Geigy Scientific Tables

Geigy Scientific Tables

Volume 3

Physical Chemistry
Composition of Blood
Hematology
Somatometric Data

Edited by C. Lentner

Eighth, revised and enlarged edition
Published by CIBA-GEIGY

ISBN 0-914168-52-5
Library of Congress Catalogue No. 81-70045

Editor: Cornelius Lentner
Associate editors: Charlotte Lentner and Anthony Wink
International Medical and Pharmaceutical Information, Ciba-Geigy Limited, Basle

American edition published by Medical Education Division, Ciba-Geigy Corporation, West Caldwell, New Jersey 07006

International edition published by Ciba-Geigy Limited, Basle, Switzerland

Printed in Switzerland

By way of explanation

This completely revised and expanded 8th edition of the *Geigy Scientific Tables* represents the continuation of a work that has stood the test of time. Its aim is to provide scientists and, in particular, doctors with a concise compendium of scientific data backed by literature references and thus to spare them much laborious searching.

The vast increase in the amount of subject matter to be included has meant that the *Geigy Scientific Tables* have had to be steadily extended, with the result that they are becoming too voluminous to be published in a single book. Dividing the book up into several separate volumes has made it possible to incorporate a number of additional chapters and has also helped to ensure that the data on the various branches of knowledge are more up-to-date than they could have been in a single-volume work.

Volume 1 contains the chapters 'Units of Measurement, Body Fluids, Composition of the Body, Nutrition', volume 2 is entitled 'Introduction to Statistics, Statistical Tables, Mathematical Formulae', and further volumes are in preparation.

CIBA-GEIGY Limited, Basle

Foreword

An improvement in the 8th edition of the *Geigy Scientific Tables*, as compared with the 7th edition, consists in the unreserved use made of the International System of Units. The International Union of Pure and Applied Chemistry (IUPAC) and the International Federation of Clinical Chemistry (IFCC) recommend that concentrations of substances whose chemical structure is sufficiently accurately known should be given using the unit mole, i.e. in terms of amount of substance concentration, substance (mole) ratio and molality[1]; it should, however, be noted that the use of the unit kilogram is fully compatible with the International System of Units[2].

The tables relating to the composition of the blood form the main body of this present volume. The application of modern techniques in analyzing blood has led to an abundance of data which does not readily lend itself to critical selection. While the analytical methods are usually given in the necessary details, the characteristics of the reference individuals (such as age, sex, body mass, genetic, ethnic and socio-economic factors) and the time of specimen collection are often not fully described as suggested by the International Federation of Clinical Chemistry[3]. Some fundamental additions have been made to the section on 'Plasma Proteins', the measurement of which is now a routine matter. The section on 'Enzymes in Plasma' has been amplified with data on erythrocyte enzymes. For hormone concentrations in the blood, the reader is referred to the chapter on 'Endocrinology', which is to appear in a subsequent volume. A completely new inclusion in the tables is the chapter on 'Complement System'.

This volume also contains some sections on the genetic aspects of hematology, the section on the HLA system being of particular concern. While the antigens of the HLA system were long regarded as important only for transplant operations (histocompatibility antigens), there is increasing recognition nowadays of links between specific HLA antigens and certain diseases.

This volume concludes with some tables giving somatometric data. In recent years the widespread use of new measurement techniques – such as sonography – and the analysis of a great deal of stored data have led to a wealth of new information on various parameters of body growth and adult body mass presented in publications which are often not easily accessible; it is hoped that this compilation will now make the data available to a wider readership.

We are sure that our readers will join us in expressing gratitude to all those who have offered us their help and advice in compiling this volume of the *Geigy Scientific Tables*. We are also indebted to all those readers who have sent us proposals for improvements or have drawn our attention to printing errors. We shall continue in the future to take account, wherever possible, of any suggestions our readers care to send us.

Basle, July 1984 *The Editors*

[1] Commission on Quantities and Units in Clinical Chemistry of the International Union of Pure and Applied Chemistry (IUPAC) and Expert Panel on Quantities and Units of the International Federation of Clinical Chemistry (IFCC): Recommendation 1973, *Pure appl. Chem.*, **37**, 519 (1974) / Approved recommendation (1978), *Clin. chim. Acta*, **96**, 157F (1979).

[2] LOWE, D.A., *A Guide to the International Recommendations on Names and Symbols for Quantities and on Units of Measurement*, WHO, Geneva, 1975.

[3] Expert Panel on Theory of Reference Values of the International Federation of Clinical Chemistry (IFCC): Part 1. The concept of reference values, *Clin. chim. Acta*, **87**, 459F (1978) / Part 2. Selection of individuals for the production of reference values, *Clin. chim. Acta*, **139**, 205F (1984).

Acknowledgments

The publishers and editors are indebted to the following for their contributions and assistance in compiling this volume of the Geigy Scientific Tables:

Prof. W. Z. Billewicz
Medical Research Council
Human Reproduction Group
Newcastle upon Tyne NE2 3BD, UK

Prof. R. Bütler
Zentrallaboratorium des Blutspendedienstes des Schweizerischen Roten Kreuzes
CH-3014 Berne, Switzerland

Prof. F. Duckert
Gerinnungs- und Fibrinolyselabor
Kantonsspital Basel
CH-4051 Basle, Switzerland

Dr. R. A. Durst
United States Department of Commerce
National Bureau of Standards
Washington, D. C. 20234, USA

Prof. H. W. Goedde
Institut für Humangenetik der Universität Hamburg
D-2000 Hamburg, Federal Republic of Germany

Prof. U. Hadding
Institut für Medizinische Mikrobiologie
Universität Mainz
D-6500 Mainz, Federal Republic of Germany

Prof. H. Heimpel
Zentrum für innere Medizin
Universität Ulm
D-7900 Ulm, Federal Republic of Germany

Prof. L. P. Holländer †
Universität Basel
Basle, Switzerland

Dr. J. J. Hoo
Institut für Humangenetik der Universität Hamburg
D-2000 Hamburg, Federal Republic of Germany

J. Hoppe-Blank
Physikalisch-Technische Bundesanstalt
D-3300 Braunschweig, Federal Republic of Germany

Prof. F. E. Hytten
Clinical Research Centre
Division of Perinatal Medicine
Northwick Park Hospital
Harrow, Middlesex HA1 3UJ, UK

Prof. H. J. Kaufmann
Kinderklinik der Freien Universität Berlin
D-1000 Berlin 19

Prof. H.-H. Kirchner
Physikalisch-Technische Bundesanstalt
D-3300 Braunschweig, Federal Republic of Germany

Prof. F. Kohler
Institut für Thermo- und Fluiddynamik
Ruhr-Universität
D-4630 Bochum, Federal Republic of Germany

Dr. H. H. Märki
Medizinische Poliklinik
Kantonsspital Winterthur
CH-8401 Winterthur, Switzerland

Prof. W. R. Mayr
Institut für Blutgruppenserologie der Universität Wien
A-1090 Vienna, Austria

R. Scherz
Zentrallaboratorium des Blutspendedienstes des Schweizerischen Roten Kreuzes
CH-3014 Berne, Switzerland

Prof. E. Schmidt and Prof. F. W. Schmidt
Zentrum für innere Medizin und Dermatologie
Medizinische Hochschule Hannover
D-3000 Hannover, Federal Republic of Germany

Prof. L. I. Woolf
The University of British Columbia
Vancouver, B. C., V6T 1W5, Canada

The publishers and editors wish to thank the following scientific bodies, journals and publishing houses for permission to reproduce data or illustrations:

Acta Medica Scandinavica, Stockholm (page 327)
Acta Paediatrica Scandinavica, Stockholm (page 101)
American Dental Association, Chicago, Ill. (page 313)
American Institute of Nutrition, Bethesda, Md. (pages 127, 129)
American Journal of Clinical Nutrition, Bethesda, Md. (pages 311, 312)
Blackwell Scientific Publications Ltd, Oxford (pages 207, 259, 260)
British Medical Association, London (page 133)
Clinical Chemistry, Winston-Salem, N. C. (pages 67, 171)
Elsevier/North-Holland Biomedical Press, Amsterdam (pages 140, 171)
Grune & Stratton, Inc., New York (pages 211, 261)
International Civil Aviation Organization, Montreal (pages 27–29)
The Lancet, London (page 69)
Lea & Febiger, Philadelphia, Pa. (page 217, with kind permission of C. A. Finch, and pages 218, 219)
Metropolitan Life Insurance Company, New York (page 326)
The C. V. Mosby Company, St. Louis, Miss. (pages 79, 83, 99, 102, 160, 203, 207, 209)
The New England Journal of Medicine, Boston, Mass. (pages 69, 70)
Radiological Society of North America, Easton, Pa. (page 318)
Radiometer A/S, Copenhagen (page 75)
Scientific American, Inc., New York (page 225)
E. & F. N. Spon Ltd, London (page 26)
Springer-Verlag, Berlin, Heidelberg, New York (pages 70, 77, 81, 143)
Georg Thieme Verlag, Stuttgart (page 91)
Year Book Medical Publishers, Chicago, Ill. (page 66)

Contents

Notes for the guidance of users

As a rule, all symbols, abbreviations, etc. used are defined or explained at the place where they occur. Zero values are indicated throughout by the figure 0.

Where necessary, exact values have been distinguished from rounded-off values by printing the last figure in bold-face type. Thus, 1.1257 is the rounded-off value of, say, 1.1257(35486...), whereas 1.125**7** is an exact number. This notation is also used for the arbitrarily defined values of constants.

In the chapter dealing with the composition of blood a 95% range for the values given is included only in cases where it has been ascertained by means of distribution-free procedures or where it has been calculated as a mean value $\pm 2s$ on the basis of a sufficiently large sample and in the presence of a normal distribution.

The biochemical nomenclature employed conforms largely to the recommendations of the International Union of Pure and Applied Chemistry (IUPAC) and of the International Union of Biochemistry (IUB)[1]; the enzyme nomenclature is based on the recommendations of the Nomenclature Committee of the International Union of Biochemistry on the Nomenclature and Classification of Enzymes (EC)[2].

The abbreviations used in the literature references are those recommended by UNESCO (*World Medical Periodicals*, 1961 and 1963)[3].

Statistical symbols

- N Size of sample
- P Centile (percentile)
- r Correlation coefficient
- s Standard deviation
- $s_{\bar{x}}$ Standard deviation of the mean
- V Coefficient of variation
- $\bar{x}$ Mean value

Base SI units

For length	meter (m)
For mass	kilogram (kg)
For time	second (s)
For electric current intensity	ampere (A)
For thermodynamic temperature	kelvin (K)
For amount of substance	mole (mol)
For luminous intensity	candela (cd)

Decimal multiples and submultiples of SI units

exa (E)	for 10^{18}	deci (d)	for 10^{-1}
peta (P)	for 10^{15}	centi (c)	for 10^{-2}
tera (T)	for 10^{12}	milli (m)	for 10^{-3}
giga (G)	for 10^{9}	micro (μ)	for 10^{-6}
mega (M)	for 10^{6}	nano (n)	for 10^{-9}
kilo (k)	for 10^{3}	pico (p)	for 10^{-12}
hecto (h)	for 10^{2}	femto (f)	for 10^{-15}
deca (da)	for 10^{1}	atto (a)	for 10^{-18}

References

[1] *Collected Tentative Rules and Recommendations of the Commission on Biochemical Nomenclature IUPAC–IUB and Related Documents*, 2nd ed., American Society of Biological Chemists, Bethesda, Md., 1975.

[2] International Union of Biochemistry, *Enzyme Nomenclature*, Recommendations 1978, Academic Press, New York, 1979; supplement 1: *Europ. J. Biochem.*, **104**, 1 (1980); supplement 2: *Europ. J. Biochem.*, **116**, 423 (1981); supplement 3: *Europ. J. Biochem.*, **125**, 1 (1982); supplement 4: *Europ. J. Biochem.*, **131**, 461 (1983).

[3] Clegg, H. A. (Ed.), *World Medical Periodicals*, 3rd ed., World Medical Association, New York, 1961, and Ware, M. (Ed.), supplement to the 3rd edition, New York, 1968.

Periodic System of the Elements*

For each element the following are given: atomic number† (ordinal number) (*italics*), symbol, and relative atomic mass[1,2]

Period	Group I a	Group I b	Group II a	Group II b	Group III a	Group III b	Group IV a	Group IV b	Group V a	Group V b	Group VI a	Group VI b	Group VII a	Group VII b	Group VIII a	Group VIII b§
1	*1.* H 1.0079															*2.* He 4.00260
2	*3.* Li 6.941^{+}		*4.* Be 9.01218			*5.* B 10.81		*6.* C 12.011		*7.* N 14.0067		*8.* O 15.9994^{+}		*9.* F 18.998403		*10.* Ne 20.179
3	*11.* Na 22.98977		*12.* Mg 24.305			*13.* Al 26.98154		*14.* Si 28.0855^{+}		*15.* P 30.97376		*16.* S 32.06		*17.* Cl 35.453		*18.* Ar 39.948
4 (3d)	*19.* K 39.0983		*20.* Ca 40.08		*21.* Sc 44.9559		*22.* Ti 47.88^{+}		*23.* V 50.9415		*24.* Cr 51.996		*25.* Mn 54.9380		*26.* Fe; 55.847^{+} *27.* Co; 58.9332 *28.* Ni 58.69	
		29. Cu 63.546^{+}		*30.* Zn 65.38		*31.* Ga 69.72		*32.* Ge 72.59^{+}		*33.* As 74.9216		*34.* Se 78.96^{+}		*35.* Br 79.904		*36.* Kr 83.80
5 (4d)	*37.* Rb 85.4678^{+}		*38.* Sr 87.62		*39.* Y 88.9059		*40.* Zr 91.22		*41.* Nb 92.9064		*42.* Mo 95.94		*43.* Tc (98)		*44.* Ru; 101.07^{+} *45.* Rh; 102.9055 *46.* Pd 106.42	
		47. Ag 107.868		*48.* Cd 112.41		*49.* In 114.82		*50.* Sn 118.69^{+}		*51.* Sb 121.75^{+}		*52.* Te 127.60^{+}		*53.* I 126.9045		*54.* Xe 131.29^{+}
6 (5d) (4f)	*55.* Cs 132.9054		*56.* Ba 137.33		*57.* La 138.9055^{+} [4f]		*72.* Hf 178.49^{+}		*73.* Ta 180.9479		*74.* W 183.85^{+}		*75.* Re 186.207		*76.* Os; 190.2 *77.* Ir; 192.22^{+} *78.* Pt 195.08^{+}	
		79. Au 196.9665		*80.* Hg 200.59^{+}		*81.* Tl 204.383		*82.* Pb 207.2		*83.* Bi 208.9804		*84.* Po (209)		*85.* At (210)		*86.* Rn (222)
7 (6d) (5f)	*87.* Fr (223)		*88.* Ra [226.0254]		*89.* Ac [227.0278] [5f]		*104.* Unq◇ (261)		*105.* Unp◇ (262)		*106.* Unh◇ (263)					

Lanthanides (rare-earth elements)

4f	*58.* Ce 140.12	*59.* Pr 140.9077	*60.* Nd 144.24^{+}	*61.* Pm (145)	*62.* Sm 150.36^{+}	*63.* Eu 151.96	*64.* Gd 157.25^{+}	*65.* Tb 158.9254	*66.* Dy 162.50^{+}	*67.* Ho 164.9304	*68.* Er 167.26^{+}	*69.* Tm 168.9342	*70.* Yb 173.04^{+}	*71.* Lu 174.967^{+}

Actinides

5f	*90.* Th [232.0381]	*91.* Pa [231.0359]	*92.* U 238.0289	*93.* Np [237.0482]	*94.* Pu (244)	*95.* Am (243)	*96.* Cm (247)	*97.* Bk (247)	*98.* Cf (251)	*99.* Es (252)	*100.* Fm (257)	*101.* Md (258)	*102.* No (259)	*103.* Lr (260)

† In physics usually referred to as nuclear charge number or proton number.

§ Also known as Group 0.

◇ The names and symbols of these elements are not yet internationally recognized.

[1] Adapted from Eucken, A. (Ed.), *Landolt-Börnstein, Zahlenwerte und Funktionen aus Physik, Chemie, Astronomie, Geophysik und Technik,* volume 1: *Atom- und Molekularphysik,* part 1: *Atome und Ionen,* 6th ed., Springer, Berlin, 1950, page 11 (modified and supplemented).

[2] Relative atomic masses: unified scale with ^{12}C as reference nuclide having the assigned value A_r (^{12}C) = **12** (International Union of Pure and Applied Chemistry (IUPAC), *Comptes rendus de la 24e conférence,* 1967, Butterworth, London, 1968, page 130). The values given are those recommended by the Commission on Atomic Weights of the IUPAC in 1979 (*Pure appl. Chem.,* **52**, 2351 [1980]). The uncertainty is ± 1 in the last decimal place except for the values marked $^{+}$, for which it is ± 3. A value in round brackets is the nucleon number (mass number) of the most stable known isotope, a value in square brackets the relative atomic mass of the best-known isotope.
Before agreement was reached on the unified ^{12}C scale, different relative mass scales were in use in physics and chemistry, namely the 'physical scale of atomic weights' based on the oxygen nuclide ^{16}O as primary standard and defined by $A_{ph}(^{16}O) = \mathbf{16}$, and the 'chemical scale of atomic weights' based on elementary oxygen, for example, on the 'naturally' occurring mixture of the stable oxygen isotopes ^{16}O, ^{17}O and ^{18}O, the primary standard being a 'mean' oxygen atom $\bar{O}$ with the definition $A_{ch}(\bar{O}) = \mathbf{16}$.

* Pages 9–60 have been compiled in collaboration with J. Hoppe-Blank and H.-H. Kirchner, Braunschweig, FRG.

Alphabetical Table of the Names of the Elements

Name	Symbol	Atomic number	Relative atomic mass 1979[1]
Actinium	Ac	89	[227.0278]
Aluminum	Al	13	26.98154
Americium	Am	95	(243)
Antimony	Sb	51	121.75^{+}
Argon	Ar	18	39.948
Arsenic	As	33	74.9216
Astatine	At	85	(210)
Barium	Ba	56	137.33
Berkelium	Bk	97	(247)
Beryllium	Be	4	9.01218
Bismuth	Bi	83	208.9804
Boron	B	5	10.81
Bromine	Br	35	79.904
Cadmium	Cd	48	112.41
Calcium	Ca	20	40.08
Californium	Cf	98	(251)
Carbon	C	6	12.011
Cerium	Ce	58	140.12
Cesium	Cs	55	132.9054
Chlorine	Cl	17	35.453
Chromium	Cr	24	51.996
Cobalt	Co	27	58.9332
Copper	Cu	29	63.546^{+}
Curium	Cm	96	(247)
Dysprosium	Dy	66	162.50^{+}
Einsteinium	Es	99	(252)
Erbium	Er	68	167.26^{+}
Europium	Eu	63	151.96
Fermium	Fm	100	(257)
Fluorine	F	9	18.998403
Francium	Fr	87	(223)
Gadolinium	Gd	64	157.25^{+}
Gallium	Ga	31	69.72
Germanium	Ge	32	72.59^{+}
Gold	Au	79	196.9665
Hafnium	Hf	72	178.49^{+}
Helium	He	2	4.00260
Holmium	Ho	67	164.9304
Hydrogen	H	1	1.0079
Indium	In	49	114.82
Iodine	I	53	126.9045
Iridium	Ir	77	192.22^{+}
Iron	Fe	26	55.847^{+}
Krypton	Kr	36	83.80
Lanthanum	La	57	138.9055^{+}
Lawrencium	Lr	103	(260)
Lead	Pb	82	207.2
Lithium	Li	3	6.941^{+}
Lutetium	Lu	71	174.967^{+}
Magnesium	Mg	12	24.305
Manganese	Mn	25	54.9380
Mendelevium	Md	101	(258)
Mercury	Hg	80	200.59^{+}
Molybdenum	Mo	42	95.94
Neodymium	Nd	60	144.24^{+}
Neon	Ne	10	20.179
Neptunium	Np	93	[237.0482]
Nickel	Ni	28	58.69
Niobium	Nb	41	92.9064
Nitrogen	N	7	14.0067
Nobelium	No	102	(259)
Osmium	Os	76	190.2
Oxygen	O	8	15.9994^{+}
Palladium	Pd	46	106.42
Phosphorus	P	15	30.97376
Platinum	Pt	78	195.08^{+}
Plutonium	Pu	94	(244)
Polonium	Po	84	(209)
Potassium	K	19	39.0983
Praseodymium	Pr	59	140.9077
Promethium	Pm	61	(145)
Protactinium	Pa	91	[231.0359]
Radium	Ra	88	[226.0254]
Radon	Rn	86	(222)
Rhenium	Re	75	186.207
Rhodium	Rh	45	102.9055
Rubidium	Rb	37	85.4678^{+}
Ruthenium	Ru	44	101.07^{+}
Samarium	Sm	62	150.36^{+}
Scandium	Sc	21	44.9559
Selenium	Se	34	78.96^{+}
Silicon	Si	14	28.0855^{+}
Silver	Ag	47	107.868
Sodium	Na	11	22.98977
Strontium	Sr	38	87.62
Sulfur	S	16	32.06
Tantalum	Ta	73	180.9479
Technetium	Tc	43	(98)
Tellurium	Te	52	127.60^{+}
Terbium	Tb	65	158.9254
Thallium	Tl	81	204.383
Thorium	Th	90	[232.0381]
Thulium	Tm	69	168.9342
Tin	Sn	50	118.69^{+}
Titanium	Ti	22	47.88^{+}
Tungsten	W	74	183.85^{+}
Unnilhexium◊	Unh◊	106	(263)
Unnilpentium◊	Unp◊	105	(262)
Unnilquadium◊	Unq◊	104	(261)
Uranium	U	92	238.0289
Vanadium	V	23	50.9415
Wolfram	W	See Tungsten	
Xenon	Xe	54	131.29^{+}
Ytterbium	Yb	70	173.04^{+}
Yttrium	Y	39	88.9059
Zinc	Zn	30	65.38
Zirconium	Zr	40	91.22

[1] Relative atomic masses: see footnote[2], page 9.
◊The names and symbols of these elements are not yet internationally recognized.

Symbol	Name	Atomic number	Relative atomic mass 1979[1]
Ac	Actinium	89	[227.0278]
Ag	Silver	47	107.868
Al	Aluminum	13	26.98154
Am	Americium	95	(243)
Ar	Argon	18	39.948
As	Arsenic	33	74.9216
At	Astatine	85	(210)
Au	Gold	79	196.9665
B	Boron	5	10.81
Ba	Barium	56	137.33
Be	Beryllium	4	9.01218
Bi	Bismuth	83	208.9804
Bk	Berkelium	97	(247)
Br	Bromine	35	79.904
C	Carbon	6	12.011
Ca	Calcium	20	40.08
Cd	Cadmium	48	112.41
Ce	Cerium	58	140.12
Cf	Californium	98	(251)
Cl	Chlorine	17	35.453
Cm	Curium	96	(247)
Co	Cobalt	27	58.9332
Cr	Chromium	24	51.996
Cs	Cesium	55	132.9054
Cu	Copper	29	63.546^{+}
Dy	Dysprosium	66	162.50^{+}
Er	Erbium	68	167.26^{+}
Es	Einsteinium	99	(252)
Eu	Europium	63	151.96
F	Fluorine	9	18.998403
Fe	Iron	26	55.847^{+}
Fm	Fermium	100	(257)
Fr	Francium	87	(223)
Ga	Gallium	31	69.72
Gd	Gadolinium	64	157.25^{+}
Ge	Germanium	32	72.59^{+}
H	Hydrogen	1	1.0079
He	Helium	2	4.00260
Hf	Hafnium	72	178.49^{+}
Hg	Mercury	80	200.59^{+}
Ho	Holmium	67	164.9304
I	Iodine	53	126.9045
In	Indium	49	114.82
Ir	Iridium	77	192.22^{+}
K	Potassium	19	39.0983
Kr	Krypton	36	83.80
La	Lanthanum	57	138.9055^{+}
Li	Lithium	3	6.941^{+}
Lr	Lawrencium	103	(260)
Lu	Lutetium	71	174.967^{+}
Md	Mendelevium	101	(258)
Mg	Magnesium	12	24.305
Mn	Manganese	25	54.9380
Mo	Molybdenum	42	95.94
N	Nitrogen	7	14.0067
Na	Sodium	11	22.98977
Nb	Niobium	41	92.9064
Nd	Neodymium	60	144.24^{+}
Ne	Neon	10	20.179
Ni	Nickel	28	58.69
No	Nobelium	102	(259)
Np	Neptunium	93	[237.0482]
O	Oxygen	8	15.9994^{+}
Os	Osmium	76	190.2
P	Phosphorus	15	30.97376
Pa	Protactinium	91	[231.0359]
Pb	Lead	82	207.2
Pd	Palladium	46	106.42
Pm	Promethium	61	(145)
Po	Polonium	84	(209)
Pr	Praseodymium	59	140.9077
Pt	Platinum	78	195.08^{+}
Pu	Plutonium	94	(244)
Ra	Radium	88	[226.0254]
Rb	Rubidium	37	85.4678^{+}
Re	Rhenium	75	186.207
Rh	Rhodium	45	102.9055
Rn	Radon	86	(222)
Ru	Ruthenium	44	101.07^{+}
S	Sulfur	16	32.06
Sb	Antimony	51	121.75^{+}
Sc	Scandium	21	44.9559
Se	Selenium	34	78.96^{+}
Si	Silicon	14	28.0855^{+}
Sm	Samarium	62	150.36^{+}
Sn	Tin	50	118.69^{+}
Sr	Strontium	38	87.62
Ta	Tantalum	73	180.9479
Tb	Terbium	65	158.9254
Tc	Technetium	43	(98)
Te	Tellurium	52	127.60^{+}
Th	Thorium	90	[232.0381]
Ti	Titanium	22	47.88^{+}
Tl	Thallium	81	204.383
Tm	Thulium	69	168.9342
U	Uranium	92	238.0289
Unh◊	Unnilhexium◊	106	(263)
Unp◊	Unnilpentium◊	105	(262)
Unq◊	Unnilquadium◊	104	(261)
V	Vanadium	23	50.9415
W	Tungsten	74	183.85^{+}
Xe	Xenon	54	131.29^{+}
Y	Yttrium	39	88.9059
Yb	Ytterbium	70	173.04^{+}
Zn	Zinc	30	65.38
Zr	Zirconium	40	91.22

[1] Relative atomic masses: see footnote[2], page 9.
◊The names and symbols of these elements are not yet internationally recognized.

Atomic number	Name (English, French, German)	Symbol	Relative atomic mass 1979[1] or relative molecular mass	Valency[16]	Melting point[2] at standard pressure[3] (unless otherwise stated) °C	Boiling point[2] at standard pressure[3] (unless otherwise stated) °C	Density[2] Gases: standard density[3] in $g\,L^{-1}$ Liquids and solids: $g\,cm^{-3}$ or relative density (20 °C/4 °C, unless otherwise stated)	*Natural abundance* Mass fraction × 100 in earth's crust, hydrosphere and atmosphere[4] %	Volume fraction × 100 in atmosphere[5] %	Mass fraction × 100 in human body[6] %	*Natural nuclides* Nuclide (nucleon number)	Mass fraction × 100 in natural isotopic mixture[17] %	Nuclidic mass[8] u	Mode of decay[7–9] (type of radiation)	Half-life[7,8,10]
1	*Hydrogen*[11] .... Hydrogène Wasserstoff	H H_2	1.0079 2.0158	1 –	– −259.14	– −252.87	– Gas 0.08988 Liquid 0.0708 (−253 °C) Solid 0.0706 (−262 °C)	0.88 –	– 0.00005	10.0 –	^{1}H(H) ^{2}H(D) ^{3}H(T)	99.985[18] 0.015[18] See[12]	1.00782522 2.01410222 3.0160497	 β^-	 12.26 y
2	*Helium*............ Hélium Helium	He	4.00260	0	< −272.2 at 26.3445 bar	−268.934	Gas 0.1785	4.2×10^{-7}	0.000524	–	^{3}He ^{4}He	1.38×10^{-4} (In air only) ~100	3.01602970 4.00260326		
3	*Lithium* .... Lithium Lithium	Li	6.941[+]	1	180.54	1347	Solid 0.534	0.006	–	3.1×10^{-6}	^{6}Li ^{7}Li	7.5 92.5	6.0151234 7.0160048		
4	*Beryllium*.......... Béryllium Beryllium	Be	9.01218	2	1278 ± 5	2970	Solid 1.848	5.3×10^{-4}	–	5×10^{-8}	^{9}Be	100	9.0121828		
5	*Boron*............. Bore Bor	B	10.81	(1, 2), 3	2079	Sublimes 2550	Solid (crystalline) 2.34 (amorphous) 2.37	0.0016	–	$<6.9 \times 10^{-5}$	^{10}B ^{11}B	20.0 80.0	10.0129385 11.00930533		
6	*Carbon*............ Carbone Kohlenstoff	C	12.011	2, (3), 4	~3550 (Sublimes 3367 ± 25)	4827	Solid (amorphous) 1.8–2.1 (graphite) 1.9–2.3 (diamond) 3.15–3.53	0.087	(CO: 0–trace CO_2: 0.0314)	18.0	^{12}C ^{13}C ^{14}C	98.90 1.10 See[13]	12.00000000 13.00335508 14.00324202	 β^-	 5.73×10^{3} y
7	*Nitrogen*........... Azote Stickstoff	N	14.0067	(1, 2), 3, (4), 5	–	–	–	0.030	–	3.0	^{14}N ^{15}N	99.63 0.37	14.00307440 15.0001093		
		N_2	28.0134	–	−209.86	−195.8	Gas 1.2506 Liquid 0.808 (−195.8 °C) Solid 1.026 (−252 °C)	–	78.084	–					
8	*Oxygen* .... Oxygène Sauerstoff	O O_2	15.9994[+] 31.9988	2 –	– −218.4	– −182.962	– Gas 1.429 Liquid 1.14 (−182.96 °C)	49.5 –	– O_2: 20.9476 O_3: $2–7 \times 10^{-6}$	65.0	^{16}O ^{17}O ^{18}O	99.762 0.038 0.200	15.99491502 16.9991333 17.99915996		
9	*Fluorine*........... Fluor Fluor	F F_2	18.998403 37.996806	1 –	– −219.62	– −188.14	– Gas 1.696 Liquid 1.108 (−188.14 °C)	0.028	–	3.7×10^{-3}	^{19}F	100	18.9984046		

10	*Neon* .... Néon Neon	Ne	20.179	0	− 248.67	− 246.048	Gas Liquid	0.89990 1.207 (− 246.048 °C)	5×10^{-7}	0.001818	–	^{20}Ne ^{21}Ne ^{22}Ne	90.51 0.27 9.22	19.9924405 20.9938474 21.9913848		
11	*Sodium* .... Sodium Natrium	Na	22.98977	1	97.81 ± 0.03	882.9	Solid	0.971	2.63	–	1.5×10^{-1}	^{23}Na	100	22.9897703		
12	*Magnesium* .... Magnésium Magnesium	Mg	24.305	2	648.8 ± 0.5	1090	Solid	1.738	1.95	–	5×10^{-2}	^{24}Mg ^{25}Mg ^{26}Mg	78.99 10.00 11.01	23.9850443 24.9858385 25.9825944		
13	*Aluminum* .... *(Aluminium)* Aluminium Aluminium	Al	26.98154	(1, 2), 3	660.37	2467	Solid	2.6989	7.57	–	8.7×10^{-5}	^{27}Al	100	26.9815406		
14	*Silicon* .... Silicium Silicium	Si	28.0855+	2, 4	1410	2355	Solid	2.33 (25 °C)	25.80	–	2×10^{-3}	^{28}Si ^{29}Si ^{30}Si	92.23 4.67 3.10	27.9769286 28.9764969 29.9737722		
15	*Phosphorus* .... Phosphore Phosphor	P	30.97376	(1), 3, (4), 5	White 44.1	White 280	Solid (white) (red) (black)	 1.82 2.20 2.25–2.69	0.09	–	1.0	^{31}P	100	30.9737633		
16	*Sulfur*............. *(Sulphur)* Soufre Schwefel	S	32.06	2, 4, 6	Rhombic 112.8 Monoclinic 119.0	444.674	Solid (rhombic) (monoclinic)	 2.07 1.957	0.048	SO_2: 0–0.0001	2.5×10^{-1}	^{32}S ^{33}S ^{34}S ^{36}S	95.02 0.75 4.21 0.002	31.9720728 32.9714591 33.9678701 35.9670791		
17	*Chlorine*.......... Chlore Chlor	Cl	35.453	1, 3, 4, 5, 7	–	–	–	–	0.19	–	1.5×10^{-1}	^{35}Cl ^{37}Cl	75.77 24.23	34.96885359 36.96590304		
		Cl_2	70.906	–	Freezing point − 100.98	− 34.6	Gas Liquid	3.214 1.56 (− 33.6 °C)								
18	*Argon*............. Argon Argon	Ar	39.948	0	Freezing point − 189.2	− 185.7	Gas	1.7837	3.6×10^{-4}	0.934	–	^{36}Ar ^{38}Ar ^{40}Ar	0.337 0.063 99.60	35.9675465 37.9627330 39.9623842		
19	*Potassium* .... Potassium Kalium	K	39.0983	1	63.65	774	Solid	0.862	2.41	–	2×10^{-1}	^{39}K ^{40}K ^{41}K	93.2581 0.0117 6.7302	38.9637089 39.9640001 40.9618270	 β− γ K	 1.28×10^{9} y
20	*Calcium*.......... Calcium Calcium	Ca	40.08	2	839 ± 2	1484	Solid	1.55	3.38	–	1.5	^{40}Ca ^{42}Ca ^{43}Ca ^{44}Ca ^{46}Ca ^{48}Ca	96.941 0.647 0.135 2.086 0.004 0.187	39.9625921 41.9586281 42.9587774 43.9554875 45.953699 47.952526		

For footnotes see page 23.

Atomic number	Name (English, French, German)	Symbol	Relative atomic mass 1979[1]	Valency[16]	Melting point[2] at standard pressure[3] (unless otherwise stated)	Boiling point[2] at standard pressure[3] (unless otherwise stated)	Density[2] Gases: standard density[3] in $g L^{-1}$ Liquids and solids: $g cm^{-3}$ or relative density (20 °C/4 °C, unless otherwise stated)		Natural abundance: Mass fraction × 100 in earth's crust, hydrosphere and atmosphere[4]	Natural abundance: Volume fraction × 100 in atmosphere[5]	Natural abundance: Mass fraction × 100 in human body[6]	Natural nuclides: Nuclide (nucleon number)	Natural nuclides: Mass fraction × 100 in natural isotopic mixture[17]	Natural nuclides: Nuclidic mass[8]	Natural nuclides: Mode of decay[7–9] (type of radiation)	Natural nuclides: Half-life[7,8,10]
					°C	°C			%	%	%		%	u		
21	*Scandium* .... Scandium Scandium	Sc	44.9559	3	1541	2831	Solid	2.989 (25 °C)	5.1×10^{-4}	–	–	^{45}Sc	100	44.9559174		
22	*Titanium* .... Titane Titan	Ti	47.88⁺	2, 3, 4	1660 ± 10	3287	Solid	4.54	0.41	–	1.3×10^{-5}	^{46}Ti	8.2	45.9526296		
												^{47}Ti	7.4	46.9517670		
												^{48}Ti	73.8	47.9479491		
												^{49}Ti	5.4	48.9478721		
												^{50}Ti	5.2	49.9447843		
23	*Vanadium* .... Vanadium Vanadium	V	50.9415	2, 3, 4, 5	1890 ± 10	3380	Solid	6.11 (18.7 °C)	0.014	–	$<2.6 \times 10^{-5}$	^{50}V	0.250	49.9471643	K	6×10^{15} y
												^{51}V	99.750	50.9439644		
24	*Chromium* .... Chrome Chrom	Cr	51.996	2, 3, 6	1857 ± 20	2672	Solid	7.18–7.20	0.019	–	2.4×10^{-6}	^{50}Cr	4.35	49.9460488		
												^{52}Cr	83.79	51.9405102		
												^{53}Cr	9.50	52.9406510		
												^{54}Cr	2.36	53.9388813		
25	*Manganese* .... Manganèse Mangan	Mn	54.9380	1, 2, 3, 4, 6, 7	1244 ± 3	1962	Solid	7.21–7.44	0.085	–	1.7×10^{-5}	^{55}Mn	100	54.9380464		
26	*Iron* .... Fer Eisen	Fe	55.847⁺	2, 3, 4, 6	1535	2750	Solid	7.874	4.7	–	6.0×10^{-3}	^{54}Fe	5.8	53.9396120		
												^{56}Fe	91.7	55.9349339		
												^{57}Fe	2.2	56.9353907		
												^{58}Fe	0.3	57.9332745		
27	*Cobalt* .... Cobalt Cobalt	Co	58.9332	2, 3	1495	2870	Solid	8.9	0.0037	–	2.1×10^{-6}	^{59}Co	100	58.9331879		
28	*Nickel* .... Nickel Nickel	Ni	58.69	0, 1, 2, 3	1453	2732	Solid	8.902 (25 °C)	0.015	–	1.4×10^{-5}	^{58}Ni	68.27	57.9353358		
												^{60}Ni	26.10	59.9307795		
												^{61}Ni	1.13	60.9310502		
												^{62}Ni	3.59	61.9283396		
												^{64}Ni	0.91	63.927956		
29	*Copper* .... Cuivre Kupfer	Cu	63.546⁺	1, 2	1083.4 ± 0.2	2567	Solid	8.96	0.010	–	1.0×10^{-4}	^{63}Cu	69.17	62.9295898		
												^{65}Cu	30.83	64.9277890		

30	*Zinc* . . . . Zinc Zink	Zn	65.38	2	419.58	907	Solid	7.133 (25 °C)	0.012	–	3.2×10^{-3}	^{64}Zn ^{66}Zn ^{67}Zn ^{68}Zn ^{70}Zn	48.6 27.9 4.1 18.8 0.6	63.929 1400 65.926 0395 66.927 1322 67.924 8481 69.925 3254		
31	*Gallium* . . . . Gallium Gallium	Ga	69.72	(1), 2, 3	29.78	2403	Liquid Solid	6.095 (29.8 °C) 5.904 (29.6 °C)	0.0014	–	–	^{69}Ga ^{71}Ga	60.1 39.9	68.925 5795 70.924 7044		
32	*Germanium* . . . . Germanium Germanium	Ge	72.59⁺	2, 4	937.4	2830	Solid	5.323 (25 °C)	5.6×10^{-1}	–	–	^{70}Ge ^{72}Ge ^{73}Ge ^{74}Ge ^{76}Ge	20.5 27.4 7.8 36.5 7.8	69.924 2520 71.922 0823 72.923 4644 73.921 1786 75.921 4042		
33	*Arsenic* . . . . Arsenic Arsen	As	74.9216	3, 5	Crystalline 817 at 28.371 bar (sublimes 613)	–	Solid (crystalline) (yellow)	 5.727 (14 °C) 2.026 (18 °C)	5.5×10^{-1}	–	2.6×10^{-5}	^{75}As	100	74.921 596		
34	*Selenium* . . . . Sélénium Selen	Se	78.96⁺	2, 4, 6	217 Gray	684.9 ± 1.0	Solid (gray) (vitreous)	 4.79 4.28	8×10^{-5}	–	1.9×10^{-5}	^{74}Se ^{76}Se ^{77}Se ^{78}Se ^{80}Se ^{82}Se	0.9 9.0 7.6 23.5 49.6 9.4	73.922 477 75.919 2117 76.919 9130 77.917 3093 79.916 5253 81.916 708		
35	*Bromine* . . . . Brome Brom	Br	79.904	1, 3, 5	− 7.2	58.78	Gas Liquid	7.59 3.12	6×10^{-4}	–	2.9×10^{-4}	^{79}Br ^{81}Br	50.69 49.31	78.918 3320 80.916 292		
36	*Krypton* . . . . Krypton Krypton	Kr	83.80	0, (2, 4)	− 156.6	− 152.30 ± 0.10	Gas	3.733	1.9×10^{-8}	0.000 114	–	^{78}Kr ^{80}Kr ^{82}Kr ^{83}Kr ^{84}Kr ^{86}Kr	0.35 2.25 11.6 11.5 57.0 17.3	77.920 401 79.916 376 81.913 482 82.914 131 83.911 5053 85.910 616		
37	*Rubidium* . . . . Rubidium Rubidium	Rb	85.4678⁺	1	38.89	688	Liquid Solid	1.475 (39 °C) 1.532	0.029	–	4.6×10^{-4}	^{85}Rb ^{87}Rb	72.17 27.83	84.911 7990 86.909 1870	 β^-	 5×10^{11} y
38	*Strontium* . . . . Strontium Strontium	Sr	87.62	2	769	1384	Solid	2.54	0.014	–	4.6×10^{-4}	^{84}Sr ^{86}Sr ^{87}Sr ^{88}Sr	0.56 9.86 7.00 82.58	83.913 4305 85.909 2763 86.908 8935 87.905 6283		
39	*Yttrium* . . . . Yttrium Yttrium	Y	88.9059	3	1522 ± 8	3338	Solid	4.469 (25 °C)	0.0026	–	–	^{89}Y	100	88.905 8667		

For footnotes see page 23.

Atomic number	Name (English, French, German)	Symbol	Relative atomic mass 1979[1]	Valency[16]	Melting point[2] at standard pressure[3] (unless otherwise stated) °C	Boiling point[2] at standard pressure[3] (unless otherwise stated) °C	Density[2] Gases: standard density[3] in $g\,L^{-1}$ Liquids and solids: $g\,cm^{-3}$ or relative density (20 °C/4 °C, unless otherwise stated)		Natural abundance: Mass fraction × 100 in earth's crust, hydrosphere and atmosphere[4] %	Natural abundance: Volume fraction × 100 in atmosphere[5] %	Natural abundance: Mass fraction × 100 in human body[6] %	Natural nuclides: Nuclide (nucleon number)	Natural nuclides: Mass fraction × 100 in natural isotopic mixture[17] %	Natural nuclides: Nuclidic mass[8] u	Natural nuclides: Mode of decay[7–9] (type of radiation)	Natural nuclides: Half-life[7,8,10]
40	*Zirconium* Zirconium Zirkon	Zr	91.22	(2, 3), 4	1852 ± 2	4377	Solid	6.506	0.021	–	6.0×10^{-4}	^{90}Zr ^{91}Zr ^{92}Zr ^{94}Zr ^{96}Zr	51.45 11.32 17.19 17.28 2.76	89.9047105 90.9056434 91.9050386 93.9063202 95.908292	 –	 $> 3.6 \times 10^{17}$ y
41	*Niobium* Niobium Niob	Nb	92.9064	2, 3, (4), 5	2468 ± 10	4742	Solid	8.57	0.0019	–	1.6×10^{-4}	^{93}Nb	100	92.9063803		
42	*Molybdenum* Molybdène Molybdän	Mo	95.94	2, 3, (4, 5), 6	2617	4612	Solid	10.22	0.0014	–	1.3×10^{-5}	^{92}Mo ^{94}Mo ^{95}Mo ^{96}Mo ^{97}Mo ^{98}Mo ^{100}Mo	14.84 9.25 15.92 16.68 9.55 24.13 9.63	91.9068083 93.9050891 94.9058369 95.9046748 96.9060227 97.9054100 99.9074775		
43	*Technetium* Technétium Technetium	Tc	(98)	(1, 2), 4, 5, 6, 7	2172	4877	Solid	11.50 (calculated)	–	–	–	$^{92-102}Tc$ $^{104,\,105}Tc$	Artificial element: all very unstable, except ^{97}Tc, ^{98}Tc, ^{99}Tc (half-lives 2.6×10^{6} y, 4.2×10^{6} y, 2.13×10^{5} y)			
44	*Ruthenium* Ruthénium Ruthenium	Ru	101.07+	1, 2, 3, 4, (5), 6, 7, 8	2310	3900	Solid	12.41	2×10^{-6}	–	–	^{96}Ru ^{98}Ru ^{99}Ru ^{100}Ru ^{101}Ru ^{102}Ru ^{104}Ru	5.52 1.88 12.7 12.6 17.0 31.6 18.7	95.907598 97.905289 98.9059369 99.9042173 100.9055766 101.9043481 103.905428		
45	*Rhodium* Rhodium Rhodium	Rh	102.9055	(1), 2, 3, 4, 5, (6)	1966 ± 3	3727 ± 100	Solid	12.41	1×10^{-7}	–	–	^{103}Rh	100	102.905512		
46	*Palladium* Palladium Palladium	Pd	106.42	2, 3, 4	1552	3140	Solid	12.02	1×10^{-6}	–	–	^{102}Pd ^{104}Pd ^{105}Pd ^{106}Pd ^{108}Pd ^{110}Pd	1.02 11.14 22.33 27.33 26.46 11.72	101.905607 103.904014 104.905086 105.903487 107.903891 109.905164		
47	*Silver* Argent Silber	Ag	107.868	1, (2), 3	961.93	2212	Solid	10.50	1×10^{-5}	–	$< 1 \times 10^{-6}$	^{107}Ag ^{109}Ag	51.83 48.17	106.905091 108.9047546		

48	*Cadmium*	Cd	112.41	2	320.9	765	Solid	8.65	3×10^{-5}	–	7.2×10^{-5}	^{106}Cd	1.25	105.906463		
	Cadmium											^{108}Cd	0.89	107.90419		
	Cadmium											^{110}Cd	12.51	109.9030101		
												^{111}Cd	12.81	110.9041855		
												^{112}Cd	24.13	111.9027628		
												^{113}Cd	12.22	112.9044074		
												^{114}Cd	28.72	113.9033668		
												^{116}Cd	7.47	115.9047615		
49	*Indium*	In	114.82	1, 2, 3	156.61	2080	Solid	7.31	1×10^{-5}	–	–	^{113}In	4.3	112.904089		
	Indium											^{115}In	95.7	114.903875	β^-	5.1×10^{14} y
	Indium															
50	*Tin*	Sn	118.69⁺	2, 4	231.9681	2270	Solid		0.0035	–	$<2.4 \times 10^{-5}$	^{112}Sn	1.0	111.904834		
	Etain						(gray)	α5.75				^{114}Sn	0.7	113.902776		
	Zinn						(white)	β7.31				^{115}Sn	0.4	114.903353		
												^{116}Sn	14.7	115.9017483		
												^{117}Sn	7.7	116.9029606		
												^{118}Sn	24.03	117.9016126		
												^{119}Sn	8.6	118.90331		
												^{120}Sn	32.4	119.9022073		
												^{122}Sn	4.6	121.9034511		
												^{124}Sn	5.6	123.905283		
51	*Antimony*	Sb	121.75⁺	3, (4), 5	630.74	1950	Solid	6.691	6.5×10^{-5}	–	1.1×10^{-5}	^{121}Sb	57.3	120.9038223		
	Antimoine											^{123}Sb	42.7	122.9042203		
	Antimon															
52	*Tellurium*	Te	127.60⁺	2, 4, 6	449.5 ± 0.3	989.8 ± 3.8	Solid	6.24	1×10^{-6}	–	1.2×10^{-5}	^{120}Te	0.096	119.904024		
	Tellure											^{122}Te	2.60	121.9030560		
	Tellur											^{123}Te	0.908	122.9042817	K	1.2×10^{13} y
												^{124}Te	4.816	123.9028302		
												^{125}Te	7.14	124.9044263		
												^{126}Te	18.95	125.9033142		
												^{128}Te	31.69	127.9044675		
												^{130}Te	33.80	129.9062319		
53	*Iodine*	I	126.9045	1, 3, 5, 7	113.5	184.35	Gas	11.27	6×10^{-6}	(I_2: 0–1×10^{-6})	1.6×10^{-5}	^{127}I	100	126.9044755		
	Iode						Solid	4.93								
	Jod															
54	*Xenon*	Xe	131.29⁺	0,(2, 4, 6)	– 111.9	– 107.1 ± 3	Gas	5.887 ± 0.009	2.4×10^{-9}	8.7×10^{-6}	–	^{124}Xe	0.10	123.90612		
	Xénon						Liquid	3.52 (– 109 °C)				^{126}Xe	0.09	125.904279		
	Xenon											^{128}Xe	1.91	127.9035323		
												^{129}Xe	26.4	128.904784		
												^{130}Xe	4.1	129.9035108		
												^{131}Xe	21.2	130.9050847		
												^{132}Xe	26.9	131.9041568		
												^{134}Xe	10.4	133.905398		
												^{136}Xe	8.9	135.907222		
55	*Cesium*	Cs	132.9054	1	28.40 ± 0.01	678.4	Solid	1.873	6.5×10^{-4}	–	2.1×10^{-6}	^{133}Cs	100	132.905463		
	Césium															
	Caesium															

For footnotes see page 23.

Atomic number	Name (English, French, German)	Symbol	Relative atomic mass 1979[1]	Valency[16]	Melting point[2] at standard pressure[3] (unless otherwise stated) °C	Boiling point[2] at standard pressure[3] (unless otherwise stated) °C	Density[2] Gases: standard density[3] in $g\,L^{-1}$ Liquids and solids: $g\,cm^{-3}$ or relative density (20 °C/4 °C, unless otherwise stated)		Natural abundance: Mass fraction × 100 in earth's crust, hydrosphere and atmosphere[4] %	Natural abundance: Volume fraction × 100 in atmosphere[5] %	Natural abundance: Mass fraction × 100 in human body[6] %	Natural nuclides: Nuclide (nucleon number)	Natural nuclides: Mass fraction × 100 in natural isotopic mixture[17] %	Natural nuclides: Nuclidic mass[8] u	Natural nuclides: Mode of decay[7–9] (type of radiation)	Natural nuclides: Half-life[7,8,10]
56	*Barium* Baryum Barium	Ba	137.33	2	725	1640	Solid	3.5	0.026	–	3.1×10^{-5}	^{130}Ba	0.106	129.906284		
												^{132}Ba	0.101	131.905045		
												^{134}Ba	2.417	133.904493		
												^{135}Ba	6.592	134.905671		
												^{136}Ba	7.854	135.904359		
												^{137}Ba	11.23	136.905815		
												^{138}Ba	71.70	137.905235		
57	*Lanthanum* Lanthane Lanthan	La	138.9055⁺	3	921	3457	Solid	6.145 (25 °C)	0.0017	–	–	^{138}La	0.09	137.907161	β^- γ K	1.12×10^{11} y
												^{139}La	99.91	138.906403		
58	*Cerium* Cérium Cer	Ce	140.12	3, 4	799	3426	Solid	6.657 (25 °C)	0.0043	–	–	^{136}Ce	0.19	135.907120		
												^{138}Ce	0.25	137.906027		
												^{140}Ce	88.48	139.905484		
												^{142}Ce	11.08	141.909300		
59	*Praseodymium* Praséodyme Praseodym	Pr	140.9077	(2), 3, 4	931	3512	Solid	α 6.773 β 6.64	5.2×10^{-4}	–	–	^{141}Pr	100	140.907698		
60	*Neodymium* Néodyme Neodym	Nd	144.24⁺	3	1021	3068	Solid	α 7.007 β 6.80	0.0022	–	–	^{142}Nd	27.16	141.907766		
												^{143}Nd	12.18	142.909856		
												^{144}Nd	23.80	143.910129	α	2.1×10^{15} y
												^{145}Nd	8.29	144.912610		
												^{146}Nd	17.19	145.91269		
												^{148}Nd	5.75	147.91648		
												^{150}Nd	5.63	149.92071		
61	*Promethium* Prométhium Promethium	Pm	(145)	3	1168 ± 6	2460	Solid	7.22 ± 0.02 (25 °C)	–	–	–	^{147}Pm	See[14]	146.915166	β^-	2.62 y
62	*Samarium* Samarium Samarium	Sm	150.36⁺	2, 3	1077 ± 5	1791	Solid	α 7.520 β 7.40	6×10^{-4}	–	–	^{144}Sm	3.1	143.912074		
												^{147}Sm	15.1	146.914925	α	1.06×10^{11} y
												^{148}Sm	11.3	147.914851	α	1.2×10^{13} y
												^{149}Sm	13.9	148.917211	α	$\sim 4 \times 10^{14}$ y
												^{150}Sm	7.4	149.917303		
												^{152}Sm	26.6	151.919755		
												^{154}Sm	22.7	153.922222		

63	*Europium* .... Europium Europium	Eu	151.96	2, 3	822	1597	Solid	5.243 (25 °C)	9.9×10^{-5}	–	–	^{151}Eu ^{153}Eu	47.8 52.2	150.919883 152.921260		
64	*Gadolinium* .... Gadolinium Gadolinium	Gd	157.25^{+}	3	1313 ± 1	3266	Solid	7.9004 (25 °C)	5.9×10^{-4}	–	–	^{152}Gd ^{154}Gd ^{155}Gd ^{156}Gd ^{157}Gd ^{158}Gd ^{160}Gd	0.20 2.1 14.8 20.6 15.7 24.8 21.8	151.919817 153.920891 154.922636 155.922143 156.923972 157.924123 159.927071	α	1.1×10^{14} y
65	*Terbium* .... Terbium Terbium	Tb	158.9254	3, 4	1356	3123	Solid	8.229	8.5×10^{-5}	–	–	^{159}Tb	100	158.925386		
66	*Dysprosium* .... Dysprosium Dysprosium	Dy	162.50^{+}	3	1412	2562	Solid	8.550 (25 °C)	4.2×10^{-4}	–	–	^{156}Dy ^{158}Dy ^{160}Dy ^{161}Dy ^{162}Dy ^{163}Dy ^{164}Dy	0.06 0.10 2.34 19.0 25.5 24.9 28.1	155.924326 157.924440 159.925231 160.926970 161.926838 162.928770 163.929218		
67	*Holmium* .... Holmium Holmium	Ho	164.9304	3	1474	2695	Solid	8.795 (25 °C)	1.1×10^{-4}	–	–	^{165}Ho	100	164.930357		
68	*Erbium* .... Erbium Erbium	Er	167.26^{+}	3	1529	2863	Solid	9.066 (25 °C)	2.3×10^{-4}	–	–	^{162}Er ^{164}Er ^{166}Er ^{167}Er ^{168}Er ^{170}Er	0.14 1.56 33.4 22.9 27.1 14.9	161.928826 163.929235 165.930324 166.932079 167.932402 169.935491		
69	*Thulium* .... Thulium Thulium	Tm	168.9342	(2) 3	1545 ± 15	1947	Solid	9.321 (25 °C)	1.9×10^{-5}	–	–	^{169}Tm	100	168.934245		
70	*Ytterbium* .... Ytterbium Ytterbium	Yb	173.04^{+}	2, 3	819	1194	Solid	α6.965 β6.54	2.5×10^{-4}	–	–	^{168}Yb ^{170}Yb ^{171}Yb ^{172}Yb ^{173}Yb ^{174}Yb ^{176}Yb	0.14 3.06 14.3 21.9 16.1 31.8 12.7	167.933925 169.934792 170.936354 171.936405 172.938234 173.938881 175.942582		
71	*Lutetium* .... Lutetium Lutetium	Lu	174.967^{+}	3	1663	3395	Solid	9.840 (25 °C)	7×10^{-5}	–	–	^{175}Lu ^{176}Lu	97.39 2.61	174.940796 175.942705	 β^- γ	 3.79×10^{10} y
72	*Hafnium* .... Hafnium Hafnium	Hf	178.49^{+}	(2, 3), 4	2227 ± 20	4602	Solid	13.31	4.2×10^{-4}	–	–	^{174}Hf ^{176}Hf ^{177}Hf ^{178}Hf ^{179}Hf ^{180}Hf	0.2 5.2 18.60 27.1 13.7 35.2	173.940140 175.941429 176.943245 177.943723 178.945840 179.946575	α	2.0×10^{15} y

For footnotes see page 23.

Atomic number	Name (English, French, German)	Symbol	Relative atomic mass 1979[1]	Valency[16]	Melting point[2] at standard pressure[3] (unless otherwise stated) °C	Boiling point[2] at standard pressure[3] (unless otherwise stated) °C	Density[2] Gases: standard density[3] in $g\,L^{-1}$ Liquids and solids: $g\,cm^{-3}$ or relative density (20 °C/4 °C, unless otherwise stated)		Natural abundance: Mass fraction × 100 in earth's crust, hydrosphere and atmosphere[4] %	Natural abundance: Volume fraction × 100 in atmosphere[5] %	Natural abundance: Mass fraction × 100 in human body[6] %	Natural nuclides: Nuclide (nucleon number)	Natural nuclides: Mass fraction × 100 in natural isotopic mixture[17] %	Natural nuclides: Nuclidic mass[8] u	Natural nuclides: Mode of decay[7–9] (type of radiation)	Natural nuclides: Half-life[7, 8, 10]
73	*Tantalum* Tantale Tantal	Ta	180.9479	(2, 3, 4), 5	2996	5425 ± 100	Solid	16.654	8×10^{-4}	–	–	^{180}Ta	0.012	179.947569	–	$> 10^{13}$ y
												^{181}Ta	99.988	180.948028		
74	*Tungsten* Tungstène Wolfram	W	183.85^{+}	2, 3, 4, 5, 6	3410 ± 20	5660	Solid	19.3	0.0064	–	–	^{180}W	0.10	179.94670		
												^{182}W	26.3	181.948248		
												^{183}W	14.3	182.950266		
												^{184}W	30.7	183.950975		
												^{186}W	28.6	185.954402		
75	*Rhenium* Rhénium Rhenium	Re	186.207	1, 2, 3, 4, 5, 6, 7	3180	5672 (estimated)	Solid	21.02	1×10^{-7}	–	–	^{185}Re	37.40	184.953007		
												^{187}Re	62.60	186.955791	β^-	4.3×10^{10} y
76	*Osmium* Osmium Osmium	Os	190.2	3, 4, 6, 8, (1, 2, 5, 7)	3045 ± 30	5027 ± 100	Solid	22.57	1×10^{-6}	–	–	^{184}Os	0.02	183.952595		
												^{186}Os	1.58	185.953883		
												^{187}Os	1.6	186.955788		
												^{188}Os	13.3	187.955877		
												^{189}Os	16.1	188.958183		
												^{190}Os	26.4	189.958482		
												^{192}Os	41.0	191.961514		
77	*Iridium* Iridium Iridium	Ir	192.22^{+}	(1, 2), 3, 4	2410	4130	Solid	22.42 (17 °C)	1×10^{-7}	–	–	^{191}Ir	37.3	190.960631		
												^{193}Ir	62.7	192.962964		
78	*Platinum* Platine Platin	Pt	195.08^{+}	(1), 2, 3, 4, (6)	1772	3827 ± 100	Solid	21.45	5×10^{-7}	–	–	^{190}Pt	0.01	189.959965	α	6×10^{11} y
												^{192}Pt	0.79	191.961078	α	$\sim 10^{15}$ y
												^{194}Pt	32.9	193.962713		
												^{195}Pt	33.8	194.964804		
												^{196}Pt	25.3	195.964965		
												^{198}Pt	7.2	197.967895		
79	*Gold* Or Gold	Au	196.9665	1, 3	1064.43	2807	Solid	19.32	5×10^{-7}	–	$< 1.4 \times 10^{-5}$	^{197}Au	100	196.966548		
80	*Mercury* Mercure Quecksilber	Hg	200.59^{+}	1, 2	– 38.842	356.58	Liquid	13.5546[15]	4×10^{-3}	–	1.9×10^{-5}	^{196}Hg	0.2	195.965822		
												^{198}Hg	10.1	197.966748		
												^{199}Hg	17.0	198.968275		
												^{200}Hg	23.1	199.968321		
												^{201}Hg	13.2	200.970304		
												^{202}Hg	29.6	201.970643		
												^{204}Hg	6.8	203.973498		

81	*Thallium* . . . . Thallium Thallium	Tl	204.383	1, 3	303.5	1457 ± 10	Solid	11.85	3×10^{-5}	–	–	^{203}Tl	29.524	202.972348		
												^{205}Tl	70.476	204.974438		
												^{206}Tl (Radium E″)	–	205.976121	β^-	4.19 min
												^{207}Tl (Actinium C″)	–	206.977441	β^-, γ	4.78 min
												^{208}Tl (Thorium C″)	–	207.982019	β^-, γ	3.1 min
												^{210}Tl (Radium C″)	–	209.990098	β^-, γ	1.3 min
82	*Lead* . . . . Plomb Blei	Pb	207.2	2, 4	327.502	1740	Solid	11.35	0.0018	–	1.7×10^{-4}	^{204}Pb	1.4	203.973049		
												^{206}Pb (Radium G)	24.1	205.974475		
												^{207}Pb	22.1	206.975903		
												^{208}Pb	52.4	207.976658		
												^{210}Pb (Radium D)	–	209.984198	β^-, α, γ	21 y
												^{211}Pb (Actinium B)	–	210.988768	β^-, γ	36.1 min
												^{212}Pb (Thorium B)	–	211.991901	β^-, γ	10.64 h
												^{214}Pb (Radium B)	–	213.999842	β^-, γ	26.8 min
83	*Bismuth* . . . . Bismuth Wismut	Bi	208.9804	(2), 3, 5	271.3	1560 ± 5	Solid	9.747	2×10^{-5}	–	–	^{209}Bi	100	208.980401	–	$>2 \times 10^{18}$ y
												^{210}Bi (Radium E)	–	209.984130	α, β^-	5.01 d
												^{211}Bi (Actinium C)	–	210.987290	α, β^-, γ	2.15 min
												^{212}Bi (Thorium C)	–	211.991286	α, β^-, γ	60.6 min
												^{214}Bi (Radium C)	–	213.998730	α, β^-, γ	19.7 min
												^{215}Bi	–	215.00185	β^-	7 min
84	*Polonium* . . . . Polonium Polonium	Po	(209)	2, 4, 6	254	962	Solid	α 9.32	2.1×10^{-14}	–	–	^{210}Po (Radium F)	–	209.982883	α, γ	138.38 d
												^{211}Po (Actinium C′)	–	210.986657	α, γ	0.52 s
												^{212}Po (Thorium C′)	–	211.988874	α	0.30 μs
												^{214}Po (Radium C′)	–	213.995212	α, γ	164 μs
												^{215}Po (Actinium A)	–	214.999449	α, β^-	0.0018 s
												^{216}Po (Thorium A)	–	216.001917	α	0.15 s
												^{218}Po (Radium A)	–	218.009007	α, β^-	3.05 min
85	*Astatine* . . . . Astatine Astatin	At	(210)	1, 3, 5	302	337	–		3×10^{-24}	–	–	^{215}At	–	214.998654	α	≈ 100 μs
												^{216}At	–	216.002426	α	≈ 300 μs
												^{218}At	–	218.008714	α, β^-	≈ 2 s
												^{219}At	–	219.01132	α, β^-	54 s

For footnotes see page 23.

Atomic number	*Name* (English, French, German)	*Symbol*	*Relative atomic mass 1979*[1]	*Valency*[16]	*Melting point*[2] *at standard pressure*[3] (unless otherwise stated) °C	*Boiling point*[2] *at standard pressure*[3] (unless otherwise stated) °C	*Density*[2] Gases: standard density[3] in $g\,L^{-1}$ Liquids and solids: $g\,cm^{-3}$ or relative density (20 °C/4 °C, unless otherwise stated)		*Natural abundance* Mass fraction × 100 in earth's crust, hydrosphere and atmosphere[4] %	Volume fraction × 100 in atmosphere[5] %	Mass fraction × 100 in human body[6] %	*Natural nuclides* Nuclide (nucleon number)	Mass fraction × 100 in natural isotopic mixture[17] %	Nuclidic mass[8] u	Mode of decay[7–9] (type of radiation)	Half-life[7, 8, 10]
86	*Radon* .... Radon Radon	Rn	(222)	0	−71	−61.8	Gas Liquid Solid	9.73 4.4 (−62 °C) 4	6.2×10^{-16}	–	–	^{219}Rn (Actinon)	–	219.009507	α γ	4.0 s
												^{220}Rn (Thoron)	–	220.011396	α γ	55 s
												^{222}Rn (Radon)	–	222.017608	α γ	3.824 d
87	*Francium* .... Francium Francium	Fr	(223)	1	27	677	–	–	1.3×10^{-21}	–	–	^{223}Fr (Actinium K)	–	223.019760	α β^- γ	22 min
88	*Radium* .... Radium Radium	Ra	[226.0254]	2	700	1140	Solid	5?	9.5×10^{-11}	–	1.4×10^{-13}	^{223}Ra (Actinium X)	–	223.018526	α γ	11.43 d
												^{224}Ra (Thorium X)	–	224.020212	α γ	3.67 d
												^{226}Ra	–	226.025436	α γ	1600 y
												^{228}Ra (Mesothorium I)	–	228.031091	β^- γ	5.75 y
89	*Actinium* .... Actinium Actinium	Ac	[227.0278]	3	1050	3200 ± 300 (estimated)	Solid	10.07 (calculated)	6.1×10^{-14}	–	–	^{227}Ac	–	227.027773	α β^- γ	21.77 y
												^{228}Ac (Mesothorium II)	–	228.031033	β^- γ	6.13 h
90	*Thorium* .... Thorium Thorium	Th	[232.0381]	(2, 3), 4	1750	~4790	Solid	11.72	0.0011	–	–	^{227}Th (Radioactinium)	–	227.027726	α γ	18.7 d
												^{228}Th (Radiothorium)	–	228.028738	α γ	1.913 y
												^{230}Th (Ionium)	–	230.033157	α γ	8.0×10^4 y
												^{231}Th (Uranium Y)	–	231.036316	β^- γ	25.5 h
												^{232}Th	100	232.038074	α γ	1.41×10^{10} y
												^{234}Th (Uranium X_1)	–	234.043633	β^- γ	24.10 d

91	*Protactinium* .... Protactinium Protactinium	Pa	[231.0359]	(2, 3), 4, 5	< 1600	–	Solid	15.37 (calculated)	9×10^{-11}	–	–	^{231}Pa	–	231.035902	α γ	3.28×10^{4} y
												^{234}Pa (Uranium X_2) (^{234m}Pa)	–	234.04343	$β^-$ γ IT	1.17 min
												^{234}Pa (Uranium Z)	–	234.04335	$β^-$ γ	6.75 h
92	*Uranium* .... Uranium Uran	U	238.0289	(2), 3, 4, (5), 6	1132.3 ± 0.8	3818	Solid	~ 18.95	2.9×10^{-4}	–	1.3×10^{-7}	^{234}U (Uranium II)	0.005	234.040975	α γ	2.44×10^{5} y
												^{235}U (Actinoura-nium)	0.72	235.043944	α γ	7.04×10^{8} y
												^{238}U (Uranium I)	99.275	238.050816	α γ	4.47×10^{9} y

[1] Atomic masses 1979 relative to the carbon isotope ^{12}C; see footnote[2], page 9.

[2] HAMMOND, C.R., in WEAST, R.C. (Ed.), *CRC Handbook of Chemistry and Physics,* 63rd ed., CRC Press, Boca Raton, Fla., 1982–1983, pages B-2 and B-73.

[3] Standard pressure p_n = 101325 Pa = 1.01325 bar = 1013.25 mbar. Standard density = density at standard pressure p_n and standard temperature T_n = 273.15 K or t_n = 0 °C.

[4] The values given (REMY, H., *Lehrbuch der anorganischen Chemie,* 12th and 13th eds., volume 2, Akademische Verlagsgesellschaft Geest & Portig, Leipzig, 1973, page 846) are total percentages in the lithosphere (outer 10 miles), hydrosphere and atmosphere.

[5] Dry atmosphere at sea level. Values from *Manual of the ICAO Standard Atmosphere,* 2nd ed., International Civil Aviation Organization, Montreal, 1964, page XVII.

[6] SCHROEDER, H.A., *J. chron. Dis.,* **18**, 217 (1965); SCHROEDER and NASON, *Clin. Chem.,* **17**, 461 (1971).

[7] HEATH, R.L., in WEAST, R.C. (Ed.), *CRC Handbook of Chemistry and Physics,* 63rd ed., CRC Press, Boca Raton, Fla., 1982–1983, page B-255.

[8] Relative to the carbon isotope ^{12}C; see footnote[2], page 9. Values from LEDERER and SHIRLEY (Eds.), *Table of Isotopes,* 7th ed., Wiley, New York, 1978, and in particular from WAPSTRA and GOVE, *Nuclear Data Tables,* **9**, 276 (1971), who also give uncertainties for the individual nuclidic masses.

[9] α = alpha particle (helium nucleus consisting of 2 protons and 2 neutrons); $β^-$ = beta particle (electron); γ = gamma ray; K = orbital electron capture (from K shell); IT = isomeric transition.

[10] y = year, d = day, h = hour, min = minute, s = second.

[11] As a result of the possibility of the two nuclei having parallel or anti-parallel spins, molecular hydrogen is a mixture of *ortho*-hydrogen (parallel spins) and *para*-hydrogen (anti-parallel spins). Under equilibrium conditions, molecular hydrogen at room temperature contains the two particles in the approximate proportions of 3 (*ortho-*) to 1 (*para-*).

[12] A decay product of ^{14}N in the atmosphere due to the action of cosmic rays. The ratio of ^{1}H to ^{3}H atoms in the atmosphere is of the order of 10^{14} (GROSSE et al., *Phys. Rev.,* **93**, 250 [1954]).

[13] A decay product of ^{14}N in the atmosphere due to the action of naturally occurring neutrons.

[14] A decay product of ^{146}Nd due to the action of naturally occurring neutrons.

[15] For internationally accepted density values for mercury at different temperatures see LINDSAY, R.B., in GRAY, D.E. (Ed.), *American Institute of Physics Handbook,* McGraw-Hill, New York, 1957, pages 2–140.

[16] Valencies which appear only rarely or are not yet confirmed are given in brackets.

[17] Representative values from IUPAC Table of Isotopic Compositions of the Elements as Determined by Mass Spectrometry (International Union of Pure and Applied Chemistry, *Pure appl. Chem.,* **52**, 2351 [1980]).

[18] In water only.

Transuranic Elements[1]

Atomic number	Name	Symbol	Relative atomic mass 1979[2]	Valency[3]	Melting point[3] °C	Boiling point[3] °C	Relative density[3] (20 °C/4 °C, unless otherwise stated)	Nuclides with longest half-life: Nuclide (nucleon number)	Nuclidic mass[4] u	Mode of decay[5,6] (type of radiation)	Half-life[5,7]
93	*Neptunium*	Np	[237.0482]	3, 4, 5, 6	640 ± 1	3902 (estimated)	Solid α20.25	^{237}Np	237.048 190	α γ	2.14 ± 10^6 y
94	*Plutonium*	Pu	(244)	3, 4, 5, 6	641	3232	Solid α19.84 (25 °C)	^{244}Pu	244.064 230	α	8.0 × 10^7 y
95	*Americium*	Am	(243)	2, 3, 4, 5, 6	944 ± 4	2607	Solid 13.67	^{243}Am	243.061 394	α γ	7.37 × 10^3 y
96	*Curium*	Cm	(247)	3, 4	1340 ± 40	–	Solid 13.51 (calculated)	^{247}Cm	247.070 38	α	1.56 × 10^7 y
97	*Berkelium*	Bk	(247)	3, 4	–	–	Solid 14 (estimated)	^{247}Bk	247.070 316	α γ	1.4 × 10^3 y
98	*Californium*	Cf	(251)	3	–	–	–	^{251}Cf	251.079 60	α γ	9.0 × 10^2 y
99	*Einsteinium*	Es	(252)	3	–	–	–	^{252}Es	252.082 86	α K γ	472 d
100	*Fermium*	Fm	(257)	3	–	–	–	^{257}Fm	257.095 146	α γ	100.5 d
101	*Mendelevium*	Md	(258)	2, 3	–	–	–	^{258}Md	–	α	56 d
102	*Nobelium*	No	(259)	2, 3	–	–	–	^{259}No	–	α K	58 min
103	*Lawrencium*	Lr	(260)	3?	–	–	–	^{260}Lr	–	α	3.0 min
104	*Unnilquadium*◊	Unq◊	(261)	–	–	–	–	–	–	–	–
105	*Unnilpentium*◊	Unp◊	(262)	–	–	–	–	–	–	–	–
106	*Unnilhexium*◊	Unh◊	(263)	–	–	–	–	–	–	–	–

[1] The transuranic elements have become known as artificially produced elements. They can be regarded as naturally occurring elements insofar as some of them have in the past occurred naturally or are still, like ^{239}Pu, identifiable in nature in very small amounts. In a sense they are elements which as a result of their short half-lives have become 'extinct'.

[2] Atomic masses 1979 relative to the carbon isotope ^{12}C; see footnote[2], page 9.

[3] HAMMOND, C.R., in WEAST, R.C. (Ed.), *CRC Handbook of Chemistry and Physics*, 63rd ed., CRC Press, Boca Raton, Fla., 1982–1983, page B-2.

[4] Relative to the carbon isotope ^{12}C; see footnote[2], page 9. Values from WAPSTRA and GOVE, *Nuclear Data Tables*, **9**, 276 (1971), who also give the uncertainties.

[5] HEATH, R.L., in WEAST, R.C. (Ed.), *CRC Handbook of Chemistry and Physics*, 63rd ed., CRC Press, Boca Raton, Fla., 1982–1983, page B-255; LEDERER and SHIRLEY (Eds.), *Table of Isotopes*, 7th ed., Wiley, New York, 1978.

[6] α = alpha particle (helium nucleus consisting of 2 protons and 2 neutrons); γ = gamma ray; K = orbital electron capture (from K shell).

[7] y = year, d = day, h = hour, min = minute, s = second.

◊ The names and symbols of these elements are not yet internationally recognized.

Electronic Configurations of the Elements[1]

Z = atomic number; E_r = resonance energy (eV); E_i = ionization energy (eV); E_{r_I} = resonance energy of singly-ionized atom (eV)

Z	Element	E_r	E_i	E_{r_I}	K	L		M			N				O				P			Q
					1s	2s	2p	3s	3p	3d	4s	4p	4d	4f	5s	5p	5d	5f	6s	6p	6d	7s
1	H	10.19	13.60	...	1																	
2	He	21.20	24.58	40.8	2																	
3	Li	1.85	5.39	62.2	2	1																
4	Be	5.28	9.32	3.96	2	2																
5	B	4.96	8.30	9.10	2	2	1															
6	C	7.48	11.26	9.29	2	2	2															
7	N	10.3	14.54	11.4	2	2	3															
8	O	9.52	13.61	14.8	2	2	4															
9	F	12.98	17.42	20.42	2	2	5															
10	Ne	16.84	21.56	26.89	2	2	6															
11	Na	2.10	5.14	33.3	2	2	6	1														
12	Mg	4.34	7.64	4.42	2	2	6	2														
13	Al	3.14	5.98	7.42	2	2	6	2	1													
14	Si	4.92	8.15	6.86	2	2	6	2	2													
15	P	6.94	10.95	8.09	2	2	6	2	3													
16	S	6.86	10.36	9.84	2	2	6	2	4													
17	Cl	9.21	13.01	11.56	2	2	6	2	5													
18	Ar	11.53	15.75	13.47	2	2	6	2	6													
19	K	1.61	4.34	20.6	2	2	6	2	6		1											
20	Ca	2.93	6.11	3.12	2	2	6	2	6		2											
21	Sc	2.32	6.56	3.40	2	2	6	2	6	1	2											
22	Ti	1.97	6.83	3.66	2	2	6	2	6	2	2											
23	V	2.24	6.74	4.40	2	2	6	2	6	3	2											
24	Cr	2.89	6.76	6.00	2	2	6	2	6	5	1											
25	Mn	3.07	7.43	4.76	2	2	6	2	6	5	2											
26	Fe	3.21	7.90	5.20	2	2	6	2	6	6	2											
27	Co	3.57	7.86	5.83	2	2	6	2	6	7	2											
28	Ni	3.54	7.63	6.39	2	2	6	2	6	8	2											
29	Cu	3.79	7.72	8.26	2	2	6	2	6	10	1											
30	Zn	4.03	9.39	5.91	2	2	6	2	6	10	2											
31	Ga	3.07	6.00	8.78	2	2	6	2	6	10	2	1										
32	Ge	4.64	8.13	8.06	2	2	6	2	6	10	2	2										
33	As	6.28	9.81	9.14	2	2	6	2	6	10	2	3										
34	Se	6.32	9.75	10.39	2	2	6	2	6	10	2	4										
35	Br	8.32	11.84	12.21	2	2	6	2	6	10	2	5										
36	Kr	10.03	13.99	15.82	2	2	6	2	6	10	2	6										
37	Rb	1.59	4.17	17.8	2	2	6	2	6	10	2	6			1							
38	Sr	2.69	5.69	2.94	2	2	6	2	6	10	2	6			2							
39	Y	1.99	6.57	2.91	2	2	6	2	6	10	2	6	1		2							
40	Zr	2.02	6.95	3.47	2	2	6	2	6	10	2	6	2		2							
41	Nb	2.97	6.77	4.13	2	2	6	2	6	10	2	6	4		1							
42	Mo	3.18	7.18	6.08	2	2	6	2	6	10	2	6	5		1							
43	Tc	2.88	7.45	4.68	2	2	6	2	6	10	2	6	6		1							
44	Ru	3.26	7.5	6.29	2	2	6	2	6	10	2	6	7		1							
45	Rh	3.35	7.7	4.97	2	2	6	2	6	10	2	6	8		1							
46	Pd	4.22	8.33	8.12	2	2	6	2	6	10	2	6	10									
47	Ag	3.66	7.58	11.1	2	2	6	2	6	10	2	6	10		1							
48	Cd	3.80	8.99	5.47	2	2	6	2	6	10	2	6	10		2							
49	In	3.02	5.78	7.82	2	2	6	2	6	10	2	6	10		2	1						
50	Sn	4.30	7.33	7.30	2	2	6	2	6	10	2	6	10		2	2						
51	Sb	5.36	8.64	9.56	2	2	6	2	6	10	2	6	10		2	3						
52	Te	5.78	9.01	8.82	2	2	6	2	6	10	2	6	10		2	4						
53	I	7.67	10.44	10.04	2	2	6	2	6	10	2	6	10		2	5						
54	Xe	8.44	12.13	11.27	2	2	6	2	6	10	2	6	10		2	6						
55	Cs	1.38	3.89	15.2	2	2	6	2	6	10	2	6	10		2	6			1			
56	Ba	2.24	5.21	2.51	2	2	6	2	6	10	2	6	10		2	6			2			
57	La	1.64	5.61	1.75	2	2	6	2	6	10	2	6	10		2	6	1		2			
58	Ce	...	6.91	2.72	2	2	6	2	6	10	2	6	10	2	2	6			2			
59	Pr	...	5.76	2.81	2	2	6	2	6	10	2	6	10	3	2	6			2			
60	Nd	...	6.31	2.63	2	2	6	2	6	10	2	6	10	4	2	6			2			
61	Pm	...	...	...	2	2	6	2	6	10	2	6	10	5	2	6			2			
62	Sm	1.71	5.6	2.63	2	2	6	2	6	10	2	6	10	6	2	6			2			
63	Eu	1.74	5.67	2.95	2	2	6	2	6	10	2	6	10	7	2	6			2			
64	Gd	1.665	6.16	3.18	2	2	6	2	6	10	2	6	10	7	2	6	1		2			
65	Tb	...	6.74	...	2	2	6	2	6	10	2	6	10	9	2	6			2			
66	Dy	...	6.82	...	2	2	6	2	6	10	2	6	10	10	2	6			2			
67	Ho	...	...	...	2	2	6	2	6	10	2	6	10	11	2	6			2			
68	Er	...	...	...	2	2	6	2	6	10	2	6	10	12	2	6			2			
69	Tm	2.62?	...	2.68	2	2	6	2	6	10	2	6	10	13	2	6			2			
70	Yb	2.23	6.2	3.35	2	2	6	2	6	10	2	6	10	14	2	6			2			
71	Lu	2.16?	5.0	3.38	2	2	6	2	6	10	2	6	10	14	2	6	1		2			
72	Hf	2.19	5.5	3.43	2	2	6	2	6	10	2	6	10	14	2	6	2		2			
73	Ta	2.44	6	3.63	2	2	6	2	6	10	2	6	10	14	2	6	3		2			
74	W	2.49	7.98	4.48	2	2	6	2	6	10	2	6	10	14	2	6	4		2			
75	Re	3.57	7.88	...	2	2	6	2	6	10	2	6	10	14	2	6	5		2			
76	Os	2.80	8.7	...	2	2	6	2	6	10	2	6	10	14	2	6	6		2			
77	Ir	4.65	9.2	...	2	2	6	2	6	10	2	6	10	14	2	6	7		2			
78	Pt	4.04	8.97	6.38	2	2	6	2	6	10	2	6	10	14	2	6	9		1			
79	Au	4.63	9.22	7.81	2	2	6	2	6	10	2	6	10	14	2	6	10		1			
80	Hg	4.89	10.43	6.38	2	2	6	2	6	10	2	6	10	14	2	6	10		2			
81	Tl	3.28	6.11	9.38	2	2	6	2	6	10	2	6	10	14	2	6	10		2	1		
82	Pb	4.33	7.42	7.35	2	2	6	2	6	10	2	6	10	14	2	6	10		2	2		
83	Bi	4.04	8.0	8.63	2	2	6	2	6	10	2	6	10	14	2	6	10		2	3		
84	Po	...	7.25	...	2	2	6	2	6	10	2	6	10	14	2	6	10		2	4		
85	At	...	...	...	2	2	6	2	6	10	2	6	10	14	2	6	10		2	5		
86	Rn	6.78	10.75	...	2	2	6	2	6	10	2	6	10	14	2	6	10		2	6		
87	Fr	...	...	...	2	2	6	2	6	10	2	6	10	14	2	6	10		2	6		1
88	Ra	2.57	5.28	2.65	2	2	6	2	6	10	2	6	10	14	2	6	10		2	6		2
89	Ac	...	...	...	2	2	6	2	6	10	2	6	10	14	2	6	10		2	6	1	2
90	Th	...	...	2.12	2	2	6	2	6	10	2	6	10	14	2	6	10		2	6	2	2
91	Pa	...	...	...	2	2	6	2	6	10	2	6	10	14	2	6	10	2	2	6	1	2
92	U	1.44	~4	3.21	2	2	6	2	6	10	2	6	10	14	2	6	10	3	2	6	1	2
93	Np	...	...	...	2	2	6	2	6	10	2	6	10	14	2	6	10	4	2	6	1	2
94	Pu	...	...	...	2	2	6	2	6	10	2	6	10	14	2	6	10	6	2	6		2
95	Am	...	...	...	2	2	6	2	6	10	2	6	10	14	2	6	10	7	2	6		2
96	Cm	...	...	...	2	2	6	2	6	10	2	6	10	14	2	6	10	7	2	6	1	2
97	Bk	...	...	...	2	2	6	2	6	10	2	6	10	14	2	6	10	9	2	6		2
98	Cf	...	...	...	2	2	6	2	6	10	2	6	10	14	2	6	10	10	2	6		2
99	Es	...	...	...	2	2	6	2	6	10	2	6	10	14	2	6	10	11	2	6		2
100	Fm	...	...	...	2	2	6	2	6	10	2	6	10	14	2	6	10	12	2	6		2
101	Md	...	...	...	2	2	6	2	6	10	2	6	10	14	2	6	10	13	2	6		2
102	No	...	...	...	2	2	6	2	6	10	2	6	10	14	2	6	10	14	2	6		2
103	Lr	...	...	...	2	2	6	2	6	10	2	6	10	14	2	6	10	14	2	6	1	2
104	Unq	...	...	...	2	2	6	2	6	10	2	6	10	14	2	6	10	14	2	6	2	2
105	Unp	...	...	...	2	2	6	2	6	10	2	6	10	14	2	6	10	14	2	6	3	2

[1] Mavrodineanu and Boiteux, *L'analyse spectrale quantitative par la flamme*, Masson, Paris, 1954, p. 116; Foster, L.S., in Weast, R.C. (Ed.), *CRC Handbook of Chemistry and Physics*, 63rd ed., CRC Press, Boca Raton, Fla., 1982–1983, page B-1; Element 105 from Waber et al., *J. chem. Phys.*, **51**, 664 (1969).

Many of the spectral emission lines listed in the tables below are readily detectable only in the hotter flames such as oxy-hydrogen or oxy-acetylene and in some cases only in the inner cone.

For further data on flame photometry see the literature[1].

Detailed flame spectra of sodium, potassium, calcium and magnesium[2]

The ionization potential of the neutral atom and excitation potential of the singly ionized atom (expressed in eV) are given in brackets. '*r*' represents a transition to ground state. The most suitable wavelengths for analysis are given in *italics*. 'I' signifies the singly ionized atom, 'II' the neutral atom.

Element	Wavelength nm	Emitter	Excitation potential eV
Na...................... (5.14; 33.3)	285.3 *r*	II	4.06
	330.2 *r*	II	3.75
	330.3 *r*	II	3.75
	568.3	II	4.03
	568.8	II	4.03
	589.0 r	II	2.10
	589.6 r	II	2.10
	818.3	II	3.61
	819.5	II	3.61
K...................... (4.34; 20.6)	344.6 *r*	II	3.59
	344.7 *r*	II	3.59
	404.4 *r*	II	3.06
	404.7 *r*	II	3.06
	693.9	II	3.40
	696.5	II	3.40
	766.5 r	II	1.61
	769.9 r	II	1.61
Ca...................... (6.11; 3.12)	*422.7 r*	II	2.93
	393.4 *r*	I	3.15
	396.8 *r*	I	3.12
	622	CaO	1.97
	554	CaO	
Mg...................... (7.64; 4.42)	277.7	II	7.17
	277.8	II	7.17
	278.0	II	7.17
	278.1	II	7.17
	278.3	II	7.17
	285.2 r	II	4.34
	333.0	II	6.43
	333.2	II	6.43
	333.7	II	6.43
	382.9	II	5.85
	383.2	II	5.85
	383.8	II	5.85
	279.6 *r*	I	4.43
	280.3 *r*	I	4.42
	371	MgO	3.49
	383	MgO	3.38

Flame lines and bands of analytical importance[2]

The emissions are arranged in order of wavelength. Inclusion does not necessarily mean that the emission is suitable for quantitative measurement of the element concerned. Band emissions are given at the most sensitive wavelength and are marked '*b*'.

Wavelength nm	Element	Wavelength nm	Element	Wavelength nm	Element
228.8	Cd	377.6	Tl	497 *b*	Ti
253.7	Hg	378.6	Ru	500 *b*	Zn
285.2	Mg	383 *b*	Mg	510 *b*	Be
303.4	Sn	385.6	Fe	518 *b*	Ti
307.6	Zn	386.0	Fe	520.5	Cr
317.5	Sn	387.3	Co	520.6	Cr
324.8	Cu	387.4	Co	520.8	Cr
326.1	Cd	396.2	Al	521 *b*	B
327.4	Cu	403.3	Ga	535.0	Tl
328.1	Ag	403.5	Mn	540 *b*	Mo
330.2	Na	404.4	K	548 *b*	B
330.3	Na	404.7	K	550 *b*	U
338.3	Ag	405.8	Pb	552 *b*	Dy
340.5	Pd	407.8	Sr	553.6	Ba
341.2	Co	410.2	In	554 *b*	Ca
341.5	Ni	417.2	Ga	560 *b*	La
343.5	Rh	420.2	Rb	562 *b*	Pr
344.6	K	421.6	Sr	565 *b*	Tb
344.7	K	422.7	Ca	570 *b*	Gd
349 *b*	Sn	425.4	Cr	570 *b*	Dy
350.2	Co	427.5	Cr	571 *b*	Pr
350.3	Rh	429.0	Cr	576 *b*	V
351.5	Ni	430.4	Nd	589.0	Na
352.5	Ni	438 *b*	La	589.5	Na
353.0	Co	442 *b*	La	600 *b*	Mo
360.5	Cr	444 *b*	Y	600 *b*	Tb
361.0	Pd	450 *b*	Nb	622 *b*	Ca
363.5	Pd	450 *b*	Gd	653 *b*	Sm
364 *b*	Te	451.1	In	660 *b*	Nd
368.3	Pb	455.4	Ba	670.8	Li
369.2	Rh	455.6	Cs	681 *b*	Sr
371 *b*	Mg	460.7	Sr	715 *b*	Ti
372 *b*	Te	460.9	Sc	766.5	K
372.0	Fe	462 *b*	Gd	769.9	K
372.3	Fe	462 *b*	Nb	780.0	Rb
372.8	Ru	466.2	Eu	794.8	Rb
373.3	Fe	467 *b*	Al	818.3	Na
373.5	Fe	471 *b*	Be	819.5	Na
373.7	Fe	472.3	Bi	852.1	Cs
374.3	Fe	481 *b*	Ce	873 *b*	Ba
374.6	Fe	483 *b*	Y	894.3	Cs
374.8	Fe	484 *b*	Al		
374.9	Fe	493.4	Ba		
375.8	Fe	495 *b*	B		

References

[1] MAVRODINEANU and BOITEUX, *L'analyse spectrale quantitative par la flamme,* Masson, Paris, 1954; DEAN, J.A., *Flame Photometry,* McGraw-Hill, New York, 1960; MACINTYRE, I., *Advanc. clin. Chem.,* **4**, 1 (1961); HERRMANN and ALKEMADE, *Flammenphotometrie,* 2nd ed., Springer, Berlin, 1960; MITCHELL and MAINES, *Progr. clin. Path.,* **5**, 99 (1973).

[2] MACINTYRE, I., in LONG, C. (Ed.), *Biochemists' Handbook,* Spon, London, 1961, page 10. Reproduced by kind permission of the author and publishers.

The ICAO standard atmosphere is fundamentally defined in terms of an ideal air assumed to be devoid of moisture, water vapor and dust. It is based on accepted *standard values for the sea-level air,* as follows:

Atmospheric pressure $p_0 = 101\,325$ Pa (= 760 torr)
Temperature $T_0 = 288.15$ K (= 15 °C)
Density $\varrho_0 = 1.2250$ kg m^{-3}
Acceleration due to gravity at 45° geographic latitude $g_0 = 9.80665$ m s^{-2}

The relative molecular mass M of air at sea level is calculated from the equation of state of a perfect gas

$$\varrho = \frac{Mp}{RT}$$

using the standard values for ϱ_0, p_0, T_0 at sea level and the universal (molar) gas constant R, which is based on the relative atomic mass of the nuclide ^{12}C = 12.

Universal gas constant $R = (8.31441 \pm 0.00026)$ J K^{-1} mol^{-1}
Molar mass of air at sea level $M_0 = 28.9644$ g mol^{-1}

Note that for the altitudes tabulated below the mean molar mass of air is assumed to be the same as at sea level (M_0).

Composition of clean, dry atmospheric air near sea level

Gas	Molar mass (g mol^{-1})	Volume fraction	Gas	Molar mass (g mol^{-1})	Volume fraction
N_2	28.0134	0.78084	CH_4	16.0426	2 × 10^{-6}
O_2	31.9988	0.209676	N_2O	44.0128	5 × 10^{-7}
Ar	39.948	9.34 × 10^{-3}	O_3	47.9982	Summer 0–7 × 10^{-8}◊
CO_2	44.0098	3.14 × 10^{-4}◊			Winter 0–2 × 10^{-7}◊
Ne	20.179	1.818 × 10^{-5}	SO_2	64.0588	0–10^{-6}◊
He	4.00260	5.24 × 10^{-6}	NO_2	46.0055	0–2 × 10^{-8}◊
Kr	83.80	1.14 × 10^{-6}	NH_3	17.0304	0 to traces◊
Xe	131.30	8.7 × 10^{-8}	CO	28.0104	0 to traces◊
H_2	2.0158	5 × 10^{-7}	I_2	253.8090	0–10^{-8}◊

◊The content of these gases may undergo significant variations from time to time or from place to place relative to the normal indicated for them.

Reference

[1] *Manual of the ICAO Standard Atmosphere,* 2nd ed., International Civil Aviation Organization, Montreal, 1964. Reproduced by kind permission of the publishers.

A one-digit number (preceded by a plus or minus sign) following the initial entry of each block indicates the power of ten by which that entry and each succeeding entry of that block should be multiplied. A change of power occurring within a block is indicated by a similar notation

Geometric altitude	Temperature	Atmospheric pressure		p/p_0	Boiling point of water	Density	ϱ/ϱ_0	Velocity of sound	Dynamic viscosity	Thermal conductivity	
m	°C	kPa	torr		°C	kg m^{-3}		m s^{-1}	Pa s	kW m^{-1} K^{-1}	kcal m^{-1} s^{-1} K^{-1}
−1000	21.501	1.13931 + 2	8.54554 + 2	1.12441 + 0	103.31	1.3470 + 0	1.0996 + 0	344.111	1.8206 − 5	25.8527 − 6	6.1748 − 6
− 950	21.176	1.13272	8.49610	1.11791	103.15	1.3407	1.0945	343.921	1.8190	25.8271	6.1687
− 900	20.851	1.12616	8.44689	1.11143	102.98	1.3344	1.0893	343.731	1.8175	25.8016	6.1626
− 850	20.526	1.11963	8.39792	1.10499	102.81	1.3281	1.0842	343.541	1.8159	25.7765	6.1566
− 800	20.201	1.11313	8.34917	1.09858	102.65	1.3219	1.0791	343.351	1.8144	25.7509	6.1505
− 750	19.876	1.10666	8.30066	1.09219	102.48	1.3157	1.0740	343.161	1.8128	25.7254	6.1444
− 700	19.550	1.10023	8.25237	1.08584	102.32	1.3095	1.0690	342.970	1.8113	25.6998	6.1383
− 650	19.225	1.09382	8.20432	1.07952	102.15	1.3033	1.0639	342.780	1.8097	25.6743	6.1323
− 600	18.900	1.08744	8.15649	1.07322	101.99	1.2971	1.0589	342.589	1.8081	25.6488	6.1262
− 550	18.575	1.08110	8.10889	1.06696	101.83	1.2910	1.0539	342.399	1.8066	25.6236	6.1201
− 500	18.250	1.07478 + 2	8.06151 + 2	1.06073 + 0	101.66	1.2849 + 0	1.0489 + 0	342.208	1.8050 − 5	25.5981 − 6	6.1140 − 6
− 450	17.925	1.06849	8.01436	1.05452	101.49	1.2788	1.0439	342.017	1.8035	25.5726	6.1079
− 400	17.600	1.06224	7.96743	1.04835	101.32	1.2727	1.0390	341.826	1.8019	25.5470	6.1018
− 350	17.275	1.05601	7.92073	1.04220	101.16	1.2667	1.0340	341.635	1.8003	25.5215	6.0957
− 300	16.950	1.04981	7.87425	1.03609	100.99	1.2607	1.0291	341.443	1.7988	25.4959	6.0896
− 250	16.625	1.04365	7.82799	1.03000	100.82	1.2547	1.0242	341.252	1.7972	25.4704	6.0835
− 200	16.300	1.03751	7.78195	1.02394	100.66	1.2487	1.0193	341.061	1.7956	25.4449	6.0774
− 150	15.975	1.03140	7.73614	1.01791	100.49	1.2427	1.0145	340.869	1.7941	25.4193	6.0713
− 100	15.650	1.02532	7.69054	1.01191	100.33	1.2368	1.0096	340.678	1.7925	25.3938	6.0652
− 50	15.325	1.01927	7.64516	1.00594	100.16	1.2309	1.0048	340.486	1.7909	25.3682	6.0591
0	15.000	1.01325 + 2	7.60000 + 2	1.00000 + 0	100.00	1.2250 + 0	1.0000 + 0	340.294	1.7894 − 5	25.3427 − 6	6.0530 − 6
50	14.675	1.00726	7.55505	9.94086 − 1	99.83	1.2191	9.9521 − 1	340.102	1.7878	25.3172	6.0469
100	14.350	1.00129	7.51032	9.88201	99.66	1.2133	9.9044	339.910	1.7862	25.2916	6.0408
150	14.025	9.95360 + 1	7.46581	9.82344	99.50	1.2075	9.8568	339.718	1.7847	25.2661	6.0347
200	13.700	9.89454	7.42151	9.76515	99.33	1.2017	9.8094	339.525	1.7831	25.2405	6.0286
250	13.375	9.83576	7.37743	9.70714	99.17	1.1959	9.7622	339.333	1.7815	25.2150	6.0225
300	13.050	9.77727	7.33356	9.64942	99.00	1.1901	9.7152	339.141	1.7800	25.1895	6.0164
350	12.725	9.71906	7.28990	9.59197	98.83	1.1844	9.6683	338.948	1.7784	25.1635	6.0102
400	12.400	9.66114	7.24645	9.53480	98.67	1.1786	9.6216	338.755	1.7768	25.1380	6.0041
450	12.075	9.60349	7.20321	9.47791	98.50	1.1729	9.5751	338.562	1.7752	25.1124	5.9980
500	11.750	9.54612 + 1	7.16018 + 2	9.42129 − 1	98.33	1.1673 + 0	9.5288 − 1	338.370	1.7737 − 5	25.0869 − 6	5.9919 − 6
550	11.425	9.48904	7.11736	9.36495	98.17	1.1616	9.4826	338.177	1.7721	25.0613	5.9858
600	11.100	9.43223	7.07475	9.30889	98.00	1.1560	9.4366	337.983	1.7705	25.0354	5.9796
650	10.775	9.37570	7.03235	9.25309	97.84	1.1504	9.3908	337.790	1.7689	25.0098	5.9735
700	10.450	9.31944	6.99015	9.19757	97.67	1.1448	9.3451	337.597	1.7673	24.9843	5.9674
750	10.126	9.26346	6.94816	9.14232	97.50	1.1392	9.2996	337.403	1.7658	24.9584	5.9612
800	9.801	9.20775	6.90638	9.08734	97.34	1.1337	9.2543	337.210	1.7642	24.9328	5.9551
850	9.476	9.15231	6.86480	9.03263	97.17	1.1281	9.2092	337.016	1.7626	24.9073	5.9490
900	9.151	9.09714	6.82342	8.97818	97.00	1.1226	9.1642	336.822	1.7610	24.8813	5.9428
950	8.826	9.04225	6.78225	8.92401	96.84	1.1171	9.1194	336.629	1.7594	24.8558	5.9367
1000	8.501	8.98762 + 1	6.74127 + 2	8.87009 − 1	96.68	1.1117 + 0	9.0748 − 1	336.435	1.7579 − 5	24.8298 − 6	5.9305 − 6
1050	8.176	8.93327	6.70050	8.81645	96.50	1.1062	9.0303	336.240	1.7563	24.8043	5.9244
1100	7.851	8.87918	6.65993	8.76307	96.34	1.1008	8.9860	336.046	1.7547	24.7783	5.9182
1150	7.526	8.82535	6.61956	8.70995	96.18	1.0954	8.9419	335.852	1.7531	24.7528	5.9121
1200	7.201	8.77180	6.57939	8.65709	96.00	1.0900	8.8979	335.657	1.7515	24.7268	5.9059
1250	6.877	8.71850	6.53941	8.60449	95.84	1.0846	8.8541	335.463	1.7499	24.7013	5.8998
1300	6.552	8.66547	6.49964	8.55215	95.68	1.0793	8.8105	335.268	1.7483	24.6753	5.8936
1350	6.227	8.61270	6.46006	8.50008	95.51	1.0740	8.7670	335.074	1.7467	24.6498	5.8875
1400	5.902	8.56020	6.42068	8.44826	95.34	1.0687	8.7237	334.879	1.7451	24.6238	5.8813
1450	5.577	8.50795	6.38149	8.39669	95.18	1.0634	8.6806	334.684	1.7436	24.5983	5.8752
1500	5.252	8.45596 + 1	6.34249 + 2	8.34539 − 1	95.01	1.0581 + 0	8.6376 − 1	334.489	1.7420 − 5	24.5723 − 6	5.8690 − 6
1550	4.927	8.40423	6.30369	8.29433	94.84	1.0529	8.5948	334.293	1.7404	24.5464	5.8628
1600	4.603	8.35276	6.26509	8.24354	94.68	1.0476	8.5521	334.098	1.7388	24.5208	5.8567
1650	4.278	8.30155	6.22667	8.19299	94.51	1.0424	8.5096	333.903	1.7372	24.4949	5.8505
1700	3.953	8.25059	6.18845	8.14270	94.34	1.0372	8.4673	333.707	1.7356	24.4689	5.8443
1750	3.628	8.19988	6.15042	8.09265	94.17	1.0321	8.4252	333.511	1.7340	24.4434	5.8382
1800	3.303	8.14943	6.11258	8.04286	94.01	1.0269	8.3832	333.316	1.7324	24.4174	5.8320
1850	2.978	8.09923	6.07492	7.99332	93.84	1.0218	8.3413	333.120	1.7308	24.3915	5.8258
1900	2.654	8.04928	6.03746	7.94402	93.68	1.0167	8.2996	332.924	1.7292	24.3659	5.8197
1950	2.329	7.99958	6.00018	7.89498	93.51	1.0116	8.2581	332.728	1.7276	24.3400	5.8135
2000	2.004	7.95014 + 1	5.96309 + 2	7.84618 − 1	93.34	1.0066 + 0	8.2168 − 1	332.532	1.7260 − 5	24.3140 − 6	5.8073 − 6
2050	1.679	7.90094	5.92619	7.79762	93.17	1.0015	8.1756	332.335	1.7244	24.2880	5.8011
2100	1.355	7.85199	5.88947	7.74931	93.01	9.9648 − 1	8.1345	332.139	1.7228	24.2621	5.7949
2150	1.030	7.80328	5.85294	7.70124	92.84	9.9147	8.0936	331.942	1.7212	24.2361	5.7887
2200	0.705	7.75482	5.81659	7.65341	92.67	9.8648	8.0529	331.746	1.7196	24.2106	5.7826
2250	0.380	7.70661	5.78043	7.60583	92.51	9.8151	8.0124	331.549	1.7180	24.1846	5.7764
2300	0.055	7.65863	5.74445	7.55849	92.34	9.7656	7.9719	331.352	1.7164	24.1587	5.7702
2350	−0.269	7.61091	5.70865	7.51138	92.17	9.7163	7.9317	331.155	1.7147	24.1327	5.7640
2400	−0.594	7.56342	5.67303	7.46452	92.01	9.6672	7.8916	330.958	1.7131	24.1068	5.7578
2450	−0.919	7.51618	5.63760	7.41789	91.84	9.6183	7.8517	330.761	1.7115	24.0808	5.7516

ICAO Standard Atmosphere

A one-digit number (preceded by a plus or minus sign) following the initial entry of each block indicates the power of ten by which that entry and each succeeding entry of that block should be multiplied

Geometric altitude	Temperature	Atmospheric pressure		p/p_0	Boiling point of water	Density	ϱ/ϱ_0	Velocity of sound	Dynamic viscosity	Thermal conductivity	
m	°C	kPa	torr		°C	kg m^{-3}		m s^{-1}	Pa s	kW m^{-1} K^{-1}	kcal m^{-1} s^{-1} K^{-1}
2500	−1.244	7.46917 + 1	5.60234 + 2	7.37150 − 1	91.67	9.5695 − 1	7.8119 − 1	330.563	1.7099 − 5	24.0548 − 6	5.7454 − 6
2550	−1.568	7.42240	5.56726	7.32534	91.51	9.5210	7.7722	330.366	1.7083	24.0289	5.7392
2600	−1.893	7.37588	5.53236	7.27942	91.34	9.4726	7.7328	330.168	1.7067	24.0029	5.7330
2650	−2.218	7.32958	5.49764	7.23374	91.17	9.4245	7.6934	329.971	1.7051	23.9770	5.7268
2700	−2.543	7.28353	5.46310	7.18829	91.01	9.3765	7.6543	329.773	1.7035	23.9510	5.7206
2750	−2.867	7.23771	5.42873	7.14307	90.84	9.3287	7.6153	329.575	1.7019	23.9250	5.7144
2800	−3.192	7.19213	5.39454	7.09808	90.67	9.2811	7.5764	329.377	1.7002	23.8991	5.7082
2850	−3.517	7.14677	5.36052	7.05332	90.50	9.2337	7.5377	329.179	1.6986	23.8727	5.7019
2900	−3.841	7.10166	5.32668	7.00879	90.33	9.1864	7.4991	328.980	1.6970	23.8468	5.6957
2950	−4.166	7.05677	5.29301	6.96449	90.17	9.1394	7.4607	328.782	1.6954	23.8208	5.6895
3000	−4.491	7.01211 + 1	5.25952 + 2	6.92042 − 1	90.01	9.0925 − 1	7.4225 − 1	328.583	1.6938 − 5	23.7948 − 6	5.6833 − 6
3050	−4.815	6.96768	5.22619	6.87657	89.84	9.0459	7.3844	328.385	1.6921	23.7689	5.6771
3100	−5.140	6.92349	5.19304	6.83295	89.67	8.9994	7.3464	328.186	1.6905	23.7429	5.6709
3150	−5.465	6.87952	5.16006	6.78956	89.50	8.9531	7.3086	327.987	1.6889	23.7165	5.6646
3200	−5.790	6.83577	5.12725	6.74638	89.34	8.9069	7.2710	327.788	1.6873	23.6906	5.6584
3250	−6.114	6.79226	5.09461	6.70344	89.16	8.8610	7.2335	327.589	1.6857	23.6646	5.6522
3300	−6.439	6.74897	5.06214	6.66071	89.00	8.8152	7.1961	327.390	1.6840	23.6387	5.6460
3350	−6.764	6.70590	5.02984	6.61821	88.83	8.7697	7.1589	327.191	1.6824	23.6123	5.6397
3400	−7.088	6.66305	4.99770	6.57592	88.67	8.7243	7.1219	326.991	1.6808	23.5863	5.6335
3450	−7.413	6.62043	4.96573	6.53386	88.50	8.6791	7.0849	326.792	1.6792	23.5604	5.6273
3500	−7.737	6.57803 + 1	4.93393 + 2	6.49201 − 1	88.33	8.6340 − 1	7.0482 − 1	326.592	1.6775 − 5	23.5340 − 6	5.6210 − 6
3550	−8.062	6.53586	4.90229	6.45039	88.16	8.5892	7.0116	326.392	1.6759	23.5080	5.6148
3600	−8.387	6.49390	4.87082	6.40898	87.99	8.5445	6.9751	326.192	1.6743	23.4817	5.6085
3650	−8.711	6.45216	4.83952	6.36778	87.83	8.5000	6.9388	325.992	1.6726	23.4557	5.6023
3700	−9.036	6.41064	4.80837	6.32681	87.66	8.4557	6.9026	325.792	1.6710	23.4298	5.5961
3750	−9.361	6.36933	4.77739	6.28604	87.49	8.4115	6.8666	325.592	1.6694	23.4034	5.5898
3800	−9.685	6.32824	4.74657	6.24549	87.32	8.3676	6.8307	325.391	1.6677	23.3774	5.5836
3850	−10.010	6.28737	4.71592	6.20515	87.16	8.3238	6.7949	325.191	1.6661	23.3510	5.5773
3900	−10.334	6.24671	4.68542	6.16503	86.99	8.2802	6.7593	324.990	1.6645	23.3251	5.5711
3950	−10.659	6.20627	4.65509	6.12511	86.82	8.2367	6.7239	324.790	1.6628	23.2987	5.5648
4000	−10.984	6.16604 + 1	4.62491 + 2	6.08541 − 1	86.65	8.1935 − 1	6.6885 − 1	324.589	1.6612 − 5	23.2727 − 6	5.5586 − 6
4050	−11.308	6.12602	4.59489	6.04591	86.49	8.1504	6.6534	324.388	1.6596	23.2464	5.5523
4100	−11.633	6.08621	4.56504	6.00663	86.32	8.1075	6.6183	324.187	1.6579	23.2200	5.5460
4150	−11.957	6.04662	4.53533	5.96755	86.15	8.0647	6.5835	323.985	1.6563	23.1940	5.5398
4200	−12.282	6.00723	4.50579	5.92867	85.98	8.0222	6.5487	323.784	1.6546	23.1677	5.5335
4250	−12.607	5.96805	4.47640	5.89001	85.82	7.9798	6.5141	323.582	1.6530	23.1417	5.5273
4300	−12.931	5.92908	4.44717	5.85154	85.65	7.9376	6.4796	323.381	1.6513	23.1153	5.5210
4350	−13.256	5.89031	4.41810	5.81329	85.48	7.8955	6.4453	323.179	1.6497	23.0889	5.5147
4400	−13.580	5.85175	4.38918	5.77523	85.32	7.8536	6.4111	322.977	1.6481	23.0626	5.5084
4450	−13.905	5.81340	4.36041	5.73738	85.14	7.8119	6.3771	322.775	1.6464	23.0366	5.5022
4500	−14.229	5.77525 + 1	4.33180 + 2	5.69973 − 1	84.98	7.7704 − 1	6.3432 − 1	322.573	1.6448 − 5	23.0102 − 6	5.4959 − 6
4550	−14.554	5.73731	4.30333	5.66228	84.81	7.7290	6.3094	322.371	1.6431	22.9839	5.4896
4600	−14.878	5.69957	4.27503	5.62503	84.64	7.6878	6.2758	322.169	1.6415	22.9575	5.4833
4650	−15.203	5.66202	4.24687	5.58798	84.47	7.6468	6.2423	321.966	1.6398	22.9315	5.4771
4700	−15.527	5.62468	4.21886	5.55113	84.30	7.6059	6.2089	321.764	1.6382	22.9051	5.4708
4750	−15.852	5.58755	4.19100	5.51448	84.14	7.5652	6.1757	321.561	1.6365	22.8788	5.4645
4800	−16.176	5.55061	4.16330	5.47802	83.97	7.5247	6.1426	321.358	1.6349	22.8524	5.4582
4850	−16.501	5.51386	4.13574	5.44176	83.80	7.4844	6.1097	321.155	1.6332	22.8260	5.4519
4900	−16.825	5.47732	4.10833	5.40570	83.63	7.4442	6.0769	320.952	1.6316	22.7996	5.4456
4950	−17.150	5.44097	4.08107	5.36982	83.47	7.4041	6.0442	320.749	1.6299	22.7733	5.4393
5000	−17.474	5.40482 + 1	4.05395 + 2	5.33415 − 1	83.29	7.3643 − 1	6.0117 − 1	320.545	1.6282 − 5	22.7473 − 6	5.4331 − 6
5050	−17.799	5.36887	4.02698	5.29866	83.13	7.3246	5.9793	320.342	1.6266	22.7209	5.4268
5100	−18.123	5.33311	4.00016	5.26337	82.96	7.2851	5.9470	320.138	1.6249	22.6945	5.4205
5150	−18.448	5.29754	3.97348	5.22827	82.79	7.2457	5.9149	319.935	1.6233	22.6682	5.4142
5200	−18.772	5.26217	3.94695	5.19335	82.62	7.2065	5.8829	319.731	1.6216	22.6418	5.4079
5250	−19.097	5.22698	3.92056	5.15863	82.45	7.1675	5.8510	319.527	1.6200	22.6154	5.4016
5300	−19.421	5.19199	3.89432	5.12410	82.29	7.1286	5.8192	319.323	1.6183	22.5890	5.3953
5350	−19.746	5.15719	3.86821	5.08975	82.12	7.0899	5.7876	319.118	1.6166	22.5627	5.3890
5400	−20.070	5.12258	3.84225	5.05560	81.95	7.0513	5.7562	318.914	1.6150	22.5359	5.3826
5450	−20.395	5.08816	3.81643	5.02162	81.78	7.0129	5.7248	318.710	1.6133	22.5095	5.3763
5500	−20.719	5.05393 + 1	3.79076 + 2	4.98784 − 1	81.61	6.9747 − 1	5.6936 − 1	318.505	1.6116 − 5	22.4831 − 6	5.3700 − 6
5550	−21.044	5.01988	3.76522	4.95424	81.45	6.9366	5.6625	318.300	1.6100	22.4567	5.3637
5600	−21.368	4.98602	3.73982	4.92082	81.28	6.8987	5.6316	318.095	1.6083	22.4304	5.3574
5650	−21.692	4.95235	3.71456	4.88759	81.11	6.8610	5.6008	317.890	1.6066	22.4040	5.3511
5700	−22.017	4.91886	3.68945	4.85453	80.94	6.8234	5.5701	317.685	1.6050	22.3776	5.3448
5750	−22.341	4.88555	3.66446	4.82166	80.77	6.7859	5.5395	317.480	1.6033	22.3508	5.3384
5800	−22.666	4.85243	3.63962	4.78898	80.60	6.7486	5.5091	317.275	1.6016	22.3244	5.3321
5850	−22.990	4.81949	3.61491	4.75647	80.43	6.7115	5.4788	317.069	1.6000	22.2981	5.3258
5900	−23.314	4.78673	3.59034	4.72414	80.26	6.6746	5.4486	316.863	1.5983	22.2717	5.3195
5950	−23.639	4.75416	3.56591	4.69199	80.09	6.6378	5.4186	316.658	1.5966	22.2449	5.3131
6000	−23.963	4.72176 + 1	3.54161 + 2	4.66001 − 1	79.92	6.6011 − 1	5.3887 − 1	316.452	1.5949 − 5	22.2185 − 6	5.3068 − 6
6050	−24.288	4.68954	3.51745	4.62822	79.76	6.5646	5.3589	316.246	1.5933	22.1921	5.3005
6100	−24.612	4.65750	3.49342	4.59660	79.59	6.5283	5.3292	316.039	1.5916	22.1653	5.2941
6150	−24.936	4.62564	3.46952	4.56516	79.42	6.4921	5.2997	315.833	1.5899	22.1390	5.2878
6200	−25.261	4.59396	3.44576	4.53389	79.25	6.4561	5.2703	315.627	1.5882	22.1126	5.2815
6250	−25.585	4.56246	3.42212	4.50279	79.08	6.4202	5.2410	315.420	1.5865	22.0858	5.2751
6300	−25.909	4.53112	3.39862	4.47187	78.91	6.3845	5.2118	315.213	1.5849	22.0594	5.2688
6350	−26.234	4.49997	3.37525	4.44112	78.75	6.3489	5.1828	315.007	1.5832	22.0326	5.2624
6400	−26.558	4.46899	3.35202	4.41055	78.57	6.3135	5.1539	314.800	1.5815	22.0062	5.2561
6450	−26.882	4.43818	3.32891	4.38014	78.40	6.2782	5.1251	314.593	1.5798	21.9794	5.2497
6500	−27.207	4.40754 + 1	3.30593 + 2	4.34991 − 1	78.24	6.2431 − 1	5.0964 − 1	314.385	1.5781 − 5	21.9531 − 6	5.2434 − 6
6550	−27.531	4.37708	3.28308	4.31984	78.07	6.2081	5.0679	314.178	1.5764	21.9263	5.2370
6600	−27.855	4.34679	3.26036	4.28995	77.90	6.1733	5.0394	313.970	1.5748	21.8999	5.2307
6650	−28.180	4.31667	3.23777	4.26022	77.73	6.1387	5.0111	313.763	1.5731	21.8731	5.2243
6700	−28.504	4.28671	3.21530	4.23066	77.56	6.1041	4.9830	313.555	1.5714	21.8467	5.2180
6750	−28.828	4.25693	3.19296	4.20126	77.39	6.0698	4.9549	313.347	1.5697	21.8199	5.2116
6800	−29.153	4.22732	3.17075	4.17204	77.23	6.0356	4.9270	313.139	1.5680	21.7931	5.2052
6850	−29.477	4.19787	3.14866	4.14297	77.05	6.0015	4.8992	312.931	1.5663	21.7668	5.1989
6900	−29.801	4.16859	3.12670	4.11408	76.88	5.9676	4.8715	312.723	1.5646	21.7400	5.1925
6950	−30.126	4.13947	3.10486	4.08534	76.71	5.9338	4.8439	312.514	1.5629	21.7136	5.1862
7000	−30.450	4.11052 + 1	3.08315 + 2	4.05677 − 1	76.55	5.9002 − 1	4.8165 − 1	312.306	1.5612 − 5	21.6868 − 6	5.1798 − 6
7050	−30.774	4.08174	3.06156	4.02836	76.37	5.8667	4.7891	312.097	1.5595	21.6600	5.1734
7100	−31.099	4.05312	3.04009	4.00012	76.20	5.8334	4.7619	311.888	1.5578	21.6332	5.1670
7150	−31.423	4.02466	3.01874	3.97203	76.03	5.8002	4.7348	311.679	1.5561	21.6068	5.1607
7200	−31.747	3.99636	2.99752	3.94411	75.86	5.7671	4.7079	311.470	1.5544	21.5800	5.1543
7250	−32.071	3.96823	2.97642	3.91634	75.69	5.7342	4.6810	311.261	1.5527	21.5532	5.1479
7300	−32.396	3.94026	2.95544	3.88873	75.52	5.7015	4.6543	311.051	1.5510	21.5264	5.1415
7350	−32.720	3.91245	2.93458	3.86128	75.36	5.6689	4.6277	310.842	1.5493	21.5001	5.1352
7400	−33.044	3.88479	2.91384	3.83399	75.18	5.6364	4.6012	310.632	1.5476	21.4733	5.1288
7450	−33.368	3.85730	2.89321	3.80686	75.02	5.6041	4.5748	310.422	1.5459	21.4465	5.1224

ICAO Standard Atmosphere

A one-digit number (preceded by a plus or minus sign) following the initial entry of each block indicates the power of ten by which that entry and each succeeding entry of that block should be multiplied. A change of power occurring within a block is indicated by a similar notation

Geometric altitude	Temperature	Atmospheric pressure		p/p_0	Boiling point of water	Density	ϱ/ϱ_0	Velocity of sound	Dynamic viscosity	Thermal conductivity	
m	°C	kPa	torr		°C	kg m^{-3}		m s^{-1}	Pa s	kW m^{-1} K^{-1}	kcal m^{-1} s^{-1} K^{-1}
7500	−33.693	3.82996 + 1	2.87271 + 2	3.77988 − 1	74.84	5.5719 − 1	4.5485 − 1	310.212	1.5442 − 5	21.4197 − 6	5.1160 − 6
7550	−34.017	3.80279	2.85232	3.75306	74.68	5.5399	4.5224	310.002	1.5425	21.3929	5.1096
7600	−34.341	3.77577	2.83206	3.72639	74.51	5.5080	4.4963	309.792	1.5408	21.3661	5.1032
7650	−34.665	3.74890	2.81191	3.69988	74.34	5.4762	4.4704	309.582	1.5391	21.3393	5.0968
7700	−34.989	3.72219	2.79187	3.67352	74.17	5.4446	4.4446	309.371	1.5374	21.3125	5.0904
7750	−35.314	3.69564	2.77196	3.64731	74.00	5.4131	4.4189	309.160	1.5357	21.2857	5.0840
7800	−35.638	3.66924	2.75215	3.62125	73.83	5.3818	4.3933	308.950	1.5340	21.2589	5.0776
7850	−35.962	3.64299	2.73247	3.59535	73.66	5.3506	4.3678	308.739	1.5323	21.2321	5.0712
7900	−36.286	3.61689	2.71289	3.56960	73.49	5.3196	4.3425	308.528	1.5305	21.2053	5.0648
7950	−36.610	3.59095	2.69343	3.54399	73.32	5.2886	4.3173	308.317	1.5288	21.1785	5.0584
8000	−36.935	3.56516 + 1	2.67409 + 2	3.51854 − 1	73.15	5.2579 − 1	4.2921 − 1	308.105	1.5271 − 5	21.1517 − 6	5.0520 − 6
8050	−37.259	3.53952	2.65486	3.49323	72.97	5.2272	4.2671	307.894	1.5254	21.1249	5.0456
8100	−37.583	3.51403	2.63574	3.46807	72.80	5.1967	4.2422	307.682	1.5237	21.0981	5.0392
8150	−37.907	3.48868	2.61673	3.44306	72.63	5.1663	4.2174	307.470	1.5220	21.0713	5.0328
8200	−38.231	3.46349	2.59783	3.41820	72.47	5.1361	4.1927	307.258	1.5202	21.0445	5.0264
8250	−38.555	3.43845	2.57905	3.39348	72.29	5.1060	4.1682	307.046	1.5185	21.0177	5.0200
8300	−38.880	3.41355	2.56037	3.36891	72.12	5.0761	4.1437	306.834	1.5168	20.9905	5.0135
8350	−39.204	3.38880	2.54181	3.34448	71.96	5.0462	4.1194	306.622	1.5151	20.9637	5.0071
8400	−39.528	3.36419	2.52335	3.32020	71.78	5.0165	4.0951	306.409	1.5134	20.9369	5.0007
8450	−39.852	3.33973	2.50500	3.29606	71.62	4.9870	4.0710	306.197	1.5116	20.9101	4.9943
8500	−40.176	3.31541 + 1	2.48677 + 2	3.27206 − 1	71.44	4.9576 − 1	4.0470 − 1	305.984	1.5099 − 5	20.8829 − 6	4.9878 − 6
8600	−40.824	3.26721	2.45061	3.22449	71.11	4.8991	3.9993	305.558	1.5065	20.8293	4.9750
8700	−41.473	3.21958	2.41489	3.17748	70.76	4.8412	3.9520	305.131	1.5030	20.7753	4.9621
8800	−42.121	3.17252	2.37959	3.13103	70.42	4.7838	3.9052	304.704	1.4995	20.7217	4.9493
8900	−42.769	3.12602	2.34470	3.08514	70.08	4.7270	3.8588	304.276	1.4961	20.6677	4.9364
9000	−43.417	3.08007 + 1	2.31024 + 2	3.03979 − 1	69.73	4.6706 − 1	3.8128 − 1	303.848	1.4926 − 5	20.6137 − 6	4.9235 − 6
9100	−44.065	3.03467	2.27619	2.99498	69.39	4.6148	3.7672	303.419	1.4891	20.5597	4.9106
9200	−44.714	2.98981	2.24254	2.95071	69.05	4.5595	3.7220	302.989	1.4856	20.5057	4.8977
9300	−45.362	2.94550	2.20930	2.90698	68.70	4.5047	3.6773	302.559	1.4822	20.4517	4.8848
9400	−46.010	2.90172	2.17647	2.86377	68.37	4.4504	3.6330	302.129	1.4787	20.3977	4.8719
9500	−46.658	2.85846	2.14402	2.82109	68.02	4.3966	3.5891	301.697	1.4752	20.3437	4.8590
9600	−47.306	2.81574	2.11198	2.77892	67.68	4.3433	3.5456	301.265	1.4717	20.2892	4.8460
9700	−47.954	2.77353	2.08032	2.73726	67.33	4.2905	3.5025	300.833	1.4682	20.2352	4.8331
9800	−48.602	2.73184	2.04905	2.69612	66.99	4.2382	3.4598	300.400	1.4647	20.1808	4.8201
9900	−49.250	2.69066	2.01816	2.65548	66.65	4.1864	3.4175	299.966	1.4612	20.1268	4.8072
10000	−49.898	2.64999 + 1	1.98765 + 2	2.61533 − 1	66.30	4.1351 − 1	3.3756 − 1	299.532	1.4577 − 5	20.0724 − 6	4.7942 − 6
10100	−50.546	2.60981	1.95752	2.57568	65.96	4.0843	3.3341	299.097	1.4541	20.0183	4.7813
10200	−51.194	2.57013	1.92776	2.53652	65.61	4.0339	3.2930	298.661	1.4506	19.9639	4.7683
10300	−51.842	2.53094	1.89836	2.49785	65.27	3.9840	3.2523	298.225	1.4471	19.9095	4.7553
10400	−52.490	2.49224	1.86934	2.45965	64.92	3.9346	3.2119	297.788	1.4436	19.8551	4.7423
10500	−53.137	2.45402	1.84067	2.42193	64.58	3.8857	3.1720	297.350	1.4400	19.8006	4.7293
10600	−53.785	2.41628	1.81236	2.38468	64.24	3.8372	3.1324	296.912	1.4365	19.7462	4.7163
10700	−54.433	2.37901	1.78441	2.34790	63.89	3.7892	3.0933	296.474	1.4329	19.6918	4.7033
10800	−55.081	2.34221	1.75680	2.31158	63.55	3.7417	3.0545	296.034	1.4294	19.6373	4.6903
10900	−55.729	2.30587	1.72955	2.27572	63.20	3.6946	3.0160	295.594	1.4258	19.5825	4.6772
11000	−56.376	2.26999 + 1	1.70263 + 2	2.24031 − 1	62.85	3.6480 − 1	2.9780 − 1	295.154	1.4223 − 5	19.5281 − 6	4.6642 − 6
11100	−56.500	2.23460	1.67609	2.20538	62.51	3.5932	2.9332	295.069	1.4216	19.5176	4.6617
11200	−56.500	2.19976	1.64996	2.17100	62.16	3.5372	2.8875	295.069	1.4216	19.5176	4.6617
11300	−56.500	2.16547	1.62423	2.13715	61.82	3.4820	2.8425	295.069	1.4216	19.5176	4.6617
11400	−56.500	2.13171	1.59891	2.10383	61.47	3.4277	2.7982	295.069	1.4216	19.5176	4.6617
11500	−56.500	2.09848	1.57399	2.07103	61.14	3.3743	2.7545	295.069	1.4216	19.5176	4.6617
11600	−56.500	2.06576	1.54945	2.03875	60.79	3.3217	2.7116	295.069	1.4216	19.5176	4.6617
11700	−56.500	2.03356	1.52530	2.00697	60.45	3.2699	2.6693	295.069	1.4216	19.5176	4.6617
11800	−56.500	2.00186	1.50152	1.97568	60.11	3.2189	2.6277	295.069	1.4216	19.5176	4.6617
11900	−56.500	1.97066	1.47812	1.94489	59.77	3.1688	2.5868	295.069	1.4216	19.5176	4.6617
12000	−56.500	1.93994 + 1	1.45508 + 2	1.91457 − 1	59.44	3.1194 − 1	2.5464 − 1	295.069	1.4216 − 5	19.5176 − 6	4.6617 − 6
12100	−56.500	1.90970	1.43240	1.88473	59.10	3.0708	2.5067	295.069	1.4216	19.5176	4.6617
12200	−56.500	1.87994	1.41007	1.85536	58.76	3.0229	2.4677	295.069	1.4216	19.5176	4.6617
12300	−56.500	1.85064	1.38809	1.82644	58.42	2.9758	2.4292	295.069	1.4216	19.5176	4.6617
12400	−56.500	1.82180	1.36646	1.79797	58.09	2.9294	2.3914	295.069	1.4216	19.5176	4.6617
12500	−56.500	1.79341	1.34517	1.76995	57.75	2.8838	2.3541	295.069	1.4216	19.5176	4.6617
12600	−56.500	1.76546	1.32420	1.74237	57.42	2.8388	2.3174	295.069	1.4216	19.5176	4.6617
12700	−56.500	1.73795	1.30357	1.71522	57.09	2.7946	2.2813	295.069	1.4216	19.5176	4.6617
12800	−56.500	1.71086	1.28325	1.68849	56.75	2.7510	2.2457	295.069	1.4216	19.5176	4.6617
12900	−56.500	1.68420	1.26326	1.66218	56.42	2.7082	2.2107	295.069	1.4216	19.5176	4.6617
13000	−56.500	1.65796 + 1	1.24357 + 2	1.63628 − 1	56.09	2.6660 − 1	2.1763 − 1	295.069	1.4216 − 5	19.5176 − 6	4.6617 − 6
13100	−56.500	1.63213	1.22420	1.61078	55.76	2.6244	2.1424	295.069	1.4216	19.5176	4.6617
13200	−56.500	1.60670	1.20512	1.58569	55.43	2.5835	2.1090	295.069	1.4216	19.5176	4.6617
13300	−56.500	1.58166	1.18634	1.56098	55.10	2.5433	2.0761	295.069	1.4216	19.5176	4.6617
13400	−56.500	1.55702	1.16786	1.53666	54.77	2.5037	2.0438	295.069	1.4216	19.5176	4.6617
13500	−56.500	1.53276	1.14967	1.51272	54.45	2.4646	2.0120	295.069	1.4216	19.5176	4.6617
13600	−56.500	1.50888	1.13176	1.48915	54.12	2.4262	1.9806	295.069	1.4216	19.5176	4.6617
13700	−56.500	1.48538	1.11412	1.46595	53.80	2.3884	1.9498	295.069	1.4216	19.5176	4.6617
13800	−56.500	1.46224	1.09677	1.44312	53.48	2.3512	1.9194	295.069	1.4216	19.5176	4.6617
13900	−56.500	1.43946	1.07968	1.42063	53.15	2.3146	1.8895	295.069	1.4216	19.5176	4.6617
14000	−56.500	1.41704 + 1	1.06286 + 2	1.39851 − 1	52.83	2.2786 − 1	1.8600 − 1	295.069	1.4216 − 5	19.5176 − 6	4.6617 − 6
14500	−56.500	1.31006	9.82628 + 1	1.29293	51.22	2.1065	1.7196	295.069	1.4216	19.5176	4.6617
15000	−56.500	1.21118	9.08460	1.19534	49.63	1.9475	1.5898	295.069	1.4216	19.5176	4.6617
15500	−56.500	1.11978	8.39901	1.10513	48.07	1.8006	1.4699	295.069	1.4216	19.5176	4.6617
16000	−56.500	1.03528	7.76525	1.02174	46.51	1.6647	1.3589	295.069	1.4216	19.5176	4.6617
16500	−56.500	9.57175 + 0	7.17940	9.44658 − 2	44.98	1.5391	1.2564	295.069	1.4216	19.5176	4.6617
17000	−56.500	8.84971	6.63783	8.73399	43.47	1.4230	1.1616	295.069	1.4216	19.5176	4.6617
17500	−56.500	8.18225	6.13719	8.07525	41.96	1.3157	1.0740	295.069	1.4216	19.5176	4.6617
18000	−56.500	7.56522	5.67438	7.46629	40.41	1.2165	9.9304 − 2	295.069	1.4216	19.5176	4.6617
18500	−56.500	6.99481	5.24654	6.90334	39.01	1.1247	9.1816	295.069	1.4216	19.5176	4.6617
19000	−56.500	6.46748 + 0	4.85101 + 1	6.38291 − 2	37.56	1.0400 − 1	8.4894 − 2	295.069	1.4216 − 5	19.5176 − 6	4.6617 − 6
19500	−56.500	5.97998	4.48536	5.90179	36.13	9.6157 − 2	7.8495	295.069	1.4216	19.5176	4.6617
20000	−56.500	5.52930	4.14732	5.45700	34.70	8.8910	7.2579	295.069	1.4216	19.5176	4.6617
21000	−55.569	4.72893	3.54699	4.66709	31.92	7.5715	6.1808	295.703	1.4267	19.5959	4.6804
22000	−54.576	4.04749	3.03587	3.99456	29.19	6.4510	5.2661	296.377	1.4322	19.6796	4.7004
23000	−53.583	3.46686	2.60036	3.42153	26.53	5.5006	4.4903	297.049	1.4376	19.7634	4.7204
24000	−52.590	2.97174	2.22899	2.93288	23.94	4.6938	3.8317	297.720	1.4430	19.8467	4.7403
25000	−51.598	2.54922	1.91207	2.51588	21.42	4.0084	3.2722	298.389	1.4484	19.9300	4.7602
26000	−50.606	2.18837	1.64141	2.15976	18.94	3.4257	2.7965	299.056	1.4538	20.0129	4.7800
27000	−49.614	1.87997	1.41009	1.85539	16.54	2.9298	2.3917	299.722	1.4592	20.0962	4.7999
28000	−48.623	1.61619 + 0	1.21225 + 1	1.59506 − 2	14.18	2.5076 − 2	2.0470 − 2	300.386	1.4646 − 5	20.1791 − 6	4.8197 − 6
29000	−47.632	1.39042	1.04290	1.37224	11.87	2.1478	1.7533	301.048	1.4699	20.2620	4.8395
30000	−46.641	1.19703	8.97846 + 0	1.18138	9.63	1.8410	1.5029	301.709	1.4753	20.3449	4.8593
31000	−45.650	1.03126	7.73508	1.01777	7.43	1.5792	1.2891	302.368	1.4806	20.4274	4.8790
32000	−44.660	8.89063 − 1	6.66852	8.77437 − 3	5.26	1.3555	1.1065	303.025	1.4859	20.5103	4.8988

Subtract from the barometer reading the amount Δp_t corresponding to the actual temperature t, *or* multiply the barometer reading by the correction factor f_t. The vapor pressure correction for air fully saturated with water vapor is already included in the conversion tables for gas volumes on pages 34–45 and can be ignored.

The correction factor f_t is calculated from the formula $f_t = 1 - \frac{(\beta - \alpha)t}{1 + \beta t}$

where

$\beta = 1.818 \times 10^{-4}\,\mathrm{K}^{-1} \approx$ volume expansion coefficient of mercury
$\alpha = 1.84 \times 10^{-5}\,\mathrm{K}^{-1} \approx$ linear expansion coefficient of brass, or
$\alpha = 8.5 \times 10^{-6}\,\mathrm{K}^{-1} \approx$ linear expansion coefficient of glass of type Standard-Flint, Jena 16III, Corning 8810, etc.

Amount Δp_t in kPa to be subtracted

Barometer temperature t °C \ Barometer reading kPa	80	81	82	83	84	85	86	87	88	89	90	91	92	93	94	95	96	97	98	99	100	101	102	103	104	105	Correction factor f_t
Brass scale																											
°C	0.	0.	0.	0.	0.	0.	0.	0.	0.	0.	0.	0.	0.	0.	0.	0.	0.	0.	0.	0.	0.	0.	0.	0.	0.	0.	0.
1	013	013	013	013	013	013	014	014	014	014	014	014	014	015	015	015	015	015	015	016	016	016	016	016	016	017	999837
2	026	026	026	027	027	027	028	028	028	029	029	029	030	030	030	031	031	031	032	032	032	032	033	033	033	034	999673
3	039	039	040	040	041	041	042	042	043	043	044	044	045	045	046	046	047	047	048	048	048	049	049	050	050	051	999510
4	052	052	053	054	054	055	056	056	057	058	058	059	060	060	061	062	062	063	064	064	065	065	066	067	067	068	999347
5	065	066	066	067	068	069	070	071	071	072	073	074	075	075	076	077	078	079	079	080	081	082	083	084	084	085	999184
6	078	079	080	081	082	083	084	085	086	087	088	089	090	091	092	093	094	095	095	096	097	098	099	100	101	102	999021
7	091	092	093	094	095	097	098	099	100	101	102	103	105	106	107	108	109	110	111	113	114	115	116	117	118	119	998858
8	104	105	107	108	109	110	112	113	114	116	117	118	120	121	122	124	125	126	127	129	130	131	133	134	135	137	998695
9	117	118	120	121	123	124	126	127	129	130	132	133	135	136	138	139	140	142	143	145	146	148	149	151	152	154	998532
10	130	132	133	135	137	138	140	141	143	145	146	148	150	151	153	154	156	158	159	161	163	164	166	168	169	171	998369
11	143	145	147	148	150	152	154	156	157	159	161	163	165	166	168	170	172	174	175	177	179	181	182	184	186	188	998206
12	156	158	160	162	164	166	168	170	172	174	176	178	180	181	183	185	187	189	191	193	195	197	199	201	203	205	998043
13	169	171	173	175	178	180	182	184	186	188	190	192	194	197	199	201	203	205	207	209	211	214	216	218	220	222	997881
14	182	184	187	189	191	193	196	198	200	203	205	207	209	212	214	216	219	221	223	225	228	230	232	235	237	239	997718
15	195	197	200	202	205	207	210	212	215	217	219	222	224	227	229	232	234	237	239	241	244	246	249	251	254	256	997556
16	208	211	213	216	218	221	224	226	229	232	234	237	239	242	245	247	250	252	255	258	260	263	265	268	271	273	997393
17	221	224	227	229	232	235	238	240	243	246	249	252	254	257	260	263	265	268	271	274	276	279	282	285	288	290	997231
18	234	237	240	243	246	249	252	255	257	260	263	266	269	272	275	278	281	284	287	290	293	296	299	301	304	307	997068
19	247	250	253	256	259	262	266	269	272	275	278	281	284	287	290	293	297	300	303	306	309	312	315	318	321	324	996906
20	260	263	267	270	273	276	280	283	286	289	293	296	299	302	306	309	312	315	319	322	325	328	332	335	338	341	996744
21	273	276	280	283	287	290	293	297	300	304	307	311	314	317	321	324	328	331	335	338	341	345	348	352	355	358	996582
22	286	290	293	297	300	304	307	311	315	318	322	325	329	332	336	340	343	347	350	354	358	361	365	368	372	375	996420
23	299	303	306	310	314	318	321	325	329	333	336	340	344	348	351	355	359	363	366	370	374	378	381	385	389	392	996257
24	312	316	320	324	327	331	335	339	343	347	351	355	359	363	367	370	374	378	382	386	390	394	398	402	406	409	996095
25	325	329	333	337	341	345	349	353	357	361	365	370	374	378	382	386	390	394	398	402	406	410	414	418	422	426	995933
26	338	342	346	350	355	359	363	367	372	376	380	384	389	393	397	401	405	410	414	418	422	427	431	435	439	443	995772
27	351	355	360	364	368	373	377	381	386	390	395	399	403	408	412	417	421	425	430	434	439	443	447	452	456	460	995610
28	364	368	373	377	382	386	391	396	400	405	409	414	418	423	427	432	436	441	446	450	455	459	464	468	473	477	995448
29	377	381	386	391	395	400	405	410	414	419	424	428	433	438	443	447	452	457	461	466	471	476	480	485	490	494	995286
30	390	394	399	404	409	414	419	424	429	433	438	443	448	453	458	463	468	472	477	482	487	492	497	502	507	511	995125
31	402	408	413	418	423	428	433	438	443	448	453	458	463	468	473	478	483	488	493	498	503	508	513	518	523	528	994963
32	415	421	426	431	436	441	447	452	457	462	467	473	478	483	488	493	499	504	509	514	519	525	530	535	540	545	994801
33	428	434	439	444	450	455	460	466	471	477	482	487	493	498	503	509	514	519	525	530	536	541	546	552	557	562	994640
34	441	447	452	458	463	469	474	480	485	491	496	502	507	513	519	524	530	535	541	546	552	557	563	568	574	579	994479
35	454	460	465	471	477	483	488	494	500	505	511	517	522	528	534	539	545	551	556	562	568	573	579	585	591	596	994317
36	467	473	479	485	490	496	502	508	514	520	525	531	537	543	549	555	561	566	572	578	584	590	596	601	607	613	994156
37	480	486	492	498	504	510	516	522	528	534	540	546	552	558	564	570	576	582	588	594	600	606	612	618	624	630	993995
38	493	499	505	511	517	524	530	536	542	548	554	561	567	573	579	585	591	598	604	610	616	622	628	635	641	647	993833
39	506	512	518	525	531	537	544	550	556	563	569	575	582	588	594	601	607	613	620	626	632	639	645	651	658	664	993672
40	519	525	532	538	545	551	558	564	571	577	583	590	596	603	609	616	622	629	635	642	648	655	661	668	674	681	993511
Glass scale																											
	0.	0.	0.	0.	0.	0.	0.	0.	0.	0.	0.	0.	0.	0.	0.	0.	0.	0.	0.	0.	0.	0.	0.	0.	0.	0.	0.
1	013	014	014	014	014	014	014	015	015	015	015	015	015	016	016	016	016	016	016	017	017	017	017	017	018	018	999827
2	027	028	028	028	029	029	029	030	030	030	031	031	031	032	032	032	033	033	033	034	034	034	035	035	036	036	999654
3	041	042	042	043	043	044	044	045	045	046	046	047	047	048	048	049	049	050	050	051	051	052	053	053	054	054	999480
4	055	056	056	057	058	058	059	060	060	061	062	063	063	064	065	065	066	067	067	068	069	069	070	071	072	072	999307
5	069	070	070	071	072	073	074	075	076	077	077	078	079	080	081	082	083	083	084	085	086	087	088	089	090	090	999134
6	083	084	085	086	087	088	089	090	091	092	093	094	095	096	097	098	099	100	101	102	103	104	105	106	108	109	998961
7	096	098	099	100	101	102	104	105	106	107	109	110	111	112	113	115	116	117	118	119	121	122	123	124	126	127	998788
8	110	112	113	114	116	117	119	120	121	123	124	125	127	128	130	131	132	134	135	137	138	139	141	142	143	145	998616
9	124	126	127	129	130	132	133	135	137	138	140	141	143	144	146	147	149	151	152	154	155	157	158	160	161	163	998443
10	138	140	141	143	145	147	148	150	152	153	155	157	159	160	162	164	166	167	169	171	172	174	176	178	179	181	998270
11	152	154	156	157	159	161	163	165	167	169	171	173	175	176	178	180	182	184	186	188	190	192	194	195	197	199	998098
12	166	168	170	172	174	176	178	180	182	184	186	188	190	192	195	197	199	201	203	205	207	209	211	213	215	217	997925
13	179	182	184	186	188	191	193	195	197	200	202	204	206	209	211	213	215	218	220	222	224	227	229	231	233	236	997752
14	193	196	198	200	203	205	208	210	212	215	217	220	222	225	227	229	232	234	237	239	242	244	246	249	251	254	997580
15	207	209	212	215	217	220	222	225	228	230	233	235	238	241	243	246	248	251	254	256	259	261	264	267	269	272	997408
16	221	223	226	229	232	235	237	240	243	246	248	251	254	257	259	262	265	268	270	273	276	279	282	284	287	290	997235
17	234	237	240	243	246	249	252	255	258	261	264	267	270	273	276	279	281	284	287	290	293	296	299	302	305	308	997063
18	248	251	254	258	261	264	267	270	273	276	279	282	286	289	292	295	298	301	304	307	310	314	317	320	323	326	996891
19	262	265	269	272	275	278	282	285	288	292	295	298	301	305	308	311	315	318	321	324	328	331	334	337	341	344	996719
20	276	279	283	286	290	293	297	300	303	307	310	314	317	321	324	328	331	334	338	341	345	348	352	355	359	362	996547
21	290	293	297	300	304	308	311	315	319	322	326	329	333	337	340	344	348	351	355	358	362	366	369	373	377	380	996375
22	303	307	311	315	318	322	326	330	334	337	341	345	349	353	356	360	364	368	372	375	379	383	387	391	394	398	996203
23	317	321	325	329	333	337	341	345	349	353	357	361	365	369	373	377	381	385	388	392	396	400	404	408	412	416	996031
24	331	335	339	343	347	352	356	360	364	368	372	376	380	385	389	393	397	401	405	409	414	418	422	426	430	434	995859
25	345	349	353	357	362	366	370	375	379	383	388	392	396	401	405	409	414	418	422	426	431	435	439	444	448	452	995687
26	358	363	367	372	376	381	385	390	394	399	403	408	412	417	421	426	430	435	439	443	448	452	457	461	466	470	995515
27	372	377	381	386	391	395	400	405	409	414	419	423	428	433	437	442	447	451	456	460	465	470	474	479	484	488	995344
28	386	391	395	400	405	410	415	420	424	429	434	439	444	448	453	458	463	468	473	477	482	487	492	497	502	506	995172
29	399	404	409	414	419	424	429	434	439	444	449	454	459	464	469	474	479	484	489	494	499	504	509	514	519	524	995001
30	413	418	424	429	434	439	444	449	455	460	465	470	475	480	486	491	496	501	506	511	517	522	527	532	537	542	994829
31	427	432	438	443	448	454	459	464	470	475	480	486	491	496	502	507	512	518	523	528	534	539	544	550	555	560	994658
32	441	446	452	457	463	468	474	479	485	490	496	501	507	512	518	523	529	534	540	545	551	556	562	567	573	578	994486
33	454	460	466	471	477	483	488	494	500	505	511	517	523	528	534	540	545	551	557	562	568	574	579	585	591	596	994315
34	468	474	480	486	491	497	503	509	515	521	527	532	538	544	550	556	562	568	573	579	585	591	597	603	609	614	994144
35	482	488	494	500	506	512	518	524	530	536	542	548	554	560	566	572	578	584	590	596	602	608	614	620	626	632	993973
36	495	502	508	514	520	526	533	539	545	551	557	564	570	576	582	588	595	601	607	613	619	626	632	638	644	650	993802
37	509	515	522	528	535	541	547	554	560	566	573	579	585	592	598	605	611	617	624	630	636	643	649	656	662	668	993631
38	523	529	536	542	549	555	562	569	575	582	588	595	601	608	614	621	627	634	640	647	654	660	667	673	680	686	993460
39	536	543	550	557	563	570	577	583	590	597	604	610	617	624	630	637	644	650	657	664	671	677	684	691	697	704	993289
40	550	557	564	571	578	584	591	598	605	612	619	626	633	640	646	653	660	667	674	681	688	695	701	708	715	722	993118

Saturation pressure of water vapor below 0 °C over ice

mPa[1]

°C	9	8	7	6	5	4	3	2	1	0
−90	1.7	2.1	2.6	3.1	3.8	4.6	5.5	6.7	8.0	9.7
−80	11.6	13.9	16.6	19.8	23.5	28.0	33.2	39.3	46.4	54.7
−70	64.4	75.8	88.9	104.2	122.0	142.5	166.2	193.6	225.2	261.5
−60	303.2	351.1	406.0	468.8	540.6	622.5	715.9	822.3	943.2	1080
−50	1236	1413	1612	1838	2092	2380	2703	3067	3476	3935
−40	4449	5026	5671	6393	7198	8097	9098	10210	11450	12830
−30	14360	16060	17940	20020	22330	24880	27690	30790	34210	37980

torr × 10⁻³

°C	9	8	7	6	5	4	3	2	1	0
−90	0.013	0.016	0.019	0.023	0.028	0.034	0.042	0.050	0.060	0.073
−80	0.087	0.104	0.124	0.148	0.176	0.210	0.249	0.294	0.348	0.410
−70	0.483	0.568	0.667	0.782	0.915	1.07	1.25	1.45	1.69	1.96
−60	2.27	2.63	3.05	3.52	4.05	4.67	5.37	6.17	7.07	8.10
−50	9.27	10.60	12.09	13.79	15.69	17.85	20.27	23.00	26.07	29.51
−40	33.37	37.70	42.54	47.95	53.99	60.73	68.24	76.58	85.88	96.23
−30	107.7	120.5	134.6	150.2	167.5	186.6	207.7	230.9	256.6	284.9

Pa[1]

°C	.9	.8	.7	.6	.5	.4	.3	.2	.1	.0
−29	38.4	38.8	39.2	39.6	40.0	40.4	40.8	41.3	41.7	42.1
−28	42.6	43.0	43.5	43.9	44.4	44.8	45.3	45.7	46.2	46.7
−27	47.2	47.7	48.1	48.6	49.1	49.6	50.1	50.7	51.2	51.7
−26	52.2	52.8	53.3	53.8	54.4	54.9	55.5	56.1	56.6	57.2
−25	57.8	58.4	59.0	59.6	60.2	60.8	61.4	62.0	62.6	63.2
−24	63.9	64.5	65.2	65.8	66.5	67.1	67.8	68.5	69.2	69.9
−23	70.6	71.3	72.0	72.7	73.4	74.1	74.9	75.6	76.3	77.1
−22	77.9	78.6	79.4	80.2	81.0	81.8	82.6	83.4	84.2	85.0
−21	85.9	86.7	87.5	88.4	89.3	90.1	91.0	91.9	92.8	93.7
−20	94.6	95.5	96.5	97.4	98.3	99.3	100.2	101.2	102.2	103.2
−19	104.2	105.2	106.2	107.2	108.2	109.2	110.3	111.4	112.4	113.5
−18	114.6	115.7	116.8	117.9	119.0	120.1	121.3	122.5	123.6	124.8
−17	126.0	127.2	128.4	129.6	130.8	132.0	133.3	134.5	135.8	137.1
−16	138.4	139.7	141.0	142.4	143.7	145.1	146.4	147.8	149.2	150.6
−15	152.0	153.4	154.8	156.2	157.7	159.2	160.7	162.2	163.7	165.2
−14	166.7	168.3	169.8	171.4	173.0	174.6	176.2	177.8	179.5	181.1
−13	182.7	184.4	186.1	187.8	189.5	191.3	193.0	194.8	196.6	198.4
−12	200.2	202.0	203.9	205.7	207.6	209.5	211.4	213.3	215.3	217.2
−11	219.1	221.1	223.1	225.1	227.1	229.2	231.3	233.4	235.5	237.6
−10	239.7	241.9	244.0	246.2	248.4	250.6	252.9	255.1	257.4	259.7
− 9	262.0	264.4	266.7	269.1	271.5	273.9	276.3	278.7	281.2	283.7
− 8	286.2	288.8	291.3	293.9	296.5	299.1	301.7	304.3	307.0	309.7
− 7	312.4	315.2	318.0	320.8	323.6	326.4	329.2	332.1	335.0	337.9
− 6	340.9	343.8	346.8	349.9	352.9	356.0	359.1	362.2	365.3	368.5
− 5	371.7	374.8	378.1	381.3	384.6	387.9	391.3	394.7	398.1	401.5
− 4	404.9	408.4	411.9	415.4	419.0	422.6	426.2	429.8	433.5	437.2
− 3	440.9	444.7	448.5	452.3	456.1	460.0	463.8	467.8	471.7	475.7
− 2	479.7	483.8	487.8	492.0	496.1	500.3	504.5	508.7	513.0	517.3
− 1	521.7	526.0	530.5	534.9	539.4	543.9	548.5	553.0	557.7	562.3
0	567.0	571.7	576.4	581.2	586.0	590.9	595.8	600.7	605.7	610.7

torr

°C	.9	.8	.7	.6	.5	.4	.3	.2	.1	.0
−29	0.288	0.291	0.294	0.297	0.300	0.303	0.306	0.310	0.313	0.316
−28	0.319	0.323	0.326	0.329	0.333	0.336	0.340	0.343	0.347	0.350
−27	0.354	0.357	0.361	0.365	0.369	0.372	0.376	0.380	0.384	0.388
−26	0.392	0.396	0.400	0.404	0.408	0.412	0.416	0.421	0.425	0.430
−25	0.433	0.438	0.442	0.447	0.451	0.456	0.460	0.465	0.470	0.474
−24	0.479	0.484	0.489	0.494	0.499	0.504	0.509	0.514	0.519	0.524
−23	0.529	0.534	0.540	0.545	0.551	0.556	0.561	0.567	0.573	0.578
−22	0.584	0.590	0.596	0.601	0.607	0.613	0.619	0.625	0.632	0.638
−21	0.644	0.650	0.657	0.663	0.670	0.676	0.683	0.689	0.696	0.703
−20	0.710	0.717	0.723	0.731	0.738	0.745	0.752	0.759	0.767	0.774
−19	0.782	0.789	0.797	0.804	0.812	0.819	0.827	0.836	0.843	0.851
−18	0.860	0.868	0.876	0.884	0.893	0.901	0.910	0.919	0.927	0.936
−17	0.945	0.954	0.963	0.972	0.981	0.990	1.000	1.009	1.019	1.028
−16	1.038	1.048	1.058	1.068	1.078	1.088	1.098	1.109	1.119	1.130
−15	1.140	1.151	1.161	1.172	1.183	1.194	1.205	1.217	1.228	1.239
−14	1.250	1.262	1.274	1.286	1.298	1.310	1.322	1.334	1.346	1.358
−13	1.370	1.383	1.396	1.409	1.421	1.435	1.448	1.461	1.475	1.488
−12	1.502	1.515	1.529	1.543	1.557	1.571	1.586	1.600	1.615	1.629
−11	1.643	1.658	1.673	1.688	1.703	1.719	1.735	1.751	1.766	1.782
−10	1.798	1.814	1.830	1.847	1.863	1.880	1.897	1.913	1.931	1.948
− 9	1.965	1.983	2.000	2.018	2.036	2.054	2.072	2.090	2.109	2.128
− 8	2.147	2.166	2.185	2.204	2.224	2.243	2.263	2.282	2.303	2.323
− 7	2.343	2.364	2.385	2.406	2.427	2.448	2.469	2.491	2.513	2.534
− 6	2.557	2.579	2.601	2.624	2.647	2.670	2.693	2.717	2.740	2.764
− 5	2.788	2.811	2.836	2.860	2.885	2.909	2.935	2.960	2.986	3.011
− 4	3.037	3.063	3.090	3.116	3.143	3.170	3.197	3.224	3.252	3.279
− 3	3.307	3.336	3.364	3.393	3.421	3.450	3.479	3.509	3.538	3.568
− 2	3.598	3.629	3.659	3.690	3.721	3.753	3.784	3.816	3.848	3.880
− 1	3.913	3.945	3.979	4.012	4.046	4.080	4.114	4.148	4.183	4.218
− 0	4.253	4.288	4.323	4.359	4.395	4.432	4.469	4.506	4.543	4.581

Saturation pressure of water vapor below 0 °C over water

Pa[1]

°C	.9	.8	.7	.6	.5	.4	.3	.2	.1	.0
−14	192.8	194.4	196.0	197.6	199.2	200.9	202.5	204.2	205.9	207.6
−13	209.3	211.0	212.7	214.4	216.2	218.0	219.7	221.5	223.3	225.2
−12	227.0	228.8	230.7	232.6	234.5	236.4	238.3	240.2	242.1	244.1
−11	246.1	248.0	250.0	252.1	254.1	256.1	258.2	260.2	262.3	264.4
−10	266.6	268.7	270.8	273.0	275.2	277.4	279.6	281.8	284.0	286.3
− 9	288.5	290.8	293.1	295.4	297.8	300.1	302.5	304.9	307.3	309.7
− 8	312.1	314.6	317.1	319.6	322.1	324.6	327.1	329.7	332.3	334.8
− 7	337.5	340.1	342.7	345.4	348.1	350.8	353.5	356.2	359.0	361.8
− 6	364.6	367.4	370.2	373.1	375.9	378.8	381.8	384.7	387.6	390.6
− 5	393.6	396.6	399.7	402.7	405.8	408.9	412.0	415.1	418.3	421.5
− 4	424.7	427.9	431.2	434.4	437.7	441.0	444.4	447.7	451.1	454.5
− 3	457.9	461.4	464.9	468.4	471.9	475.4	479.0	482.6	486.2	489.8
− 2	493.5	497.2	500.9	504.6	508.4	512.1	516.0	519.8	523.6	527.5
− 1	531.4	535.4	539.3	543.3	547.3	551.4	555.4	559.5	563.7	567.8
− 0	572.0	576.2	580.4	584.7	588.9	593.3	597.6	602.0	606.4	610.8

torr

°C	.9	.8	.7	.6	.5	.4	.3	.2	.1	.0
−14	1.446	1.458	1.470	1.482	1.494	1.507	1.519	1.532	1.544	1.557
−13	1.570	1.582	1.595	1.608	1.622	1.635	1.648	1.662	1.675	1.689
−12	1.703	1.716	1.730	1.744	1.759	1.773	1.787	1.802	1.816	1.831
−11	1.846	1.861	1.876	1.891	1.906	1.921	1.936	1.952	1.968	1.983
−10	1.999	2.015	2.031	2.048	2.064	2.080	2.097	2.114	2.130	2.147
− 9	2.164	2.181	2.199	2.216	2.234	2.251	2.269	2.287	2.305	2.323
− 8	2.341	2.360	2.378	2.397	2.416	2.435	2.454	2.473	2.492	2.512
− 7	2.531	2.551	2.571	2.591	2.611	2.631	2.651	2.672	2.693	2.714
− 6	2.734	2.756	2.777	2.798	2.820	2.842	2.863	2.885	2.908	2.930
− 5	2.952	2.975	2.998	3.021	3.044	3.067	3.090	3.114	3.138	3.161
− 4	3.185	3.210	3.234	3.259	3.283	3.308	3.333	3.358	3.384	3.409
− 3	3.435	3.461	3.487	3.513	3.539	3.566	3.593	3.620	3.647	3.674
− 2	3.701	3.729	3.757	3.785	3.813	3.841	3.870	3.899	3.928	3.957
− 1	3.986	4.016	4.045	4.075	4.105	4.136	4.166	4.197	4.228	4.259
− 0	4.290	4.322	4.353	4.385	4.417	4.450	4.482	4.515	4.548	4.581

Saturation pressure of water vapor above 100 °C

kPa

°C	0	1	2	3	4	5	6	7	8	9
100	101.33	104.99	108.77	112.67	116.67	120.80	125.05	129.40	133.91	138.51
110	143.26	148.15	153.15	158.31	163.62	169.05	174.64	180.38	186.28	192.34
120	198.54	204.89	211.46	218.16	225.02	232.11	239.33	246.76	254.36	262.16
130	270.13	278.30	286.70	295.26	304.08	312.94	322.15	331.73	341.39	351.28
140	361.4	371.8	382.3	393.1	404.2	415.5	427.1	438.9	451.0	463.5
150	476.0	488.9	502.2	515.5	529.3	543.4	557.8	572.4	587.3	602.6
160	618.1	634.0	650.2	666.6	683.5	700.8	718.2	736.1	754.4	773.0
170	792.1	811.3	831.1	851.0	871.7	892.5	913.6	935.3	957.3	979.8
180	1002.6	1025.8	1049.5	1073.6	1098.2	1123.1	1148.7	1174.6	1200.9	1227.7
190	1255.0	1282.6	1310.7	1339.5	1368.6	1398.4	1428.6	1459.2	1490.5	1522.2
200	1554.4	1587.3	1620.6	1654.3	1688.7	1723.7	1759.5	1795.6	1832.2	1869.5
210	1907.2	1945.8	1985.0	2024.5	2064.9	2105.5	2147.1	2189.2	2232.1	2275.5
220	2319.2	2364.0	2409.5	2455.5	2502.0	2549.5	2597.5	2646.3	2695.8	2746.0
230	2796.9	2848.4	2900.7	2953.6	3007.5	3062.1	3117.5	3173.4	3230.3	3287.9
240	3346.5	3405.5	3465.6	3526.3	3588.0	3650.5	3713.8	3777.8	3842.9	3908.6
250	3975.4	4042.9	4111.4	4180.6	4251.0	4322.0	4394.0	4467.0	4540.9	4615.5
260	4691.3	4767.8	4845.4	4923.9	5003.5	5084.0	5165.2	5247.8	5331.1	5415.5
270	5501.0	5587.6	5675.0	5763.5	5853.1	5943.6	6035.4	6128.0	6222.1	6317.1
280	6413.4	6510.6	6608.8	6708.3	6809.1	6911.2	7014.3	7118.8	7224.4	7331.3
290	7439	7548	7659	7771	7884	7999	8114	8232	8349	8470
300	8590	8713	8837	8961	9087	9214	9342	9473	9606	9736
310	9869	10005	10143	10281	10421	10563	10705	10849	10995	11142
320	11291	11442	11594	11748	11903	12059	12217	12376	12538	12702
330	12867	13033	13202	13372	13543	13716	13892	14069	14248	14429
340	14611	14794	14980	15165	15356	15547	15742	15936	16134	16333
350	16532	16735	16939	17145	17353	17563	17775	17991	18209	18429
360	18651	18875	19102	19331	19563	19801	20041	20282	20526	20774
370	21024	21276	21533	21794	22060	(←critical temperature)				

atm[2]

°C	0	1	2	3	4	5	6	7	8	9
100	1.0000	1.0362	1.0735	1.1120	1.1514	1.1922	1.2341	1.2771	1.3216	1.3670
110	1.4139	1.4621	1.5115	1.5624	1.6148	1.6684	1.7236	1.7802	1.8384	1.8982
120	1.9594	2.0221	2.0869	2.1531	2.2208	2.2907	2.3620	2.4353	2.5103	2.5873
130	2.6660	2.7466	2.8295	2.9140	3.0010	3.0885	3.1794	3.2739	3.3693	3.4669
140	3.567	3.669	3.773	3.880	3.989	4.101	4.215	4.332	4.451	4.574
150	4.698	4.825	4.956	5.088	5.224	5.363	5.505	5.649	5.796	5.947
160	6.100	6.257	6.417	6.579	6.746	6.916	7.088	7.265	7.445	7.629
170	7.817	8.007	8.202	8.399	8.603	8.808	9.017	9.231	9.448	9.670
180	9.895	10.124	10.358	10.596	10.838	11.084	11.337	11.592	11.852	12.116
190	12.386	12.658	12.936	13.220	13.507	13.801	14.099	14.401	14.710	15.023
200	15.341	15.665	15.994	16.327	16.666	17.012	17.365	17.721	18.082	18.451
210	18.823	19.204	19.590	19.980	20.379	20.780	21.190	21.606	22.029	22.457
220	22.889	23.331	23.780	24.234	24.693	25.162	25.635	26.117	26.605	27.101
230	27.603	28.112	28.628	29.150	29.682	30.221	30.767	31.319	31.881	32.449
240	33.027	33.610	34.203	34.802	35.411	36.028	36.652	37.284	37.926	38.575
250	39.234	39.900	40.576	41.259	41.954	42.655	43.365	44.086	44.815	45.551
260	46.300	47.055	47.820	48.595	49.381	50.175	50.977	51.792	52.614	53.447
270	54.291	55.145	56.008	56.881	57.766	58.659	59.565	60.479	61.407	62.345
280	63.295	64.255	65.224	66.206	67.201	68.208	69.226	70.257	71.299	72.354
290	73.42	74.49	75.59	76.69	77.81	78.94	80.08	81.24	82.40	83.59
300	84.78	85.99	87.21	88.44	89.68	90.94	92.20	93.49	94.80	96.09
310	97.40	98.74	100.10	101.47	102.85	104.25	105.65	107.07	108.51	109.96
320	111.43	112.92	114.42	115.94	117.47	119.01	120.57	122.14	123.74	125.36
330	126.99	128.63	130.29	131.97	133.66	135.37	137.10	138.85	140.62	142.40
340	144.20	146.01	147.84	149.67	151.55	153.44	155.36	157.28	159.23	161.19
350	163.16	165.16	167.17	169.21	171.26	173.33	175.43	177.56	179.71	181.88
360	184.07	186.28	188.52	190.78	193.07	195.42	197.79	200.17	202.58	205.02
370	207.49	209.98	212.51	215.09	217.72	(←critical temperature)				

[1] *Smithsonian Meteorological Tables*, 6th ed., Smithsonian Institution, Washington (D.C.), 1966.

[2] KEYES, F. G., *Int. crit. Tab.*, **3**, 233 (1928).

Saturation pressure in kPa[1]

°C	.0	.1	.2	.3	.4	.5	.6	.7	.8	.9
0	0.611	0.615	0.620	0.624	0.629	0.633	0.638	0.643	0.647	0.652
1	0.657	0.661	0.666	0.671	0.676	0.681	0.686	0.690	0.695	0.700
2	0.705	0.711	0.716	0.721	0.726	0.731	0.736	0.742	0.747	0.752
3	0.758	0.763	0.768	0.774	0.779	0.785	0.790	0.796	0.802	0.807
4	0.813	0.819	0.824	0.830	0.836	0.842	0.848	0.854	0.860	0.866
5	0.872	0.878	0.884	0.890	0.897	0.903	0.909	0.915	0.922	0.928
6	0.935	0.941	0.948	0.954	0.961	0.967	0.974	0.981	0.988	0.994
7	1.001	1.008	1.015	1.022	1.029	1.036	1.043	1.051	1.058	1.065
8	1.072	1.080	1.087	1.094	1.102	1.109	1.117	1.124	1.132	1.140
9	1.147	1.155	1.163	1.171	1.179	1.187	1.195	1.203	1.211	1.219
10	1.227	1.236	1.244	1.252	1.261	1.269	1.278	1.286	1.295	1.303
11	1.312	1.321	1.330	1.338	1.347	1.356	1.365	1.374	1.383	1.393
12	1.402	1.411	1.420	1.430	1.439	1.449	1.458	1.468	1.477	1.487
13	1.497	1.507	1.517	1.527	1.537	1.547	1.557	1.567	1.577	1.587
14	1.598	1.608	1.619	1.629	1.640	1.650	1.661	1.672	1.683	1.694
15	1.704	1.715	1.726	1.738	1.749	1.760	1.771	1.783	1.794	1.806
16	1.817	1.829	1.841	1.852	1.864	1.876	1.888	1.900	1.912	1.925
17	1.937	1.949	1.961	1.974	1.986	1.999	2.012	2.024	2.037	2.050
18	2.063	2.076	2.089	2.102	2.116	2.129	2.142	2.156	2.169	2.183
19	2.196	2.210	2.224	2.238	2.252	2.266	2.280	2.294	2.309	2.323
20	2.337	2.352	2.366	2.381	2.396	2.411	2.426	2.441	2.456	2.471
21	2.486	2.501	2.517	2.532	2.548	2.564	2.579	2.595	2.611	2.627
22	2.643	2.659	2.675	2.692	2.708	2.725	2.741	2.758	2.775	2.792
23	2.809	2.826	2.843	2.860	2.877	2.895	2.912	2.930	2.948	2.965
24	2.983	3.001	3.019	3.037	3.056	3.074	3.092	3.111	3.130	3.148
25	3.167	3.186	3.205	3.224	3.243	3.263	3.282	3.302	3.321	3.341
26	3.361	3.381	3.401	3.421	3.441	3.462	3.482	3.503	3.523	3.544
27	3.565	3.586	3.607	3.628	3.650	3.671	3.692	3.714	3.736	3.758
28	3.780	3.802	3.824	3.846	3.869	3.891	3.914	3.937	3.959	3.982
29	4.006	4.029	4.052	4.076	4.099	4.123	4.147	4.171	4.195	4.219
30	4.243	4.267	4.292	4.317	4.341	4.366	4.391	4.417	4.442	4.467
31	4.493	4.518	4.544	4.570	4.596	4.622	4.649	4.675	4.702	4.728
32	4.755	4.782	4.809	4.836	4.864	4.891	4.919	4.947	4.975	5.003
33	5.031	5.059	5.087	5.116	5.145	5.174	5.203	5.232	5.261	5.290
34	5.320	5.350	5.380	5.410	5.440	5.470	5.500	5.531	5.562	5.593
35	5.624	5.655	5.686	5.718	5.749	5.781	5.813	5.845	5.877	5.910
36	5.942	5.975	6.008	6.041	6.074	6.107	6.141	6.174	6.208	6.242
37	6.276	6.311	6.345	6.380	6.414	6.449	6.484	6.520	6.555	6.591
38	6.626	6.662	6.699	6.735	6.771	6.808	6.845	6.882	6.919	6.956
39	6.993	7.031	7.069	7.107	7.145	7.183	7.222	7.261	7.299	7.339
40	7.378	7.417	7.457	7.497	7.537	7.577	7.617	7.658	7.698	7.739
41	7.780	7.822	7.863	7.905	7.947	7.989	8.031	8.073	8.116	8.159
42	8.202	8.245	8.288	8.332	8.375	8.419	8.464	8.508	8.553	8.597
43	8.642	8.688	8.733	8.779	8.824	8.870	8.917	8.963	9.010	9.056
44	9.103	9.151	9.198	9.246	9.294	9.342	9.390	9.439	9.487	9.536
45	9.586	9.635	9.685	9.734	9.784	9.835	9.885	9.936	9.987	10.038
46	10.089	10.141	10.193	10.245	10.297	10.350	10.403	10.456	10.509	10.562
47	10.616	10.670	10.724	10.778	10.833	10.888	10.943	10.998	11.054	11.110
48	11.166	11.222	11.279	11.336	11.393	11.450	11.507	11.565	11.623	11.681
49	11.740	11.799	11.858	11.917	11.977	12.037	12.097	12.157	12.218	12.279
50	12.340	12.401	12.463	12.525	12.587	12.649	12.712	12.775	12.838	12.901
51	12.965	13.029	13.093	13.158	13.223	13.288	13.353	13.419	13.484	13.551
52	13.617	13.684	13.751	13.818	13.886	13.954	14.022	14.091	14.160	14.229
53	14.298	14.368	14.438	14.508	14.578	14.649	14.720	14.791	14.863	14.935
54	15.007	15.080	15.153	15.226	15.299	15.373	15.447	15.521	15.596	15.671
55	15.746	15.822	15.897	15.974	16.050	16.127	16.204	16.282	16.359	16.438
56	16.516	16.595	16.674	16.753	16.833	16.913	16.993	17.074	17.155	17.236
57	17.318	17.400	17.482	17.565	17.648	17.731	17.815	17.899	17.983	18.068
58	18.153	18.238	18.324	18.410	18.496	18.583	18.670	18.758	18.845	18.934
59	19.022	19.111	19.200	19.289	19.379	19.469	19.560	19.651	19.742	19.834
60	19.926	20.018	20.111	20.205	20.298	20.392	20.486	20.581	20.676	20.771
61	20.867	20.963	21.059	21.156	21.253	21.351	21.449	21.548	21.646	21.745
62	21.845	21.945	22.045	22.146	22.247	22.348	22.450	22.552	22.654	22.758
63	22.861	22.965	23.070	23.174	23.279	23.385	23.491	23.597	23.703	23.811
64	23.918	24.026	24.134	24.243	24.352	24.462	24.572	24.682	24.793	24.904
65	25.016	25.128	25.241	25.354	25.467	25.581	25.695	25.810	25.925	26.040
66	26.156	26.273	26.390	26.507	26.625	26.743	26.861	26.980	27.100	27.220
67	27.340	27.461	27.582	27.704	27.826	27.949	28.072	28.196	28.320	28.445
68	28.570	28.696	28.821	28.948	29.075	29.202	29.330	29.458	29.586	29.715
69	29.845	29.975	30.106	30.237	30.369	30.501	30.634	30.767	30.900	31.034
70	31.169	31.304	31.439	31.575	31.712	31.849	31.987	32.125	32.263	32.402
71	32.542	32.682	32.822	32.963	33.105	33.247	33.389	33.533	33.676	33.820
72	33.965	34.110	34.256	34.403	34.550	34.697	34.845	34.993	35.142	35.291
73	35.441	35.591	35.743	35.894	36.046	36.199	36.352	36.506	36.661	36.815
74	36.971	37.127	37.284	37.441	37.599	37.757	37.916	38.075	38.235	38.395
75	38.556	38.718	38.880	39.043	39.206	39.370	39.534	39.699	39.865	40.031
76	40.198	40.365	40.534	40.702	40.871	41.041	41.211	41.382	41.553	41.725
77	41.898	42.071	42.245	42.420	42.595	42.771	42.947	43.124	43.302	43.480
78	43.659	43.838	44.018	44.199	44.380	44.562	44.745	44.928	45.111	45.296
79	45.481	45.667	45.853	46.040	46.228	46.416	46.605	46.794	46.985	47.176
80	47.367	47.559	47.752	47.945	48.139	48.334	48.529	48.725	48.922	49.119
81	49.317	49.516	49.715	49.916	50.117	50.318	50.520	50.723	50.926	51.130
82	51.335	51.541	51.747	51.954	52.162	52.370	52.579	52.789	52.999	53.210
83	53.422	53.635	53.848	54.062	54.277	54.492	54.708	54.925	55.143	55.361
84	55.580	55.799	56.020	56.241	56.462	56.685	56.908	57.132	57.357	57.583
85	57.809	58.036	58.264	58.493	58.722	58.952	59.183	59.414	59.646	59.879
86	60.113	60.348	60.583	60.819	61.056	61.294	61.532	61.772	62.012	62.252
87	62.494	62.736	62.979	63.223	63.468	63.713	63.959	64.207	64.455	64.703
88	64.953	65.203	65.454	65.706	65.959	66.212	66.466	66.722	66.978	67.234
89	67.492	67.750	68.009	68.269	68.530	68.792	69.055	69.318	69.582	69.847
90	70.113	70.380	70.647	70.916	71.185	71.455	71.726	71.998	72.271	72.545
91	72.819	73.094	73.370	73.647	73.925	74.204	74.484	74.764	75.046	75.328
92	75.611	75.895	76.180	76.466	76.752	77.040	77.329	77.618	77.909	78.200
93	78.492	78.785	79.079	79.374	79.669	79.966	80.263	80.562	80.861	81.162
94	81.463	81.765	82.069	82.373	82.678	82.984	83.291	83.599	83.908	84.217
95	84.528	84.840	85.152	85.466	85.780	86.096	86.412	86.730	87.048	87.368
96	87.688	88.009	88.331	88.655	88.979	89.304	89.630	89.957	90.286	90.615
97	90.945	91.276	91.608	91.942	92.276	92.611	92.947	93.284	93.623	93.962
98	94.302	94.643	94.985	95.328	95.673	96.018	96.365	96.712	97.061	97.410
99	97.761	98.113	98.465	98.819	99.174	99.530	99.887	100.245	100.604	100.964
100	101.325									

[1] *Smithsonian Meteorological Tables*, 6th ed., Smithsonian Institution, Washington (D.C.), 1966.

Boiling point in °C

kPa	.0	.1	.2	.3	.4	.5	.6	.7	.8	.9
0		−16.52	−12.90	−8.35	−5.02	−2.40	−0.21	+1.90	3.78	5.46
1	6.99	8.38	9.67	10.87	11.99	13.04	14.03	14.97	15.86	16.71
2	17.52	18.29	19.04	19.75	20.44	21.10	21.74	22.36	22.96	23.54
3	24.10	24.65	25.18	25.70	26.21	26.70	27.18	27.65	28.10	28.55
4	28.99	29.41	29.83	30.24	30.65	31.04	31.43	31.80	32.18	32.54
5	32.90	33.26	33.60	33.94	34.28	34.61	34.93	35.25	35.57	35.88
6	36.19	36.49	36.79	37.08	37.37	37.66	37.94	38.22	38.49	38.76
7	39.03	39.29	39.55	39.81	40.07	40.32	40.57	40.82	41.06	41.30
8	41.54	41.77	42.01	42.24	42.47	42.69	42.92	43.14	43.36	43.58
9	43.79	44.00	44.22	44.43	44.63	44.84	45.04	45.24	45.44	45.64
10	45.84	46.03	46.23	46.42	46.61	46.79	46.98	47.17	47.35	47.53
11	47.72	47.89	48.07	48.25	48.42	48.60	48.77	48.94	49.11	49.28
12	49.45	49.62	49.78	49.95	50.11	50.27	50.43	50.59	50.75	50.91
13	51.07	51.22	51.38	51.53	51.68	51.83	51.99	52.14	52.28	52.43
14	52.58	52.72	52.87	53.01	53.16	53.30	53.44	53.58	53.72	53.86
15	54.00	54.14	54.28	54.41	54.55	54.68	54.82	54.95	55.08	55.21
16	55.35	55.48	55.61	55.73	55.86	55.99	56.12	56.24	56.37	56.49
17	56.62	56.74	56.87	56.99	57.11	57.23	57.35	57.47	57.59	57.71
18	57.93	57.98	58.07	58.18	58.30	58.42	58.53	58.64	58.76	58.87
19	58.99	59.10	59.21	59.32	59.43	59.54	59.65	59.76	59.87	59.98
20	60.09	60.20	60.31	60.41	60.52	60.63	60.73	60.84	60.94	61.04
21	61.15	61.25	61.36	61.46	61.56	61.66	61.76	61.86	61.97	62.07
22	62.17	62.26	62.36	62.46	62.56	62.66	62.76	62.85	62.95	63.05
23	63.14	63.24	63.33	63.43	63.52	63.62	63.71	63.81	63.90	63.99
24	64.09	64.18	64.27	64.36	64.45	64.54	64.64	64.72	64.82	64.91
25	64.99	65.08	65.17	65.26	65.35	65.44	65.53	65.61	65.70	65.79
26	65.87	65.96	66.05	66.13	66.22	66.30	66.39	66.47	66.56	66.64
27	66.72	66.81	66.89	66.97	67.06	67.14	67.22	67.31	67.39	67.47
28	67.55	67.63	67.71	67.79	67.87	67.95	68.03	68.11	68.19	68.27
29	68.35	68.43	68.51	68.59	68.66	68.74	68.82	68.90	68.97	69.05
30	69.13	69.20	69.28	69.36	69.43	69.51	69.58	69.66	69.73	69.81
31	69.88	69.96	70.03	70.10	70.18	70.25	70.33	70.40	70.47	70.54
32	70.62	70.69	70.76	70.83	70.91	70.98	71.05	71.12	71.19	71.26
33	71.33	71.40	71.47	71.54	71.61	71.68	71.75	71.82	71.89	71.96
34	72.03	72.10	72.17	72.24	72.30	72.37	72.44	72.51	72.58	72.64
35	72.71	72.78	72.84	72.91	72.98	73.05	73.11	73.18	73.24	73.31
36	73.38	73.44	73.51	73.57	73.64	73.70	73.77	73.83	73.90	73.96
37	74.02	74.09	74.15	74.22	74.28	74.34	74.41	74.47	74.53	74.60
38	74.66	74.72	74.78	74.85	74.91	74.97	75.03	75.10	75.16	75.22
39	75.28	75.34	75.40	75.46	75.52	75.58	75.65	75.71	75.77	75.83
40	75.89	75.95	76.01	76.07	76.13	76.19	76.25	76.31	76.36	76.42
41	76.48	76.54	76.60	76.66	76.72	76.77	76.83	76.89	76.95	77.01
42	77.06	77.12	77.18	77.24	77.29	77.35	77.41	77.46	77.52	77.58
43	77.63	77.69	77.75	77.80	77.86	77.92	77.97	78.03	78.08	78.14
44	78.19	78.25	78.30	78.36	78.42	78.47	78.53	78.58	78.64	78.69
45	78.74	78.80	78.85	78.91	78.96	79.01	79.07	79.12	79.18	79.23
46	79.28	79.34	79.39	79.44	79.50	79.55	79.60	79.66	79.71	79.76
47	79.81	79.86	79.92	79.97	80.02	80.07	80.12	80.18	80.23	80.28
48	80.33	80.38	80.44	80.49	80.54	80.59	80.64	80.69	80.74	80.79
49	80.84	80.89	80.94	81.00	81.05	81.09	81.15	81.20	81.25	81.30
50	81.35	81.40	81.45	81.49	81.54	81.59	81.64	81.69	81.74	81.79
51	81.84	81.89	81.94	81.99	82.03	82.08	82.13	82.18	82.23	82.28
52	82.33	82.37	82.42	82.47	82.52	82.57	82.61	82.66	82.71	82.76
53	82.80	82.85	82.90	82.94	82.99	83.04	83.09	83.13	83.18	83.23
54	83.27	83.32	83.37	83.41	83.46	83.51	83.55	83.60	83.65	83.69
55	83.74	83.78	83.83	83.87	83.92	83.97	84.01	84.06	84.10	84.15
56	84.19	84.24	84.28	84.33	84.37	84.42	84.46	84.51	84.55	84.60
57	84.64	84.69	84.73	84.78	84.82	84.86	84.91	84.95	85.00	85.04
58	85.09	85.13	85.17	85.22	85.26	85.31	85.35	85.39	85.44	85.48
59	85.52	85.57	85.61	85.65	85.70	85.74	85.78	85.83	85.87	85.91
60	85.95	86.00	86.04	86.08	86.12	86.17	86.21	86.25	86.29	86.33
61	86.38	86.42	86.46	86.50	86.55	86.59	86.63	86.67	86.71	86.75
62	86.80	86.84	86.88	86.92	86.96	87.00	87.05	87.09	87.13	87.17
63	87.21	87.25	87.29	87.33	87.37	87.41	87.46	87.50	87.54	87.58
64	87.62	87.66	87.70	87.74	87.78	87.82	87.86	87.90	87.94	87.98
65	88.02	88.06	88.10	88.14	88.18	88.22	88.26	88.30	88.34	88.38
66	88.42	88.46	88.50	88.54	88.57	88.61	88.65	88.69	88.73	88.77
67	88.81	88.85	88.89	88.93	88.96	89.00	89.04	89.08	89.12	89.16
68	89.20	89.23	89.27	89.31	89.35	89.39	89.43	89.46	89.50	89.54
69	89.58	89.62	89.66	89.69	89.73	89.77	89.81	89.84	89.88	89.92
70	89.96	90.00	90.03	90.07	90.11	90.14	90.18	90.22	90.26	90.29
71	90.33	90.37	90.41	90.44	90.48	90.52	90.55	90.59	90.63	90.66
72	90.70	90.74	90.77	90.81	90.85	90.88	90.92	90.96	90.99	91.03
73	91.06	91.10	91.14	91.17	91.21	91.25	91.28	91.32	91.35	91.39
74	91.43	91.46	91.50	91.53	91.57	91.61	91.64	91.68	91.71	91.75
75	91.78	91.82	91.85	91.89	91.93	91.96	92.00	92.03	92.07	92.10
76	92.14	92.17	92.21	92.24	92.28	92.31	92.35	92.38	92.41	92.45
77	92.48	92.52	92.55	92.59	92.62	92.66	92.69	92.73	92.76	92.80
78	92.83	92.86	92.90	92.93	92.97	93.00	93.04	93.07	93.10	93.14
79	93.17	93.20	93.24	93.27	93.31	93.34	93.37	93.41	93.44	93.48
80	93.51	93.54	93.58	93.61	93.64	93.68	93.71	93.74	93.78	93.81
81	93.84	93.88	93.91	93.94	93.98	94.01	94.04	94.08	94.11	94.14
82	94.18	94.21	94.24	94.27	94.31	94.34	94.37	94.41	94.44	94.47
83	94.50	94.54	94.57	94.60	94.63	94.67	94.70	94.73	94.76	94.79
84	94.83	94.86	94.89	94.92	94.96	94.99	95.02	95.05	95.09	95.12
85	95.15	95.18	95.21	95.24	95.28	95.31	95.34	95.37	95.40	95.44
86	95.47	95.50	95.53	95.56	95.59	95.62	95.66	95.69	95.72	95.75
87	95.78	95.81	95.85	95.88	95.91	95.94	95.97	96.00	96.03	96.06
88	96.09	96.13	96.16	96.19	96.22	96.25	96.28	96.31	96.34	96.37
89	96.40	96.43	96.47	96.50	96.53	96.56	96.59	96.62	96.65	96.68
90	96.71	96.74	96.77	96.80	96.83	96.86	96.89	96.92	96.95	96.98
91	97.01	97.04	97.07	97.10	97.13	97.16	97.19	97.22	97.25	97.29
92	97.32	97.34	97.37	97.40	97.43	97.46	97.49	97.52	97.55	97.58
93	97.61	97.64	97.67	97.70	97.73	97.76	97.79	97.82	97.85	97.88
94	97.91	97.94	97.97	98.00	98.03	98.06	98.08	98.11	98.14	98.17
95	98.20	98.23	98.26	98.29	98.32	98.35	98.38	98.40	98.43	98.46
96	98.49	98.52	98.55	98.58	98.61	98.64	98.66	98.69	98.72	98.75
97	98.78	98.81	98.84	98.87	98.89	98.92	98.95	98.98	99.01	99.04
98	99.06	99.09	99.12	99.15	99.18	99.21	99.24	99.26	99.29	99.32
99	99.35	99.37	99.40	99.43	99.46	99.49	99.52	99.54	99.57	99.60
100	99.63	99.66	99.69	99.71	99.74	99.76	99.79	99.82	99.85	99.88
101	99.90	99.93	99.96	99.99 (100 for 101.325 kPa)						

Conversion of Saturated Gas Volumes to Values at Body Temperature (37 °C) 65–104 kPa

The table gives factors for conversion of spirometer values to lung values calculated from the formula

$$f = \frac{(p - p_{t,\mathrm{H_2O}})(1 + 37\alpha)}{(p - p_{37\,°\mathrm{C},\mathrm{H_2O}})(1 + \alpha t)}$$

p: measured pressure of the spirometer volume in kPa.
t: measured temperature of the spirometer volume in °C.
$p_{t,\mathrm{H_2O}}$ and $p_{37\,°\mathrm{C},\mathrm{H_2O}}$: pressure of water vapor at the measured temperature of the spirometer volume and at 37 °C in the lungs respectively in kPa.
α: volume coefficient of expansion of air in K^{-1} (see also next page).

kPa	65	66	67	68	69	70	71	72	73	74	75	76	77	78	79	80	81	82	83	84
°C	1.	1.	1.	1.	1.	1.	1.	1.	1.	1.	1.	1.	1.	1.	1.	1.	1.	1.	1.	1.
0	2454	2435	2417	2400	2384	2368	2352	2337	2322	2308	2294	2281	2268	2255	2243	2231	2219	2208	2197	2186
1	2399	2381	2364	2347	2330	2314	2299	2284	2269	2255	2242	2228	2215	2203	2191	2179	2167	2156	2145	2134
2	2345	2327	2310	2293	2277	2261	2246	2231	2217	2203	2189	2176	2163	2151	2139	2127	2116	2105	2094	2083
3	2290	2272	2255	2239	2223	2207	2192	2177	2163	2150	2136	2123	2111	2099	2087	2075	2064	2053	2042	2032
4	2235	2217	2201	2184	2168	2153	2138	2124	2110	2097	2083	2071	2058	2046	2034	2023	2012	2001	1991	1980
5	2180	2162	2146	2130	2114	2099	2084	2070	2057	2043	2030	2018	2005	1994	1982	1971	1960	1949	1939	1929
6	2124	2107	2091	2075	2059	2045	2030	2016	2003	1990	1977	1964	1952	1941	1929	1918	1908	1897	1887	1877
7	2068	2051	2035	2020	2005	1990	1976	1962	1949	1936	1923	1911	1899	1888	1877	1866	1855	1845	1835	1825
8	2012	1995	1980	1964	1949	1935	1921	1908	1895	1882	1869	1857	1846	1835	1824	1813	1802	1792	1782	1773
9	1955	1939	1923	1908	1894	1880	1866	1853	1840	1827	1815	1804	1792	1781	1770	1760	1749	1739	1730	1720
10	1898	1882	1867	1852	1838	1824	1810	1797	1785	1773	1761	1749	1738	1727	1716	1706	1696	1686	1677	1668
11	1840	1825	1810	1795	1781	1768	1754	1742	1729	1717	1706	1694	1683	1673	1662	1652	1642	1633	1624	1614
12	1782	1767	1752	1738	1724	1711	1698	1686	1673	1662	1650	1639	1629	1618	1608	1598	1588	1579	1570	1561
13	1723	1708	1694	1680	1667	1654	1641	1629	1617	1606	1595	1584	1573	1563	1553	1543	1534	1525	1516	1507
14	1663	1649	1635	1622	1609	1596	1584	1572	1560	1549	1538	1528	1517	1507	1498	1488	1479	1470	1462	1453
15	1603	1589	1576	1563	1550	1538	1526	1514	1503	1492	1481	1471	1461	1451	1442	1433	1424	1415	1407	1399
16	1543	1529	1516	1503	1491	1479	1467	1456	1445	1434	1424	1414	1404	1395	1386	1377	1368	1360	1351	1343
17	1481	1468	1455	1442	1430	1419	1408	1397	1386	1376	1366	1356	1347	1338	1329	1320	1312	1303	1296	1288
18	1418	1406	1393	1381	1370	1358	1348	1337	1327	1317	1307	1298	1289	1280	1271	1263	1255	1247	1239	1232
19	1355	1343	1331	1319	1308	1297	1287	1277	1267	1257	1248	1239	1230	1222	1213	1205	1197	1190	1182	1175
20	1291	1279	1268	1256	1246	1235	1225	1215	1206	1197	1188	1179	1171	1162	1154	1147	1139	1132	1124	1117
21	1226	1214	1203	1193	1182	1172	1163	1153	1144	1135	1127	1118	1110	1102	1095	1087	1080	1073	1066	1059
22	1160	1149	1138	1128	1118	1109	1099	1090	1082	1073	1065	1057	1049	1042	1034	1027	1020	1014	1007	1001
23	1092	1082	1072	1062	1053	1044	1035	1026	1018	1010	1002	0995	0987	0980	0973	0966	0960	0953	0947	0941
24	1024	1014	1005	0995	0986	0978	0970	0961	0954	0946	0939	0931	0925	0918	0911	0905	0898	0892	0886	0881
25	0954	0945	0936	0927	0919	0911	0903	0896	0888	0881	0874	0867	0861	0854	0848	0842	0836	0831	0825	0820
26	0883	0875	0866	0858	0850	0843	0836	0828	0822	0815	0808	0802	0796	0790	0784	0778	0773	0768	0762	0757
27	0811	0803	0795	0788	0781	0774	0767	0760	0754	0748	0742	0736	0730	0725	0719	0714	0709	0704	0699	0694
28	0737	0730	0723	0716	0709	0703	0697	0691	0685	0679	0674	0668	0663	0658	0653	0648	0644	0639	0635	0630
29	0662	0656	0649	0643	0637	0631	0625	0620	0615	0609	0604	0600	0595	0590	0586	0581	0577	0573	0569	0565
30	0586	0580	0574	0568	0563	0558	0553	0548	0543	0539	0534	0530	0526	0521	0517	0514	0510	0506	0503	0499
31	0507	0502	0497	0492	0488	0483	0479	0474	0470	0466	0462	0458	0455	0451	0448	0444	0441	0438	0435	0432
32	0427	0423	0419	0415	0411	0407	0403	0399	0396	0392	0389	0386	0383	0380	0377	0374	0371	0368	0366	0363
33	0346	0342	0339	0335	0332	0329	0326	0323	0320	0317	0314	0312	0309	0307	0304	0302	0300	0298	0295	0293
34	0262	0260	0257	0254	0252	0249	0247	0245	0243	0240	0238	0236	0234	0232	0231	0229	0227	0225	0224	0222
35	0177	0175	0173	0171	0170	0168	0166	0165	0163	0162	0161	0159	0158	0157	0155	0154	0153	0152	0151	0149
36	0089	0089	0088	0087	0086	0085	0084	0083	0083	0082	0081	0080	0080	0079	0078	0078	0077	0077	0076	0076

kPa	85	86	87	88	89	90	91	92	93	94	95	96	97	98	99	100	101	102	103	104
°C	1.	1.	1.	1.	1.	1.	1.	1.	1.	1.	1.	1.	1.	1.	1.	1.	1.	1.	1.	1.
0	2175	2165	2155	2145	2136	2126	2117	2108	2100	2091	2083	2075	2067	2059	2052	2044	2037	2030	2023	2016
1	2124	2114	2104	2094	2085	2076	2067	2058	2050	2041	2033	2025	2017	2010	2002	1995	1988	1981	1974	1967
2	2073	2063	2053	2044	2034	2025	2017	2008	1999	1991	1983	1975	1968	1960	1953	1945	1938	1931	1925	1918
3	2022	2012	2002	1993	1984	1975	1966	1957	1949	1941	1933	1925	1917	1910	1903	1896	1889	1882	1875	1869
4	1970	1961	1951	1942	1933	1924	1915	1907	1899	1891	1883	1875	1868	1860	1853	1846	1839	1832	1826	1819
5	1919	1909	1900	1891	1882	1873	1865	1856	1848	1840	1833	1825	1818	1810	1803	1796	1790	1783	1776	1770
6	1867	1858	1848	1839	1831	1822	1814	1806	1798	1790	1782	1775	1767	1760	1753	1746	1740	1733	1727	1721
7	1815	1806	1797	1788	1780	1771	1763	1755	1747	1739	1732	1724	1717	1710	1703	1697	1690	1684	1677	1671
8	1763	1754	1745	1737	1728	1720	1712	1704	1696	1689	1681	1674	1667	1660	1653	1647	1640	1634	1628	1622
9	1711	1702	1693	1685	1676	1668	1660	1653	1645	1638	1630	1623	1616	1610	1603	1596	1590	1584	1578	1572
10	1658	1650	1641	1633	1625	1617	1609	1601	1594	1586	1579	1572	1566	1559	1552	1546	1540	1534	1528	1522
11	1606	1597	1589	1580	1572	1564	1557	1549	1542	1535	1528	1521	1515	1508	1502	1495	1489	1483	1477	1472
12	1552	1544	1536	1528	1520	1512	1505	1497	1490	1483	1476	1470	1463	1457	1451	1445	1439	1433	1427	1421
13	1499	1491	1482	1475	1467	1459	1452	1445	1438	1431	1425	1418	1412	1406	1399	1393	1388	1382	1376	1371
14	1445	1437	1429	1421	1414	1406	1399	1392	1386	1379	1372	1366	1360	1354	1348	1342	1336	1331	1325	1320
15	1390	1383	1375	1368	1360	1353	1346	1339	1333	1326	1320	1314	1308	1302	1296	1290	1285	1279	1274	1269
16	1336	1328	1321	1313	1306	1299	1293	1286	1280	1273	1267	1261	1255	1249	1244	1238	1233	1228	1223	1217
17	1280	1273	1266	1259	1252	1245	1238	1232	1226	1220	1214	1208	1202	1197	1191	1186	1181	1175	1170	1166
18	1224	1217	1210	1203	1197	1190	1184	1178	1172	1166	1160	1154	1149	1143	1138	1133	1128	1123	1118	1113
19	1168	1161	1154	1148	1141	1135	1129	1123	1117	1111	1106	1100	1095	1090	1085	1080	1075	1070	1065	1061
20	1111	1104	1098	1091	1085	1079	1073	1067	1062	1056	1051	1046	1041	1036	1031	1026	1021	1017	1012	1008
21	1053	1046	1040	1034	1028	1023	1017	1011	1006	1001	0996	0991	0986	0981	0976	0972	0967	0963	0958	0954
22	0994	0988	0982	0977	0971	0965	0960	0955	0950	0945	0940	0935	0930	0926	0921	0917	0912	0908	0904	0900
23	0935	0929	0924	0918	0913	0908	0902	0897	0893	0888	0883	0879	0874	0870	0865	0861	0857	0853	0849	0845
24	0875	0870	0864	0859	0854	0849	0844	0839	0835	0830	0826	0822	0817	0813	0809	0805	0801	0798	0794	0790
25	0814	0809	0804	0799	0794	0790	0785	0781	0776	0772	0768	0764	0760	0756	0752	0748	0745	0741	0738	0734
26	0752	0748	0743	0738	0734	0730	0725	0721	0717	0713	0709	0705	0702	0698	0694	0691	0688	0684	0681	0678
27	0690	0685	0681	0677	0673	0669	0665	0661	0657	0653	0650	0646	0643	0639	0636	0633	0630	0627	0624	0621
28	0626	0622	0618	0614	0610	0607	0603	0599	0596	0593	0589	0586	0583	0580	0577	0574	0571	0568	0565	0563
29	0561	0558	0554	0550	0547	0544	0540	0537	0534	0531	0528	0525	0522	0519	0517	0514	0511	0509	0506	0504
30	0496	0492	0489	0486	0483	0480	0477	0474	0471	0469	0466	0463	0461	0458	0456	0453	0451	0449	0446	0444
31	0429	0426	0423	0420	0418	0415	0412	0410	0407	0405	0403	0400	0398	0396	0394	0392	0390	0388	0386	0384
32	0361	0358	0356	0353	0351	0349	0347	0345	0342	0340	0338	0337	0335	0333	0331	0329	0327	0326	0324	0322
33	0291	0289	0287	0285	0283	0282	0280	0278	0276	0275	0273	0272	0270	0268	0267	0266	0264	0263	0261	0260
34	0221	0219	0217	0216	0215	0213	0212	0210	0209	0208	0207	0205	0204	0203	0202	0201	0200	0199	0198	0197
35	0148	0147	0146	0145	0144	0143	0143	0142	0141	0140	0139	0138	0137	0137	0136	0135	0134	0134	0133	0132
36	0075	0074	0074	0073	0073	0072	0072	0072	0071	0071	0070	0070	0069	0069	0069	0068	0068	0067	0067	0067

The following remarks are applicable to any other gas in place of air without appreciable error (see under 'Basis of calculation', below).

Explanation of the tables

kPa: Values in the uppermost line of each table: observed pressure p in kPa of the measured gas volume. Under many conditions of measurement this will be the same as the ambient (atmospheric) pressure (10^5 Pa = 1 bar = 0.986923267 atm), for example the observed barometric pressure after correction for temperature. Correction for pressure of water vapor under conditions of saturation is also provided for in the table (see under '*sat.*', below).

°C: Values in the extreme left-hand column: observed temperature t in °C of the measured gas volume.

dry: Factor for the conversion of the measured volume of *dry* gas to *normal conditions* (0 °C, 101.325 kPa, dry). Normal gas volumes are indicated by the abbreviation NTP (normal temperature and pressure). American lung specialists have introduced the abbreviation STPD (standard temperature and pressure, dry).

sat.: Factor for the conversion of the measured volume of gas *saturated with water vapor* to normal conditions (0 °C, 101.325 kPa, dry). Gases may be assumed to be saturated with water vapor if they are in contact with water. This applies to the air in the lungs and to exhaled air, as also to spirometer air (if not dried). For the pressure of saturated water vapor at various temperatures see pages 31 and 32.

Use of the tables

Conversion of measured gas volumes to normal conditions (NTP)

The measured volume is multiplied by the factor appropriate to the conditions of measurement (temperature, pressure, dry or saturated).

Examples. 1. What is the volume at NTP of 1.6 L of dry gas measured at 25°C and 94.9 kPa? Required volume at NTP: 1.6 L × 0.8579 = 1.3726 L (NTP).

2. What is the volume at NTP of 1.6 L of gas saturated with water vapor and measured at 25 °C and 94.9 kPa? Required volume at NTP: 1.6 L × 0.8293 = 1.3269 L (NTP). This is the type of calculation required to convert spirometer values to NTP.

Conversion of measured volumes to other conditions

The measured volume is multiplied by the appropriate conversion factor to NTP and the resulting value divided by the conversion factor corresponding to the required conditions (temperature, pressure, dry or saturated).

Examples. 1. What will be the volume occupied by 1.6 L of gas measured at 25 °C and 97.3 kPa in contact with water when warmed at constant pressure to 37 °C? Required volume: 1.6 L × 0.8509/7909 = 1.7214 L. This is the type of calculation required to convert spirometer values to lung values. The expression BTPS (body temperature and pressure, saturated) is frequently used to indicate gas volumes under lung conditions, for example 37 °C, atmospheric pressure, saturated with water vapor. For direct conversion factors for spirometer to lung values see page 33.

2. What will be the volume occupied by 1.6 L of dry gas measured at 0 °C and 80.0 kPa after saturation with water vapor, warming to 25 °C and compression to 101.325 kPa? Required volume: 1.6 L × 0.7895/0.8871 = 1.4240 L.

Basis of calculation

The conversion factors have been calculated on the basis of the following formulae:

dry: $\frac{p}{101.325(1+\alpha t)}$ *saturated:* $\frac{p - p_{H_2O}}{101.325(1+\alpha t)}$

p, t: Pressure in kPa and temperature in °C of the measured gas volume.

p_{H_2O}: Pressure of saturated water vapor at the temperature t (see pp. 31 and 32).

α: Volume coefficient of thermal expansion of the gas between 0 and 100 °C at a constant pressure of 101.325 kPa. In these tables the value for air, 0.003670 K^{-1} (REGNAULT, 1842), has been used. Under the same conditions the value for an ideal gas is 0.003661 K^{-1}, for nitrogen 0.003671 K^{-1}, for carbon monoxide 0.003669 K^{-1}, for carbon dioxide 0.003723 K^{-1}, for acetylene 0.003739 K^{-1}. The conversion factors are therefore clearly applicable without sensible error to other gases in addition to air.

Note that in calculating the factors the 4th decimal place has been obtained by rounding off upwards or downwards. Any discrepancies with factors given in other tables (e.g. in the *Handbook of Chemistry and Physics*) are due to the use of other values for the expansion coefficient or conversion factors.

Conversion factors*

kPa	80.0		80.1		80.2		80.3		80.4		80.5		80.6		80.7		80.8		80.9		81.0		81.1	
°C	dry	*sat.*	dry	*sat.*	dry	*sat.*	dry	*sat.*	dry	*sat.*	dry	*sat.*	dry	*sat.*	dry	*sat.*	dry	*sat.*	dry	*sat.*	dry	*sat.*	dry	*sat.*
	0.	*0.*	0.	*0.*	0.	*0.*	0.	*0.*	0.	*0.*	0.	*0.*	0.	*0.*	0.	*0.*	0.	*0.*	0.	*0.*	0.	*0.*	0.	*0.*
0	7895	*7835*	7905	*7845*	7915	*7855*	7925	*7865*	7935	*7875*	7945	*7884*	7955	*7894*	7964	*7904*	7974	*7914*	7984	*7924*	7994	*7934*	8004	*7944*
1	7867	*7802*	7876	*7812*	7886	*7822*	7896	*7831*	7906	*7841*	7916	*7851*	7926	*7861*	7935	*7871*	7945	*7881*	7955	*7890*	7965	*7900*	7975	*7910*
2	7838	*7769*	7848	*7779*	7857	*7788*	7867	*7798*	7877	*7808*	7887	*7818*	7897	*7828*	7906	*7837*	7916	*7847*	7926	*7857*	7936	*7867*	7946	*7877*
3	7809	*7735*	7819	*7745*	7829	*7755*	7839	*7765*	7848	*7774*	7858	*7784*	7868	*7794*	7878	*7804*	7887	*7814*	7897	*7823*	7907	*7833*	7917	*7843*
4	7781	*7702*	7791	*7712*	7801	*7722*	7810	*7731*	7820	*7741*	7830	*7751*	7840	*7760*	7849	*7770*	7859	*7780*	7869	*7790*	7878	*7799*	7888	*7809*
5	7753	*7669*	7763	*7678*	7772	*7688*	7782	*7698*	7792	*7707*	7802	*7717*	7811	*7727*	7821	*7736*	7831	*7746*	7840	*7756*	7850	*7766*	7860	*7775*
6	7725	*7635*	7735	*7645*	7745	*7654*	7754	*7664*	7764	*7674*	7774	*7683*	7783	*7693*	7793	*7703*	7803	*7712*	7812	*7722*	7822	*7732*	7831	*7741*
7	7698	*7601*	7707	*7611*	7717	*7621*	7727	*7630*	7736	*7640*	7746	*7649*	7755	*7659*	7765	*7669*	7775	*7678*	7784	*7688*	7794	*7698*	7803	*7707*
8	7670	*7567*	7680	*7577*	7689	*7587*	7699	*7596*	7709	*7606*	7718	*7615*	7728	*7625*	7737	*7635*	7747	*7644*	7756	*7654*	7766	*7663*	7776	*7673*
9	7643	*7533*	7652	*7543*	7662	*7552*	7672	*7562*	7681	*7572*	7691	*7581*	7700	*7591*	7710	*7600*	7719	*7610*	7729	*7619*	7738	*7629*	7748	*7638*
10	7616	*7499*	7625	*7509*	7635	*7518*	7644	*7528*	7654	*7537*	7663	*7547*	7673	*7556*	7683	*7566*	7692	*7575*	7702	*7585*	7711	*7594*	7721	*7604*
11	7589	*7465*	7599	*7474*	7608	*7484*	7617	*7493*	7627	*7503*	7636	*7512*	7646	*7521*	7655	*7531*	7665	*7540*	7674	*7550*	7684	*7559*	7693	*7569*
12	7562	*7430*	7572	*7439*	7581	*7449*	7591	*7458*	7600	*7468*	7610	*7477*	7619	*7487*	7629	*7496*	7638	*7505*	7647	*7515*	7657	*7524*	7666	*7534*
13	7536	*7395*	7545	*7404*	7555	*7414*	7564	*7423*	7574	*7433*	7583	*7442*	7592	*7451*	7602	*7461*	7611	*7470*	7621	*7480*	7630	*7489*	7639	*7498*
14	7510	*7360*	7519	*7369*	7528	*7378*	7538	*7388*	7547	*7397*	7556	*7406*	7566	*7416*	7575	*7425*	7585	*7435*	7594	*7444*	7603	*7453*	7613	*7463*
15	7483	*7324*	7493	*7333*	7502	*7343*	7511	*7352*	7521	*7361*	7530	*7371*	7540	*7380*	7549	*7390*	7558	*7399*	7568	*7408*	7577	*7418*	7586	*7427*
16	7457	*7288*	7467	*7297*	7476	*7307*	7485	*7316*	7495	*7325*	7504	*7335*	7513	*7344*	7523	*7353*	7532	*7363*	7541	*7372*	7551	*7381*	7560	*7391*
17	7432	*7252*	7441	*7261*	7450	*7270*	7460	*7280*	7469	*7289*	7478	*7298*	7487	*7308*	7497	*7317*	7506	*7326*	7515	*7335*	7525	*7345*	7534	*7354*
18	7406	*7215*	7415	*7224*	7425	*7234*	7434	*7243*	7443	*7252*	7452	*7261*	7462	*7271*	7471	*7280*	7480	*7289*	7489	*7298*	7499	*7308*	7508	*7317*
19	7381	*7178*	7390	*7187*	7399	*7197*	7408	*7206*	7418	*7215*	7427	*7224*	7436	*7233*	7445	*7243*	7455	*7252*	7464	*7261*	7473	*7270*	7482	*7280*
20	7355	*7141*	7365	*7150*	7374	*7159*	7383	*7168*	7392	*7177*	7401	*7187*	7411	*7196*	7420	*7205*	7429	*7214*	7438	*7223*	7447	*7233*	7457	*7242*
21	7330	*7103*	7340	*7112*	7349	*7121*	7358	*7130*	7367	*7139*	7376	*7148*	7385	*7158*	7395	*7167*	7404	*7176*	7413	*7185*	7422	*7194*	7431	*7203*
22	7306	*7064*	7315	*7073*	7324	*7082*	7333	*7092*	7342	*7101*	7351	*7110*	7360	*7119*	7369	*7128*	7379	*7137*	7388	*7146*	7397	*7155*	7406	*7165*
23	7281	*7025*	7290	*7034*	7299	*7043*	7308	*7052*	7317	*7062*	7326	*7071*	7335	*7080*	7345	*7089*	7354	*7098*	7363	*7107*	7372	*7116*	7381	*7125*
24	7256	*6986*	7265	*6995*	7274	*7004*	7283	*7013*	7293	*7022*	7302	*7031*	7311	*7040*	7320	*7049*	7329	*7058*	7338	*7067*	7347	*7076*	7356	*7085*
25	7232	*6946*	7241	*6955*	7250	*6964*	7259	*6973*	7268	*6982*	7277	*6991*	7286	*7000*	7295	*7009*	7304	*7018*	7313	*7027*	7322	*7036*	7331	*7045*
26	7208	*6905*	7217	*6914*	7226	*6923*	7235	*6932*	7244	*6941*	7253	*6950*	7262	*6959*	7271	*6968*	7280	*6977*	7289	*6986*	7298	*6995*	7307	*7004*
27	7184	*6863*	7193	*6872*	7202	*6881*	7211	*6890*	7219	*6899*	7228	*6908*	7237	*6917*	7246	*6926*	7255	*6935*	7264	*6944*	7273	*6953*	7282	*6962*
28	7160	*6821*	7169	*6830*	7178	*6839*	7187	*6848*	7195	*6857*	7204	*6866*	7213	*6875*	7222	*6884*	7231	*6893*	7240	*6902*	7249	*6911*	7258	*6920*
29	7136	*6779*	7145	*6788*	7154	*6796*	7163	*6805*	7172	*6814*	7181	*6823*	7189	*6832*	7198	*6841*	7207	*6850*	7216	*6859*	7225	*6868*	7234	*6877*
30	7112	*6735*	7121	*6744*	7130	*6753*	7139	*6762*	7148	*6771*	7157	*6780*	7166	*6788*	7175	*6797*	7183	*6806*	7192	*6815*	7201	*6824*	7210	*6833*
31	7089	*6691*	7098	*6700*	7107	*6708*	7115	*6717*	7124	*6726*	7133	*6735*	7142	*6744*	7151	*6753*	7160	*6762*	7169	*6771*	7177	*6779*	7186	*6788*
32	7066	*6646*	7074	*6654*	7083	*6663*	7092	*6672*	7101	*6681*	7110	*6690*	7119	*6699*	7127	*6707*	7136	*6716*	7145	*6725*	7154	*6734*	7163	*6743*
33	7042	*6600*	7051	*6608*	7060	*6617*	7069	*6626*	7078	*6635*	7086	*6644*	7095	*6652*	7104	*6661*	7113	*6670*	7122	*6679*	7131	*6688*	7139	*6696*
34	7019	*6553*	7028	*6561*	7037	*6570*	7046	*6579*	7055	*6588*	7063	*6597*	7072	*6605*	7081	*6614*	7090	*6623*	7098	*6632*	7107	*6640*	7116	*6649*
35	6997	*6505*	7005	*6514*	7014	*6522*	7023	*6531*	7032	*6540*	7040	*6549*	7049	*6557*	7058	*6566*	7067	*6575*	7075	*6584*	7084	*6592*	7093	*6601*
36	6974	*6456*	6983	*6465*	6991	*6473*	7000	*6482*	7009	*6491*	7018	*6500*	7026	*6508*	7035	*6517*	7044	*6526*	7052	*6534*	7061	*6543*	7070	*6552*
37	6951	*6406*	6960	*6415*	6969	*6423*	6978	*6432*	6986	*6441*	6995	*6450*	7004	*6458*	7012	*6467*	7021	*6476*	7030	*6484*	7038	*6493*	7047	*6502*
38	6929	*6355*	6938	*6364*	6946	*6372*	6955	*6381*	6964	*6390*	6972	*6398*	6981	*6407*	6990	*6416*	6998	*6424*	7007	*6433*	7016	*6442*	7024	*6450*
39	6907	*6303*	6915	*6312*	6924	*6320*	6933	*6329*	6941	*6338*	6950	*6346*	6959	*6355*	6967	*6364*	6976	*6372*	6985	*6381*	6993	*6389*	7002	*6398*
40	6885	*6250*	6893	*6258*	6902	*6267*	6911	*6276*	6919	*6284*	6928	*6293*	6936	*6301*	6945	*6310*	6954	*6319*	6962	*6327*	6971	*6336*	6979	*6344*
41	6863	*6195*	6871	*6204*	6880	*6213*	6888	*6221*	6897	*6230*	6906	*6238*	6914	*6247*	6923	*6255*	6931	*6264*	6940	*6273*	6949	*6281*	6957	*6290*
42	6841	*6140*	6849	*6148*	6858	*6157*	6867	*6165*	6875	*6174*	6884	*6182*	6892	*6191*	6901	*6199*	6909	*6208*	6918	*6217*	6926	*6225*	6935	*6234*

kPa	81.2		81.3		81.4		81.5		81.6		81.7		81.8		81.9		82.0		82.1		82.2		82.3	
°C	dry	sat.	dry	sat.	dry	sat.	dry	sat.	dry	sat.	dry	sat.	dry	sat.	dry	sat.	dry	sat.	dry	sat.	dry	sat.	dry	sat.
	0.	0.	0.	0.	0.	0.	0.	0.	0.	0.	0.	0.	0.	0.	0.	0.	0.	0.	0.	0.	0.	0.	0.	0.
0	8014	7954	8024	7963	8034	7973	8043	7983	8053	7993	8063	8003	8073	8013	8083	8023	8093	8032	8103	8042	8113	8052	8122	8062
1	7985	7920	7994	7930	8004	7940	8014	7949	8024	7959	8034	7969	8044	7979	8053	7989	8063	7999	8073	8008	8083	8018	8093	8028
2	7955	7886	7965	7896	7975	7906	7985	7916	7995	7926	8004	7935	8014	7945	8024	7955	8034	7965	8044	7975	8053	7984	8063	7994
3	7927	7853	7936	7862	7946	7872	7956	7882	7966	7892	7975	7901	7985	7911	7995	7921	8005	7931	8014	7940	8024	7950	8034	7960
4	7898	7819	7908	7829	7917	7838	7927	7848	7937	7858	7947	7867	7956	7877	7966	7887	7976	7897	7985	7906	7995	7916	8005	7926
5	7869	7785	7879	7795	7889	7804	7898	7814	7908	7824	7918	7833	7928	7843	7937	7853	7947	7862	7957	7872	7966	7882	7976	7892
6	7841	7751	7851	7761	7860	7770	7870	7780	7880	7789	7889	7799	7899	7809	7909	7818	7918	7828	7928	7838	7938	7847	7947	7857
7	7813	7717	7823	7726	7832	7736	7842	7746	7852	7755	7861	7765	7871	7775	7880	7784	7890	7794	7900	7803	7909	7813	7919	7823
8	7785	7682	7795	7692	7804	7702	7814	7711	7824	7721	7833	7730	7843	7740	7852	7750	7862	7759	7872	7769	7881	7778	7891	7788
9	7758	7648	7767	7658	7777	7667	7786	7677	7796	7686	7805	7696	7815	7705	7824	7715	7834	7724	7844	7734	7853	7744	7863	7753
10	7730	7613	7740	7623	7749	7632	7759	7642	7768	7651	7778	7661	7787	7670	7797	7680	7806	7689	7816	7699	7825	7709	7835	7718
11	7703	7578	7712	7588	7722	7597	7731	7607	7741	7616	7750	7626	7760	7635	7769	7645	7779	7654	7788	7664	7798	7673	7807	7683
12	7676	7543	7685	7553	7695	7562	7704	7572	7714	7581	7723	7591	7732	7600	7742	7609	7751	7619	7761	7628	7770	7638	7780	7647
13	7649	7508	7658	7517	7668	7527	7677	7536	7687	7546	7696	7555	7705	7564	7715	7574	7724	7583	7734	7593	7743	7602	7753	7611
14	7622	7472	7632	7482	7641	7491	7650	7500	7660	7510	7669	7519	7679	7529	7688	7538	7697	7547	7707	7557	7716	7566	7725	7575
15	7596	7436	7605	7446	7614	7455	7624	7464	7633	7474	7642	7483	7652	7492	7661	7502	7671	7511	7680	7520	7689	7530	7699	7539
16	7569	7400	7579	7409	7588	7419	7597	7428	7607	7437	7616	7447	7625	7456	7635	7465	7644	7475	7653	7484	7663	7493	7672	7503
17	7543	7363	7552	7373	7562	7382	7571	7391	7580	7400	7590	7410	7599	7419	7608	7428	7618	7438	7627	7447	7636	7456	7645	7465
18	7517	7326	7526	7336	7536	7345	7545	7354	7554	7363	7564	7373	7573	7382	7582	7391	7591	7400	7601	7410	7610	7419	7619	7428
19	7491	7289	7501	7298	7510	7307	7519	7317	7528	7326	7538	7335	7547	7344	7556	7353	7565	7363	7574	7372	7584	7381	7593	7390
20	7466	7251	7475	7260	7484	7269	7493	7279	7503	7288	7512	7297	7521	7306	7530	7315	7539	7325	7549	7334	7558	7343	7567	7352
21	7440	7213	7450	7222	7459	7231	7468	7240	7477	7249	7486	7258	7495	7268	7505	7277	7514	7286	7523	7295	7532	7304	7541	7313
22	7415	7174	7424	7183	7433	7192	7443	7201	7452	7210	7461	7219	7470	7229	7479	7238	7488	7247	7497	7256	7506	7265	7516	7274
23	7390	7134	7399	7143	7408	7153	7417	7162	7426	7171	7436	7180	7445	7189	7454	7198	7463	7207	7472	7216	7481	7225	7490	7234
24	7365	7095	7374	7104	7383	7113	7392	7122	7401	7131	7410	7140	7420	7149	7429	7158	7438	7167	7447	7176	7456	7185	7465	7194
25	7340	7054	7349	7063	7358	7072	7367	7081	7377	7090	7386	7099	7395	7108	7404	7117	7413	7126	7422	7135	7431	7144	7440	7153
26	7316	7013	7325	7022	7334	7031	7343	7040	7352	7049	7361	7058	7370	7067	7379	7076	7388	7085	7397	7094	7406	7103	7415	7112
27	7291	6971	7300	6980	7309	6989	7318	6998	7327	7007	7336	7016	7345	7025	7354	7034	7363	7043	7372	7052	7381	7061	7390	7070
28	7267	6929	7276	6938	7285	6947	7294	6956	7303	6965	7312	6974	7321	6982	7330	6991	7339	7000	7348	7009	7357	7018	7365	7027
29	7243	6886	7252	6895	7261	6903	7270	6912	7279	6921	7288	6930	7296	6939	7305	6948	7314	6957	7323	6966	7332	6975	7341	6984
30	7219	6842	7228	6851	7237	6860	7246	6868	7255	6877	7263	6886	7272	6895	7281	6904	7290	6913	7299	6922	7308	6931	7317	6940
31	7195	6797	7204	6806	7213	6815	7222	6824	7231	6833	7240	6841	7248	6850	7257	6859	7266	6868	7275	6877	7284	6886	7293	6895
32	7172	6752	7180	6760	7189	6769	7198	6778	7207	6787	7216	6796	7225	6805	7233	6813	7242	6822	7251	6831	7260	6840	7269	6849
33	7148	6705	7157	6714	7166	6723	7175	6732	7183	6740	7192	6749	7201	6758	7210	6767	7219	6776	7227	6784	7236	6793	7245	6802
34	7125	6658	7134	6667	7142	6676	7151	6684	7160	6693	7169	6702	7177	6711	7186	6719	7195	6728	7204	6737	7213	6746	7221	6755
35	7102	6610	7110	6618	7119	6627	7128	6636	7137	6645	7145	6653	7154	6662	7163	6671	7172	6680	7180	6688	7189	6697	7198	6706
36	7079	6561	7087	6569	7096	6578	7105	6587	7113	6595	7122	6604	7131	6613	7140	6622	7148	6630	7157	6639	7166	6648	7174	6656
37	7056	6510	7064	6519	7073	6528	7082	6536	7090	6545	7099	6554	7108	6563	7117	6571	7125	6580	7134	6589	7143	6597	7151	6606
38	7033	6459	7042	6468	7050	6476	7059	6485	7068	6494	7076	6502	7085	6511	7094	6520	7102	6528	7111	6537	7120	6546	7128	6554
39	7010	6407	7019	6415	7028	6424	7036	6433	7045	6441	7054	6450	7062	6458	7071	6467	7079	6476	7088	6484	7097	6493	7105	6502
40	6988	6353	6997	6362	7005	6370	7014	6379	7022	6387	7031	6396	7040	6405	7048	6413	7057	6422	7065	6430	7074	6439	7083	6448
41	6966	6298	6974	6307	6983	6315	6991	6324	7000	6333	7009	6341	7017	6350	7026	6358	7034	6367	7043	6375	7051	6384	7060	6393
42	6944	6242	6952	6251	6961	6259	6969	6268	6978	6276	6986	6285	6995	6293	7003	6302	7012	6311	7021	6319	7029	6328	7038	6336

kPa	82.4		82.5		82.6		82.7		82.8		82.9		83.0		83.1		83.2		83.3		83.4		83.5	
°C	dry	sat.	dry	sat.	dry	sat.	dry	sat.	dry	sat.	dry	sat.	dry	sat.	dry	sat.	dry	sat.	dry	sat.	dry	sat.	dry	sat.
	0.	0.	0.	0.	0.	0.	0.	0.	0.	0.	0.	0.	0.	0.	0.	0.	0.	0.	0.	0.	0.	0.	0.	0.
0	8132	8072	8142	8082	8152	8092	8162	8102	8172	8111	8182	8121	8191	8131	8201	8141	8211	8151	8221	8161	8231	8171	8241	8181
1	8103	8038	8112	8048	8122	8058	8132	8067	8142	8077	8152	8087	8162	8097	8171	8107	8181	8117	8191	8126	8201	8136	8211	8146
2	8073	8004	8083	8014	8093	8024	8102	8033	8112	8043	8122	8053	8132	8063	8142	8073	8151	8082	8161	8092	8171	8102	8181	8112
3	8044	7970	8053	7979	8063	7989	8073	7999	8083	8009	8092	8019	8102	8028	8112	8038	8122	8048	8132	8058	8141	8067	8151	8077
4	8015	7936	8024	7945	8034	7955	8044	7965	8053	7974	8063	7984	8073	7994	8083	8004	8092	8013	8102	8023	8112	8033	8122	8043
5	7986	7901	7995	7911	8005	7921	8015	7930	8024	7940	8034	7950	8044	7959	8054	7969	8063	7979	8073	7988	8083	7998	8092	8008
6	7957	7867	7967	7876	7976	7886	7986	7896	7996	7905	8005	7915	8015	7925	8025	7934	8034	7944	8044	7954	8054	7963	8063	7973
7	7929	7832	7938	7842	7948	7851	7957	7861	7967	7871	7977	7880	7986	7890	7996	7900	8006	7909	8015	7919	8025	7928	8034	7938
8	7900	7798	7910	7807	7919	7817	7929	7826	7939	7836	7948	7845	7958	7855	7967	7865	7977	7874	7987	7884	7996	7893	8006	7903
9	7872	7763	7882	7772	7891	7782	7901	7791	7910	7801	7920	7810	7930	7820	7939	7830	7949	7839	7958	7849	7968	7858	7977	7868
10	7844	7728	7854	7737	7863	7747	7873	7756	7882	7766	7892	7775	7901	7785	7911	7794	7921	7804	7930	7813	7940	7823	7949	7832
11	7817	7692	7826	7702	7836	7711	7845	7721	7855	7730	7864	7740	7874	7749	7883	7759	7893	7768	7902	7778	7912	7787	7921	7797
12	7789	7657	7799	7666	7808	7676	7818	7685	7827	7694	7836	7704	7846	7713	7855	7723	7865	7732	7874	7742	7884	7751	7893	7761
13	7762	7621	7771	7630	7781	7640	7790	7649	7800	7659	7809	7668	7818	7677	7828	7687	7837	7696	7847	7706	7856	7715	7866	7725
14	7735	7585	7744	7594	7754	7604	7763	7613	7772	7622	7782	7632	7791	7641	7801	7651	7810	7660	7819	7669	7829	7679	7838	7688
15	7708	7549	7717	7558	7727	7567	7736	7577	7745	7586	7755	7595	7764	7605	7773	7614	7783	7623	7792	7633	7801	7642	7811	7651
16	7681	7512	7691	7521	7700	7530	7709	7540	7718	7549	7728	7558	7737	7568	7746	7577	7756	7586	7765	7596	7774	7605	7784	7614
17	7655	7475	7664	7484	7673	7493	7683	7503	7692	7512	7701	7521	7710	7530	7720	7540	7729	7549	7738	7558	7748	7568	7757	7577
18	7628	7437	7638	7447	7647	7456	7656	7465	7665	7474	7675	7484	7684	7493	7693	7502	7702	7511	7712	7521	7721	7530	7730	7539
19	7602	7400	7611	7409	7621	7418	7630	7427	7639	7436	7648	7446	7658	7455	7667	7464	7676	7473	7685	7483	7694	7492	7704	7501
20	7576	7361	7585	7370	7595	7380	7604	7389	7613	7398	7622	7407	7631	7416	7641	7426	7650	7435	7659	7444	7668	7453	7677	7462
21	7550	7323	7560	7332	7569	7341	7578	7350	7587	7359	7596	7368	7605	7378	7614	7387	7624	7396	7633	7405	7642	7414	7651	7423
22	7525	7283	7534	7292	7543	7302	7552	7311	7561	7320	7570	7329	7579	7338	7589	7347	7598	7356	7607	7366	7616	7375	7625	7384
23	7499	7244	7508	7253	7517	7262	7527	7271	7536	7280	7545	7289	7554	7298	7563	7307	7572	7316	7581	7325	7590	7335	7599	7344
24	7474	7203	7483	7212	7492	7222	7501	7231	7510	7240	7519	7249	7528	7258	7537	7267	7547	7276	7556	7285	7565	7294	7574	7303
25	7449	7163	7458	7172	7467	7181	7476	7190	7485	7199	7494	7208	7503	7217	7512	7226	7521	7235	7530	7244	7539	7253	7548	7262
26	7424	7121	7433	7130	7442	7139	7451	7148	7460	7157	7469	7166	7478	7175	7487	7184	7496	7193	7505	7202	7514	7211	7523	7220
27	7399	7079	7408	7088	7417	7097	7426	7106	7435	7115	7444	7124	7453	7133	7462	7142	7471	7151	7480	7160	7489	7169	7498	7178
28	7374	7036	7383	7045	7392	7054	7401	7063	7410	7072	7419	7081	7428	7090	7437	7099	7446	7108	7455	7117	7464	7126	7473	7135
29	7350	6993	7359	7002	7368	7010	7377	7019	7386	7028	7395	7037	7404	7046	7412	7055	7421	7064	7430	7073	7439	7082	7448	7091
30	7326	6948	7335	6957	7343	6966	7352	6975	7361	6984	7370	6993	7379	7002	7388	7011	7397	7020	7406	7028	7415	7037	7423	7046
31	7302	6903	7310	6912	7319	6921	7328	6930	7337	6939	7346	6948	7355	6957	7364	6965	7372	6974	7381	6983	7390	6992	7399	7001
32	7278	6858	7286	6866	7295	6875	7304	6884	7313	6893	7322	6902	7331	6911	7339	6919	7348	6928	7357	6937	7366	6946	7375	6955
33	7254	6811	7263	6820	7271	6828	7280	6837	7289	6846	7298	6855	7307	6864	7315	6872	7324	6881	7333	6890	7342	6899	7351	6908
34	7230	6763	7239	6772	7248	6781	7256	6790	7265	6798	7274	6807	7283	6816	7291	6825	7300	6833	7309	6842	7318	6851	7327	6860
35	7207	6715	7215	6723	7224	6732	7233	6741	7242	6750	7250	6758	7259	6767	7268	6776	7277	6785	7285	6793	7294	6802	7303	6811
36	7183	6665	7192	6674	7201	6683	7209	6691	7218	6700	7227	6709	7236	6718	7244	6726	7253	6735	7262	6744	7270	6752	7279	6761
37	7160	6615	7169	6623	7177	6632	7186	6641	7195	6649	7203	6658	7212	6667	7221	6675	7230	6684	7238	6693	7247	6702	7256	6710
38	7137	6563	7146	6572	7154	6580	7163	6589	7172	6598	7180	6606	7189	6615	7198	6624	7206	6632	7215	6641	7224	6650	7232	6658
39	7114	6510	7123	6519	7131	6528	7140	6536	7149	6545	7157	6553	7166	6562	7174	6571	7183	6579	7192	6588	7200	6597	7209	6605
40	7091	6456	7100	6465	7108	6474	7117	6482	7126	6491	7134	6499	7143	6508	7151	6517	7160	6525	7169	6534	7177	6542	7186	6551
41	7069	6401	7077	6410	7086	6418	7094	6427	7103	6436	7112	6444	7120	6453	7129	6461	7137	6470	7146	6478	7154	6487	7163	6496
42	7046	6345	7055	6353	7063	6362	7072	6370	7080	6379	7089	6388	7097	6396	7106	6405	7115	6413	7123	6422	7132	6430	7140	6439

kPa	83.6		83.7		83.8		83.9		84.0		84.1		84.2		84.3		84.4		84.5		84.6		84.7	
°C	dry	*sat.*	dry	*sat.*	dry	*sat.*	dry	*sat.*	dry	*sat.*	dry	*sat.*	dry	*sat.*	dry	*sat.*	dry	*sat.*	dry	*sat.*	dry	*sat.*	dry	*sat.*
	0.	*0.*	0.	*0.*	0.	*0.*	0.	*0.*	0.	*0.*	0.	*0.*	0.	*0.*	0.	*0.*	0.	*0.*	0.	*0.*	0.	*0.*	0.	*0.*
0	8251	*8190*	8261	*8200*	8270	*8210*	8280	*8220*	8290	*8230*	8300	*8240*	8310	*8250*	8320	*8259*	8330	*8269*	8340	*8279*	8349	*8289*	8359	*8299*
1	8221	*8156*	8230	*8166*	8240	*8176*	8250	*8185*	8260	*8195*	8270	*8205*	8280	*8215*	8289	*8225*	8299	*8235*	8309	*8244*	8319	*8254*	8329	*8264*
2	8191	*8121*	8200	*8131*	8210	*8141*	8220	*8151*	8230	*8161*	8240	*8170*	8249	*8180*	8259	*8190*	8269	*8200*	8279	*8210*	8289	*8219*	8298	*8229*
3	8161	*8087*	8171	*8097*	8180	*8106*	8190	*8116*	8200	*8126*	8210	*8136*	8219	*8145*	8229	*8155*	8239	*8165*	8249	*8175*	8258	*8184*	8268	*8194*
4	8131	*8052*	8141	*8062*	8151	*8072*	8160	*8081*	8170	*8091*	8180	*8101*	8190	*8111*	8199	*8120*	8209	*8130*	8219	*8140*	8229	*8149*	8238	*8159*
5	8102	*8017*	8112	*8027*	8121	*8037*	8131	*8047*	8141	*8056*	8150	*8066*	8160	*8076*	8170	*8085*	8180	*8095*	8189	*8105*	8199	*8114*	8209	*8124*
6	8073	*7983*	8083	*7992*	8092	*8002*	8102	*8012*	8112	*8021*	8121	*8031*	8131	*8041*	8141	*8050*	8150	*8060*	8160	*8070*	8169	*8079*	8179	*8089*
7	8044	*7948*	8054	*7957*	8063	*7967*	8073	*7977*	8083	*7986*	8092	*7996*	8102	*8005*	8111	*8015*	8121	*8025*	8131	*8034*	8140	*8044*	8150	*8054*
8	8015	*7913*	8025	*7922*	8035	*7932*	8044	*7941*	8054	*7951*	8063	*7961*	8073	*7970*	8082	*7980*	8092	*7989*	8102	*7999*	8111	*8008*	8121	*8018*
9	7987	*7877*	7996	*7887*	8006	*7896*	8016	*7906*	8025	*7916*	8035	*7925*	8044	*7935*	8054	*7944*	8063	*7954*	8073	*7963*	8082	*7973*	8092	*7982*
10	7959	*7842*	7968	*7851*	7978	*7861*	7987	*7870*	7997	*7880*	8006	*7889*	8016	*7899*	8025	*7908*	8035	*7918*	8044	*7927*	8054	*7937*	8063	*7947*
11	7931	*7806*	7940	*7816*	7949	*7825*	7959	*7835*	7968	*7844*	7978	*7853*	7987	*7863*	7997	*7872*	8006	*7882*	8016	*7891*	8025	*7901*	8035	*7910*
12	7903	*7770*	7912	*7780*	7922	*7789*	7931	*7798*	7940	*7808*	7950	*7817*	7959	*7827*	7969	*7836*	7978	*7846*	7988	*7855*	7997	*7865*	8007	*7874*
13	7875	*7734*	7884	*7743*	7894	*7753*	7903	*7762*	7913	*7772*	7922	*7781*	7931	*7790*	7941	*7800*	7950	*7809*	7960	*7819*	7969	*7828*	7979	*7838*
14	7847	*7697*	7857	*7707*	7866	*7716*	7876	*7726*	7885	*7735*	7894	*7744*	7904	*7754*	7913	*7763*	7923	*7773*	7932	*7782*	7941	*7791*	7951	*7801*
15	7820	*7661*	7830	*7670*	7839	*7679*	7848	*7689*	7858	*7698*	7867	*7708*	7876	*7717*	7886	*7726*	7895	*7736*	7904	*7745*	7914	*7754*	7923	*7764*
16	7793	*7624*	7802	*7633*	7812	*7642*	7821	*7652*	7830	*7661*	7840	*7670*	7849	*7680*	7858	*7689*	7868	*7698*	7877	*7708*	7886	*7717*	7896	*7726*
17	7766	*7586*	7775	*7595*	7785	*7605*	7794	*7614*	7803	*7623*	7813	*7633*	7822	*7642*	7831	*7651*	7840	*7661*	7850	*7670*	7859	*7679*	7868	*7688*
18	7739	*7548*	7749	*7558*	7758	*7567*	7767	*7576*	7776	*7585*	7786	*7595*	7795	*7604*	7804	*7613*	7813	*7622*	7823	*7632*	7832	*7641*	7841	*7650*
19	7713	*7510*	7722	*7519*	7731	*7529*	7741	*7538*	7750	*7547*	7759	*7556*	7768	*7566*	7777	*7575*	7787	*7584*	7796	*7593*	7805	*7603*	7814	*7612*
20	7686	*7472*	7696	*7481*	7705	*7490*	7714	*7499*	7723	*7508*	7732	*7518*	7742	*7527*	7751	*7536*	7760	*7545*	7769	*7554*	7778	*7564*	7788	*7573*
21	7660	*7433*	7669	*7442*	7679	*7451*	7688	*7460*	7697	*7469*	7706	*7478*	7715	*7487*	7724	*7497*	7734	*7506*	7743	*7515*	7752	*7524*	7761	*7533*
22	7634	*7393*	7643	*7402*	7653	*7411*	7662	*7420*	7671	*7429*	7680	*7439*	7689	*7448*	7698	*7457*	7707	*7466*	7716	*7475*	7726	*7484*	7735	*7493*
23	7608	*7353*	7618	*7362*	7627	*7371*	7636	*7380*	7645	*7389*	7654	*7398*	7663	*7407*	7672	*7417*	7681	*7426*	7690	*7435*	7699	*7444*	7709	*7453*
24	7583	*7312*	7592	*7321*	7601	*7330*	7610	*7339*	7619	*7349*	7628	*7358*	7637	*7367*	7646	*7376*	7655	*7385*	7664	*7394*	7673	*7403*	7683	*7412*
25	7557	*7271*	7566	*7280*	7575	*7289*	7584	*7298*	7593	*7307*	7602	*7316*	7612	*7325*	7621	*7334*	7630	*7343*	7639	*7352*	7648	*7361*	7657	*7370*
26	7532	*7229*	7541	*7238*	7550	*7247*	7559	*7256*	7568	*7265*	7577	*7274*	7586	*7283*	7595	*7292*	7604	*7301*	7613	*7310*	7622	*7319*	7631	*7328*
27	7507	*7187*	7516	*7196*	7525	*7205*	7534	*7214*	7543	*7223*	7552	*7232*	7561	*7241*	7570	*7250*	7579	*7259*	7588	*7268*	7597	*7277*	7606	*7285*
28	7482	*7144*	7491	*7152*	7500	*7161*	7509	*7170*	7518	*7179*	7527	*7188*	7536	*7197*	7544	*7206*	7553	*7215*	7562	*7224*	7571	*7233*	7580	*7242*
29	7457	*7100*	7466	*7109*	7475	*7118*	7484	*7126*	7493	*7135*	7502	*7144*	7511	*7153*	7519	*7162*	7528	*7171*	7537	*7180*	7546	*7189*	7555	*7198*
30	7432	*7055*	7441	*7064*	7450	*7073*	7459	*7082*	7468	*7091*	7477	*7100*	7486	*7108*	7495	*7117*	7503	*7126*	7512	*7135*	7521	*7144*	7530	*7153*
31	7408	*7010*	7417	*7019*	7426	*7027*	7434	*7036*	7443	*7045*	7452	*7054*	7461	*7063*	7470	*7072*	7479	*7081*	7488	*7090*	7496	*7098*	7505	*7107*
32	7384	*6964*	7392	*6972*	7401	*6981*	7410	*6990*	7419	*6999*	7428	*7008*	7437	*7017*	7445	*7025*	7454	*7034*	7463	*7043*	7472	*7052*	7481	*7061*
33	7359	*6917*	7368	*6925*	7377	*6934*	7386	*6943*	7395	*6952*	7403	*6961*	7412	*6969*	7421	*6978*	7430	*6987*	7439	*6996*	7447	*7005*	7456	*7013*
34	7335	*6869*	7344	*6877*	7353	*6886*	7362	*6895*	7370	*6904*	7379	*6912*	7388	*6921*	7397	*6930*	7406	*6939*	7414	*6948*	7423	*6956*	7432	*6965*
35	7312	*6820*	7320	*6828*	7329	*6837*	7338	*6846*	7346	*6855*	7355	*6863*	7364	*6872*	7373	*6881*	7381	*6890*	7390	*6898*	7399	*6907*	7408	*6916*
36	7288	*6770*	7297	*6779*	7305	*6787*	7314	*6796*	7323	*6805*	7331	*6813*	7340	*6822*	7349	*6831*	7358	*6840*	7366	*6848*	7375	*6857*	7384	*6866*
37	7264	*6719*	7273	*6728*	7282	*6736*	7290	*6745*	7299	*6754*	7308	*6762*	7316	*6771*	7325	*6780*	7334	*6788*	7342	*6797*	7351	*6806*	7360	*6815*
38	7241	*6667*	7250	*6676*	7258	*6684*	7267	*6693*	7276	*6702*	7284	*6710*	7293	*6719*	7301	*6728*	7310	*6736*	7319	*6745*	7327	*6754*	7336	*6762*
39	7218	*6614*	7226	*6623*	7235	*6631*	7244	*6640*	7252	*6648*	7261	*6657*	7269	*6666*	7278	*6674*	7287	*6683*	7295	*6692*	7304	*6700*	7313	*6709*
40	7195	*6560*	7203	*6568*	7212	*6577*	7220	*6585*	7229	*6594*	7238	*6603*	7246	*6611*	7255	*6620*	7263	*6628*	7272	*6637*	7281	*6646*	7289	*6654*
41	7172	*6504*	7180	*6513*	7189	*6521*	7197	*6530*	7206	*6538*	7214	*6547*	7223	*6556*	7232	*6564*	7240	*6573*	7249	*6581*	7257	*6590*	7266	*6599*
42	7149	*6447*	7157	*6456*	7166	*6465*	7174	*6473*	7183	*6482*	7192	*6490*	7200	*6499*	7209	*6507*	7217	*6516*	7226	*6524*	7234	*6533*	7243	*6541*

kPa	84.8		84.9		85.0		85.1		85.2		85.3		85.4		85.5		85.6		85.7		85.8		85.9	
°C	dry	*sat.*	dry	*sat.*	dry	*sat.*	dry	*sat.*	dry	*sat.*	dry	*sat.*	dry	*sat.*	dry	*sat.*	dry	*sat.*	dry	*sat.*	dry	*sat.*	dry	*sat.*
	0.	*0.*	0.	*0.*	0.	*0.*	0.	*0.*	0.	*0.*	0.	*0.*	0.	*0.*	0.	*0.*	0.	*0.*	0.	*0.*	0.	*0.*	0.	*0.*
0	8369	*8309*	8379	*8319*	8389	*8329*	8399	*8338*	8409	*8348*	8418	*8358*	8428	*8368*	8438	*8378*	8448	*8388*	8458	*8398*	8468	*8408*	8478	*8417*
1	8339	*8274*	8348	*8284*	8358	*8294*	8368	*8303*	8378	*8313*	8388	*8323*	8398	*8333*	8407	*8343*	8417	*8353*	8427	*8362*	8437	*8372*	8447	*8382*
2	8308	*8239*	8318	*8249*	8328	*8259*	8338	*8268*	8347	*8278*	8357	*8288*	8367	*8298*	8377	*8308*	8387	*8317*	8396	*8327*	8406	*8337*	8416	*8347*
3	8278	*8204*	8288	*8214*	8297	*8223*	8307	*8233*	8317	*8243*	8327	*8253*	8337	*8263*	8346	*8272*	8356	*8282*	8366	*8292*	8376	*8302*	8385	*8311*
4	8248	*8169*	8258	*8179*	8267	*8188*	8277	*8198*	8287	*8208*	8297	*8218*	8306	*8227*	8316	*8237*	8326	*8247*	8336	*8256*	8345	*8266*	8355	*8276*
5	8218	*8134*	8228	*8143*	8238	*8153*	8247	*8163*	8257	*8173*	8267	*8182*	8276	*8192*	8286	*8202*	8296	*8211*	8306	*8221*	8315	*8231*	8325	*8240*
6	8189	*8099*	8198	*8108*	8208	*8118*	8218	*8127*	8227	*8137*	8237	*8147*	8247	*8156*	8256	*8166*	8266	*8176*	8276	*8185*	8285	*8195*	8295	*8205*
7	8159	*8063*	8169	*8073*	8179	*8082*	8188	*8092*	8198	*8102*	8208	*8111*	8217	*8121*	8227	*8131*	8236	*8140*	8246	*8150*	8256	*8159*	8265	*8169*
8	8130	*8028*	8140	*8037*	8150	*8047*	8159	*8056*	8169	*8066*	8178	*8076*	8188	*8085*	8198	*8095*	8207	*8104*	8217	*8114*	8226	*8123*	8236	*8133*
9	8102	*7992*	8111	*8001*	8121	*8011*	8130	*8021*	8140	*8030*	8149	*8040*	8159	*8049*	8168	*8059*	8178	*8068*	8187	*8078*	8197	*8087*	8207	*8097*
10	8073	*7956*	8082	*7966*	8092	*7975*	8101	*7985*	8111	*7994*	8120	*8004*	8130	*8013*	8139	*8023*	8149	*8032*	8159	*8042*	8168	*8051*	8178	*8061*
11	8044	*7920*	8054	*7929*	8063	*7939*	8073	*7948*	8082	*7958*	8092	*7967*	8101	*7977*	8111	*7986*	8120	*7996*	8130	*8005*	8139	*8015*	8149	*8024*
12	8016	*7884*	8026	*7893*	8035	*7902*	8044	*7912*	8054	*7921*	8063	*7931*	8073	*7940*	8082	*7950*	8092	*7959*	8101	*7969*	8111	*7978*	8120	*7988*
13	7988	*7847*	7997	*7856*	8007	*7866*	8016	*7875*	8026	*7885*	8035	*7894*	8045	*7904*	8054	*7913*	8063	*7922*	8073	*7932*	8082	*7941*	8092	*7951*
14	7960	*7810*	7970	*7820*	7979	*7829*	7988	*7838*	7998	*7848*	8007	*7857*	8016	*7866*	8026	*7876*	8035	*7885*	8045	*7895*	8054	*7904*	8063	*7913*
15	7932	*7773*	7942	*7782*	7951	*7792*	7960	*7801*	7970	*7810*	7979	*7820*	7989	*7829*	7998	*7839*	8007	*7848*	8017	*7857*	8026	*7867*	8035	*7876*
16	7905	*7736*	7914	*7745*	7924	*7754*	7933	*7764*	7942	*7773*	7952	*7782*	7961	*7791*	7970	*7801*	7980	*7810*	7989	*7819*	7998	*7829*	8007	*7838*
17	7878	*7698*	7887	*7707*	7896	*7716*	7905	*7726*	7915	*7735*	7924	*7744*	7933	*7753*	7943	*7763*	7952	*7772*	7961	*7781*	7971	*7791*	7980	*7800*
18	7851	*7660*	7860	*7669*	7869	*7678*	7878	*7687*	7888	*7697*	7897	*7706*	7906	*7715*	7915	*7724*	7925	*7734*	7934	*7743*	7943	*7752*	7952	*7761*
19	7824	*7621*	7833	*7630*	7842	*7639*	7851	*7649*	7860	*7658*	7870	*7667*	7879	*7676*	7888	*7686*	7897	*7695*	7907	*7704*	7916	*7713*	7925	*7722*
20	7797	*7582*	7806	*7591*	7815	*7600*	7824	*7610*	7834	*7619*	7843	*7628*	7852	*7637*	7861	*7646*	7870	*7656*	7880	*7665*	7889	*7674*	7898	*7683*
21	7770	*7542*	7779	*7552*	7789	*7561*	7798	*7570*	7807	*7579*	7816	*7588*	7825	*7597*	7834	*7607*	7844	*7616*	7853	*7625*	7862	*7634*	7871	*7643*
22	7744	*7503*	7753	*7512*	7762	*7521*	7771	*7530*	7780	*7539*	7790	*7548*	7799	*7557*	7808	*7566*	7817	*7576*	7826	*7585*	7835	*7594*	7844	*7603*
23	7718	*7462*	7727	*7471*	7736	*7480*	7745	*7489*	7754	*7498*	7763	*7508*	7772	*7517*	7781	*7526*	7790	*7535*	7800	*7544*	7809	*7553*	7818	*7562*
24	7692	*7421*	7701	*7430*	7710	*7439*	7719	*7448*	7728	*7457*	7737	*7466*	7746	*7475*	7755	*7485*	7764	*7494*	7773	*7503*	7782	*7512*	7791	*7521*
25	7666	*7379*	7675	*7389*	7684	*7398*	7693	*7407*	7702	*7416*	7711	*7425*	7720	*7434*	7729	*7443*	7738	*7452*	7747	*7461*	7756	*7470*	7765	*7479*
26	7640	*7337*	7649	*7346*	7658	*7355*	7667	*7364*	7676	*7373*	7685	*7382*	7694	*7391*	7703	*7400*	7712	*7409*	7721	*7418*	7730	*7427*	7739	*7436*
27	7615	*7294*	7624	*7303*	7633	*7312*	7642	*7321*	7650	*7330*	7659	*7339*	7668	*7348*	7677	*7357*	7686	*7366*	7695	*7375*	7704	*7384*	7713	*7393*
28	7589	*7251*	7598	*7260*	7607	*7269*	7616	*7278*	7625	*7287*	7634	*7296*	7643	*7305*	7652	*7314*	7661	*7323*	7670	*7331*	7679	*7340*	7688	*7349*
29	7564	*7207*	7573	*7216*	7582	*7225*	7591	*7233*	7600	*7242*	7609	*7251*	7618	*7260*	7627	*7269*	7635	*7278*	7644	*7287*	7653	*7296*	7662	*7305*
30	7539	*7162*	7548	*7171*	7557	*7180*	7566	*7189*	7575	*7197*	7584	*7206*	7592	*7215*	7601	*7224*	7610	*7233*	7619	*7242*	7628	*7251*	7637	*7260*
31	7514	*7116*	7523	*7125*	7532	*7134*	7541	*7143*	7550	*7152*	7559	*7160*	7567	*7169*	7576	*7178*	7585	*7187*	7594	*7196*	7603	*7205*	7612	*7214*
32	7490	*7070*	7498	*7078*	7507	*7087*	7516	*7096*	7525	*7105*	7534	*7114*	7543	*7123*	7551	*7131*	7560	*7140*	7569	*7149*	7578	*7158*	7587	*7167*
33	7465	*7022*	7474	*7031*	7483	*7040*	7491	*7049*	7500	*7057*	7509	*7066*	7518	*7075*	7527	*7084*	7535	*7093*	7544	*7101*	7553	*7110*	7562	*7119*
34	7441	*6974*	7449	*6983*	7458	*6991*	7467	*7000*	7476	*7009*	7485	*7018*	7493	*7027*	7502	*7035*	7511	*7044*	7520	*7053*	7528	*7062*	7537	*7070*
35	7416	*6925*	7425	*6933*	7434	*6942*	7443	*6951*	7451	*6960*	7460	*6968*	7469	*6977*	7478	*6986*	7486	*6995*	7495	*7003*	7504	*7012*	7513	*7021*
36	7392	*6874*	7401	*6883*	7410	*6892*	7419	*6901*	7427	*6909*	7436	*6918*	7445	*6927*	7453	*6935*	7462	*6944*	7471	*6953*	7480	*6962*	7488	*6970*
37	7369	*6823*	7377	*6832*	7386	*6841*	7395	*6849*	7403	*6858*	7412	*6867*	7421	*6875*	7429	*6884*	7438	*6893*	7447	*6901*	7455	*6910*	7464	*6919*
38	7345	*6771*	7353	*6780*	7362	*6788*	7371	*6797*	7379	*6806*	7388	*6814*	7397	*6823*	7405	*6832*	7414	*6840*	7423	*6849*	7431	*6858*	7440	*6866*
39	7321	*6717*	7330	*6726*	7338	*6735*	7347	*6743*	7356	*6752*	7364	*6761*	7373	*6769*	7382	*6778*	7390	*6787*	7399	*6795*	7408	*6804*	7416	*6812*
40	7298	*6663*	7306	*6671*	7315	*6680*	7324	*6689*	7332	*6697*	7341	*6706*	7349	*6714*	7358	*6723*	7367	*6732*	7375	*6740*	7384	*6749*	7392	*6758*
41	7275	*6607*	7283	*6616*	7292	*6624*	7300	*6633*	7309	*6641*	7317	*6650*	7326	*6659*	7335	*6667*	7343	*6676*	7352	*6684*	7360	*6693*	7369	*6701*
42	7251	*6550*	7260	*6559*	7268	*6567*	7277	*6576*	7286	*6584*	7294	*6593*	7303	*6601*	7311	*6610*	7320	*6618*	7328	*6627*	7337	*6636*	7345	*6644*

kPa	86.0		86.1		86.2		86.3		86.4		86.5		86.6		86.7		86.8		86.9		87.0		87.1	
°C	dry	*sat.*	dry	*sat.*	dry	*sat.*	dry	*sat.*	dry	*sat.*	dry	*sat.*	dry	*sat.*	dry	*sat.*	dry	*sat.*	dry	*sat.*	dry	*sat.*	dry	*sat.*
	0.	*0.*	0.	*0.*	0.	*0.*	0.	*0.*	0.	*0.*	0.	*0.*	0.	*0.*	0.	*0.*	0.	*0.*	0.	*0.*	0.	*0.*	0.	*0.*
0	8488	*8427*	8497	*8437*	8507	*8447*	8517	*8457*	8527	*8467*	8537	*8477*	8547	*8486*	8557	*8496*	8566	*8506*	8576	*8516*	8586	*8526*	8596	*8536*
1	8457	*8392*	8466	*8402*	8476	*8412*	8486	*8421*	8496	*8431*	8506	*8441*	8516	*8451*	8525	*8461*	8535	*8471*	8545	*8480*	8555	*8490*	8565	*8500*
2	8426	*8357*	8435	*8366*	8445	*8376*	8455	*8386*	8465	*8396*	8475	*8406*	8484	*8415*	8494	*8425*	8504	*8435*	8514	*8445*	8524	*8455*	8533	*8464*
3	8395	*8321*	8405	*8331*	8415	*8341*	8424	*8350*	8434	*8360*	8444	*8370*	8454	*8380*	8463	*8389*	8473	*8399*	8483	*8409*	8493	*8419*	8502	*8428*
4	8365	*8286*	8374	*8295*	8384	*8305*	8394	*8315*	8404	*8325*	8413	*8334*	8423	*8344*	8433	*8354*	8443	*8363*	8452	*8373*	8462	*8383*	8472	*8393*
5	8335	*8250*	8344	*8260*	8354	*8269*	8364	*8279*	8373	*8289*	8383	*8299*	8393	*8308*	8402	*8318*	8412	*8328*	8422	*8337*	8432	*8347*	8441	*8357*
6	8305	*8214*	8314	*8224*	8324	*8234*	8334	*8243*	8343	*8253*	8353	*8263*	8363	*8272*	8372	*8282*	8382	*8292*	8392	*8301*	8401	*8311*	8411	*8321*
7	8275	*8179*	8285	*8188*	8294	*8198*	8304	*8208*	8313	*8217*	8323	*8227*	8333	*8236*	8342	*8246*	8352	*8256*	8362	*8265*	8371	*8275*	8381	*8284*
8	8245	*8143*	8255	*8152*	8265	*8162*	8274	*8171*	8284	*8181*	8293	*8191*	8303	*8200*	8313	*8210*	8322	*8219*	8332	*8229*	8341	*8239*	8351	*8248*
9	8216	*8107*	8226	*8116*	8235	*8126*	8245	*8135*	8254	*8145*	8264	*8154*	8273	*8164*	8283	*8173*	8293	*8183*	8302	*8193*	8312	*8202*	8321	*8212*
10	8187	*8070*	8197	*8080*	8206	*8089*	8216	*8099*	8225	*8108*	8235	*8118*	8244	*8127*	8254	*8137*	8263	*8146*	8273	*8156*	8282	*8165*	8292	*8175*
11	8158	*8034*	8168	*8043*	8177	*8053*	8187	*8062*	8196	*8072*	8206	*8081*	8215	*8091*	8225	*8100*	8234	*8110*	8244	*8119*	8253	*8129*	8263	*8138*
12	8130	*7997*	8139	*8006*	8148	*8016*	8158	*8025*	8167	*8035*	8177	*8044*	8186	*8054*	8196	*8063*	8205	*8073*	8215	*8082*	8224	*8092*	8233	*8101*
13	8101	*7960*	8110	*7969*	8120	*7979*	8129	*7988*	8139	*7998*	8148	*8007*	8158	*8017*	8167	*8026*	8176	*8035*	8186	*8045*	8195	*8054*	8205	*8064*
14	8073	*7923*	8082	*7932*	8092	*7942*	8101	*7951*	8110	*7960*	8120	*7970*	8129	*7979*	8138	*7988*	8148	*7998*	8157	*8007*	8167	*8017*	8176	*8026*
15	8045	*7885*	8054	*7895*	8063	*7904*	8073	*7913*	8082	*7923*	8091	*7932*	8101	*7941*	8110	*7951*	8120	*7960*	8129	*7969*	8138	*7979*	8148	*7988*
16	8017	*7847*	8026	*7857*	8035	*7866*	8045	*7875*	8054	*7885*	8063	*7894*	8073	*7903*	8082	*7913*	8091	*7922*	8101	*7931*	8110	*7941*	8119	*7950*
17	7989	*7809*	7998	*7818*	8008	*7828*	8017	*7837*	8026	*7846*	8036	*7856*	8045	*7865*	8054	*7874*	8063	*7883*	8073	*7893*	8082	*7902*	8091	*7911*
18	7962	*7771*	7971	*7780*	7980	*7789*	7989	*7798*	7999	*7808*	8008	*7817*	8017	*7826*	8026	*7835*	8036	*7845*	8045	*7854*	8054	*7863*	8063	*7872*
19	7934	*7732*	7944	*7741*	7953	*7750*	7962	*7759*	7971	*7769*	7980	*7778*	7990	*7787*	7999	*7796*	8008	*7805*	8017	*7815*	8027	*7824*	8036	*7833*
20	7907	*7692*	7916	*7701*	7926	*7711*	7935	*7720*	7944	*7729*	7953	*7738*	7962	*7747*	7972	*7757*	7981	*7766*	7990	*7775*	7999	*7784*	8008	*7793*
21	7880	*7652*	7889	*7662*	7899	*7671*	7908	*7680*	7917	*7689*	7926	*7698*	7935	*7707*	7944	*7717*	7954	*7726*	7963	*7735*	7972	*7744*	7981	*7753*
22	7853	*7612*	7863	*7621*	7872	*7630*	7881	*7639*	7890	*7649*	7899	*7658*	7908	*7667*	7917	*7676*	7927	*7685*	7936	*7694*	7945	*7703*	7954	*7713*
23	7827	*7571*	7836	*7580*	7845	*7589*	7854	*7599*	7863	*7608*	7872	*7617*	7881	*7626*	7891	*7635*	7900	*7644*	7909	*7653*	7918	*7662*	7927	*7671*
24	7800	*7530*	7810	*7539*	7819	*7548*	7828	*7557*	7837	*7566*	7846	*7575*	7855	*7584*	7864	*7593*	7873	*7602*	7882	*7612*	7891	*7621*	7900	*7630*
25	7774	*7488*	7783	*7497*	7792	*7506*	7801	*7515*	7810	*7524*	7819	*7533*	7828	*7542*	7838	*7551*	7847	*7560*	7856	*7569*	7865	*7578*	7874	*7587*
26	7748	*7445*	7757	*7454*	7766	*7463*	7775	*7472*	7784	*7481*	7793	*7490*	7802	*7499*	7811	*7508*	7820	*7517*	7829	*7526*	7838	*7535*	7847	*7545*
27	7722	*7402*	7731	*7411*	7740	*7420*	7749	*7429*	7758	*7438*	7767	*7447*	7776	*7456*	7785	*7465*	7794	*7474*	7803	*7483*	7812	*7492*	7821	*7501*
28	7697	*7358*	7706	*7367*	7715	*7376*	7723	*7385*	7732	*7394*	7741	*7403*	7750	*7412*	7759	*7421*	7768	*7430*	7777	*7439*	7786	*7448*	7795	*7457*
29	7671	*7314*	7680	*7323*	7689	*7332*	7698	*7341*	7707	*7349*	7716	*7358*	7725	*7367*	7734	*7376*	7742	*7385*	7751	*7394*	7760	*7403*	7769	*7412*
30	7646	*7269*	7655	*7277*	7664	*7286*	7672	*7295*	7681	*7304*	7690	*7313*	7699	*7322*	7708	*7331*	7717	*7340*	7726	*7349*	7735	*7357*	7744	*7366*
31	7621	*7222*	7629	*7231*	7638	*7240*	7647	*7249*	7656	*7258*	7665	*7267*	7674	*7276*	7683	*7284*	7691	*7293*	7700	*7302*	7709	*7311*	7718	*7320*
32	7596	*7176*	7604	*7184*	7613	*7193*	7622	*7202*	7631	*7211*	7640	*7220*	7649	*7229*	7657	*7237*	7666	*7246*	7675	*7255*	7684	*7264*	7693	*7273*
33	7571	*7128*	7579	*7137*	7588	*7145*	7597	*7154*	7606	*7163*	7615	*7172*	7623	*7181*	7632	*7189*	7641	*7198*	7650	*7207*	7659	*7216*	7667	*7225*
34	7546	*7079*	7555	*7088*	7564	*7097*	7572	*7105*	7581	*7114*	7590	*7123*	7599	*7132*	7607	*7141*	7616	*7149*	7625	*7158*	7634	*7167*	7642	*7176*
35	7521	*7030*	7530	*7038*	7539	*7047*	7548	*7056*	7556	*7065*	7565	*7073*	7574	*7082*	7583	*7091*	7591	*7100*	7600	*7108*	7609	*7117*	7618	*7126*
36	7497	*6979*	7506	*6988*	7514	*6996*	7523	*7005*	7532	*7014*	7541	*7023*	7549	*7031*	7558	*7040*	7567	*7049*	7575	*7057*	7584	*7066*	7593	*7075*
37	7473	*6927*	7481	*6936*	7490	*6945*	7499	*6954*	7508	*6962*	7516	*6971*	7525	*6980*	7534	*6988*	7542	*6997*	7551	*7006*	7560	*7014*	7568	*7023*
38	7449	*6875*	7457	*6884*	7466	*6892*	7475	*6901*	7483	*6909*	7492	*6918*	7501	*6927*	7509	*6935*	7518	*6944*	7527	*6953*	7535	*6961*	7544	*6970*
39	7425	*6821*	7433	*6830*	7442	*6838*	7451	*6847*	7459	*6856*	7468	*6864*	7477	*6873*	7485	*6882*	7494	*6890*	7503	*6899*	7511	*6907*	7520	*6916*
40	7401	*6766*	7410	*6775*	7418	*6783*	7427	*6792*	7435	*6801*	7444	*6809*	7453	*6818*	7461	*6826*	7470	*6835*	7479	*6844*	7487	*6852*	7496	*6861*
41	7377	*6710*	7386	*6719*	7395	*6727*	7403	*6736*	7412	*6744*	7420	*6753*	7429	*6762*	7438	*6770*	7446	*6779*	7455	*6787*	7463	*6796*	7472	*6804*
42	7354	*6653*	7363	*6661*	7371	*6670*	7380	*6678*	7388	*6687*	7397	*6695*	7405	*6704*	7414	*6712*	7422	*6721*	7431	*6730*	7440	*6738*	7448	*6747*

kPa	87.2		87.3		87.4		87.5		87.6		87.7		87.8		87.9		88.0		88.1		88.2		88.3	
°C	dry	*sat.*	dry	*sat.*	dry	*sat.*	dry	*sat.*	dry	*sat.*	dry	*sat.*	dry	*sat.*	dry	*sat.*	dry	*sat.*	dry	*sat.*	dry	*sat.*	dry	*sat.*
	0.	*0.*	0.	*0.*	0.	*0.*	0.	*0.*	0.	*0.*	0.	*0.*	0.	*0.*	0.	*0.*	0.	*0.*	0.	*0.*	0.	*0.*	0.	*0.*
0	8606	*8546*	8616	*8556*	8626	*8565*	8636	*8575*	8645	*8585*	8655	*8595*	8665	*8605*	8675	*8615*	8685	*8625*	8695	*8634*	8705	*8644*	8715	*8654*
1	8575	*8510*	8584	*8520*	8594	*8530*	8604	*8539*	8614	*8549*	8624	*8559*	8634	*8569*	8643	*8579*	8653	*8589*	8663	*8598*	8673	*8608*	8683	*8618*
2	8543	*8474*	8553	*8484*	8563	*8494*	8573	*8504*	8582	*8513*	8592	*8523*	8602	*8533*	8612	*8543*	8622	*8553*	8631	*8562*	8641	*8572*	8651	*8582*
3	8512	*8438*	8522	*8448*	8532	*8458*	8542	*8468*	8551	*8477*	8561	*8487*	8571	*8497*	8581	*8507*	8590	*8516*	8600	*8526*	8610	*8536*	8620	*8546*
4	8481	*8402*	8491	*8412*	8501	*8422*	8511	*8432*	8520	*8441*	8530	*8451*	8540	*8461*	8550	*8470*	8559	*8480*	8569	*8490*	8579	*8500*	8588	*8509*
5	8451	*8366*	8461	*8376*	8470	*8386*	8480	*8395*	8490	*8405*	8499	*8415*	8509	*8425*	8519	*8434*	8528	*8444*	8538	*8454*	8548	*8463*	8558	*8473*
6	8421	*8330*	8430	*8340*	8440	*8350*	8450	*8359*	8459	*8369*	8469	*8379*	8478	*8388*	8488	*8398*	8498	*8408*	8507	*8417*	8517	*8427*	8527	*8436*
7	8390	*8294*	8400	*8304*	8410	*8313*	8419	*8323*	8429	*8333*	8439	*8342*	8448	*8352*	8458	*8361*	8467	*8371*	8477	*8381*	8487	*8390*	8496	*8400*
8	8361	*8258*	8370	*8267*	8380	*8277*	8389	*8286*	8399	*8296*	8408	*8306*	8418	*8315*	8428	*8325*	8437	*8334*	8447	*8344*	8456	*8354*	8466	*8363*
9	8331	*8221*	8340	*8231*	8350	*8240*	8359	*8250*	8369	*8259*	8379	*8269*	8388	*8279*	8398	*8288*	8407	*8298*	8417	*8307*	8426	*8317*	8436	*8326*
10	8301	*8185*	8311	*8194*	8320	*8204*	8330	*8213*	8339	*8223*	8349	*8232*	8358	*8242*	8368	*8251*	8377	*8261*	8387	*8270*	8397	*8280*	8406	*8289*
11	8272	*8148*	8282	*8157*	8291	*8167*	8300	*8176*	8310	*8186*	8319	*8195*	8329	*8204*	8338	*8214*	8348	*8223*	8357	*8233*	8367	*8242*	8376	*8252*
12	8243	*8110*	8252	*8120*	8262	*8129*	8271	*8139*	8281	*8148*	8290	*8158*	8300	*8167*	8309	*8177*	8319	*8186*	8328	*8195*	8337	*8205*	8347	*8214*
13	8214	*8073*	8223	*8082*	8233	*8092*	8242	*8101*	8252	*8111*	8261	*8120*	8271	*8130*	8280	*8139*	8289	*8148*	8299	*8158*	8308	*8167*	8318	*8177*
14	8185	*8035*	8195	*8045*	8204	*8054*	8214	*8064*	8223	*8073*	8232	*8082*	8242	*8092*	8251	*8101*	8261	*8110*	8270	*8120*	8279	*8129*	8289	*8139*
15	8157	*7998*	8166	*8007*	8176	*8016*	8185	*8026*	8194	*8035*	8204	*8044*	8213	*8054*	8222	*8063*	8232	*8072*	8241	*8082*	8250	*8091*	8260	*8100*
16	8129	*7959*	8138	*7969*	8147	*7978*	8157	*7987*	8166	*7997*	8175	*8006*	8185	*8015*	8194	*8025*	8203	*8034*	8213	*8043*	8222	*8052*	8231	*8062*
17	8101	*7921*	8110	*7930*	8119	*7939*	8128	*7949*	8138	*7958*	8147	*7967*	8156	*7976*	8166	*7986*	8175	*7995*	8184	*8004*	8193	*8014*	8203	*8023*
18	8073	*7882*	8082	*7891*	8091	*7900*	8100	*7909*	8110	*7919*	8119	*7928*	8128	*7937*	8137	*7947*	8147	*7956*	8156	*7965*	8165	*7974*	8175	*7984*
19	8045	*7842*	8054	*7852*	8063	*7861*	8073	*7870*	8082	*7879*	8091	*7889*	8100	*7898*	8110	*7907*	8119	*7916*	8128	*7925*	8137	*7935*	8146	*7944*
20	8017	*7803*	8027	*7812*	8036	*7821*	8045	*7830*	8054	*7839*	8063	*7849*	8073	*7858*	8082	*7867*	8091	*7876*	8100	*7885*	8109	*7895*	8119	*7904*
21	7990	*7762*	7999	*7772*	8008	*7781*	8018	*7790*	8027	*7799*	8036	*7808*	8045	*7817*	8054	*7827*	8063	*7836*	8073	*7845*	8082	*7854*	8091	*7863*
22	7963	*7722*	7972	*7731*	7981	*7740*	7990	*7749*	8000	*7758*	8009	*7767*	8018	*7776*	8027	*7786*	8036	*7795*	8045	*7804*	8054	*7813*	8063	*7822*
23	7936	*7680*	7945	*7690*	7954	*7699*	7963	*7708*	7972	*7717*	7982	*7726*	7991	*7735*	8000	*7744*	8009	*7753*	8018	*7762*	8027	*7771*	8036	*7781*
24	7909	*7639*	7918	*7648*	7927	*7657*	7937	*7666*	7946	*7675*	7955	*7684*	7964	*7693*	7973	*7702*	7982	*7711*	7991	*7720*	8000	*7729*	8009	*7739*
25	7883	*7596*	7892	*7605*	7901	*7615*	7910	*7624*	7919	*7633*	7928	*7642*	7937	*7651*	7946	*7660*	7955	*7669*	7964	*7678*	7973	*7687*	7982	*7696*
26	7856	*7554*	7865	*7563*	7874	*7572*	7883	*7581*	7892	*7590*	7901	*7599*	7910	*7608*	7919	*7617*	7928	*7626*	7937	*7635*	7946	*7644*	7955	*7653*
27	7830	*7510*	7839	*7519*	7848	*7528*	7857	*7537*	7866	*7546*	7875	*7555*	7884	*7564*	7893	*7573*	7902	*7582*	7911	*7591*	7920	*7600*	7929	*7609*
28	7804	*7466*	7813	*7475*	7822	*7484*	7831	*7493*	7840	*7502*	7849	*7510*	7858	*7519*	7867	*7528*	7876	*7537*	7885	*7546*	7894	*7555*	7902	*7564*
29	7778	*7421*	7787	*7430*	7796	*7439*	7805	*7448*	7814	*7456*	7823	*7465*	7832	*7474*	7841	*7483*	7850	*7492*	7858	*7501*	7867	*7510*	7876	*7519*
30	7752	*7375*	7761	*7384*	7770	*7393*	7779	*7402*	7788	*7411*	7797	*7420*	7806	*7429*	7815	*7437*	7824	*7446*	7832	*7455*	7841	*7464*	7850	*7473*
31	7727	*7329*	7736	*7338*	7745	*7346*	7753	*7355*	7762	*7364*	7771	*7373*	7780	*7382*	7789	*7391*	7798	*7400*	7807	*7409*	7815	*7417*	7824	*7426*
32	7702	*7282*	7710	*7290*	7719	*7299*	7728	*7308*	7737	*7317*	7746	*7326*	7754	*7335*	7763	*7343*	7772	*7352*	7781	*7361*	7790	*7370*	7799	*7379*
33	7676	*7233*	7685	*7242*	7694	*7251*	7703	*7260*	7712	*7269*	7720	*7277*	7729	*7286*	7738	*7295*	7747	*7304*	7756	*7313*	7764	*7321*	7773	*7330*
34	7651	*7184*	7660	*7193*	7669	*7202*	7678	*7211*	7686	*7220*	7695	*7228*	7704	*7237*	7713	*7246*	7721	*7255*	7730	*7263*	7739	*7272*	7748	*7281*
35	7626	*7134*	7635	*7143*	7644	*7152*	7653	*7161*	7661	*7169*	7670	*7178*	7679	*7187*	7688	*7196*	7696	*7204*	7705	*7213*	7714	*7222*	7723	*7231*
36	7602	*7084*	7610	*7092*	7619	*7101*	7628	*7110*	7637	*7119*	7645	*7127*	7654	*7136*	7663	*7145*	7671	*7153*	7680	*7162*	7689	*7171*	7698	*7180*
37	7577	*7032*	7586	*7040*	7594	*7049*	7603	*7058*	7612	*7066*	7621	*7075*	7629	*7084*	7638	*7093*	7647	*7101*	7655	*7110*	7664	*7119*	7673	*7127*
38	7553	*6979*	7561	*6987*	7570	*6996*	7579	*7005*	7587	*7013*	7596	*7022*	7605	*7031*	7613	*7039*	7622	*7048*	7631	*7057*	7639	*7065*	7648	*7074*
39	7528	*6925*	7537	*6933*	7546	*6942*	7554	*6951*	7563	*6959*	7572	*6968*	7580	*6976*	7589	*6985*	7597	*6994*	7606	*7002*	7615	*7011*	7623	*7020*
40	7504	*6869*	7513	*6878*	7522	*6887*	7530	*6895*	7539	*6904*	7547	*6912*	7556	*6921*	7565	*6930*	7573	*6938*	7582	*6947*	7590	*6955*	7599	*6964*
41	7480	*6813*	7489	*6822*	7498	*6830*	7506	*6839*	7515	*6847*	7523	*6856*	7532	*6864*	7540	*6873*	7549	*6882*	7558	*6890*	7566	*6899*	7575	*6907*
42	7457	*6755*	7465	*6764*	7474	*6772*	7482	*6781*	7491	*6789*	7499	*6798*	7508	*6807*	7516	*6815*	7525	*6824*	7534	*6832*	7542	*6841*	7551	*6849*

kPa	88.4		88.5		88.6		88.7		88.8		88.9		89.0		89.1		89.2		89.3		89.4		89.5	
°C	dry	sat.	dry	sat.	dry	sat.	dry	sat.	dry	sat.	dry	sat.	dry	sat.	dry	sat.	dry	sat.	dry	sat.	dry	sat.	dry	sat.
	0.	0.	0.	0.	0.	0.	0.	0.	0.	0.	0.	0.	0.	0.	0.	0.	0.	0.	0.	0.	0.	0.	0.	0.
0	8724	8664	8734	8674	8744	8684	8754	8694	8764	8704	8774	8713	8784	8723	8793	8733	8803	8743	8813	8753	8823	8763	8833	8773
1	8693	8628	8702	8638	8712	8648	8722	8657	8732	8667	8742	8677	8751	8687	8761	8697	8771	8707	8781	8716	8791	8726	8801	8736
2	8661	8592	8671	8602	8680	8611	8690	8621	8700	8631	8710	8641	8720	8651	8729	8660	8739	8670	8749	8680	8759	8690	8769	8700
3	8629	8555	8639	8565	8649	8575	8659	8585	8668	8594	8678	8604	8688	8614	8698	8624	8707	8633	8717	8643	8727	8653	8737	8663
4	8598	8519	8608	8529	8618	8539	8627	8548	8637	8558	8647	8568	8657	8577	8666	8587	8676	8597	8686	8607	8695	8616	8705	8626
5	8567	8483	8577	8492	8587	8502	8596	8512	8606	8521	8616	8531	8625	8541	8635	8551	8645	8560	8654	8570	8664	8580	8674	8589
6	8536	8446	8546	8456	8556	8465	8565	8475	8575	8485	8585	8494	8594	8504	8604	8514	8614	8523	8623	8533	8633	8543	8643	8552
7	8506	8410	8516	8419	8525	8429	8535	8438	8544	8448	8554	8458	8564	8467	8573	8477	8583	8487	8592	8496	8602	8506	8612	8515
8	8476	8373	8485	8382	8495	8392	8504	8402	8514	8411	8523	8421	8533	8430	8543	8440	8552	8449	8562	8459	8571	8469	8581	8478
9	8445	8336	8455	8345	8465	8355	8474	8365	8484	8374	8493	8384	8503	8393	8512	8403	8522	8412	8531	8422	8541	8431	8551	8441
10	8416	8299	8425	8308	8435	8318	8444	8327	8454	8337	8463	8346	8473	8356	8482	8365	8492	8375	8501	8384	8511	8394	8520	8403
11	8386	8261	8395	8271	8405	8280	8414	8290	8424	8299	8433	8309	8443	8318	8452	8328	8462	8337	8471	8347	8481	8356	8490	8366
12	8356	8224	8366	8233	8375	8243	8385	8252	8394	8262	8404	8271	8413	8281	8423	8290	8432	8299	8441	8309	8451	8318	8460	8328
13	8327	8186	8337	8196	8346	8205	8355	8214	8365	8224	8374	8233	8384	8243	8393	8252	8402	8261	8412	8271	8421	8280	8431	8290
14	8298	8148	8307	8157	8317	8167	8326	8176	8336	8186	8345	8195	8354	8204	8364	8214	8373	8223	8383	8233	8392	8242	8401	8251
15	8269	8110	8279	8119	8288	8128	8297	8138	8307	8147	8316	8157	8325	8166	8335	8175	8344	8185	8353	8194	8363	8203	8372	8213
16	8241	8071	8250	8080	8259	8090	8268	8099	8278	8108	8287	8118	8296	8127	8306	8136	8315	8146	8324	8155	8334	8164	8343	8174
17	8212	8032	8221	8041	8231	8051	8240	8060	8249	8069	8259	8079	8268	8088	8277	8097	8286	8106	8296	8116	8305	8125	8314	8134
18	8184	7993	8193	8002	8202	8011	8212	8021	8221	8030	8230	8039	8239	8048	8249	8058	8258	8067	8267	8076	8276	8085	8286	8095
19	8156	7953	8165	7962	8174	7972	8183	7981	8193	7990	8202	7999	8211	8008	8220	8018	8230	8027	8239	8036	8248	8045	8257	8055
20	8128	7913	8137	7922	8146	7931	8155	7941	8165	7950	8174	7959	8183	7968	8192	7977	8201	7987	8211	7996	8220	8005	8229	8014
21	8100	7872	8109	7881	8118	7891	8128	7900	8137	7909	8146	7918	8155	7927	8164	7936	8173	7946	8183	7955	8192	7964	8201	7973
22	8073	7831	8082	7840	8091	7850	8100	7859	8109	7868	8118	7877	8127	7886	8137	7895	8146	7904	8155	7913	8164	7923	8173	7932
23	8045	7790	8054	7799	8064	7808	8073	7817	8082	7826	8091	7835	8100	7844	8109	7853	8118	7862	8127	7872	8136	7881	8145	7890
24	8018	7748	8027	7757	8036	7766	8045	7775	8054	7784	8064	7793	8073	7802	8082	7811	8091	7820	8100	7829	8109	7838	8118	7847
25	7991	7705	8000	7714	8009	7723	8018	7732	8027	7741	8036	7750	8045	7759	8054	7768	8064	7777	8073	7786	8082	7795	8091	7804
26	7964	7662	7973	7671	7982	7680	7991	7689	8000	7698	8009	7707	8018	7716	8028	7725	8037	7734	8046	7743	8055	7752	8064	7761
27	7938	7618	7947	7627	7956	7636	7965	7645	7974	7654	7983	7663	7992	7672	8001	7681	8010	7690	8019	7699	8028	7708	8037	7716
28	7911	7573	7920	7582	7929	7591	7938	7600	7947	7609	7956	7618	7965	7627	7974	7636	7983	7645	7992	7654	8001	7663	8010	7672
29	7885	7528	7894	7537	7903	7546	7912	7555	7921	7564	7930	7572	7939	7581	7948	7590	7957	7599	7965	7608	7974	7617	7983	7626
30	7859	7482	7868	7491	7877	7500	7886	7509	7895	7517	7904	7526	7912	7535	7921	7544	7930	7553	7939	7562	7948	7571	7957	7580
31	7833	7435	7842	7444	7851	7453	7860	7462	7869	7471	7878	7479	7886	7488	7895	7497	7904	7506	7913	7515	7922	7524	7931	7533
32	7807	7388	7816	7396	7825	7405	7834	7414	7843	7423	7852	7432	7860	7441	7869	7449	7878	7458	7887	7467	7896	7476	7905	7485
33	7782	7339	7791	7348	7800	7357	7808	7365	7817	7374	7826	7383	7835	7392	7844	7401	7852	7409	7861	7418	7870	7427	7879	7436
34	7757	7290	7765	7299	7774	7307	7783	7316	7792	7325	7800	7334	7809	7342	7818	7351	7827	7360	7836	7369	7844	7377	7853	7386
35	7731	7239	7740	7248	7749	7257	7758	7266	7766	7274	7775	7283	7784	7292	7793	7301	7801	7309	7810	7318	7819	7327	7828	7336
36	7706	7188	7715	7197	7724	7206	7732	7214	7741	7223	7750	7232	7759	7241	7767	7249	7776	7258	7785	7267	7793	7275	7802	7284
37	7681	7136	7690	7145	7699	7153	7707	7162	7716	7171	7725	7179	7733	7188	7742	7197	7751	7206	7760	7214	7768	7223	7777	7232
38	7657	7083	7665	7091	7674	7100	7683	7109	7691	7117	7700	7126	7709	7135	7717	7143	7726	7152	7735	7161	7743	7169	7752	7178
39	7632	7028	7641	7037	7649	7046	7658	7054	7667	7063	7675	7071	7684	7080	7692	7089	7701	7097	7710	7106	7718	7115	7727	7123
40	7608	6973	7616	6981	7625	6990	7633	6998	7642	7007	7651	7016	7659	7024	7668	7033	7676	7042	7685	7050	7694	7059	7702	7067
41	7583	6916	7592	6925	7600	6933	7609	6942	7618	6950	7626	6959	7635	6967	7643	6976	7652	6985	7661	6993	7669	7002	7678	7010
42	7559	6858	7568	6866	7576	6875	7585	6884	7593	6892	7602	6901	7611	6909	7619	6918	7628	6926	7636	6935	7645	6943	7653	6952

kPa	89.6		89.7		89.8		89.9		90.0		90.1		90.2		90.3		90.4		90.5		90.6		90.7	
°C	dry	sat.	dry	sat.	dry	sat.	dry	sat.	dry	sat.	dry	sat.	dry	sat.	dry	sat.	dry	sat.	dry	sat.	dry	sat.	dry	sat.
	0.	0.	0.	0.	0.	0.	0.	0.	0.	0.	0.	0.	0.	0.	0.	0.	0.	0.	0.	0.	0.	0.	0.	0.
0	8843	8783	8853	8792	8863	8802	8872	8812	8882	8822	8892	8832	8902	8842	8912	8852	8922	8861	8932	8871	8942	8881	8951	8891
1	8810	8746	8820	8756	8830	8766	8840	8775	8850	8785	8860	8795	8869	8805	8879	8815	8889	8825	8899	8834	8909	8844	8919	8854
2	8778	8709	8788	8719	8798	8729	8808	8739	8818	8749	8827	8758	8837	8768	8847	8778	8857	8788	8867	8798	8876	8807	8886	8817
3	8747	8673	8756	8682	8766	8692	8776	8702	8786	8712	8795	8721	8805	8731	8815	8741	8825	8751	8834	8760	8844	8770	8854	8780
4	8715	8636	8725	8646	8734	8655	8744	8665	8754	8675	8764	8684	8773	8694	8783	8704	8793	8714	8802	8723	8812	8733	8822	8743
5	8683	8599	8693	8609	8703	8618	8713	8628	8722	8638	8732	8647	8742	8657	8751	8667	8761	8677	8771	8686	8780	8696	8790	8706
6	8652	8562	8662	8572	8672	8581	8681	8591	8691	8601	8701	8610	8710	8620	8720	8630	8730	8639	8739	8649	8749	8659	8759	8668
7	8621	8525	8631	8535	8641	8544	8650	8554	8660	8564	8669	8573	8679	8583	8689	8592	8698	8602	8708	8612	8718	8621	8727	8631
8	8591	8488	8600	8497	8610	8507	8619	8517	8629	8526	8639	8536	8648	8545	8658	8555	8667	8565	8677	8574	8686	8584	8696	8593
9	8560	8451	8570	8460	8579	8470	8589	8479	8598	8489	8608	8498	8617	8508	8627	8517	8637	8527	8646	8536	8656	8546	8665	8556
10	8530	8413	8539	8423	8549	8432	8558	8442	8568	8451	8577	8461	8587	8470	8596	8480	8606	8489	8615	8499	8625	8508	8635	8518
11	8500	8375	8509	8385	8519	8394	8528	8404	8538	8413	8547	8423	8557	8432	8566	8442	8576	8451	8585	8461	8595	8470	8604	8480
12	8470	8337	8479	8347	8489	8356	8498	8366	8508	8375	8517	8385	8527	8394	8536	8403	8545	8413	8555	8422	8564	8432	8574	8441
13	8440	8299	8450	8309	8459	8318	8468	8327	8478	8337	8487	8346	8497	8356	8506	8365	8516	8374	8525	8384	8534	8393	8544	8403
14	8411	8261	8420	8270	8429	8279	8439	8289	8448	8298	8458	8308	8467	8317	8476	8326	8486	8336	8495	8345	8505	8355	8514	8364
15	8381	8222	8391	8231	8400	8241	8409	8250	8419	8259	8428	8269	8438	8278	8447	8288	8456	8297	8466	8306	8475	8316	8484	8325
16	8352	8183	8362	8192	8371	8202	8380	8211	8390	8220	8399	8230	8408	8239	8418	8248	8427	8258	8436	8267	8446	8276	8455	8286
17	8324	8144	8333	8153	8342	8162	8351	8171	8361	8181	8370	8190	8379	8199	8389	8209	8398	8218	8407	8227	8416	8236	8426	8246
18	8295	8104	8304	8113	8313	8122	8323	8132	8332	8141	8341	8150	8350	8159	8360	8169	8369	8178	8378	8187	8387	8196	8397	8206
19	8266	8064	8276	8073	8285	8082	8294	8091	8303	8101	8313	8110	8322	8119	8331	8128	8340	8138	8349	8147	8359	8156	8368	8165
20	8238	8023	8247	8032	8257	8042	8266	8051	8275	8060	8284	8069	8293	8078	8303	8088	8312	8097	8321	8106	8330	8115	8339	8124
21	8210	7982	8219	7991	8228	8001	8238	8010	8247	8019	8256	8028	8265	8037	8274	8046	8283	8056	8293	8065	8302	8074	8311	8083
22	8182	7941	8191	7950	8200	7959	8210	7968	8219	7977	8228	7987	8237	7996	8246	8005	8255	8014	8264	8023	8274	8032	8283	8041
23	8155	7899	8164	7908	8173	7917	8182	7926	8191	7935	8200	7944	8209	7953	8218	7963	8227	7972	8236	7981	8246	7990	8255	7999
24	8127	7856	8136	7866	8145	7875	8154	7884	8163	7893	8172	7902	8181	7911	8190	7920	8200	7929	8209	7938	8218	7947	8227	7956
25	8100	7813	8109	7822	8118	7831	8127	7841	8136	7850	8145	7859	8154	7868	8163	7877	8172	7886	8181	7895	8190	7904	8199	7913
26	8073	7770	8082	7779	8091	7788	8100	7797	8109	7806	8118	7815	8127	7824	8136	7833	8145	7842	8154	7851	8163	7860	8172	7869
27	8046	7725	8055	7734	8064	7743	8073	7752	8082	7761	8090	7770	8099	7779	8108	7788	8117	7797	8126	7806	8135	7815	8144	7824
28	8019	7681	8028	7689	8037	7698	8046	7707	8055	7716	8064	7725	8073	7734	8081	7743	8090	7752	8099	7761	8108	7770	8117	7779
29	7992	7635	8001	7644	8010	7653	8019	7662	8028	7671	8037	7679	8046	7688	8055	7697	8064	7706	8072	7715	8081	7724	8090	7733
30	7966	7589	7975	7597	7984	7606	7992	7615	8001	7624	8010	7633	8019	7642	8028	7651	8037	7660	8046	7669	8055	7677	8064	7686
31	7940	7541	7948	7550	7957	7559	7966	7568	7975	7577	7984	7586	7993	7595	8002	7603	8010	7612	8019	7621	8028	7630	8037	7639
32	7913	7494	7922	7502	7931	7511	7940	7520	7949	7529	7958	7538	7966	7547	7975	7555	7984	7564	7993	7573	8002	7582	8011	7591
33	7888	7445	7896	7453	7905	7462	7914	7471	7923	7480	7932	7489	7940	7498	7949	7506	7958	7515	7967	7524	7976	7533	7984	7542
34	7862	7395	7871	7404	7879	7413	7888	7421	7897	7430	7906	7439	7914	7448	7923	7456	7932	7465	7941	7474	7950	7483	7958	7492
35	7836	7344	7845	7353	7854	7362	7863	7371	7871	7379	7880	7388	7889	7397	7897	7406	7906	7414	7915	7423	7924	7432	7932	7441
36	7811	7293	7820	7302	7828	7310	7837	7319	7846	7328	7854	7336	7863	7345	7872	7354	7881	7363	7889	7371	7898	7380	7907	7389
37	7786	7240	7794	7249	7803	7258	7812	7266	7820	7275	7829	7284	7838	7292	7846	7301	7855	7310	7864	7318	7873	7327	7881	7336
38	7761	7187	7769	7195	7778	7204	7787	7213	7795	7221	7804	7230	7813	7239	7821	7247	7830	7256	7838	7265	7847	7273	7856	7282
39	7736	7132	7744	7141	7753	7149	7762	7158	7770	7166	7779	7175	7787	7184	7796	7192	7805	7201	7813	7210	7822	7218	7831	7227
40	7711	7076	7719	7085	7728	7093	7737	7102	7745	7110	7754	7119	7763	7128	7771	7136	7780	7145	7788	7153	7797	7162	7806	7171
41	7686	7019	7695	7027	7703	7036	7712	7045	7721	7053	7729	7062	7738	7070	7746	7079	7755	7088	7763	7096	7772	7105	7781	7113
42	7662	6960	7670	6969	7679	6978	7687	6986	7696	6995	7705	7003	7713	7012	7722	7020	7730	7029	7739	7037	7747	7046	7756	7055

kPa	90.8		90.9		91.0		91.1		91.2		91.3		91.4		91.5		91.6		91.7		91.8		91.9	
°C	dry	sat.	dry	sat.	dry	sat.	dry	sat.	dry	sat.	dry	sat.	dry	sat.	dry	sat.	dry	sat.	dry	sat.	dry	sat.	dry	sat.
	0.	0.	0.	0.	0.	0.	0.	0.	0.	0.	0.	0.	0.	0.	0.	0.	0.	0.	0.	0.	0.	0.	0.	0.
0	8961	8901	8971	8911	8981	8921	8991	8931	9001	8940	9011	8950	9020	8960	9030	8970	9040	8980	9050	8990	9060	9000	9070	9010
1	8928	8864	8938	8874	8948	8884	8958	8893	8968	8903	8978	8913	8987	8923	8997	8933	9007	8943	9017	8952	9027	8962	9037	8972
2	8896	8827	8906	8837	8916	8846	8925	8856	8935	8866	8945	8876	8955	8886	8965	8895	8974	8905	8984	8915	8994	8925	9004	8935
3	8864	8790	8873	8799	8883	8809	8893	8819	8903	8829	8912	8838	8922	8848	8932	8858	8942	8868	8952	8878	8961	8887	8971	8897
4	8832	8753	8841	8762	8851	8772	8861	8782	8871	8791	8880	8801	8890	8811	8900	8821	8909	8830	8919	8840	8929	8850	8939	8860
5	8800	8715	8809	8725	8819	8735	8829	8744	8839	8754	8848	8764	8858	8773	8868	8783	8877	8793	8887	8803	8897	8812	8906	8822
6	8768	8678	8778	8688	8788	8697	8797	8707	8807	8717	8816	8726	8826	8736	8836	8745	8845	8755	8855	8765	8865	8774	8874	8784
7	8737	8640	8746	8650	8756	8660	8766	8669	8775	8679	8785	8689	8795	8698	8804	8708	8814	8717	8823	8727	8833	8737	8843	8746
8	8706	8603	8715	8612	8725	8622	8734	8632	8744	8641	8754	8651	8763	8660	8773	8670	8782	8680	8792	8689	8802	8699	8811	8708
9	8675	8565	8684	8575	8694	8584	8703	8594	8713	8603	8723	8613	8732	8622	8742	8632	8751	8642	8761	8651	8770	8661	8780	8670
10	8644	8527	8654	8537	8663	8546	8673	8556	8682	8565	8692	8575	8701	8584	8711	8594	8720	8603	8730	8613	8739	8622	8749	8632
11	8614	8489	8623	8499	8633	8508	8642	8518	8651	8527	8661	8537	8670	8546	8680	8555	8689	8565	8699	8574	8708	8584	8718	8593
12	8583	8451	8593	8460	8602	8470	8612	8479	8621	8489	8631	8498	8640	8507	8649	8517	8659	8526	8668	8536	8678	8545	8687	8555
13	8553	8412	8563	8422	8572	8431	8581	8440	8591	8450	8600	8459	8610	8469	8619	8478	8629	8488	8638	8497	8647	8506	8657	8516
14	8523	8373	8533	8383	8542	8392	8551	8401	8561	8411	8570	8420	8580	8430	8589	8439	8598	8448	8608	8458	8617	8467	8627	8477
15	8494	8334	8503	8344	8512	8353	8522	8362	8531	8372	8540	8381	8550	8390	8559	8400	8569	8409	8578	8418	8587	8428	8597	8437
16	8464	8295	8474	8304	8483	8314	8492	8323	8502	8332	8511	8341	8520	8351	8529	8360	8539	8369	8548	8379	8557	8388	8567	8397
17	8435	8255	8444	8264	8454	8274	8463	8283	8472	8292	8481	8302	8491	8311	8500	8320	8509	8329	8519	8339	8528	8348	8537	8357
18	8406	8215	8415	8224	8424	8233	8434	8243	8443	8252	8452	8261	8462	8271	8471	8280	8480	8289	8489	8298	8499	8308	8508	8317
19	8377	8175	8386	8184	8396	8193	8405	8202	8414	8211	8423	8221	8432	8230	8442	8239	8451	8243	8460	8258	8469	8267	8479	8276
20	8348	8134	8358	8143	8367	8152	8376	8161	8385	8170	8394	8180	8404	8189	8413	8198	8422	8207	8431	8216	8440	8226	8450	8235
21	8320	8092	8329	8101	8338	8111	8348	8120	8357	8129	8366	8138	8375	8147	8384	8156	8393	8166	8403	8175	8412	8184	8421	8193
22	8292	8050	8301	8060	8310	8069	8319	8078	8328	8087	8337	8096	8347	8105	8356	8114	8365	8123	8374	8133	8383	8142	8392	8151
23	8264	8008	8273	8017	8282	8026	8291	8035	8300	8044	8309	8054	8318	8063	8327	8072	8337	8081	8346	8090	8355	8099	8364	8108
24	8236	7965	8245	7974	8254	7983	8263	7992	8272	8002	8281	8011	8290	8020	8299	8029	8308	8038	8317	8047	8327	8056	8336	8065
25	8208	7922	8217	7931	8226	7940	8235	7949	8244	7958	8253	7967	8262	7976	8271	7985	8280	7994	8290	8003	8299	8012	8308	8021
26	8181	7878	8190	7887	8199	7896	8208	7905	8217	7914	8226	7923	8235	7932	8244	7941	8253	7950	8262	7959	8271	7968	8280	7977
27	8153	7833	8162	7842	8171	7851	8180	7860	8189	7869	8198	7878	8207	7887	8216	7896	8225	7905	8234	7914	8243	7923	8252	7932
28	8126	7788	8135	7797	8144	7806	8153	7815	8162	7824	8171	7833	8180	7842	8189	7851	8198	7860	8207	7868	8216	7877	8225	7886
29	8099	7742	8108	7751	8117	7760	8126	7769	8135	7778	8144	7787	8153	7795	8162	7804	8171	7813	8180	7822	8188	7831	8197	7840
30	8072	7695	8081	7704	8090	7713	8099	7722	8108	7731	8117	7740	8126	7749	8135	7757	8144	7766	8152	7775	8161	7784	8170	7793
31	8046	7648	8055	7657	8064	7665	8072	7674	8081	7683	8090	7692	8099	7701	8108	7710	8117	7719	8126	7728	8134	7736	8143	7745
32	8019	7599	8028	7608	8037	7617	8046	7626	8055	7635	8064	7644	8072	7652	8081	7661	8090	7670	8099	7679	8108	7688	8117	7697
33	7993	7550	8002	7559	8011	7568	8020	7577	8028	7586	8037	7594	8046	7603	8055	7612	8064	7621	8072	7630	8081	7638	8090	7647
34	7967	7500	7976	7509	7985	7518	7993	7527	8002	7535	8011	7544	8020	7553	8029	7562	8037	7571	8046	7579	8055	7588	8064	7597
35	7941	7449	7950	7458	7959	7467	7967	7476	7976	7484	7985	7493	7994	7502	8002	7511	8011	7519	8020	7528	8029	7537	8037	7546
36	7915	7397	7924	7406	7933	7415	7942	7424	7950	7432	7959	7441	7968	7450	7976	7459	7985	7467	7994	7476	8003	7485	8011	7493
37	7890	7345	7899	7353	7907	7362	7916	7371	7925	7379	7933	7388	7942	7397	7951	7405	7959	7414	7968	7423	7977	7431	7985	7440
38	7864	7291	7873	7299	7882	7308	7890	7317	7899	7325	7908	7334	7916	7343	7925	7351	7934	7360	7942	7369	7951	7377	7960	7386
39	7839	7235	7848	7244	7857	7253	7865	7261	7874	7270	7882	7279	7891	7287	7900	7296	7908	7305	7917	7313	7926	7322	7934	7330
40	7814	7179	7823	7188	7831	7196	7840	7205	7849	7214	7857	7222	7866	7231	7874	7239	7883	7248	7892	7257	7900	7265	7909	7274
41	7789	7122	7798	7130	7806	7139	7815	7148	7824	7156	7832	7165	7841	7173	7849	7182	7858	7190	7866	7199	7875	7208	7884	7216
42	7764	7063	7773	7072	7782	7080	7790	7089	7799	7097	7807	7106	7816	7114	7824	7123	7833	7131	7841	7140	7850	7149	7859	7157

kPa	92.0		92.1		92.2		92.3		92.4		92.5		92.6		92.7		92.8		92.9		93.0		93.1	
°C	dry	sat.	dry	sat.	dry	sat.	dry	sat.	dry	sat.	dry	sat.	dry	sat.	dry	sat.	dry	sat.	dry	sat.	dry	sat.	dry	sat.
	0.	0.	0.	0.	0.	0.	0.	0.	0.	0.	0.	0.	0.	0.	0.	0.	0.	0.	0.	0.	0.	0.	0.	0.
0	9080	9019	9090	9029	9099	9039	9109	9049	9119	9059	9129	9069	9139	9079	9149	9088	9159	9098	9169	9108	9178	9118	9188	9128
1	9046	8982	9056	8992	9066	9002	9076	9011	9086	9021	9096	9031	9105	9041	9115	9051	9125	9061	9135	9070	9145	9080	9155	9090
2	9014	8944	9023	8954	9033	8964	9043	8974	9053	8984	9063	8993	9072	9003	9082	9013	9092	9023	9102	9033	9112	9042	9121	9052
3	8981	8907	8991	8917	9000	8926	9010	8936	9020	8946	9030	8956	9039	8965	9049	8975	9059	8985	9069	8995	9078	9004	9088	9014
4	8948	8869	8958	8879	8968	8889	8978	8898	8987	8908	8997	8918	9007	8928	9016	8937	9026	8947	9036	8957	9046	8967	9055	8976
5	8916	8832	8926	8841	8935	8851	8945	8861	8955	8870	8965	8880	8974	8890	8984	8899	8994	8909	9003	8919	9013	8928	9023	8938
6	8884	8794	8894	8803	8903	8813	8913	8823	8923	8832	8932	8842	8942	8852	8952	8861	8961	8871	8971	8881	8981	8890	8990	8900
7	8852	8756	8862	8766	8872	8775	8881	8785	8891	8794	8900	8804	8910	8814	8920	8823	8929	8833	8939	8843	8948	8852	8958	8862
8	8821	8718	8830	8728	8840	8737	8849	8747	8859	8756	8869	8766	8878	8775	8888	8785	8897	8795	8907	8804	8917	8814	8926	8823
9	8789	8680	8799	8689	8808	8699	8818	8708	8828	8718	8837	8728	8847	8737	8856	8747	8866	8756	8875	8766	8885	8775	8894	8785
10	8758	8641	8768	8651	8777	8660	8787	8670	8796	8680	8806	8689	8815	8699	8825	8708	8834	8718	8844	8727	8853	8737	8863	8746
11	8727	8603	8737	8612	8746	8622	8756	8631	8765	8641	8775	8650	8784	8660	8794	8669	8803	8679	8813	8688	8822	8698	8832	8707
12	8697	8564	8706	8574	8716	8583	8725	8593	8735	8602	8744	8611	8753	8621	8763	8630	8772	8640	8782	8649	8791	8659	8801	8668
13	8666	8525	8676	8535	8685	8544	8694	8553	8704	8563	8713	8572	8723	8582	8732	8591	8742	8601	8751	8610	8760	8619	8770	8629
14	8636	8486	8645	8495	8655	8505	8664	8514	8674	8524	8683	8533	8692	8542	8702	8552	8711	8561	8720	8570	8730	8580	8739	8589
15	8606	8447	8615	8456	8625	8465	8634	8475	8643	8484	8653	8493	8662	8503	8671	8512	8681	8521	8690	8531	8699	8540	8709	8549
16	8576	8407	8585	8416	8595	8425	8604	8435	8613	8444	8623	8453	8632	8463	8641	8472	8651	8481	8660	8491	8669	8500	8679	8509
17	8546	8367	8556	8376	8565	8385	8574	8394	8584	8404	8593	8413	8602	8422	8612	8432	8621	8441	8630	8450	8639	8459	8649	8469
18	8517	8326	8526	8335	8536	8345	8545	8354	8554	8363	8563	8372	8573	8382	8582	8391	8591	8400	8600	8409	8610	8419	8619	8428
19	8488	8285	8497	8294	8506	8304	8516	8313	8525	8322	8534	8331	8543	8341	8552	8350	8562	8359	8571	8368	8580	8377	8589	8387
20	8459	8244	8468	8253	8477	8262	8486	8272	8496	8281	8505	8290	8514	8299	8523	8308	8532	8317	8542	8327	8551	8336	8560	8345
21	8430	8202	8439	8211	8448	8221	8457	8230	8467	8239	8476	8248	8485	8257	8494	8266	8503	8276	8512	8285	8522	8294	8531	8303
22	8401	8160	8410	8169	8420	8178	8429	8187	8438	8197	8447	8206	8456	8215	8465	8224	8474	8233	8484	8242	8493	8251	8502	8260
23	8373	8117	8382	8126	8391	8135	8400	8145	8409	8154	8418	8163	8428	8172	8437	8181	8446	8190	8455	8199	8464	8208	8473	8217
24	8345	8074	8354	8083	8363	8092	8372	8101	8381	8110	8390	8119	8399	8129	8408	8138	8417	8147	8426	8156	8435	8165	8444	8174
25	8317	8030	8326	8039	8335	8048	8344	8057	8353	8067	8362	8076	8371	8085	8380	8094	8389	8103	8398	8112	8407	8121	8416	8130
26	8289	7986	8298	7995	8307	8004	8316	8013	8325	8022	8334	8031	8343	8040	8352	8049	8361	8058	8370	8067	8379	8076	8388	8085
27	8261	7941	8270	7950	8279	7959	8288	7968	8297	7977	8306	7986	8315	7995	8324	8004	8333	8013	8342	8022	8351	8031	8360	8040
28	8234	7895	8243	7904	8252	7913	8260	7922	8269	7931	8278	7940	8287	7949	8296	7958	8305	7967	8314	7976	8323	7985	8332	7994
29	8206	7849	8215	7858	8224	7867	8233	7876	8242	7885	8251	7894	8260	7902	8269	7911	8278	7920	8287	7929	8295	7938	8304	7947
30	8179	7802	8188	7811	8197	7820	8206	7829	8215	7838	8224	7846	8233	7855	8241	7864	8250	7873	8259	7882	8268	7891	8277	7900
31	8152	7754	8161	7763	8170	7772	8179	7781	8188	7790	8197	7798	8205	7807	8214	7816	8223	7825	8232	7834	8241	7843	8250	7852
32	8125	7705	8134	7714	8143	7723	8152	7732	8161	7741	8170	7750	8178	7758	8187	7767	8196	7776	8205	7785	8214	7794	8223	7803
33	8099	7656	8108	7665	8116	7674	8125	7682	8134	7691	8143	7700	8152	7709	8160	7718	8169	7726	8178	7735	8187	7744	8196	7753
34	8072	7606	8081	7614	8090	7623	8099	7632	8108	7641	8116	7649	8125	7658	8134	7667	8143	7676	8151	7685	8160	7693	8169	7702
35	8046	7554	8055	7563	8064	7572	8072	7581	8081	7589	8090	7598	8099	7607	8107	7616	8116	7624	8125	7633	8134	7642	8142	7651
36	8020	7502	8029	7511	8038	7520	8046	7528	8055	7537	8064	7546	8072	7554	8081	7563	8090	7572	8099	7581	8107	7589	8116	7598
37	7994	7449	8003	7458	8012	7466	8020	7475	8029	7484	8038	7492	8046	7501	8055	7510	8064	7518	8072	7527	8081	7536	8090	7544
38	7968	7395	7977	7403	7986	7412	7994	7421	8003	7429	8012	7438	8020	7446	8029	7455	8038	7464	8046	7472	8055	7481	8064	7490
39	7943	7339	7951	7348	7960	7356	7969	7365	7977	7374	7986	7382	7995	7391	8003	7400	8012	7408	8021	7417	8029	7425	8038	7434
40	7917	7282	7926	7291	7935	7300	7943	7308	7952	7317	7960	7326	7969	7334	7978	7343	7986	7351	7995	7360	8003	7369	8012	7377
41	7892	7225	7901	7233	7909	7242	7918	7250	7926	7259	7935	7268	7944	7276	7952	7285	7961	7293	7969	7302	7978	7311	7987	7319
42	7867	7166	7876	7174	7884	7183	7893	7191	7901	7200	7910	7208	7918	7217	7927	7226	7935	7234	7944	7243	7953	7251	7961	7260

kPa	93.2		93.3		93.4		93.5		93.6		93.7		93.8		93.9		94.0		94.1		94.2		94.3	
°C	dry	sat.	dry	sat.	dry	sat.	dry	sat.	dry	sat.	dry	sat.	dry	sat.	dry	sat.	dry	sat.	dry	sat.	dry	sat.	dry	sat.
	0.	0.	0.	0.	0.	0.	0.	0.	0.	0.	0.	0.	0.	0.	0.	0.	0.	0.	0.	0.	0.	0.	0.	0.
0	9198	9138	9208	9148	9218	9158	9228	9167	9238	9177	9247	9187	9257	9197	9267	9207	9277	9217	9287	9227	9297	9237	9307	9246
1	9164	9100	9174	9110	9184	9120	9194	9129	9204	9139	9214	9149	9223	9159	9233	9169	9243	9179	9253	9188	9263	9198	9273	9208
2	9131	9062	9141	9072	9151	9082	9160	9091	9170	9101	9180	9111	9190	9121	9200	9131	9209	9140	9219	9150	9229	9160	9239	9170
3	9098	9024	9108	9034	9117	9043	9127	9053	9137	9063	9147	9073	9157	9083	9166	9092	9176	9102	9186	9112	9196	9122	9205	9131
4	9065	8986	9075	8996	9085	9005	9094	9015	9104	9025	9114	9035	9123	9044	9133	9054	9143	9064	9153	9074	9162	9083	9172	9093
5	9032	8948	9042	8958	9052	8967	9061	8977	9071	8987	9081	8996	9091	9006	9100	9016	9110	9025	9120	9035	9129	9045	9139	9054
6	9000	8910	9010	8919	9019	8929	9029	8939	9039	8948	9048	8958	9058	8968	9068	8977	9077	8987	9087	8997	9097	9006	9106	9016
7	8968	8871	8977	8881	8987	8891	8997	8900	9006	8910	9016	8920	9025	8929	9035	8939	9045	8948	9054	8958	9064	8968	9074	8977
8	8936	8833	8945	8843	8955	8852	8965	8862	8974	8871	8984	8881	8993	8891	9003	8900	9012	8910	9022	8919	9032	8929	9041	8938
9	8904	8794	8914	8804	8923	8814	8933	8823	8942	8833	8952	8842	8961	8852	8971	8861	8980	8871	8990	8880	9000	8890	9009	8900
10	8873	8756	8882	8765	8892	8775	8901	8784	8911	8794	8920	8803	8930	8813	8939	8822	8949	8832	8958	8841	8968	8851	8977	8860
11	8841	8717	8851	8726	8860	8736	8870	8745	8879	8755	8889	8764	8898	8774	8908	8783	8917	8793	8927	8802	8936	8812	8946	8821
12	8810	8678	8820	8687	8829	8697	8838	8706	8848	8715	8857	8725	8867	8734	8876	8744	8886	8753	8895	8763	8905	8772	8914	8782
13	8779	8638	8789	8648	8798	8657	8808	8667	8817	8676	8826	8685	8836	8695	8845	8704	8855	8714	8864	8723	8873	8732	8883	8742
14	8749	8599	8758	8608	8767	8617	8777	8627	8786	8636	8796	8646	8805	8655	8814	8664	8824	8674	8833	8683	8842	8692	8852	8702
15	8718	8559	8728	8568	8737	8578	8746	8587	8756	8596	8765	8606	8774	8615	8784	8624	8793	8634	8802	8643	8812	8652	8821	8662
16	8688	8519	8697	8528	8707	8537	8716	8547	8725	8556	8735	8565	8744	8575	8753	8584	8763	8593	8772	8602	8781	8612	8791	8621
17	8658	8478	8667	8487	8677	8497	8686	8506	8695	8515	8704	8524	8714	8534	8723	8543	8732	8552	8742	8562	8751	8571	8760	8580
18	8628	8437	8637	8446	8647	8456	8656	8465	8665	8474	8674	8483	8684	8493	8693	8502	8702	8511	8711	8520	8721	8530	8730	8539
19	8599	8396	8608	8405	8617	8414	8626	8424	8635	8433	8645	8442	8654	8451	8663	8461	8672	8470	8682	8479	8691	8488	8700	8497
20	8569	8354	8578	8363	8588	8373	8597	8382	8606	8391	8615	8400	8624	8409	8634	8419	8643	8428	8652	8437	8661	8446	8670	8455
21	8540	8312	8549	8321	8558	8330	8567	8340	8577	8349	8586	8358	8595	8367	8604	8376	8613	8385	8622	8395	8632	8404	8641	8413
22	8511	8270	8520	8279	8529	8288	8538	8297	8547	8306	8557	8315	8566	8324	8575	8334	8584	8343	8593	8352	8602	8361	8611	8370
23	8482	8226	8491	8236	8500	8245	8509	8254	8519	8263	8528	8272	8537	8281	8546	8290	8555	8299	8564	8308	8573	8318	8582	8327
24	8454	8183	8463	8192	8472	8201	8481	8210	8490	8219	8499	8228	8508	8237	8517	8246	8526	8256	8535	8265	8544	8274	8553	8283
25	8425	8139	8434	8148	8443	8157	8452	8166	8461	8175	8470	8184	8479	8193	8488	8202	8497	8211	8506	8220	8516	8229	8525	8238
26	8397	8094	8406	8103	8415	8112	8424	8121	8433	8130	8442	8139	8451	8148	8460	8157	8469	8166	8478	8175	8487	8184	8496	8193
27	8369	8049	8378	8058	8387	8067	8396	8076	8405	8085	8414	8094	8423	8103	8432	8112	8441	8121	8450	8130	8459	8139	8468	8148
28	8341	8003	8350	8012	8359	8021	8368	8030	8377	8039	8386	8047	8395	8056	8404	8065	8413	8074	8422	8083	8430	8092	8439	8101
29	8313	7956	8322	7965	8331	7974	8340	7983	8349	7992	8358	8001	8367	8010	8376	8018	8385	8027	8394	8036	8403	8045	8411	8054
30	8286	7909	8295	7918	8304	7926	8313	7935	8321	7944	8330	7953	8339	7962	8348	7971	8357	7980	8366	7989	8375	7998	8384	8006
31	8259	7860	8267	7869	8276	7878	8285	7887	8294	7896	8303	7905	8312	7914	8321	7922	8329	7931	8338	7940	8347	7949	8356	7958
32	8231	7811	8240	7820	8249	7829	8258	7838	8267	7847	8276	7856	8284	7864	8293	7873	8302	7882	8311	7891	8320	7900	8329	7909
33	8204	7762	8213	7770	8222	7779	8231	7788	8240	7797	8248	7806	8257	7814	8266	7823	8275	7832	8284	7841	8293	7850	8301	7858
34	8178	7711	8186	7720	8195	7728	8204	7737	8213	7746	8222	7755	8230	7764	8239	7772	8248	7781	8257	7790	8265	7799	8274	7807
35	8151	7659	8160	7668	8169	7677	8177	7685	8186	7694	8195	7703	8204	7712	8212	7720	8221	7729	8230	7738	8239	7747	8247	7755
36	8125	7607	8133	7615	8142	7624	8151	7633	8160	7642	8168	7650	8177	7659	8186	7668	8194	7676	8203	7685	8212	7694	8221	7703
37	8098	7553	8107	7562	8116	7570	8125	7579	8133	7588	8142	7597	8151	7605	8159	7614	8168	7623	8177	7631	8185	7640	8194	7649
38	8072	7498	8081	7507	8090	7516	8098	7524	8107	7533	8116	7542	8124	7550	8133	7559	8142	7568	8150	7576	8159	7585	8168	7594
39	8046	7443	8055	7451	8064	7460	8072	7469	8081	7477	8090	7486	8098	7494	8107	7503	8116	7512	8124	7520	8133	7529	8141	7538
40	8021	7386	8029	7394	8038	7403	8047	7412	8055	7420	8064	7429	8072	7437	8081	7446	8090	7455	8098	7463	8107	7472	8115	7480
41	7995	7328	8004	7336	8012	7345	8021	7353	8029	7362	8038	7371	8047	7379	8055	7388	8064	7396	8072	7405	8081	7413	8089	7422
42	7970	7268	7978	7277	7987	7285	7995	7294	8004	7303	8012	7311	8021	7320	8030	7328	8038	7337	8047	7345	8055	7354	8064	7362

kPa	94.4		94.5		94.6		94.7		94.8		94.9		95.0		95.1		95.2		95.3		95.4		95.5	
°C	dry	sat.	dry	sat.	dry	sat.	dry	sat.	dry	sat.	dry	sat.	dry	sat.	dry	sat.	dry	sat.	dry	sat.	dry	sat.	dry	sat.
	0.	0.	0.	0.	0.	0.	0.	0.	0.	0.	0.	0.	0.	0.	0.	0.	0.	0.	0.	0.	0.	0.	0.	0.
0	9317	9256	9326	9266	9336	9276	9346	9286	9356	9296	9366	9306	9376	9315	9386	9325	9396	9335	9405	9345	9415	9355	9425	9365
1	9282	9218	9292	9228	9302	9238	9312	9247	9322	9257	9332	9267	9341	9277	9351	9287	9361	9297	9371	9306	9381	9316	9391	9326
2	9249	9180	9258	9189	9268	9199	9278	9209	9288	9219	9298	9229	9307	9238	9317	9248	9327	9258	9337	9268	9347	9278	9356	9287
3	9215	9141	9225	9151	9235	9161	9244	9170	9254	9180	9264	9190	9274	9200	9283	9209	9293	9219	9303	9229	9313	9239	9322	9248
4	9182	9103	9191	9112	9201	9122	9211	9132	9221	9142	9230	9151	9240	9161	9250	9171	9260	9181	9269	9190	9279	9200	9289	9210
5	9149	9064	9158	9074	9168	9084	9178	9093	9187	9103	9197	9113	9207	9122	9217	9132	9226	9142	9236	9151	9246	9161	9255	9171
6	9116	9026	9125	9035	9135	9045	9145	9055	9154	9064	9164	9074	9174	9083	9183	9093	9193	9103	9203	9112	9212	9122	9222	9132
7	9083	8987	9093	8997	9102	9006	9112	9016	9122	9025	9131	9035	9141	9045	9151	9054	9160	9064	9170	9073	9179	9083	9189	9093
8	9051	8948	9060	8958	9070	8967	9080	8977	9089	8986	9099	8996	9108	9006	9118	9015	9128	9025	9137	9034	9147	9044	9156	9054
9	9019	8909	9028	8919	9038	8928	9047	8938	9057	8947	9066	8957	9076	8966	9086	8976	9095	8986	9105	8995	9114	9005	9124	9014
10	8987	8870	8996	8879	9006	8889	9015	8898	9025	8908	9034	8918	9044	8927	9053	8937	9063	8946	9072	8956	9082	8965	9091	8975
11	8955	8831	8965	8840	8974	8850	8983	8859	8993	8869	9002	8878	9012	8887	9021	8897	9031	8906	9040	8916	9050	8925	9059	8935
12	8924	8791	8933	8800	8942	8810	8952	8819	8961	8829	8971	8838	8980	8848	8990	8857	8999	8867	9009	8876	9018	8886	9028	8895
13	8892	8751	8902	8761	8911	8770	8921	8780	8930	8789	8939	8798	8949	8808	8958	8817	8968	8827	8977	8836	8987	8845	8996	8855
14	8861	8711	8871	8721	8880	8730	8889	8739	8899	8749	8908	8758	8918	8768	8927	8777	8936	8786	8946	8796	8955	8805	8965	8815
15	8830	8671	8840	8680	8849	8690	8859	8699	8868	8708	8877	8718	8887	8727	8896	8737	8905	8746	8915	8755	8924	8765	8933	8774
16	8800	8630	8809	8640	8818	8649	8828	8658	8837	8668	8846	8677	8856	8686	8865	8696	8874	8705	8884	8714	8893	8724	8902	8733
17	8769	8589	8779	8599	8788	8608	8797	8617	8807	8627	8816	8636	8825	8645	8834	8655	8844	8664	8853	8673	8862	8682	8872	8692
18	8739	8548	8748	8558	8758	8567	8767	8576	8776	8585	8786	8595	8795	8604	8804	8613	8813	8622	8823	8632	8832	8641	8841	8650
19	8709	8507	8718	8516	8728	8525	8737	8534	8746	8544	8755	8553	8765	8562	8774	8571	8783	8580	8792	8590	8802	8599	8811	8608
20	8679	8465	8689	8474	8698	8483	8707	8492	8716	8501	8725	8511	8735	8520	8744	8529	8753	8538	8762	8547	8771	8557	8781	8566
21	8650	8422	8659	8431	8668	8440	8677	8450	8687	8459	8696	8468	8705	8477	8714	8486	8723	8495	8732	8505	8742	8514	8751	8523
22	8621	8379	8630	8388	8639	8397	8648	8407	8657	8416	8666	8425	8675	8434	8684	8443	8694	8452	8703	8461	8712	8470	8721	8480
23	8591	8336	8600	8345	8610	8354	8619	8363	8628	8372	8637	8381	8646	8390	8655	8399	8664	8409	8673	8418	8682	8427	8691	8436
24	8562	8292	8571	8301	8581	8310	8590	8319	8599	8328	8608	8337	8617	8346	8626	8355	8635	8364	8644	8373	8653	8383	8662	8392
25	8534	8247	8543	8256	8552	8265	8561	8274	8570	8283	8579	8293	8588	8302	8597	8311	8606	8320	8615	8329	8624	8338	8633	8347
26	8505	8202	8514	8211	8523	8220	8532	8229	8541	8238	8550	8247	8559	8256	8568	8265	8577	8274	8586	8283	8595	8292	8604	8301
27	8477	8156	8486	8165	8495	8174	8504	8183	8513	8192	8522	8201	8530	8210	8539	8219	8548	8228	8557	8237	8566	8246	8575	8255
28	8448	8110	8457	8119	8466	8128	8475	8137	8484	8146	8493	8155	8502	8164	8511	8173	8520	8182	8529	8191	8538	8200	8547	8209
29	8420	8063	8429	8072	8438	8081	8447	8090	8456	8099	8465	8108	8474	8117	8483	8125	8492	8134	8501	8143	8510	8152	8518	8161
30	8393	8015	8401	8024	8410	8033	8419	8042	8428	8051	8437	8060	8446	8069	8455	8078	8464	8086	8473	8095	8481	8104	8490	8113
31	8365	7967	8374	7976	8383	7984	8391	7993	8400	8002	8409	8011	8418	8020	8427	8029	8436	8038	8445	8047	8453	8055	8462	8064
32	8337	7917	8346	7926	8355	7935	8364	7944	8373	7953	8382	7962	8390	7970	8399	7979	8408	7988	8417	7997	8426	8006	8435	8015
33	8310	7867	8319	7876	8328	7885	8337	7894	8345	7902	8354	7911	8363	7920	8372	7929	8381	7938	8389	7946	8398	7955	8407	7964
34	8283	7816	8292	7825	8301	7834	8309	7843	8318	7851	8327	7860	8336	7869	8344	7878	8353	7886	8362	7895	8371	7904	8380	7913
35	8256	7764	8265	7773	8274	7782	8282	7790	8291	7799	8300	7808	8309	7817	8317	7825	8326	7834	8335	7843	8344	7852	8352	7860
36	8229	7711	8238	7720	8247	7729	8255	7737	8264	7746	8273	7755	8282	7764	8290	7772	8299	7781	8308	7790	8316	7798	8325	7807
37	8203	7657	8211	7666	8220	7675	8229	7683	8237	7692	8246	7701	8255	7710	8264	7718	8272	7727	8281	7736	8290	7744	8298	7753
38	8176	7602	8185	7611	8194	7620	8202	7628	8211	7637	8220	7646	8228	7654	8237	7663	8246	7672	8254	7680	8263	7689	8272	7698
39	8150	7546	8159	7555	8167	7564	8176	7572	8185	7581	8193	7589	8202	7598	8210	7607	8219	7615	8228	7624	8236	7633	8245	7641
40	8124	7489	8133	7498	8141	7506	8150	7515	8158	7523	8167	7532	8176	7541	8184	7549	8193	7558	8201	7566	8210	7575	8219	7584
41	8098	7431	8107	7439	8115	7448	8124	7456	8132	7465	8141	7474	8150	7482	8158	7491	8167	7499	8175	7508	8184	7516	8192	7525
42	8072	7371	8081	7379	8089	7388	8098	7397	8106	7405	8115	7414	8124	7422	8132	7431	8141	7439	8149	7448	8158	7456	8166	7465

kPa	95.6		95.7		95.8		95.9		96.0		96.1		96.2		96.3		96.4		96.5		96.6		96.7	
°C	dry	*sat.*	dry	*sat.*	dry	*sat.*	dry	*sat.*	dry	*sat.*	dry	*sat.*	dry	*sat.*	dry	*sat.*	dry	*sat.*	dry	*sat.*	dry	*sat.*	dry	*sat.*
	0.	*0.*	0.	*0.*	0.	*0.*	0.	*0.*	0.	*0.*	0.	*0.*	0.	*0.*	0.	*0.*	0.	*0.*	0.	*0.*	0.	*0.*	0.	*0.*
0	9435	*9375*	9445	*9385*	9455	*9394*	9465	*9404*	9474	*9414*	9484	*9424*	9494	*9434*	9504	*9444*	9514	*9454*	9524	*9464*	9534	*9473*	9544	*9483*
1	9400	*9336*	9410	*9346*	9420	*9356*	9430	*9365*	9440	*9375*	9450	*9385*	9459	*9395*	9469	*9405*	9479	*9415*	9489	*9424*	9499	*9434*	9509	*9444*
2	9366	*9297*	9376	*9307*	9386	*9317*	9396	*9327*	9405	*9336*	9415	*9346*	9425	*9356*	9435	*9366*	9445	*9376*	9454	*9385*	9464	*9395*	9474	*9405*
3	9332	*9258*	9342	*9268*	9352	*9278*	9362	*9288*	9371	*9297*	9381	*9307*	9391	*9317*	9401	*9327*	9410	*9336*	9420	*9346*	9430	*9356*	9440	*9366*
4	9298	*9219*	9308	*9229*	9318	*9239*	9328	*9249*	9337	*9258*	9347	*9268*	9357	*9278*	9367	*9287*	9376	*9297*	9386	*9307*	9396	*9317*	9405	*9326*
5	9265	*9180*	9275	*9190*	9284	*9200*	9294	*9210*	9304	*9219*	9313	*9229*	9323	*9239*	9333	*9248*	9343	*9258*	9352	*9268*	9362	*9277*	9372	*9287*
6	9232	*9141*	9241	*9151*	9251	*9161*	9261	*9170*	9270	*9180*	9280	*9190*	9290	*9199*	9299	*9209*	9309	*9219*	9319	*9228*	9328	*9238*	9338	*9248*
7	9199	*9102*	9208	*9112*	9218	*9122*	9228	*9131*	9237	*9141*	9247	*9150*	9256	*9160*	9266	*9170*	9276	*9179*	9285	*9189*	9295	*9199*	9305	*9208*
8	9166	*9063*	9175	*9073*	9185	*9082*	9195	*9092*	9204	*9101*	9214	*9111*	9223	*9121*	9233	*9130*	9243	*9140*	9252	*9149*	9262	*9159*	9271	*9169*
9	9133	*9024*	9143	*9033*	9152	*9043*	9162	*9052*	9172	*9062*	9181	*9072*	9191	*9081*	9200	*9091*	9210	*9100*	9219	*9110*	9229	*9119*	9238	*9129*
10	9101	*8984*	9111	*8994*	9120	*9003*	9130	*9013*	9139	*9022*	9149	*9032*	9158	*9041*	9168	*9051*	9177	*9060*	9187	*9070*	9196	*9079*	9206	*9089*
11	9069	*8944*	9078	*8954*	9088	*8963*	9097	*8973*	9107	*8982*	9116	*8992*	9126	*9001*	9135	*9011*	9145	*9020*	9154	*9030*	9164	*9039*	9173	*9049*
12	9037	*8904*	9046	*8914*	9056	*8923*	9065	*8933*	9075	*8942*	9084	*8952*	9094	*8961*	9103	*8971*	9113	*8980*	9122	*8990*	9132	*8999*	9141	*9008*
13	9005	*8864*	9015	*8874*	9024	*8883*	9034	*8893*	9043	*8902*	9052	*8911*	9062	*8921*	9071	*8930*	9081	*8940*	9090	*8949*	9100	*8959*	9109	*8968*
14	8974	*8824*	8983	*8833*	8993	*8843*	9002	*8852*	9011	*8861*	9021	*8871*	9030	*8880*	9040	*8890*	9049	*8899*	9058	*8908*	9068	*8918*	9077	*8927*
15	8943	*8783*	8952	*8793*	8961	*8802*	8971	*8811*	8980	*8821*	8989	*8830*	8999	*8839*	9008	*8849*	9018	*8858*	9027	*8867*	9036	*8877*	9046	*8886*
16	8912	*8742*	8921	*8752*	8930	*8761*	8940	*8770*	8949	*8780*	8958	*8789*	8968	*8798*	8977	*8808*	8986	*8817*	8996	*8826*	9005	*8836*	9014	*8845*
17	8881	*8701*	8890	*8710*	8899	*8720*	8909	*8729*	8918	*8738*	8927	*8747*	8937	*8757*	8946	*8766*	8955	*8775*	8965	*8785*	8974	*8794*	8983	*8803*
18	8850	*8659*	8860	*8669*	8869	*8678*	8878	*8687*	8887	*8696*	8897	*8706*	8906	*8715*	8915	*8724*	8924	*8733*	8934	*8743*	8943	*8752*	8952	*8761*
19	8820	*8617*	8829	*8627*	8838	*8636*	8848	*8645*	8857	*8654*	8866	*8663*	8875	*8673*	8885	*8682*	8894	*8691*	8903	*8700*	8912	*8710*	8921	*8719*
20	8790	*8575*	8799	*8584*	8808	*8593*	8817	*8603*	8827	*8612*	8836	*8621*	8845	*8630*	8854	*8639*	8863	*8648*	8873	*8658*	8882	*8667*	8891	*8676*
21	8760	*8532*	8769	*8541*	8778	*8550*	8787	*8560*	8797	*8569*	8806	*8578*	8815	*8587*	8824	*8596*	8833	*8605*	8842	*8615*	8851	*8624*	8861	*8633*
22	8730	*8489*	8739	*8498*	8748	*8507*	8758	*8516*	8767	*8525*	8776	*8534*	8785	*8544*	8794	*8553*	8803	*8562*	8812	*8571*	8821	*8580*	8831	*8589*
23	8701	*8445*	8710	*8454*	8719	*8463*	8728	*8472*	8737	*8481*	8746	*8490*	8755	*8500*	8764	*8509*	8773	*8518*	8782	*8527*	8792	*8536*	8801	*8545*
24	8671	*8401*	8680	*8410*	8689	*8419*	8698	*8428*	8708	*8437*	8717	*8446*	8726	*8455*	8735	*8464*	8744	*8473*	8753	*8482*	8762	*8491*	8771	*8500*
25	8642	*8356*	8651	*8365*	8660	*8374*	8669	*8383*	8678	*8392*	8687	*8401*	8696	*8410*	8705	*8419*	8714	*8428*	8723	*8437*	8732	*8446*	8742	*8455*
26	8613	*8310*	8622	*8319*	8631	*8328*	8640	*8337*	8649	*8346*	8658	*8355*	8667	*8364*	8676	*8373*	8685	*8382*	8694	*8391*	8703	*8400*	8712	*8409*
27	8584	*8264*	8593	*8273*	8602	*8282*	8611	*8291*	8620	*8300*	8629	*8309*	8638	*8318*	8647	*8327*	8656	*8336*	8665	*8345*	8674	*8354*	8683	*8363*
28	8556	*8217*	8565	*8226*	8574	*8235*	8583	*8244*	8592	*8253*	8601	*8262*	8609	*8271*	8618	*8280*	8627	*8289*	8636	*8298*	8645	*8307*	8654	*8316*
29	8527	*8170*	8536	*8179*	8545	*8188*	8554	*8197*	8563	*8206*	8572	*8215*	8581	*8224*	8590	*8233*	8599	*8241*	8608	*8250*	8617	*8259*	8626	*8268*
30	8499	*8122*	8508	*8131*	8517	*8140*	8526	*8149*	8535	*8158*	8544	*8166*	8553	*8175*	8561	*8184*	8570	*8193*	8579	*8202*	8588	*8211*	8597	*8220*
31	8471	*8073*	8480	*8082*	8489	*8091*	8498	*8100*	8507	*8109*	8516	*8117*	8524	*8126*	8533	*8135*	8542	*8144*	8551	*8153*	8560	*8162*	8569	*8171*
32	8443	*8023*	8452	*8032*	8461	*8041*	8470	*8050*	8479	*8059*	8488	*8068*	8496	*8076*	8505	*8085*	8514	*8094*	8523	*8103*	8532	*8112*	8541	*8121*
33	8416	*7973*	8425	*7982*	8433	*7990*	8442	*7999*	8451	*8008*	8460	*8017*	8469	*8026*	8477	*8034*	8486	*8043*	8495	*8052*	8504	*8061*	8513	*8070*
34	8388	*7921*	8397	*7930*	8406	*7939*	8415	*7948*	8423	*7957*	8432	*7965*	8441	*7974*	8450	*7983*	8458	*7992*	8467	*8000*	8476	*8009*	8485	*8018*
35	8361	*7869*	8370	*7878*	8379	*7887*	8387	*7895*	8396	*7904*	8405	*7913*	8413	*7922*	8422	*7930*	8431	*7939*	8440	*7948*	8448	*7957*	8457	*7965*
36	8334	*7816*	8343	*7825*	8351	*7833*	8360	*7842*	8369	*7851*	8377	*7860*	8386	*7868*	8395	*7877*	8404	*7886*	8412	*7894*	8421	*7903*	8430	*7912*
37	8307	*7762*	8316	*7770*	8324	*7779*	8333	*7788*	8342	*7796*	8350	*7805*	8359	*7814*	8368	*7822*	8376	*7831*	8385	*7840*	8394	*7849*	8403	*7857*
38	8280	*7706*	8289	*7715*	8298	*7724*	8306	*7732*	8315	*7741*	8324	*7750*	8332	*7758*	8341	*7767*	8350	*7776*	8358	*7784*	8367	*7793*	8376	*7802*
39	8254	*7650*	8262	*7659*	8271	*7667*	8280	*7676*	8288	*7684*	8297	*7693*	8305	*7702*	8314	*7710*	8323	*7719*	8331	*7728*	8340	*7736*	8349	*7745*
40	8227	*7592*	8236	*7601*	8244	*7609*	8253	*7618*	8262	*7627*	8270	*7635*	8279	*7644*	8287	*7653*	8296	*7661*	8305	*7670*	8313	*7678*	8322	*7687*
41	8201	*7534*	8210	*7542*	8218	*7551*	8227	*7559*	8235	*7568*	8244	*7576*	8252	*7585*	8261	*7594*	8270	*7602*	8278	*7611*	8287	*7619*	8295	*7628*
42	8175	*7474*	8183	*7482*	8192	*7491*	8201	*7499*	8209	*7508*	8218	*7516*	8226	*7525*	8235	*7533*	8243	*7542*	8252	*7551*	8260	*7559*	8269	*7568*

kPa	96.8		96.9		97.0		97.1		97.2		97.3		97.4		97.5		97.6		97.7		97.8		97.9	
°C	dry	*sat.*	dry	*sat.*	dry	*sat.*	dry	*sat.*	dry	*sat.*	dry	*sat.*	dry	*sat.*	dry	*sat.*	dry	*sat.*	dry	*sat.*	dry	*sat.*	dry	*sat.*
	0.	*0.*	0.	*0.*	0.	*0.*	0.	*0.*	0.	*0.*	0.	*0.*	0.	*0.*	0.	*0.*	0.	*0.*	0.	*0.*	0.	*0.*	0.	*0.*
0	9553	*9493*	9563	*9503*	9573	*9513*	9583	*9523*	9593	*9533*	9603	*9542*	9613	*9552*	9623	*9562*	9632	*9572*	9642	*9582*	9652	*9592*	9662	*9602*
1	9518	*9454*	9528	*9464*	9538	*9474*	9548	*9483*	9558	*9493*	9568	*9503*	9577	*9513*	9587	*9523*	9597	*9533*	9607	*9542*	9617	*9552*	9627	*9562*
2	9484	*9415*	9494	*9425*	9503	*9434*	9513	*9444*	9523	*9454*	9533	*9464*	9543	*9474*	9552	*9483*	9562	*9493*	9572	*9503*	9582	*9513*	9592	*9523*
3	9449	*9375*	9459	*9385*	9469	*9395*	9479	*9405*	9488	*9414*	9498	*9424*	9508	*9434*	9518	*9444*	9527	*9453*	9537	*9463*	8547	*9473*	9557	*9483*
4	9415	*9336*	9425	*9346*	9435	*9356*	9444	*9365*	9454	*9375*	9464	*9385*	9474	*9394*	9483	*9404*	9493	*9414*	9503	*9424*	9512	*9433*	9522	*9443*
5	9381	*9297*	9391	*9306*	9401	*9316*	9410	*9326*	9420	*9336*	9430	*9345*	9439	*9355*	9449	*9365*	9459	*9374*	9468	*9384*	9478	*9394*	9488	*9403*
6	9348	*9257*	9357	*9267*	9367	*9277*	9377	*9286*	9386	*9296*	9396	*9306*	9406	*9315*	9415	*9325*	9425	*9335*	9434	*9344*	9444	*9354*	9454	*9364*
7	9314	*9218*	9324	*9227*	9333	*9237*	9343	*9247*	9353	*9256*	9362	*9266*	9372	*9276*	9381	*9285*	9391	*9295*	9401	*9304*	9410	*9314*	9420	*9324*
8	9281	*9178*	9291	*9188*	9300	*9197*	9310	*9207*	9319	*9216*	9329	*9226*	9338	*9236*	9348	*9245*	9358	*9255*	9367	*9264*	9377	*9274*	9386	*9284*
9	9248	*9138*	9258	*9148*	9267	*9157*	9277	*9167*	9286	*9177*	9296	*9186*	9305	*9196*	9315	*9205*	9324	*9215*	9334	*9224*	9343	*9234*	9353	*9243*
10	9215	*9098*	9225	*9108*	9234	*9117*	9244	*9127*	9253	*9136*	9263	*9146*	9272	*9156*	9282	*9165*	9291	*9175*	9301	*9184*	9310	*9194*	9320	*9203*
11	9183	*9058*	9192	*9068*	9202	*9077*	9211	*9087*	9221	*9096*	9230	*9106*	9240	*9115*	9249	*9125*	9259	*9134*	9268	*9144*	9278	*9153*	9287	*9163*
12	9150	*9018*	9160	*9027*	9169	*9037*	9179	*9046*	9188	*9056*	9198	*9065*	9207	*9075*	9217	*9084*	9226	*9094*	9236	*9103*	9245	*9112*	9254	*9122*
13	9118	*8977*	9128	*8987*	9137	*8996*	9147	*9006*	9156	*9015*	9165	*9024*	9175	*9034*	9184	*9043*	9194	*9053*	9203	*9062*	9213	*9072*	9222	*9081*
14	9087	*8937*	9096	*8946*	9105	*8955*	9115	*8965*	9124	*8974*	9133	*8983*	9143	*8993*	9152	*9002*	9162	*9012*	9171	*9021*	9180	*9030*	9190	*9040*
15	9055	*8896*	9064	*8905*	9074	*8914*	9083	*8924*	9092	*8933*	9102	*8942*	9111	*8952*	9120	*8961*	9130	*8970*	9139	*8980*	9148	*8989*	9158	*8998*
16	9024	*8854*	9033	*8863*	9042	*8873*	9052	*8882*	9061	*8891*	9070	*8901*	9079	*8910*	9089	*8919*	9098	*8929*	9107	*8938*	9117	*8947*	9126	*8957*
17	8992	*8812*	9002	*8822*	9011	*8831*	9020	*8840*	9030	*8850*	9039	*8859*	9048	*8868*	9057	*8877*	9067	*8887*	9076	*8896*	9085	*8905*	9095	*8915*
18	8961	*8770*	8971	*8780*	8980	*8789*	8989	*8798*	8998	*8807*	9008	*8817*	9017	*8826*	9026	*8835*	9035	*8845*	9045	*8854*	9054	*8863*	9063	*8872*
19	8931	*8728*	8940	*8737*	8949	*8747*	8958	*8756*	8968	*8765*	8977	*8774*	8986	*8783*	8995	*8793*	9004	*8802*	9014	*8811*	9023	*8820*	9032	*8830*
20	8900	*8685*	8909	*8694*	8919	*8704*	8928	*8713*	8937	*8722*	8946	*8731*	8955	*8740*	8965	*8750*	8974	*8759*	8983	*8768*	8992	*8777*	9001	*8786*
21	8870	*8642*	8879	*8651*	8888	*8660*	8897	*8670*	8906	*8679*	8916	*8688*	8925	*8697*	8934	*8706*	8943	*8715*	8952	*8724*	8961	*8734*	8971	*8743*
22	8840	*8598*	8849	*8607*	8858	*8617*	8867	*8626*	8876	*8635*	8885	*8644*	8894	*8653*	8904	*8662*	8913	*8671*	8922	*8681*	8931	*8690*	8940	*8699*
23	8810	*8554*	8819	*8563*	8828	*8572*	8837	*8581*	8846	*8591*	8855	*8600*	8864	*8609*	8873	*8618*	8883	*8627*	8892	*8636*	8901	*8645*	8910	*8654*
24	8780	*8510*	8789	*8519*	8798	*8528*	8807	*8537*	8816	*8546*	8825	*8555*	8834	*8564*	8844	*8573*	8853	*8582*	8862	*8591*	8871	*8600*	8880	*8609*
25	8751	*8464*	8760	*8473*	8769	*8482*	8778	*8491*	8787	*8500*	8796	*8509*	8805	*8519*	8814	*8528*	8823	*8537*	8832	*8546*	8841	*8555*	8850	*8564*
26	8721	*8418*	8730	*8427*	8739	*8436*	8748	*8445*	8757	*8454*	8766	*8463*	8775	*8472*	8784	*8481*	8793	*8491*	8802	*8500*	8811	*8509*	8820	*8518*
27	8692	*8372*	8701	*8381*	8710	*8390*	8719	*8399*	8728	*8408*	8737	*8417*	8746	*8426*	8755	*8435*	8764	*8444*	8773	*8453*	8782	*8462*	8791	*8471*
28	8663	*8325*	8672	*8334*	8681	*8343*	8690	*8352*	8699	*8361*	8708	*8370*	8717	*8379*	8726	*8388*	8735	*8396*	8744	*8405*	8753	*8414*	8762	*8423*
29	8634	*8277*	8643	*8286*	8652	*8295*	8661	*8304*	8670	*8313*	8679	*8322*	8688	*8331*	8697	*8340*	8706	*8348*	8715	*8357*	8724	*8366*	8733	*8375*
30	8606	*8229*	8615	*8238*	8624	*8246*	8633	*8255*	8641	*8264*	8650	*8273*	8659	*8282*	8668	*8291*	8677	*8300*	8686	*8309*	8695	*8318*	8704	*8326*
31	8578	*8179*	8586	*8188*	8595	*8197*	8604	*8206*	8613	*8215*	8622	*8224*	8631	*8233*	8640	*8241*	8648	*8250*	8657	*8259*	8666	*8268*	8675	*8277*
32	8549	*8129*	8558	*8138*	8567	*8147*	8576	*8156*	8585	*8165*	8594	*8174*	8602	*8182*	8611	*8191*	8620	*8200*	8629	*8209*	8638	*8218*	8647	*8227*
33	8521	*8079*	8530	*8087*	8539	*8096*	8548	*8105*	8557	*8114*	8565	*8123*	8574	*8131*	8583	*8140*	8592	*8149*	8601	*8158*	8609	*8167*	8618	*8175*
34	8494	*8027*	8502	*8036*	8511	*8044*	8520	*8053*	8529	*8062*	8537	*8071*	8546	*8079*	8555	*8088*	8645	*8097*	8573	*8106*	8581	*8115*	8590	*8123*
35	8466	*7974*	8475	*7983*	8483	*7992*	8492	*8000*	8501	*8009*	8510	*8018*	8518	*8027*	8527	*8035*	8536	*8044*	8545	*8053*	8553	*8062*	8562	*8070*
36	8439	*7921*	8447	*7929*	8456	*7938*	8465	*7947*	8473	*7955*	8482	*7964*	8491	*7973*	8500	*7982*	8508	*7990*	8517	*7999*	8526	*8008*	8534	*8016*
37	8411	*7866*	8420	*7875*	8429	*7883*	8437	*7892*	8446	*7901*	8455	*7909*	8463	*7918*	8472	*7927*	8481	*7935*	8489	*7944*	8498	*7953*	8507	*7961*
38	8384	*7810*	8393	*7819*	8401	*7828*	8410	*7836*	8419	*7845*	8427	*7854*	8436	*7862*	8445	*7871*	8453	*7880*	8462	*7888*	8471	*7897*	8479	*7906*
39	8357	*7754*	8366	*7762*	8375	*7771*	8383	*7779*	8392	*7788*	8400	*7797*	8409	*7805*	8418	*7814*	8426	*7823*	8435	*7831*	8444	*7840*	8452	*7848*
40	8330	*7696*	8339	*7704*	8348	*7713*	8356	*7721*	8365	*7730*	8374	*7739*	8382	*7747*	8391	*7756*	8399	*7764*	8408	*7773*	8417	*7782*	8425	*7790*
41	8304	*7637*	8313	*7645*	8321	*7654*	8330	*7662*	8338	*7671*	8347	*7679*	8355	*7688*	8364	*7697*	8373	*7705*	8381	*7714*	8390	*7722*	8398	*7731*
42	8278	*7576*	8286	*7585*	8295	*7593*	8303	*7602*	8312	*7610*	8320	*7619*	8329	*7627*	8337	*7636*	8346	*7645*	8454	*7653*	8363	*7662*	8372	*7670*

kPa	98.0		98.1		98.2		98.3		98.4		98.5		98.6		98.7		98.8		98.9		99.0		99.1	
°C	dry	*sat.*	dry	*sat.*	dry	*sat.*	dry	*sat.*	dry	*sat.*	dry	*sat.*	dry	*sat.*	dry	*sat.*	dry	*sat.*	dry	*sat.*	dry	*sat.*	dry	*sat.*
	0.	*0.*	0.	*0.*	0.	*0.*	0.	*0.*	0.	*0.*	0.	*0.*	0.	*0.*	0.	*0.*	0.	*0.*	0.	*0.*	0.	*0.*	0.	*0.*
0	9672	*9612*	9682	*9621*	9692	*9631*	9701	*9641*	9711	*9651*	9721	*9661*	9731	*9671*	9741	*9681*	9751	*9691*	9761	*9700*	9771	*9710*	9780	*9720*
1	9636	*9572*	9646	*9582*	9656	*9592*	9666	*9601*	9676	*9611*	9686	*9621*	9695	*9631*	9705	*9641*	9715	*9651*	9725	*9660*	9735	*9670*	9745	*9680*
2	9601	*9532*	9611	*9542*	9621	*9552*	9631	*9562*	9641	*9571*	9650	*9581*	9660	*9591*	9670	*9601*	9680	*9611*	9690	*9620*	9699	*9630*	9709	*9640*
3	9567	*9493*	9576	*9502*	9586	*9512*	9596	*9522*	9606	*9532*	9615	*9541*	9625	*9551*	9635	*9561*	9645	*9571*	9654	*9580*	9664	*9590*	9674	*9600*
4	9532	*9453*	9542	*9463*	9551	*9472*	9561	*9482*	9571	*9492*	9581	*9501*	9590	*9511*	9600	*9521*	9610	*9531*	9619	*9540*	9629	*9550*	9639	*9560*
5	9498	*9413*	9507	*9423*	9517	*9432*	9527	*9442*	9536	*9452*	9546	*9462*	9556	*9471*	9565	*9481*	9575	*9491*	9585	*9500*	9594	*9510*	9604	*9520*
6	9463	*9373*	9473	*9383*	9483	*9392*	9492	*9402*	9502	*9412*	9512	*9421*	9521	*9431*	9531	*9441*	9541	*9450*	9550	*9460*	9560	*9470*	9570	*9479*
7	9430	*9333*	9439	*9343*	9449	*9353*	9458	*9362*	9468	*9372*	9478	*9381*	9487	*9391*	9497	*9401*	9507	*9410*	9516	*9420*	9526	*9430*	9535	*9439*
8	9396	*9293*	9406	*9303*	9415	*9312*	9425	*9322*	9434	*9332*	9444	*9341*	9454	*9351*	9463	*9360*	9473	*9370*	9482	*9379*	9492	*9389*	9501	*9399*
9	9363	*9253*	9372	*9263*	9382	*9272*	9391	*9282*	9401	*9291*	9410	*9301*	9420	*9310*	9429	*9320*	9439	*9329*	9449	*9339*	9458	*9349*	9468	*9358*
10	9329	*9213*	9339	*9222*	9348	*9232*	9358	*9241*	9368	*9251*	9377	*9260*	9387	*9270*	9396	*9279*	9406	*9289*	9415	*9298*	9425	*9308*	9434	*9317*
11	9297	*9172*	9306	*9182*	9316	*9191*	9325	*9201*	9334	*9210*	9344	*9220*	9353	*9229*	9363	*9238*	9372	*9248*	9382	*9257*	9391	*9267*	9401	*9276*
12	9264	*9131*	9273	*9141*	9283	*9150*	9292	*9160*	9302	*9169*	9311	*9179*	9321	*9188*	9330	*9198*	9339	*9207*	9349	*9216*	9358	*9226*	9368	*9235*
13	9231	*9090*	9241	*9100*	9250	*9109*	9260	*9119*	9269	*9128*	9279	*9138*	9288	*9147*	9297	*9156*	9307	*9166*	9316	*9175*	9326	*9185*	9335	*9194*
14	9199	*9049*	9209	*9059*	9218	*9068*	9227	*9077*	9237	*9087*	9246	*9096*	9256	*9106*	9265	*9115*	9274	*9124*	9284	*9134*	9293	*9143*	9302	*9152*
15	9167	*9008*	9177	*9017*	9186	*9027*	9195	*9036*	9205	*9045*	9214	*9055*	9223	*9064*	9233	*9073*	9242	*9083*	9251	*9092*	9261	*9101*	9270	*9111*
16	9135	*8966*	9145	*8975*	9154	*8985*	9163	*8994*	9173	*9003*	9182	*9013*	9191	*9022*	9201	*9031*	9210	*9041*	9219	*9050*	9229	*9059*	9238	*9069*
17	9104	*8924*	9113	*8933*	9122	*8942*	9132	*8952*	9141	*8961*	9150	*8970*	9160	*8980*	9169	*8989*	9178	*8998*	9187	*9008*	9197	*9017*	9206	*9026*
18	9073	*8882*	9082	*8891*	9091	*8900*	9100	*8909*	9110	*8919*	9119	*8928*	9128	*8937*	9137	*8946*	9147	*8956*	9156	*8965*	9165	*8974*	9174	*8983*
19	9041	*8839*	9051	*8848*	9060	*8857*	9069	*8866*	9078	*8876*	9088	*8885*	9097	*8894*	9106	*8903*	9115	*8913*	9124	*8922*	9134	*8931*	9143	*8940*
20	9010	*8796*	9020	*8805*	9029	*8814*	9038	*8823*	9047	*8832*	9056	*8842*	9066	*8851*	9075	*8860*	9084	*8869*	9093	*8878*	9102	*8888*	9112	*8897*
21	8980	*8752*	8989	*8761*	8998	*8770*	9007	*8779*	9016	*8789*	9026	*8798*	9035	*8807*	9044	*8816*	9053	*8825*	9062	*8834*	9071	*8844*	9081	*8853*
22	8949	*8708*	8958	*8717*	8968	*8726*	8977	*8735*	8986	*8744*	8995	*8754*	9004	*8763*	9013	*8772*	9022	*8781*	9031	*8790*	9041	*8799*	9050	*8808*
23	8919	*8663*	8928	*8672*	8937	*8682*	8946	*8691*	8955	*8700*	8965	*8709*	8974	*8718*	8983	*8727*	8992	*8736*	9001	*8745*	9010	*8754*	9019	*8763*
24	8889	*8618*	8898	*8627*	8907	*8636*	8916	*8646*	8925	*8655*	8934	*8664*	8943	*8673*	8952	*8682*	8961	*8691*	8971	*8700*	8980	*8709*	8989	*8718*
25	8859	*8573*	8868	*8582*	8877	*8591*	8886	*8600*	8895	*8609*	8904	*8618*	8913	*8627*	8922	*8636*	8931	*8645*	8940	*8654*	8949	*8663*	8958	*8672*
26	8829	*8527*	8838	*8536*	8847	*8545*	8856	*8554*	8865	*8563*	8874	*8572*	8883	*8581*	8892	*8590*	8901	*8599*	8910	*8608*	8919	*8617*	8928	*8626*
27	8800	*8480*	8809	*8489*	8818	*8498*	8827	*8507*	8836	*8516*	8845	*8525*	8854	*8534*	8863	*8543*	8872	*8552*	8881	*8561*	8890	*8570*	8899	*8579*
28	8771	*8432*	8780	*8441*	8788	*8450*	8797	*8459*	8806	*8468*	8815	*8477*	8824	*8486*	8833	*8495*	8842	*8504*	8851	*8513*	8860	*8522*	8869	*8531*
29	8741	*8384*	8750	*8393*	8759	*8402*	8768	*8411*	8777	*8420*	8786	*8429*	8795	*8438*	8804	*8447*	8813	*8456*	8822	*8464*	8831	*8473*	8840	*8482*
30	8713	*8335*	8721	*8344*	8730	*8353*	8739	*8362*	8748	*8371*	8757	*8380*	8766	*8389*	8775	*8398*	8784	*8406*	8793	*8415*	8801	*8424*	8810	*8433*
31	8684	*8286*	8693	*8295*	8702	*8303*	8710	*8312*	8719	*8321*	8728	*8330*	8737	*8339*	8746	*8348*	8755	*8357*	8764	*8366*	8772	*8374*	8781	*8383*
32	8655	*8235*	8664	*8244*	8673	*8253*	8682	*8262*	8691	*8271*	8700	*8280*	8708	*8288*	8717	*8297*	8726	*8306*	8735	*8315*	8744	*8324*	8753	*8333*
33	8627	*8184*	8636	*8193*	8645	*8202*	8653	*8211*	8662	*8219*	8671	*8228*	8680	*8237*	8689	*8246*	8697	*8255*	8706	*8263*	8715	*8272*	8724	*8281*
34	8599	*8132*	8608	*8141*	8616	*8150*	8625	*8158*	8634	*8167*	8643	*8176*	8652	*8185*	8660	*8194*	8669	*8202*	8678	*8211*	8687	*8220*	8695	*8229*
35	8571	*8079*	8580	*8088*	8588	*8097*	8597	*8105*	8606	*8114*	8615	*8123*	8623	*8132*	8632	*8140*	8641	*8149*	8650	*8158*	8658	*8167*	8667	*8175*
36	8543	*8025*	8552	*8034*	8561	*8043*	8569	*8051*	8578	*8060*	8587	*8069*	8595	*8077*	8604	*8086*	8613	*8095*	8622	*8104*	8630	*8112*	8639	*8121*
37	8516	*7970*	8524	*7979*	8533	*7988*	8542	*7996*	8550	*8005*	8559	*8014*	8568	*8022*	8576	*8031*	8585	*8040*	8594	*8048*	8602	*8057*	8611	*8066*
38	8488	*7914*	8497	*7923*	8505	*7932*	8514	*7940*	8523	*7949*	8531	*7958*	8540	*7966*	8549	*7975*	8557	*7983*	8566	*7992*	8575	*8001*	8583	*8009*
39	8461	*7857*	8469	*7866*	8478	*7874*	8487	*7883*	8495	*7892*	8504	*7900*	8513	*7909*	8521	*7918*	8530	*7926*	8539	*7935*	8547	*7943*	8556	*7952*
40	8434	*7799*	8442	*7807*	8451	*7816*	8460	*7825*	8468	*7833*	8477	*7842*	8485	*7850*	8494	*7859*	8503	*7868*	8511	*7876*	8520	*7885*	8528	*7893*
41	8407	*7739*	8415	*7748*	8424	*7757*	8433	*7765*	8441	*7774*	8450	*7782*	8458	*7791*	8467	*7800*	8475	*7808*	8484	*7817*	8493	*7825*	8501	*7834*
42	8380	*7679*	8389	*7687*	8397	*7696*	8406	*7704*	8414	*7713*	8423	*7722*	8431	*7730*	8440	*7739*	8449	*7747*	8457	*7756*	8466	*7764*	8474	*7773*

kPa	99.2		99.3		99.4		99.5		99.6		99.7		99.8		99.9		100.0		100.1		100.2		100.3	
°C	dry	*sat.*	dry	*sat.*	dry	*sat.*	dry	*sat.*	dry	*sat.*	dry	*sat.*	dry	*sat.*	dry	*sat.*	dry	*sat.*	dry	*sat.*	dry	*sat.*	dry	*sat.*
	0.	*0.*	0.	*0.*	0.	*0.*	0.	*0.*	0.	*0.*	0.	*0.*	0.	*0.*	0.	*0.*	0.	*0.*	0.	*0.*	0.	*0.*	0.	*0.*
0	9790	*9730*	9800	*9740*	9810	*9750*	9820	*9760*	9830	*9769*	9840	*9779*	9849	*9789*	9859	*9799*	9869	*9809*	9879	*9819*	9889	*9829*	9899	*9839*
1	9754	*9690*	9764	*9700*	9774	*9710*	9784	*9719*	9794	*9729*	9804	*9739*	9813	*9749*	9823	*9759*	9833	*9769*	9843	*9778*	9853	*9788*	9863	*9798*
2	9719	*9650*	9729	*9660*	9739	*9669*	9748	*9679*	9758	*9689*	9768	*9699*	9778	*9709*	9788	*9718*	9797	*9728*	9807	*9738*	9817	*9748*	9827	*9758*
3	9684	*9610*	9693	*9619*	9703	*9629*	9713	*9639*	9723	*9649*	9732	*9658*	9742	*9668*	9752	*9678*	9762	*9688*	9772	*9698*	9781	*9707*	9791	*9717*
4	9649	*9570*	9658	*9579*	9668	*9589*	9678	*9599*	9688	*9608*	9697	*9618*	9707	*9628*	9717	*9638*	9726	*9647*	9736	*9657*	9746	*9667*	9756	*9677*
5	9614	*9529*	9624	*9539*	9633	*9549*	9643	*9558*	9653	*9568*	9662	*9578*	9672	*9588*	9682	*9597*	9691	*9607*	9701	*9617*	9711	*9626*	9720	*9636*
6	9579	*9489*	9589	*9499*	9599	*9508*	9608	*9518*	9618	*9528*	9628	*9537*	9637	*9547*	9647	*9557*	9657	*9566*	9666	*9576*	9676	*9586*	9686	*9595*
7	9545	*9449*	9555	*9458*	9564	*9468*	9574	*9478*	9584	*9487*	9593	*9497*	9603	*9506*	9612	*9516*	9622	*9526*	9632	*9535*	9641	*9545*	9651	*9555*
8	9511	*9408*	9521	*9418*	9530	*9427*	9540	*9437*	9549	*9447*	9559	*9456*	9569	*9466*	9578	*9475*	9588	*9485*	9597	*9495*	9607	*9504*	9616	*9514*
9	9477	*9368*	9487	*9377*	9496	*9387*	9506	*9396*	9515	*9406*	9525	*9415*	9535	*9425*	9544	*9435*	9554	*9444*	9563	*9454*	9573	*9463*	9582	*9473*
10	9444	*9327*	9453	*9336*	9463	*9346*	9472	*9355*	9482	*9365*	9491	*9374*	9501	*9384*	9510	*9394*	9520	*9403*	9529	*9413*	9539	*9422*	9548	*9432*
11	9410	*9286*	9420	*9295*	9429	*9305*	9439	*9314*	9448	*9324*	9458	*9333*	9467	*9343*	9477	*9352*	9486	*9362*	9496	*9371*	9505	*9381*	9515	*9390*
12	9377	*9245*	9387	*9254*	9396	*9264*	9406	*9273*	9415	*9283*	9425	*9292*	9434	*9301*	9443	*9311*	9453	*9320*	9462	*9330*	9472	*9339*	9481	*9349*
13	9344	*9203*	9354	*9213*	9363	*9222*	9373	*9232*	9382	*9241*	9392	*9251*	9401	*9260*	9410	*9269*	9420	*9279*	9429	*9288*	9439	*9298*	9448	*9307*
14	9312	*9162*	9321	*9171*	9331	*9181*	9340	*9190*	9349	*9199*	9359	*9209*	9368	*9218*	9378	*9228*	9387	*9237*	9396	*9246*	9406	*9256*	9415	*9265*
15	9279	*9120*	9289	*9129*	9298	*9139*	9308	*9148*	9317	*9157*	9326	*9167*	9336	*9176*	9345	*9186*	9354	*9195*	9364	*9204*	9373	*9214*	9382	*9223*
16	9247	*9078*	9257	*9087*	9266	*9097*	9275	*9106*	9285	*9115*	9294	*9125*	9303	*9134*	9313	*9143*	9322	*9152*	9331	*9162*	9340	*9171*	9350	*9180*
17	9215	*9035*	9225	*9045*	9234	*9054*	9243	*9063*	9252	*9073*	9262	*9082*	9271	*9091*	9280	*9100*	9290	*9110*	9299	*9119*	9308	*9128*	9318	*9138*
18	9184	*8993*	9193	*9002*	9202	*9011*	9211	*9020*	9221	*9030*	9230	*9039*	9239	*9048*	9248	*9057*	9258	*9067*	9267	*9076*	9276	*9085*	9285	*9094*
19	9152	*8950*	9161	*8959*	9171	*8968*	9180	*8977*	9189	*8986*	9198	*8996*	9207	*9005*	9217	*9014*	9226	*9023*	9235	*9033*	9244	*9042*	9254	*9051*
20	9121	*8906*	9130	*8915*	9139	*8924*	9148	*8934*	9158	*8943*	9167	*8952*	9176	*8961*	9185	*8970*	9194	*8979*	9204	*8989*	9213	*8998*	9222	*9007*
21	9090	*8862*	9099	*8871*	9108	*8880*	9117	*8889*	9126	*8899*	9136	*8908*	9145	*8917*	9154	*8926*	9163	*8935*	9172	*8944*	9181	*8954*	9191	*8963*
22	9059	*8818*	9068	*8827*	9077	*8836*	9086	*8845*	9095	*8854*	9105	*8863*	9114	*8872*	9123	*8881*	9132	*8891*	9141	*8900*	9150	*8909*	9159	*8918*
23	9028	*8773*	9037	*8782*	9046	*8791*	9056	*8800*	9065	*8809*	9074	*8818*	9083	*8827*	9092	*8836*	9101	*8845*	9110	*8854*	9119	*8864*	9128	*8873*
24	8998	*8727*	9007	*8736*	9016	*8745*	9025	*8754*	9034	*8763*	9043	*8773*	9052	*8782*	9061	*8791*	9070	*8800*	9079	*8809*	9088	*8818*	9098	*8827*
25	8968	*8681*	8977	*8690*	8986	*8699*	8995	*8708*	9004	*8717*	9013	*8726*	9022	*8735*	9031	*8744*	9040	*8754*	9049	*8763*	9058	*8772*	9067	*8781*
26	8937	*8635*	8946	*8644*	8955	*8653*	8964	*8662*	8974	*8671*	8983	*8680*	8992	*8689*	9001	*8698*	9010	*8707*	9019	*8716*	9028	*8725*	9037	*8734*
27	8908	*8588*	8917	*8596*	8926	*8605*	8935	*8614*	8944	*8623*	8953	*8632*	8961	*8641*	8970	*8650*	8979	*8659*	8988	*8668*	8997	*8677*	9006	*8686*
28	8878	*8540*	8887	*8549*	8896	*8558*	8905	*8567*	8914	*8575*	8923	*8584*	8932	*8593*	8941	*8602*	8950	*8611*	8959	*8620*	8967	*8629*	8976	*8638*
29	8849	*8491*	8857	*8500*	8866	*8509*	8875	*8518*	8884	*8527*	8893	*8536*	8902	*8545*	8911	*8554*	8920	*8563*	8929	*8571*	8938	*8580*	8947	*8589*
30	8819	*8442*	8828	*8451*	8837	*8460*	8846	*8469*	8855	*8478*	8864	*8487*	8873	*8495*	8882	*8504*	8890	*8513*	8899	*8522*	8908	*8531*	8917	*8540*
31	8790	*8392*	8799	*8401*	8808	*8410*	8817	*8419*	8826	*8428*	8835	*8436*	8843	*8445*	8852	*8454*	8861	*8463*	8870	*8472*	8879	*8481*	8888	*8490*
32	8761	*8341*	8770	*8350*	8779	*8359*	8788	*8368*	8797	*8377*	8806	*8386*	8814	*8394*	8823	*8403*	8832	*8412*	8841	*8421*	8850	*8430*	8858	*8439*
33	8733	*8290*	8741	*8299*	8750	*8307*	8759	*8316*	8768	*8325*	8777	*8334*	8785	*8343*	8794	*8351*	8803	*8360*	8812	*8369*	8821	*8378*	8829	*8387*
34	8704	*8237*	8713	*8246*	8722	*8255*	8730	*8264*	8739	*8272*	8748	*8281*	8757	*8290*	8766	*8299*	8774	*8308*	8783	*8316*	8792	*8325*	8801	*8334*
35	8676	*8184*	8685	*8193*	8693	*8201*	8702	*8210*	8711	*8219*	8720	*8228*	8728	*8236*	8737	*8245*	8746	*8254*	8755	*8263*	8763	*8271*	8772	*8280*
36	8648	*8130*	8656	*8138*	8665	*8147*	8674	*8156*	8683	*8165*	8691	*8173*	8700	*8182*	8709	*8191*	8717	*8199*	8726	*8208*	8735	*8217*	8744	*8226*
37	8620	*8074*	8628	*8083*	8637	*8092*	8646	*8101*	8655	*8109*	8663	*8118*	8672	*8127*	8681	*8135*	8689	*8144*	8698	*8153*	8707	*8161*	8715	*8170*
38	8592	*8018*	8601	*8027*	8609	*8035*	8618	*8044*	8627	*8053*	8635	*8061*	8644	*8070*	8653	*8079*	8661	*8087*	8670	*8096*	8679	*8105*	8687	*8113*
39	8564	*7961*	8573	*7969*	8582	*7978*	8590	*7987*	8599	*7995*	8608	*8004*	8616	*8013*	8625	*8021*	8634	*8030*	8642	*8038*	8651	*8047*	8659	*8056*
40	8537	*7902*	8546	*7911*	8554	*7919*	8563	*7928*	8571	*7937*	8580	*7945*	8589	*7954*	8597	*7962*	8606	*7971*	8614	*7980*	8623	*7988*	8632	*7997*
41	8510	*7842*	8518	*7851*	8527	*7860*	8536	*7868*	8544	*7877*	8553	*7885*	8561	*7894*	8570	*7902*	8578	*7911*	8587	*7920*	8596	*7928*	8604	*7937*
42	8483	*7781*	8491	*7790*	8500	*7798*	8508	*7807*	8517	*7816*	8526	*7824*	8534	*7833*	8543	*7841*	8551	*7850*	8560	*7858*	8568	*7867*	8577	*7875*

kPa	100.4		100.5		100.6		100.7		100.8		100.9		101.0		101.1		101.2	
°C	dry	*sat.*	dry	*sat.*	dry	*sat.*	dry	*sat.*	dry	*sat.*	dry	*sat.*	dry	*sat.*	dry	*sat.*	dry	*sat.*
0	0.9909	0.9848	0.9919	0.9858	0.9928	0.9868	0.9938	0.9878	0.9948	0.9888	0.9958	0.9898	0.9968	0.9908	0.9978	0.9917	0.9988	0.9927
1	0.9872	0.9808	0.9882	0.9818	0.9892	0.9828	0.9902	0.9837	0.9912	0.9847	0.9922	0.9857	0.9931	0.9867	0.9941	0.9877	0.9951	0.9887
2	0.9837	0.9767	0.9846	0.9777	0.9856	0.9787	0.9866	0.9797	0.9876	0.9807	0.9885	0.9816	0.9895	0.9826	0.9905	0.9836	0.9915	0.9846
3	0.9801	0.9727	0.9811	0.9737	0.9820	0.9746	0.9830	0.9756	0.9840	0.9766	0.9850	0.9776	0.9859	0.9785	0.9869	0.9795	0.9879	0.9805
4	0.9765	0.9686	0.9775	0.9696	0.9785	0.9706	0.9795	0.9715	0.9804	0.9725	0.9814	0.9735	0.9824	0.9745	0.9833	0.9754	0.9843	0.9764
5	0.9730	0.9646	0.9740	0.9655	0.9750	0.9665	0.9759	0.9675	0.9769	0.9684	0.9779	0.9694	0.9788	0.9704	0.9798	0.9713	0.9808	0.9723
6	0.9695	0.9605	0.9705	0.9615	0.9715	0.9624	0.9724	0.9634	0.9734	0.9644	0.9744	0.9653	0.9753	0.9663	0.9763	0.9673	0.9772	0.9682
7	0.9661	0.9564	0.9670	0.9574	0.9680	0.9583	0.9689	0.9593	0.9699	0.9603	0.9709	0.9612	0.9718	0.9622	0.9728	0.9632	0.9738	0.9641
8	0.9626	0.9523	0.9636	0.9533	0.9645	0.9542	0.9655	0.9552	0.9664	0.9562	0.9674	0.9571	0.9684	0.9581	0.9693	0.9590	0.9703	0.9600
9	0.9592	0.9482	0.9601	0.9492	0.9611	0.9501	0.9621	0.9511	0.9630	0.9521	0.9640	0.9530	0.9649	0.9540	0.9659	0.9549	0.9668	0.9559
10	0.9558	0.9441	0.9567	0.9451	0.9577	0.9460	0.9586	0.9470	0.9596	0.9479	0.9606	0.9489	0.9615	0.9498	0.9625	0.9508	0.9634	0.9517
11	0.9524	0.9400	0.9534	0.9409	0.9543	0.9419	0.9553	0.9428	0.9562	0.9438	0.9572	0.9447	0.9581	0.9457	0.9591	0.9466	0.9600	0.9476
12	0.9491	0.9358	0.9500	0.9368	0.9510	0.9377	0.9519	0.9387	0.9529	0.9396	0.9538	0.9405	0.9547	0.9415	0.9557	0.9424	0.9566	0.9434
13	0.9457	0.9316	0.9467	0.9326	0.9476	0.9335	0.9486	0.9345	0.9495	0.9354	0.9505	0.9364	0.9514	0.9373	0.9523	0.9382	0.9533	0.9392
14	0.9424	0.9274	0.9434	0.9284	0.9443	0.9293	0.9453	0.9303	0.9462	0.9312	0.9471	0.9321	0.9481	0.9331	0.9490	0.9340	0.9500	0.9350
15	0.9392	0.9232	0.9401	0.9242	0.9410	0.9251	0.9420	0.9260	0.9429	0.9270	0.9438	0.9279	0.9448	0.9288	0.9457	0.9298	0.9467	0.9307
16	0.9359	0.9190	0.9368	0.9199	0.9378	0.9208	0.9387	0.9218	0.9396	0.9227	0.9406	0.9236	0.9415	0.9246	0.9424	0.9255	0.9434	0.9264
17	0.9327	0.9147	0.9336	0.9156	0.9345	0.9165	0.9355	0.9175	0.9364	0.9184	0.9373	0.9193	0.9383	0.9203	0.9392	0.9212	0.9401	0.9221
18	0.9295	0.9104	0.9304	0.9113	0.9313	0.9122	0.9322	0.9131	0.9332	0.9141	0.9341	0.9150	0.9350	0.9159	0.9360	0.9169	0.9369	0.9178
19	0.9263	0.9060	0.9272	0.9069	0.9281	0.9079	0.9290	0.9088	0.9300	0.9097	0.9309	0.9106	0.9318	0.9116	0.9327	0.9125	0.9337	0.9134
20	0.9231	0.9016	0.9240	0.9025	0.9250	0.9035	0.9259	0.9044	0.9268	0.9053	0.9277	0.9062	0.9286	0.9071	0.9296	0.9081	0.9305	0.9090
21	0.9200	0.8972	0.9209	0.8981	0.9218	0.8990	0.9227	0.8999	0.9236	0.9009	0.9246	0.9018	0.9255	0.9027	0.9264	0.9036	0.9273	0.9045
22	0.9168	0.8927	0.9178	0.8936	0.9187	0.8945	0.9196	0.8954	0.9205	0.8964	0.9214	0.8973	0.9223	0.8982	0.9232	0.8991	0.9242	0.9000
23	0.9137	0.8882	0.9147	0.8891	0.9156	0.8900	0.9165	0.8909	0.9174	0.8918	0.9183	0.8927	0.9192	0.8936	0.9201	0.8945	0.9210	0.8955
24	0.9107	0.8836	0.9116	0.8845	0.9125	0.8854	0.9134	0.8863	0.9143	0.8872	0.9152	0.8881	0.9161	0.8890	0.9170	0.8900	0.9179	0.8909
25	0.9076	0.8790	0.9085	0.8799	0.9094	0.8808	0.9103	0.8817	0.9112	0.8826	0.9121	0.8835	0.9130	0.8844	0.9139	0.8853	0.9148	0.8862
26	0.9046	0.8743	0.9055	0.8752	0.9064	0.8761	0.9073	0.8770	0.9082	0.8779	0.9091	0.8788	0.9100	0.8797	0.9109	0.8806	0.9118	0.8815
27	0.9015	0.8695	0.9024	0.8704	0.9033	0.8713	0.9042	0.8722	0.9051	0.8731	0.9060	0.8740	0.9069	0.8749	0.9078	0.8758	0.9087	0.8767
28	0.8985	0.8647	0.8994	0.8656	0.9003	0.8665	0.9012	0.8674	0.9021	0.8683	0.9030	0.8692	0.9039	0.8701	0.9048	0.8710	0.9057	0.8719
29	0.8956	0.8598	0.8964	0.8607	0.8973	0.8616	0.8982	0.8625	0.8991	0.8634	0.9000	0.8643	0.9009	0.8652	0.9018	0.8661	0.9027	0.8670
30	0.8926	0.8549	0.8935	0.8558	0.8944	0.8567	0.8953	0.8575	0.8962	0.8584	0.8970	0.8593	0.8979	0.8602	0.8988	0.8611	0.8997	0.8620
31	0.8897	0.8498	0.8905	0.8507	0.8914	0.8516	0.8923	0.8525	0.8932	0.8534	0.8941	0.8543	0.8950	0.8552	0.8959	0.8560	0.8967	0.8569
32	0.8867	0.8447	0.8876	0.8456	0.8885	0.8465	0.8894	0.8474	0.8903	0.8483	0.8911	0.8492	0.8920	0.8500	0.8929	0.8509	0.8938	0.8518
33	0.8838	0.8395	0.8847	0.8404	0.8856	0.8413	0.8865	0.8422	0.8874	0.8431	0.8882	0.8439	0.8891	0.8448	0.8900	0.8457	0.8909	0.8466
34	0.8809	0.8343	0.8818	0.8351	0.8827	0.8360	0.8836	0.8369	0.8845	0.8378	0.8853	0.8387	0.8862	0.8395	0.8871	0.8404	0.8880	0.8413
35	0.8781	0.8289	0.8790	0.8298	0.8798	0.8306	0.8807	0.8315	0.8816	0.8324	0.8825	0.8333	0.8833	0.8341	0.8842	0.8350	0.8851	0.8359
36	0.8752	0.8234	0.8761	0.8243	0.8770	0.8252	0.8779	0.8261	0.8787	0.8269	0.8796	0.8278	0.8805	0.8287	0.8813	0.8295	0.8822	0.8304
37	0.8724	0.8179	0.8733	0.8187	0.8741	0.8196	0.8750	0.8205	0.8759	0.8213	0.8768	0.8222	0.8776	0.8231	0.8785	0.8240	0.8794	0.8248
38	0.8696	0.8122	0.8705	0.8131	0.8713	0.8139	0.8722	0.8148	0.8731	0.8157	0.8739	0.8165	0.8748	0.8174	0.8757	0.8183	0.8765	0.8191
39	0.8668	0.8064	0.8677	0.8073	0.8685	0.8082	0.8694	0.8090	0.8703	0.8099	0.8711	0.8107	0.8720	0.8116	0.8728	0.8125	0.8737	0.8133
40	0.8640	0.8005	0.8649	0.8014	0.8658	0.8023	0.8666	0.8031	0.8675	0.8040	0.8683	0.8048	0.8692	0.8057	0.8701	0.8066	0.8709	0.8074
41	0.8613	0.7945	0.8621	0.7954	0.8630	0.7963	0.8638	0.7971	0.8647	0.7980	0.8656	0.7988	0.8664	0.7997	0.8673	0.8005	0.8681	0.8014
42	0.8585	0.7884	0.8594	0.7893	0.8602	0.7901	0.8611	0.7910	0.8620	0.7918	0.8628	0.7927	0.8637	0.7935	0.8645	0.7944	0.8654	0.7952

kPa	101.3		101.4		101.5		101.6		101.7		101.8		101.9		102.0		102.1	
°C	dry	*sat.*	dry	*sat.*	dry	*sat.*	dry	*sat.*	dry	*sat.*	dry	*sat.*	dry	*sat.*	dry	*sat.*	dry	*sat.*
0	0.9998	0.9937	1.0007	0.9947	1.0017	0.9957	1.0027	0.9967	1.0037	0.9977	1.0047	0.9987	1.0057	0.9996	1.0067	1.0006	1.0076	1.0016
1	0.9961	0.9896	0.9971	0.9906	0.9981	0.9916	0.9990	0.9926	1.0000	0.9936	1.0010	0.9946	1.0020	0.9955	1.0030	0.9965	1.0040	0.9975
2	0.9925	0.9856	0.9934	0.9865	0.9944	0.9875	0.9954	0.9885	0.9964	0.9895	0.9974	0.9905	0.9983	0.9914	0.9993	0.9924	1.0003	0.9934
3	0.9889	0.9815	0.9898	0.9824	0.9908	0.9834	0.9918	0.9844	0.9928	0.9854	0.9937	0.9863	0.9947	0.9873	0.9957	0.9883	0.9967	0.9893
4	0.9853	0.9774	0.9863	0.9784	0.9872	0.9793	0.9882	0.9803	0.9892	0.9813	0.9902	0.9822	0.9911	0.9832	0.9921	0.9842	0.9931	0.9852
5	0.9817	0.9733	0.9827	0.9743	0.9837	0.9752	0.9846	0.9762	0.9856	0.9772	0.9866	0.9781	0.9876	0.9791	0.9885	0.9801	0.9895	0.9810
6	0.9782	0.9692	0.9792	0.9701	0.9801	0.9711	0.9811	0.9721	0.9821	0.9730	0.9830	0.9740	0.9840	0.9750	0.9850	0.9759	0.9859	0.9769
7	0.9747	0.9651	0.9757	0.9660	0.9766	0.9670	0.9776	0.9680	0.9786	0.9689	0.9795	0.9699	0.9805	0.9709	0.9814	0.9718	0.9824	0.9728
8	0.9712	0.9610	0.9722	0.9619	0.9732	0.9629	0.9741	0.9638	0.9751	0.9648	0.9760	0.9658	0.9770	0.9667	0.9779	0.9677	0.9789	0.9686
9	0.9678	0.9568	0.9687	0.9578	0.9697	0.9587	0.9707	0.9597	0.9716	0.9607	0.9726	0.9616	0.9735	0.9626	0.9745	0.9635	0.9754	0.9645
10	0.9644	0.9527	0.9653	0.9536	0.9663	0.9546	0.9672	0.9555	0.9682	0.9565	0.9691	0.9574	0.9701	0.9584	0.9710	0.9593	0.9720	0.9603
11	0.9610	0.9485	0.9619	0.9495	0.9629	0.9504	0.9638	0.9514	0.9648	0.9523	0.9657	0.9533	0.9667	0.9542	0.9676	0.9552	0.9685	0.9561
12	0.9576	0.9443	0.9585	0.9453	0.9595	0.9462	0.9604	0.9472	0.9614	0.9481	0.9623	0.9491	0.9633	0.9500	0.9642	0.9509	0.9651	0.9519
13	0.9542	0.9401	0.9552	0.9411	0.9561	0.9420	0.9571	0.9430	0.9580	0.9439	0.9589	0.9448	0.9599	0.9458	0.9608	0.9467	0.9618	0.9477
14	0.9509	0.9359	0.9518	0.9368	0.9528	0.9378	0.9537	0.9387	0.9547	0.9397	0.9556	0.9406	0.9565	0.9415	0.9575	0.9425	0.9584	0.9434
15	0.9476	0.9316	0.9485	0.9326	0.9495	0.9335	0.9504	0.9345	0.9513	0.9354	0.9523	0.9363	0.9532	0.9373	0.9541	0.9382	0.9551	0.9391
16	0.9443	0.9274	0.9452	0.9283	0.9462	0.9292	0.9471	0.9302	0.9480	0.9311	0.9490	0.9320	0.9499	0.9330	0.9508	0.9339	0.9518	0.9348
17	0.9410	0.9230	0.9420	0.9240	0.9429	0.9249	0.9438	0.9258	0.9448	0.9268	0.9457	0.9277	0.9466	0.9286	0.9475	0.9296	0.9485	0.9305
18	0.9378	0.9187	0.9387	0.9196	0.9397	0.9206	0.9406	0.9215	0.9415	0.9224	0.9424	0.9233	0.9434	0.9243	0.9443	0.9252	0.9452	0.9261
19	0.9346	0.9143	0.9355	0.9152	0.9364	0.9162	0.9374	0.9171	0.9383	0.9180	0.9392	0.9189	0.9401	0.9199	0.9410	0.9208	0.9420	0.9217
20	0.9314	0.9099	0.9323	0.9108	0.9332	0.9117	0.9341	0.9127	0.9351	0.9136	0.9360	0.9145	0.9369	0.9154	0.9378	0.9163	0.9387	0.9173
21	0.9282	0.9054	0.9291	0.9064	0.9300	0.9073	0.9310	0.9082	0.9319	0.9091	0.9328	0.9100	0.9337	0.9109	0.9346	0.9119	0.9355	0.9128
22	0.9251	0.9009	0.9260	0.9018	0.9269	0.9028	0.9278	0.9037	0.9287	0.9046	0.9296	0.9055	0.9305	0.9064	0.9315	0.9073	0.9324	0.9082
23	0.9219	0.8964	0.9228	0.8973	0.9238	0.8982	0.9247	0.8991	0.9256	0.9000	0.9265	0.9009	0.9274	0.9018	0.9283	0.9027	0.9292	0.9036
24	0.9188	0.8918	0.9197	0.8927	0.9206	0.8936	0.9215	0.8945	0.9225	0.8954	0.9234	0.8963	0.9243	0.8972	0.9252	0.8981	0.9261	0.8990
25	0.9157	0.8871	0.9166	0.8880	0.9175	0.8889	0.9184	0.8898	0.9194	0.8907	0.9203	0.8916	0.9212	0.8925	0.9221	0.8934	0.9230	0.8943
26	0.9127	0.8824	0.9136	0.8833	0.9145	0.8842	0.9154	0.8851	0.9163	0.8860	0.9172	0.8869	0.9181	0.8878	0.9190	0.8887	0.9199	0.8896
27	0.9096	0.8776	0.9105	0.8785	0.9114	0.8794	0.9123	0.8803	0.9132	0.8812	0.9141	0.8821	0.9150	0.8830	0.9159	0.8839	0.9168	0.8848
28	0.9066	0.8728	0.9075	0.8737	0.9084	0.8746	0.9093	0.8754	0.9102	0.8763	0.9111	0.8772	0.9120	0.8781	0.9129	0.8790	0.9138	0.8799
29	0.9036	0.8679	0.9045	0.8687	0.9054	0.8696	0.9063	0.8705	0.9072	0.8714	0.9080	0.8723	0.9089	0.8732	0.9098	0.8741	0.9107	0.8750
30	0.9006	0.8629	0.9015	0.8638	0.9024	0.8647	0.9033	0.8655	0.9042	0.8664	0.9050	0.8673	0.9059	0.8682	0.9068	0.8691	0.9077	0.8700
31	0.8976	0.8578	0.8985	0.8587	0.8994	0.8596	0.9003	0.8605	0.9012	0.8614	0.9021	0.8622	0.9029	0.8631	0.9038	0.8640	0.9047	0.8649
32	0.8947	0.8527	0.8956	0.8536	0.8964	0.8545	0.8973	0.8553	0.8982	0.8562	0.8991	0.8571	0.9000	0.8580	0.9009	0.8589	0.9017	0.8598
33	0.8918	0.8475	0.8926	0.8483	0.8935	0.8492	0.8944	0.8501	0.8953	0.8510	0.8962	0.8519	0.8970	0.8527	0.8979	0.8536	0.8988	0.8545
34	0.8888	0.8422	0.8897	0.8430	0.8906	0.8439	0.8915	0.8448	0.8924	0.8457	0.8932	0.8466	0.8941	0.8474	0.8950	0.8483	0.8959	0.8492
35	0.8860	0.8368	0.8868	0.8376	0.8877	0.8385	0.8886	0.8394	0.8895	0.8403	0.8903	0.8411	0.8912	0.8420	0.8921	0.8429	0.8929	0.8438
36	0.8831	0.8313	0.8840	0.8322	0.8848	0.8330	0.8857	0.8339	0.8866	0.8348	0.8874	0.8356	0.8883	0.8365	0.8892	0.8374	0.8901	0.8383
37	0.8802	0.8257	0.8811	0.8266	0.8820	0.8274	0.8828	0.8283	0.8837	0.8292	0.8846	0.8300	0.8854	0.8309	0.8863	0.8318	0.8872	0.8326
38	0.8774	0.8200	0.8783	0.8209	0.8791	0.8217	0.8800	0.8226	0.8809	0.8235	0.8817	0.8243	0.8826	0.8252	0.8835	0.8261	0.8843	0.8269
39	0.8746	0.8142	0.8754	0.8151	0.8763	0.8159	0.8772	0.8168	0.8780	0.8177	0.8789	0.8185	0.8798	0.8194	0.8806	0.8202	0.8815	0.8211
40	0.8718	0.8083	0.8726	0.8091	0.8735	0.8100	0.8744	0.8109	0.8752	0.8117	0.8761	0.8126	0.8769	0.8134	0.8778	0.8143	0.8787	0.8152
41	0.8690	0.8023	0.8699	0.8031	0.8707	0.8040	0.8716	0.8048	0.8724	0.8057	0.8733	0.8065	0.8741	0.8074	0.8750	0.8083	0.8759	0.8091
42	0.8662	0.7961	0.8671	0.7970	0.8679	0.7978	0.8688	0.7987	0.8697	0.7995	0.8705	0.8004	0.8714	0.8012	0.8722	0.8021	0.8731	0.8029

kPa	102.2		102.3		102.4		102.5		102.6		102.7		102.8		102.9		103.0	
°C	dry	*sat.*	dry	*sat.*	dry	*sat.*	dry	*sat.*	dry	*sat.*	dry	*sat.*	dry	*sat.*	dry	*sat.*	dry	*sat.*
0	1.0086	*1.0026*	1.0096	*1.0036*	1.0106	*1.0046*	1.0116	*1.0056*	1.0126	*1.0066*	1.0136	*1.0075*	1.0146	*1.0085*	1.0155	*1.0095*	1.0165	*1.0105*
1	1.0049	*0.9985*	1.0059	*0.9995*	1.0069	*1.0005*	1.0079	*1.0014*	1.0089	*1.0024*	1.0099	*1.0034*	1.0108	*1.0044*	1.0118	*1.0054*	1.0128	*1.0064*
2	1.0013	*0.9944*	1.0023	*0.9954*	1.0032	*0.9963*	1.0042	*0.9973*	1.0052	*0.9983*	1.0062	*0.9993*	1.0072	*1.0003*	1.0081	*1.0012*	1.0091	*1.0022*
3	0.9977	*0.9903*	0.9986	*0.9912*	0.9996	*0.9922*	1.0006	*0.9932*	1.0016	*0.9942*	1.0025	*0.9951*	1.0035	*0.9961*	1.0045	*0.9971*	1.0055	*0.9981*
4	0.9940	*0.9861*	0.9950	*0.9871*	0.9960	*0.9881*	0.9970	*0.9891*	0.9979	*0.9900*	0.9989	*0.9910*	0.9999	*0.9920*	1.0009	*0.9929*	1.0018	*0.9939*
5	0.9905	*0.9820*	0.9914	*0.9830*	0.9924	*0.9839*	0.9934	*0.9849*	0.9943	*0.9859*	0.9953	*0.9869*	0.9963	*0.9878*	0.9972	*0.9888*	0.9982	*0.9898*
6	0.9869	*0.9779*	0.9879	*0.9788*	0.9888	*0.9798*	0.9898	*0.9808*	0.9908	*0.9817*	0.9917	*0.9827*	0.9927	*0.9837*	0.9937	*0.9846*	0.9946	*0.9856*
7	0.9834	*0.9737*	0.9843	*0.9747*	0.9853	*0.9757*	0.9863	*0.9766*	0.9872	*0.9776*	0.9882	*0.9786*	0.9891	*0.9795*	0.9901	*0.9805*	0.9911	*0.9814*
8	0.9799	*0.9696*	0.9808	*0.9705*	0.9818	*0.9715*	0.9827	*0.9725*	0.9837	*0.9734*	0.9847	*0.9744*	0.9856	*0.9753*	0.9866	*0.9763*	0.9875	*0.9773*
9	0.9764	*0.9654*	0.9773	*0.9664*	0.9783	*0.9673*	0.9793	*0.9683*	0.9802	*0.9692*	0.9812	*0.9702*	0.9821	*0.9712*	0.9831	*0.9721*	0.9840	*0.9731*
10	0.9729	*0.9612*	0.9739	*0.9622*	0.9748	*0.9632*	0.9758	*0.9641*	0.9767	*0.9651*	0.9777	*0.9660*	0.9786	*0.9670*	0.9796	*0.9679*	0.9805	*0.9689*
11	0.9695	*0.9571*	0.9704	*0.9580*	0.9714	*0.9589*	0.9723	*0.9599*	0.9733	*0.9608*	0.9742	*0.9618*	0.9752	*0.9627*	0.9761	*0.9637*	0.9771	*0.9646*
12	0.9661	*0.9528*	0.9670	*0.9538*	0.9680	*0.9547*	0.9689	*0.9557*	0.9699	*0.9566*	0.9708	*0.9576*	0.9718	*0.9585*	0.9727	*0.9595*	0.9737	*0.9604*
13	0.9627	*0.9486*	0.9636	*0.9495*	0.9646	*0.9505*	0.9655	*0.9514*	0.9665	*0.9524*	0.9674	*0.9533*	0.9684	*0.9543*	0.9693	*0.9552*	0.9702	*0.9561*
14	0.9593	*0.9443*	0.9603	*0.9453*	0.9612	*0.9462*	0.9622	*0.9472*	0.9631	*0.9481*	0.9640	*0.9490*	0.9650	*0.9500*	0.9659	*0.9509*	0.9669	*0.9519*
15	0.9560	*0.9401*	0.9569	*0.9410*	0.9579	*0.9419*	0.9588	*0.9429*	0.9597	*0.9438*	0.9607	*0.9447*	0.9616	*0.9457*	0.9626	*0.9466*	0.9635	*0.9476*
16	0.9527	*0.9358*	0.9536	*0.9367*	0.9546	*0.9376*	0.9555	*0.9386*	0.9564	*0.9395*	0.9574	*0.9404*	0.9583	*0.9413*	0.9592	*0.9423*	0.9602	*0.9432*
17	0.9494	*0.9314*	0.9503	*0.9323*	0.9513	*0.9333*	0.9522	*0.9342*	0.9531	*0.9351*	0.9540	*0.9361*	0.9550	*0.9370*	0.9559	*0.9379*	0.9568	*0.9388*
18	0.9461	*0.9270*	0.9471	*0.9280*	0.9480	*0.9289*	0.9489	*0.9298*	0.9498	*0.9307*	0.9508	*0.9317*	0.9517	*0.9326*	0.9526	*0.9335*	0.9535	*0.9344*
19	0.9429	*0.9226*	0.9438	*0.9236*	0.9447	*0.9245*	0.9457	*0.9254*	0.9466	*0.9263*	0.9475	*0.9272*	0.9484	*0.9282*	0.9493	*0.9291*	0.9503	*0.9300*
20	0.9397	*0.9182*	0.9406	*0.9191*	0.9415	*0.9200*	0.9424	*0.9209*	0.9433	*0.9219*	0.9443	*0.9228*	0.9452	*0.9237*	0.9461	*0.9246*	0.9470	*0.9255*
21	0.9365	*0.9137*	0.9374	*0.9146*	0.9383	*0.9155*	0.9392	*0.9164*	0.9401	*0.9173*	0.9410	*0.9183*	0.9420	*0.9192*	0.9429	*0.9201*	0.9438	*0.9210*
22	0.9333	*0.9091*	0.9342	*0.9101*	0.9351	*0.9110*	0.9360	*0.9119*	0.9369	*0.9128*	0.9378	*0.9137*	0.9388	*0.9146*	0.9397	*0.9155*	0.9406	*0.9165*
23	0.9301	*0.9046*	0.9310	*0.9055*	0.9319	*0.9064*	0.9329	*0.9073*	0.9338	*0.9082*	0.9347	*0.9091*	0.9356	*0.9100*	0.9365	*0.9109*	0.9374	*0.9118*
24	0.9270	*0.8999*	0.9279	*0.9008*	0.9288	*0.9017*	0.9297	*0.9027*	0.9306	*0.9036*	0.9315	*0.9045*	0.9324	*0.9054*	0.9333	*0.9063*	0.9342	*0.9072*
25	0.9239	*0.8952*	0.9248	*0.8961*	0.9257	*0.8970*	0.9266	*0.8980*	0.9275	*0.8989*	0.9284	*0.8998*	0.9293	*0.9007*	0.9302	*0.9016*	0.9311	*0.9025*
26	0.9208	*0.8905*	0.9217	*0.8914*	0.9226	*0.8923*	0.9235	*0.8932*	0.9244	*0.8941*	0.9253	*0.8950*	0.9262	*0.8959*	0.9271	*0.8968*	0.9280	*0.8977*
27	0.9177	*0.8857*	0.9186	*0.8866*	0.9195	*0.8875*	0.9204	*0.8884*	0.9213	*0.8893*	0.9222	*0.8902*	0.9231	*0.8911*	0.9240	*0.8920*	0.9249	*0.8929*
28	0.9146	*0.8808*	0.9155	*0.8817*	0.9164	*0.8826*	0.9173	*0.8835*	0.9182	*0.8844*	0.9191	*0.8853*	0.9200	*0.8862*	0.9209	*0.8871*	0.9218	*0.8880*
29	0.9116	*0.8759*	0.9125	*0.8768*	0.9134	*0.8777*	0.9143	*0.8786*	0.9152	*0.8794*	0.9161	*0.8803*	0.9170	*0.8812*	0.9179	*0.8821*	0.9187	*0.8830*
30	0.9086	*0.8709*	0.9095	*0.8718*	0.9104	*0.8727*	0.9113	*0.8735*	0.9122	*0.8744*	0.9130	*0.8753*	0.9139	*0.8762*	0.9148	*0.8771*	0.9157	*0.8780*
31	0.9056	*0.8658*	0.9065	*0.8667*	0.9074	*0.8676*	0.9083	*0.8685*	0.9091	*0.8693*	0.9100	*0.8702*	0.9109	*0.8711*	0.9118	*0.8720*	0.9127	*0.8729*
32	0.9026	*0.8606*	0.9035	*0.8615*	0.9044	*0.8624*	0.9053	*0.8633*	0.9062	*0.8642*	0.9070	*0.8651*	0.9079	*0.8659*	0.9088	*0.8668*	0.9097	*0.8677*
33	0.8997	*0.8554*	0.9006	*0.8563*	0.9014	*0.8571*	0.9023	*0.8580*	0.9032	*0.8589*	0.9041	*0.8598*	0.9050	*0.8607*	0.9058	*0.8615*	0.9067	*0.8624*
34	0.8967	*0.8501*	0.8976	*0.8509*	0.8985	*0.8518*	0.8994	*0.8527*	0.9003	*0.8536*	0.9011	*0.8544*	0.9020	*0.8553*	0.9029	*0.8562*	0.9038	*0.8571*
35	0.8938	*0.8446*	0.8947	*0.8455*	0.8956	*0.8464*	0.8964	*0.8473*	0.8973	*0.8481*	0.8982	*0.8490*	0.8991	*0.8499*	0.8999	*0.8508*	0.9008	*0.8516*
36	0.8909	*0.8391*	0.8918	*0.8400*	0.8927	*0.8409*	0.8935	*0.8417*	0.8944	*0.8426*	0.8953	*0.8435*	0.8962	*0.8444*	0.8970	*0.8452*	0.8979	*0.8461*
37	0.8880	*0.8335*	0.8889	*0.8344*	0.8898	*0.8353*	0.8907	*0.8361*	0.8915	*0.8370*	0.8924	*0.8379*	0.8933	*0.8387*	0.8941	*0.8396*	0.8950	*0.8405*
38	0.8852	*0.8278*	0.8861	*0.8287*	0.8869	*0.8295*	0.8878	*0.8304*	0.8887	*0.8313*	0.8895	*0.8321*	0.8904	*0.8330*	0.8913	*0.8339*	0.8921	*0.8347*
39	0.8823	*0.8220*	0.8832	*0.8228*	0.8841	*0.8237*	0.8849	*0.8246*	0.8858	*0.8254*	0.8867	*0.8263*	0.8875	*0.8272*	0.8884	*0.8280*	0.8893	*0.8289*
40	0.8795	*0.8160*	0.8804	*0.8169*	0.8812	*0.8177*	0.8821	*0.8186*	0.8830	*0.8195*	0.8838	*0.8203*	0.8847	*0.8212*	0.8855	*0.8221*	0.8864	*0.8229*
41	0.8767	*0.8100*	0.8776	*0.8108*	0.8784	*0.8117*	0.8793	*0.8125*	0.8801	*0.8134*	0.8810	*0.8143*	0.8819	*0.8151*	0.8827	*0.8160*	0.8836	*0.8168*
42	0.8739	*0.8038*	0.8748	*0.8046*	0.8756	*0.8055*	0.8765	*0.8064*	0.8773	*0.8072*	0.8782	*0.8081*	0.8791	*0.8089*	0.8799	*0.8098*	0.8808	*0.8106*

kPa	103.1		103.2		103.3		103.4		103.5		103.6		103.7		103.8		103.9	
°C	dry	*sat.*	dry	*sat.*	dry	*sat.*	dry	*sat.*	dry	*sat.*	dry	*sat.*	dry	*sat.*	dry	*sat.*	dry	*sat.*
0	1.0175	*1.0115*	1.0185	*1.0125*	1.0195	*1.0135*	1.0205	*1.0144*	1.0215	*1.0154*	1.0225	*1.0164*	1.0234	*1.0174*	1.0244	*1.0184*	1.0254	*1.0194*
1	1.0138	*1.0073*	1.0148	*1.0083*	1.0158	*1.0093*	1.0167	*1.0103*	1.0177	*1.0113*	1.0187	*1.0123*	1.0197	*1.0132*	1.0207	*1.0142*	1.0217	*1.0152*
2	1.0101	*1.0032*	1.0111	*1.0042*	1.0121	*1.0052*	1.0130	*1.0061*	1.0140	*1.0071*	1.0150	*1.0081*	1.0160	*1.0091*	1.0170	*1.0101*	1.0179	*1.0110*
3	1.0064	*0.9990*	1.0074	*1.0000*	1.0084	*1.0010*	1.0094	*1.0020*	1.0103	*1.0029*	1.0113	*1.0039*	1.0123	*1.0049*	1.0133	*1.0059*	1.0142	*1.0068*
4	1.0028	*0.9949*	1.0038	*0.9959*	1.0047	*0.9968*	1.0057	*0.9978*	1.0067	*0.9988*	1.0077	*0.9998*	1.0086	*1.0007*	1.0096	*1.0017*	1.0106	*1.0027*
5	0.9992	*0.9907*	1.0002	*0.9917*	1.0011	*0.9927*	1.0021	*0.9936*	1.0031	*0.9946*	1.0040	*0.9956*	1.0050	*0.9965*	1.0060	*0.9975*	1.0069	*0.9985*
6	0.9956	*0.9866*	0.9966	*0.9875*	0.9975	*0.9885*	0.9985	*0.9895*	0.9995	*0.9904*	1.0004	*0.9914*	1.0014	*0.9924*	1.0024	*0.9933*	1.0033	*0.9943*
7	0.9920	*0.9824*	0.9930	*0.9834*	0.9940	*0.9843*	0.9949	*0.9853*	0.9959	*0.9862*	0.9968	*0.9872*	0.9978	*0.9882*	0.9988	*0.9891*	0.9997	*0.9901*
8	0.9885	*0.9782*	0.9895	*0.9792*	0.9904	*0.9801*	0.9914	*0.9811*	0.9923	*0.9821*	0.9933	*0.9830*	0.9942	*0.9840*	0.9952	*0.9849*	0.9962	*0.9859*
9	0.9850	*0.9740*	0.9859	*0.9750*	0.9869	*0.9759*	0.9878	*0.9769*	0.9888	*0.9778*	0.9898	*0.9788*	0.9907	*0.9798*	0.9917	*0.9807*	0.9926	*0.9817*
10	0.9815	*0.9698*	0.9824	*0.9708*	0.9834	*0.9717*	0.9844	*0.9727*	0.9853	*0.9736*	0.9863	*0.9746*	0.9872	*0.9755*	0.9882	*0.9765*	0.9891	*0.9774*
11	0.9780	*0.9656*	0.9790	*0.9665*	0.9799	*0.9675*	0.9809	*0.9684*	0.9818	*0.9694*	0.9828	*0.9703*	0.9837	*0.9713*	0.9847	*0.9722*	0.9856	*0.9732*
12	0.9746	*0.9613*	0.9755	*0.9623*	0.9765	*0.9632*	0.9774	*0.9642*	0.9784	*0.9651*	0.9793	*0.9661*	0.9803	*0.9670*	0.9812	*0.9680*	0.9822	*0.9689*
13	0.9712	*0.9571*	0.9721	*0.9580*	0.9731	*0.9590*	0.9740	*0.9599*	0.9750	*0.9608*	0.9759	*0.9618*	0.9768	*0.9627*	0.9778	*0.9637*	0.9787	*0.9646*
14	0.9678	*0.9528*	0.9687	*0.9537*	0.9697	*0.9547*	0.9706	*0.9556*	0.9715	*0.9565*	0.9725	*0.9575*	0.9734	*0.9584*	0.9744	*0.9594*	0.9753	*0.9603*
15	0.9644	*0.9485*	0.9654	*0.9494*	0.9663	*0.9504*	0.9672	*0.9513*	0.9682	*0.9522*	0.9691	*0.9532*	0.9700	*0.9541*	0.9710	*0.9550*	0.9719	*0.9560*
16	0.9611	*0.9441*	0.9620	*0.9451*	0.9629	*0.9460*	0.9639	*0.9469*	0.9648	*0.9479*	0.9657	*0.9488*	0.9667	*0.9497*	0.9676	*0.9507*	0.9685	*0.9516*
17	0.9578	*0.9398*	0.9587	*0.9407*	0.9596	*0.9416*	0.9605	*0.9426*	0.9615	*0.9435*	0.9624	*0.9444*	0.9633	*0.9453*	0.9643	*0.9463*	0.9652	*0.9472*
18	0.9545	*0.9354*	0.9554	*0.9363*	0.9563	*0.9372*	0.9572	*0.9381*	0.9582	*0.9391*	0.9591	*0.9400*	0.9600	*0.9409*	0.9609	*0.9418*	0.9619	*0.9428*
19	0.9512	*0.9309*	0.9521	*0.9319*	0.9530	*0.9328*	0.9540	*0.9337*	0.9549	*0.9346*	0.9558	*0.9355*	0.9567	*0.9365*	0.9576	*0.9374*	0.9586	*0.9383*
20	0.9479	*0.9265*	0.9489	*0.9274*	0.9498	*0.9283*	0.9507	*0.9292*	0.9516	*0.9301*	0.9525	*0.9310*	0.9535	*0.9320*	0.9544	*0.9329*	0.9553	*0.9338*
21	0.9447	*0.9219*	0.9456	*0.9228*	0.9465	*0.9238*	0.9475	*0.9247*	0.9484	*0.9256*	0.9493	*0.9265*	0.9502	*0.9274*	0.9511	*0.9283*	0.9520	*0.9293*
22	0.9415	*0.9174*	0.9424	*0.9183*	0.9433	*0.9192*	0.9442	*0.9201*	0.9452	*0.9210*	0.9461	*0.9219*	0.9470	*0.9228*	0.9479	*0.9238*	0.9488	*0.9247*
23	0.9383	*0.9127*	0.9392	*0.9137*	0.9401	*0.9146*	0.9410	*0.9155*	0.9420	*0.9164*	0.9429	*0.9173*	0.9438	*0.9182*	0.9447	*0.9191*	0.9456	*0.9200*
24	0.9351	*0.9081*	0.9361	*0.9090*	0.9370	*0.9099*	0.9379	*0.9108*	0.9388	*0.9117*	0.9397	*0.9126*	0.9406	*0.9135*	0.9415	*0.9144*	0.9424	*0.9153*
25	0.9320	*0.9034*	0.9329	*0.9043*	0.9338	*0.9052*	0.9347	*0.9061*	0.9356	*0.9070*	0.9365	*0.9079*	0.9374	*0.9088*	0.9383	*0.9097*	0.9392	*0.9106*
26	0.9289	*0.8986*	0.9298	*0.8995*	0.9307	*0.9004*	0.9316	*0.9013*	0.9325	*0.9022*	0.9334	*0.9031*	0.9343	*0.9040*	0.9352	*0.9049*	0.9361	*0.9058*
27	0.9258	*0.8938*	0.9267	*0.8947*	0.9276	*0.8956*	0.9285	*0.8965*	0.9294	*0.8974*	0.9303	*0.8983*	0.9312	*0.8992*	0.9321	*0.9001*	0.9330	*0.9010*
28	0.9227	*0.8889*	0.9236	*0.8898*	0.9245	*0.8907*	0.9254	*0.8916*	0.9263	*0.8925*	0.9272	*0.8933*	0.9281	*0.8942*	0.9290	*0.8951*	0.9299	*0.8960*
29	0.9196	*0.8839*	0.9205	*0.8848*	0.9214	*0.8857*	0.9223	*0.8866*	0.9232	*0.8875*	0.9241	*0.8884*	0.9250	*0.8893*	0.9259	*0.8902*	0.9268	*0.8910*
30	0.9166	*0.8789*	0.9175	*0.8798*	0.9184	*0.8807*	0.9193	*0.8815*	0.9202	*0.8824*	0.9210	*0.8833*	0.9219	*0.8842*	0.9228	*0.8851*	0.9237	*0.8860*
31	0.9136	*0.8738*	0.9145	*0.8747*	0.9154	*0.8755*	0.9162	*0.8764*	0.9171	*0.8773*	0.9180	*0.8782*	0.9189	*0.8791*	0.9198	*0.8800*	0.9207	*0.8809*
32	0.9106	*0.8686*	0.9115	*0.8695*	0.9123	*0.8703*	0.9132	*0.8712*	0.9141	*0.8721*	0.9150	*0.8730*	0.9159	*0.8739*	0.9168	*0.8748*	0.9176	*0.8756*
33	0.9076	*0.8633*	0.9085	*0.8642*	0.9094	*0.8651*	0.9102	*0.8660*	0.9111	*0.8668*	0.9120	*0.8677*	0.9129	*0.8686*	0.9138	*0.8695*	0.9146	*0.8704*
34	0.9046	*0.8580*	0.9055	*0.8588*	0.9064	*0.8597*	0.9073	*0.8606*	0.9081	*0.8615*	0.9090	*0.8623*	0.9099	*0.8632*	0.9108	*0.8641*	0.9117	*0.8650*
35	0.9017	*0.8525*	0.9026	*0.8534*	0.9034	*0.8543*	0.9043	*0.8551*	0.9052	*0.8560*	0.9061	*0.8569*	0.9069	*0.8578*	0.9078	*0.8586*	0.9087	*0.8595*
36	0.8988	*0.8470*	0.8996	*0.8478*	0.9005	*0.8487*	0.9014	*0.8496*	0.9023	*0.8505*	0.9031	*0.8513*	0.9040	*0.8522*	0.9049	*0.8531*	0.9057	*0.8539*
37	0.8959	*0.8413*	0.8967	*0.8422*	0.8976	*0.8431*	0.8985	*0.8439*	0.8993	*0.8448*	0.9002	*0.8457*	0.9011	*0.8465*	0.9020	*0.8474*	0.9028	*0.8483*
38	0.8930	*0.8356*	0.8938	*0.8365*	0.8947	*0.8373*	0.8956	*0.8382*	0.8964	*0.8391*	0.8973	*0.8399*	0.8982	*0.8408*	0.8990	*0.8417*	0.8999	*0.8425*
39	0.8901	*0.8297*	0.8910	*0.8306*	0.8918	*0.8315*	0.8927	*0.8323*	0.8936	*0.8332*	0.8944	*0.8341*	0.8953	*0.8349*	0.8962	*0.8358*	0.8970	*0.8366*
40	0.8873	*0.8238*	0.8881	*0.8246*	0.8890	*0.8255*	0.8898	*0.8264*	0.8907	*0.8272*	0.8916	*0.8281*	0.8924	*0.8289*	0.8933	*0.8298*	0.8942	*0.8307*
41	0.8844	*0.8177*	0.8853	*0.8186*	0.8862	*0.8194*	0.8870	*0.8203*	0.8879	*0.8211*	0.8887	*0.8220*	0.8896	*0.8228*	0.8904	*0.8237*	0.8913	*0.8246*
42	0.8816	*0.8115*	0.8825	*0.8123*	0.8833	*0.8132*	0.8842	*0.8141*	0.8850	*0.8149*	0.8859	*0.8158*	0.8868	*0.8166*	0.8876	*0.8175*	0.8885	*0.8183*

kPa	104.0		104.1		104.2		104.3		104.4		104.5		104.6		104.7		104.8	
°C	dry	sat.	dry	sat.	dry	sat.	dry	sat.	dry	sat.	dry	sat.	dry	sat.	dry	sat.	dry	sat.
0	1.0264	1.0204	1.0274	1.0214	1.0284	1.0223	1.0294	1.0233	1.0303	1.0243	1.0313	1.0253	1.0323	1.0263	1.0333	1.0273	1.0343	1.0283
1	1.0226	1.0162	1.0236	1.0172	1.0246	1.0182	1.0256	1.0191	1.0266	1.0201	1.0276	1.0211	1.0285	1.0221	1.0295	1.0231	1.0305	1.0241
2	1.0189	1.0120	1.0199	1.0130	1.0209	1.0140	1.0219	1.0150	1.0228	1.0159	1.0238	1.0169	1.0248	1.0179	1.0258	1.0189	1.0268	1.0199
3	1.0152	1.0078	1.0162	1.0088	1.0172	1.0098	1.0182	1.0108	1.0191	1.0117	1.0201	1.0127	1.0211	1.0137	1.0221	1.0147	1.0230	1.0156
4	1.0116	1.0036	1.0125	1.0046	1.0135	1.0056	1.0145	1.0066	1.0154	1.0075	1.0164	1.0085	1.0174	1.0095	1.0184	1.0105	1.0193	1.0114
5	1.0079	0.9995	1.0089	1.0004	1.0098	1.0014	1.0108	1.0024	1.0118	1.0033	1.0128	1.0043	1.0137	1.0053	1.0147	1.0062	1.0157	1.0072
6	1.0043	0.9953	1.0053	0.9962	1.0062	0.9972	1.0072	0.9982	1.0081	0.9991	1.0091	1.0001	1.0101	1.0011	1.0110	1.0020	1.0120	1.0030
7	1.0007	0.9911	1.0017	0.9920	1.0026	0.9930	1.0036	0.9939	1.0045	0.9949	1.0055	0.9959	1.0065	0.9968	1.0074	0.9978	1.0084	0.9988
8	0.9971	0.9868	0.9981	0.9878	0.9990	0.9888	1.0000	0.9897	1.0010	0.9907	1.0019	0.9916	1.0029	0.9926	1.0038	0.9936	1.0048	0.9945
9	0.9936	0.9826	0.9945	0.9836	0.9955	0.9845	0.9964	0.9855	0.9974	0.9864	0.9984	0.9874	0.9993	0.9884	1.0003	0.9893	1.0012	0.9903
10	0.9901	0.9784	0.9910	0.9793	0.9920	0.9803	0.9929	0.9812	0.9939	0.9822	0.9948	0.9831	0.9958	0.9841	0.9967	0.9850	0.9977	0.9860
11	0.9866	0.9741	0.9875	0.9751	0.9885	0.9760	0.9894	0.9770	0.9904	0.9779	0.9913	0.9789	0.9923	0.9798	0.9932	0.9808	0.9942	0.9817
12	0.9831	0.9699	0.9840	0.9708	0.9850	0.9717	0.9859	0.9727	0.9869	0.9736	0.9878	0.9746	0.9888	0.9755	0.9897	0.9765	0.9907	0.9774
13	0.9797	0.9656	0.9806	0.9665	0.9815	0.9674	0.9825	0.9684	0.9834	0.9693	0.9844	0.9703	0.9853	0.9712	0.9863	0.9722	0.9872	0.9731
14	0.9762	0.9612	0.9772	0.9622	0.9781	0.9631	0.9791	0.9641	0.9800	0.9650	0.9809	0.9659	0.9819	0.9669	0.9828	0.9678	0.9838	0.9688
15	0.9728	0.9569	0.9738	0.9578	0.9747	0.9588	0.9757	0.9597	0.9766	0.9606	0.9775	0.9616	0.9785	0.9625	0.9794	0.9635	0.9803	0.9644
16	0.9695	0.9525	0.9704	0.9535	0.9713	0.9544	0.9723	0.9553	0.9732	0.9563	0.9741	0.9572	0.9751	0.9581	0.9760	0.9591	0.9769	0.9600
17	0.9661	0.9481	0.9671	0.9491	0.9680	0.9500	0.9689	0.9509	0.9698	0.9518	0.9708	0.9528	0.9717	0.9537	0.9726	0.9546	0.9736	0.9556
18	0.9628	0.9437	0.9637	0.9446	0.9646	0.9456	0.9656	0.9465	0.9665	0.9474	0.9674	0.9483	0.9684	0.9493	0.9693	0.9502	0.9702	0.9511
19	0.9595	0.9392	0.9604	0.9402	0.9613	0.9411	0.0623	0.9420	0.9632	0.9429	0.9641	0.9438	0.9650	0.9448	0.9660	0.9457	0.9669	0.9466
20	0.9562	0.9347	0.9571	0.9356	0.9581	0.9366	0.9590	0.9375	0.9599	0.9384	0.9608	0.9393	0.9617	0.9402	0.9627	0.9412	0.9636	0.9421
21	0.9530	0.9302	0.9539	0.9311	0.9548	0.9320	0.9557	0.9329	0.9566	0.9338	0.9575	0.9348	0.9585	0.9357	0.9594	0.9366	0.9603	0.9375
22	0.9497	0.9256	0.9506	0.9265	0.9515	0.9274	0.9525	0.9283	0.9534	0.9292	0.9543	0.9302	0.9552	0.9311	0.9561	0.9320	0.9570	0.9329
23	0.9465	0.9209	0.9474	0.9219	0.9483	0.9228	0.9492	0.9237	0.9501	0.9246	0.9511	0.9255	0.9520	0.9264	0.9529	0.9273	0.9538	0.9282
24	0.9433	0.9163	0.9442	0.9172	0.9451	0.9181	0.9460	0.9190	0.9469	0.9199	0.9478	0.9208	0.9488	0.9217	0.9497	0.9226	0.9506	0.9235
25	0.9401	0.9115	0.9410	0.9124	0.9420	0.9133	0.9429	0.9142	0.9438	0.9151	0.9447	0.9160	0.9456	0.9169	0.9465	0.9178	0.9474	0.9187
26	0.9370	0.9067	0.9379	0.9076	0.9388	0.9085	0.9397	0.9094	0.9406	0.9103	0.9415	0.9112	0.9424	0.9121	0.9433	0.9130	0.9442	0.9139
27	0.9339	0.9019	0.9348	0.9027	0.9357	0.9036	0.9366	0.9045	0.9375	0.9054	0.9384	0.9063	0.9393	0.9072	0.9401	0.9081	0.9410	0.9090
28	0.9308	0.8969	0.9317	0.8978	0.9325	0.8987	0.9334	0.8996	0.9343	0.9005	0.9352	0.9014	0.9361	0.9023	0.9370	0.9032	0.9379	0.9041
29	0.9277	0.8919	0.9286	0.8928	0.9295	0.8937	0.9303	0.8946	0.9312	0.8955	0.9321	0.8964	0.9330	0.8973	0.9339	0.8982	0.9348	0.8991
30	0.9246	0.8869	0.9255	0.8878	0.9264	0.8887	0.9273	0.8895	0.9282	0.8904	0.9290	0.8913	0.9299	0.8922	0.9308	0.8931	0.9317	0.8940
31	0.9216	0.8817	0.9224	0.8826	0.9233	0.8835	0.9242	0.8844	0.9251	0.8853	0.9260	0.8862	0.9269	0.8871	0.9278	0.8879	0.9286	0.8888
32	0.9185	0.8765	0.9194	0.8774	0.9203	0.8783	0.9212	0.8792	0.9221	0.8801	0.9229	0.8809	0.9238	0.8818	0.9247	0.8827	0.9256	0.8836
33	0.9155	0.8712	0.9164	0.8721	0.9173	0.8730	0.9182	0.8739	0.9190	0.8748	0.9199	0.8756	0.9208	0.8765	0.9217	0.8774	0.9226	0.8783
34	0.9125	0.8659	0.9134	0.8667	0.9143	0.8676	0.9152	0.8685	0.9160	0.8694	0.9169	0.8702	0.9178	0.8711	0.9187	0.8720	0.9196	0.8729
35	0.9096	0.8604	0.9104	0.8613	0.9113	0.8621	0.9122	0.8630	0.9131	0.8639	0.9139	0.8648	0.9148	0.8656	0.9157	0.8665	0.9166	0.8674
36	0.9066	0.8548	0.9075	0.8557	0.9084	0.8566	0.9092	0.8574	0.9101	0.8583	0.9110	0.8592	0.9118	0.8600	0.9127	0.8609	0.9136	0.8618
37	0.9037	0.8492	0.9046	0.8500	0.9054	0.8509	0.9063	0.8518	0.9072	0.8526	0.9080	0.8535	0.9089	0.8544	0.9098	0.8552	0.9106	0.8561
38	0.9008	0.8434	0.9016	0.8443	0.9025	0.8451	0.9034	0.8460	0.9042	0.8469	0.9051	0.8477	0.9060	0.8486	0.9068	0.8495	0.9077	0.8503
39	0.8979	0.8375	0.8987	0.8384	0.8996	0.8392	0.9005	0.8401	0.9013	0.8410	0.9022	0.8418	0.9031	0.8427	0.9039	0.8436	0.9048	0.8444
40	0.8950	0.8315	0.8959	0.8324	0.8967	0.8332	0.8976	0.8341	0.8985	0.8350	0.8993	0.8358	0.9002	0.8367	0.9010	0.8375	0.9019	0.8384
41	0.8922	0.8254	0.8930	0.8263	0.8939	0.8271	0.8947	0.8280	0.8956	0.8288	0.8964	0.8297	0.8973	0.8306	0.8982	0.8314	0.8990	0.8323
42	0.8893	0.8192	0.8902	0.8200	0.8910	0.8209	0.8919	0.8217	0.8927	0.8226	0.8936	0.8235	0.8945	0.8243	0.8953	0.8252	0.8962	0.8260

kPa	104.9		105.0		105.1		105.2		105.3		105.4		105.5		105.6		105.7	
°C	dry	sat.	dry	sat.	dry	sat.	dry	sat.	dry	sat.	dry	sat.	dry	sat.	dry	sat.	dry	sat.
0	1.0353	1.0293	1.0363	1.0302	1.0373	1.0312	1.0382	1.0322	1.0392	1.0332	1.0402	1.0342	1.0412	1.0352	1.0422	1.0362	1.0432	1.0371
1	1.0315	1.0250	1.0325	1.0260	1.0335	1.0270	1.0344	1.0280	1.0354	1.0290	1.0364	1.0300	1.0374	1.0309	1.0384	1.0319	1.0394	1.0329
2	1.0277	1.0208	1.0287	1.0218	1.0297	1.0228	1.0307	1.0238	1.0317	1.0248	1.0326	1.0257	1.0336	1.0267	1.0346	1.0277	1.0356	1.0287
3	1.0240	1.0166	1.0250	1.0176	1.0260	1.0186	1.0269	1.0195	1.0279	1.0205	1.0289	1.0215	1.0299	1.0225	1.0308	1.0234	1.0318	1.0244
4	1.0203	1.0124	1.0213	1.0134	1.0222	1.0143	1.0232	1.0153	1.0242	1.0163	1.0252	1.0173	1.0261	1.0182	1.0271	1.0192	1.0281	1.0202
5	1.0166	1.0082	1.0176	1.0091	1.0186	1.0101	1.0195	1.0111	1.0205	1.0121	1.0215	1.0130	1.0224	1.0140	1.0234	1.0150	1.0244	1.0159
6	1.0130	1.0039	1.0139	1.0049	1.0149	1.0059	1.0159	1.0068	1.0168	1.0078	1.0178	1.0088	1.0188	1.0097	1.0197	1.0107	1.0207	1.0117
7	1.0094	0.9997	1.0103	1.0007	1.0113	1.0016	1.0122	1.0026	1.0132	1.0036	1.0142	1.0045	1.0151	1.0055	1.0161	1.0065	1.0170	1.0074
8	1.0058	0.9955	1.0067	0.9964	1.0077	0.9974	1.0086	0.9984	1.0096	0.9993	1.0105	1.0003	1.0115	1.0012	1.0125	1.0022	1.0134	1.0031
9	1.0022	0.9912	1.0031	0.9922	1.0041	0.9931	1.0050	0.9941	1.0060	0.9950	1.0070	0.9960	1.0079	0.9970	1.0089	0.9979	1.0098	0.9989
10	0.9986	0.9870	0.9996	0.9879	1.0005	0.9889	1.0015	0.9898	1.0024	0.9908	1.0034	0.9917	1.0043	0.9927	1.0053	0.9936	1.0062	0.9946
11	0.9951	0.9827	0.9961	0.9836	0.9970	0.9846	0.9980	0.9855	0.9989	0.9865	0.9999	0.9874	1.0008	0.9884	1.0018	0.9893	1.0027	0.9903
12	0.9916	0.9784	0.9926	0.9793	0.9935	0.9802	0.9944	0.9812	0.9954	0.9821	0.9963	0.9831	0.9973	0.9840	0.9982	0.9850	0.9992	0.9859
13	0.9881	0.9740	0.9891	0.9750	0.9900	0.9759	0.9910	0.9769	0.9919	0.9778	0.9928	0.9787	0.9938	0.9797	0.9947	0.9806	0.9957	0.9816
14	0.9847	0.9697	0.9856	0.9706	0.9866	0.9716	0.9875	0.9725	0.9884	0.9734	0.9894	0.9744	0.9903	0.9753	0.9913	0.9763	0.9922	0.9772
15	0.9813	0.9653	0.9822	0.9663	0.9831	0.9672	0.9841	0.9681	0.9850	0.9691	0.9859	0.9700	0.9869	0.9709	0.9878	0.9719	0.9887	0.9728
16	0.9779	0.9609	0.9788	0.9619	0.9797	0.9628	0.9807	0.9637	0.9816	0.9647	0.9825	0.9656	0.9835	0.9665	0.9844	0.9674	0.9853	0.9684
17	0.9745	0.9565	0.9754	0.9574	0.9763	0.9583	0.9773	0.9593	0.9782	0.9602	0.9791	0.9611	0.9801	0.9621	0.9810	0.9630	0.9819	0.9639
18	0.9711	0.9520	0.9721	0.9530	0.9730	0.9539	0.9739	0.9548	0.9748	0.9557	0.9758	0.9567	0.9767	0.9576	0.9776	0.9585	0.9785	0.9594
19	0.9678	0.9475	0.9687	0.9485	0.9696	0.9494	0.9706	0.9503	0.9715	0.9512	0.9724	0.9522	0.9733	0.9531	0.9743	0.9540	0.9752	0.9549
20	0.9645	0.9430	0.9654	0.9439	0.9663	0.9448	0.9672	0.9458	0.9682	0.9467	0.9691	0.9476	0.9700	0.9485	0.9709	0.9494	0.9718	0.9504
21	0.9612	0.9384	0.9621	0.9393	0.9630	0.9403	0.9640	0.9412	0.9649	0.9421	0.9658	0.9430	0.9667	0.9439	0.9676	0.9448	0.9685	0.9458
22	0.9579	0.9338	0.9589	0.9347	0.9598	0.9356	0.9607	0.9365	0.9616	0.9375	0.9625	0.9384	0.9634	0.9393	0.9643	0.9402	0.9652	0.9411
23	0.9547	0.9291	0.9556	0.9300	0.9565	0.9310	0.9574	0.9319	0.9583	0.9328	0.9592	0.9337	0.9602	0.9346	0.9611	0.9355	0.9620	0.9364
24	0.9515	0.9244	0.9524	0.9253	0.9533	0.9262	0.9542	0.9271	0.9551	0.9280	0.9560	0.9290	0.9569	0.9299	0.9578	0.9308	0.9587	0.9317
25	0.9483	0.9196	0.9492	0.9206	0.9501	0.9215	0.9510	0.9224	0.9519	0.9233	0.9528	0.9242	0.9537	0.9251	0.9546	0.9260	0.9555	0.9269
26	0.9451	0.9148	0.9460	0.9157	0.9469	0.9166	0.9478	0.9175	0.9487	0.9184	0.9496	0.9193	0.9505	0.9202	0.9514	0.9211	0.9523	0.9220
27	0.9419	0.9099	0.9428	0.9108	0.9437	0.9117	0.9446	0.9126	0.9455	0.9135	0.9464	0.9144	0.9473	0.9153	0.9482	0.9162	0.9491	0.9171
28	0.9388	0.9050	0.9397	0.9059	0.9406	0.9068	0.9415	0.9077	0.9424	0.9086	0.9433	0.9095	0.9442	0.9104	0.9451	0.9112	0.9460	0.9121
29	0.9357	0.9000	0.9366	0.9009	0.9375	0.9017	0.9384	0.9026	0.9393	0.9035	0.9402	0.9044	0.9410	0.9053	0.9419	0.9062	0.9428	0.9071
30	0.9326	0.8949	0.9335	0.8958	0.9344	0.8967	0.9353	0.8975	0.9362	0.8984	0.9370	0.8993	0.9379	0.9002	0.9388	0.9011	0.9397	0.9020
31	0.9295	0.8897	0.9304	0.8906	0.9313	0.8915	0.9322	0.8924	0.9331	0.8933	0.9340	0.8941	0.9348	0.8950	0.9357	0.8959	0.9366	0.8968
32	0.9265	0.8845	0.9274	0.8854	0.9282	0.8862	0.9291	0.8871	0.9300	0.8880	0.9309	0.8889	0.9318	0.8898	0.9327	0.8907	0.9335	0.8915
33	0.9234	0.8792	0.9243	0.8800	0.9252	0.8809	0.9261	0.8818	0.9270	0.8827	0.9278	0.8836	0.9287	0.8844	0.9296	0.8853	0.9305	0.8862
34	0.9204	0.8738	0.9213	0.8746	0.9222	0.8755	0.9231	0.8764	0.9239	0.8773	0.9248	0.8781	0.9257	0.8790	0.9266	0.8799	0.9275	0.8808
35	0.9174	0.8683	0.9183	0.8691	0.9192	0.8700	0.9201	0.8709	0.9209	0.8717	0.9218	0.8726	0.9227	0.8735	0.9236	0.8744	0.9244	0.8752
36	0.9145	0.8627	0.9153	0.8635	0.9162	0.8644	0.9171	0.8653	0.9180	0.8662	0.9188	0.8670	0.9197	0.8679	0.9206	0.8688	0.9214	0.8696
37	0.9115	0.8570	0.9124	0.8578	0.9132	0.8587	0.9141	0.8596	0.9150	0.8605	0.9159	0.8613	0.9167	0.8622	0.9176	0.8631	0.9185	0.8639
38	0.9086	0.8512	0.9094	0.8520	0.9103	0.8529	0.9112	0.8538	0.9120	0.8546	0.9129	0.8555	0.9138	0.8564	0.9146	0.8572	0.9155	0.8581
39	0.9057	0.8453	0.9065	0.8461	0.9074	0.8470	0.9082	0.8479	0.9091	0.8487	0.9100	0.8496	0.9108	0.8505	0.9117	0.8513	0.9126	0.8522
40	0.9028	0.8393	0.9036	0.8401	0.9045	0.8410	0.9053	0.8418	0.9062	0.8427	0.9071	0.8436	0.9079	0.8444	0.9088	0.8453	0.9096	0.8461
41	0.8999	0.8331	0.9007	0.8340	0.9016	0.8349	0.9025	0.8357	0.9033	0.8366	0.9042	0.8374	0.9050	0.8383	0.9059	0.8391	0.9067	0.8400
42	0.8970	0.8269	0.8979	0.8277	0.8987	0.8286	0.8996	0.8294	0.9004	0.8303	0.9013	0.8312	0.9021	0.8320	0.9030	0.8329	0.9039	0.8337

The vital functions of highly developed organisms are closely dependent on the internal aqueous medium and on the maintenance of extreme constancy of its chemical and physical properties. A knowledge of some of the properties of aqueous solutions is therefore essential to an understanding of water and electrolyte balance and how it changes under pathological conditions.

In spite of the advances made in physical chemistry there remain considerable gaps in our knowledge of aqueous solutions. The properties of solutions with concentrations up to about 0.01 mol kg^{-1} can now be calculated with great accuracy, but for solutions of higher concentration it is necessary to introduce empirical correction factors in order to reconcile measured with theoretical values. In biology and medicine, however, this is of little importance since the approximate formulae derived from theory are sufficiently accurate for most practical purposes.

Definitions of the concepts atom, molecule and ion

A molecule of a substance is that group of elementary particles existing as kinetic unit in the gaseous phase of the substance at low concentration. The number concentration of molecules $C_i = N_i/V$ and their kinetic energy determine the mechanical and thermal properties of ideal gases. Molecules can be made up of one kind of element only or of various elements in combination. The smallest part of an element identifiable in compounds of which the element forms a part is known as an atom.

The 'chemical bonds' binding atoms together to form molecules are usually more than one order of magnitude stronger than the attractive forces between molecules. For this reason the molecules of a substance are often recognizable as units even in the condensed state. This does not apply, however, to many groups of substances, in particular metals and salts; here the term molecule is used in the purely formal sense as the sum of the atoms given in the empirical formula.

Salts are not made up of atoms bound together by orientated forces but of electrically charged atoms – known as ions – situated at the center of a spherically symmetrical electric field. Atoms are transformed into positive ions (cations) by loss of electrons and into negative ions (anions) by capture of electrons. Since the chemical properties of a particle are determined by the number of electrons it possesses, the properties of ions are completely different from those of the corresponding atoms.

Electrolytes

When an electric current is passed through a fused salt or its solution in water (or other polar solvent) chemical changes occur at the places where the current enters and leaves (the electrodes). This process is known as electrolysis, and a substance undergoing it as an electrolyte. Current passing through an electrolyte is carried by material particles, the ions. Positively charged ions (cations), which migrate in the electric field to the cathode, are indicated by one or more plus signs ($|z|+$), depending on their valency z, placed after their symbol as a superscript; in the same way negatively charged ions (anions), which migrate to the anode, are indicated by minus signs ($|z|-$) as a superscript. (For example magnesium ion = Mg^{2+}, nitrate ion = NO_3^-.)

That the ions already exist in the solution and are not formed when the electric field is applied can be demonstrated by measuring properties dependent only on the number of particles present in the solution, such as osmotic pressure, freezing-point depression, etc. (see below). The dissolution of a salt is therefore understood as the statistical distribution of the positive and negative ions forming the solid crystal lattice. This separation of oppositely charged particles is made easier by (1) a higher dielectric constant of the solvent, and (2) a stronger ion–dipole interaction between the ions of the solute and the polar molecules of the solvent (known as solvation or, for water, hydration of the ions). In respect to both (1) and (2) water occupies an almost unique position among solvents.

A solution in which the solute consists primarily of (solvated or hydrated) ions is known as a 'strong' electrolyte (the term electrolyte is also used to describe the solute itself). The amount of substance n contains $N = nN_A$ particles (N_A: Avogadro constant). When the substance is dissolved, each particle dissociates into ν_+ (dissociation number of the positive ions) positive ions with the charge number z_+ together with ν_- (dissociation number of the negative ions) negative ions with the charge number z_-, i.e. into $\nu = \nu_+ + \nu_-$ ions (or ion complexes). For example:

$NaCl$ $\quad \nu_+ = 1, \nu_- = 1, \nu = 2$ and $z_+ = 1, z_- = -1$
$CaCl_2$ $\quad \nu_+ = 1, \nu_- = 2, \nu = 3$ and $z_+ = 2, z_- = -1$
$K_3Fe(CN)_6$ $\quad \nu_+ = 3, \nu_- = 1, \nu = 4$ and $z_+ = 1, z_- = -3$
{$K_3Fe(CN)_6$ dissociates into 3 K^+ and 1 $[Fe(CN)_6]^{3-}$.}

Other substances dissociate in solution partly into ions and partly into molecules. These and their solutions are known as 'weak' electrolytes. They include particularly the weak acids and bases (almost all organic acids and bases, carbonic acid, hydrogen sulfide, etc.). The fraction of the total number of molecules dissociated into ions is known as the degree of dissociation $\alpha = N_i/N$. Dissolution of a weak electrolyte, in which the amount of substance $n = N/N_A$ of the particles is dissolved in the form of ions, gives rise to $N(\nu\alpha + 1 - \alpha)$ particles as (positive and negative) ions, for example, the amount of substance of the ions in the solution is $n(\nu\alpha + 1 - \alpha)$. The degree of dissociation α depends to a great extent on the concentration of the solution: the weaker the solution the more complete the dissociation and the closer the degree of dissociation approaches to 1.

Ideal dilute solutions

The thermodynamic treatment of dilute solutions makes use of the concept of the ideal dilute solution. This is a solution in which the molecules of the solute are completely surrounded by solvent molecules, so that any further addition of solvent results in no further interactions between solvent and solute. Under these conditions the properties of the solvent molecules in the solution depend only on the number of dissolved particles and not on their individual properties. Thus the lowering of the vapor pressure of the solvent due to the presence of the solute is proportional to the molar concentration x_i of the solute, and the same applies to the osmotic pressure, freezing-point depression and boiling-point elevation.

The osmotic pressure and freezing-point depression of an ideal dilute aqueous solution are expressed as follows:

Osmotic pressure (ideal)

$$\Pi_{id} = R \times T \times \frac{M_1}{V_{m_1}} \times \nu \times m_2 = R \times T \times n_2 \times \frac{M_1}{V_{m_1}} \times \frac{\nu}{\overline{m}} \qquad \textbf{(1)}$$

$[m_2 = n_2/\overline{m}]$

where R = (molar) gas constant (= 8.31441 J mol^{-1} K^{-1}); T = thermodynamic temperature; M_1 = molar mass of water; V_{m_1} = molar volume of water; m_2 = molality, n_2 = amount of substance, $\overline{m}$ = mass of the solute; ν = dissociation number, or number of particles into which the solute dissociates at complete dissociation (to be replaced by the factor $\nu\alpha + 1 - \alpha$ when dissociation is not complete; see above). In the case of water the value of M_1/V_{m_1}, measured in kg m^{-3}, equals 1000 to a good approximation.

Freezing-point depression (ideal)

$$\Delta T_{id} = \left(\frac{\Delta T_{id}}{\nu \times m_2}\right) \times \nu \times m_2 \qquad \textbf{(2)}$$

where $\Delta T_{id}/(\nu \times m_2)$ = molar freezing-point depression of water, or 'cryoscopic constant' (= 1.86 K mol^{-1} kg).

(For calculation of the osmotic pressure and freezing-point depression of solutions with molalities between 10 mmol kg^{-1} and 740 mmol kg^{-1} see page 48.)

Real solutions

The higher the solute concentration the wider the solution diverges from the concept of the ideal dilute solution. This divergence can be compensated for by means of a correction factor known as the osmotic coefficient ϕ (= 1 for ideal dilute solutions). At any given concentration a real solution diverges more widely from the ideal solution as the interactions between the particles in it become stronger. For ionic solutions, the correction by an osmotic coefficient ϕ differing from 1 is therefore greater than for mixed phases, for example, for solutions in which the solutes are not dissociated, and for solutions containing multivalent ions it is particularly large.

For very dilute ionic solutions the coefficient ϕ can be calculated by means of the DEBYE-HÜCKEL limiting law. Experimentally, it can be obtained from the relationship

$$\phi = \frac{\Delta T}{\Delta T_{id}} = \frac{1}{1.86 \text{ K mol}^{-1}\text{kg}} \times \frac{\Delta T}{\nu \times m_2} \qquad \textbf{(3)}$$

where ΔT is the actual freezing-point depression. In most reference books the magnitude $\Delta T/m_2$ as a function of the molality m_2 is given in place of the osmotic coefficient ϕ. To obtain ϕ, this is simply divided by $\nu \times 1.86$ K mol^{-1} kg.

In solutions of weak electrolytes the osmotic properties (freezing-point depression, osmotic pressure, etc.) depend mainly on the number of particles, which is a function of the concentration; in other words, they vary with the degree of dissociation α. In this case the divergence from the ideal dilute solution is of importance only in very precise physicochemical measurements, particularly as the ionic concentration remains low.

Measures of concentration

The concentration of a dilute solution is usually expressed as its molality $m_i = n_i/m_0$ in mol kg^{-1} (amount of substance of the solute in relation to the mass m_0 of the solvent) or as the amount of substance concentration $c_i = n_i/V$ in mol L^{-1} (amount of substance of the solute in relation to volume V of the solution; this was formerly termed the 'molarity' or, in the case of the 'amount of equivalent concentration' $c_{eq,i} = z_i n_i/V$ in mol L^{-1}, the 'normality').

The use of 1 L solution as reference magnitude has great advantages in volumetric analysis but also the disadvantage of being temperature-dependent (see Table 1).

Table 1 *Temperature-dependence of the amount of substance concentration of aqueous solutions*

Temperature t	Factor	Temperature t	Factor
14 °C	1.0010	21 °C	0.9998
15 °C	1.0009	22 °C	0.9996
16 °C	1.0007	23 °C	0.9994
17 °C	1.0006	24 °C	0.9991
18 °C	1.0004	25 °C	0.9989
19 °C	1.0002	26 °C	0.9986
20 °C	1.0000	27 °C	0.9983

These data are valid for solutions with the amount of substance concentration 0.1 mol L^{-1} where the cubic thermal expansion coefficient for glass[1] $\alpha = 0.000027$ K^{-1}. The reference temperature is 20 °C. For the other temperatures given in the table the amount of substance concentration is obtained by multiplication using the appropriate factor.

Table 2 *Calculation of molality for serum according to the relative density of serum*[2]

Relative density d of the serum	Mass fraction of water w_{i,H_2O} in the serum	Mass concentration of water ϱ_{i,H_2O} in the serum	$\frac{1000}{\varrho_{i,H_2O}}$
	g kg^{-1}	g L^{-1}	L kg^{-1}
1	2	3	4
1.015	952	966	1.035
1.016	948	964	1.038
1.017	945	961	1.040
1.018	942	959	1.043
1.019	939	957	1.045
1.020	936	954	1.048
1.021	932	952	1.051
1.022	929	949	1.053
1.023	926	947	1.056
1.024	923	945	1.059
1.025	919	942	1.061
1.026	916	940	1.064
1.027	913	938	1.067
1.028	910	935	1.069
1.029	906	933	1.072
1.030	903	930	1.075
1.031	900	928	1.078
1.032	897	925	1.081
1.033	894	923	1.083
1.034	890	921	1.086

Conversion of the amount of substance concentration c_i of a component of the serum (in mmol L^{-1}) *into the molality m_i of the component of the serum water* (in mmol kg^{-1}): multiply by the factor in column 4.
Conversion of the molality m_i of a component of the serum water (in mmol kg^{-1}) *into the amount of substance concentration c_i of the component of the serum* (in mmol L^{-1}): multiply by the factor in column 3 and divide by 1000.

Freezing-point depression values are always given for concentrations of the solution expressed as molality.

In extremely dilute aqueous solutions the amount of substance concentration and the molality can be assumed to be nearly equal; with increasing concentration they deviate more and more to an extent depending on the specific volume of the solute(s). The amount of substance concentration and molality of the serum cannot therefore be compared (high specific volume of the proteins); to do this, the usual mass concentration values, given in mg L^{-1} serum, etc., employed to express the molality of a serum component must be converted into its amount of substance concentration in the serum.

This conversion can be made by means of either the relative density of the serum or by using the mass concentration of the proteins in the serum. The former method is the more accurate and appropriate factors are given in Table 2.

Example. The freezing-point depression of the serum is 0.54 K, corresponding to a molality $m_i = 290$ mmol kg^{-1}. The amount of substance concentration in a normal serum (relative density 1.026) is accordingly 290 mmol kg^{-1} × 0.940 kg L^{-1} (factor 940 in column 3 of Table 2 divided by 1000).

Calculation of the mass concentration of the water in the serum follows from the mass concentration of the proteins in the serum in accordance with the following formula[3]:

$$\varrho_{i,H_2O} = 984 \text{ g L}^{-1} - (0.718 \times \varrho_{i,Pr}) \qquad (4)$$

where ϱ_{i,H_2O} = mass concentration of the water in the serum in g L^{-1}; and $\varrho_{i,Pr}$ = mass concentration of the proteins in the serum in g L^{-1}. The mass concentration of the minerals and other serum components in sera with a normal lipid concentration is already allowed for, namely by using 984 g L^{-1} instead of 1000 g L^{-1}. For conversion of amount of substance concentration into mass concentration and vice versa see page 64.

In the following text only the molality will be used. It should be noted that 'molarity', or amount of substance concentration, and molality are sometimes confused. To avoid such confusion, amount of substance concentration and molality should always be related to the *undissociated* component; otherwise they should be clearly specified, for instance 'the molality of all osmotically active particles'.

Osmotic amount of substance concentration, osmolality

The terms osmotic amount of substance concentration $c_{i,osm}$ (in mol L^{-1})* and osmolality $m_{i,osm}$ (in mol kg^{-1})* indicate respectively the amount of substance concentration and molality an ideal solution of a nondissociating solute must possess in order to exert the same osmotic pressure as the solution under consideration. The terms are not used in the physicochemical field but find considerable application in the sphere of biology and medicine[4]. As is clear from the definition, the (real) osmolality is a quantity capable of experimental determination. It can also be calculated from the molality of the solution provided: 1) the number of molecular fragments (for weak electrolytes the degree of dissociation α) and 2) the correction factor (osmotic coefficient ϕ) from the ideal to the real state are known.

If weak electrolytes are excluded, the *ideal osmolality* $m_{i,osm(id)}$ can be obtained by multiplying the molality by the number of molecular fragments. Multiplication of this by the osmotic coefficient ϕ gives the *(real) osmolality* $m_{i,osm(real)}$ as defined above:

$$m_{i,osm(id)} = m_2 \times \nu \text{ in the unit mol kg}^{-1} \qquad (5)$$

$$m_{i,osm(real)} = m_{i,osm(id)} \times \phi = m_2 \times \nu \times \phi = \Delta T/(1.86 \text{ K mol}^{-1}\text{kg}) \text{ in the unit mol kg}^{-1} \qquad (6)$$

For mixed solutions $m_2 \times \nu$ is replaced by the sum for each of the component solutes:

$$\sum_{i=2}^{n} m_i \times \nu_i = m_2 \times \nu_2 + m_3 \times \nu_3 + \ldots$$

For the sake of simplicity it is assumed that there is no change in the osmotic coefficient when passing from a simple to a mixed solution.

References

1 KOLTHOFF, I. M., *Die Maßanalyse,* part 2, Springer, Berlin, 1928, page 30.
2 SUNDERMAN, F. W., *J. biol. Chem.*, **113**, 111 (1936).
3 WELT, L. G., in DUNCAN, G. G. (Ed.), *Diseases of Metabolism,* 5th ed., Saunders, Philadelphia, 1964, page 449.
4 NETTER, H., *Theoretische Biochemie,* Springer, Berlin, 1959, page 108.

*Earlier termed 'osm L^{-1}' and 'osm kg^{-1}' respectively.

(Solvent: 1 kg water)

(Real) osmolality	Freezing-point depression ΔT	Osmotic pressure at 0 °C	Osmotic pressure at 38 °C
mmol kg⁻¹	K	kPa◇	kPa◇
1	2	3	4
10	0.019	23	26
20	0.037	45	52
30	0.056	68	78
40	0.074	91	103
50	0.093	114	129
60	0.112	136	155
70	0.130	159	181
80	0.149	182	207
90	0.167	204	233
100	0.186	227	259
110	0.205	250	285
120	0.223	273	310
130	0.242	295	336
140	0.260	318	362
150	0.279	341	388
160	0.298	363	414
170	0.316	386	440
180	0.335	409	466
190	0.353	432	492
200	0.372	454	517
210	0.391	477	543
220	0.409	500	569
230	0.428	522	595
240	0.446	545	621
250	0.465	568	647
260	0.484	590	673
270	0.502	613	698
280	0.521	636	724
290	0.539	659	750
300	0.558	681	776
310	0.577	704	802
320	0.595	727	828
330	0.614	749	854
340	0.632	772	880
350	0.651	795	905
360	0.669	818	931
370	0.688	840	957
380	0.707	863	983
390	0.725	886	1010

(Real) osmolality	Freezing-point depression ΔT	Osmotic pressure at 0 °C	Osmotic pressure at 38 °C
mmol kg⁻¹	K	kPa◇	kPa◇
1	2	3	4
400	0.744	908	1035
410	0.762	931	1061
420	0.781	954	1087
430	0.800	977	1112
440	0.818	999	1138
450	0.837	1022	1164
460	0.855	1045	1190
470	0.874	1067	1216
480	0.893	1090	1242
490	0.911	1113	1268
500	0.930	1136	1294
510	0.948	1158	1319
520	0.967	1181	1345
530	0.986	1204	1371
540	1.004	1226	1397
550	1.023	1249	1423
560	1.041	1272	1449
570	1.060	1295	1475
580	1.079	1317	1500
590	1.097	1340	1526
600	1.116	1363	1552
610	1.134	1385	1578
620	1.153	1408	1604
630	1.172	1431	1630
640	1.190	1453	1656
650	1.209	1476	1682
660	1.227	1499	1707
670	1.246	1522	1733
680	1.265	1544	1759
690	1.283	1567	1785
700	1.302	1590	1811
710	1.320	1612	1837
720	1.339	1635	1863
730	1.358	1658	1889
740	1.376	1681	1914

Freezing-point depression ΔT	(Real) osmolality	Osmotic pressure at 0 °C	Osmotic pressure at 38 °C
K	mmol kg⁻¹	kPa◇	kPa◇
5	6	7	8
0.01	5.4	12	14
0.02	10.8	24	28
0.03	16.1	37	42
0.04	21.5	49	56
0.05	26.9	61	70
0.06	32.3	73	83
0.07	37.6	85	97
0.08	43.0	98	111
0.09	48.4	110	125
0.10	53.8	122	139
0.11	59.1	134	153
0.12	64.5	147	167
0.13	69.9	159	181
0.14	75.3	171	195
0.15	80.7	183	209
0.16	86.0	195	223
0.17	91.4	208	236
0.18	96.8	220	250
0.19	102.2	232	264
0.20	107.5	244	278
0.21	112.9	256	292
0.22	118.3	269	306
0.23	123.7	281	320
0.24	129.1	293	334
0.25	134.4	305	348
0.26	139.8	318	362
0.27	145.2	330	376
0.28	150.6	342	390
0.29	155.9	354	403
0.30	161.3	366	417
0.31	166.7	379	431
0.32	172.1	391	445
0.33	177.4	403	459
0.34	182.8	415	473
0.35	188.2	427	487
0.36	193.6	440	501
0.37	199.0	452	515
0.38	204.3	464	529
0.39	209.7	476	543

Freezing-point depression ΔT	(Real) osmolality	Osmotic pressure at 0 °C	Osmotic pressure at 38 °C
K	mmol kg⁻¹	kPa◇	kPa◇
5	6	7	8
0.40	215.1	488	556
0.41	220.5	501	570
0.42	225.8	513	584
0.43	231.2	525	598
0.44	236.6	537	612
0.45	242.0	550	626
0.46	247.4	562	640
0.47	252.7	574	654
0.48	258.1	586	668
0.49	263.5	598	682
0.50	268.9	611	696
0.51	274.2	623	704
0.52	279.6	635	723
0.53	285.0	647	737
0.54	290.4	659	751
0.55	295.7	672	765
0.56	301.1	684	779
0.57	306.5	696	793
0.58	311.9	708	807
0.59	317.3	721	821
0.60	322.6	733	835
0.61	328.0	745	849
0.62	333.4	757	862
0.63	338.8	769	876
0.64	344.1	782	890
0.65	349.5	794	904
0.66	354.9	806	918
0.67	360.3	818	932
0.68	365.7	830	946
0.69	371.0	843	960
0.70	376.4	855	974
0.71	381.8	867	988
0.72	387.2	879	1002
0.73	392.5	891	1016
0.74	397.9	904	1029

◇ 1 kPa = 10^{-2} bar = 0.00986923267 atm.

Use of the tables above and on the next page

Calculation of the osmolality of blood serum from the freezing-point depression

Columns 5 and 6 of the above table show that the freezing-point depression of 0.54 K for blood serum corresponds to an osmolality of 290 mmol kg⁻¹.

Calculations for NaCl and glucose solutions (table on page 49)

(a) The *masses of NaCl, glucose or fructose required to yield a particular ideal osmolality* are given in columns 1 and 2 and in columns 1 and 6. Columns 7 and 8 give the corresponding energy values for glucose and fructose.

(b) The *ideal osmolalities corresponding to given masses of NaCl, glucose or fructose* are given in columns 12 and 13 and in columns 12 and 14. Columns 15 and 16 again give the corresponding energy values for glucose and fructose.

(c) The *values of the osmotic coefficient* ϕ and its reciprocal $1/\phi$ for NaCl and glucose are given in columns 1 and 4 and 1 and 5 (NaCl) and in columns 1 and 10 and 1 and 11 (glucose), with the values in column 1 being read as real osmolalities.

Example 1. Required is the mass of NaCl necessary to yield a solution with a (real) osmolality of 500 mmol kg⁻¹.

From equation (**5**) the ideal osmolality = real osmolality ϕ = 500/0.9180 = 500 × 1.0893 = 544.65 mmol kg⁻¹. From (a) above, the corresponding mass lies midway between 15.780 g and 16.072 g. The mass of NaCl which must be dissolved in 1 kg H_2O to yield an osmolality of 500 mmol kg⁻¹ is therefore 15.9 g.

The inconvenience of first calculating the ideal osmolality can be avoided by calculating the required mass of NaCl or glucose direct from column 2 or column 6. To do this, the mass given in column 2 or 6 obtained by entering the required (real) osmolality in column 1 is multiplied by the corresponding value for $1/\phi$ read off from column 5 or 11. The above example gives the result (14.611 × 1.0893) g = 15.916 g NaCl.

Example 2. It is desired to raise the osmolality of a solution from 400 mmol kg⁻¹ to 500 mmol kg⁻¹ by addition of NaCl. Here the calculation is simplified by assuming that the osmotic coefficient ϕ does not change when the solution becomes a mixed solution. $1/\phi$ for NaCl at 500 mmol kg⁻¹ is 1.0893. Since 100 mmol kg⁻¹ are to be added by means of NaCl, the required mass (see example 1) is (2.922 × 1.0893) = 3.183 g.

(d) *Exact calculations for isotonic solutions.* These can be made as shown in examples 1 and 2 below. More simply, the values required can be read off from columns 1 and 3 (NaCl) or 1 and 9 (glucose) of the table on the next page.

Example 1. To obtain a NaCl or glucose solution with an osmolality of 300 mmol kg⁻¹, 9.463 g NaCl or 53.312 g glucose must be dissolved in 1 kg water.

Example 2. It is desired to raise the osmolality of a solution from 200 mmol kg⁻¹ to 300 mmol kg⁻¹ by addition of NaCl. Since the additional osmolality is 100 mmol kg⁻¹ (column 1), the required mass of NaCl is 3.154 g (column 3). The value for glucose is obtained in a similar manner.

Values in columns 3–5 and 9–11 have been calculated for the relevant (real) osmolalities (in mmol kg^{-1}) and mass contents in 1 kg water (see introductory remarks, page 48)

	Common salt (NaCl, molar mass M = 58.443 g mol^{-1})				D-Glucose* ($C_6H_{12}O_6$, molar mass M = 180.16 g mol^{-1})							Common salt (NaCl)	D-Glucose* ($C_6H_{12}O_6$)		
Ideal osmolality	Corresponds to a mass of	Mass necessary when the osmolality in column 1 is to be added to bring the total to 300 mmol kg^{-1}◇	Osmotic coefficient§ ϕ	Osmotic coefficient§ $1/\phi$	Corresponds to a mass of	Corresponds to an energy value of	Corresponds to an energy value of	Mass necessary when the osmolality in column 1 is to be added to bring the total to 300 mmol kg^{-1}◇	Osmotic coefficient§ ϕ	Osmotic coefficient§ $1/\phi$	Mass	Corresponds to an ideal osmolality of	Corresponds to an ideal osmolality of	Corresponds to an energy value of	Corresponds to an energy value of
mmol kg^{-1}◇	g	g			g	kJ	kcal†	g			g	mmol kg^{-1}◇	mmol kg^{-1}◇	kJ	kcal†
1	2	3	4	5	6	7	8	9	10	11	12	13	14	15	16
10	0.292	0.315	0.9778	1.0227	1.802	31.54	7.54	1.777	1.0005	0.9995	1	34.22	5.55	17.50	4.18
20	0.584	0.630	0.9703	1.0306	3.603	63.07	15.07	3.554	1.0009	0.9991	2	68.44	11.10	35.01	8.36
30	0.877	0.947	0.9653	1.0359	5.405	94.61	22.60	5.331	1.0014	0.9986	3	102.66	16.65	52.51	12.55
40	1.169	1.262	0.9612	1.0404	7.206	126.1	30.14	7.108	1.0018	0.9982	4	136.89	22.20	70.02	16.73
50	1.461	1.577	0.9579	1.0440	9.008	157.7	37.67	8.885	1.0023	0.9977	5	171.11	27.75	87.52	20.91
60	1.753	1.892	0.9550	1.0471	10.810	189.2	45.21	10.662	1.0028	0.9972	6	205.33	33.30	105.0	25.09
70	2.046	2.208	0.9525	1.0499	12.611	220.7	52.74	12.439	1.0032	0.9968	7	239.55	38.85	122.5	29.27
80	2.338	2.524	0.9503	1.0523	14.413	252.3	60.28	14.217	1.0037	0.9963	8	273.77	44.41	140.0	33.46
90	2.630	2.839	0.9482	1.0546	16.214	283.8	67.81	15.994	1.0041	0.9959	9	307.99	49.96	157.5	37.64
100	2.922	3.154	0.9463	1.0567	18.016	315.3	75.34	17.771	1.0046	0.9954	**10**	342.22	55.51	175.0	41.82
110	3.214	3.469	0.9448	1.0584	19.818	346.9	82.88	19.548	1.0051	0.9949	11	376.44	61.06	192.5	46.00
120	3.507	3.785	0.9432	1.0602	21.619	378.4	90.41	21.325	1.0055	0.9945	12	410.66	66.61	210.0	50.18
130	3.799	4.101	0.9418	1.0618	23.421	410.0	97.95	23.102	1.0060	0.9940	13	444.88	72.16	227.5	54.37
140	4.091	4.416	0.9405	1.0633	25.222	441.5	105.5	24.879	1.0064	0.9936	14	479.10	77.71	245.1	58.55
150	4.383	4.731	0.9392	1.0647	27.024	473.0	113.0	26.656	1.0069	0.9931	15	513.32	83.26	262.6	62.73
160	4.675	5.047	0.9380	1.0661	28.826	504.6	120.6	28.433	1.0074	0.9927	16	547.54	88.81	280.1	66.91
170	4.968	5.362	0.9368	1.0675	30.627	536.1	128.1	30.210	1.0078	0.9923	17	581.77	94.36	297.6	71.09
180	5.260	5.678	0.9357	1.0687	32.429	567.6	135.6	31.987	1.0083	0.9918	18	615.99	99.91	315.1	75.28
190	5.552	5.993	0.9347	1.0699	34.230	599.2	143.1	33.764	1.0087	0.9914	19	650.21	105.46	332.6	79.46
200	5.844	6.308	0.9337	1.0710	36.032	630.7	150.7	35.541	1.0092	0.9909	**20**	684.43	111.01	350.1	83.64
210	6.137	6.624	0.9328	1.0720	37.834	662.2	158.2	37.318	1.0097	0.9904	21	718.65	116.56	367.6	87.82
220	6.429	6.939	0.9319	1.0731	39.635	693.8	165.8	39.096	1.0101	0.9900	22	752.87	122.11	385.1	92.00
230	6.721	7.255	0.9311	1.0740	41.437	725.3	173.3	40.873	1.0106	0.9895	23	787.09	127.66	402.6	96.19
240	7.013	7.570	0.9304	1.0748	43.238	756.8	180.8	42.650	1.0110	0.9891	24	821.32	133.22	420.1	100.4
250	7.305	7.885	0.9297	1.0756	45.040	788.4	188.4	44.427	1.0115	0.9886	25	855.54	138.77	437.6	104.6
260	7.598	8.201	0.9290	1.0764	46.842	819.9	195.9	46.204	1.0120	0.9881	26	889.76	144.32	455.1	108.7
270	7.890	8.516	0.9283	1.0772	48.643	851.4	203.4	47.981	1.0124	0.9878	27	923.98	149.87	472.6	112.9
280	8.182	8.832	0.9276	1.0780	50.445	883.0	211.0	49.758	1.0129	0.9873	28	958.20	155.42	490.1	117.1
290	8.474	9.147	0.9270	1.0787	52.246	914.5	218.5	51.535	1.0133	0.9869	29	992.42	160.97	507.6	121.3
300	8.766	9.463	0.9264	1.0794	54.048	946.0	226.0	53.312	1.0138	0.9864	**30**	1026.65	166.52	525.1	125.5
310	9.059	These values are obtained by dividing those in column 2 by 0.9264 or multiplying them by 1.0794 (= ϕ or $1/\phi$ for NaCl at an osmolality of 300 mmol kg^{-1}).	0.9258	1.0801	55.850	977.6	233.6	These values are obtained by dividing those in column 6 by 1.0138 or multiplying them by 0.9864 (= ϕ or $1/\phi$ for glucose at an osmolality of 300 mmol kg^{-1}).	1.0143	0.9859	31	1060.87	172.06	542.6	129.6
320	9.351		0.9252	1.0808	57.651	1009	241.1		1.0147	0.9855	32	1095.09	177.62	560.1	133.8
330	9.643		0.9246	1.0815	59.453	1041	248.6		1.0152	0.9850	33	1129.31	183.17	577.6	138.0
340	9.935		0.9241	1.0821	61.254	1072	256.2		1.0156	0.9846	34	1163.53	188.72	595.1	142.2
350	10.228		0.9236	1.0827	63.056	1104	263.7		1.0161	0.9842	35	1197.75	194.27	612.6	146.4
360	10.520		0.9232	1.0832	64.858	1135	271.2		1.0166	0.9837	36	1231.97	199.82	630.1	150.6
370	10.812		0.9227	1.0838	66.659	1167	278.8		1.0170	0.9833	37	1266.20	205.37	647.6	154.7
380	11.104		0.9223	1.0842	68.461	1198	286.3		1.0175	0.9828	38	1300.42	210.92	665.1	158.9
390	11.396		0.9219	1.0847	70.262	1230	293.8		1.0179	0.9824	39	1334.64	216.47	682.6	163.1
400	11.689		0.9215	1.0852	72.064	1261	301.4		1.0183	0.9820	**40**	1368.86	222.03	700.2	167.3
410	11.981		0.9211	1.0857	73.866	1293	308.9		1.0187	0.9816	41	1403.08	227.58	717.7	171.5
420	12.273		0.9207	1.0861	75.667	1324	316.4		1.0192	0.9812	42	1437.30	233.13	735.2	175.6
430	12.565		0.9204	1.0864	77.469	1356	324.0		1.0196	0.9808	43	1471.52	238.68	752.7	179.8
440	12.857		0.9200	1.0868	79.270	1388	331.5		1.0201	0.9803	44	1505.75	244.23	770.2	184.0
450	13.150		0.9196	1.0874	81.072	1419	339.0		1.0205	0.9799	45	1539.97	249.78	787.7	188.2
460	13.442		0.9192	1.0878	82.874	1451	346.6		1.0209	0.9795	46	1574.19	255.33	805.2	192.4
470	13.734		0.9189	1.0882	84.675	1482	354.1		1.0214	0.9790	47	1608.41	260.88	822.7	196.6
480	14.026		0.9185	1.0887	86.477	1514	361.6		1.0218	0.9787	48	1642.63	266.43	840.2	200.7
490	14.319		0.9182	1.0891	88.278	1545	369.2		1.0222	0.9783	49	1676.85	271.98	857.7	204.9
500	14.611		0.9180	1.0893	90.080	1577	376.7		1.0226	0.9779	**50**	1711.08	277.53	875.2	209.1
510	14.903		0.9177	1.0897	91.882	1608	384.3		1.0230	0.9775	51	1745.30	283.08	892.7	213.3
520	15.195		0.9174	1.0900	93.683	1640	391.8		1.0234	0.9771	52	1779.52	288.63	910.2	217.5
530	15.487		0.9172	1.0903	95.485	1671	399.3		1.0238	0.9767	53	1813.74	294.18	927.7	221.6
540	15.780		0.9170	1.0905	97.286	1703	406.9		1.0242	0.9764	54	1847.96	299.73	945.2	225.8
550	16.072		0.9167	1.0908	99.088	1734	414.4		1.0245	0.9761	55	1882.18	305.28	962.7	230.0
560	16.364		0.9165	1.0911	100.890	1766	421.9		1.0249	0.9757	56	1916.40	310.84	980.2	234.2
570	16.656		0.9163	1.0913	102.691	1797	429.5		1.0253	0.9753	57	1950.63	316.39	997.7	238.4
580	16.948		0.9161	1.0916	104.493	1829	437.0		1.0256	0.9750	58	1984.85	321.94	1015	242.6
590	17.241		0.9159	1.0918	106.294	1861	444.5		1.0260	0.9747	59	2019.07	327.49	1033	246.7
600	17.533		0.9157	1.0921	108.096	1892	452.1		1.0263	0.9744	**60**	2053.29	333.04	1050	250.9
610	17.825		0.9155	1.0923	109.898	1924	459.6		1.0267	0.9740	61	2087.51	338.59	1068	255.1
620	18.117		0.9153	1.0925	111.699	1955	467.1		1.0270	0.9737	62	2121.73	344.14	1085	259.3
630	18.410		0.9152	1.0927	113.501	1987	474.7		1.0273	0.9734	63	2155.95	349.69	1103	263.5
640	18.702		0.9150	1.0929	115.302	2018	482.2		1.0276	0.9731	64	2190.18	355.24	1120	267.6
650	18.994		0.9148	1.0931	117.104	2050	489.7		1.0279	0.9729	65	2224.40	360.79	1138	271.8
660	19.286		0.9146	1.0934	118.906	2081	497.3		1.0282	0.9726	66	2258.62	366.34	1155	276.0
670	19.578		0.9145	1.0935	120.707	2113	504.8		1.0285	0.9723	67	2292.84	371.89	1173	280.2
680	19.871		0.9144	1.0936	122.509	2144	512.3		1.0288	0.9720	68	2327.06	377.44	1190	284.3
690	20.163		0.9142	1.0938	124.310	2176	519.9		1.0291	0.9717	69	2361.28	382.99	1207	288.6
700	20.455		0.9140	1.0941	126.112	2207	527.4		1.0293	0.9715	**70**	2395.51	388.55	1225	292.7
710	20.747		0.9139	1.0942	127.914	2239	534.9		1.0296	0.9713	71	2429.73	394.09	1243	296.9
720	21.039		0.9137	1.0945	129.715	2271	542.5		1.0298	0.9711	72	2463.95	399.65	1260	301.1
730	21.332		0.9135	1.0947	131.517	2302	550.0		1.0300	0.9709	73	2498.17	405.20	1278	305.3
740	21.624		0.9134	1.0948	133.318	2334	557.5		1.0302	0.9707	74	2532.39	410.75	1295	309.5

*Since the elementary compositions of glucose and fructose are the same, columns 6–8 and 14–16 can also be used for fructose. Note, however, that the osmotic coefficient ϕ for fructose is not the same as that for glucose.

◇Earlier termed 'mosm kg^{-1}'.

§Values for NaCl obtained by interpolation from the data of SCATCHARD and PRENTISS, *J. Amer. chem. Soc.*, **55**, 4355 (1933); values for glucose from ROTH, W. A., *Z. phys. Chem.*, **43**, 539 (1903).

†LOEWY's value for the energy value of 1 g carbohydrate (4.182 kcal g^{-1}) has been used; 1 kcal$_{15}$ = 4.1855 kJ.

No.	Electrolyte		Reference mass 1 g (unless otherwise stated)											Reference amount of substance (osmotic) 10 mmol (unless otherwise stated)							
	Name	Chemical formula	Molar mass M	Maximum mass concentration		Amount of substance of the undissociated electrolyte	Cation			Anion			Osmotic amount of substance concentration*	Undissociated electrolyte		Cation			Anion		
				Cold⁷	Hot⁷		Nature (symbol)	Amount of substance	Mass	Nature (symbol)	Amount of substance	Mass		Mass	Amount of substance	Nature (symbol)	Amount of substance	Mass	Nature (symbol)	Amount of substance	Mass
			g mol^{-1}	g L^{-1}	g L^{-1}	mmol		mmol	mg		mmol	mg	mmol L^{-1}	g	mmol		mmol	mg		mmol	mg
1	2	3	4	5	6	7	8	9	10	11	12	13	14	15	16	17	18	19	20	21	22
	Calcium (Ca)																				
1	Calcium acetate	$Ca(C_2H_3O_2)_2 + H_2O$	176.18	436^{0}	343^{100}	5.68	Ca^{2+}	5.68	227	$C_2H_3O_2^-$	11.35	670	17.03	0.587	3⅓	Ca^{2+}	3⅓	134	$C_2H_3O_2^-$	6⅔	394
2		$Ca(C_2H_3O_2)_2 + 2\,H_2O$	194.20	347^{20}	335^{80}	5.15	Ca^{2+}	5.15	206	$C_2H_3O_2^-$	10.30	608	15.45	0.647	3⅓	Ca^{2+}	3⅓	134	$C_2H_3O_2^-$	6⅔	394
3	Calcium chloride	$CaCl_2 + 2\,H_2O$	147.02	977^{0}	3260^{60}	6.80	Ca^{2+}	6.80	273	Cl^-	13.60	482	20.40	0.490	3⅓	Ca^{2+}	3⅓	134	Cl^-	6⅔	236
4		$CaCl_2 + 6\,H_2O$	219.08	2790^{0}	5360^{20}	4.56	Ca^{2+}	4.56	183	Cl^-	9.13	324	13.69	0.730	3⅓	Ca^{2+}	3⅓	134	Cl^-	6⅔	236
5	Calcium citrate	$Ca_3(C_6H_5O_7)_2 + 4\,H_2O$	570.50	0.85^{18}	0.96^{23}	1.75	Ca^{2+}	5.26	211	$C_6H_5O_7^{3-}$	3.50	663	8.76	1.141	2	Ca^{2+}	6	240	$C_6H_5O_7^{3-}$	4	756
6	Calcium D-gluconate	$Ca(C_6H_{11}O_7)_2 + H_2O$	448.39	33^{15}	...	2.23	Ca^{2+}	2.23	89	$C_6H_{11}O_7^-$	4.46	870	6.69	1.495	3⅓	Ca^{2+}	3⅓	134	$C_6H_{11}O_7^-$	6⅔	1301
7	Calcium thiosulfate	$CaS_2O_3 + 6\,H_2O$	260.29	1000^{3}	d	3.84	Ca^{2+}	3.84	154	$S_2O_3^{2-}$/S	3.84	431/246	7.68	1.301	5	Ca^{2+}	5	200	$S_2O_3^{2-}$ S	5 ...	561 321
8	Calcium lactate	$Ca(C_3H_5O_3)_2 + 5\,H_2O$	308.30	31^{0}	79^{30}	3.24	Ca^{2+}	3.24	130	$C_3H_5O_3^-$	6.49	578	9.73	1.028	3⅓	Ca^{2+}	3⅓	134	$C_3H_5O_3^-$	6⅔	594
9	Calcium levulinate	$Ca(C_5H_7O_3)_2 + 2\,H_2O$	306.33	...	...	3.26	Ca^{2+}	3.26	131	$C_5H_7O_3^-$	6.53	752	9.79	1.021	3⅓	Ca^{2+}	3⅓	134	$C_5H_7O_3^-$	6⅔	767
10	Calcium hydrogen phosphate	$CaHPO_4 + 2\,H_2O$	172.09	0.316^{38}	0.75^{100}	5.81	Ca^{2+}	5.81	233	HPO_4^{2-}/P	5.81	558/180	11.62	0.860	5	Ca^{2+}	5	200	HPO_4^{2-} P	5 ...	480 155
	Chlorine (Cl)																				
11	Hydrochloric acid (10%)																				
	1 g	(0.1 g HCl)	36.46	∞	∞	2.74	H^+	2.74	2.8	Cl^-	2.74	97.2	5.48	1.823	5	H^+	5	5	Cl^-	5	177
	1 ml	(0.1047 g HCl)	36.46	∞	∞	2.87	H^+	2.87	2.9	Cl^-	2.87	101.8	5.74	1.741	5	H^+	5	5	Cl^-	5	177
12	Ammonium chloride	NH_4Cl	53.49	297^{0}	758^{100}	18.69	NH_4^+	18.69	337	Cl^-	18.69	663	37.39	0.267	5	NH_4^+	5	90	Cl^-	5	177
	See also Calcium (**3**, **4**), Potassium (**20**), Magnesium (**13**, **14**), and Sodium (**28**)																				
	Magnesium (Mg)																				
13	Magnesium chloride	$MgCl_2$	95.21	542.5^{20}	727^{100}	10.50	Mg^{2+}	10.50	255	Cl^-	21.01	745	31.51	0.317	3⅓	Mg^{2+}	3⅓	81	Cl^-	6⅔	236
14		$MgCl_2 + 6\,H_2O$	203.30	1670	3670	4.92	Mg^{2+}	4.92	120	Cl^-	9.84	349	14.76	0.678	3⅓	Mg^{2+}	3⅓	81	Cl^-	6⅔	236
15	Magnesium hydroxide	$Mg(OH)_2$	58.32	0.009^{18}	0.04^{100}	17.15	Mg^{2+}	17.14	417												
16	Magnesium sulfate	$MgSO_4 + 7\,H_2O$	246.47	710^{20}	910^{40}	4.06	Mg^{2+}	4.06	98.7	SO_4^{2-}/S	4.06	390/130	8.11	1.232	5	Mg^{2+}	5	122	SO_4^{2-} S	5 ...	480 160
	Phosphorus (P)																				
	See Calcium (**10**), Potassium (**23**, **24**), and Sodium (**35–39**)																				

1	2	3	4	5	6	7	8	9	10	11	12	13	14	15	16	17	18	19	20	21	22
	Potassium (K)																				
17	Potassium acetate	$K(C_2H_3O_2)$	98.14	2530^{20}	4920^{62}	10.19	K^+	10.19	398	$C_2H_3O_2^-$	10.19	602	20.38	0.491	5	K^+	5	195	$C_2H_3O_2^-$	5	295
18	Potassium bicarbonate	$KHCO_3$	100.11	224	600^{60}	9.99	K^+	9.99	391	HCO_3^-	9.99	609	19.98	0.501	5	K^+	5	195	HCO_3^-	5	305
19	Potassium bromide	KBr	119.00	534.8^{0}	1020^{100}	8.40	K^+	8.40	328	Br^-	8.40	671	16.81	0.595	5	K^+	5	195	Br^-	5	400
20	Potassium chloride	KCl	74.55	347^{20}	567^{100}	13.41	K^+	13.41	524	Cl^-	13.41	476	26.83	0.373	5	K^+	5	195	Cl^-	5	177
21	Potassium citrate	$K_3(C_6H_5O_7) + H_2O$	324.41	1670^{15}	1997^{31}	3.08	K^+	9.25	362	$C_6H_5O_7^{3-}$	3.08	583	12.33	0.811	2½	K^+	7½	293	$C_6H_5O_7^{3-}$	2½	473
22	Potassium D-gluconate	$K(C_6H_{11}O_7)$	234.25	...	...	4.27	K^+	4.27	167	$C_6H_{11}O_7^-$	4.27	833	8.54	1.171	5	K^+	5	195	$C_6H_{11}O_7^-$	5	976
23	Potassium dihydrogen phosphate	KH_2PO_4	136.09	330^{25}	835^{90}	7.35	K^+ H^+	7.35 7.35	287 7.4	HPO_4^{2-}/P	7.35	705/228	22.04	0.454	3⅓	K^+ H^+	3⅓ 3⅓	130 3.3	HPO_4^{2-} P	3⅓ ...	320 103
24	Dipotassium hydrogen phosphate	K_2HPO_4	174.18	1670^{20}	v.s.	5.74	K^+	11.48	449	HPO_4^{2-}/P	5.74	551/178	17.22	0.581	3⅓	K^+	6⅔	261	HPO_4^{2-} P	3⅓ ...	320 103
	Sodium (Na)																				
25	Sodium acetate	$Na(C_2H_3O_2) + 3\,H_2O$	136.08	762^{0}	1388^{50}	7.35	Na^+	7.35	169	$C_2H_3O_2^-$	7.35	434	14.70	0.680	5	Na^+	5	115	$C_2H_3O_2^-$	5	295
26	Sodium bicarbonate◊	$NaHCO_3$	84.01	69^{0}	164^{60}	11.90	Na^+	11.90	274	HCO_3^-	11.90	726	23.81	0.420	5	Na^+	5	115	HCO_3^-	5	305
27	Sodium bromide	NaBr	102.89	1160^{50}	1210^{100}	9.72	Na^+	9.72	223	Br^-	9.72	777	19.44	0.514	5	Na^+	5	115	Br^-	5	400
28	Sodium chloride	NaCl	58.44	357^{0}	391.2^{100}	17.11	Na^+	17.11	393	Cl^-	17.11	607	34.22	0.292	5	Na^+	5	115	Cl^-	5	177
29	Disodium hydrogen citrate	$Na_2H(C_6H_5O_7) + 1½\,H_2O$	263.11	v.s.	v.s.	3.80	Na^+	7.60	175	$H(C_6H_5O_7)^{2-}$	3.80	723	11.40	0.658	2½	Na^+ H^+	5 2½	115 2.5	$C_6H_5O_7^{3-}$	2½	473
							Na^+ H^+	7.60 3.80	175 3.83	$C_6H_5O_7^{3-}$	3.80	719	15.20								
30	Sodium citrate	$Na_3(C_6H_5O_7) + 2\,H_2O$	294.10	720^{25}	1670^{100}	3.40	Na^+	10.19	235	$C_6H_5O_7^{3-}$	3.40	643	13.60	0.735	2½	Na^+	7½	172	$C_6H_5O_7^{3-}$	2½	473
31		$Na_3(C_6H_5O_7) + 5½\,H_2O$	357.16	926^{25}	2500^{100}	2.80	Na^+	8.40	193	$C_6H_5O_7^{3-}$	2.80	529	11.20	0.893	2½	Na^+	7½	172	$C_6H_5O_7^{3-}$	2½	473
32	Sodium thiosulfate	$Na_2S_2O_3$	158.10	500	2310^{100}	6.32	Na^+	12.65	291	$S_2O_3^{2-}/S$	6.32	709/406	18.98	0.527	3⅓	Na^+	6⅔	153	$S_2O_3^{2-}$ S	3⅓ ...	374 214
33	Sodium lactate◊	$Na(C_3H_5O_3)$	112.06	v.s.	...	8.92	Na^+	8.92	205	$C_3H_5O_3^-$	8.92	795	17.84	0.560	5	Na^+	5	115	$C_3H_5O_3^-$	5	445
34	Sodium 4-aminosalicylate	$Na(C_7H_6O_3N) + 2\,H_2O$	211.15	...	...	4.74	Na^+	4.74	109	$C_7H_6O_3N^-$	4.74	720	9.47	1.056	5	Na^+	5	115	$C_7H_6O_3N^-$	5	761
35	Sodium dihydrogen phosphate	$NaH_2PO_4 + H_2O$	137.99	599^{0}	4270^{100}	7.25	Na^+ H^+	7.25 7.25	167 7.3	HPO_4^{2-}/P	7.25	696/224	21.74	0.460	3⅓	Na^+ H^+	3⅓ 3⅓	77 3.3	HPO_4^{2-}	3⅓	320
36		$NaH_2PO_4 + 2\,H_2O$	156.01	v.s.	v.s.	6.41	Na^+ H^+	6.41 6.41	147 6.5	HPO_4^{2-}/P	6.41	615/199	19.23	0.520	3⅓	Na^+ H^+	3⅓ 3⅓	77 3.3	HPO_4^{2-} P	3⅓ ...	320 103
37	Disodium hydrogen phosphate	Na_2HPO_4	141.96	...	...	7.04	Na^+	14.09	324	HPO_4^{2-}/P	7.04	676/218	21.13	0.473	3⅓	Na^+	6⅔	153	HPO_4^{2-} P	3⅓ ...	320 103
38		$Na_2HPO_4 + 2\,H_2O$	177.99	1000^{50}	1170^{80}	5.62	Na^+	11.24	258	HPO_4^{2-}/P	5.62	539/174	16.85	0.593	3⅓	Na^+	6⅔	153	HPO_4^{2-} P	3⅓ ...	320 103
39		$Na_2HPO_4 + 12\,H_2O$	358.14	41.5	874^{34}	2.79	Na^+	5.58	128	HPO_4^{2-}/P	2.79	268/86.5	8.38	1.194	3⅓	Na^+	6⅔	153	HPO_4^{2-} P	3⅓ ...	320 103
40	Sodium salicylate	$Na(C_7H_5O_3)$	160.10	1110^{15}	1250^{25}	6.25	Na^+	6.25	144	$C_7H_5O_3^-$	6.25	856	12.49	0.801	5	Na^+	5	115	$C_7H_5O_3^-$	5	686
41	Sodium sulfate	Na_2SO_4	142.04	47.6^{0}	427^{100}	7.04	Na^+	14.08	324	SO_4^{2-}/S	7.04	676/226	21.12	0.473	3⅓	Na^+	6⅔	153	SO_4^{2-} S	3⅓ ...	320 107
42	(Glauber's salt)	$Na_2SO_4 + 10\,H_2O$	322.19	110^{0}	927^{30}	3.10	Na^+	6.21	143	SO_4^{2-}/S	3.10	298/100	9.31	1.074	3⅓	Na^+	6⅔	153	SO_4^{2-} S	3⅓ ...	320 107
	Sulfur (S) See Calcium (**7**), Magnesium (**16**), and Sodium (**32, 41, 42**)																				

[1] HAMMOND, C.R., in WEAST, R.C. (Ed.), *CRC Handbook of Chemistry and Physics,* 63rd ed., CRC Press, Boca Raton, Fla., 1982–1983, page B-73. The elevated figures are the temperatures in °C (v.s. = very soluble; d = decomposes).

* On the assumption of complete dissociation. See under 'Osmotic amount of substance concentration', page 47.

◊ The mass of the sodium in 1 g sodium bicarbonate is the same as that in 1.33 g sodium lactate. The mass of the sodium in 1 g sodium lactate is the same as that in 0.75 g sodium bicarbonate.

No.	Electrolyte	Chemical formula		
1	2	3	4	5
	Calcium (Ca) 1 g Ca^{2+} has an amount of substance of 24.95 mmol. 1 mmol Ca^{2+} has a mass of 40.08 mg.		*1 g Ca^{2+} corresponds to*	*1 mmol Ca^{2+} corresponds to*
1	Calcium acetate	$Ca(C_2H_3O_2)_2 + H_2O$	4.396 g	176.18 mg
2		$Ca(C_2H_3O_2)_2 + 2\,H_2O$	4.845 g	194.20 mg
3	Calcium chloride	$CaCl_2 + 2\,H_2O$	3.668 g	147.02 mg
4		$CaCl_2 + 6\,H_2O$	5.466 g	219.08 mg
5	Calcium citrate	$Ca_3(C_6H_5O_7)_2 + 4\,H_2O$	4.745 g	190.17 mg
6	Calcium D-gluconate	$Ca(C_6H_{11}O_7)_2 + H_2O$	11.187 g	448.39 mg
7	Calcium thiosulfate	$CaS_2O_3 + 6\,H_2O$	6.494 g	260.29 mg
8	Calcium lactate	$Ca(C_3H_5O_3)_2 + 5\,H_2O$	7.692 g	308.30 mg
9	Calcium levulinate	$Ca(C_5H_7O_3)_2 + 2\,H_2O$	7.643 g	306.33 mg
10	Calcium hydrogen phosphate	$CaHPO_4 + 2\,H_2O$	4.294 g	172.09 mg
	Chlorine (Cl) 1 g Cl^- has an amount of substance of 28.21 mmol. 1 mmol Cl^- has a mass of 35.453 mg.		*1 g Cl^- corresponds to*	*1 mmol Cl^- corresponds to*
11	Hydrochloric acid (10% solution)	HCl (10%)	10.28 g 9.823 ml	364.6 mg 348.24 µl
12	Ammonium chloride	NH_4Cl	1.509 g	53.49 mg
3	Calcium chloride	$CaCl_2 + 2\,H_2O$	2.073 g	73.51 mg
4		$CaCl_2 + 6\,H_2O$	3.090 g	109.55 mg
20	Potassium chloride	KCl	2.103 g	74.56 mg
13	Magnesium chloride	$MgCl_2$	1.343 g	47.61 mg
14		$MgCl_2 + 6\,H_2O$	2.867 g	101.66 mg
28	Sodium chloride	NaCl	1.648 g	58.44 mg
	Magnesium (Mg) 1 g Mg^{2+} has an amount of substance of 41.14 mmol. 1 mmol Mg^{2+} has a mass of 24.305 mg.		*1 g Mg^{2+} corresponds to*	*1 mmol Mg^{2+} corresponds to*
13	Magnesium chloride	$MgCl_2$	3.917 g	95.21 mg
14		$MgCl_2 + 6\,H_2O$	8.365 g	203.30 mg
16	Magnesium sulfate	$MgSO_4 + 7\,H_2O$	10.141 g	246.47 mg
	Phosphorus (P) *At pH 4.3:* 1 g P corresponds to 32.28 mmol $H_2PO_4^-$ ions. 1 mmol $H_2PO_4^-$ ions corresponds to 30.97 mg P. *At pH 7.4 and 38 °C:* 1 g P corresponds to 31.19 mmol phosphate ions (i.e. ca. 20% $H_2PO_4^-$ ions and 80% HPO_4^{2-} ions). 1 mmol phosphate ions (i.e. ca. 20% $H_2PO_4^-$ ions and 80% HPO_4^{2-} ions) corresponds to 31.05 mg P. *At pH 9.6:* 1 g P corresponds to 32.28 mmol HPO_4^{2-} ions. 1 mmol HPO_4^{2-} ions corresponds to 30.97 mg P.		*1 g P corresponds to*	
10	Calcium hydrogen phosphate	$CaHPO_4 + 2\,H_2O$	5.556 g	
23	Potassium dihydrogen phosphate	KH_2PO_4	4.394 g	
24	Dipotassium hydrogen phosphate	K_2HPO_4	5.624 g	
35	Sodium dihydrogen phosphate	$NaH_2PO_4 + H_2O$	4.455 g	
36		$NaH_2PO_4 + 2\,H_2O$	5.037 g	
37	Disodium hydrogen phosphate	Na_2HPO_4	4.583 g	
38		$Na_2HPO_4 + 2\,H_2O$	5.746 g	
39		$Na_2HPO_4 + 12\,H_2O$	11.563 g	

No.	Electrolyte	Chemical formula		
1	2	3	4	5
	Potassium (K) 1 g K^+ has an amount of substance of 25.58 mmol. 1 mmol K^+ has a mass of 39.098 mg.		*1 g K^+ corresponds to*	*1 mmol K^+ corresponds to*
17	Potassium acetate	$K(C_2H_3O_2)$	2.510 g	98.14 mg
18	Potassium bicarbonate	$KHCO_3$	2.560 g	100.11 mg
19	Potassium bromide	KBr	3.044 g	119.00 mg
20	Potassium chloride	KCl	1.907 g	74.55 mg
21	Potassium citrate	$K_3(C_6H_5O_7) + H_2O$	2.766 g	108.14 mg
22	Potassium D-gluconate	$K(C_6H_{11}O_7)$	5.991 g	234.25 mg
23	Potassium dihydrogen phosphate	KH_2PO_4	3.480 g	136.09 mg
24	Dipotassium hydrogen phosphate	K_2HPO_4	2.227 g	87.09 mg
	Sodium (Na) 1 g Na^+ has an amount of substance of 43.50 mmol. 1 mmol Na^+ has a mass of 22.99 mg.		*1 g Na^+ corresponds to*	*1 mmol Na^+ corresponds to*
25	Sodium acetate	$Na(C_2H_3O_2) + 3\,H_2O$	5.919 g	136.08 mg
26	Sodium bicarbonate	$NaHCO_3$	3.654 g	84.01 mg
28	Sodium chloride (common salt)	NaCl	2.542 g	58.44 mg
29	Disodium hydrogen citrate	$Na_2H(C_6H_5O_7) + 1\frac{1}{2}\,H_2O$	5.722 g	131.56 mg
30	Sodium citrate	$Na_3(C_6H_5O_7) + 2\,H_2O$	4.264 g	98.03 mg
31		$Na_3(C_6H_5O_7) + 5\frac{1}{2}\,H_2O$	5.178 g	119.05 mg
32	Sodium thiosulfate	$Na_2S_2O_3$	3.438 g	79.05 mg
33	Sodium lactate	$Na(C_3H_5O_3)$	4.874 g	112.06 mg
34	Sodium 4-aminosalicylate	$Na(C_7H_6O_3N) + 2\,H_2O$	9.185 g	211.15 mg
35	Sodium dihydrogen phosphate	$NaH_2PO_4 + H_2O$	6.002 g	137.99 mg
36		$NaH_2PO_4 + 2\,H_2O$	6.786 g	156.01 mg
37	Disodium hydrogen phosphate	Na_2HPO_4	3.087 g	70.98 mg
38		$Na_2HPO_4 + 2\,H_2O$	3.871 g	88.99 mg
39		$Na_2HPO_4 + 12\,H_2O$	7.789 g	179.07 mg
40	Sodium salicylate	$Na(C_7H_5O_3)$	6.964 g	160.10 mg
41	Sodium sulfate	Na_2SO_4	3.089 g	71.02 mg
42	(Glauber's salt)	$Na_2SO_4 + 10\,H_2O$	7.007 g	161.10 mg
	Sulfur (S) 1 g S corresponds to 31.19 mmol SO_4^{2-} ions. 1 mmol SO_4^{2-} ions corresponds to 32.06 mg S.		*1 g S corresponds to*	
7	Calcium thiosulfate	$CaS_2O_3 + 6\,H_2O$	4.059 g	
16	Magnesium sulfate	$MgSO_4 + 7\,H_2O$	7.688 g	
32	Sodium thiosulfate	$Na_2S_2O_3$	2.466 g	
41	Sodium sulfate	Na_2SO_4	4.430 g	
42	(Glauber's salt)	$Na_2SO_4 + 10\,H_2O$	10.050 g	

Carbon dioxide (CO_2) and bicarbonate ions (HCO_3^-)
1 g CO_2 corresponds to 1.387 g HCO_3^- ions and to 22.72 mmol HCO_3^- ions.
At 0 °C and 101 325 Pa, a CO_2 volume fraction 0.01 corresponds to a mass concentration of 27.41 mg L^{-1} of HCO_3^- ions in the dissolved gas* and to an amount of substance concentration of 0.449 mmol L^{-1}.
1 mmol HCO_3^- ions has a mass of 61.02 mg and corresponds to 44.01 mg CO_2. An amount of substance concentration of 1 mmol L^{-1} HCO_3^- ions in the dissolved gas* corresponds to a mass concentration of 61.02 mg L^{-1} and at 0 °C and 101 325 Pa has a CO_2 volume fraction 0.0223.

Serum proteins[1]
At pH 7.4 and 38 °C and an albumin/globulin ratio of 1.6:
1 g serum protein corresponds to 0.241 mmol ionized serum protein.
1 mmol ionized serum protein corresponds to 4.15 g serum protein.

[1] VAN SLYKE et al., *J. biol. Chem.*, **79**, 769 (1928).
*The conversion factors (44.9 and 0.0223) given here for CO_2 volume fractions into mmol L^{-1} of CO_2 and vice versa are derived from the molar volume of this gas (22.257 L mol^{-1} at 0 °C and 101 325 Pa). The conversion factor 0.0224 (or 2.24 when the volume fraction is given in %) often used in the medical literature is mistakenly based on the molar volume of ideal gases (22.414 L mol^{-1}). For practical purposes the difference between the 2 factors is negligible.

Solutions of Salts and other Reagents with the Amount of Substance Concentration c_i = 0.1 mol L^{-1}

Name of substance	Molar mass M	System relative to the amount of substance n (H)	Mass concentration ϱ_i of the system (at c_i = 0.1 mol L^{-1})
	g mol^{-1}		g L^{-1}
1	2	3	4
Acetic acid	60.05	$C_2H_4O_2$	6.005
Ammonia	17.03	NH_3	1.703
Ammonium chloride	53.49	NH_4Cl	5.349
Ammonium hydroxide	35.05	NH_4OH	3.505
Ammonium nitrate	80.04	NH_4NO_3	8.004
Ammonium sulfate	132.14	$\frac{1}{2}(NH_4)_2SO_4$	6.607
Ammonium thiocyanate	76.12	NH_4CNS	7.612
Barium carbonate	197.35	$\frac{1}{2}BaCO_3$	9.868
Barium chloride dihydrate	244.28	$\frac{1}{2}[BaCl_2 + 2\,H_2O]$	12.214
Barium hydroxide octahydrate	315.48	$\frac{1}{2}[Ba(OH)_2 + 8\,H_2O]$	15.774
Barium oxide	153.34	$\frac{1}{2}BaO$	7.667
Borax. See Sodium tetraborate decahydrate			
Boric acid (orthoboric acid)	61.83	$\frac{1}{3}H_3BO_3$	2.061
Bromine	159.81	$\frac{1}{2}Br_2$	7.991
Calcium carbonate	100.09	$\frac{1}{2}CaCO_3$	5.005
Calcium chloride	110.99	$\frac{1}{2}CaCl_2$	5.550
Calcium chloride hexahydrate	219.08	$\frac{1}{2}[CaCl_2 + 6\,H_2O]$	10.954
Calcium hydroxide	74.09	$\frac{1}{2}Ca(OH)_2$	3.705
Calcium oxide	56.08	$\frac{1}{2}CaO$	2.804
Carbon dioxide	44.01	$\frac{1}{2}CO_2$	2.201
Chlorine	70.91	$\frac{1}{2}Cl_2$	3.546
Citric acid hydrate	210.14	$\frac{1}{3}[C_6H_8O_7 + H_2O]$	7.005
Copper oxide	79.55	$\frac{1}{2}CuO$	3.978
Copper sulfate pentahydrate	249.68	$\frac{1}{2}[CuSO_4 + 5\,H_2O]$	12.484
Hydrobromic acid	80.91	HBr	8.091
Hydrochloric acid	36.46	HCl	3.646
Hydrocyanic acid	27.03	HCN	2.703
Hydroiodic acid	127.91	HI	12.791
Iodine	253.81	$\frac{1}{2}I_2$	12.691
Lactic acid	90.08	$C_3H_6O_3$	9.008
Lead carbonate	267.20	$\frac{1}{2}PbCO_3$	13.360
Lead oxide	223.19	$\frac{1}{2}PbO$	11.160
Magnesium carbonate	84.31	$\frac{1}{2}MgCO_3$	4.216
Magnesium chloride	95.21	$\frac{1}{2}MgCl_2$	4.761
Magnesium chloride hexahydrate	203.30	$\frac{1}{2}[MgCl_2 + 6\,H_2O]$	10.165
Magnesium oxide	40.31	$\frac{1}{2}MgO$	2.016
Malic acid	134.09	$\frac{1}{2}C_4H_6O_5$	6.705
Manganese sulfate	151.00	$\frac{1}{2}MnSO_4$	7.550
Mercuric chloride (corrosive sublimate)	271.50	$\frac{1}{2}HgCl_2$	13.575
Nitric acid	63.01	HNO_3	6.301
Nitrous acid	47.01	HNO_2	4.701
Oxalic acid	90.04	$\frac{1}{2}C_2H_2O_4$	4.502
Oxalic acid dihydrate	126.07	$\frac{1}{2}[C_2H_2O_4 + 2\,H_2O]$	6.304
Phosphoric acid	98.00	$\frac{1}{3}H_3PO_4$	3.267
Potassium bicarbonate	100.12	$KHCO_3$	10.012
Potassium bitartrate	188.18	$C_4H_5O_6K$	18.818
Potassium carbonate	138.21	$\frac{1}{2}K_2CO_3$	6.911
Potassium chloride	74.56	KCl	7.456
Potassium cyanide	65.12	KCN	6.512
Potassium dichromate	294.19	$\frac{1}{6}K_2Cr_2O_7$	4.903
Potassium hydroxide	56.11	KOH	5.611
Potassium oxide	94.20	$\frac{1}{2}K_2O$	4.710
Potassium permanganate in acid medium	158.04	$\frac{1}{5}KMnO_4$	3.161
Potassium permanganate for Mn determination	158.04	$\frac{1}{3}KMnO_4$	5.268
Potassium tartrate	226.28	$\frac{1}{2}C_4H_4O_6K_2$	11.314
Potassium tetraoxalate dihydrate	254.20	$\frac{1}{3}[KH_3(C_2O_4)_2 + 2\,H_2O]$	8.473
Silver nitrate	169.87	$AgNO_3$	16.987
Sodium bicarbonate	84.01	$NaHCO_3$	8.401
Sodium carbonate	105.99	$\frac{1}{2}Na_2CO_3$	5.300
Sodium chloride	58.44	$NaCl$	5.844
Sodium hydroxide	40.00	$NaOH$	4.000
Sodium oxide	61.98	$\frac{1}{2}Na_2O$	3.099
Sodium phosphate (disodium hydrogen phosphate) dihydrate	177.99	$\frac{1}{2}[Na_2HPO_4 + 2\,H_2O]$	8.900
Sodium phosphate (trisodium phosphate) dodecahydrate	380.12	$\frac{1}{3}[Na_3PO_4 + 12\,H_2O]$	12.671
Sodium sulfide	78.04	$\frac{1}{2}Na_2S$	3.902
Sodium tetraborate	201.22	$\frac{1}{2}Na_2B_4O_7$	10.061
Sodium tetraborate decahydrate (borax)	381.37	$\frac{1}{2}[Na_2B_4O_7 + 10\,H_2O]$	19.069
Succinic acid	118.09	$\frac{1}{2}C_4H_6O_4$	5.905
Sulfuric acid	98.07	$\frac{1}{2}H_2SO_4$	4.904
Sulfur trioxide	80.06	$\frac{1}{2}SO_3$	4.003
Tartaric acid	150.09	$\frac{1}{2}C_4H_6O_6$	7.505
Zinc sulfate heptahydrate	287.54	$\frac{1}{2}[ZnSO_4 + 7\,H_2O]$	14.377

Definition of the pH value

Ionic activity[1,2]

The relationship between activity and concentration is given by

$$a = \gamma m \quad (1)$$

where a is the ionic activity, γ is the activity coefficient and m is the solute concentration in molality (moles of solute per kilogram of solvent). The activity coefficient reflects interactions among solute species which result in deviations from ideality, i.e. the equality of activity and concentration. As the solute concentration approaches 0, the activity coefficient becomes 1.

Experimentally, it is only possible to obtain mean activity coefficients for combinations of ions. Since single ion activity coefficients cannot be measured or defined uniquely, it has proved advantageous to express certain thermodynamic properties, such as pH, in terms of 'conventional' single ion activity coefficients. The pH convention set forth by BATES and GUGGENHEIM[3] for the chloride ion activity coefficient only applies to dilute (not greater than 0.1 mol kg^{-1}) aqueous solutions where mean activity coefficients generally display considerable uniformity. The use of this convention in the assignment of pH values is described below.

Dissociation constant of water[2]

The relationship between the activities of hydrogen and hydroxy ions in an aqueous solution is given by the equilibrium between these ions and water molecules:

$$H_2O \rightleftharpoons H^+ + OH^-$$

If solutes are present in such low concentrations that the activity of water can be considered 1, the equilibrium constant can be written as follows:

$$K_w = a_H a_{OH} = m_H \gamma_H m_{OH} \gamma_{OH} \quad (2)$$

where K_w is the dissociation (or ion product) constant of water, a_i is the activity, m_i the molality and γ_i the activity coefficient of the indicated ions. The charges of the ions appearing in subscripts are omitted in the interest of simplified notation when no confusion is likely to result. Since the dissociation of pure water is extremely small, the ionic activity coefficients in equation (2) can therefore be considered 1. As a result, for a neutral aqueous solution where the value of K_w is 1.008×10^{-14} $mol^2\,kg^{-2}$ at 25 °C,

$$m_H = m_{OH} = \sqrt{K_w} \approx 1 \times 10^{-7} \text{ mol kg}^{-1} \quad (3)$$

Consequently, for dilute aqueous solutions at approximately 25 °C, the numerical values of the concentration and molality are almost identical and the neutral point ($c_H = c_{OH}$) occurs at a hydrogen ion concentration of 1×10^{-7} mol L^{-1}. If solutes are added to the solution which contribute hydrogen ions (dissociation of acids, hydrolysis of salts, etc.), it follows from equation (2) that the activity of the hydroxyl ions must be reduced. In the same way, additional hydroxyl ions will cause a decrease in the hydrogen ion activity. In the former case, the solution is said to be 'acid', i.e. $c_H > 1 \times 10^{-7}$ mol L^{-1}, and in the latter, 'alkaline'. Because the dissociation constant, K_w, is a function of temperature, the neutral point will vary accordingly, for example; at 0 °C: $c_H = 1 \times 10^{-7.5}$ mol L^{-1}, and at 60 °C: $c_H = 1 \times 10^{-6.5}$ mol L^{-1}.

Temperature-dependence of the dissociation constant of water (K_W)[2]

Temperature t	$K_W \times 10^{14}$	$-\log K_W$	Temperature t	$K_W \times 10^{14}$	$-\log K_W$
0 °C.......	0.1139	14.943	35 °C	2.089	13.680
5 °C.......	0.1846	14.734	40 °C	2.919	13.535
10 °C	0.2920	14.535	45 °C	4.018	13.396
15 °C	0.4505	14.346	50 °C	5.474	13.262
20 °C	0.6809	14.167	55 °C	7.297	13.137
25 °C	1.008	13.996	60 °C	9.614	13.017
30 °C	1.469	13.833			

Sørensen pH scale[2,4]

In 1909, the Danish chemist SØRENSEN described the unique influence of hydrogen ion concentration on biochemical reactions[4]. In this work, he compared the concepts of 'degree of acidity' with 'total acidity', and devised colorimetric and electrometric methods

*This chapter on 'pH Value, Scales, and Standards' (pages 54–57) has been compiled by R. A. DURST, United States Department of Commerce, National Bureau of Standards, Washington, D.C., USA.

Values of $RT\ln 10/F$* as a function of temperature

Temperature t	$RT\ln 10/F$ (V)	Temperature t	$RT\ln 10/F$ (V)
0 °C.............	0.054199	50 °C	0.064120
5 °C.............	0.055191	55 °C	0.065112
10 °C	0.056183	60 °C	0.066104
15 °C	0.057175	65 °C	0.067096
20 °C	0.058167	70 °C	0.068089
25 °C	0.059160	75 °C	0.069080
30 °C	0.060151	80 °C	0.070073
35 °C	0.061144	85 °C	0.071065
38 °C	0.061739	90 °C	0.072057
40 °C............	0.062136	95 °C............	0.073049
45 °C	0.063128	100 °C	0.074041

* ln 10 = 2.30259; R in J $mol^{-1}\,K^{-1}$ (= 8.31441); F in C mol^{-1} (= 96484.56); T in K ($t = T - 273.15$ K).

for the c_H determination including suitable buffers and indicators. He also proposed the exponential scheme for representing the hydrogen ion concentration

$$\text{pH} = 10^{-c_H} = -\log c_H \quad (4)$$

where p, the first letter of the word 'power', was called the hydrogen ion exponent but was later changed to pH. To measure the pH of a solution, SØRENSEN chose the cell

$$\text{Hg, Hg}_2\text{Cl}_2 \,|\, 0.1 \text{ mol L}^{-1} \text{ KCl} \,\vdots\vdots\, \text{sat. KCl} \,\vdots\vdots\, \text{solution } X \,|\, \text{H}_2; \text{Pt} \quad (5)$$

(sat. = saturated)

the electromotive force of which (E_X) is compared to that (E_S) of an identical cell containing, in place of solution X, a standard solution S having a known c_H, for example, an HCl solution of c_H = 1 mol L^{-1}. For this purpose, the hydrogen gas electrode could be replaced by any other electrode responsive to hydrogen ions, for example, the glass electrode. Similarly, other reference electrodes could be used in place of the calomel electrode. It is only necessary that comparison measurements be made under identical conditions. Accordingly, if the c_H = 1 mol L^{-1} Sørensen standard solution is used, the pH of solution X is given by

$$\text{pH}_X = \frac{(E_S - E_X)F}{RT\ln 10} \quad (6)$$

where F is the Faraday constant, R the molar gas constant and T the thermodynamic temperature in K.

Subsequently, it was recognized that the potential of electrometric cells used for hydrogen ion measurements actually reveal changes in activity rather than concentration and a new definition of pH was proposed[5]:

$$\text{pH} = -\log a_H \quad (7)$$

Conventional pH scale[1–3,6–8]

Thermodynamically, the activity of a single ionic species, such as the hydrogen ion, is an inexact quantity and a conventional pH scale must be adopted to provide reference pH values. The definition of pH is operational in terms of the method used to measure it and the reference solutions with assigned pH values. The operational cell is similar to that used by SØRENSEN

$$\text{Hg, Hg}_2\text{Cl}_2 \,|\, \text{KCl}(\geq 3.5 \text{ mol L}^{-1}) \,\vdots\vdots\, \text{solution S or } X \,|\, \text{H}_2; \text{Pt} \quad (8)$$

but instead of merely using a single standard solution, c_H = 1 mol L^{-1}, a series of pH_S reference solutions is available for calibration of the operational cell. The pH_X of a test solution is then obtained from:

$$\text{pH}_X = \text{pH}_S + \frac{(E_S - E_X)F}{RT\ln 10} \quad (9)$$

The interpretation of the pH values calculated by this equation obviously depends to a large extent on the significance of the number assigned to the standard solution. If imperfections in this method of comparison could be ignored, the pH value would derive its character exclusively from that of pH_S. A consideration of various possible standard pH scales reveals that none can be thermodynamically exact and consequently the conventional pH scale has been adopted internationally. The method of defining the conventional scale has been approached in 2 ways, both methods giving comparable pH values.

pH values for primary and secondary standard reference solutions

Temperature t	Primary reference standards						Secondary reference standards		
	Potassium hydrogen tartrate, saturated at 25 °C	Potassium dihydrogen citrate 0.1 mol kg^{-1}	Disodium hydrogen phosphate 0.025 mol kg^{-1} + potassium dihydrogen phosphate 0.025 mol kg^{-1}	Disodium hydrogen phosphate 0.03043 mol kg^{-1} + potassium dihydrogen phosphate 0.008695 mol kg^{-1}	Sodium tetraborate 0.1 mol kg^{-1}	Sodium hydrogen carbonate 0.025 mol kg^{-1} + sodium carbonate 0.025 mol kg^{-1}	Potassium tetroxalate 0.05 mol kg^{-1}	Tris(hydroxymethyl)aminomethane 0.01667 mol kg^{-1} + tris(hydroxymethyl)aminomethane hydrochloride 0.0500 mol kg^{-1}	Calcium hydroxide, saturated at 25 °C
	pH								
0 °C	–	3.863	6.982	7.534	9.460	10.321	1.666	8.471	13.423
5 °C	–	3.840	6.949	7.501	9.392	10.248	1.668	8.303	13.207
10 °C	–	3.820	6.921	7.472	9.331	10.181	1.670	8.142	13.003
15 °C	–	3.802	6.898	7.449	9.276	10.120	1.672	7.988	12.810
20 °C	–	3.788	6.878	7.430	9.227	10.064	1.675	7.840	12.627
25 °C	3.557	3.776	6.863	7.415	9.183	10.014	1.679	7.699	12.454
30 °C	3.552	3.766	6.851	7.403	9.143	9.968	1.683	7.563	12.289
35 °C	3.549	3.759	6.842	7.394	9.107	9.928	1.688	7.433	12.133
37 °C	3.548	3.756	6.839	7.392	9.093	9.912	1.690	7.382	12.073
40 °C	3.547	3.754	6.836	7.388	9.074	9.891	1.694	7.307	11.984
45 °C	3.547	3.750	6.832	7.385	9.044	9.859	1.700	7.186	11.841
50 °C	3.549	3.749	6.831	7.384	9.017	9.831	1.707	7.070	11.705
60 °C	3.560	–	6.835	–	8.968	–	1.723	–	11.449
70 °C	3.580	–	6.843	–	8.928	–	1.743	–	–
80 °C	3.610	–	6.857	–	8.891	–	1.766	–	–
90 °C	3.650	–	6.874	–	8.857	–	1.792	–	–
95 °C	3.674	–	6.884	–	8.841	–	1.806	–	–

The multiple primary standard pH scale developed in the USA[6] and adopted by the International Union of Pure and Applied Chemistry (IUPAC)[7] and most other countries with national pH scales[8] is based on pH values assigned to a series of 7 primary buffer solutions. The assignment of pH values is carried out by means of an electrochemical cell without liquid junction. The first step is the determination of the acidity function, $p(a_H \gamma_{Cl})$ for a series of buffer solutions containing small added concentrations of a soluble chloride salt. The electromotive force of cells of the type

$$\text{Ag, AgCl} \mid \text{buffer solution, Cl}^- \mid \text{H}_2\text{; Pt(Pd)} \qquad \textbf{(10)}$$

is measured for each solution under carefully controlled conditions. From the known values of the chloride ion concentration and the standard electromotive force, $E°$, the acidity function is readily obtained from the measured electromotive force, E, by the equation

$$p(a_H \gamma_{Cl}) = \frac{(E° - E)F}{RT \ln 10} + \log m_{Cl} \qquad \textbf{(11)}$$

The limiting value of this acidity function, $p(a_H \gamma_{Cl})°$, i.e. the limit approached as the molality of added NaCl approaches 0, can be obtained by extrapolation. The pa_H of the buffer solution is then computed from $p(a_H \gamma_{Cl})°$ by the introduction of a conventional single ionic activity coefficient for the chloride ion:

$$pa_H = p(a_H \gamma_{Cl}) + \log \gamma_{Cl} \qquad \textbf{(12)}$$

The quantity γ_{Cl} has no independent thermodynamic definition, and the Bates-Guggenheim convention[3] has been adopted for the evaluation of $\log \gamma_{Cl}$

$$\log \gamma_{Cl} = \frac{-A I^{1/2}}{1 + 1.5 I^{1/2}} \qquad \textbf{(13)}$$

where A is the Debye-Hückel slope and I is the ionic strength of the buffer. The primary standards have pH values in the range 3–10 and are chosen for their reproducibility, stability, buffer capacity and ease of preparation. For these standard buffer solutions

$$pH_S = pa_H \qquad \textbf{(14)}$$

An important property of a primary buffer solution is the absence of any significant residual liquid junction potential when used in the operational cell (**8**). Thus, the tris buffer, which exhibits an abnormal liquid junction potential with certain types of reference electrode junctions, and buffers such as potassium tetroxalate and calcium hydroxide which, because they are outside the intermediate pH region (3–11), show variable liquid junction potentials, are designated as secondary pH standards. These secondary standards are provided for special purposes, however, such as biological compatibility or calibration at pH extremes.

The single primary standard pH scale, introduced in Great Britain in 1950[7], is based on only one of the standards comprising the multiple primary standard pH scale, the 0.05 mol kg^{-1} potassium hydrogen phthalate buffer. Since the assignment of the pH values to this buffer is carried out in cell (**10**), the 2 pH scales are identical at the point defined by this buffer and show only small deviations at other pH values. To provide additional calibration points on the British pH scale, a series of secondary pH standards is assigned pH values by direct comparison to the primary pH standard using an operational cell with a well-defined liquid junction

$$\text{Pd; H}_2 \left| \begin{matrix}\text{Primary}\\ \text{standard}\end{matrix} \right\vdots\vdots\ \text{KCl} \geq 3.5\ \text{mol L}^{-1} \vdots\vdots \left. \begin{matrix}\text{Secondary}\\ \text{standard}\end{matrix} \right| \text{H}_2\text{; Pt} \qquad \textbf{(15)}$$

The basis for this difference in approach is the contention that only 1 point is required to define the pH scale, the other parameter

pH_{OS} values for operational standard reference solutions

Temperature t	Potassium tetraoxalate 0.1 mol kg^{-1}	Potassium tetraoxalate 0.05 mol kg^{-1}	Sodium hydrogen diglycolate 0.05 mol kg^{-1}	Potassium hydrogen tartrate, saturated	Acetic acid 0.1 mol dm^{-3} + sodium acetate 0.1 mol dm^{-3}	Acetic acid 0.01 mol dm^{-3} + sodium acetate 0.01 mol dm^{-3}	Piperazine phosphate 0.02 mol kg^{-1}	Disodium hydrogen phosphate 0.025 mol kg^{-1} + potassium dihydrogen phosphate 0.025 mol kg^{-1}	Disodium hydrogen phosphate 0.03043 mol kg^{-1} + potassium dihydrogen phosphate 0.008695 mol kg^{-1}	Disodium hydrogen phosphate 0.04 mol kg^{-1} + potassium dihydrogen phosphate 0.01 mol kg^{-1}	Tris hydrochloride 0.05 mol kg^{-1} + tris 0.01667 mol kg^{-1}	Sodium tetraborate 0.05 mol kg^{-1}	Sodium tetraborate 0.01 mol kg^{-1}	Sodium hydrogen carbonate 0.025 mol kg^{-1} + sodium carbonate 0.025 mol kg^{-1}	Calcium hydroxide, saturated at 20 °C
	pH_{OS}														
0 °C	–	–	–	–	4.664	4.729	–	6.961	7.506	–	8.399	9.475	9.451	10.273	13.360
5 °C	–	–	3.466	–	4.657	4.722	6.477	6.935	7.482	7.512	8.238	9.409	9.388	10.212	13.159
10 °C	–	1.638	3.470	–	4.652	4.717	6.419	6.912	7.460	7.488	8.083	9.347	9.329	10.154	12.965
15 °C	–	1.642	3.476	–	4.647	4.714	6.364	6.891	7.441	7.466	7.933	9.288	9.275	10.098	12.780
20 °C	1.475	1.644	3.484	–	4.645	4.712	6.310	6.873	7.423	7.445	7.788	9.233	9.225	10.045	12.602
25 °C	1.479	1.646	3.492	3.556	4.644	4.713	6.259	6.857	7.406	7.428	7.648	9.182	9.179	9.995	12.431
30 °C	1.483	1.648	3.502	3.549	4.643	4.715	6.209	6.843	7.390	7.414	7.513	9.134	9.138	9.948	12.267
37 °C	1.490	1.649	3.519	3.544	4.647	4.722	6.143	6.828	7.369	7.404	7.332	9.074	9.086	9.889	12.049
40 °C	1.493	1.650	3.527	3.542	4.650	4.726	6.116	6.823	–	–	7.257	9.051	9.066	9.866	11.959
50 °C	1.503	1.653	3.558	3.544	4.663	4.743	6.030	6.814	–	–	7.018	8.983	9.009	9.800	11.678
60 °C	1.513	1.660	3.595	3.553	4.684	4.768	5.952	6.817	–	–	6.794	8.932	8.965	9.753	11.423
70 °C	1.52	1.671	–	3.570	4.713	4.800	–	6.830	–	–	–	8.898	8.932	9.728	11.192
80 °C	1.53	1.689	–	3.596	4.75	4.839	–	6.85	–	–	–	8.88	8.91	9.725	10.984
90 °C	1.53	1.72	–	3.627	4.80	4.88	–	6.90	–	–	–	8.84	8.90	9.75	10.80
95 °C	1.53	1.73	–	3.649	4.83	4.91	–	6.92	–	–	–	8.89	8.89	9.77	10.71

pH values for the reference value standard (RVS) of 0.05 mol kg^{-1} potassium hydrogen phthalate at various temperatures

Temperature t	pH_{RVS}	Temperature t	pH_{RVS}
0 °C	4.000	50 °C	4.050
5 °C	3.998	55 °C	4.064
10 °C	3.997	60 °C	4.080
15 °C	3.998	65 °C	4.097
20 °C	4.001	70 °C	4.116
25 °C	4.005	75 °C	4.137
30 °C	4.011	80 °C	4.159
35 °C	4.018	85 °C	4.183
37 °C	4.022	90 °C	4.21
40 °C	4.027	95 °C	4.24
45 °C	4.038		

being the theoretical pH electrode response slope, RTF^{-1}. However, in order to apply the theoretical slope to the operational cell, in which a glass electrode replaces the ideal hydrogen gas electrode, one must calibrate the cell with 2 standard solutions, S_1 and S_2, which bracket the pH of the test solution X. By this procedure, it is assumed that the electromotive force of the cell varies linearly with pH within the range of the standards but that the pH electrode response slope is not necessarily equal to the theoretical RTF^{-1}. The pH of the test solution is then given by

$$pH_X = pH_{S_1} + \frac{E_{S_1} - E_X}{E_{S_1} - E_{S_2}} (pH_{S_2} - pH_{S_1}) \tag{16}$$

This operational definition of the measured pH has been endorsed by many national standardization organizations and recommended by the IUPAC.

IUPAC pH scale[9]

As a compromise measure to unify the 2 pH scales, IUPAC has recommended a 3-level pH scale which retains the advantages of both the previously endorsed multiple primary standard approach and that based on the definition by a single primary standard and associated operational standards.

Reference value pH standard

Potassium hydrogen phthalate has been more extensively studied[10,11] than any other pH buffer material and, on this basis,

pD_S values of NBS standards as a function of temperature[2]

Temperature t	Solutes in heavy water solution and their molalities		
	Potassium dideuterium citrate, 0.05 mol kg^{-1}	KD_2PO_4, 0.025 mol kg^{-1} Na_2DPO_4, 0.025 mol kg^{-1}	$NaDCO_3$, 0.025 mol kg^{-1} Na_2CO_3, 0.025 mol kg^{-1}
	pD_S		
5 °C	4.378	7.537	10.996
10 °C	4.352	7.504	10.924
15 °C	4.330	7.475	10.856
20 °C	4.310	7.450	10.794
25 °C	4.293	7.429	10.737
30 °C	4.279	7.411	10.684
35 °C	4.268	7.397	10.637
40 °C	4.259	7.386	10.595
45 °C	4.253	7.380	10.558
50 °C	4.250	7.377	10.527

Approximate pH values of reagent solutions at room temperature[2]

Aqueous solution	Concentration mol L^{-1}	pH
Ammonia	0.1	11.3
Ammonium chloride	0.1	4.6
Ammonium dihydrogen phosphate	0.1	4.0
Ammonium oxalate	0.1	6.4
Ammonium sulfate	0.1	5.5
Barbital sodium	0.1	9.4
Benzoic acid	saturated	2.8
Boric acid	0.1	5.3
Calcium hydroxide	saturated	12.4
Citric acid	0.1	2.1
Diammonium hydrogen phosphate	0.1	7.9
Disodium hydrogen phosphate	0.1	9.2
Hydrochloric acid	0.1	1.1
Oxalic acid	0.1	1.3
Potassium acetate	0.1	9.7
Potassium aluminum sulfate	0.1	4.2
Potassium bicarbonate	0.1	8.2
Potassium carbonate	0.1	11.5
Potassium dihydrogen phosphate	0.1	4.5
Salicylic acid	saturated	2.4
Sodium acetate	0.1	8.9
Sodium benzoate	0.1	8.0
Sodium bisulfate	0.1	1.4
Sodium carbonate	0.1	11.5
Sodium dihydrogen phosphate	0.1	4.5
Sodium hydrogen sulfate	0.1	8.3
Sodium hydroxide	0.1	12.9
Sodium tetraborate decahydrate	0.1	9.4
Succinic acid	0.1	2.7
Tartaric acid	0.1	2.0
Trichloroacetic acid	0.1	1.2

has been designated the reference value pH standard (RVS). The pH values are assigned to an 0.05 $mol\,kg^{-1}$ solution of this buffer using the cell (**10**) without liquid junction.

Primary pH standards

Substances which have the characteristics of high purity, solution stability, low residual liquid junction potential, pH value between 3 and 11, and which are available as a certified reference material are designated primary reference pH standards (PS). At the present time, there are 6 primary reference standards, not including the reference value pH standard. Their pH values are assigned using the same type of cell (**10**) used in certification of the reference value standard[6].

In addition, there are 3 secondary pH standards certified in the same way but which exhibit excessive residual liquid junction potentials and/or fall outside of the intermediate pH region (3–11). These secondary standards are not recognized in the new IUPAC pH scale.

Operational pH standards

The next level of standards, operational standards (OS), have pH values assigned by direct comparison to the reference value standard in a cell (**15**) with liquid junction which is formed in a 1 mm capillary tube:

$$Pd; H_2 \mid RVS \vdots\vdots KCl \geq 3.5\ mol\,kg^{-1} \vdots\vdots OS \mid H_2; Pt \qquad (\mathbf{17})$$

Consequently, the pH_{OS} incorporates a residual liquid junction potential error into the assigned values, but these errors are usually not significant in most practical pH measurements. At present, there are 15 solutions for which pH_{OS} values have been assigned. In contrast to the reference value and primary pH standards, which are usually certified and issued by national standards organizations and metrological laboratories, operational standards can be produced as needed by individual laboratories for specialized purposes.

References

[1] IUPAC: Manual of symbols and terminology for physicochemical quantities and units, *Pure appl. Chem.,* **51**, 1 (1979).
[2] BATES, R.G., *Determination of pH, Theory and Practice,* 2nd ed., Wiley, New York, 1973.
[3] BATES and GUGGENHEIM, *Pure appl. Chem.,* **1**, 163 (1960).
[4] SØRENSEN, S.P., *Biochem. Z.,* **21**, 131 (1909) and *C. R. Lab. Carlsberg,* **8**, 1 (1909).
[5] SØRENSEN and LINDERSTRØM-LANG, *C. R. Lab. Carlsberg,* **15**, No. 6 (1924).
[6] DURST, R.A., *Standardization of pH Measurements,* Standard reference materials, National Bureau of Standards special publication 260-53, U.S. Govt. Printing Office, Washington, D.C., 1975.
[7] British Standards Institution, *Specification for pH Scale,* BS 1647, London, 1961.
[8] DURST and CALI, *Pure appl. Chem.,* **50**, 1485 (1978).
[9] COVINGTON et al., Definition of pH scales, standard reference values, measurement of pH, and related terminology, IUPAC Recommendation (provisional), *Pure appl. Chem.,* **55**, 1467 (1983).
[10] HETZER et al., *J. Res. Nat. Bur. Stand.,* **81A**, 21 (1977).
[11] BÜTIKOFER and COVINGTON, *Analyt. chim. Acta,* **108**, 179 (1979).
[12] HARNED and OWEN, *The Physical Chemistry of Electrolyte Solutions,* 3rd ed., Reinhold, New York, 1958.

Buffer Solutions*

Buffer solutions (or buffers) are solutions whose pH value is to a large degree insensitive to the addition of other substances. It is important to realize, however, that the pH value of a buffer solution not only changes when acids or bases are added or on dilution but also when the temperature changes or neutral salts are added. In accurate work, therefore, it is important to check the pH value electrometrically after all the ingredients have been added. The extent to which the pH values of buffer solutions vary when acids or bases are added or the temperature changes is shown in the following tables. In general, dilution to half the concentration changes the pH value by only some hundredths of a unit (buffer No. 1 in the table is an exception in that the change amounts to a pH value of ca. 0.15); addition of neutral salt 0.1 mol L^{-1} may change the pH value by ca. 0.1.

In the table below the solutions are classified into general buffers (mostly in use for the last 75 years), universal buffers with a low buffering capacity but a wide pH range, and buffers for biological media with a moderate pH range but containing stable ingredients (phosphate and borate, for example, often undergo secondary reactions with biological media). An important property is often the transparency to ultraviolet light. Occasionally it is desirable to have a volatile buffer which can be readily removed[1] (examples are buffers Nos. 20 and 21) but the use of very volatile systems makes a close control of the pH essential. Most of the older pH data found in the literature relate to the SØRENSEN scale, and it should be noted that the values given in the following table of buffers are on the conventional pH scale.

*This chapter on 'Buffer Solutions' (pages 58–60) has been compiled by F. KOHLER, Institut für Thermo- und Fluiddynamik, Ruhr-Universität, Bochum, FRG.

Both stock and buffer solutions should be made up with distilled water free of CO_2. Only standard reagents should be used. If there is any doubt as to the purity or water content of solutions their amount of substance concentration must be checked by titration. The volumes x (in mL) of stock solutions required to make up a buffer solution of the desired pH value are given in the table on page 60.

References

[1] For a list of volatile buffers see MICHL, H., in HEFTMANN, E. (Ed.), *Chromatography,* 3rd. ed., van Nostrand Reinhold, New York, 1975, page 288, and PERRIN and DEMPSEY, *Buffers for pH and Metal Ion Control,* Chapman & Hall, London, 1974.
[2] CLARK and LUBS, *J. Bact.*, **2**, 1 (1917).
[3] SØRENSEN, S.P., *Biochem. Z.*, **21**, 131 (1909), and **22**, 352 (1909); *Ergebn. Physiol.*, **12**, 393 (1912); WALBUM, L.E., *Biochem. Z.*, **107**, 219 (1920).
[4] MICHAELIS, L., *J. biol. Chem.*, **87**, 33 (1930).
[5] MCILVAINE, T. C., *J. biol. Chem.*, **49**, 183 (1921).
[6] TEORELL and STENHAGEN, *Biochem. Z.*, **299**, 416 (1938).
[7] BRITTON and WELFORD, *J. chem. Soc.*, **1**, 1848 (1937).
[8] WALPOLE, G.S., *J. chem. Soc.*, **105**, 2501 (1914).
[9] GOMORI, G., in COLOWICK and KAPLAN (Eds.), *Methods in Enzymology*, volume 1, Academic Press, New York, 1955, page 138.
[10] GREEN, A.A., *J. Amer. chem. Soc.*, **55**, 2331 (1933).
[11] STAFFORD et al., *Biochim. biophys. Acta*, **18**, 318 (1955); KREBS, H.A., unpublished, 1957.
[12] SMITH and SMITH, *Biol. Bull.*, **96**, 233 (1949).
[13] SEMENZA et al., *Helv. chim. Acta*, **45**, 2306 (1962).
[14] GOMORI, G., *Proc. Soc. exp. Biol. (N. Y.)*, **68**, 354 (1948).
[15] MERTZ and OWEN, *Proc. Soc. exp. Biol. (N. Y.)*, **43**, 204 (1940).
[16] BEISENHERZ et al., *Z. Naturforsch.*, **8b**, 555 (1953).
[17] LEONIS, J., *C. R. Lab. Carlsberg, Sér. chim.*, **26**, 357 (1948).
[18] DELORY and KING, *Biochem. J.*, **39**, 245 (1945).

No.	Name	Range of pH value	Temperature	Δ pH/K
	General buffers			
1	KCl/HCl (CLARK and LUBS)[2]	1.0–2.2	Room	0
2	Glycine/HCl (SØRENSEN)[3]	1.2–3.4	Room	0
3	Na citrate/HCl (SØRENSEN)[3]	1.2–5.0	Room	0
4	K biphthalate/HCl (CLARK and LUBS)[2]	2.4–4.0	20 °C	+0.001
5	K biphthalate/NaOH (CLARK and LUBS)[2]	4.2–6.2	20 °C	
6	Na citrate/NaOH (SØRENSEN)[3]	5.2–6.6	20 °C	+0.004
7	Phosphate (SØRENSEN)[3]	5.0–8.0	20 °C	−0.003
8	Barbital-Na/HCl (MICHAELIS)[4]	7.0–9.0	18 °C	
9	Na borate/HCl (SØRENSEN)[3]	7.8–9.2	20 °C	−0.005
10	Glycine/NaOH (SØRENSEN)[3]	8.6–12.8	20 °C	−0.025
11	Na borate/NaOH (SØRENSEN)[3]	9.4–10.6	20 °C	−0.01
	Universal buffers			
12	Citric acid/phosphate (MCILVAINE)[5]	2.2–7.8	21 °C	
13	Citrate-phosphate-borate/HCl (TEORELL and STENHAGEN)[6]	2.0–12.0	20 °C	
14	BRITTON-ROBINSON[7]	2.6–11.8	25 °C	at low pH: 0 at high pH: −0.02
	Buffers for biological media			
15	Acetate (WALPOLE)[8–10]	3.8–5.6	25 °C	
16	Dimethylglutaric acid/NaOH[11]	3.2–7.6	21 °C	
17	Piperazine/HCl[12,13]	4.6–6.4 8.8–10.6	20 °C	
18	Tetraethylethylenediamine*[13]	5.0–6.8 8.2–10.0	20 °C	
19	Tris maleate[9,14]	5.2–8.6	23 °C	
20	Dimethylaminoethylamine*[13]	5.6–7.4 8.6–10.4	20 °C	
21	Imidazole/HCl[15]	6.2–7.8	25 °C	
22	Triethanolamine/HCl[16]	7.0–8.8	25 °C	
23	N-Dimethylaminoleucylglycine/NaOH[17]	7.0–8.8	23 °C	−0.015
24	Tris/HCl[9]	7.2–9.0	23 °C	−0.02
25	2-Amino-2-methylpropane-1,3-diol/HCl[9,14]	7.8–10.0	23 °C	
26	Carbonate (DELORY and KING)[9,18]	9.2–10.8	20 °C	

*Can be combined with tris buffer to give a cationic universal buffer (see SEMENZA et al.[13]).

When not otherwise specified, both stock and buffer solutions should be made up with distilled water free of CO_2. Only standard reagents should be used. If there is any doubt as to the purity or water content of solutions their amount of substance concentration must be checked by titration. The volumes x (in mL) of stock solutions required to make up a buffer solution of the desired pH value are given in the table on the next page.

No.	Stock solutions and their amount of substance concentrations, or mass and/or volume contents of the solutes		Composition of the buffer
	A	*B*	
1	KCl 0.2 mol L^{-1} (14.91 g L^{-1})	HCl 0.2 mol L^{-1}	25 mL *A* + *x* mL *B* made up to 100 mL
2	Glycine 0.1 mol L^{-1} + NaCl 0.1 mol L^{-1} (1 L solution contains 7.507 g glycine + 5.844 g NaCl)	HCl 0.1 mol L^{-1}	*x* mL *A* + (100 − *x*) mL *B*
3	Disodium citrate 0.1 mol L^{-1} (1 L solution contains 21.01 g citric acid monohydrate + 200 mL NaOH 1 mol L^{-1})	HCl 0.1 mol L^{-1}	*x* mL *A* + (100 − *x*) mL *B*
4	Potassium biphthalate 0.1 mol L^{-1} (20.42 g L^{-1})	HCl 0.1 mol L^{-1}	50 mL *A* + *x* mL *B* made up to 100 mL
5	As No. 4	NaOH 0.1 mol L^{-1}	50 mL *A* + *x* mL *B* made up to 100 mL
6	As No. 3	NaOH 0.1 mol L^{-1}	*x* mL *A* + (100 − *x*) mL *B*
7	Potassium dihydrogen phosphate 1/15 mol L^{-1} (9.073 g L^{-1})	Disodium phosphate 1/15 mol L^{-1} ($Na_2HPO_4 \cdot 2\,H_2O$, 11.87 g L^{-1})	*x* mL *A* + (100 − *x*) mL *B*
8	Barbital-Na 0.1 mol L^{-1} (20.62 g L^{-1})	HCl 0.1 L^{-1}	*x* mL *A* + (100 − *x*) mL *B*
9	Boric acid, half-neutralized, 0.2 mol L^{-1} (corresponds to 0.05 mol L^{-1} borax solution; 1 L solution contains 12.37 g boric acid + 100 mL NaOH 1 mol L^{-1})	HCl 0.1 mol L^{-1}	*x* mL *A* + (100 − *x*) mL *B*
10	As No. 2	NaOH 0.1 mol L^{-1}	*x* mL *A* + (100 − *x*) mL *B*
11	As No. 9	NaOH 0.1 mol L^{-1}	*x* mL *A* + (100 − *x*) mL *B*
12	Citric acid 0.1 mol L^{-1} (citric acid monohydrate 21.01 g L^{-1})	Disodium phosphate 0.2 mol L^{-1} ($Na_2HPO_4 \cdot 2\,H_2O$, 35.60 g L^{-1})	*x* mL *A* + (100 − *x*) mL *B*
13	To 100 mL citric acid and 100 mL phosphoric acid solution, each equivalent to 100 mL NaOH 1 mol L^{-1}, add 3.54 g boric acid and 343 mL NaOH 1 mol L^{-1} and make up to 1 L of solution	HCl 0.1 L^{-1}	20 mL *A* + *x* mL *B* made up to 100 L
14	Citric acid, potassium hydrogen phosphate, barbital and boric acid, all 0.02857 mol L^{-1} (1 L solution contains 6.004 g citric acid monohydrate, 3.888 g potassium hydrogen phosphate, 5.263 g barbital, 1.767 g boric acid)	NaOH 0.2 mol L^{-1}	100 mL *A* + *x* mL *B*
15	Sodium acetate 0.1 mol L^{-1} (1 L solution contains 8.204 g $C_2H_3O_2Na$ or 13.61 g $C_2H_3O_2Na \cdot 3\,H_2O$)	Acetic acid 0.1 mol L^{-1} (6.005 g L^{-1})	*x* mL *A* + (100 − *x*) mL *B*
16a	Dimethylglutaric acid 0.1 mol L^{-1} (16.02 g L^{-1})	NaOH 0.2 mol L^{-1}	(a) 100 mL *A* + *x* mL *B* made up to 1000 mL
16b	Dimethylglutaric acid 0.1 mol L^{-1} (16.02 g L^{-1})	NaOH 0.2 mol L^{-1}	(b) 100 mL *A* + *x* mL *B* + 5.844 g NaCl made up to 1000 mL NaCl − 0.1 mol L^{-1}
17	Piperazine 1 mol L^{-1} (86.14 g L^{-1})	HCl 0.1 mol L^{-1}	5 mL *A* + *x* mL *B* made up to 100 mL
18	Tetraethylethylenediamine 1 mol L^{-1} (172.32 g L^{-1})	HCl 0.1 mol L^{-1}	5 mL *A* + *x* mL *B* made up to 100 mL
19	Tris acid maleate 0.2 mol L^{-1} [1 L solution contains 24.23 g tris(hydroxymethyl)aminomethane + 23.21 g maleic acid or 19.61 g maleic anhydride]	NaOH 0.2 mol L^{-1}	25 mL *A* + *x* mL *B* made up to 100 mL
20	Dimethylaminoethylamine 1 mol L^{-1} (88 g L^{-1})	HCl 0.1 mol L^{-1}	5 mL *A* + *x* mL *B* made up to 100 mL
21	Imidazole 0.2 mol L^{-1} (13.62 g L^{-1})	HCl 0.1 mol L^{-1}	25 mL *A* + *x* mL *B* made up to 100 mL
22	Triethanolamine 0.5 mol L^{-1} + ethylenediaminetetraacetic acid disodium salt (1 L solution contains 74.60 g $C_6H_{15}O_3N$ + 20 g $C_{10}H_{14}O_8N_2 \cdot Na_2 \cdot 2\,H_2O$)	HCl 0.05 mol L^{-1}	10 mL *A* + *x* mL *B* made up to 100 mL
23	N-Dimethylaminoleucylglycine 0.1 mol L^{-1} + NaCl 0.2 mol L^{-1} (1 L solution contains 24.33 g $C_{10}H_{20}O_3N_2 \cdot ½\,H_2O$ + 11.69 g NaCl)	NaOH 1 mol L^{-1} 100 mL made up to 1 L with solution *A*	*x* mL *A* + (100 − *x*) mL *B*
24	Tris 0.2 mol L^{-1} [tris(hydroxymethyl)aminomethane 24.23 g L^{-1}]	HCl 0.1 mol L^{-1}	25 mL *A* + *x* mL *B* made up to 100 mL
25	2-Amino-2-methylpropane-1,3-diol 0.1 mol L^{-1} (10.51 g L^{-1})	HCl 0.1 mol L^{-1}	50 mL *A* + *x* mL *B* made up to 100 mL
26	Sodium carbonate anhydrous 0.1 mol L^{-1} (10.60 g L^{-1})	Sodium bicarbonate 0.1 mol L^{-1} (8.401 g L^{-1})	*x* mL *A* + (100 − *x*) mL *B*

Buffer Solutions

The table gives the volumes x (in mL) of the stock solutions listed on page 59 required to make up a buffer solution of the desired pH value

pH	1	2	3	4	5	6	7	8	9	10	11	12	13	14	15	16a	16b	17	18	19	20	21	22	23	24	25	26	pH
1.0	54.2	...	...	...	...	...	...	...	...	...	...	...	...	...	...	...	...	...	...	...	...	...	...	...	...	...	...	1.0
1.2	36.0	11.1	9.0	...	...	...	...	...	...	...	...	...	...	...	...	...	...	...	...	...	...	...	...	...	...	...	...	1.2
1.4	23.2	26.4	17.9	...	...	...	...	...	...	...	...	...	...	...	...	...	...	...	...	...	...	...	...	...	...	...	...	1.4
1.6	14.7	36.2	23.6	...	...	...	...	...	...	...	...	...	...	...	...	...	...	...	...	...	...	...	...	...	...	...	...	1.6
1.8	9.3	43.9	27.6	...	...	...	...	...	...	...	...	...	...	...	...	...	...	...	...	...	...	...	...	...	...	...	...	1.8
2.0	5.9	50.7	30.2	...	...	...	...	...	...	...	...	...	74.4	...	...	...	...	...	...	...	...	...	...	...	...	...	...	2.0
2.2	3.8	56.5	32.2	...	...	...	...	...	...	...	...	98.8	68.8	...	...	...	...	...	...	...	...	...	...	...	...	...	...	2.2
2.4	...	62.3	34.1	41.0	...	...	...	...	...	...	...	94.5	64.6	...	...	...	...	...	...	...	...	...	...	...	...	...	...	2.4
2.6	...	68.4	36.0	34.3	...	...	...	...	...	...	...	90.0	61.3	1.6	...	...	...	...	...	...	...	...	...	...	...	...	...	2.6
2.8	...	74.7	37.9	27.8	...	...	...	...	...	...	...	85.1	58.9	3.6	...	...	...	...	...	...	...	...	...	...	...	...	...	2.8
3.0	...	81.0	39.9	21.6	...	...	...	...	...	...	...	80.3	56.9	5.7	...	...	...	...	...	...	...	...	...	...	...	...	...	3.0
3.2	...	86.2	42.1	15.9	...	...	...	...	...	...	...	76.0	55.2	7.8	...	7.0	14.4	...	...	...	...	...	...	...	...	...	...	3.2
3.4	...	90.3	44.8	10.9	...	...	...	...	...	...	...	72.0	53.9	9.9	...	13.3	20.9	...	...	...	...	...	...	...	...	...	...	3.4
3.6	...	...	47.8	6.7	...	...	...	...	...	...	...	68.4	52.9	11.7	...	20.7	26.8	...	...	...	...	...	...	...	...	...	...	3.6
3.8	...	...	51.2	3.3	...	...	...	...	...	...	...	65.1	51.8	13.5	10.9	26.3	32.4	...	...	...	...	...	...	...	...	...	...	3.8
4.0	...	...	55.1	0.0	...	...	...	...	...	...	...	62.0	50.7	15.3	16.6	32.4	36.6	...	...	...	...	...	...	...	...	...	...	4.0
4.2	...	...	60.0	...	3.0	...	...	...	...	...	...	59.1	49.7	17.5	23.9	36.2	40.3	...	...	...	...	...	...	...	...	...	...	4.2
4.4	...	...	66.4	...	6.7	...	...	...	...	...	...	56.4	48.6	19.7	33.5	39.3	43.1	...	...	...	...	...	...	...	...	...	...	4.4
4.6	...	...	74.9	...	11.1	...	...	...	...	...	...	53.7	47.5	21.9	44.9	41.3	45.7	94.3	...	...	...	...	...	...	...	...	...	4.6
4.8	...	...	85.6	...	16.5	...	...	...	...	...	...	51.2	46.4	24.1	56.6	43.5	48.3	91.5	...	...	...	...	...	...	...	...	...	4.8
5.0	...	...	100.0	...	22.6	...	99.2	...	...	...	...	49.0	45.4	26.3	67.8	45.7	51.5	87.8	94.3	...	...	...	...	...	...	...	...	5.0
5.2	...	...	...	...	28.8	87.1	98.4	...	...	...	...	46.9	44.3	28.6	76.8	48.4	53.6	83.6	91.5	3.2	...	...	...	...	...	...	...	5.2
5.4	...	...	...	...	34.4	78.0	97.3	...	...	...	...	44.7	43.2	31.0	84.0	51.3	58.2	77.6	87.8	5.0	...	...	...	...	...	...	...	5.4
5.6	...	...	...	...	39.1	70.3	95.5	...	...	...	...	42.4	42.0	33.4	89.3	55.0	63.6	71.8	83.1	7.3	94.3	...	...	...	...	...	...	5.6
5.8	...	...	...	...	42.4	64.5	92.8	...	...	...	...	40.0	40.8	35.8	...	58.8	68.7	66.5	77.6	9.7	91.7	...	...	...	...	...	...	5.8
6.0	...	...	...	...	45.0	60.3	88.9	...	...	...	...	37.4	39.7	38.3	...	63.9	73.6	61.8	71.7	12.4	88.0	...	...	...	...	...	...	6.0
6.2	...	...	...	...	46.7	57.2	83.0	...	...	...	...	34.5	38.4	40.8	...	69.5	78.5	58.2	66.4	15.2	83.3	43.4	...	...	...	...	...	6.2
6.4	...	...	...	...	...	54.8	75.4	...	...	...	...	31.4	37.0	43.3	...	74.1	83.3	55.5	61.7	17.9	77.9	40.4	...	...	...	...	...	6.4
6.6	...	...	...	...	...	53.2	65.3	...	...	...	...	27.9	35.6	45.8	...	83.5	87.4	...	58.0	20.8	72.0	36.5	...	...	...	...	...	6.6
6.8	...	...	...	...	...	...	53.4	...	...	...	...	23.5	34.2	48.3	...	87.4	91.0	...	55.3	22.2	66.6	31.4	...	...	...	...	...	6.8
7.0	...	...	...	...	...	...	41.3	53.3	...	...	...	19.0	32.9	50.9	...	90.0	93.2	...	...	23.7	61.9	25.4	86.2	86.4	...	...	...	7.0
7.2	...	...	...	...	...	...	29.6	55.0	...	...	...	13.8	31.7	53.4	...	91.8	94.9	...	...	25.2	58.1	19.6	79.6	80.6	44.7	...	...	7.2
7.4	...	...	...	...	...	...	19.7	57.6	...	...	...	9.8	30.6	55.8	...	93.0	95.8	...	...	26.7	55.3	14.6	71.3	72.8	42.0	...	...	7.4
7.6	...	...	...	...	...	...	12.8	60.8	...	...	...	6.8	29.6	58.2	...	93.8	96.8	...	...	28.6	...	10.2	62.0	63.2	39.3	...	...	7.6
7.8	...	...	...	...	...	...	7.4	65.2	53.0	...	...	4.6	28.8	60.5	...	...	...	...	...	31.2	...	6.6	52.0	52.1	33.7	43.9	...	7.8
8.0	...	...	...	...	...	...	3.7	70.6	55.4	...	...	...	28.1	62.8	...	...	...	...	...	33.9	...	...	42.0	41.1	27.9	41.6	...	8.0
8.2	...	...	...	...	...	...	...	75.9	58.0	...	...	...	27.6	65.0	...	...	...	...	46.4	36.9	...	...	31.9	31.4	22.9	38.4	...	8.2
8.4	...	...	...	...	...	...	...	81.2	62.1	...	...	...	27.0	67.2	...	...	...	...	43.9	39.9	...	...	22.5	23.0	17.3	34.8	...	8.4
8.6	...	...	...	...	...	...	...	86.2	66.9	94.7	...	...	26.3	69.3	...	...	...	...	40.9	42.7	45.4	...	16.0	15.9	13.0	30.7	...	8.6
8.8	...	...	...	...	...	...	...	90.1	73.6	92.0	...	...	25.2	71.3	...	...	...	45.5	36.8	...	42.8	...	11.7	10.3	8.8	23.3	...	8.8
9.0	...	...	...	...	...	...	...	93.2	83.5	88.4	...	...	24.0	73.2	...	...	...	43.2	31.8	...	39.2	...	...	...	5.3	17.7	...	9.0
9.2	...	...	...	...	...	...	...	...	95.6	84.0	...	...	22.6	75.1	...	...	...	40.0	26.2	...	34.7	...	...	...	...	13.3	10.0	9.2
9.4	...	...	...	...	...	...	...	...	...	78.9	87.0	...	21.4	77.0	...	...	...	35.8	20.4	...	29.3	...	...	...	...	9.2	18.4	9.4
9.6	...	...	...	...	...	...	...	...	...	73.2	75.5	...	20.2	78.8	...	...	...	30.8	15.2	...	23.6	...	...	...	...	5.2	29.3	9.6
9.8	...	...	...	...	...	...	...	...	...	67.2	65.1	...	19.0	80.4	...	...	...	25.0	10.8	...	19.0	...	...	...	...	4.1	42.0	9.8
10.0	...	...	...	...	...	...	...	...	...	62.5	59.6	...	18.1	81.8	...	...	...	19.4	7.4	...	13.1	...	...	...	...	2.3	53.4	10.0
10.2	...	...	...	...	...	...	...	...	...	58.8	56.4	...	17.1	83.1	...	...	...	14.3	...	...	9.2	...	...	...	...	...	63.7	10.2
10.4	...	...	...	...	...	...	...	...	...	55.7	54.1	...	16.5	84.3	...	...	...	10.0	...	...	6.2	...	...	...	...	...	73.1	10.4
10.6	...	...	...	...	...	...	...	...	...	53.6	52.3	...	16.0	85.4	...	...	...	6.9	...	...	...	...	...	...	...	...	81.2	10.6
10.8	...	...	...	...	...	...	...	...	...	52.2	...	...	15.5	86.5	...	...	...	...	...	...	...	...	...	...	...	...	87.9	10.8
11.0	...	...	...	...	...	...	...	...	...	51.2	...	...	14.7	87.8	...	...	...	...	...	...	...	...	...	...	...	...	...	11.0
11.2	...	...	...	...	...	...	...	...	...	50.4	...	...	13.5	89.3	...	...	...	...	...	...	...	...	...	...	...	...	...	11.2
11.4	...	...	...	...	...	...	...	...	...	49.5	...	...	11.7	91.3	...	...	...	...	...	...	...	...	...	...	...	...	...	11.4
11.6	...	...	...	...	...	...	...	...	...	48.7	...	...	9.1	94.5	...	...	...	...	...	...	...	...	...	...	...	...	...	11.6
11.8	...	...	...	...	...	...	...	...	...	47.6	...	...	5.5	99.0	...	...	...	...	...	...	...	...	...	...	...	...	...	11.8
12.0	...	...	...	...	...	...	...	...	...	46.0	...	...	1.3	...	...	...	...	...	...	...	...	...	...	...	...	...	...	12.0
12.2	...	...	...	...	...	...	...	...	...	43.2	...	...	...	...	...	...	...	...	...	...	...	...	...	...	...	...	...	12.2
12.4	...	...	...	...	...	...	...	...	...	39.1	...	...	...	...	...	...	...	...	...	...	...	...	...	...	...	...	...	12.4
12.6	...	...	...	...	...	...	...	...	...	31.8	...	...	...	...	...	...	...	...	...	...	...	...	...	...	...	...	...	12.6
12.8	...	...	...	...	...	...	...	...	...	21.4	...	...	...	...	...	...	...	...	...	...	...	...	...	...	...	...	...	12.8

Indicators are usually made up as solutions in water at a concentration of 1 $g L^{-1}$ with the addition of ethanol. For titrations to an end-point of definite pH it is advantageous to use mixed indicators as described in the literature[1].

References

[1] KOLTHOFF and MENZEL, *Die Maßanalyse,* part 2, 2nd ed., Springer, Berlin, 1931, page 64; REMY, H., *Lehrbuch der anorganischen Chemie,* vol. 1, 13th ed., Akademische Verlagsgesellschaft Geest & Portig, Leipzig, 1970, p. 1001.

Indicator	Acid side	Range of pH value	Alkaline side	Indicator	Acid side	Range of pH value	Alkaline side
Cresol red, 1st range	red	0.2–1.8	yellow	Chlorophenol red	yellow	5.0–6.9	purple
m-Cresol purple, 1st range	red	1.2–2.8	yellow	Bromothymol blue	yellow	6.0–7.6	blue
Thymol blue, 1st range	red	1.2–2.8	yellow	*m*-Nitrophenol	colorless	6.6–8.6	yellow
Metanil yellow	red	1.2–2.3	yellow	Neutral red	red	6.8–8.0	yellow
Tropeolin 00 (orange IV)	red	1.4–3.2	yellow	Phenol red	yellow	6.8–8.4	red
2,6-Dinitrophenol	colorless	1.7–4.4	yellow	Rosolic acid	brown	6.9–8.0	red
Benzyl orange	red	1.9–3.3	yellow	Cresol red, 2nd range	yellow	7.2–8.8	purple
2,4-Dinitrophenol	colorless	2.0–4.7	yellow	α-Naphtholphthalein	brown	7.3–8.7	green
p-Dimethylaminoazobenzene	red	2.9–4.0	yellow	Orange I (tropeolin 000 No. 1)	yellow	7.6–8.9	rose
Bromophenol blue	yellow	3.0–4.6	violet	*m*-Cresol purple, 2nd range	yellow	7.6–9.2	purple
Congo red	blue	3.0–5.0	red	Thymol blue, 2nd range	yellow	8.0–9.6	blue
Bromochlorophenol blue	yellow	3.0–4.6	purple	*o*-Cresolphthalein	colorless	8.2–9.8	red
Methyl orange	red	3.1–4.4	yellow	Phenolphthalein	colorless	8.3–10.0	red
Bromocresol green	yellow	3.8–5.4	blue	Thymolphthalein	colorless	9.3–10.5	blue
2,5-Dinitrophenol	colorless	4.0–5.8	yellow	β-Naphthol violet	yellow	10.0–12.0	violet
Methyl red	red	4.2–6.3	yellow	Alizarin yellow R	yellow	10.0–12.1	brown
Azolitmin (litmus)	red	4.4–6.6	blue	Alizarin yellow GG	yellow	10.0–12.0	orange
Propyl red	red	4.6–6.6	yellow	Nitramine	colorless	10.8–13.0	brown
p-Nitrophenol	colorless	4.7–7.9	yellow	POIRRIER blue	blue	11.0–13.0	red
Bromocresol purple	yellow	4.8–6.8	purple	Tropeolin 0 (resorcin yellow)	yellow	11.1–12.7	orange
Bromophenol red	yellow	4.8–6.8	purple				

Conversion factors for compounds

To convert		Factor	To convert		Factor
g Acetone	into g acetoacetic acid	1.758	g Acetoacetic acid	into g acetone	0.5689
g Acetone	into g 3-hydroxybutyric acid	1.793	g 3-Hydroxybutyric acid	into g acetone	0.5579
g Protein-N	into g protein	6.25	g Protein	into g protein-N	0.16
g Ammonia-N	into g ammonia	1.216	g Ammonia	into g ammonia-N	0.8225
g Creatine-N	into g creatine	3.121	g Creatine	into g creatine-N	0.3204
g Creatinine-N	into g creatinine	2.692	g Creatinine	into g creatinine-N	0.3715
g Urea-N	into g urea	2.144	g Urea	into g urea-N	0.4664
g Uric acid-N	into g uric acid	3.001	g Uric acid	into g uric acid-N	0.3333
g Lipid phosphorus	into g phospholipids	23.5			
g Lipid phosphorus	into g phosphatidylcholine	25	g Phosphatidylcholine	into g lipid phosphorus	0.040

Relative molecular masses $(M_i)_r$ of organic compounds

1 mol of a substance has a mass of $(M_i)_r \times$ g; 1 g of a substance has an amount of substance of $\frac{1}{(M_i)_r} \times$ mol or $\frac{1}{(M_i)_r} \times 10^3$ mmol

Substance	$(M_i)_r$	$\frac{1}{(M_i)_r} \times 10^3$	Substance	$(M_i)_r$	$\frac{1}{(M_i)_r} \times 10^3$
Acetaldehyde	44.05	22.701	Adenosine 3′,5′-phosphate	329.21	3.0376
Acetic acid	60.05	16.653	Adenosine triphosphate	507.18	1.9717
Acetoacetic acid	102.09	9.7953	S-Adenosylmethionine	399.44	2.5035
Acetoin	88.11	11.349	Adipic acid	146.14	6.8428
Acetone	58.08	17.218	Alanine	89.09	11.225
Acetonitrile	41.05	24.361	Allantoin	158.12	6.3243
Acetylcholine	163.22	6.1267	Aminoacetone	73.09	13.682
N-Acetylhistamine	153.18	6.5283	2(α)-Aminoadipic acid	161.16	6.2050
Acetylkynurenine	250.25	3.9960	*o*-Aminobenzoic acid	137.14	7.2918
N-Acetyllysine	188.23	5.3126	*p*-Aminobenzoic acid	137.14	7.2918
N-Acetylneuraminic acid	309.27	3.2334	2(α)-Aminobutyric acid	103.12	9.6974
cis-Aconitic acid	174.11	5.7435	*o*-Aminohippuric acid	194.19	5.1496
Adenine	135.13	7.4003	Aminoimidazolecarboxamide	126.12	7.9290
Adenosine	267.24	3.7420	3(β)-Aminoisobutyric acid	103.12	9.6974
Adenosine diphosphate	427.20	2.3408	5(δ)-Aminolevulinic acid	131.13	7.6260
Adenosine monophosphate	347.22	2.8800	[Ammonia	17.03	58.720]

Substance	$(M_i)_r$	$\frac{1}{(M_i)_r} \times 10^3$
Anserine	240.26	4.1622
Arabinose	150.13	6.6609
Arabitol	152.15	6.5725
Arginine	174.20	5.7405
Argininosuccinic acid	290.28	3.4449
Ascorbic acid	176.13	5.6776
Asparagine	132.12	7.5689
Aspartic acid	133.10	7.5131
Benzoic acid	122.12	8.1887
Bile acids	400*	2.50*
Bilirubin	584.67	1.7104
Biopterin	237.22	4.2155
Biotin	244.31	4.0932
2,3-Bisphosphoglyceric acid	266.04	3.7588
Bufotenine	204.27	4.8955
Butanone	72.11	13.868
2,3-Butylene glycol	90.12	11.096
Butyric acid	88.11	11.349
Cadaverine	102.18	9.7867
Caproic acid	116.16	8.6088
Carbamoylaspartic acid	176.13	5.6776
4(γ)-Carboxyglutamic acid	191.14	5.2318
Carnitine	161.20	6.2035
Carnosine	226.23	4.4203
β-Carotene	536.88	1.8626
Chenodeoxycholic acid	392.58	2.5473
Cholecalciferol	384.64	2.5998
Cholesterol	386.66	2.5863
Cholic acid	408.58	2.4475
Choline	121.18	8.2522
Citric acid	192.13	5.2048
Citrulline	175.19	5.7081
Coproporphyrin	654.72	1.5274
Corticosterone	346.47	2.8863
Cortisol	362.47	2.7588
Cortisone	360.45	2.7743
Creatine	131.13	7.6260
Creatinine	113.12	8.8402
p-Cresol	108.14	9.2473
Cyanocobalamin	1355.38	0.7378
Cystamine	152.27	6.5673
Cystathionine	222.26	4.4992
Cysteic acid	169.15	5.9119
Cysteine	121.15	8.2542
5-S-Cysteinyldopa	348.33	2.8708
Cystine	240.29	4.1616
Cytidine monophosphate	323.20	3.0941
Dehydroepiandrosterone	289.44	3.4549
Deoxycholic acid	392.58	2.5473
11-Deoxycorticosterone	330.47	3.0260
Deoxyuridine	228.21	4.3819
Diglycerides	621*	1.610*
Dihydroxyacetone phosphate	170.06	5.8803
Dihydroxybutyric acid	120.10	8.3264
erythro-2,3-Dihydroxybutyric acid	120.10	8.3264
1,25-Dihydroxycholecalciferol	416.64	2.4002
Dihydroxymandelic acid	184.15	5.4304
Dihydroxyphenylacetic acid	168.15	5.9471
3,4-Dihydroxyphenylalanine	197.19	5.0713
3,4-Dihydroxyphenylglycol	170.16	5.8768
3,4-Dihydroxyphenylpropionic acid	182.18	5.4891
3,4-Dimethoxyphenylethylamine	181.23	5.5179
Dimethylamine	45.08	22.183
N^2,N^2-Dimethylguanosine	311.30	3.2123
Dimethylsulfone	94.13	10.624
N,N-Dimethyltryptamine	188.27	5.3115
4,5-Dioxovaleric acid	130.10	7.6864
Dopa (3,4-dihydroxyphenylalanine)	197.19	5.0713
Dopamine	153.18	6.5283
Epinephrine	183.21	5.4582
Ergothioneine	229.30	4.3611
Erythritol	122.12	8.1887
Estradiol	272.39	3.6712
Estriol	288.39	3.4675
Ethanol	46.07	21.706
Ethanolamine	61.08	16.372
Ethylmalonic acid	132.12	7.5689
Fatty acids	282*	3.546*
Flavin adenine dinucleotide (FAD)	785.56	1.2730
Flavin mononucleotide (FMN)	456.35	2.1913
Formic acid	46.03	21.725
Formiminoglutamic acid	174.16	5.7418
Fructose	180.16	5.5506
Fructose 1,6-bisphosphate	340.12	2.9401
Fructose 6-phosphate	260.14	3.8441
Fucose	164.16	6.0916
Fumaric acid	116.07	8.6155
Furane-2,5-dicarboxylic acid	156.09	6.4066
Galactose	180.16	5.5506
Galactose 1-phosphate	260.14	3.8441
Glucaric acid (as lactone)	192.13	5.2048
Glucosamine	179.17	5.5813
Glucose	180.16	5.5506
Glucose 1,6-bisphosphate	340.12	2.9401
Glucose 6-phosphate	260.14	3.8441
Glucuronic acid	194.14	5.1509
Glutamic acid	147.13	6.7967
Glutamine	146.15	6.8423
4(γ)-Glutamylcysteine	250.27	3.9957
Glutaric acid	132.12	7.5689
Glutathione	307.32	3.2539
Glyceraldehyde 3-phosphate	170.06	5.8803
Glycerol	92.09	10.859
Glycine	75.07	13.321
Glycolic acid	76.05	13.149
Glyoxylic acid	74.04	13.506
Guanidine	59.07	16.929
Guanidinoacetic acid	117.11	8.5390
Guanidinobutyric acid	146.17	6.8413
Guanidinopropionic acid	132.14	7.5677
Guanidinosuccinic acid	175.14	5.7097
Guanine	151.13	6.6168
Guanosine	283.24	3.5306
Guanosine 3′,5′-phosphate	345.21	2.8968
Guanosine triphosphate	523.18	1.9114
Hippuric acid	179.18	5.5810
Histamine	111.15	8.9969
Histidine	155.16	6.4450
Homoarginine	188.23	5.3126
Homocarnosine	240.26	4.1622
Homocitrulline	189.21	5.2851
Homocystine	268.35	3.7265
3-Hydroxyanthranilic acid	153.14	6.5300
p-Hydroxybenzoic acid	138.12	7.2401
3-Hydroxybutyric acid	104.11	9.6052
25-Hydroxycholecalciferol	400.64	2.4960
o-Hydroxyhippuric acid	195.17	5.1237
Hydroxyindoleacetic acid	191.19	5.2304
3-Hydroxykynurenine	224.22	4.4599
Hydroxylysine	162.19	6.1656
4-Hydroxy-3-methoxybenzoic acid	168.15	5.9471
4-Hydroxy-3-methoxymandelic acid	198.18	5.0459

*Data are for this class of substance as it occurs in the blood.

Substance	$(M_i)_r$	$\frac{1}{(M_i)_r} \times 10^3$
4-Hydroxy-3-methoxyphenylacetic acid	182.18	5.4891
4-Hydroxy-3-methoxyphenylethanol	168.19	5.9457
4-Hydroxy-3-methoxyphenylglycol	184.19	5.4292
Hydroxyphenylacetic acid	152.15	6.5725
p-Hydroxyphenylethanolamine (octopamine)	153.18	6.5283
p-Hydroxyphenyllactic acid	182.18	5.4891
Hydroxyproline	131.13	7.6260
5-Hydroxytryptophan	220.23	4.5407
Hypoxanthine	136.11	7.3470
Imidazoleacetic acid	126.11	7.9296
Imidazolelactic acid	156.14	6.4045
3-Indoleacetic acid	175.19	5.7081
Indoleacryloylglycine	244.25	4.0942
3-Indolelactic acid	205.21	4.8731
3-Indoxylsulfuric acid	213.21	4.6902
Inosine triphosphate	508.17	1.9678
myo-Inositol	180.16	5.5506
Isobutyric acid	88.11	11.349
Isoleucine	131.17	7.6237
Isovaleric acid	102.13	9.7914
Isovalerylglycine	159.18	6.2822
Kynurenic acid	189.17	5.2863
Kynurenine	208.22	4.8026
Lactic acid	90.08	11.101
Lactose	342.30	2.9214
Lauric acid	200.32	4.9920
Leucine	131.17	7.6237
Linoleic acid	280.45	3.5657
Lipoic acid	206.32	4.8468
Lithocholic acid	376.58	2.6555
Lysine	146.19	6.8404
Malic acid	134.09	7.4577
Mannitol	182.17	5.4894
Mannoheptulose	210.18	4.7578
Mannose	180.16	5.5506
Melatonin	232.28	4.3051
Metanephrine	197.23	5.0702
Methionine	149.21	6.7020
5-Methoxytryptamine	190.24	5.2565
3-Methoxytyramine	167.21	5.9805
Methyladipic acid	160.17	6.2434
Methylamine	31.06	32.196
Methylglutaric acid	146.14	6.8428
Methylguanidine	73.10	13.680
Methylguanine	165.15	6.0551
Methylhistidine	169.18	5.9109
2-Methyl-3-hydroxybutyric acid	106.12	9.4233
7-Methyl-8-hydroxyguanine	181.15	5.5203
1-Methylhypoxanthine	150.14	6.6605
1-Methyl-4-imidazoleacetic acid	140.14	7.1357
Methylinosine	282.26	3.5428
Methylmalonic acid	118.09	8.4681
1-Methylnicotinamide	137.16	7.2908
Methylpimelic acid	174.20	5.7405
1-Methyl-2-pyridone-5-carboxamide	152.15	6.5725
Methylsuberic acid	188.22	5.3129
Methylsuccinic acid	132.12	7.5689
5-Methyltetrahydrofolic acid	459.46	2.1765
Mevalonic acid	148.16	6.7495
Monoglycerides	357*	2.801*
Myristic acid	228.37	4.3789
Nicotinamide adenine dinucleotide (NAD)	663.43	1.5073
Nicotinamide adenine dinucleotide phosphate (NADP)	743.41	1.3452
Nicotinic acid	123.11	8.1228
Norepinephrine	169.18	5.9109
Normetanephrine	183.21	5.4582
Octulose 1,8-bisphosphate	400.17	2.4989
Oleic acid	282.47	3.5402
Ornithine	132.16	7.5666
Orotic acid	156.10	6.4061
Oxalacetic acid	132.07	7.5717
Oxalic acid	90.04	11.106
2-Oxoglutaric acid	146.10	6.8446
2-Oxoisocaproic acid	130.14	7.6840
2-Oxoisovaleric acid	116.12	8.6118
2-Oxo-3-methylvaleric acid	130.14	7.6840
Palmitic acid	256.43	3.8999
Palmitoleic acid	254.41	3.9307
Pantothenic acid	219.24	4.5612
Phenol	94.11	10.626
Phenylacetic acid	136.15	7.3448
Phenylacetylglutamine	264.28	3.7839
Phenylalanine	165.19	6.0536
2-Phenylethylamine	121.18	8.2522
Phenylpropionic acid	150.18	6.6587
Phosphoenolpyruvic acid	168.04	5.9510
Phosphoethanolamine	141.06	7.0892
2-Phosphoglyceric acid	186.06	5.3746
Phospholipids	774*	1.292*
5-Phosphoribosyl 1-diphosphate	390.07	2.5636
Pipecolic acid	129.16	7.7423
Piperidine	85.15	11.744
Porphobilinogen	226.23	4.4203
Pregnanediol	320.51	3.1200
Pregnanetriol	336.51	2.9717
Progesterone	314.47	3.1800
Proline	115.13	8.6858
Propionic acid	74.08	13.499
Prostaglandin E_1	354.49	2.8210
Prostaglandin E_2	352.47	2.8371
Prostaglandin $F_{2\alpha}$	354.49	2.8210
Protoporphyrin	562.67	1.7772
Pteroylglutamic acid	441.40	2.2655
Putreanine	160.22	6.2414
Putrescine	88.15	11.344
Pyridoxal	167.16	5.9823
Pyridoxal phosphate	247.14	4.0463
Pyridoxamine	168.20	5.9453
Pyridoxic acid	183.16	5.4597
Pyridoxine	169.18	5.9109
Pyrocatechol	110.11	9.0818
Pyrrole-2-carboxylic acid	111.10	9.0009
Pyruvic acid	88.06	11.356
Quinolinic acid	167.12	5.9837
Raffinose	504.44	1.9824
Retinol	286.46	3.4909
Rhamnose	164.16	6.0916
Ribitol	152.15	6.5725
Riboflavin	376.37	2.6570
Ribose	150.13	6.6609
Ribose 5-phosphate	230.11	4.3457
5-Ribosyluracil	244.20	4.0950
Sarcosine	89.09	11.225
Sebacic acid	202.25	4.9444
Sedoheptulose 1,7-bisphosphate	370.14	2.7017
Serine	105.09	9.5157
Serotonin	176.22	5.6747
Sorbitol	182.17	5.4894
Spermidine	145.25	6.8847
Spermine	202.34	4.9422
Stearic acid	284.48	3.5152

*Data are for this class of substance as it occurs in the blood.

Substance	$(M_i)_r$	$\frac{1}{(M_i)_r} \times 10^3$	Substance	$(M_i)_r$	$\frac{1}{(M_i)_r} \times 10^3$
Suberic acid	174.20	5.7405	Tryptophan	204.23	4.8964
Succinic acid	118.09	8.4681	Tyramine	137.18	7.2897
6-Succinoaminopurine	251.20	3.9809	Tyrosine	181.19	5.5191
Sucrose	342.30	2.9214	Ubiquinone-10	863.36	1.1583
6-Sulfatoxyskatole	227.23	4.4008	Uracil	112.09	8.9214
Tartaric acid	150.09	6.6627	Urea	60.06	16.650
Taurine	125.14	7.9911	Uric acid	168.11	5.9485
Testosterone	288.43	3.4670	Uridine	244.21	4.0948
Thiamine	265.35	3.7686	Uridine diphosphate	404.16	2.4743
Threitol	122.12	8.1887	Urocanic acid	138.13	7.2396
Threonine	119.12	8.3949	Uroporphyrin	830.76	1.2037
Thyroxine	776.87	1.2872	Valine	117.15	8.5361
α-Tocopherol	430.71	2.3217	Xanthine	152.11	6.5742
Triglycerides	885*	1.130*	Xanthurenic acid	205.17	4.8740
erythro-2,3,4-Trihydroxybutyric acid	136.10	7.3475	Xylitol	152.15	6.5725
Triiodothyronine	650.98	1.5361	Xylose	150.13	6.6609
Tryptamine	160.22	6.2414	Xylulose	150.13	6.6609

*Data are for this class of substance as it occurs in the blood.

Conversion of amount of substance concentration into mass concentration and vice versa

When the basic quantity *amount of substance,* with the SI base unit mole (mol), was introduced, the General Conference on Weights and Measures deliberately refrained from an analogous redefinition of the equivalent (Eq or val) since the further use of this unit is now not recommended.

When concentration data are presented in clinical chemistry and hematology, volume (in liter or its decimal fractions) should be used as reference quantity for liquids and mass (in kilogram or its decimal fractions) as reference quantity for solids[1]; to be avoided are concentration data expressed for example in g%, ppm (parts per million) or ppb (parts per billion) since these units do not make it clear whether the reference quantity is mass or volume.

Conversion of amount of substance concentration into mass concentration

Amount of substance concentration $c_i = n_i/V$ (in mol L^{-1}) is converted into mass concentration $\varrho_i = \bar{m}_i/V$ (in g L^{-1}) by means of the following relationship:

$$\varrho_i = c_i \times M_i$$

Conversion of mass concentration into amount of substance concentration

Mass concentration $\varrho_i = \bar{m}_i/V$ (in g L^{-1}) is converted into amount of substance concentration $c_i = n_i/V$ (in mol L^{-1}) by means of the following relationship:

$$c_i = \frac{n_i}{\bar{m}_i} \times \varrho_i = \frac{\varrho_i}{M_i}$$

where n_i = amount of substance; $\bar{m}_i$ = mass; $M_i = (M_i)_r \times \text{g mol}^{-1}$ = molar mass [$(M_i)_r$ = relative molecular mass].

Reference

[1] *Z. klin. Chem.*, **11**, 93 (1973), and **12**, 180 (1974).

Blood volume* (for references see page 67)

The term blood volume (BV) - more precisely, total or whole blood volume - denotes the amount of blood that is present in the vascular system. In healthy individuals it is correlated with fat-free body mass[1,2]. The fraction of blood mass in relation to body mass is about 0.075 in a normally built, healthy man, and about 0.070 in a normally built, healthy woman[3]. As a rule, about 70% is found in the venous, 20% in the arterial, and about 5% in the capillary segment of the vascular system[4]. The blood volume is composed of a liquid component, the plasma volume (PV), and a cellular component more than 95% of which consists of erythrocytes and it is therefore usually equated with the erythrocyte volume (EV).

The plasma volume can be measured by the older dye dilution methods[5] or by the newer radioisotope dilution methods (page 215); the erythrocyte volume can be measured by labeling these cells with ^{51}Cr or ^{99}Tc^{m} (page 215). The most accurate total-blood-volume values are obtained by addition of the separately measured components[2,6,9]:

$$BV = PV + EV$$

*This section on 'Blood Volume' (pages 65–67) has been compiled in collaboration with H. Heimpel, Zentrum für innere Medizin, Universität Ulm, Ulm, FRG.

In clinical practice, a frequently used method is to measure the erythrocyte volume and then calculate the plasma volume and blood volume with the aid of the hematocrit:

$$PV = EV \times \frac{1 - \text{hematocrit}}{\text{hematocrit}}$$

$$BV = EV \times \frac{1}{\text{hematocrit}}$$

[Hematocrit: fraction of erythrocyte volume in relation to blood volume of a venous sample; normally about 0.44.]

This calculation of plasma volume from erythrocyte volume neglects the fact that the ratio of the cellular component to the plasma component in the entire vascular system is about 10% lower than that in the blood of the great veins[2,6–9]. Moreover, (using the micromethod) plasma trapping of the order of 2% occurs when the blood is centrifuged for 5 minutes at 10000 *g*[7]. An approximative correction can be made by means of appropriate correction factors:

Corrected total hematocrit = venous hematocrit × 0.91 × 0.98

Since blood-volume values are used almost exclusively as comparative values, these corrections are generally omitted in diagnostics and clinical research. In many diseases, for example in erythrocytosis, splenomegaly or cardiac failure, the distribution of

Table 1 *Blood, plasma and erythrocyte volumes in relation to different body dimensions in adult reference subjects (determination of erythrocyte volume with ^{51}Cr, the other values calculated via hematocrit without correction for body hematocrit or residual plasma)*

	201 men[15]			101 women[16]		
	Mean	Reference values*	Coefficient of variation	Mean	Reference values*	Coefficient of variation
	mL		%	mL		%
Blood volume	4490		12.6	3600		11.8
		$a \times 52.1 - 4700$	10.1		$a \times 35.73 - 2320$	10.2
		$b \times 41.0 + 1530$	8.9		$b \times 47.16 + 864$	8.9
		$a \times 28.5 + b \times 31.6 - 2820$	8.1		$a \times 16.52 + b \times 38.46 - 1369$	8.6
		$c \times 3140 - 1410$	8.1		$c \times 2885 - 1131$	8.6
Plasma volume	2460		13.2	2130		12.9
		$a \times 29.7 - 2770$	10.7		$a \times 21.09 - 1362$	11.4
		$b \times 19.6 + 1050$	10.7		$b \times 28.89 + 455$	10.0
		$a \times 19.9 + b \times 13.1 - 2000$	9.7		$a \times 9.03 + b \times 24.13 - 766$	9.8
		$c \times 1580 - 520$	9.8		$c \times 1747 - 733$	9.8
Erythrocyte volume	2030		14.2	1470		12.0
		$a \times 22.4 - 1930$	12.2		$a \times 14.64 - 957$	10.4
		$b \times 21.4 + 490$	9.7		$b \times 18.26 + 409$	9.5
		$a \times 8.6 + b \times 18.6 - 830$	9.4		$a \times 7.49 + b \times 14.32 - 603$	9.1
		$c \times 1550 - 890$	9.4		$c \times 1138 - 397$	9.1

*a: Body length in cm; b: body mass in kg; c: body surface in m^2 as determined by the formula of Du Bois and Du Bois.

Table 2 *Blood, plasma and erythrocyte volumes of reference subjects relative to body mass*

Subjects	Number	Methods	Blood volume		Plasma volume		Erythrocyte volume		Reference
			Mean	s	Mean	s	Mean	s	
			mL/kg						
Male and female infants born prematurely, 4 hours	36	RISA, Hkt$_v$ × 0.87	79.7	6.7	46.9	7.4	32.4	3.5	21
Male and female infants born at term, 4 hours	15	RISA, Hkt$_v$ × 0.87	73.9	5.8	40.3	3.6	32.4	2.6	21
Men	10	^{51}Cr*	71.4	–	41.1	5.6	30.3	5.6	22
Men	25	^{32}P, RISA	73.7	–	43.6	5.8	30.1	5.7	23
Men	22	^{51}Cr, RISA	71.0	6.3	43.5	4.6	27.5	3.4	24
Women	11	^{51}Cr, RISA	69.6	8.4	44.0	4.5	25.9	4.3	24
Men, at sea level	16	^{51}Cr, Hkt$_v$	[60.0]	–	[33.0]	–	27.1	3.7	20
Men, at 1600 m above sea level	19	^{51}Cr, Hkt$_v$	[58.7]	–	[31.9]	–	26.8	3.2	20
Men, at 3100 m above sea level	39	^{51}Cr, Hkt$_v$	[66.8]	–	[35.2]	–	31.8	6.7	20

RISA: ^{131}I-human serum albumin; Hkt$_v$: venous hematocrit.

*Separate labeling of plasma proteins with ^{51}CrCl$_2$ and of erythrocytes with Na$_2$^{51}CrO$_4$.

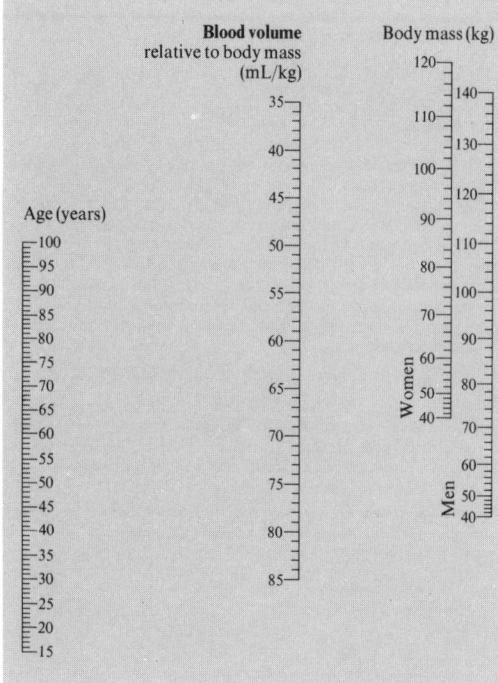

Fig. 1. Nomogram for obtaining blood volume from age and body mass of adults[17].

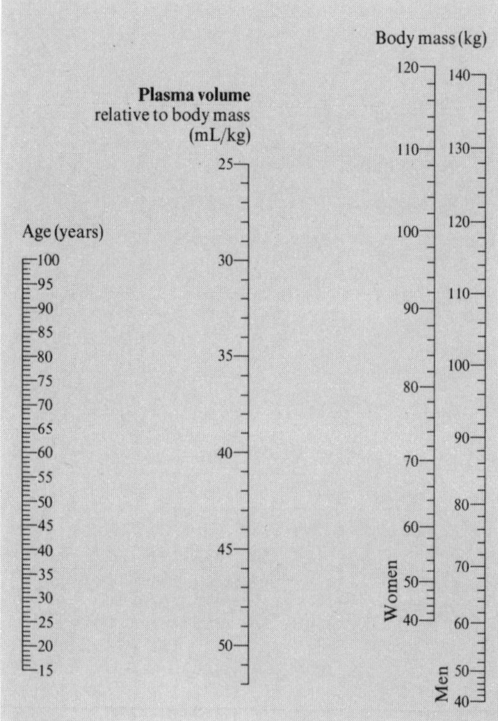

Fig. 2. Nomogram for obtaining plasma volume from age and body mass of adults[17].

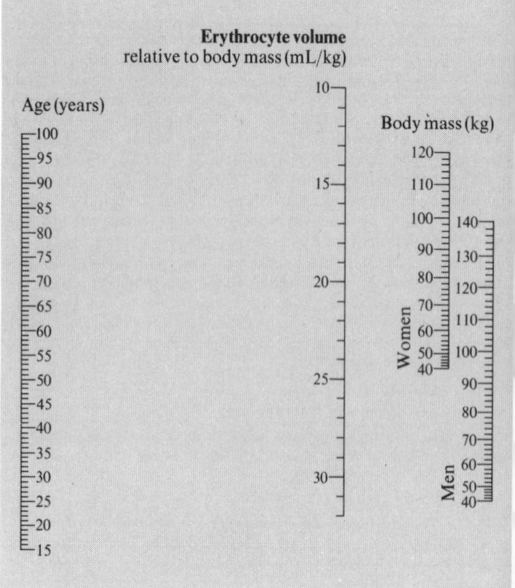

Fig. 3. Nomogram for obtaining erythrocyte volume from age and body mass of adults[17].

the cellular and plasma components in various vascular regions changes so drastically that calculation of the plasma volume from the erythrocyte volume and the hematocrit, and conversely, is not permissible. In such cases reliable blood-volume values can be obtained only by simultaneous measurement of both components[2, 10].

The decision whether to measure the erythrocyte volume or the plasma volume depends precisely on what information is being sought. Owing to the passage of plasma constituents into and out of the extravascular space the plasma volume is subject to a greater extent to short-term variations, which are partly dependent on the condition of the study. In standing and sitting positions it is lower than in the recumbent position, and it is higher at high than at low temperatures[2, 11, 12]. The influence of these factors varies with the size of the protein molecule to which the radioactive substance is bound.

Blood volume is correlated with body mass to a moderate degree only, even in healthy individuals of the same age, mainly because of physiological variations in the proportion of adipose tissue. The correlation with body surface is decidedly closer[13, 14]. The best estimates are derived from formulas or nomograms in which

Table 3 *Blood, plasma and erythrocyte volumes relative to body mass in newborn and infants[25] (determination of plasma volume with ^{131}I-human serum albumin, other values calculated via hematocrit with correction factor of 0.91 for body hematocrit)*

Age	Number	Blood volume		Plasma volume		Erythrocyte volume
		Mean	s	Mean	s	Mean
		mL/kg				
0–33 hours	8	80.9	4.7	43.8	4.7	37.1
2–4 days	10	84.6	8.2	46.8	6.1	37.8
8–30 days	5	84.0	6.7	51.8	5.6	32.2
1 month	5	78.8	6.9	53.0	4.5	25.8
2 months	5	80.0	7.6	54.8	5.7	25.2
3–4 months	7	77.4	8.6	54.8	8.0	22.6
5–6 months	5	75.6	8.3	52.2	6.3	23.4
7–9 months	6	81.0	10.2	56.3	5.7	24.7
10–12 months	6	83.8	11.3	58.3	8.4	25.5

body mass and body length are considered (Table 1 and Figs. 1 to 3)[13,15,16,27]. See Table 2 for additional reference data.

At the time of birth the erythrocyte volume relative to body mass is 10–20% greater[25] than in older children and adults if the umbilical cord is cut immediately, and 30–50% greater[21,25] if it is cut at a later time. During the first month after birth, the erythrocyte volume relative to body mass drops to values below those of adults, while the plasma volume is markedly increased (Table 3). Studies using radioisotope-dilution methods have scarcely ever been performed in older children[26].

The blood volume increases during pregnancy by about 30%, while the plasma volume increases by about 40% and the erythrocyte volume by about 20%[18,19]. This greater increase of the plasma volume as compared with the erythrocyte volume results in a lower hematocrit in the peripheral blood: this is known as physiological anemia of pregnancy.

Acclimatization to high altitudes leads via the stimulus of hypoxia and the erythropoietin regulatory cycle primarily to an increase in erythrocyte volume and secondarily to increases in plasma and blood volume[20].

References

[1] HUFF and FELLER, *J. clin. Invest.*, **35**, 1 (1956).
[2] WRIGHT et al., *Semin. nucl. Med.*, **5**, 63 (1975).
[3] OLESEN, K.H., in BROŽEK, J. (Ed.), *Human Body Composition*, Pergamon, Oxford, 1965, page 177.
[4] MARTIN et al., *Brit. J. Haemat.*, **54**, 337 (1983).
[5] SJÖSTRAND, T., *Physiol. Rev.*, **33**, 202 (1953).
[6] International Committee for Standardization in Haematology (ICSH), *Brit. J. Haemat.*, **25**, 801 (1973).
[7] International Committee for Standardization in Haematology (ICSH), *J. nucl. Med.*, **21**, 793 (1980).
[8] FAIRBANKS and TAUXE, in BERGNER and LUSHBAUGH (Eds.), *Compartments, Pools and Spaces in Medical Physiology*, US Atomic Energy Commission, Oak Ridge (Tenn.), 1967, page 283.
[9] MOLLISON, P.L., *Blood Transfusion in Clinical Medicine*, 7th ed., Blackwell, Oxford, 1983.
[10] FUDENBERG et al., *Blood*, **17**, 71 (1961).
[11] BASS and HENSCHEL, *Physiol. Rev.*, **36**, 128 (1956).
[12] GREGERSEN and RAWSON, *Physiol. Rev.*, **39**, 307 (1959).
[13] NADLER et al., *Surgery*, **51**, 224 (1962).
[14] RETZLAFF et al., *Blood*, **33**, 649 (1969).
[15] WENNESLAND et al., *J. clin. Invest.*, **38**, 1065 (1959).
[16] BROWN et al., *J. clin. Invest.*, **41**. 2182 (1962).
[17] DAGHER et al., *Advanc. Surg.*, **1**, 69 (1965).
[18] CHESLEY, L.C., *Amer. J. Obstet. Gynec.*, **112**, 440 (1972).
[19] HYTTEN and LIND, *Diagnostic Indices in Pregnancy*, CIBA-GEIGY Ltd., Basle, 1974.
[20] WEIL et al., *J. clin. Invest.*, **47**, 1627 (1968).
[21] SAIGAL et al., *Pediatrics*, **49**, 406 (1972).
[22] GRAY and FRANK, *J. clin. Invest.*, **32**, 1000 (1953).
[23] BRADY et al., *Surg. Gynec. Obstet.*, **97**, 25 (1953).
[24] DISSMANN et al., *Klin. Wschr.*, **49**, 915 (1971).
[25] LINDERKAMP et al., *Klin. Pädiat.*, **186**, 511 (1974).
[26] LINDERKAMP et al., *Europ. J. Pediat.*, **125**, 143 (1977).
[27] PAYNE, R.W., *J. clin. Path.*, **31**, 1003 (1978).

Physicochemical data (for references see pages 70 and 71)

↓See text below	B Blood, P Plasma, S Serum, Erys Erythrocytes, Grcs Granulocytes, Lkcs Leukocytes, Plts Platelets	SI unit	Mean	s	95% range (extreme range in brackets)	Other units	Mean	s	95% range (extreme range in brackets)	Reference
↓ **Relative density** .. (d_4^{25})	B 20 men .... (a)	–	1.0595	0.0021	–	...	...	...	...	1
	B 17 women .... (a)	–	–	–	(1.0523–1.0604)	...	...	...	...	1
	P 20 men .... (a)	–	1.0269	0.0009	–	...	...	...	...	1
	S	–	–	–	(1.024–1.028)	...	...	...	...	2
	Erys 20 men .... (a)	–	1.0964	0.0018	–	...	...	...	...	1
	Lkcs	–	–	–	(1.07–1.08)	...	...	...	...	3
	Plts 20 men	–	1.0645	0.0015	–	...	...	...	...	4
↓ **Density** (20.0 °C)	P 20 samples...........	kg/L	1.0262	1.8	–	...	...	...	...	6
	Erys 20 samples	kg/L	1.0941	3.6	–	...	...	...	...	6
↓ **Freezing-point depression**	S 75 subjects...........	K	0.540	0.014	0.512–0.568	°C	0.540	0.014	0.512–0.568	7

Relative density. Values determined (a) by the copper sulfate method according to PHILLIPS et al.[5]. – The relative density of whole blood is dependent on the erythrocyte content, while that of the plasma and serum depends primarily on the protein concentration. See Figure 1 regarding temperature dependence. The relative density of whole blood tends to be lower in the afternoon and after meals but higher at night and after physical exertion. The plasma values are pathologically *increased* in cholera, dysentery, severe burns and plasmacytoma; the whole-blood values are *decreased* in anemias and the plasma values in dropsical kidney diseases.

Density. Values determined by the mechanical oscillator technique. All other aspects are covered by the text under 'Relative density'.

Freezing-point depression. Values for whole blood and serum are virtually identical. The erythrocytes are in osmotic equilibrium with the serum[8].

Osmolality. This is generally determined by way of the freezing-point depression[14–16]. Values determined by measurement of vapor pressure tend to be lower than those given here[17]. The contribution of electrolytes to osmolality is approximately 96%, and that of glucose and nonprotein nitrogen substances approximately %. Between the 5th and 10th week of pregnancy the osmolality

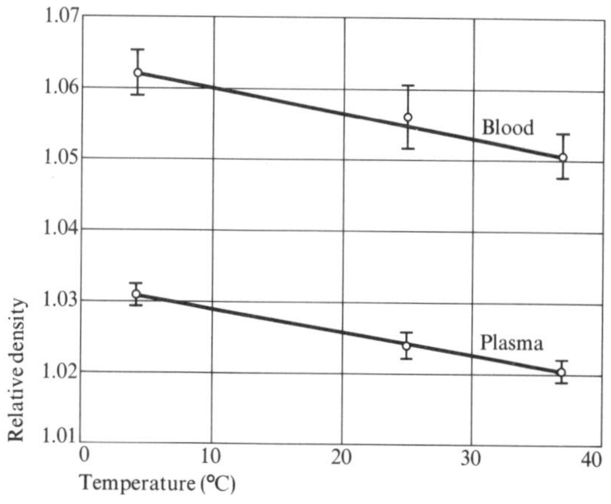

Fig. 1. Relative density of blood or plasma in relation to the temperature, referred to water at 4 °C[75].

↑↓See text on previous page and below	B Blood, P Plasma, S Serum, Erys Erythrocytes, Grcs Granulocytes, Lkcs Leukocytes, Plts Platelets	SI unit	Mean	s	95% range (extreme range in brackets)	Other units	Mean	s	95% range (extreme range in brackets)	Reference
↑**Osmolality**	P(S) Cord blood, 36 newborn	mmol/kg	284	6.5	271–297	mosm/kg	284	6.5	271–297	9
	– 10 newborn, 12 hours .	mmol/kg	293	6	–	mosm/kg	293	6	–	9
	– 14 children, 1–3 months (breast milk)	mmol/kg	284	4.5	–	mosm/kg	284	4.5	–	10
	– 9 children, 1–3 months (cow's milk preparations)	mmol/kg	294	5	–	mosm/kg	294	5	–	10
	– 22 children, 6–11 months	mmol/kg	282	5.2	–	mosm/kg	282	5.2	–	11
	– 50 subjects	mmol/kg	289	4	281–297	mosm/kg	289	4	281–297	12
	– 56 subjects	mmol/kg	286	4.2	281–297 (276–295)	mosm/kg	286	4.2	(276–295)	13
↓**Osmotic pressure** (at 0 °C)	S	kPa	660	–	–	mmHg	4950	–	–	–
						atm	6.51	–	–	–
↓**Oncotic pressure** (at 0 °C)	S	kPa	3.24	–	(2.75–4.71)	mmHg	24.3	–	(20.6–35.3)	21
(at 25–28 °C)	S 15 subjects	kPa	3.40	0.20	–	mmHg	25.5	1.5	–	77
↓**Viscosity**										
Relative viscosity (at 18 °C)	B 21 subjects	–	4.75	–	(3.80–5.70)	...	...	...	...	25
	P 21 subjects	–	2.01	0.17	–	...	...	...	...	25
	S 25 subjects	–	1.88	0.15	–	...	...	...	...	25
Kinematic viscosity (at 37.7 °C) ...	B 14 men	$mm^2 s^{-1}$	2.91	0.28	–	cSt	2.91	0.28	–	26
(at 37 °C)	S 49 subjects	$mm^2 s^{-1}$	1.15	3.5	(1.05–1.24)	cSt	1.15	3.5	(1.05–1.24)	27
Dynamic viscosity (at 37 °C, shear rate 230 s^{-1})	B 110 newborn	mPa s	5.5	1.1	3.3–7.7	cP	5.5	1.1	3.3–7.7	28
	B 117 men	mPa s	4.59	0.485	3.62–5.56	cP	4.59	0.485	3.62–5.56	29
	B 108 women	mPa s	3.95	0.467	3.02–4.88	cP	3.95	0.467	3.02–4.88	29
(at 37 °C)	P 20 newborn	mPa s	1.46	0.33	–	cP	1.46	0.33	–	78
	P 20 women	mPa s	1.75	0.40	–	cP	1.75	0.40	–	78
	P 25 subjects	mPa s	1.24	0.04	–	cP	1.24	0.04	–	82
	S 25 subjects	mPa s	1.11	0.03	–	cP	1.11	0.03	–	82
	S 30 subjects	mPa s	1.115	0.065	–	cP	1.115	0.065	–	30
(at 25 °C)	P	mPa s	–	–	1.50–1.72	cP	–	–	1.50–1.72	79

declines by about 10 mmol/kg[80]. Age and sex differences among children and adults – amounting, however, to at most only a few mmol/kg – are due to different urea levels. *High values* are found in hyperosmolar diabetic coma without ketoacidosis (400 mmol/kg to 450 mmol/kg)[18], in dehydration (inadequate liquid intake in stroke, diabetes insipidus, etc.), and in ethanol intoxication[13,19,76] (Fig.2), and *low values* in the presence of sodium depletion and water intoxication (down to 183–235 mmol/kg according to one publication[20]).

Osmotic pressure. Calculated from the value of freezing-point depression (page 48). The level of the osmotic pressure is determined chiefly by the crystalloid constituents of the plasma; colloids account for a partial pressure amounting to about 0.5% of the total osmotic pressure.

Oncotic pressure. The oncotic pressure – or colloid-osmotic pressure – can be calculated roughly from the serum albumin and globulin concentrations using the formula of KEYS[22]. A more precise calculation takes into account the oncotic pressures of the individual serum-protein fractions[23]. The greater part of the oncotic pressure is exerted by albumin; fibrinogen does not influence the oncotic pressure of the plasma to a measurable degree[24] so that the oncotic pressure of the plasma may be equated with that of the serum. In the newborn the oncotic pressure is lower than in adults[81].

Viscosity. Determination of relative viscosity by Hess viscosimeter, of kinematic viscosity by capillary viscosimeter, and of dynamic viscosity by the cone-plate viscosimeter. – The viscosity of whole blood depends mainly on the blood-cell content, the plasma-protein concentration, and the temperature. Whole blood is not a newtonian fluid but a pseudoplastic one; that is to say, its viscosity varies with the shear rate (Fig.3)[31–33]. In healthy individuals, the viscosity of whole blood at a given rate of shear is determined primarily by the erythrocyte content (Fig.4). At shear rates above 100 s^{-1}, whole blood may be considered, for all practical purposes, as a newtonian fluid, its viscosity varying linearly with the hematocrit at a normal erythrocyte content (Fig.5)[34]. – *Pathological variations*[32,33,35]: The viscosity of whole blood is increased (hyperviscosity syndrome) in polycythemia, leukemia[36], sickle-cell anemia[37], and other erythrocyte deformations as well as at increased concentrations of some plasma proteins – as of IgM (macroglobulinemia), IgA (myeloma), IgG (myeloma), IgG complexes (collagenoses), and fibrinogen (hyperfibrinogenemia).

Surface tension. Fasting blood, determined by torsion balance.

Refractive index. Determined by Pulfrich refractometer. The refractive index of the serum is dependent primarily on the protein content of the serum and may therefore be used for determination of the latter (see e.g. DRICKMAN and MCKEON[40]). Refractometric determination of protein is unreliable at high serum concentrations of urea, sugar, lipids, and bilirubin.

Specific conductivity. The specific conductivity and the total protein content of the serum permit determination of the total cation content of the serum.

↑↓See text on pages 68–70	B Blood, P Plasma, S Serum, Erys Erythrocytes, Grcs Granulocytes, Lkcs Leukocytes, Plts Platelets	SI unit	Mean	*s*	95% range (extreme range in brackets)	Other units	Mean	*s*	95% range (extreme range in brackets)	Reference
↑**Surface tension** (at 20 °C)	S 82 subjects, 20–30 years	$mN\,m^{-1}$	56.2	–	–	$dyn\,cm^{-1}$	56.2	–	–	38
↑**Refractive index** (at 20 °C)	S	...	...	...	(1.34846–1.35132)	...	...	...	...	39
Specific heat	B	$kJ\,K^{-1}kg^{-1}$	3.64	–	–	$cal\,grd^{-1}g^{-1}$	0.87	–	–	41
	P	$kJ\,K^{-1}kg^{-1}$	3.93	–	–	$cal\,grd^{-1}g^{-1}$	0.94	–	–	41
	Erys	$kJ\,K^{-1}kg^{-1}$	3.22	–	–	$cal\,grd^{-1}g^{-1}$	0.77	–	–	41
↑**Specific conductivity** (at 25 °C)..	S	$S\,m^{-1}$	1.190	–	(1.173–1.229)	...	...	...	...	42
↓**Electrophoretic mobility** (toward anode)..........	Erys ....(a)	...	...	...	...	$10^{-4}cm^2V^{-1}s^{-1}$	1.080	0.008	–	43
	Erys 28 subjects .....(b)	...	...	...	...	$10^{-4}cm^2V^{-1}s^{-1}$	1.270	0.017	–	44
	Grcs 28 subjects .....(b)	...	...	...	...	$10^{-4}cm^2V^{-1}s^{-1}$	0.840	0.025	–	44
	Lkcs 28 subjects .....(b)	...	...	...	...	$10^{-4}cm^2V^{-1}s^{-1}$	1.060	0.027	–	44
	Plts 28 subjects ......(b)	...	...	...	...	$10^{-4}cm^2V^{-1}s^{-1}$	0.120	0.050	–	44
↓**Surface density of electrical charge**	Erys	$mC\,m^{-2}$	11.7	–	–	$esE\,cm^{-2}$	3500	–	–	46
↓**Redox potential**.	B Venous........... (a)	mV	–	–	– 260 to – 300	...	...	...	...	50
	B Venous........... (b)	mV	–	–	– 12 to – 52	...	...	...	...	50
↓**pH**.............	....	...	...	...	...	...	...	...	...	...

Electrophoretic mobility. (a) pH 7.2 (NaCl solution and phosphate buffer); (b) citrated blood. – The electrophoretic mobility of the blood cells is determined chiefly by the carboxy groups of the sialic acid that is present at the cell surface[45–47]. The mobility is a value which is highly characteristic for each type of blood cell; that of the erythrocytes is independent of race, sex, age or blood group[48]. *Increased* leukocyte mobility[44,47] is encountered in chronic and acute myeloses, in lymphadenosis, in Hodgkin's disease, and in the presence of tumors with bone metastases. The mobility of the erythrocytes is reduced by the serum of cancer patients[49].

Surface density of electrical charge. This is calculated from the electrophoretic mobility. Assuming an erythrocyte surface area of 163 µm², the electrical charge of 1 erythrocyte is 5.2 mC.

Redox potential. Redox potential (a) against calomel electrode; (b) against hydrogen electrode. – The range indicated covers 83% of 550 measurements, determined in vitro by the method of ZIEGLER[51] using a weakly polarized platinum electrode. The redox potential of the blood is dependent on the dehydroascorbic acid/ascorbic acid ratio.

pH (Table 1). Blood, plasma: All the values given were determined potentiometrically; the reference buffers used were those of

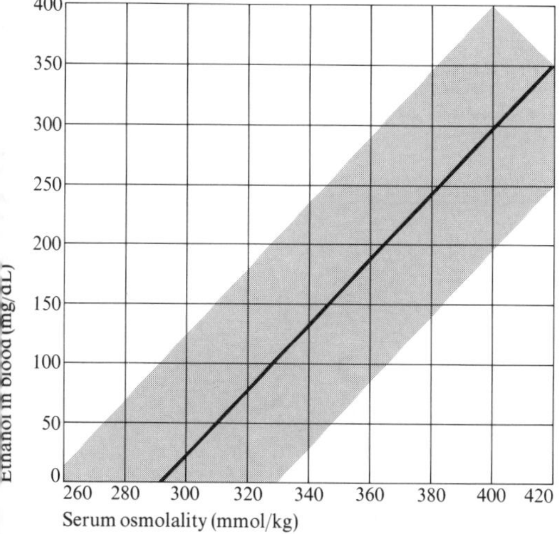

Fig. 2. Correlation between blood ethanol level and serum osmolality. Regression line with 95% confidence range[76].

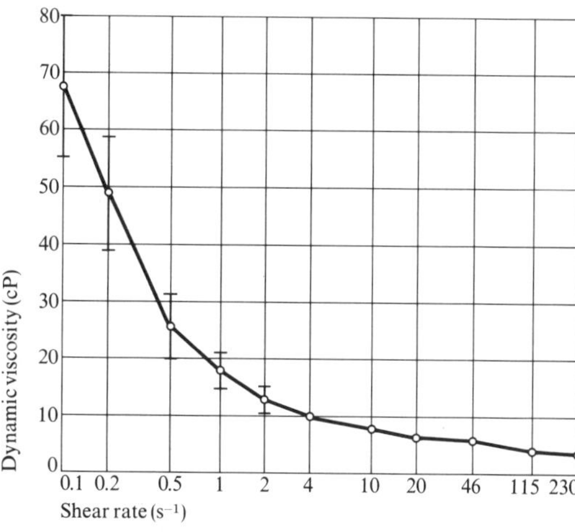

Fig. 3. Dependence of dynamic viscosity of whole blood (hematocrit 0.45, 37 °C) on shear rate (measurement with cone-plate viscosimeter, $\bar{x}$ and $s_{\bar{x}}$)[35].

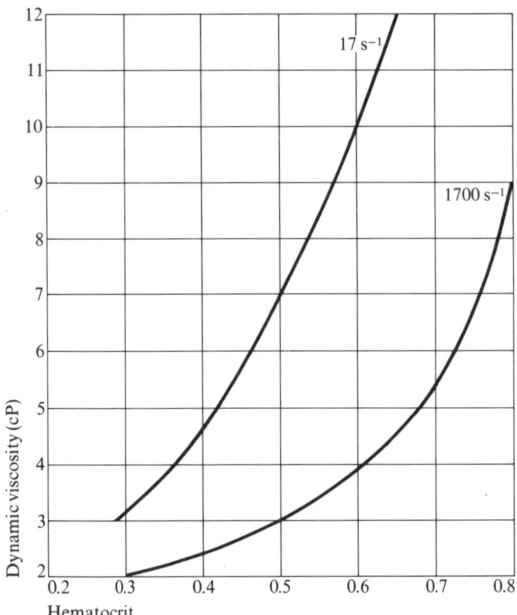

Fig. 4. Dependence of dynamic viscosity of whole blood (37 °C) on hematocrit at two extreme shear rates (measurement with cone-plate viscosimeter)[35].

the National Bureau of Standards (page 56). See the literature concerning the measuring technique[57,64–66]. The measurement temperature of 37 °C is preferable to 38 °C[57,66]. The following relation is applicable to the temperature dependence: $\Delta pH/\Delta T = -0.0146\,K^{-1}$ in adults; $\Delta pH/\Delta T = -0.0128\,K^{-1}$ in children. Heparin, but not oxalate, citrate or EDTA, is suitable as anticoagulant[65]. In subjects at complete rest, there is no difference between the pH values of plasma and whole blood[64]. During physical exercise, the arterial plasma is slightly more alkaline than the arterial

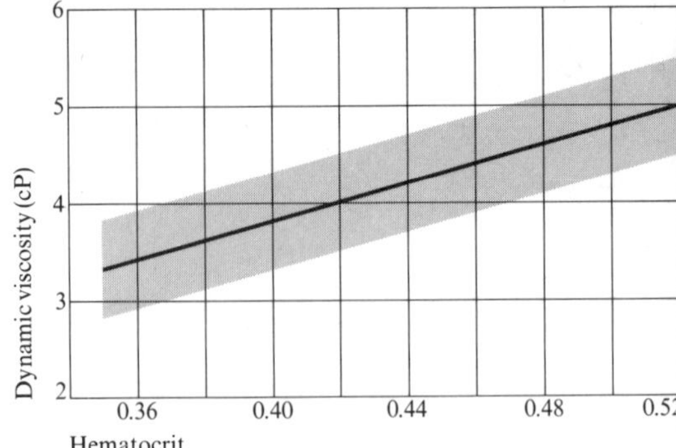

Fig. 5. Dynamic viscosity of whole blood (37 °C) in normal range of hematocrit at a shear rate of 230 s^{-1} (measurement with cone-plate viscosimeter, $\bar{x} \pm s$)[34].

whole blood (maximum difference 0.10 pH units at oxygen saturation of 98%). The pH of capillary blood agrees well with that of arterial blood[57,67]. Venous plasma from an extremity is up to 0.03 pH units less alkaline than arterial plasma[67]. In the newborn, the pH of the blood is lower[52,68,69] but it reaches adult values within the first few postnatal months[53,54,70]. During pregnancy the blood pH is slightly increased[71]. The lower normal limit for fetal capillary blood during labor has been set at 7.25[72]. In the presence of acute derangements of the acid-base balance the pH may briefly drop to 6.7 (e.g. in lactacidosis) or rise to 7.8 (e.g. in pyloric stenosis)[57,73]. In the case of chronic disturbances it usually varies between 7.2 and 7.5. The pH may also temporarily decrease to 6.8 during extreme physical exertion[74].

References

1 VAN SLYKE et al., *J. biol. Chem.*, **183**, 349 (1950).
2 LEAKE et al., *Amer. J. Physiol.*, **81**, 493 (1927).
3 GRAHAM et al., *Blood*, **10**, 467 (1955).
4 TULLIS, J. L., *Blood*, **7**, 891 (1952).
5 PHILLIPS et al., *J. biol. Chem.*, **183**, 305 (1950).
6 HINGHOFER-SZALKAY et al., *Klin. Wschr.* **57**, 1163 (1979).
7 OLMSTEAD and ROTH, *Amer. J. med. Sci.*, **233**, 392 (1957).
8 WILLIAMS et al., *J. clin. Invest.*, **38**, 1587 (1959).

Table 1 *pH value of blood at different ages*

Material	Measured at	Subjects	Age	Number	Mean	s	(Extreme range)	Reference
Blood, umbilical vein	37 °C	Newborn		45	7.320	0.055	(7.178–7.414)	52
Blood, umbilical artery	37 °C	Newborn		27	7.242	0.059	(7.111–7.375)	52
Blood, arterial	37 °C	Newborn	5–10 minutes	44	7.207	0.051	(7.091–7.302)	52
Blood, arterial	37 °C	Newborn	60 minutes	43	7.332	0.031	(7.261–7.394)	52
Blood, arterial	37 °C	Newborn	24 hours	72	7.369	0.032	(7.290–7.448)	52
Blood, arterial	38 °C	Children	10–90 days	24	7.379	0.028	–	53
Blood, arterial	38 °C	Children	90–360 days	47	7.400	0.019	–	53
Blood, arterial	38 °C	Children	7–15 years	30	7.41	0.025	(7.365–7.455)	54
Blood, arterial	38 °C	Adults		40	7.40	0.020	–	55
Blood, capillary	37 °C	Children	3–12 months	32	7.380	0.027	–	56
Blood, capillary	37 °C	Children	1–3 years	16	7.381	0.033	–	56
Blood, capillary	37 °C	Children	3–15 years	49	7.407	0.031	–	56
Blood, capillary	37 °C	Men	23–45 years	20	7.405	0.015	–	57
Blood, capillary	37 °C	Women	20–37 years	20	7.413	0.011	–	57
Plasma, arterial	37 °C	Adults		20	7.39	0.018	–	58
Plasma, arterial	37 °C	Adults		14	7.42	0.03	–	59
Plasma, venous	38 °C	Adults		22	7.34	0.037	–	60
Erythrocytes (a)	37 °C	Adults		20	7.19	0.022	–	58
Erythrocytes (b)	37 °C	Adults		14	7.12	0.03	–	59
Erythrocytes (c)	37 °C	Adults		14	7.22	0.04	–	59
Erythrocytes (c)	37 °C	Children	4 months to 3 years	70	7.18	0.05	–	61
Leukocytes (d)	–	Adults		13	7.07	0.04	–	62
Platelets (e)	–	Adults		–	7.08	0.08	–	63

(a) pH determination in hemolyzate; (b) by DMO method; (c) via chloride concentration; (d) at a plasma pH of 7.38 and a CO_2 pressure of 5.5 kPa; (e) at a milieu pH of 7.4 and a CO_2 pressure of 5.33 kPa.

[9] GAUTIER, E., in JONXIS et al. (Eds.), *Nutricia Symposium on the Adaptation of the Newborn Infant to Extra-Uterine Life,* Kroese, Leiden, 1964, page 83.
[10] DAVIES, D.P., *Brit. med. J.,* **2**, 340 (1973).
[11] HELLERSTEIN et al., *Amer. J. Dis. Child.,* **112**, 298 (1966).
[12] HENDRY, E.B., *Clin. Chem.,* **7**, 156 (1961), and **8**, 246 (1962).
[13] GLASSER et al., *Amer. J. clin. Path.,* **60**, 695 (1973).
[14] JOHNSON and HOCH, *Stand. Meth. clin. Chem.,* **5**, 159 (1965); WARHOL et al., *Arch. intern. Med.,* **116**, 743 (1965).
[15] DORMANDY, T.L., *Lancet,* **1**, 267 (1967).
[16] HARAWAY and BECKER, *J. Amer. med. Ass.,* **205**, 506 (1968).
[17] LIPSON and JOHNSON, *Arthr. and Rheum.,* **10**, 294 (1967).
[18] FRICK, P.G., *Schweiz. med. Wschr.,* **98**, 1562 (1968).
[19] ROBINSON and LOEB, *New Engl. J. Med.,* **284**, 1253 (1971).
[20] AYUS et al., *Amer. J. Med.,* **72**, 43 (1982).
[21] KEYS and HILL, *J. exp. Biol.,* **11**, 28 (1934).
[22] KEYS, A., *J. phys. Chem.,* **42**, 11 (1938).
[23] OTT, H., *Klin. Wschr.,* **34**, 1079 (1956).
[24] WUHRMANN and MÄRKI, *Dysproteinämien and Paraproteinämien,* Schwabe, Basle, 1963, page 156.
[25] WATSON, W.C., *Lancet,* **2**, 366 (1957).
[26] STRUMIA and PHILLIPS, *Amer. J. clin. Path.,* **39**, 464 (1963).
[27] SHEARN et al., *Arch. intern. Med.,* **112**, 684 (1963), and *J. Lab. clin. Med.,* **61**, 677 (1963).
[28] MACKINTOSH and WALKER, *Arch. Dis. Childh.,* **48**, 547 (1973).
[29] ROSENBLATT et al., *J. Lab. clin. Med.,* **65**, 202 (1965).
[30] MCMILLAN, D.E., *J. clin. Invest.,* **53**, 1071 (1974).
[31] WELLS and MERRILL, *J. clin. Invest.,* **41**, 1591 (1962).
[32] MERRILL, E.W., *Physiol. Rev.,* **49**, 863 (1969).
[33] LA CELLE and WEED, *Progr. Hemat.,* **7**, 1 (1971).
[34] BOLLINGER et al., *Klin. Wschr.,* **45**, 939 (1967).
[35] WELLS, R., *New Engl. J. Med.,* **283**, 183 (1970); BLOCH and MAKI, *Sem. Hemat.,* **10**, 113 (1973).
[36] LICHTMAN, M.A., *J. clin. Invest.,* **52**, 350 (1973); PRESTON et al., *Brit. med. J.,* **1**, 476 (1978).
[37] KLUG et al., *Arch. intern. Med.,* **133**, 577 (1974).
[38] KÜNZEL, O., *Ergebn. inn. Med. Kinderheilk.,* **60**, 565 (1941).
[39] FRANK, H., in HENNING, N. (Ed.), *Klinische Laboratoriumsdiagnostik,* 2nd ed., Urban & Schwarzenberg, Munich, 1960, page 1.
[40] DRICKMAN and MCKEON, *Amer. J. clin. Path.,* **38**, 392 (1962).
[41] MENDLOWITZ, M., *Science,* **107**, 97 (1948).
[42] SUNDERMAN, F.W., *Amer. J. clin. Path.,* **15**, 219 (1945); LUFKIN and SUNDERMAN, *Techn. Bull. Reg. med. Technol.,* **7**, 118 (1946).
[43] SACHTLEBEN and RUHENSTROTH-BAUER, *Nature,* **192**, 982 (1961).
[44] RUHENSTROTH-BAUER et al., *Münch. med. Wschr.,* **103**, 794 (1961).
[45] COOK et al., *Nature,* **191**, 44 (1961).
[46] EYLAR et al., *J. biol. Chem.,* **237**, 1992 (1962).
[47] RUEFF, F., *Die Zellelektrophorese in der klinischen Diagnostik,* Lehmann, Munich, 1964.
[48] BANGHAM et al., *Nature,* **182**, 642 (1958).
[49] ROTTINO and ANGERS, *Proc. N. Y. St. Ass. publ. Hlth Lab.,* **41**, 9 (1961), and *Clin. Chem.,* **8**, 579 (1962); GRACE et al., *Amer. Rev. resp. Dis.,* **88**, 652 (1963).
[50] MÜNKER, G., *Redoxpotential-, Eisen-, Kupfer- und Vitamin-C-Veränderungen im Blut unter einer Behandlung, die Einfluß auf das redoxaktive Geschehen nimmt,* thesis, Freiburg i. Br., 1963.
[51] ZIEGLER, E., *Messung und Bedeutung des Redoxpotentials im Blut in vivo und in vitro,* suppl. 10, Arzneimittel-Forschung, Editio Cantor, Aulendorf, 1960.
[52] KOCH and WENDEL, *Biol. Neonat. (Basel),* **12**, 136 (1968).
[53] BARTELS and WENNER, *Klin. Wschr.,* **43**, 437 (1965).
[54] LIAPPIS and KALLFELZ, *Klin. Wschr.,* **50**, 471 (1972).
[55] SCHWAB and WISSER, *Klin. Wschr.,* **40**, 713 (1962).
[56] VÁVROVÁ et al., *Poumon,* **25**, 1121 (1969).
[57] SIGGAARD-ANDERSEN, O., *The Acid-Base Status of the Blood,* 4th ed., Munksgaard, Copenhagen, 1974; SIGGAARD-ANDERSEN, O., *Scand. J. clin. Lab. Invest.,* **15**, suppl. 70, 1 (1963); ASTRUP and SIGGAARD-ANDERSEN, *Advanc. clin. Chem.,* **6**, 1 (1963).
[58] PURCELL et al., *Clin. Chem.,* **7**, 536 (1961).
[59] TUSHAN et al., *Arch. intern. Med.,* **125**, 967 (1970).
[60] FUNDER and WIETH, *Scand. J. clin. Lab. Invest.,* **18**, 167 (1966).
[61] HELLERSTEIN, S., *J. Lab. clin. Med.,* **79**, 559 (1972).
[62] LEVIN and BARON, *Clin. Sci.,* **52**, 325 (1977).
[63] ZIEVE and SOLOMON, *J. clin. Invest.,* **45**, 1251 (1966).
[64] GAMBINO, S.R., *Amer. J. clin. Path.,* **32**, 285 (1959).
[65] GAMBINO et al., *Stand. Meth. clin. Chem.,* **5**, 169 (1965).
[66] RICHTERICH, R., *Klinische Chemie,* 3rd ed., Karger, Basle, 1971; ALBERS, C., in KOENIG, W. (Ed.), *Klinisch-physiologische Untersuchungsmethoden,* Thieme, Stuttgart, 1972, page 163.
[67] GAMBINO, S.R., *Amer. J. clin. Path.,* **32**, 298 (1959).
[68] ROOTH, G., *Acta paediat. (Uppsala),* **52**, 22 (1963).
[69] RÄIHÄ, N.C., *Pediatrics,* **32**, 1025 (1963).
[70] RIEGEL, K., *Klin. Wschr.,* **41**, 249 (1963).
[71] SJÖSTEDT, S., *Amer. J. Obstet. Gynec.,* **84**, 775 (1962).
[72] KUBLI et al., *Amer. J. Obstet. Gynec.,* **104**, 1190 (1969).
[73] LENTNER, C., *Klinisch wichtige Parameter des Elektrolytstoffwechsels,* in preparation.
[74] KINDERMANN et al., *Dtsch. med. Wschr.,* **99**, 1372 (1974).
[75] TRUDNOWSKI and RICO, *Clin. Chem.,* **20**, 615 (1974).
[76] CHAMPION et al., *Lancet,* **1**, 1402 (1975).
[77] RACKOW et al., *Chest,* **72**, 709 (1977).
[78] BUCHAN, P.C., *Brit. J. Haemat.,* **45**, 97 (1980).
[79] STUART and KENNY, *J. clin. Path.,* **33**, 417 (1980).
[80] DAVISON et al., *Brit. J. Obstet. Gynaec.,* **88**, 472 (1981).
[81] WU et al., *Pediatrics,* **68**, 814 (1981).
[82] LETCHER et al., *Amer. J. Med.,* **70**, 1195 (1981).

Blood gases (for pH values see page 70; for references see page 77)

Normal values are given on pages 72–74. They apply to sea level and may be used for altitudes up to about 200 m above sea level. In individuals who live at high altitudes, the carbon dioxide pressure (p_{CO_2}) is reduced because of chronic hyperventilation, while the pH is normal owing to complete renal compensation as a result of which the plasma bicarbonate concentration is lowered.

For gas analysis, blood samples have to be secured under anaerobic conditions. Even when the blood samples are stored anaerobically, consideration has to be given to changes due to coagulation, glycolysis, auto-oxidation and sedimentation. Venous blood from peripheral subcutaneous veins is usually not suitable. Mixed venous blood is obtained from the pulmonary artery, and arterial blood by puncture of the femoral, brachial or radial artery. Capillary blood, obtainable by deep puncture of the warmed finger tip or the ear lobe, can be used for measurement of acid–base parameters[1] but is less suitable for the measurement of oxygen content[2]. Values of the acid–base status should be measured at 37 °C and not, as previously customary, at 38 °C[1]. When use is made of nomograms, the temperature to which they are applicable must be considered.

Methods[3–5]. Carbon dioxide, oxygen, nitrogen, and carbon monoxide are generally determined manometrically according to VAN SLYKE or by the micromodification of KOPP-NATELSON. Oxygen and carbon monoxide contents can also be determined by mass spectrography or gas chromatography. Spectrophotometric methods are available for the determination of oxygen capacity and oxygen saturation. The bicarbonate concentration can be determined by titration, the oxygen tension polarographically, and the carbon dioxide pressure potentiometrically. Not measured values of the CO_2-bicarbonate system can be calculated by way of the dissociation equation of carbonic acid, or read off from nomograms (page 75)[4,13,19,23].

Comments on tables on pages 72–74:

Carbon dioxide pressure. Partial pressure of carbon dioxide (p_{CO_2}) in gaseous phase in equilibrium with blood.

Carbon dioxide content. Content of CO_2 extractable with strong acids in blood collected and examined in the absence of air. Of this amount, about 5% is physically dissolved in the plasma, 94% is bicarbonate and 1% composed of carbamino compounds; in the erythrocytes, about 7% is physically dissolved, while 82% consists of bicarbonate and 11% of carbamino compounds (for details see ALBRITTON[13]). The proportions of carbonic acid and carbonate are small.

Bicarbonate concentration. The bicarbonate concentration in the plasma is generally calculated from the carbon dioxide content, the physically dissolved CO_2, but not the carbamino CO_2, being subtracted from the total CO_2. Plasma values determined by titration roughly agree with the calculated ones.

Standard bicarbonate. Bicarbonate concentration in plasma of whole blood containing oxygen-saturated hemoglobin and equilibrated to $p_{CO_2} = 5.33$ kPa (= 40 mmHg) at 37 °C. For nomographic determination of standard bicarbonate, see the literature[4,5]. The alkali reserve (carbon dioxide-combining power) is the carbon dioxide content of anaerobically separated plasma equilibrated to $p_{CO_2} = 5.33$ kPa (= 40 mmHg) at room temperature; these values, however, are not perfectly reproducible.

Base excess. Base concentration corresponding to titration with a strong acid up to pH 7.40 at $p_{CO_2} = 5.33$ kPa (= 40 mmHg) at 37 °C. Negative values conform to titration with a strong base (also called base deficit). At a blood hemoglobin concentration of

(Continued on page 76)

↑See text on page 71	Material	Method	SI unit	Mean	s	95% range (extreme range in brackets)	Other units	Mean	s	95% range (extreme range in brackets)	Reference
Carbon dioxide											
↑CO_2 pressure	Blood, umbilical artery, 27 newborn (37 °C)	Potentiometric	kPa	6.55	0.77	(4.7–8.0)	mmHg	49.1	5.8	(35–60)	6
	Blood, umbilical vein, 44 newborn (37 °C)	Potentiometric	kPa	5.04	0.75	(3.5–6.9)	mmHg	37.8	5.6	(26–52)	6
	Blood, arterial:										
	43 newborn, 5–10 minutes (37 °C)	Potentiometric	kPa	6.15	0.93	(4.7–8.7)	mmHg	46.1	7.0	(35–65)	6
	43 newborn, 60 minutes (37 °C)	Potentiometric	kPa	4.81	0.56	(3.7–6.0)	mmHg	36.1	4.2	(28–45)	6
	71 newborn, 24 hours (37 °C)	Potentiometric	kPa	4.45	0.41	(3.6–5.3)	mmHg	33.4	3.1	(27–40)	6
	24 children, 10–90 days (37 °C)	Calculated	kPa	4.60	0.53	–	mmHg	34.5	4.0	–	14
	24 children, 10–90 days (38 °C)	Calculated	kPa	4.80	0.53	–	mmHg	36.0	4.0	–	14
	47 children, 90–360 days (37 °C)	Calculated	kPa	4.45	0.43	3.59–5.31	mmHg	33.4	3.2	27.0–39.8	14
	47 children, 90–360 days (38 °C)	Calculated	kPa	4.65	0.43	3.79–5.51	mmHg	34.9	3.2	28.5–41.3	14
	30 children, 7–15 years (38 °C)	Calculated	kPa	4.88	0.46	–	mmHg	36.6	3.44	–	8
	40 adults, 19–51 years (38 °C)	Calculated	kPa	4.87	0.47	3.93–5.81	mmHg	36.5	3.56	29.4–43.6	8
	15 adults	Calculated	kPa	5.00	0.30	–	mmHg	37.5	2.23	–	15
	24 men, <30 years	Potentiometric	kPa	5.24	0.49	–	mmHg	39.3	3.7	–	9
	11 men, >60 years	Potentiometric	kPa	5.17	0.42	–	mmHg	38.8	3.16	–	9
	50 men	Calculated	kPa	5.32	0.24	4.84–5.80	mmHg	39.9	1.8	36.3–43.5	12
	Blood, venous, 50 men	Calculated	kPa	6.65	0.25	6.15–7.15	mmHg	49.9	1.9	46.1–53.7	12
	Blood, capillary:										
	20 men (37 °C)	Calculated	kPa	5.24	0.36	–	mmHg	39.3	2.7	–	4
	20 women (37 °C)	Calculated	kPa	4.85	0.37	–	mmHg	36.4	2.8	–	4
↑Carbon dioxide content	Blood, umbilical artery, 29 newborn	Gas chromatography	mmol/L	19.8	–	(13.6–25.6)	vol %	44.1	–	(30.3–57.0)	10
	Blood, umbilical vein, 32 newborn	Gas chromatography	mmol/L	17.0	–	(11.1–21.2)	vol %	37.8	–	(24.7–47.2)	10
	Blood, arterial:										
	9 children, 3–11 years	Manometry	mmol/L	20.9	1.1	(19.3–22.4)	vol %	46.4	2.4	(43.0–49.8)	11
	50 men	Manometry	mmol/L	21.6	0.6	20.4–22.8	vol %	48.1	1.3	45.5–50.7	12
	Blood, venous, 50 men	Manometry	mmol/L	24.6	0.7	23.2–26.0	vol %	54.8	1.6	51.6–58.0	12
	Plasma, arterial:										
	15 adults	Manometry	mmol/L	26.1	1.83	–	vol %	58.1	4.07	–	15
	50 men	Manometry	mmol/L	26.6	0.99	24.6–28.6	vol %	59.2	2.20	44.8–63.8	5
	50 women	Manometry	mmol/L	25.6	1.43	22.7–28.5	vol %	57.0	3.11	50.8–63.8	5
	Plasma, capillary:										
	20 men	Calculated	mmol/L	25.9	1.3	–	vol %	57.7	2.9	–	4
	20 women	Calculated	mmol/L	24.2	1.7	–	vol %	53.9	3.8	–	4
	Plasma, venous:										
	7 men	Manometry	mmol/L	30.3	1.31	(28.6–31.9)	vol %	67.4	2.92	(63.7–71.0)	16
	8 women	Manometry	mmol/L	27.8	1.45	(24.9–29.2)	vol %	61.9	3.23	(55.4–65.0)	16
↑Bicarbonate concentration	Plasma, adults	Titrimetry	mmol/L	–	–	21–30	...	...	...	...	17
	Plasma, arterial, 15 adults	Calculated	mmol/L	24.9	1.79	–	...	...	...	...	15

↑↓ See text on pages 71 and 76	Material	Method	SI unit	Mean	s	95% range (extreme range in brackets)	Other units	Mean	s	95% range (extreme range in brackets)	Reference
↑Bicarbonate concentration *(continued)*	Plasma, capillary:										
	20 men	Calculated	mmol/L	24.7	1.2	–	...	...	...	...	4
	20 women	Calculated	mmol/L	23.1	1.5	–	...	...	...	...	4
↑Standard bicarbonate	Plasma, umbilical artery, 27 newborn	Calculated	mmol/L	18.7	1.8	(14–21.0)	...	...	...	...	6
	Plasma, umbilical vein, 44 newborn	Calculated	mmol/L	20.0	1.4	(15.5–22.5)	...	...	...	...	6
	Plasma, arterial:										
	42 newborn, 5–10 minutes	Calculated	mmol/L	16.7	1.6	(12.5–20.5)	...	...	...	...	6
	42 newborn, 60 minutes	Calculated	mmol/L	19.2	1.2	(16.0–21.5)	...	...	...	...	6
	71 newborn, 24 hours	Calculated	mmol/L	20.2	1.3	(18.0–23.5)	...	...	...	...	6
	24 children, 10–90 days	Calculated	mmol/L	21.5	1.5	–	...	...	...	...	14
	47 children, 90–360 days	Calculated	mmol/L	22.0	1.1	19.8–24.2	...	...	...	...	14
	30 children, 7–15 years	Calculated	mmol/L	23.4	1.68	–	...	...	...	...	8
	40 adults, 19–51 years	Calculated	mmol/L	22.8	1.48	19.9–25.7	...	...	...	...	8
	Plasma, capillary:										
	20 men	Calculated	mmol/L	24.7	1.1	–	...	...	...	...	4
	20 women	Calculated	mmol/L	24.0	1.0	–	...	...	...	...	4
↑Base excess	Blood, umbilical artery, 16 newborn	Calculated	mmol/L	–9.9	–	–	...	...	...	...	10
	Blood, umbilical vein:										
	16 newborn	Calculated	mmol/L	–6.4	–	–	...	...	...	...	10
	Newborn	Calculated	mmol/L	–9.5	–	–16.6 to –2.5	...	...	...	...	18
	Blood, capillary:										
	49 children, 3–15 years	Calculated	mmol/L	–0.82	1.62	–4.06 to 2.42	...	...	...	...	21
	20 men	Calculated	mmol/L	–0.1	1.2	–	...	...	...	...	4
	20 women	Calculated	mmol/L	–1.0	1.1	–	...	...	...	...	4
↓Buffer bases	Blood, umbilical vein	Calculated	mmol/L	37.2	–	30.8–43.7	...	...	...	...	18
	Blood, arterial, 153 men	Calculated	mmol/L	48.4	–	46–52	...	...	...	...	19
	Blood, capillary:										
	49 children, 3–15 years	Calculated	mmol/L	47.5	2.7	42.1–52.9	...	...	...	...	21
	20 men	Calculated	mmol/L	48.6	2.3	–	...	...	...	...	4
	20 women	Calculated	mmol/L	46.9	2.2	–	...	...	...	...	4
↓Carbon monoxide											
Carbon monoxide content	Blood, 70 nonsmokers	Gas chromatography	mmol/L	0.072	0.025	0.022–0.122	vol%	0.161	0.055	0.051–0.271	20
	Blood, 23 smokers	Gas chromatography	mmol/L	0.350	0.178	–	vol%	0.784	0.396	–	20
Oxygen											
↓Oxygen pressure	Blood, umbilical artery, 29 newborn	Polarographic	kPa	2.12	0.51	(0.93–3.1)	mmHg	15.9	3.8	(7–23)	6
	Blood, umbilical vein, 45 newborn	Polarographic	kPa	3.65	0.76	(2.0–5.3)	mmHg	27.4	5.7	(15–40)	6

↓See text on pages 76 and 77	Material	Method	SI unit	Mean	s	95% range (extreme range in brackets)	Other units	Mean	s	95% range (extreme range in brackets)	Reference
↓Oxygen pressure *(continued)*	Blood, arterial:										
	42 newborn, 5–10 minutes	Polarographic	kPa	6.61	1.32	(4.4–10)	mmHg	49.6	9.9	(33–75)	6
	31 newborn, 60 minutes	Polarographic	kPa	8.44	1.51	(5.1–11)	mmHg	63.3	11.3	(38–83)	6
	62 newborn, 24 hours	Polarographic	kPa	9.69	1.27	(7.2–13)	mmHg	72.7	9.5	(54–95)	6
	12 children, 1–4 weeks	Polarographic	kPa	11.4	0.99	–	mmHg	85.6	7.45	–	7
	13 children, 4–16 months	Polarographic	kPa	10.4	1.53	–	mmHg	78.0	11.5	–	7
	30 children, 7–15 years	Polarographic	kPa	10.6	1.12	–	mmHg	79.7	8.4	–	8
	40 adults, 19–51 years	Polarographic	kPa	10.7	0.84	9.02–12.4	mmHg	80.6	6.29	68.0–93.2	8
	28 men, <30 years	Polarographic	kPa	12.1	1.11	–	mmHg	91.0	8.3	–	9
	10 men, >60 years	Polarographic	kPa	10.6	1.13	–	mmHg	79.7	8.5	–	9
↓Oxygen content	Blood, umbilical artery, 29 newborn	Gas chromatography	mmol/L	1.83	–	(0.17–3.43)	vol%	4.1	–	(0.4–7.7)	10
	Blood, umbilical vein, 32 newborn	Gas chromatography	mmol/L	5.49	–	(2.78–7.41)	vol%	12.3	–	(6.2–16.6)	10
	Blood, arterial:										
	9 children, 3–11 years	Manometry	mmol/L	6.96	0.41	(6.11–7.63)	vol%	15.6	0.93	(13.7–17.1)	11
	50 men	Manometry	mmol/L	8.74	0.53	7.68–9.70	vol%	19.6	1.2	17.2–22.0	12
	Blood, venous, 50 men	Manometry	mmol/L	5.76	0.58	4.60–6.92	vol%	12.9	1.3	10.3–15.5	12
↓Oxygen capacity	Blood, umbilical artery, 21 newborn	Calculated	mmol/L	9.05	0.80	(7.32–10.6)	vol%	20.3	1.8	(16.4–23.7)	6
	Blood, umbilical vein, 36 newborn	Calculated	mmol/L	8.88	0.76	(7.36–10.8)	vol%	19.9	1.7	(16.5–24.1)	6
	Blood, arterial:										
	38 newborn, 5–10 minutes	Calculated	mmol/L	9.86	0.85	(8.12–11.7)	vol%	22.1	1.9	(18.2–26.3)	6
	37 newborn, 60 minutes	Calculated	mmol/L	10.0	0.85	(8.48–11.6)	vol%	22.5	1.9	(19.0–25.9)	6
	62 newborn, 24 hours	Calculated	mmol/L	9.86	1.03	(7.50–12.5)	vol%	22.1	2.3	(16.8–28.0)	6
	12 children, 1–4 weeks	Manometry	mmol/L	9.10	1.31	–	vol%	20.4	2.93	–	7
	13 children, 4–16 months	Manometry	mmol/L	6.19	0.79	–	vol%	13.9	1.78	–	7
	50 men	Manometry	mmol/L	9.33	0.58	8.17–10.6	vol%	20.9	1.3	18.3–23.5	12
	Blood, venous, 50 men	Manometry	mmol/L	9.29	0.58	8.13–10.5	vol%	20.8	1.3	18.2–23.4	12
↓Oxygen saturation	Blood, umbilical artery, 19 newborn	Spectrophotometry	mol/mol	0.30	0.09	(0.09–0.51)	%	29.5	9.4	(9.0–51.4)	6
	Blood, umbilical vein, 35 newborn	Spectrophotometry	mol/mol	0.60	0.13	(0.34–0.86)	%	60.0	12.5	(33.8–85.6)	6
	Blood, arterial:										
	31 newborn, 5–10 minutes	Spectrophotometry	mol/mol	0.809	0.104	(0.575–0.935)	%	80.9	10.4	(57.5–93.5)	6
	29 newborn, 60 minutes	Spectrophotometry	mol/mol	0.922	0.055	(0.721–0.973)	%	92.2	5.5	(72.1–97.3)	6
	17 newborn, 24 hours	Spectrophotometry	mol/mol	0.968	0.017	(0.939–0.988)	%	96.8	1.7	(93.9–98.8)	6
	12 children, 1–4 weeks	Manometry	mol/mol	0.952	0.0311	–	%	95.2	3.11	–	7
	13 children, 4–16 months	Manometry	mol/mol	0.925	0.0323	–	%	92.5	3.23	–	7
	50 men	Manometry	mol/mol	0.939	0.010	0.919–0.959	%	93.9	1.0	91.9–95.9	12
	Blood, venous, 50 men	Manometry	mol/mol	0.618	0.037	0.544–0.692	%	61.8	3.7	54.4–69.2	12
	Blood, capillary, 40 adults	Spectrophotometry	mol/mol	0.966	0.012	0.942–0.990	%	96.6	1.2	94.2–99.0	4

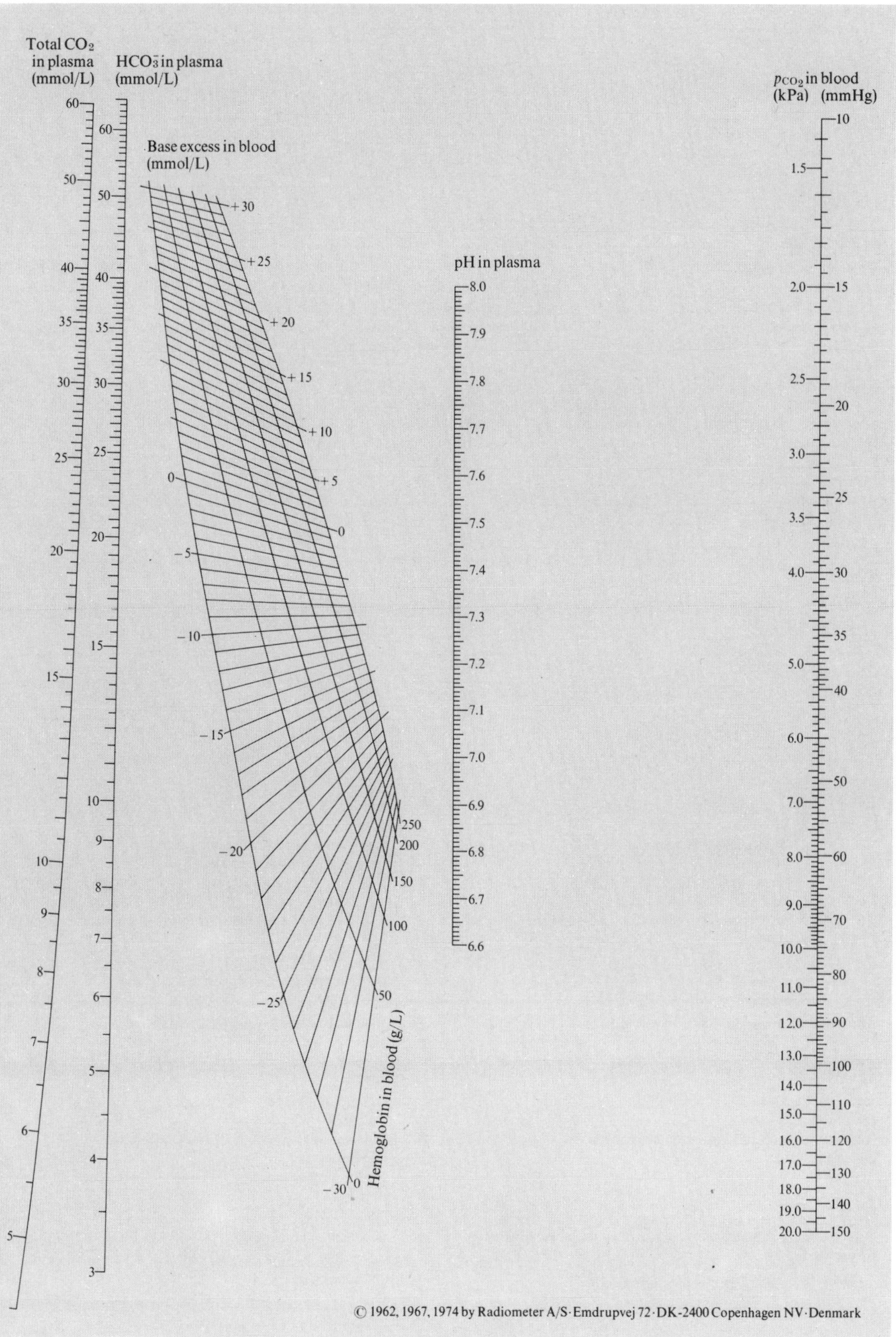

Fig. 1. Nomogram of acid–base status in blood at 37 °C (SIGGAARD-ANDERSEN[4]).

Table 1 *Half-saturation pressure of O_2 (p_{50}) in the blood, erythrocytic 2,3-bisphosphoglycerate, and fetal hemoglobin in relation to age*

Subjects	Age	p_{50} ($t = 37\,°C$; $p_{CO_2} = 5.33$ kPa; pH = 7.4)				2,3-Bisphosphoglycerate in erythrocytes	Substance fraction of fetal to total hemoglobin	Reference
		Mean	s	Mean	s	Mean	Mean	
		kPa		mmHg		mmol/L	%	
13 premature infants	1–3 days	2.65	0.19	19.9	1.44	4.00	74.8	26
11 premature infants	>3 days	2.89	0.25	21.7	1.88	5.54	69.7	26
10 full-term infants	1st day	2.87	0.21	21.5	1.57	3.94	59.1	26
7 full-term infants	2–4 days	2.83	0.18	21.2	1.35	3.93	54.2	26
9 children	5–10 days	3.05	0.19	22.9	1.40	4.93	53.7	26
10 children	11–20 days	3.15	0.18	23.6	1.33	4.80	50.3	26
8 children	21–30 days	3.28	0.19	24.6	1.45	4.59	42.8	26
11 children	31–60 days	3.32	0.18	24.9	1.38	4.31	34.6	26
11 children	61–120 days	3.56	0.35	26.7	2.64	4.73	19.4	26
10 children	121–210 days	3.67	0.32	27.5	2.43	4.77	7.0	26
17 children	>7 months	3.63	0.21	27.2	1.59	4.41	4.1	26
8 children	5.6 years	3.67	0.15	27.5	1.09	3.99	1.2	26
10 adults		3.45	0.17	25.9	1.28	4.11	–	26
27 adults	18–39 years	3.65	0.15	27.4	1.1	4.72	–	27
10 adults	40–59 years	3.72	0.09	27.9	0.7	4.36	–	27
25 adults	60–89 years	3.91	0.15	29.3	1.1	4.56	–	27
32 men	41 years	3.35	0.15	25.1	1.1	4.52	–	28
59 women	27 years	3.55	0.15	26.6	1.1	5.28	–	28
25 men	23.3 years	3.51	0.05	26.3	0.4	3.43	–	29
25 women	20.9 years	3.77	0.05	28.3	0.4	3.53	–	29

Table 2 *Some causes of displacement of the oxygen-binding curve of hemoglobin*[30,31]

Leftward displacement Increase of oxygen affinity (reduction of p_{50})	*Rightward displacement* Decrease of oxygen affinity (increase of p_{50})
Direct effect Decrease of: Temperature Hydrogen ion concentration CO_2 pressure Erythrocyte concentration of 2,3-bisphosphoglycerate Erythrocyte concentration of adenosine triphosphate Ionic strength Increase of: Carboxyhemoglobin Methemoglobin Abnormal hemoglobins (e.g. Hb Malmö)	*Direct effect* Increase of: Temperature Hydrogen ion concentration CO_2 pressure Erythrocyte concentration of 2,3-bisphosphoglycerate Erythrocyte concentration of adenosine triphosphate Ionic strength Decrease of: Erythrocyte concentration of zinc[32] Abnormal hemoglobins (e.g. Hb Kansas)
Indirect effect of decrease of 2,3-bisphosphoglycerate concentration in erythrocytes Increased hydrogen ion concentration Hexokinase deficiency Reduced concentration of inorganic phosphate Old erythrocytes	*Indirect effect of increase of 2,3-bisphosphoglycerate concentration in erythrocytes* Decreased hydrogen ion concentration Pyruvate kinase deficiency Increased concentration of inorganic phosphate Young erythrocytes

150 g/L approximately the following relation holds true between the deviation of standard bicarbonate from the normal value and base excess:

ΔStandard bicarbonate × 1.2 = base excess

For determination of base excess, see the nomogram on page 75 (Fig. 1).

Buffer bases. Sum of concentrations of basic anions having a buffering effect, bicarbonate, hemoglobin and plasma protein in whole blood. For determination of buffer base values, see the nomograms of SINGER and HASTINGS[22] or of VON MENGDEN et al.[23].

Carbon monoxide. For the proportion of carboxyhemoglobin to total hemoglobin, see page 98.

Oxygen pressure. Partial pressure of oxygen (p_{O_2}) in gaseous phase in equilibrium with blood.

Oxygen content. Oxygen content of blood collected and examined in absence of air. Approximately 99% is bound to hemoglo-

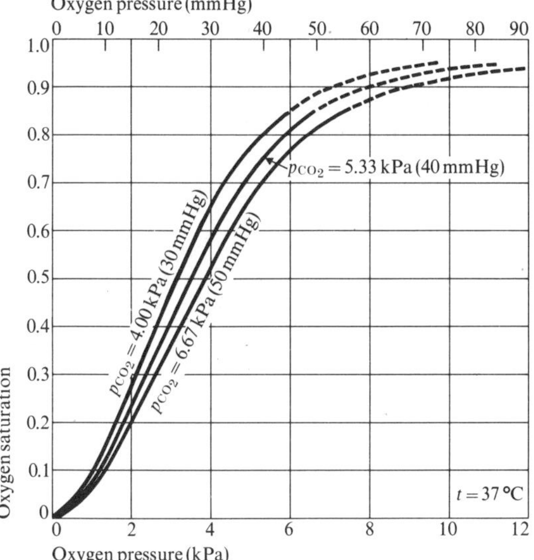

Fig. 2. Oxygen-binding curves of hemoglobin in blood at 37 °C in relation to CO_2 pressure[24].

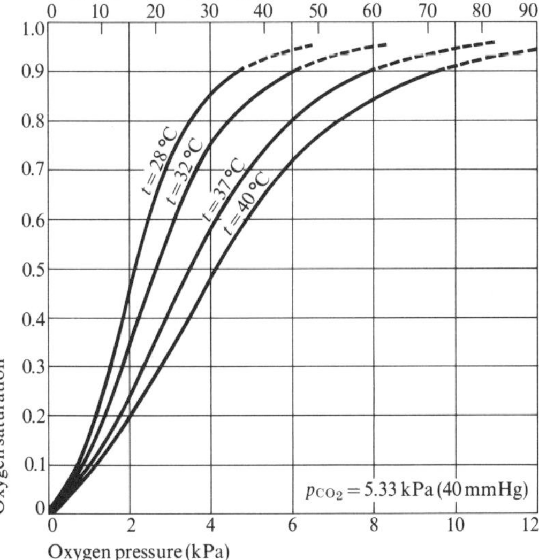

Fig. 3. Oxygen-binding curves of hemoglobin in blood at p_{CO_2} = 5.33 kPa in relation to temperature[24].

bin, while the remainder is physically dissolved (see also ALBRITTON[13]).

Oxygen capacity. Oxygen content of O_2-saturated blood (maximum possible content). The oxygen capacity is frequently equated with the amount of hemoglobin that can be bound to O_2 and calculated from the hemoglobin content, physically dissolved O_2 being ignored. For practical purposes it may be assumed that 1 g of hemoglobin binds in vivo 1.34 mL of O_2 (Hüfner number).

Oxygen saturation. Substance fraction of oxyhemoglobin in relation to total hemoglobin

$$S_{O_2} = \frac{[HbO_2]}{[HbO_2] + [Hb]}$$

other forms of hemoglobin being ignored (page 99). If only deoxygenated hemoglobin is present, the oxygen saturation is 0; if all of the hemoglobin is present as oxyhemoglobin, the oxygen saturation amounts to 1 (previously indicated as 100%).

The oxygen saturation of the hemoglobin is determined, according to the law of mass action, by the partial pressure of oxygen. This relation can be represented graphically by the oxygen-binding curve (Figs. 2 and 3), which is also called an oxyhemoglobin dissociation curve. The theoretical background for the S shape is still being clarified[25].

A measure of the slope of the curve is the half-saturation pressure of O_2 (p_{50}), that is, that partial pressure of O_2 at which the oxygen saturation amounts to 0.5 (50% of the hemoglobin is present as oxyhemoglobin). Normal values of p_{50} are presented in Table 1. The slope of the curve, hence the p_{50} value, is affected by a number of factors, among which pH, p_{CO_2}, and the concentrations of certain phosphates, notably 2,3-bisphosphoglycerate in the erythrocytes (page 113), are the most important (Table 2). The dependence of the oxygen-binding curve on pH and p_{CO_2} is known as the Bohr effect. Indirectly, by way of the 2,3-bisphosphoglycerate concentration, the p_{50} value is also influenced by hormones (thyroid hormones, corticosteroids)[33]. The steeper slope of the oxygen-binding curve for fetal blood (reduced p_{50} values) is attributable to the fact that 2,3-bisphosphoglycerate is bound to a lesser extent by Hb F than by Hb A so that oxygen is released less readily from the fetal oxyhemoglobin than from adult hemoglobin[34].

References

[1] GAMBINO et al., *Ann. N. Y. Acad. Sci.,* **133**, 259 (1966).
[2] GAMBINO, S.R., *Stand. Meth. clin. Chem.,* **6**, 171 (1970).
[3] BARTELS et al., *Lungenfunktionsprüfungen,* Springer, Berlin, 1959; CONSOLAZIO et al., *Physiological Measurements of Metabolic Functions in Man,* McGraw-Hill, New York, 1963, pages 99 and 132; RICHTERICH, R., *Klinische Chemie,* 3rd ed., Karger, Basle, 1971; ALBERS, C., in KOENIG, W. (Ed.), *Klinisch-physiologische Untersuchungsmethoden,* Thieme, Stuttgart, 1972, page 163.
[4] SIGGAARD-ANDERSEN, O., *Scand. J. clin. Lab. Invest.,* **15**, suppl. 70 (1963); ASTRUP and SIGGAARD-ANDERSEN, *Advanc. clin. Chem.* **6**, 1 (1963); SIGGAARD-ANDERSEN, O., *The Acid–Base Status of the Blood,* 4th ed., Munksgaard, Copenhagen, 1974.
[5] MØLLER, B., *Acta med. scand.,* **165**, suppl. 348, 1 (1959).
[6] KOCH and WENDEL, *Biol. Neonat. (Basel),* **12**, 136 (1968).
[7] RIEGEL, K., *Klin. Wschr.,* **41**, 249 (1963).
[8] LIAPPIS and KALLFELZ, *Klin. Wschr.,* **50**, 471 (1972).
[9] ULMER and REICHEL, *Klin. Wschr.,* **41**, 1 (1963).
[10] ROOTH, G., *Acta paediat. (Uppsala),* **52**, 22 (1963).
[11] KENNEDY and SOKOLOFF, *J. clin. Invest.,* **36**, 1130 (1957).
[12] GIBBS et al., *J. biol. Chem.,* **144**, 325 (1942).
[13] ALBRITTON, E.C. (Ed.), *Standard Values in Blood,* Saunders, Philadelphia, 1952, page 120; BARTELS and OPITZ, in DITTMER and GREBE (Eds.), *Handbook of Respiration,* Saunders, Philadelphia, 1958, page 56.
[14] BARTELS and WENNER, *Klin. Wschr.,* **43**, 437 (1965).
[15] SCHWAB, M., *Klin. Wschr.,* **40**, 765 (1962).
[16] GAMBINO, S.R., *Amer. J. clin. Path.,* **32**, 294 (1959).
[17] HODES, M.E., *Stand. Meth. clin. Chem.,* **1**, 19 (1953).
[18] SALING, E., *Das Kind im Bereich der Geburtshilfe,* Thieme, Stuttgart, 1966.
[19] SINGER and HASTINGS, in DITTMER, D.S. (Ed.), *Blood and Other Body Fluids,* Federation of American Societies for Experimental Biology, Washington, 1961, page 183.
[20] MCCREDIE and JOSE, *J. appl. Physiol.,* **22**, 863 (1967).
[21] VÁVROVÁ et al., *Poumon,* **25**, 1121 (1969).
[22] SINGER and HASTINGS, *Medicine (Baltimore),* **27**, 223 (1948).
[23] VON MENGDEN et al., in THEWS, G. (Ed.), *Nomogramme zum Säure–Basen-Status des Blutes und zum Atemgastransport,* Springer, Berlin, 1971, page 1.
[24] GROTE, J., in THEWS, G. (Ed.), *Nomogramme zum Säure–Basen-Status des Blutes und zum Atemgastransport,* Springer, Berlin, 1971, page 47.
[25] PERUTZ, M.F., *Brit. med. Bull.,* **32**, 195 (1976); KILMARTIN, J.V., *Brit. med. Bull.,* **32**, 209 (1976); BALDWIN, J.M., *Brit. med. Bull.,* **32**, 213 (1976).
[26] VERSMOLD et al., *Resp. Physiol.,* **18**, 14 (1973).
[27] TWEEDDALE et al., *Clin. Sci.,* **51**, 185 (1976).
[28] ARTURSON and ROBERT, *Acta anaesth. scand.,* suppl. 45, 22 (1971).
[29] HUMPELER and AMOR, *Pflügers Arch. ges. Physiol.,* **343**, 151 (1973).
[30] SHAPPELL and LENFANT, *Anaesthesiology,* **37**, 127 (1972).
[31] CANIZARO et al., *Ann. Surg.,* **180**, 364 (1974).
[32] OELSHLEGEL et al., *Biochem. biophys. Res. Commun.,* **53**, 560 (1973).
[33] THOMAS et al., *Amer. J. Med.,* **57**, 331 (1974).
[34] NELSON, N.M., in SMITH and NELSON, *The Physiology of the Newborn Infant,* 4th ed., Thomas, Springfield, 1976, page 117.

Inorganic substances (for references see pages 88 and 89)

↓See text below	B Blood, P Plasma, S Serum, Erys Erythrocytes, Lkcs Leukocytes, Plts Platelets	Amount of substance				Mass				Reference
		Unit	Mean	*s*	95% range (extreme range in brackets)	Unit	Mean	*s*	95% range (extreme range in brackets)	
↓**Water**	B	mol/L	47.2	–	(46.0–48.0)	g/L	850	–	(830–865)	1
	P	mol/L	52.4	–	(51.6–53.0)	g/L	945	–	(930–955)	1
	P 7 newborn, 1 day	mol/kg	51.4	0.3	–	g/kg	927	5	–	11
	P 34 children, 6–11 months	mol/kg	51.1	1.6	–	g/kg	921	29	–	2
	Erys 6 newborn, 1 day	mol/kg	36.3	0.4	–	g/kg	654	7	–	11
	Erys 70 children, 4–36 months	mol/kg	36.8	0.49	35.8–37.8	g/kg	664	8.9	646–682	5
	Erys 50 adults	mol/kg	37.8	0.8	36.2–39.4	g/kg	681	14	654–709	3
	Erys 128 adults	mol/kg	37.0	0.5	36.0–38.0	g/kg	666	9	648–684	4
	Lkcs	mol/kg	40.2	–	–	g/kg	725	–	–	6
	Plts 7 men	mol/kg	39.7	0.8	(38.8–41.2)	g/kg	715	15	(699–742)	153
↓**Dry mass**	B (a)	...	...	...	...	g/L	210	–	(195–230)	–
	P (a)	...	...	...	...	g/L	80	–	(75–100)	–
	Erys 128 adults	...	...	...	...	g/kg	334	9	316–352	4
	Lkcs 15 adults	...	...	...	...	g/kg	265	12	–	60
↓**Bicarbonate**	P Arterial, 15 adults	mmol/L	24.9	1.79	–	...	...	...	...	9
	Erys 9 adults	mmol/L	11.2	0.15	(10.8–12.0)	...	...	...	...	10
↓**Chloride**	P(S) 50 newborn, 2 days (a)	mmol/L	110	4.5	101–119	g/L	3.90	0.16	3.58–4.22	12
	– 515 infants, children (b)	mmol/L	103.2	2.64	98–109	g/L	3.66	0.094	3.47–3.85	13
	– 65 adults (b)	mmol/L	103.7	1.90	100–108	g/L	3.68	0.067	3.55–3.81	13
	– 31 adults (c)	mmol/L	104	–	101–109	g/L	3.69	–	3.58–3.86	14
	– 246 adults (d)	mmol/L	–	–	98–107	g/L	–	–	3.47–3.79	15
	Erys 37 adults	mmol/L	67.9	4.9	58.1–77.7	g/L	2.41	0.17	2.07–2.75	16
	Erys 70 children, 4–36 months	mmol/kg	47.6	2.8	42.0–53.2	g/kg	1.69	0.10	1.49–1.89	5

Water. Erythrocyte water content increases with decreasing hemoglobin content[7]. In man plasma water content is highest in the supine position and decreases during muscular activity. In leukocytes the water content depends on type and degree of maturity[8].

Dry mass. (a) Calculated from water content and relative density. – In whole blood, about 90% of the dry mass are organic substances.

Bicarbonate. The values shown were obtained by calculation. See also pages 72 and 73. – *Pathological* changes reflect the metabolic component of disturbances of acid-base status. Extreme metabolic alkalosis (values to 70 mmol/L) in pyloric stenosis and in chloride diarrhea; lowest values below 5 mmol/L in ammonium chloride intoxication, diabetic acidosis, lactacidosis, methylmalonic acidosis, and in intoxications with methanol, ethylene glycol, and paraldehyde.

Chloride. Data determined (a) mercurimetrically; (b) potentiometrically; (c) colorimetrically; (d) by automated technique. – *Pathological* alterations reflect either disturbances of sodium metabolism (page 81) or the metabolic component of acidoses and alkaloses. The highest values – up to 170 mmol/L – are found in osmotic diuresis plus inadequate water intake, in the presence of a deranged thirst-regulating mechanism, nephrogenic diabetes insipidus and enteral bicarbonate loss; the lowest values – down to 30 mmol/L – occur in the presence of gastrointestinal chloride loss (vomiting, chloride diarrhea) (Table 1).

Phosphorus. In the erythrocytes, phosphorus is found for the most part in the form of phosphoric acid esters (nucleotides, sugar phosphates and bisphosphoglycerate); inorganic phosphate occurs in small amounts only. In the serum, lipid phosphorus predominates (see 'Phospholipids', page 116), and nearly all the inorganic phosphorus is in the form of orthophosphate.

Inorganic phosphorus in serum. It should be determined in fasting serum. See the literature regarding methods[25]. At pH 7.4 the serum phosphate is made up of about 80% primary phosphate and about 20% secondary phosphate; small quantities are bound to proteins[26].

The serum phosphate level is increased in the first few days after birth[18,27,28]. In children it is decidedly higher than in adults but

Table 1a *Differentiation of hyperchloridemia[143] (highest recorded values about 170 mmol/L)*

In hypernatremia:	*In acidosis:*
NaCl intoxication	Renal tubular acidoses
Lesions in hypothalamic-neurohypophyseal region	Ammonium chloride administration
Osmotic diuresis (see sodium [Table 4a, page 82])	Ureteral enterostomy
Hyperosmolar coma without ketoacidosis	Diarrhea
Nephrogenic diabetes insipidus	(Hyperventilation)
Primary hyperparathyroidism	

Table 1b *Differentiation of hypochloridemia[143] (lowest recorded values about 30 mmol/L)*

In hyponatremia:	*In alkalosis:*
Water intoxication	Loss of gastric acid (anorexia nervosa, pyloric stenosis, gastrointestinal fistulae)
Acute renal failure	Chloride diarrhea
Cardiac, hepatic insufficiency	Cushing's syndrome
Excessive vasopressin secretion	Primary hyperaldosteronism (Conn's syndrome)
Addison's disease	
Administration of diuretics	
Bartter's syndrome	

toward the end of skeletal ossification it approaches the adult level[31,32]. See Figure 1 concerning sex and age dependence. See the literature on phosphate metabolism[33]. The serum phosphate level is *pathologically* elevated in hypoparathyroidism, pseudohypoparathyroidism, and renal insufficiency (up to 7.1 mmol/L). It is reduced (to 0.32 mmol/L and below) in hyperparathyroidism,

↑ See text on previous page	B Blood, P Plasma, S Serum, Erys Erythrocytes, Lkcs Leukocytes, Plts Platelets	Amount of substance				Mass				Reference
		Unit	Mean	s	95% range (extreme range in brackets)	Unit	Mean	s	95% range (extreme range in brackets)	
↑ Phosphorus										
Total phosphorus ...	B 42 subjects	mmol/L	11.9	–	(10.1–14.3)	mg/L	370	–	(314–443)	17
	P 42 subjects	mmol/L	3.62	–	(2.87–4.81)	mg/L	112	–	(89–149)	17
	Erys 42 subjects	mmol/L	23.2	–	(19.7–28.0)	mg/L	719	–	(609–867)	17
↑ Inorganic phosphorus	P(S) Umbilical vein, 43 newborn	mmol/L	1.84	0.28	1.29–2.40	mg/L	57	8.7	40–74	18
	– 126 newborn, 1st day	mmol/L	2.03	0.32	1.39–2.67	mg/L	63	10	43–83	18
	– 23 children, 6 months to 6 years	mmol/L	1.82	0.26	–	mg/L	56.5	8.1	–	19
	– 44 children, 6–12 years	mmol/L	1.64	0.18	1.28–2.00	mg/L	50.9	5.7	39.5–62.3	19
	– 46 youths, 12–20 years	mmol/L	1.54	0.25	1.05–2.05	mg/L	47.8	7.6	32.6–63.0	19
	– 144 men	mmol/L	–	–	0.71–1.36	mg/L	–	–	22–42	15
	– 139 women	mmol/L	–	–	0.77–1.36	mg/L	–	–	24–42	15
	Erys 30 adults	mmol/L	0.087	0.036	(0.03–0.13)	mg/L	2.7	1.1	(1–4)	20
	Plts	mmol/kg	1.59	–	–	mg/kg	49.2	–	–	21
Phosphoric acid ester phosphorus .... (without lipid phosphorus)	B 42 subjects	mmol/L	7.46	–	(6.01–9.23)	mg/L	231	–	(186–286)	17
	P 42 subjects	mmol/L	1.10	–	(0.81–1.45)	mg/L	34	–	(25–45)	17
	Erys 42 subjects	mmol/L	16.0	–	(12.3–19.0)	mg/L	497	–	(385–587)	17
Lipid phosphorus ...	P 42 subjects	mmol/L	2.68	–	(2.23–3.13)	mg/L	83	–	(69–97)	17
	Erys 20 subjects	mmol/L	4.42	0.21	(4.13–4.81)	mg/L	137	6.5	(128–149)	24
	Lkcs 4 subjects	mmol/10^{12}	9.0	1.7	–	mg/10^{12}	280	53	–	29
	Plts 9 subjects	mmol/10^{12}	0.57	0.13	–	mg/10^{12}	1.68	0.39	–	30
Inorganic pyrophosphate	P 94 subjects	µmol/L	1.8	0.58	0.64–2.96	...	...	...	...	22
	P 15 adults	µmol/L	2.72	0.29	(1.90–4.00)	...	...	...	...	129
	S 15 adults	µmol/L	6.09	0.73	(3.40–9.10)	...	...	...	...	129
	Erys 11 specimens	µmol/10^{12}	1.74	0.91	–	...	...	...	...	129
	Plts 6 subjects	µmol/10^{12}	–	–	(14–31)	...	...	...	...	23

disturbances of calcium or phosphate absorption, vitamin D-deficiency rickets, vitamin D-resistant osteomalacia, renal tubular acidosis (Albright type), Fanconi's syndrome, phosphate diabetes, and intravenous hyperalimentation.

Sulfur. (a) Plasma values calculated from whole blood and erythrocyte values. – Approximately 95% of the sulfur in the blood is contained in the proteins. The fraction of sulfuric acid esters contains indoxyl sulfate (page 97) and other conjugated sulfuric acids, while the neutral sulfur fraction contains free sulfur-bearing amino acids, glutathione, ergothioneine and other compounds. The serum concentration of inorganic sulfate is increased in cases of renal failure[36].

Bromide. The bromide level of the blood appears to be subject to wide individual variations. It is increased after bromide medication. A concentration above 31 mmol/L is certain to be toxic[40].

Fluoride. The concentration in the serum increases after fluoride intake[41].

Iodine. (a) Approximately 0.05% of thyroxine and 0.5% of triiodothyronine are present in the serum in free form. – A minor proportion of the iodine in the serum is in the form of inorganic iodide, the concentration of which is affected by iodine intake; the major portion is composed of thyroxine and triiodothyronine, all but traces of which are bound to serum proteins. Two methods of estimating organic-bound iodine in serum are available[49–51]: one gives the protein-bound iodine (PBI), the other the butanol-extractable iodine (BEI). PBI consists of the thyroxine iodine and triiodothyronine iodine and, if present, the iodine of mono-iodotyrosine, diiodotyrosine, iodinated proteins and iodinated organic compounds such as radiographic contrast media, for example[49–51]. BEI is more specific since it does not estimate the iodotyrosines and iodinated proteins. In view of the relative non-specificity of the methods, direct assay of the serum thyroxine and triiodothyronine is recommended for thyroid diagnosis.

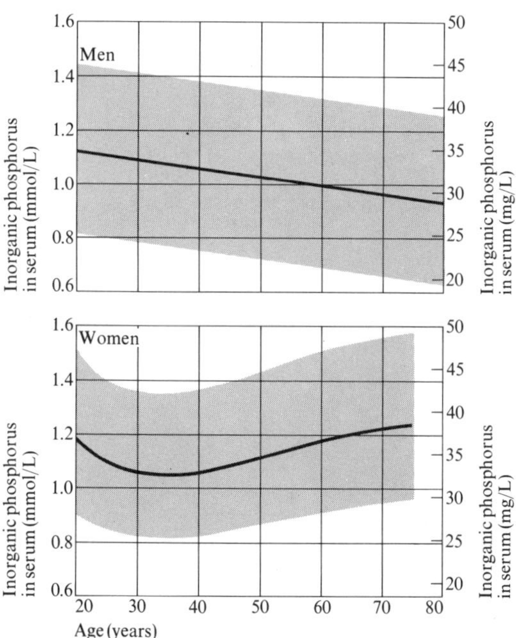

Fig. 1. Concentration of inorganic phosphorus in serum of men and women in relation to age (regression line and 95% range)[74].

↑ See text on previous page	B Blood, P Plasma, S Serum, Erys Erythrocytes, Lkcs Leukocytes, Plts Platelets	Amount of substance				Mass				Reference
		Unit	Mean	s	95% range (extreme range in brackets)	Unit	Mean	s	95% range (extreme range in brackets)	
↑ Sulfur										
Total sulfur	B	mmol/L	38.1	–	–	mg/L	1220	–	–	34
	P (a)	mmol/L	24.3	–	–	mg/L	780	–	–	–
	Erys	mmol/L	59.3	–	–	mg/L	1900	–	–	34
Protein sulfur	B	mmol/L	36.8	–	–	mg/L	1180	–	–	34
	P (a)	mmol/L	23.1	–	–	mg/L	740	–	–	–
	Erys	mmol/L	58.0	–	–	mg/L	1860	–	–	34
Nonprotein sulfur	P 16 adults	mmol/L	1.05	–	(0.92–1.17)	mg/L	33.8	–	(29.5–37.5)	35
Inorganic sulfate sulfur	P 16 adults	mmol/L	0.49	–	(0.31–0.58)	mg/L	15.7	–	(10.0–18.5)	35
Sulfuric acid ester sulfur	P 16 adults	mmol/L	0.12	–	(0.08–0.20)	mg/L	3.9	–	(2.5–6.5)	35
Neutral sulfur	P 16 adults	mmol/L	0.44	–	(0.28–0.61)	mg/L	14.2	–	(9.0–19.5)	35
Inorganic sulfate	P(S) Newborn, 1st day	mmol/L	0.47	–	0.29–0.95	...	...	...	...	155
	– Children, 36 months	mmol/L	0.33	–	0.22–0.67	...	...	...	...	155
	– 10 adults	mmol/L	0.33	–	0.22–0.43	...	...	...	...	155
	– 88 adults	mmol/L	0.33	0.09	0.15–0.51	...	...	...	...	36
↑ Bromide	B 5 adults	µmol/kg	49	25	–	mg/kg	3.9	2.0	–	37
	B 35 men	µmol/L	43.3	8.6	(33.0–67.2)	mg/L	3.46	0.69	(2.64–5.37)	38
	B 38 women	µmol/L	50.6	9.6	(32.9–73.8)	mg/L	4.04	0.77	(2.63–5.90)	38
	P(S) 35 men	µmol/L	63.6	11.8	(49.4–90.7)	mg/L	5.08	0.94	(3.95–7.25)	38
	– 38 women	µmol/L	64.3	5.8	(42.8–93.2)	mg/L	5.14	0.46	(3.42–7.45)	38
	– 10 subjects	µmol/L	60.9	25.3	(16.0–93.6)	mg/L	4.87	2.02	(1.28–7.48)	39
↑ Fluoride										
– total	P 66 subjects, 21–30 years	µmol/L	4.74	1.75	–	µg/L	90	33	–	42
	P 39 subjects, > 60 years	µmol/L	6.58	2.14	–	µg/L	125	41	–	42
– ionized	P 66 subjects, 21–30 years	µmol/L	2.84	1.36	–	µg/L	54	26	–	42
	P 39 subjects, > 60 years	µmol/L	3.89	1.61	–	µg/L	74	31	–	42
	S 26 subjects	µmol/L	1.95	0.49	(0.84–2.90)	µg/L	37	9	(16–55)	43
↑ Iodine										
– total	S 12 subjects	nmol/L	410	–	(300–470)	µg/L	52	–	(38–60)	44
– inorganic	P	nmol/L	–	–	6–47	µg/L	–	–	0.8–6.0	45
– protein-bound	S 12 subjects	nmol/L	380	–	(280–440)	µg/L	48	–	(35–56)	44
	S 125 subjects	nmol/L	410	78	250–570	µg/L	52	10	32–72	46
Thyroxine iodine	S 241 adults	nmol/L	320	76	165–470	µg/L	40.6	9.7	21–60	47
– not protein-bound	S (a)	nmol/L	~0.16	–	–	µg/L	~0.02	–	–	–
Triiodothyronine iodine	S 31 adults	nmol/L	10	1.3	–	µg/L	1.3	0.16	–	48
– not protein-bound	S (a)	nmol/L	~0.08	–	–	µg/L	~0.01	–	–	–

Table 2 *Clinical reference ranges of protein-bound serum iodine*[51]

	nmol/L
Children	
Cord blood	390–790
1st week	630–1260
2nd week	360–830
3 weeks to 3 months	320–830
3 months to 5 years	320–670
5 years to puberty	320–550
Men	
Puberty to 18 years	280–510
> 18 years	280–590
Women	
Not using oral contraceptives	320–630
Using oral contraceptives	360–1060
Pregnancy, 3rd week to end of 2nd trimester	360–910
Pregnancy, 3rd trimester to 1 week post partum	590–1060

PBI: for various reference ranges see Table 2. Both normal values and values up to about 1700 nmol/L are found in hyperthyroidism; in hypothyroidism the iodine concentration varies between 180 nmol/L and 300 nmol/L[51].

Cyanide. Fatal poisoning can occur at blood levels of about 100 µmol/L (2.5 mg/L)[53,56]. There is an equilibrium between cyanide and thiocyanate in the plasma[55].

Borate. Sizable amounts of borate, for example, owing to increased transdermal absorption during use of boric acid-containing preparations, are toxic.

Silicate. The concentration is independent of age, sex, or diseases (including silicosis).

Potassium. All the values shown were determined by flame photometry. – The potassium concentration in the plasma is about 10% lower than that in the serum since potassium is released from the platelets during coagulation[65,66]. In non-deproteinized serum the potassium concentration is approximately 5% lower than in a protein-free filtrate.

The cord serum shows significantly higher values than the maternal serum[11,27]. In newborn and nursing infants the serum level

↑See text on previous page	B Blood, P Plasma, S Serum, Erys Erythrocytes, Lkcs Leukocytes, Plts Platelets	Amount of substance				Mass				Reference
		Unit	Mean	*s*	95% range (extreme range in brackets)	Unit	Mean	*s*	95% range (extreme range in brackets)	
Thiocyanate	B 30 nonsmokers	μmol/L	30.7	28.8	(10–166)	...	...	...	...	53
	24 smokers	μmol/L	59.8	26.1	(18–110)	...	...	...	...	53
	P 40 nonsmokers	μmol/L	20.2	9.5	–	...	...	...	...	54
	23 smokers	μmol/L	82.0	41.0	–	...	...	...	...	54
↑ **Cyanide**	B 29 nonsmokers	μmol/L	2.9	2.4	(0–11.7)	...	...	...	...	53
	27 smokers	μmol/L	6.8	4.2	(1.3–19.4)	...	...	...	...	53
↑ **Borate** (as boron)	B 34 children	μmol/L	23	–	(0–116)	mg/L	0.25	–	(0–1.25)	57
Nitrite	B	μmol/L	0.17	–	(0–0.35)	μg/L	8	–	(0–16)	58
Nitrate	B 30 newborn, 0–7 days	μmol/L	47.8	18.7	–	mg/L	2.96	1.16	–	52
	– 30 children, 1 week to 1½ years	μmol/L	37.1	19.7	–	mg/L	2.30	1.22	–	52
	– 30 children, 1½–15 years	μmol/L	29.7	16.6	–	mg/L	1.84	1.03	–	52
	– 40 adults	μmol/L	37.7	15.4	–	mg/L	2.34	0.95	–	52
↑ **Silicate** (as SiO_2)	B 264 subjects	μmol/L	138	40	58–218	mg/L	8.3	2.4	3.5–13.1	59
↑ **Potassium**	P 50 newborn, 2 days	mmol/L	4.56	0.56	3.4–5.7	mg/L	178	22	130–220	12
	P 57 children, 1–35 months	mmol/L	4.6	0.5	3.6–5.6	mg/L	180	20	140–220	61
	P 57 adults	mmol/L	4.03	–	3.5–4.6	mg/L	158	–	140–180	62
	P 10 newborn, 1 day	mmol/kg	4.65	0.13	–	mg/kg	182	5.1	–	11
	S 65 adults	mmol/L	4.10	0.29	3.5–4.7	mg/L	160	11	140–180	13
	S 115 men	mmol/L	–	–	3.6–4.8	mg/L	–	–	140–190	15
	S 118 women	mmol/L	–	–	3.6–4.6	mg/L	–	–	140–180	15
	S 37 adults	mmol/L	4.05	0.34	3.4–4.7	mg/L	158	13	132–184	16
	Erys 37 adults	mmol/L	88	6	76–100	g/L	3.44	0.24	2.97–3.91	16
	Erys 157 adults	mmol/L	99.1	5.3	88.5–110	g/L	3.87	0.21	3.46–4.30	63
	Erys 30 adults	mmol/L	102	3.9	94–110	g/L	4.00	0.15	3.68–4.30	144
	Erys 10 newborn, 1 day	mmol/kg	97.3	1.6	–	g/kg	3.80	0.06	–	11
	Erys 70 children, 4–36 months	mmol/kg	91.8	3.2	85.4–98.2	g/kg	3.59	0.13	3.33–3.85	5
	Plts 7 subjects	mmol/kg	69.1	–	(65–71)	g/kg	2.70	–	(2.54–2.78)	64
	Plts ('pure'), 7 subjects	mmol/kg	122	27	(62–151)	g/kg	4.39	1.06	(2.42–5.92)	153
	Relative to solids: Lkcs 15 adults	mmol/kg	379	21	–	g/kg	14.8	0.82	–	60

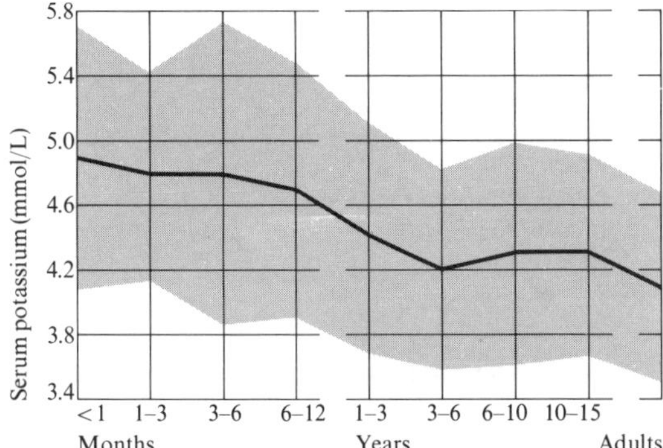

Fig. 2. Potassium concentration in serum in relation to age (means and 95% range)[13].

of potassium is increased (Fig. 2); in children and adults it is independent of age and sex[67]. See Tables 3a and 3b for pathological changes in serum potassium values.

Sodium. Data (a) determined by neutron activation; all others by means of flame photometry. – In non-deproteinized serum the sodium concentration is about 5% lower than in the protein-free filtrate. Differences in normal values may be due to different standards[69].

Table 3a *Differentiation of hyperkalemia*[143] *(highest recorded values about 10 mmol/L)*

Excessive potassium intake:
Particularly with intravenous administration
In renal insufficiency

Escape of intracellular potassium:
Fasting
Muscle trauma
Myocardial infarction
Administration of succinylcholine
Hyperkalemic periodic paralysis
Malignant hyperpyrexia
Hypothermia
Acidoses (diabetic ketoacidosis, lactacidosis, methanol and salicylate intoxications)

Renal potassium retention:
Anuric phase of renal insufficiency
Acute tubular necrosis
Administration of spironolactone, triamterene, amiloride
Addison's disease
Congenital adrenocortical hyperplasia with salt depletion (sodium deficiency)

During pregnancy, the sodium concentration in plasma[71] declines and that in the erythrocytes[27] tends to be lower than in non-pregnant women. The serum sodium levels of neonates and their mothers are for the most part equal but the sodium concentration

↑ See text on previous page	B Blood, P Plasma, S Serum, Erys Erythrocytes, Lkcs Leukocytes, Plts Platelets	Amount of substance				Mass				Reference
		Unit	Mean	s	95% range (extreme range in brackets)	Unit	Mean	s	95% range (extreme range in brackets)	
↑ **Sodium**	P(S) 50 newborn, 2 days	mmol/L	144	5.7	133–155	g/L	3.31	0.13	3.05–3.57	12
	– 518 infants and children	mmol/L	139.1	2.02	135–143	g/L	3.20	0.046	3.11–3.29	13
	– 65 adults	mmol/L	140.0	2.38	135–145	g/L	3.22	0.055	3.11–3.33	13
	– 246 adults	mmol/L	–	–	134–143	g/L	–	–	3.08–3.29	15
	– 20 adults (a)	mmol/L	142.6	2.45	(138–146)	g/L	3.28	0.056	(3.17–3.36)	68
	– 10 newborn, 1 day	mmol/kg	140	0.3	–	g/kg	3.22	0.07	–	11
	Erys 159 adults	mmol/L	7.35	1.26	4.83–9.87	mg/L	169	29	111–227	63
	Erys 30 adults	mmol/L	6.2	0.8	4.6–7.8	mg/L	143	18	106–179	144
	Erys 10 newborn, 1 day	mmol/kg	10.3	0.79	–	mg/kg	237	18	–	11
	Erys 70 children, 4–36 months	mmol/kg	8.8	1.6	5.6–12.0	mg/kg	200	37	130–280	5
	Plts 7 subjects	mmol/kg	27	–	(25–28)	mg/kg	621	–	(575–644)	64
	Relative to solids:									
	Lkcs 15 adults	mmol/kg	119	17	–	g/kg	2.74	0.39	–	60

Table 3b *Differentiation of hypokalemia*[143] *(lowest recorded values about 1 mmol/L)*

Inadequate potassium intake:
Prolonged fasting
Enteral malabsorption

Passage of potassium into cells:
Alkalosis
Hypokalemic periodic paralysis
Administration of insulin

Potassium loss with digestive juices:
Vomiting (pyloric stenosis, anorexia nervosa)
Diarrhea (malabsorption syndrome, intestinal infections, laxative abuse, Verner-Morrison syndrome)

Renal potassium loss:
Ureteral enterostomy
Administration of diuretics (thiazides etc.)
Polyuric phase of renal insufficiency
Impairment of tubular function (pyelonephritis, renal tubular acidosis, Liddle's syndrome)
Quinine intoxication
Administration of corticosteroids
Cushing's syndrome
Primary hyperaldosteronism (Conn's syndrome)
Deficiency of steroid 17α-monooxygenase
Administration of carbenoxolone
Secondary hyperaldosteronism (renovascular, essential and malignant hypertension, pheochromocytoma, Bartter's syndrome, postoperative hypokalemia)
(Hyperthyroidism)

of the erythrocytes is higher in newborn than in their mothers[11,27]. The serum sodium level remains nearly constant throughout life except for slightly higher values in the neonate. *Pathological* changes in the serum level of sodium are summarized in Table 4. The sodium concentration in the erythrocytes is increased in hyperthyroidism[70].

Calcium. Determination of data (a) by the EDTA method; (b) by atomic absorption; (c) by means of an ion-specific electrode (ionized calcium). – EDTA titration and atomic absorption are the preferred methods of determining calcium[78,79]. Values obtained by flame photometry or oxalate precipitation tend to be higher[80,81]. Ionized calcium can be determined directly with the aid of a calcium electrode or, if the protein concentration is known, from the total calcium concentration (Fig. 3). 35–50% of the serum calcium is bound to proteins, 50–60% is ionized, and 5–10% complexed with organic acids[82].

In the course of pregnancy the serum level of total calcium decreases about 10%[83], but that of ionized calcium increases slightly[164]. In the newborn it is slightly lower than in older children. See Figure 4 regarding the age and sex dependence in adults. See the literature concerning calcium metabolism[33,76]. *Pathologi-*

Table 4a *Differentiation of hypernatremia*[143] *(highest recorded values in the range 170–200 mmol/L)*

Excessive sodium intake at inadequate water intake (young children are particularly at risk)

Sodium retention:
Administration of mineralocorticoids
Primary hyperaldosteronism (Conn's syndrome)
Cushing's syndrome

Excessive water depletion:
Lesions in hypothalamic–hypophyseal area (hypophyseal diabetes insipidus in cerebral trauma, etc.)
Osmotic diuresis following excessive protein intake, gastrointestinal hemorrhages, mannitol infusions, urea infusions, and in connection with hyperglucosemia
Disturbances in mechanism of urine concentration (renal tubular acidosis, nephrogenic diabetes insipidus, hyperthyroidism)
Loss through lungs and skin (fever); tracheotomy
Diarrhea

Table 4b *Differentiation of hyponatremia*[143] *(lowest recorded values about 90 mmol/L)*

Excessive water intake at inadequate sodium intake (rare, e.g. after enemas, gastric lavage)

Expansion of extracellular fluid:
After mannitol infusions
In hyperglucosemia

Water retention:
Acute renal failure
Hepatic and cardiac insufficiency
Excessive secretion of vasopressin
Hypothyroidism

Increased loss of sodium with digestive juices:
Pyloric stenosis
Electrolyte-losing villous adenoma of large intestine

Renal sodium loss:
Diuretics
Addison's disease
Congenital adrenocortical hyperplasia
Bartter's syndrome
Salt-losing nephritis

↑ See text on previous page	B Blood, P Plasma, S Serum, Erys Erythrocytes, Lkcs Leukocytes, Plts Platelets	Amount of substance				Mass				Reference
		Unit	Mean	s	95% range (extreme range in brackets)	Unit	Mean	s	95% range (extreme range in brackets)	
↑**Calcium**	P(S) Umbilical vein, 57 newborn .... (a)	mmol/L	2.59	0.15	2.29–2.89	mg/L	104	6.2	97–116	18
	– 132 newborn, 1st day ... (a)	mmol/L	2.22	0.19	1.84–2.60	mg/L	89	7.7	74–104	18
	– 27 children, 6 months to 6 years .... (b)	mmol/L	2.51	0.09	–	mg/L	100.5	3.5	–	19
	– 45 children, 6–12 years . (b)	mmol/L	2.46	0.06	2.34–2.58	mg/L	98.4	2.3	93.8–103	19
	– 47 youths, 12–20 years .. (b)	mmol/L	2.43	0.07	2.29–2.57	mg/L	97.5	2.7	92.1–103	19
	– 132 men................ (a)	mmol/L	–	–	2.25–2.59	mg/L	–	–	90–104	15
	– 116 women............. (a)	mmol/L	–	–	2.17–2.54	mg/L	–	–	87–102	15
	– 81 adults .... (b)	mmol/L	2.44	0.10	2.24–2.64	mg/L	97.8	4	89.8–106	72
	– 40 adults .... (b)	mmol/L	2.42	0.15	2.12–2.72	mg/L	97	6	85–109	73
	Erys 14 adults............ (b)	µmol/L	24.9	8.2	–	mg/L	0.99	0.33	–	141
	Erys 39 adults............ (b)	µmol/L	19	9	–	mg/L	0.76	0.36	–	145
	Plts 20 subjects........... (b)	mmol/10^{12}	1.5	0.4	–	mg/10^{12}	60	15	–	146
– ultrafiltratable.....	S 40 adults	mmol/L	1.37	0.10	1.17–1.57	mg/L	55	4	47–63	73
– ionized...........	P(S) 40 newborn, 1st day · (c)	mmol/L	1.02	0.15	(0.62–1.2)	mg/L	41	6	(25–50)	75
	– 7 children, 6 months to 6 years .... (c)	mmol/L	1.10	0.06	–	mg/L	44.1	2.5	–	19
	– 28 children, 6–12 years . (c)	mmol/L	1.15	0.06	–	mg/L	45.9	2.6	–	19
	– 32 youths, 12–20 years .. (c)	mmol/L	1.08	0.06	–	mg/L	43.3	2.5	–	19
	– 81 adults .... (c)	mmol/L	1.22	0.045	1.13–1.32	mg/L	48.7	1.8	45.1–52.3	72
	– 40 adults .... (c)	mmol/L	1.26	0.035	1.19–1.33	mg/L	50.7	1.4	47.9–53.5	73

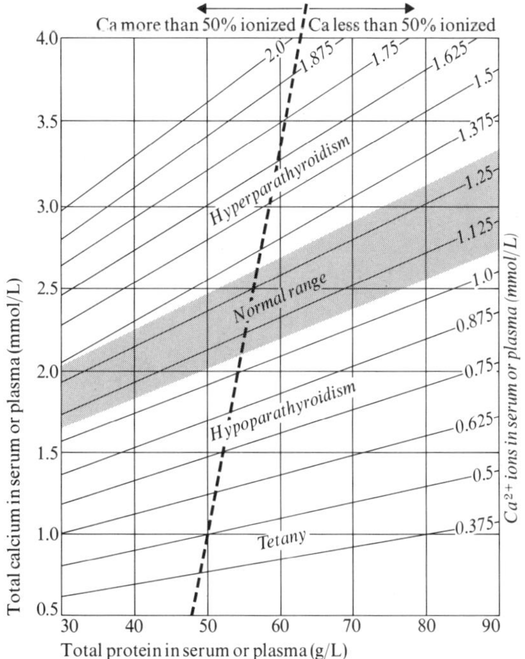

Fig. 3. Determination of Ca^{2+} ion concentration in serum or plasma from total calcium and total protein concentration [77].

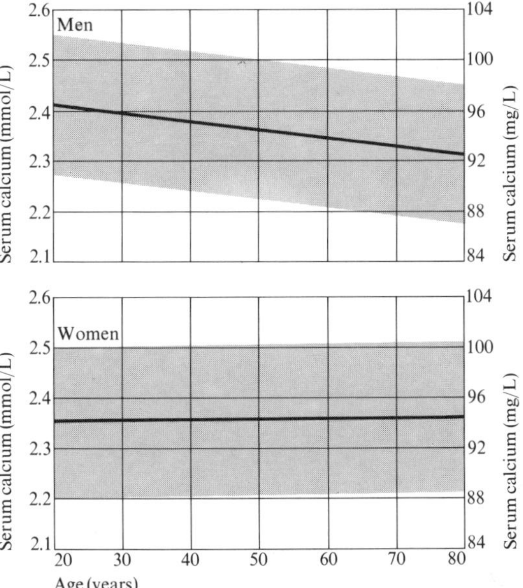

Fig. 4. Calcium concentration in serum of men and women in relation to age (regression line and 95% range)[74].

cal changes in the serum level of calcium are summarized in Table 5.

The calcium of the erythrocytes is contained in the membrane. The concentration in the erythrocytes is increased in sickle-cell anemia[141] and in hereditary spherocytosis[142].

Magnesium. All the data for the serum were determined by atomic absorption. – Use is also made of a fluorimetric assay with 8-hydroxyquinoline[85]. Normal values determined by various methods have been cited by Seelig and Berger[86]. About 30% of the serum magnesium is bound to protein, 55–60% is ionized, and 10–15% bound in complexes[87,88].

In the course of pregnancy the serum level of magnesium decreases by 10–20%[83]. In the newborn it is slightly lower than in older children and adults[86]. No age or sex dependence has been found in adults[89]. See the literature regarding magnesium metabolism[33,90,143]. *Pathological* changes in the serum concentration of magnesium are presented in Table 6.

Iron. Data determined (a) by atomic absorption, (b) by neutron activation, and all others by means of colorimetry. – The cus-

↑ See text on previous page	B Blood, P Plasma, S Serum, Erys Erythrocytes, Lkcs Leukocytes, Plts Platelets	Amount of substance				Mass				Reference
		Unit	Mean	s	95% range (extreme range in brackets)	Unit	Mean	s	95% range (extreme range in brackets)	
↑**Magnesium**	P(S) Umbilical vein, 19 newborn	mmol/L	0.71	0.12	–	mg/L	17.2	3.0	–	18
	– 104 newborn, 1st day	mmol/L	0.70	0.13	0.44–0.96	mg/L	16.9	3.1	10.7–23.1	18
	– 20 children, 6 months to 6 years	mmol/L	0.82	0.06	–	mg/L	20.0	1.4	–	19
	– 40 children, 6–12 years	mmol/L	0.78	0.05	0.68–0.88	mg/L	19.0	1.1	16.8–21.2	19
	– 39 youths, 12–20 years......	mmol/L	0.78	0.05	0.68–0.88	mg/L	18.9	1.3	16.3–21.5	19
	– 31 adults	mmol/L	0.78	0.04	–	mg/L	19.0	1.0	–	84
	– 67 men	mmol/L	–	–	0.68–0.93	mg/L	–	–	16.6–22.7	15
	– 85 women	mmol/L	–	–	0.65–0.98	mg/L	–	–	15.7–23.7	15
	Erys 27 adults	mmol/L	2.30	0.17	–	mg/L	55.9	4.1	–	84
	Erys 43 men.................	mmol/L	1.95	0.19	–	mg/L	47.5	4.5	–	147
	Erys 30 women..............	mmol/L	2.03	0.21	–	mg/L	49.4	5.2	–	147
	Erys 70 children, 4–36 months	mmol/kg	2.21	0.25	1.71–2.71	mg/kg	53.7	6.1	41.5–65.9	5
– ultrafiltratable.....	S 22 adults	mmol/L	0.58	0.025	–	mg/L	14.1	0.61	–	84

Table 5
Differentiation of changes in serum concentration of calcium[143]

Hypercalcemia (values up to about 6 mmol/L)

Increased enteral absorption:
Milk-alkali syndrome
Vitamin D intoxication
Vitamin D hypersensitivity (idiopathic hypercalcemia of young children, sarcoidosis, hypothyroidism)

Increased bone resorption:
Primary hyperparathyroidism
Ectopic hyperparathyroidism
Malignant disease with bone involvement
Vitamin D intoxication
Osteoporosis of inactivity
Hyperthyroidism
Familial hypophosphatasia
(Administration of thiazides)
(Polyuric phase of acute renal failure)

Hypocalcemia (values down to 1 mmol/L)

Impaired enteral absorption:
Vitamin D deficiency (rickets, osteomalacia)
Vitamin D resistance or disturbed vitamin D metabolism
Hereditary pseudodeficiency rickets
Malabsorption syndrome
Whipple's disease
Gastrectomy
Chronic renal insufficiency
Administration of anticonvulsants

Impaired bone resorption:
Hypoparathyroidism
Pseudohypoparathyroidism
(Hypomagnesemia)

Table 6
Differentiation of changes in serum concentration of magnesium[143]

Hypermagnesemia (values up to about 5 mmol/L)

Excessive magnesium intake:
Intravenous
Enteral
Oral (only in renal insufficiency)

Escape of intracellular magnesium:
Fasting
Acidosis (diabetic ketoacidosis)

Renal magnesium retention:
Advanced renal insufficiency

Hypomagnesemia (values down to 0.1 mmol/L)

Inadequate magnesium intake:
Prolonged fasting
Disturbed enteral absorption (hypoparathyroidism, persistent familial hypomagnesemia)

Passage of magnesium into cells:
Administration of insulin

Magnesium loss with digestive juices:
Vomiting (pyloric stenosis, anorexia nervosa)
Diarrhea (malabsorption syndrome, intestinal infections, laxative abuse, Verner-Morrison syndrome)

Renal magnesium loss:
Polyuric phase of renal insufficiency
Damage to tubular function (pyelonephritis, renal tubular acidosis, Liddle's syndrome)
Primary hyperaldosteronism (Conn's syndrome)
Bartter's syndrome
Chronic alcoholism
(Hyperparathyroidism)
(Hyperthyroidism)

tomary reagents for colorimetric iron assay are 1,10-phenanthroline, 2,2′-bipyridyl, and bathophenanthroline[69,78]; the latter reagent has been included in an ICSH standard[96]. The major portion of the iron in the blood is contained in the hemoglobin of the erythrocytes (iron content of hemoglobin 0.347%). In the serum, iron is present in its trivalent form and is almost completely bound to the protein transferrin insofar as the iron-binding capacity of transferrin is not exceeded. One molecule of transferrin is able to bind 2 ions of iron, and normally about $^1/_3$ of the protein is saturated with iron (Table 7). Several µg/L of iron in the serum are present in the form of the iron-containing storage protein ferritin[152].

The serum iron level varies widely both intra- and interindividually[91]: it is about 30% lower in the evening than in the morning; in women the average level is about 10–20% lower than in men, and it is about 30% lower during menstruation than in the intermenstruum. Pregnant women tend to have low values if iron is not prescribed for them. In the neonate, the iron level drops from high values in the umbilical blood to low values on the first postna-

↑See text on page 83	B Blood, P Plasma, S Serum, Erys Erythrocytes, Lkcs Leukocytes, Plts Platelets	Amount of substance				Mass				Reference
		Unit	Mean	s	95% range (extreme range in brackets)	Unit	Mean	s	95% range (extreme range in brackets)	
↑**Iron**	B Men	mmol/L	–	–	(7.9–10.0)	mg/L	–	–	(440–560)	92
	B Women	mmol/L	–	–	(7.5–8.6)	mg/L	–	–	(420–480)	92
	P(S) Men	µmol/L	–	–	13.4–31.3	mg/L	–	–	0.75–1.75	93
	– Women	µmol/L	–	–	11.6–29.5	mg/L	–	–	0.65–1.65	93
	– 104 men (a)	µmol/L	18.0	–	11.2–27.0	mg/L	1.01	–	0.63–1.51	94
	– 136 women (a)	µmol/L	16.5	–	10.0–27.0	mg/L	0.92	–	0.56–1.51	94
	– 70 women (using ovulation inhibitors) (a)	µmol/L	19.3	–	10.0–32.0	mg/L	1.08	–	0.56–1.79	95
	Plts 7 subjects (b)	µmol/kg	220	52	(147–294)	mg/kg	12.3	2.9	(8.2–16.4)	153

Table 7 *Iron concentration, total iron-binding capacity (TIBC), and transferrin saturation of serum*

Subjects	Serum iron		TIBC		Transferrin saturation		Method	Reference
	Mean	95% range (extreme range in brackets)	Mean	95% range (extreme range in brackets)	Mean	95% range (extreme range in brackets)		
	µmol/L				%			
17 children	15.4	(4.8–27.4)	72.3	(33.5–117)	21	(13–32)	1,10-Phenanthroline	98
46 adults	19.3	(9.8–33.1)	65.7	(44.8–84.5)	29	(14–49)	Bathophenanthroline	99
224 adults	18.3	11.5–29.9	54.6	44.6–70.7	34	20–52	Bathophenanthroline	100

Table 8
Hematocrit values and serum levels of iron in children[97]

Age	Number	Hematocrit		Serum iron			
		Mean	s	Mean	s	Mean	s
				µmol/L		mg/L	
1–5 days	7	0.57	0.14	12.2	3.6	0.68	0.20
6–10 days	14	0.53	0.10	20.6	5.4	1.15	0.30
11–20 days	20	0.53	0.09	22.4	5.6	1.25	0.31
21–30 days	26	0.43	0.07	23.6	4.3	1.32	0.24
31–60 days	43	0.36	0.05	21.3	5.4	1.19	0.30
61–90 days	26	0.33	0.03	17.0	3.9	0.95	0.22
4th to 6th month	48	0.35	0.04	12.5	4.3	0.70	0.24
7th to 12th month	10	0.36	0.04	10.6	2.1	0.59	0.12
1st year	19	0.37	0.04	13.4	3.9	0.75	0.22
2nd to 6th year	95	0.38	0.03	21.5	6.1	1.20	0.34
7th to 14th year	152	0.39	0.04	24.7	8.2	1.38	0.46

tal day, followed by a rise, another decline and then another rise (Table 8)[97,98]. Details on iron metabolism and on *pathological* changes in the serum iron level (Table 9) may be found in the literature[91,93,101].

Copper. Data determined (a) by atomic absorption; (b) by neutron activation, and all others by means of colorimetry. – The reagents commonly used for colorimetric assays are diethyl dithiocarbamate, bathocuproin, oxalyl dihydrazide, and cuprizone[78,103]. 60% of the copper in the erythrocytes is bound to the protein erythrocuprein (superoxide dismutase); in the serum about 93% is bound to the α_2-globulin ceruloplasmin. The remaining 7% of the serum copper is bound to albumin and amino acids and represents the transport form of copper in the blood ('directly reacting' or 'free' copper).

The serum copper level is more stable than the serum iron level[97]. Intraindividual variations of 0.9–1.3 µmol/L are common. In women, the serum copper is 10–20% higher than in men; it increases under the action of estrogens (oral ovulation inhibitors, pregnancy). In the newborn it is considerably lower than in the mother since ceruloplasmin cannot cross the placental barrier. The serum copper level begins to rise in the week after birth and during

Table 9 *Differentiation of changes in serum iron levels*[91]

Hyperferremia (toxic symptoms if total iron-binding capacity is exceeded)
Acute iron intoxication Protracted alimentary or treatment-induced iron overload Hemosiderosis due to transfusions Primary hemochromatosis Cirrhosis of the liver, acute hepatic necrosis Cutaneous porphyria Megaloblastic anemias Sideroachrestic anemias Thalassemias Erythroleukemia Pancytopenia Acute hemolytic anemias Atypical transferrin
Hypoferremia (values down to 2 µmol/L)
Iron deficiency anemias (alimentary, blood loss, gastrointestinal diseases) Atransferrinemia Copper deficiency Infections Rheumatic diseases Carcinomas Lymphogranulomatosis Chronic renal diseases

childhood it reaches values higher than those found in adults[102,105]. See the literature concerning copper metabolism and *pathological* changes in the serum level of copper (Table 10)[91,103,106]. In Wilson's disease, the serum concentration of free copper is increased, but that of ceruloplasmin is decreased.

Zinc. Data determined (a) colorimetrically; (b) by means of atomic absorption; (c) by neutron activation. – 30–40% of the

↑See text on previous page	B Blood, P Plasma, S Serum, Erys Erythrocytes, Lkcs Leukocytes, Plts Platelets	Amount of substance				Mass				Reference
		Unit	Mean	s	95% range (extreme range in brackets)	Unit	Mean	s	95% range (extreme range in brackets)	
↑**Copper**.............	P(S) 15 newborn, at birth.....	µmol/L	4.56	1.83	–	mg/L	0.29	0.12	–	102
	– 133 children, 2 years........	µmol/L	22.0	–	14.9–29.3	mg/L	1.40	–	0.95–1.86	103
	– 133 children, 6 years........	µmol/L	20.3	–	13.1–27.4	mg/L	1.29	–	0.83–1.74	103
	– 133 children, 10 years.......	µmol/L	18.4	–	11.3–25.5	mg/L	1.17	–	0.72–1.62	103
	– 104 men.................(a)	µmol/L	15.5	–	10.0–24.5	mg/L	0.98	–	0.64–1.56	94
	– 136 women..............(a)	µmol/L	17.0	–	10.2–29.0	mg/L	1.08	–	0.65–1.84	94
	– 70 women (using ovulation inhibitors)...............(a)	µmol/L	23.7	–	11.3–32.0	mg/L	1.51	–	0.72–2.03	95
	– 135 men....................	µmol/L	17.2	–	12.7–21.6	mg/L	1.09	–	0.81–1.37	104
	– 100 women................	µmol/L	18.9	–	13.7–24.1	mg/L	1.20	–	0.87–1.53	104
	– 72 pregnant women, 3rd trimester	µmol/L	37.6	–	23.6–49.9	mg/L	2.39	–	1.50–3.17	104
	Erys 50 adults................	µmol/L	14.4	1.4	11.6–17.2	mg/L	0.92	0.089	0.74–1.10	131
	Erys 20 adults................	µmol/L	14.0	–	10.4–17.6	mg/L	0.89	–	0.66–1.12	104
	Erys 10 pregnant women, 3rd trimester	µmol/L	11.8	–	7.5–16.1	mg/L	0.75	–	0.48–1.02	104
	Plts 7 subjects................	µmol/kg	21.9	3.9	(17.8–29.6)	mg/kg	1.39	0.25	(1.13–1.88)	153
Directly reacting copper..............	S 19 adults...................	µmol/L	1.59	0.25	(0.80–2.01)	µg/L	101	16	(51–128)	132
	S 30 adults...................	µmol/L	1.10	–	0–3.2	µg/L	70	–	0–200	104
	S 10 pregnant women, 3rd trimester...............	µmol/L	4.6	–	1.5–8.7	µg/L	290	–	100–550	104
↑**Zinc**	P 26 children, 3–13 years..(b)	µmol/L	13.6	2.0	(9.6–18.0)	mg/L	0.89	0.13	(0.63–1.18)	109
	P 89 adults................(b)	µmol/L	14.7	1.8	(11.0–17.6)	mg/L	0.96	0.12	(0.72–1.15)	109
	P 104 men.................(b)	µmol/L	14.2	–	11.1–18.6	mg/L	0.93	–	0.73–1.22	94
	P 136 women..............(b)	µmol/L	13.0	–	10.0–17.0	mg/L	0.85	–	0.65–1.11	94
	S Cord blood, 115 newborn............(b)	µmol/L	14.0	2.20	9.6–18.4	mg/L	0.918	0.144	0.63–1.21	108
	S 25 adults................(b)	µmol/L	14.5	1.68	–	mg/L	0.946	0.110	–	108
	S 126 adults..............(a)	µmol/L	16.7	3.1	10.5–22.9	mg/L	1.09	0.20	0.69–1.49	107
	Erys 32 newborn ....(a)	µmol/L	58	17	–	mg/L	3.8	1.10	–	107
	Erys 16 children, 4–11 months............(a)	µmol/L	119	26	–	mg/L	7.8	1.70	–	107
	Erys 12 children, 1–5 years (a)	µmol/L	162	23	–	mg/L	10.6	1.52	–	107
	Erys 84 adults.............(a)	µmol/L	190	28	134–246	mg/L	12.4	1.80	8.8–16.0	107
	Erys 29 adults.............(c)	µmol/10^{12}	14.8	2.4	–	mg/10^{12}	0.97	0.16	–	110
	Lkcs 29 adults.............(c)	µmol/10^{12}	214	159	(57–670)	mg/10^{12}	14.0	10.4	(3.7–44)	110
	Plts 7 subjects.............(c)	µmol/kg	737	168	(500–1046)	mg/kg	49.2	11.0	(32.7–68.4)	153

Table 10 *Differentiation of changes in serum copper levels*[91]

Hypercupremia (values above 50 µmol/L)
Copper intoxication Infections Rheumatic diseases Carcinomas Lymphogranulomatosis After operation After myocardial infarction Certain anemias
Hypocupremia (values down to 1.5 µmol/L)
Nephrotic syndrome Malabsorption syndrome (particularly kinky-hair syndrome) Copper-deficient diet in infants Wilson's disease

serum zinc is bound to α_2-macroglobulin, and approximately 60% is loosely associated with albumin[111].

The zinc concentration in the serum tends to be higher than that in the plasma since zinc is released from the platelets during coagulation[109]. The plasma values are lower in children than in adults[102,109]. During pregnancy they are approximately 20% lower[107,109], whereas the erythrocyte and leukocyte values show no significant changes[112]. Data on zinc metabolism may be found in the literature[113]. The plasma levels are *reduced* in atrophic cirrhosis of the liver, pneumonia and tuberculosis and on the first few days after a myocardial infarction[109,114] as well as in acrodermatitis enteropathica[133]. *Elevated* values are seen in the porphyrias[115].

Chromium. Many of the data on serum chromium concentrations reported in the literature seem to be unduly high so that the clinical implications of these data are doubtful[158].

Lead. Data determined (a) by atomic absorption; (b) by colorimetry; and (c) by isotope dilution. – Almost all published plasma values seem to be unduly high[162]. The concentration in the blood is related to the intake of lead from the inspired air and to nutrition, and it therefore varies from one place to another[150]. Whole blood values in excess of 1.9 µmol/L are suggestive of an abnormal lead intake, and values about 2.9 µmol/L must be considered toxic[128] (Fig. 2, page 99).

Lithium. The therapeutic range extends from 0.6 mmol/L to 1.5 mmol/L; toxic values begin near 2.0 mmol/L[127].

Manganese. Some published data on serum manganese levels appear unduly high so that the clinical implications of these data are doubtful[159].

↑↓See text on previous page and on next page	B Blood, P Plasma, S Serum, Erys Erythrocytes, Lkcs Leukocytes, Plts Platelets	Amount of substance				Mass				Reference
		Unit	Mean	s	95% range (extreme range in brackets)	Unit	Mean	s	95% range (extreme range in brackets)	
Trace metals of minor importance										
Aluminum	B 39 men	nmol/L	185	104	(19–482)	µg/L	5.0	2.8	(0.5–13.0)	148
	P(S) 39 men	nmol/L	237	82	(30–408)	µg/L	6.4	2.2	(0.8–11.0)	148
	– 8 subjects	nmol/L	138	44	(78–230)	µg/L	3.72	1.20	(2.1–6.2)	156
	– 14 samples	nmol/L	78	82	(0–282)	µg/L	2.1	2.2	(0–7.6)	157
Antimony	P 5 subjects	nmol/L	4.3	1.6	–	µg/L	0.52	0.19	–	154
	Plts 5 subjects	nmol/kg	148	214	(17–468)	µg/kg	18	26	(2.1–57)	154
Arsenic	B 8 subjects	nmol/kg	53	41	–	µg/kg	4	3.1	–	37
	S 11 subjects	nmol/L	14.3	6.0	(6.1–24.3)	µg/L	1.07	0.45	(0.46–1.82)	126
Cadmium	B 44 nonsmokers	nmol/L	4.9	–	(1.8–11)	µg/L	0.55	–	(0.2–1.2)	125
	B 45 smokers	nmol/L	19	–	(4–68)	µg/L	2.1	–	(0.5–7.6)	125
	P 7 subjects	nmol/L	9.0	3.9	–	µg/L	1.01	0.44	–	154
	Plts 7 subjects	nmol/kg	55	30	(28–109)	µg/kg	6.2	3.4	(3.1–12.2)	154
Cesium	P 7 subjects	nmol/L	6.4	1.7	–	µg/L	0.85	0.22	–	154
	S 36 adults	nmol/L	5.6	1.5	(3.4–8.9)	µg/L	0.74	0.20	(0.45–1.18)	119
	Erys 36 adults	nmol/kg	36.3	15.8	(16.5–83)	µg/kg	4.82	2.10	(2.19–11.0)	119
	Plts 7 subjects	nmol/kg	412	144	(269–639)	µg/kg	54.8	19.2	(35.8–84.9)	154
↑**Chromium**	S 14 adults	nmol/L	3.08	1.60	(0.73–6.75)	µg/L	0.160	0.083	(0.0382–0.351)	134
	P 7 subjects	nmol/L	8.6	2.9	–	µg/L	0.45	0.15	–	154
	Plts 7 subjects	nmol/kg	117	48	(69–190)	µg/kg	6.1	2.5	(3.6–9.9)	154
Cobalt	S 20 subjects	nmol/L	1.83	1.02	(0.67–4.60)	µg/L	0.108	0.060	(0.039–0.271)	134
	P 7 subjects	nmol/L	5.6	3.7	–	µg/L	0.33	0.22	–	154
	Plts 7 subjects	nmol/kg	127	85	(31–249)	µg/kg	7.5	5.0	(1.8–14.7)	154
Gold	B 5 adults	nmol/kg	0.28	0.15	–	ng/kg	55	30	–	37
	P 7 subjects	nmol/L	0.24	0.26	–	ng/L	48	51	–	154
	Plts 7 subjects	nmol/kg	1.1	1.1	(0–2.5)	ng/kg	220	220	(0–500)	154
↑**Lead**	B 20 newborn, 1–8 days ...(a)	µmol/L	0.67	0.22	(0.3–1.1)	µg/L	138	45	(70–230)	123
	B 801 samples ...(b)	µmol/L	0.82	0.53	<1.9	µg/L	170	110	<400	124
	B 19 men ...(a)	µmol/L	0.77	0.24	(0.54–1.43)	µg/L	160	49	(111–295)	120
	B 15 women ...(a)	µmol/L	0.46	0.12	(0.37–0.69)	µg/L	96	25	(76–142)	120
	B 103 men ...(a)	µmol/L	1.08	0.31	–	µg/L	224	64	–	149
	B 83 women ...(a)	µmol/L	0.92	0.27	–	µg/L	191	56	–	149
	S ...(c)	nmol/L	~0.1	–	–	ng/L	~20	–	–	162
↑**Lithium**	P	µmol/L	4.5	–	–	µg/L	31	–	–	118
↑**Manganese**	B 14 adults ...(a)	nmol/L	154	43	–	µg/L	8.44	2.37	–	116
	P 14 adults ...(a)	nmol/L	11	3.3	–	µg/L	0.59	0.18	–	116
	S 46 adults ...(b)	nmol/L	10	2.4	(7–19)	µg/L	0.57	0.13	(0.38–1.04)	117
	Erys 46 adults ...(b)	nmol/kg	270	89	(150–670)	µg/kg	15.0	4.9	(8.1–36.9)	117
↓**Mercury**	B Cord blood, 100 newborn	nmol/L	6.2	7.0	(0–30)	µg/L	1.24	1.4	(0–6)	139
	B 100 mothers, birth	nmol/L	5.0	6.0	(0–40)	µg/L	1.01	1.2	(0–8)	139
	B 83 subjects	nmol/L	11.6	5.5	–	µg/L	2.33	1.11	–	137
↓**Molybdenum**	S 30 adults	nmol/L	6.0	2.2	(2.9–12.2)	µg/L	0.58	0.21	(0.28–1.17)	151
	P 7 subjects	nmol/L	6.1	2.4	–	µg/L	0.59	0.23	–	154
	Plts 7 subjects	nmol/kg	35	14	(19–50)	µg/kg	3.4	1.3	(1.8–4.8)	154
Nickel	B 17 subjects	nmol/L	82	22	(49–120)	µg/L	4.8	1.3	(2.9–7.0)	130
	S 19 men	nmol/L	53	17	(19–77)	µg/L	3.1	1.0	(1.1–4.5)	120
	S 15 women	nmol/L	46	20	(7–78)	µg/L	2.7	1.2	(0.4–4.6)	120
Rubidium	P 7 subjects	µmol/L	1.8	0.23	–	µg/L	150	20	–	154
	S 5 subjects	µmol/L	0.98	0.24	–	µg/L	83.8	20.2	–	138
	S 36 adults	µmol/L	2.0	0.47	(1.1–3.2)	µg/L	170	40	(90–270)	119
	Erys 36 adults	µmol/kg	50.1	11.5	(31.1–84.7)	mg/kg	4.28	0.98	(2.66–7.24)	119
	Plts 7 subjects	µmol/kg	122	35	(82–180)	mg/kg	10.4	3.0	(7.0–15.4)	154

↓See text below	B Blood, P Plasma, S Serum, Erys Erythrocytes, Lkcs Leukocytes, Plts Platelets	Amount of substance				Mass				Reference
		Unit	Mean	s	95% range (extreme range in brackets)	Unit	Mean	s	95% range (extreme range in brackets)	
↓**Selenium**	B 6 subjects	µmol/kg	1.5	0.6	–	µg/kg	120	50	–	37
	S Cord blood, 38 newborn	µmol/L	0.49	0.10	–	µg/L	38.8	7.8	–	122
	S 20 adults	µmol/L	0.95	0.25	–	µg/L	75.3	19.9	–	122
	P 7 subjects	µmol/L	0.84	0.10	–	µg/L	66	8	–	154
	P 253 subjects	µmol/L	1.8	0.4	1.0–2.6	µg/L	144	29	86–202	121
	Erys 251 subjects	µmol/L	3.0	0.8	1.4–4.6	µg/L	236	60	116–356	121
	Plts 7 subjects	µmol/kg	9.90	1.61	(7.90–11.9)	µg/kg	782	127	(624–937)	154
Silver	P 6 subjects	nmol/L	6.3	5.8	–	µg/L	0.68	0.63	–	154
	Plts 6 subjects	nmol/kg	270	170	(110–500)	µg/kg	29	18	(12–54)	154
Strontium	S 5 subjects	µmol/L	0.37	0.10	–	µg/L	32.2	9	–	138
Tin	S 5 subjects	µmol/L	0.313	0.107	–	µg/L	37.2	12.8	–	138
Vanadium	S 6 men	nmol/L	0.92	0.22	(0.69–1.30)	ng/L	47	11	(35–66)	140
	S 8 women	nmol/L	0.47	0.10	(0.33–0.61)	ng/L	24	5	(17–31)	140

Mercury. Erythrocytes contain inorganic mercury and methylmercury in comparable amounts; in plasma inorganic mercury predominates[163].

Molybdenum. The concentration in the erythrocytes is below the detection limit of 6 nmol/kg[135].

Selenium. The blood selenium concentration reflects the selenium content of the soil; it varies geographically, with age, and with the diet[160]. The plasma levels of selenium are consistently lower than the selenium concentrations in the erythrocytes[161]. At birth, the blood level of selenium is lower than in adults and it decreases even further during the first month after birth[161].

References

1 Davis et al., *Science,* **118**, 276 (1953).
2 Hellerstein et al., *Amer. J. Dis. Child.,* **112**, 298 (1966).
3 Valberg et al., *J. clin. Invest.,* **44**, 379 (1965).
4 Funder and Wieth, *Scand. J. clin. Lab. Invest.,* **18**, 167 (1966).
5 Hellerstein, S., *J. Lab. clin. Med.,* **79**, 559 (1972).
6 Edmondson et al., *Europ. J. clin. Invest.,* **4**, 329 (1974).
7 von Bubnoff and Riecker, *Klin. Wschr.,* **39**, 724 (1961).
8 Rigas, D.A., *J. Lab. clin. Med.,* **58**, 234 (1961).
9 Schwab, M., *Klin. Wschr.,* **40**, 765 (1962).
10 Sommerkamp and Bomke, *Klin. Wschr.,* **42**, 392 (1964).
11 Bengtsson et al., *Acta paediat. scand.,* **59**, 192 (1970).
12 Izquierdo et al., *Clin. chim. Acta,* **30**, 343 (1970).
13 Liappis, N., *Mschr. Kinderheilk.,* **120**, 138 (1972).
14 Cotlove et al., *Stand. Meth. clin. Chem.,* **3**, 81 (1961).
15 Roberts, L.B., *Clin. chim. Acta,* **16**, 69 (1967).
16 Marongiu et al., *Klin. Wschr.,* **44**, 1405 (1966).
17 Helve, O., *Acta med. scand.,* **125**, 505 (1946).
18 Snodgrass et al., *Arch. Dis. Childh.,* **48**, 279 (1973).
19 Arnaud et al., *Pediat. Res.,* **7**, 485 (1973).
20 Skaug and Natvig, *Scand. J. clin. Lab. Invest.,* **9**, 39 (1957).
21 Karpatkin, S., *Ann Rev. Med.,* **23**, 101 (1972).
22 Silcox and McCarty, *J. clin. Invest.,* **52**, 1863 (1973).
23 Silcox et al., *J. clin. Invest.,* **52**, 1595 (1973).
24 Reed et al., *J. Lab. clin. Med.,* **56**, 281 (1960).
25 Power, M.H., *Stand. Meth. clin. Chem.,* **1**, 84 (1953); Dryer and Routh, *Stand. Meth. clin. Chem.,* **4**, 191 (1963).
26 Walser, M., *J. clin. Invest.,* **40**, 723 (1961).
27 Österlund, K., *Ann. Paediat. Fenn.,* **1**, suppl. 4 (1955).
28 Connelly et al., *Pediatrics,* **30**, 425 (1962).
29 Gottfried, E.L., *J. Lipid Res.,* **8**, 321 (1967).
30 Safrit et al., *Lipids,* **7**, 60 (1972).
31 McNair and Stickler, *New Engl. J. Med.,* **281**, 511 (1969).
32 Greenberg et al., *J. clin. Endocr.,* **20**, 364 (1960).
33 Fourman and Royer, *Calcium Metabolism and the Bone,* 2nd ed., Blackwell, Oxford, 1968; Nordin, B.E. (Ed.), *Calcium, Phosphate and Magnesium Metabolism,* Churchill, Edinburgh, 1976.
34 Larizza, P., *Fisiol. e Med.,* **6**, 203 (1935), quoted in Flaschenträger and Lehnartz (Eds.), *Physiologische Chemie,* volume II/1a, Springer, Berlin, 1954, page 415.
35 Sturm and Pothmann, *Z. klin. Med.,* **137**, 467 (1940).
36 Miller et al., *J. Lab. clin. Med.,* **58**, 656 (1961).
37 Brune et al., *Clin. chim. Acta,* **13**, 285 (1966).
38 Stump et al., *Clin. Biochem.,* **10**, 127 (1977).
39 Versieck and Cornelis, *Analyt. chim. Acta,* **116**, 217 (1980).
40 Arieff, A.J., *J. Amer. med. Ass.,* **180**, 1075 (1961).
41 Büttner et al., *Dtsch. med. Wschr.,* **98**, 751 (1973); Maheshwari et al., *Amer. J. clin. Nutr.,* **34**, 2679 (1981).
42 Singer and Ophaug, *Clin. Chem.,* **25**, 523 (1979).
43 Hall et al., *Clin. Chem.,* **18**, 1455 (1972).
44 Sanz et al., *Clin. chim. Acta,* **1**, 570 (1956).
45 Wayne et al., *Clinical Aspects of Iodine Metabolism,* Blackwell, Oxford, 1964.
46 Farrell and Richmond, *Clin. chim. Acta,* **6**, 620 (1961).
47 Lee et al., *Clin. Chem.,* **18**, 422 (1972).
48 Sterling et al., *J. clin. Invest.,* **48**, 1150 (1969).
49 Berger, S., in Tietz, N.W. (Ed.), *Fundamentals of Clinical Chemistry,* Saunders, Philadelphia, 1970, page 587.
50 Clark, F., *J. clin. Path.,* **28**, 207 (1975).
51 Acland, J.D., *J. clin. Path.,* **24**, 187 (1971).
52 Hegesh and Shiloah, *Clin. chim. Acta,* **125**, 107 (1982).
53 Symington et al., *Lancet,* **2**, 91 (1978).
54 Dastur et al., *Brit. med. J.,* **3**, 260 (1972).
55 Pettigrew and Fell, *Clin. Chem.,* **18**, 996 (1972).
56 Hillman et al., *Postgrad. med. J.,* **50**, 171 (1974).
57 Fisher and Freimuth, *J. invest. Derm.,* **30**, 85 (1958).
58 Hinsberg, K., in Flaschenträger and Lehnartz (Eds.), *Physiologische Chemie,* volume II/1a, Springer, Berlin, 1954, page 415.
59 Worth, G., *Klin. Wschr.,* **30**, 82 (1952).
60 Edmondson et al., *Lancet,* **1**, 1003 (1975).
61 Hellerstein et al., *J. Lab. clin. Med.,* **76**, 10 (1970).
62 Schoeppe and Brecht, *Med. Klin.,* **64**, 736 (1969).
63 Smith, E.K., *Clin. Sci.* **42**, 447 (1972).
64 Hartmann et al., *J. clin. Invest.,* **37**, 699 (1958).
65 Pfleiderer, T., *Klin. Wschr.,* **42**, 640 (1964).
66 Staib et al., *Chirurg,* **32**, 453 (1961); Lum and Gambino, *Amer. J. clin. Path.,* **61**, 108 (1974).
67 Videbaek and Ackermann, *J. Geront.,* **8**, 63 (1953).
68 Bergström and Hultman, *Lancet,* **1**, 1132 (1962).
69 Richterich, R., *Klinische Chemie,* 3rd ed., Karger, Basle, 1971.
70 Cole and Waddell, *J. clin. Endocr.,* **42**, 1056 (1976).
71 Davison et al., *Brit. J. Obstet. Gynaec.,* **88**, 472 (1981).
72 Fuchs et al., *Klin. Wschr.,* **50**, 824 (1972).
73 Studer et al., *Schweiz. med. Wschr.,* **102**, 305 (1972).
74 Keating et al., *J. Lab. clin. Med.,* **73**, 825 (1969).
75 Brown et al., *Pediatrics,* **49**, 841 (1972).
76 Root and Harrison, *J. Pediat.,* **88**, 1 and 117 (1976).
77 McLean and Hastings, *Amer. J. med. Sci.,* **189**, 601 (1935).
78 Weissman and Pileggi, in Henry et al. (Eds.), *Clinical Chemistry,* 2nd ed., Harper & Row, Hagerstown, Md., 1974, page 639.
79 Bowers and Pybus, *Stand. Meth. clin. Chem.,* **7**, 143 (1972).
80 Stewart and Dunlop, *Clinical Chemistry in Practical Medicine,* 6th ed., Livingstone, Edinburgh, 1962, page 236.
81 Wilkinson, R.H., *J. clin. Path.,* **10**, 126 (1957).
82 Myers, W.P. *Advanc. intern. Med.,* **11**, 163 (1962).
83 Hytten and Lind, *Diagnostic Indices in Pregnancy,* CIBA-GEIGY Ltd., Basle, 1974.
84 Alfrey et al., *J. Lab. clin. Med.,* **84**, 153 (1974).
85 Thiers, R.E., *Stand. Meth. clin. Chem.,* **5**, 131 (1965).
86 Seelig and Berger, *New Engl. J. Med.,* **290**, 974 (1974).
87 Walser, M., *J. clin. Invest.,* **40**, 723 (1961).
88 Prasad et al., *J. Lab. clin. Med.,* **58**, 531 (1961).
89 Stewart et al., *J. Lab. clin. Med.,* **61**, 858 (1963).
90 Wacker, W.E., *Magnesium and Man,* Harvard University Press, Cambridge, Mass., 1980; Wacker and Parisi, *New Engl. J. Med.,* **278**, 658, 712 and 772 (1968).

91 LENTNER and EGGSTEIN, *Leading Symptoms: Laboratory Values,* CIBA-GEIGY Ltd., Basle, 1976.
92 SACHS et al., *Arch. intern. Med.,* **52**, 366 (1933); **55**, 227 (1935); **71**, 489 (1943).
93 FAIRBANKS et al., *Clinical Disorders of Iron Metabolism,* 2nd ed., Grune & Stratton, New York, 1971.
94 HEINEMANN, G., *Z. klin. Chem.,* **10**, 467 (1972).
95 HEINEMANN, G., *Med. Klin.,* **69**, 892 (1974).
96 International Committee for Standardization in Haematology, *Brit. J. Haemat.,* **38**, 291 (1978).
97 GLADTKE and RIND, *Klin. Wschr.,* **44**, 88 (1966).
98 STURGEON, P., *Pediatrics,* **13**, 107 (1954).
99 CARD et al., *Canad. med. Ass. J.,* **90**, 618 (1964).
00 GABBE et al., *Clin. chim. Acta,* **119**, 51 (1982).
01 MOORE and BROWN, *Der Eisenstoffwechsel,* Documenta Geigy, Acta clinica, No. 7, Basle, 1967; HALLBERG et al. (Eds.), *Iron Deficiency,* Academic Press, London, 1970; BOTHWELL et al., *Iron Metabolism in Man,* Blackwell, Oxford, 1979.
02 HENKIN et al., *J. Pediat.,* **82**, 831 (1973).
03 SASS-KORTSAK, A., *Advanc. clin. Chem.,* **8**, 1 (1965); SASS-KORTSAK. A., in SCHWIEGK, H. (Ed.), *Handbuch der inneren Medizin,* 5th ed., volume 7, part 1, Springer, Berlin, 1974, page 627.
04 CARTWRIGHT and WINTROBE, *Amer. J. clin. Nutr.,* **14**, 224 (1964).
05 BAKWIN et al., *Pediatrics,* **27**, 642 (1961).
06 ADELSTEIN and VALLEE, in COMAR and BRONNER (Eds.), *Mineral Metabolism,* volume 2, part B, Academic Press, New York, 1962, page 371; SCHEINBERG and STERNLIEB, in BONDY, P. K. (Ed.), *Duncan's Diseases of Metabolism,* 6th ed., Saunders, Philadelphia, 1969, page 1321.
07 BERFENSTAM, R., *Acta Paediat. (Uppsala),* **41**, suppl. 87 (1952).
08 MERET and HENKIN, *Clin. Chem.,* **17**, 369 (1971).
09 HALSTED and SMITH, *Lancet,* **1**, 322 (1970).
10 DENNES et al., *Biochem. J.,* **78**, 578 (1961).
11 PARISI and VALLEE, *Biochemistry,* **9**, 2421 (1970).
12 FREDRICKS et al., *J. clin. Invest.,* **43**, 304 (1964).
13 VALLEE, B. L., in COMAR and BRONNER (Eds.), *Mineral Metabolism,* volume 2, part B, Academic Press, New York, 1962, page 443; VALLEE, B. L., *Physiol. Rev.,* **39**, 443 (1959); MIKAC-DEVIĆ, D., *Advanc. clin. Chem.,* **13**, 271 (1970).
14 MCBEAN et al., *Clin. chim. Acta,* **50**, 43 (1974).
15 ROMAN, W., *Amer. J. clin. Nutr.,* **22**, 1290 (1969).
16 COTZIAS et al., *J. Lab. clin. Med.,* **67**, 836 (1966).
17 VERSIECK et al., *Clin. Chem.,* **20**, 1141 (1974).
18 SCHROEDER and NASON, *Clin. Chem.,* **17**, 461 (1971).
19 VERSIECK et al., *Clin. Chem.,* **23**, 1301 (1977).
20 HOHNADEL et al., *Clin. Chem.,* **19**, 1288 (1973).
21 DICKSON and TOMLINSON, *Clin. chim. Acta,* **16**, 311 (1967).
22 PERONA et al., *Brit. J. Haemat.,* **42**, 567 (1979).
23 KUBASIK and VOLOSIN, *Clin. Chem.,* **18**, 1415 (1972).
24 GOLDWATER and HOOVER, *Arch. environm. Hlth.* **15**, 60 (1967).
25 ULANDER and AXELSON, *Lancet,* **1**, 682 (1974).
126 DAMSGAARD et al., quoted from VERSIECK and CORNELIS, *Analyt. chim. Acta,* **116**, 217 (1980) [reference 45].
127 CRAMMER et al., *Brit. med. J.,* **3**, 650 (1974).
128 BERMAN, E., *Amer. J. clin. Path.,* **36**, 549 (1961); Bureau of Community Environmental Management, *Pediatrics,* **48**, 464 (1971).
129 LUST and SEEGMILLER, *Clin. chim. Acta,* **66**, 241 (1976).
130 NOMOTO and SUNDERMAN, *Clin. Chem.,* **16**, 477 (1970).
131 SCUDDER et al., *Clin. chim. Acta,* **69**, 397 (1976).
132 FROMMER, D. J., *Clin. chim. Acta,* **68**, 303 (1976).
133 LOMBECK et al., *Z. Kinderheilk.,* **120**, 181 (1975); LEUPOLD et al., *Helv. paediat. Acta,* **31**, 109 (1976); LUNGAROTTI et al., *Helv. paediat. Acta,* **31**, 117 (1976).
134 VERSIECK et al., *Clin. Chem.,* **24**, 303 (1978).
135 BAERT et al., *Clin. chim. Acta,* **68**, 355 (1976).
136 LOMBECK et al., *Clin. chim. Acta,* **64**, 57 (1975).
137 TEJNING, S., quoted from VERSIECK and CORNELIS, *Analyt. chim. Acta,* **116**, 217 (1980) [reference 169].
138 ALFREY et al., *Kidney Int.,* **7**, suppl. 2, 85 (1975).
139 PITKIN et al., *Proc. Soc. exp. Biol. (N. Y.),* **151**, 565 (1976).
140 CORNELIS et al., in *Nuclear Activation Techniques in the Life Sciences,* International Atomic Energy Agency, Vienna, 1979, page 165.
141 EATON et al., *Nature,* **246**, 105 (1973).
142 FEIG and BASSILIAN, *Pediat. Res.,* **9**, 928 (1975).
143 LENTNER, C., *Klinisch wichtige Parameter des Elektrolytstoffwechsels,* in preparation.
144 FORTES MAYER and STARKEY, *Clin. Chem.,* **23**, 275 (1977).
145 PALEK, J., *J. Lab. clin. Med.,* **89**, 1365 (1977).
146 CRETER et al., *Acta haemat. (Basel),* **57**, 168 (1977).
147 PETERSEN et al., *Acta med. scand.,* **201**, 31 (1977).
148 BURATTI et al., *Clin. chim. Acta,* **141**, 253 (1984).
149 VALLOTON et al., *Schweiz. med. Wschr.,* **103**, 547 (1973).
150 RABINOWITZ et al., *J. Lab. clin. Med.,* **90**, 238 (1977).
151 VERSIECK et al., *Clin. chim. Acta,* **87**, 135 (1978).
152 MUNRO and LINDER, *Physiol. Rev.,* **58**, 317 (1978).
153 KIEM et al., *Clin. Chem.,* **25**, 705 (1979).
154 KASPEREK et al., *Clin. Chem.,* **25**, 711 (1979).
155 COLE and SCRIVER, *Clin. chim. Acta,* **107**, 135 (1980).
156 VERSIECK and CORNELIS, *New Engl. J. Med.,* **302**, 468 (1980).
157 ALDERMAN and GITELMAN, *Clin. Chem.,* **26**, 258 (1980).
158 VERSIECK et al., *J. Amer. med. Ass.,* **242**, 1613 (1979).
159 VERSIECK et al., *Clin. Chem.,* **26**, 531 (1980).
160 MCKENZIE et al., *Amer. J. clin. Nutr.,* **31**, 1413 (1978); SCHRAUZER and WHITE, *Bioinorganic Chem.,* **8**, 303 (1978).
161 THOMSON and ROBINSON, *Amer. J. clin. Nutr.,* **33**, 303 (1980).
162 EVERSON and PATTERSON, *Clin. Chem.,* **26**, 1603 (1980).
163 KUHNERT et al., *Amer. J. Obstet. Gynec.,* **139**, 209 (1981).
164 FOGH-ANDERSEN and SCHULTZ-LARSEN, *Acta obstet. gynec. scand.,* **60**, 309 (1981).

Nitrogenous substances (for references see pages 105 and 106)

↓ See text below	B Blood, P Plasma, S Serum, Erys Erythrocytes, Grcs Granulocytes, Lkcs Leukocytes, Plts Platelets	Amount of substance				Mass				Reference
		Unit	Mean	s	95% range (extreme range in brackets)	Unit	Mean	s	95% range (extreme range in brackets)	
↓ **Total nitrogen**	B	mol/L	2.45	–	(2.14–2.93)	g/L	34.3	–	(30.0–41.0)	1
	S	mol/L	0.935	–	(0.86–1.02)	g/L	13.1	–	(12.0–14.3)	1
	Erys	mol/L	–	–	(4.1–4.4)	g/L	–	–	(57–62)	2
	Erys 50 subjects	mol/kg	3.95	0.13	3.69–4.21	g/kg	55.3	1.8	51.7–58.9	3
	Erys 28 subjects	mol/10^{12}	0.329	0.030	–	g/10^{12}	4.61	0.42	–	4
	Lkcs 28 subjects	mol/10^{12}	0.71	0.49	–	g/10^{12}	10	6.9	–	4
	Plts 5 subjects	mmol/10^{12}	–	–	(22–28)	g/10^{12}	–	–	(0.31–0.39)	5

Total nitrogen. The data apply to chemically bound nitrogen. The reference method for the determination of total nitrogen in biological material is the KJELDAHL technique[6]. – The total nitrogen concentration in the plasma is slightly higher than that in the serum, because of the former's fibrinogen content. – The fraction of protein nitrogen relative to total nitrogen is more than 99% in the erythrocytes, more than 96% in the serum, about 80% in the leukocytes, and approximately 90% in the platelets. Hemoglobin accounts for 94% of the total erythrocyte nitrogen.

Nonprotein nitrogen (NPN). High-protein diet: Nonprotein nitrogen increased, the fraction of urea nitrogen ranging up to 90%. Low-protein diet: Nonprotein nitrogen decreased, the fraction of urea nitrogen 50% or less[9]. Toward the end of pregnancy the NPN content of the blood is reduced and the fraction of urea nitrogen is low[9]. Nonprotein nitrogen is *pathologically* increased in various renal diseases, in obstruction of the urinary tract, burns and shock; it is decreased in cases of severe liver damage. See also under 'Urea'.

Urea. Assay methods: Cleavage with urease and determination of ammonia (NH_3) with Nessler's reagent[11] or, preferably, with Berthelot's reagent[12,13]; automated techniques using diacetylmonoxime[14,15] or diacetyl[16]. The blood urea nitrogen (BUN) concentration can be roughly calculated from the blood NPN concentration by the following formula[17] (BUN and NPN in mg/L):

$$BUN = \frac{NPN - 100}{1.07}$$

The urea concentration in the blood depends primarily on protein intake, urine volume, and functional state of the kidney. In the adult, the urea level rises with increasing age[15,16]. It falls by about 25% during the course of pregnancy[18]. The urea level is *pathologically* increased in cases of increased degradation of organ protein

↑↓ See text on previous page and below	B Blood, P Plasma, S Serum, Erys Erythrocytes, Grcs Granulocytes, Lkcs Leukocytes, Plts Platelets	Amount of substance				Mass				Reference
		Unit	Mean	s	95% range (extreme range in brackets)	Unit	Mean	s	95% range (extreme range in brackets)	
↑ Nonprotein nitrogen	B Cord blood, 20 newborn	mmol/L	22.2	2.39	(17.1–27.9)	mg/L	311	33.4	(240–390)	7
	B 21 newborn, 5–6 days	mmol/L	19.0	2.31	(14.6–22.9)	mg/L	266	32.3	(205–320)	7
	B 25 children, 1–6 years	mmol/L	23.1	2.55	(19.3–29.3)	mg/L	324	35.7	(270–410)	7
	B 30 adults	mmol/L	23.6	4.00	(18.6–35.4)	mg/L	331	56.0	(260–495)	7
	B 58 men	mmol/L	19.7	2.63	14.4–25.0	mg/L	276	36.9	202–350	8
	B 46 women	mmol/L	18.6	2.79	13.0–24.2	mg/L	261	39.1	183–339	8
	P 58 men	mmol/L	17.8	2.56	12.7–22.9	mg/L	249	35.9	177–321	8
	P 46 women	mmol/L	15.9	3.00	9.90–21.9	mg/L	223	42.0	139–307	8
	Erys 58 men	mmol/L	22.1	3.49	15.1–29.1	mg/L	309	48.9	211–407	8
	Erys 49 women	mmol/L	22.7	4.62	13.5–31.9	mg/L	318	64.7	189–447	8
↑ Urea	B 42 men	mmol/L	4.53	0.97	2.59–6.47	mg/L	272	58	156–388	8
	B 31 women	mmol/L	4.01	0.92	–	mg/L	241	55	–	8
	P 42 men	mmol/L	5.08	1.07	2.94–7.22	mg/L	305	64	177–433	8
	P 31 women	mmol/L	3.96	0.97	–	mg/L	238	58	–	8
	S Cord blood, 25 newborn	mmol/L	3.60	0.48	(2.68–4.78)	mg/L	216	29	(161–287)	7
	S 21 newborn, 5–6 days	mmol/L	3.35	0.52	(2.50–4.50)	mg/L	201	31	(150–270)	7
	S 25 children, 1–6 years	mmol/L	5.21	0.60	(4.31–6.78)	mg/L	313	36	(259–407)	7
	S 30 adults	mmol/L	5.46	0.82	(4.21–7.96)	mg/L	328	49	(253–478)	7
	S 10 young men:									
	Protein intake 0.5 g d^{-1} kg^{-1}	mmol/L	3.21	0.48	–	mg/L	193	29	–	10
	Protein intake 1.5 g d^{-1} kg^{-1}	mmol/L	6.43	1.18	–	mg/L	386	71	–	10
	Protein intake 2.5 g d^{-1} kg^{-1}	mmol/L	7.58	1.20	–	mg/L	455	72	–	10
	Erys 42 men	mmol/L	3.86	0.98	1.90–5.82	mg/L	232	59	114–350	8
	Erys 31 women	mmol/L	2.96	1.00	–	mg/L	178	60	–	8
↓ Creatine	P 10 adults	µmol/L	34	12	–	mg/L	4.5	1.6	–	22
	S 14 newborn, 1st day	µmol/L	84.0	23.2	–	mg/L	11.0	3.0	–	28
	S 14 newborn, 4th day	µmol/L	138	37.8	–	mg/L	18.1	5.0	–	28
	S 14 newborn, 7th day	µmol/L	91.5	23.9	–	mg/L	12.0	3.1	–	28
	S 14 children, 0–14 years	µmol/L	53	21	(17–82)	mg/L	6.9	2.7	(2.2–10.8)	21
	S 9 men, 18–40 years	µmol/L	19	5	(11–30)	mg/L	2.5	0.7	(1.4–3.9)	21
	Erys	µmol/L	429	–	–	mg/L	56.2	–	–	23
	Relative to hemoglobin:									
	Erys 10 adults	µmol/g	1.13	0.32	–	µg/g	148	42	–	22
	Erys 10 men	µmol/g	1.24	0.24	(0.7–1.8)	µg/g	163	31	(92–240)	24

(e.g. in fever, after operations), of impaired renal excretion and urinary tract obstruction; it is often lowered in dehydrated patients after administration of nitrogen-free solutions[19] and occasionally also in liver diseases[20]. For interpretation of the urea values, see LENTNER and EGGSTEIN[17].

Creatine. Serum and plasma values determined enzymatically. – Other methods: Jaffé reaction (see under 'Creatinine'); fluorimetry with ninhydrin. The serum creatine level is raised with diets of high meat content.

Creatinine. Values given are 'true' creatinine values. The Jaffé reaction (alkaline picrate) usually used for the determination of creatine and creatinine values is not specific, and glucose, acetoacetic acid, acetone, ascorbic acid, pyruvate, etc. interfere with it. The values obtained differ according to the pretreatment of the specimens. Those obtained by the customary automated techniques represent total chromogens (Table 1). The serum values are increased after creatinine intake (e.g. in the form of roast meat)[242]. They are essentially proportional to muscle mass and therefore higher in men than in women, and higher in adults than in children. Pregnant women have a lower creatinine level[18]. The creatinine concentration in the serum is *pathologically* increased when renal excretion is impaired; it is decreased in the early stage of diabetes. For interpretation of the creatinine values, see LENTNER and EGGSTEIN[17].

Guanidino compounds. Whether guanidine, methylguanidine and guanidinopropionic acid are normal constituents of plasma remains doubtful[192,272]. The concentration of guanidino compounds is increased in chronic renal failure[30,31,192,272].

Table 1 *Creatinine concentration in plasma (automated ferricyanide method)*

Age	Males			Females			Reference
	Number	Mean (µmol/L)	s (µmol/L)	Number	Mean (µmol/L)	s (µmol/L)	
1 year	9	36	9	8	31	4	26
2 years	18	38	11	13	40	6	26
3 years	30	41	10	24	37	7	26
4 years	49	40	10	28	42	11	26
5 years	50	44	10	44	41	10	26
6 years	62	46	11	44	42	10	26
7 years	59	48	12	50	46	11	26
8 years	60	50	14	61	47	10	26
9 years	52	52	14	61	49	10	26
10 years	58	54	19	46	49	11	26
11 years	56	55	12	57	53	11	26
12 years	67	57	14	54	52	11	26
13 years	53	60	19	41	55	12	26
14 years	44	64	21	30	57	11	26
15 years	40	67	19	22	59	19	26
16 years	24	65	20	16	57	13	26
17 years	22	71	16	12	62	18	26
18–20 years	19	80	15	15	64	17	26
15–65 years	65	88	9	58	72	9	27

↑↓ See text on previous page and below	B Blood, P Plasma, S Serum, Erys Erythrocytes, Grcs Granulocytes, Lkcs Leukocytes, Plts Platelets	Amount of substance				Mass				Reference
		Unit	Mean	s	95% range (extreme range in brackets)	Unit	Mean	s	95% range (extreme range in brackets)	
↑**Creatinine**	S 14 newborn, 1st day	µmol/L	73.5	15.0	–	mg/L	8.31	1.70	–	28
	S 13 newborn, 4th day	µmol/L	43.3	37.9	–	mg/L	4.90	4.29	–	28
	S 12 newborn, 7th day	µmol/L	30.1	26.0	–	mg/L	3.40	2.94	–	28
	S 63 men	µmol/L	72	–	57–93	mg/L	8.2	–	6.4–10.5	25
	S 55 women	µmol/L	60	–	50–80	mg/L	6.8	–	5.6–9.1	25
	Erys	µmol/L	40	–	–	mg/L	4.5	–	–	23
	Erys 6 subjects	µmol/L	100	24	–	mg/L	11.3	2.7	–	272
	Relative to hemoglobin: Erys 10 adults	µmol/g	0.36	0.11	–	µg/g	40.8	13.0	–	22
Guanidine	S 9 subjects	µmol/L	0.24	0.08	–	µg/L	14.1	4.9	–	29
	P 6 subjects	–	–	–	0	–	–	–	0	272
	Erys 6 subjects	–	–	–	0	–	–	–	0	272
↑**Guanidino-acetic acid**	P 98 subjects	µmol/L	19	8	3–37	mg/L	2.3	1.0	0.3–4.3	30
	P 9 subjects	µmol/L	–	–	(0–6.3)	mg/L	–	–	(0–0.74)	31
	P 6 subjects	µmol/L	2.8	0.9	–	mg/L	0.33	0.11	–	272
	Erys 6 subjects	µmol/L	2.3	0.9	–	mg/L	0.27	0.11	–	272
↑**Guanidinosuccinic acid**	P 9 subjects	µmol/L	–	–	(0–3.3)	mg/L	–	–	(0–0.58)	31
	P 6 subjects	µmol/L	0.4	0.2	–	mg/L	0.07	0.035	–	272
	Erys 6 subjects	µmol/L	0.2	0.5	–	mg/L	0.035	0.09	–	272
↓**Ammonia** (as NH_3)	B 25 adults (a)	µmol/L	28	7.6	(15–41)	mg/L	0.47	0.13	(0.26–0.69)	32
	B 120 men (c)	µmol/L	36	–	17–68	mg/L	0.62	–	0.29–1.16	33
	B 80 women (c)	µmol/L	44	–	21–82	mg/L	0.75	–	0.36–1.39	33
	B 35 subjects (b)	µmol/L	20	4.9	(11–29)	mg/L	0.34	0.084	(0.19–0.49)	34
	P 52 newborn, 0–3 days (a)	µmol/L	27.5	3.6	–	mg/L	0.47	0.061	–	39
	P 15 newborn, 0–3 days (a)	µmol/L	60	20	(34–102)	mg/L	1.02	0.34	(0.58–17.4)	41
	P 36 children, 1 month to 14 years (a)	µmol/L	25	–	(13–38)	mg/L	0.43	–	(0.22–0.65)	41
	P 15 adults (a)	µmol/L	19	3.0	(13–28)	mg/L	0.32	0.051	(0.22–0.47)	244
	P 102 adults (c)	µmol/L	29	8.2	13–46	mg/L	0.50	0.14	0.22–0.78	35
	P 64 men (c)	µmol/L	35	–	20–58	mg/L	0.60	–	0.34–0.99	36
	P 51 women (c)	µmol/L	29	–	17–51	mg/L	0.49	–	0.29–0.87	36
	P 23 subjects (b)	µmol/L	16.9	6.75	–	mg/L	0.287	0.115	–	48

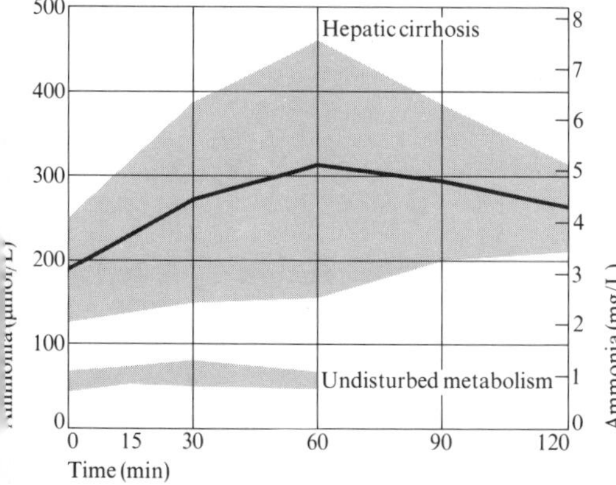

Fig. 1. Blood ammonia values (means and 95% range) after oral administration of 56 mmol (3 g) of ammonium chloride to patients with hepatic cirrhosis and in individuals with an undisturbed metabolism[42].

Ammonia. Values determined (a) with ion exchanger, Nessler's reagent; (b) with an ion-specific electrode; (c) enzymatically. Methods using alkali that release ammonia – with subsequent separation by distillation or diffusion – give higher values than those shown in the table, since ammonia is split off from glutamine and other amino acids by alkali[37,50].

Physiological variations: At normal blood pH nearly all the ammonia is present in the form of ammonium ions (NH_4^+) but with increasing pH the proportion of NH_3 also increases. The cell membranes are permeable to NH_3 but not to NH_4^+[38]. In healthy individuals the ammonium level remains within narrow limits even after intake of protein or ammonium salts. The normal values in capillary and arterial blood tend to be higher than those in venous blood[40,243,245]. In newborn with normal body mass the ammonia level seems not to differ significantly from that in older children and adults[39].

Pathological variations: With increasingly severe liver damage, there is a growing tendency to hyperammonemia – particularly after intake of protein or ammonium salts (Fig. 1)[40,42,43,244]. In precomatose states levels of 160 µmol/L (s 90 µmol/L), and in hepatic coma levels of 280 µmol/L (s 140 µmol/L)[44] have been found. Hyperammonemia has been demonstrated in premature infants[39,45], in leukemia[46], and in Reye's syndrome[47]. Hyperammonemia is encountered – especially after protein intake – in various hereditary metabolic disturbances of the urea cycle, such as carbamoyl-phosphate synthetase deficiency, ornithine carbamoyltransferase deficiency, argininosuccinic aciduria, hypercitrullinemia, and hyperargininemia; the ammonium concentrations range up to more than 1500 µmol/L[50,246]. Intermittent hyperammonemia is found in cases of familial protein intolerance[49].

↓ See text below	B Blood, P Plasma, S Serum, Erys Erythrocytes, Grcs Granulocytes, Lkcs Leukocytes, Plts Platelets	Amount of substance Unit	Mean	s	95% range (extreme range in brackets)	Mass Unit	Mean	s	95% range (extreme range in brackets)	Reference
↓ Amino acids										
– free, total	P 36 boys, 6–18 years	mmol/L	3.06	0.30	2.46–3.66	...	...	...	...	51
	P 34 girls, 6–18 years	mmol/L	3.01	0.36	2.29–3.73	...	...	...	...	51
	P 83 men	mmol/L	3.43	0.31	2.81–4.05	...	...	...	...	51
	P 92 women	mmol/L	3.08	0.38	2.32–3.84	...	...	...	...	51
	Grcs Men	$mmol/10^{12}$	26.5	–	–	...	...	...	...	212
	Grcs Women	$mmol/10^{12}$	38.5	–	–	...	...	...	...	212
– free, total, as α-amino-N	B 53 men (a)	mmol/L	4.4	0.45	3.5–5.3	mg/L	61	6.3	48–74	8
	B 53 women (a)	mmol/L	4.2	0.39	3.4–5.0	mg/L	59	5.4	48–70	8
	P 53 men (a)	mmol/L	3.0	0.31	2.4–3.6	mg/L	42	4.3	33–51	8
	P 53 women (a)	mmol/L	2.8	0.38	2.0–3.6	mg/L	39	5.3	20–50	8
	P 11 men (b)	mmol/L	3.22	0.21	(2.9–3.6)	mg/L	45.1	2.9	(41–50)	53
	P 10 women (b)	mmol/L	2.89	0.36	(2.2–3.4)	mg/L	40.5	5.1	(31–47)	53
	P 14 adults (c)	mmol/L	3.4	0.29	(2.8–4.0)	mg/L	47	4	(39–55)	52
	P 20 children, 2–10 years (d)	mmol/L	2.94	0.32	(2.6–3.7)	mg/L	41.2	4.5	(36–52)	54
	P 20 adults (d)	mmol/L	3.97	0.60	(2.6–5.0)	mg/L	55.6	8.4	(36–70)	54
	S Cord blood, 25 newborn (a)	mmol/L	5.48	1.4	(1.6–8.6)	mg/L	76.8	20	(23–120)	55
	S 32 children, 6 weeks to 11 years (a)	mmol/L	3.58	0.93	(2.1–5.4)	mg/L	50.1	13	(30–75)	55
	Erys 53 men (a)	mmol/L	6.2	0.54	5.1–7.29	mg/L	87	7.6	72–102	8
	Erys 53 women (a)	mmol/L	6.4	0.54	5.3–7.50	mg/L	90	7.5	75–105	8
	Plts 5 subjects	$mmol/10^{12}$	–	–	(0.41–0.66)	$mg/10^{12}$	–	–	(5.8–9.2)	5

Table 2 *Free amino acids in plasma of newborn infants, children, and adults*

Amino acid	46 newborn[69] <2500 g (1st day) Mean	s	25 newborn[74] >2500 g (1st day) Mean	s	22–40 newborn[248] breast-fed (1–21 days) Mean	80% range	Children (6–18 years)[51] 36 boys Mean	s	34 girls Mean	s	Adults[51] 83 men Mean	s	92 women Mean	s
	µmol/L													
Alanine	375	50	330	55	235	163–387	355	76	369	88	419	89	373	87
α-Aminobutyric acid	25	–	15	6	14	7.8–21	24	6	22	7	26	8	22	8
Arginine	50	20	54	17	47	30–84	92	19	84	20	89	26	75	24
Asparagine	–	–	–	–	53	43–87	48	7	46	7	49	7	47	9
Aspartic acid	10	10	8	4	–	–	6	4	6	4	–	–	–	–
Citrulline	12*	6*	7**	3**	13	5.8–20	36	8	33	7	37	9	35	10
Cystine/2	130	20	122	26	104	68–124	91	20	96	19	118	17	109	24
Glutamine	905	250	764	140	610	468–755	600	70	591	66	645	64	578	85
Glutamic acid	65	35	52	25	56	36–98	35	14	37	14	60	16	46	13
Glycine	460	275	344	69	183	120–228	234	34	230	36	236	42	300	114
Histidine	75	20	77	16	66	44–85	86	10	84	10	89	11	83	14
Hydroxyproline	40	40	32	–	40	28–55	24	13	20	12	20	11	16	9
Isoleucine	40	20	40	8	49	32–71	69	13	64	13	84	18	64	13
Leucine	70	25	72	18	103	73–160	134	20	119	20	160	27	122	23
Lysine	190	60	200	46	148	92–210	175	29	164	28	198	31	183	34
Methionine	35	5	29	8	20	13–29	27	5	26	5	32	6	27	5
Ornithine	90	20	92	25	84	49–116	51	15	47	14	65	18	54	18
Phenylalanine	80	20	79	14	41	23–63	60	8	55	8	65	9	56	8
Proline	230	75	185	33	212	162–283	198	63	172	57	239	70	168	49
Serine	134*	38*	141**	28**	109	80–143	121	25	127	27	114	23	127	29
Taurine	180	75	141	40	50	27–96	104	62	116	62	162	60	141	57
Threonine	215	60	217	21	104	76–134	140	28	138	32	146	22	154	40
Tryptophan	30	15	32	17	44	25–69	57	11	53	11	60	15	50	13
Tyrosine	120	100	70	17	72	45–117	68	10	65	11	72	15	61	13
Valine	130	50	137	39	153	108–184	232	28	214	29	252	37	209	31

* 31 newborn[196]. ** 8 newborn[196].

Amino acids

Free amino acids. The α-amino-N values shown were determined (a) colorimetrically with ninhydrin; (b) gasometrically with ninhydrin; (c) by the naphthoquinone reaction; and (d) spectrophotometrically with fluorodinitrobenzene. – The concentration of α-amino nitrogen is a measure of the amino-acid concentration

(Continued on page 9

Table 3 *Free amino acids in serum of children and adults*

Amino acid	12 children (16 days to 4 months)[75]		12 children (2–13 years)[75]		Children (5–10 years)[76]				Children (10–15 years)[76]				Adults[67]					
					30 boys		28 girls		34 boys		29 girls		38 men		28 women		10 women (OC users)	
	Mean	s	Mean	s	Mean	s	Mean	s	Mean	s	Mean	s	Mean	s	Mean	s	Mean	s
	μmol/L																	
Alanine	293	53	272	36	365	103	367	82	390	95	415	99	404	94	377	108	345	102
Arginine	63	10	85	15	85	19	95	18	97	19	95	14	92	22	96	25	92	21
Aspartic acid	19	2	16	3	–	–	–	–	–	–	–	–	21	5	20	5	23	6
Citrulline	–	–	–	–	30	8	31	8	32	11	29	9	46	10	40	11	34	14
Cystine/2	83	17	87	13	88	21	88	17	82	16	87	14	109	18	107	23	98	14
Glutamic acid	–	–	–	–	–	–	–	–	–	–	–	–	226	85	214	71	244	63
Glycine	213	35	220	33	259	71	262	47	262	38	269	49	242	44	258	64	224	62
Histidine	79	14	80	14	74	17	87	16	77	14	81	16	77	12	70	16	75	12
Isoleucine	40	8	44	6	47	12	48	9	51	13	50	11	81	18	56	12	55	12
Leucine	78	21	91	13	106	19	110	22	105	21	105	20	157	30	115	23	114	18
Lysine	135	28	131	20	162	23	183	24	169	34	187	35	222	50	196	53	194	36
Methionine	18	3	16	3	17	4	18	5	18	6	18	6	26	6	21	7	24	6
Ornithine	50	11	46	8	78	18	87	15	70	20	73	16	85	24	67	19	57	17
Phenylalanine	53	10	47	5	51	9	51	11	48	9	47	12	57	13	48	11	47	8
Proline	195	52	178	33	216	70	208	67	235	77	217	91	274	62	218	63	187	34
Serine	131	28	121	14	147	35	157	19	143	29	148	30	137	35	142	35	136	24
Taurine	–	–	–	–	97	23	94	21	72	24	86	20	67	25	66	17	58	12
Threonine	178*	33*	145*	16*	147	41	158	33	146	40	158	44	207	58	193	58	197	39
Tyrosine	54	21	46	8	61	13	66	14	64	16	67	17	72	12	63	15	56	15
Valine	161	38	181	20	212	35	221	25	220	33	218	41	274	53	214	41	213	31

*Threonine + asparagine calculated as threonine. OC: oral contraceptives.

Table 4 *Free amino acids in plasma and blood cells*

Amino acid	20 men[249]						7 adults[215]		1 man[60]			22 men[212]		12 women[212]	
	Blood		Plasma		Erythrocytes (calc.)		Erythrocytes (washed)		Erythrocytes	Leukocytes	Platelets	Granulocytes		Granulocytes	
	Mean	s	Mean	s	Mean	s	Mean	s				Mean	s	Mean	s
	μmol/L						μmol/kg					mmol/10^{12}			
Alanine	310	62	320	67	298	76	237	71	350	6610	2700	1.66	0.51	4.13	0.89
β-Alanine	–	–	–	–	–	–	6	5	–	–	–	–	–	–	–
α-Aminobutyric acid	22	7	26	8	25	23	–	–	–	–	–	–	–	–	–
Arginine	57	14	79	23	29	18	5	5	0	330	530	trace	–	trace	–
Asparagine	84	30	62	20	118	43	93	22	–	–	–	–	–	–	–
Aspartic acid	140	44	7	3	306	80	322	127	370	3500	2700	1.28	0.36	1.40	0.33
Citrulline	37	5	34	9	36	5	–	–	–	–	–	trace	–	0.88	0.29
Cystine/2 + cysteine*	–	–	99	19	–	–	trace	–	0	370	0	–	–	–	–
Glutamine	509	106	538	93	469	118	287	68	–	–	–	1.15	0.31	1.44	0.48
Glutamic acid	137	35	33	12	277	82	146	56	(320)	(7360)	(3160)	1.41	0.51	2.40	0.73
Glycine	288	48	240	49	354	71	266	65	370	5080	3650	1.14	0.41	2.04	0.76
Histidine	84	12	89	12	77	15	50	10	140	630	310	0.23	0.11	0.60	0.29
Isoleucine	58	9	62	11	52	11	13	9	40	2900	1200	0.37	0.19	1.19	0.64
Leucine	119	12	132	15	102	14	23	16	400	6300	1880	1.07	0.36	3.59	1.43
Lysine	153	21	167	25	134	27	90	26	130	2360	1220	1.63	0.74	3.53	0.80
Methionine	18	4	24	5	12	7	1	0	trace	1750	380	0.30	0.13	0.85	0.37
Ornithine	88	18	64	21	121	33	96	35	–	–	–	0.35	0.14	0.27	0.12
Phenylalanine	49	/	53	8	44	9	9	4	40	2480	850	0.40	0.16	1.14	0.52
Proline	160	34	183	43	129	31	78	24	170	2100	1020	–	–	–	–
Serine	131	22	122	23	144	26	103	26	150	5100	3650	1.19	0.45	1.90	0.82
Taurine	185	39	53	13	152	–	91	36	36	26000	21000	12.4	4.60	9.06	1.80
Threonine	128	19	142	26	109	20	75	25	160	3400	1550	0.88	0.41	1.48	0.53
Tryptophan	–	–	45	9	–	–	1	1	–	–	–	–	–	–	–
Tyrosine	53	11	54	11	52	13	25	7	50	1970	780	0.32	0.13	0.91	0.41
Valine	201	24	235	31	155	30	59	19	330	3750	1500	0.70	0.33	1.71	0.75

*Concentrations in plasma of adults: cystine about 42 μmol/L, cysteine about 33 μmol/L[82].

Table 5 *Other amino acids and related compounds in the blood*

Amino acid	Material	Subjects	Unit	Mean	s	(Extreme range)	Reference
β-Alanine	Serum	11 men	μmol/L	3.00	0.85	–	193
	Serum	12 women	μmol/L	1.76	0.74	–	193
β-Aminoisobutyric acid	Plasma	9 children	μmol/L	–	–	(0–trace)	77
	Serum	11 men	μmol/L	1.03	0.34	–	193
	Serum	12 women	μmol/L	0.75	0.33	–	193
Carnosine	Plasma	12 children, 6 days to 3 months	μmol/L	3.1	7.5	–	68
Cystathionine	Plasma	33 newborn, 1–21 days	μmol/L	1.0	–	(0.3–5.5)	248
	Plasma	12 children, 6 days to 3 months	μmol/L	–	–	(<0.9)	68
Cysteine homocysteine disulfide	Plasma	24 men	μmol/L	3.3	0.8	–	79
	Plasma	24 women	μmol/L	2.4	0.2	–	79
5-S-Cysteinyldopa	Serum	20 subjects	nmol/L	8.6	–	(1.2–37)	261
Cystinylglycine	Plasma	54 adults	μmol/L	13.6	3.6	(6.7–20.4)	269
3,4-Dihydroxyphenylalanine	Plasma	5 subjects	nmol/L	7.23	0.97	–	250
γ-Glutamylcysteine	Blood	28 adults	μmol/L	25	8	–	218
	Plasma	7 adults	μmol/L	4.0	0.8	–	218
	Erythrocytes, washed	7 adults	μmol/L	22	5	–	218
Glutathione	Blood	28 adults	mmol/L	1.09	0.20	–	218
	Plasma	7 adults	mmol/L	4.5	0.7	–	218
	Erythrocytes, washed	20 newborn (cord blood)	mmol/L	2.57	0.44	–	91
	Erythrocytes, washed	20 adults	mmol/L	2.18	0.29	–	91
	Erythrocytes, washed	20 adults	mmol/L	2.45	0.18	–	92
	Erythrocytes, washed	7 adults	mmol/L	2.33	0.13	–	218
	Erythrocytes, washed	20 newborn	$\mu mol/10^{12}$	339	44	–	219
	Erythrocytes, washed	22 children, adults	$\mu mol/10^{12}$	217	38	–	219
	Erythrocytes, washed	20 adults	$\mu mol/10^{12}$	231	32	–	92
Glutathione, oxidized	Erythrocytes, washed		μmol/L	–	–	(<5)	93
Homocitrulline	Plasma	12 children, 6 days to 3 months	μmol/L	–	–	(<12)	68
Hydroxylysine	Serum	60 subjects	μmol/L	–	–	(1.8–3.2)	220
N^{π}-Methylhistidine	Plasma	15 children	μmol/L	9.1	7.2	–	251
	Plasma	9 children	μmol/L	–	–	(0–20)	77
	Plasma	77 subjects	μmol/L	4	8	–	80
N^{τ}-Methylhistidine	Plasma	35 newborn, 1–21 days	μmol/L	3.0	–	(0.3–5.9)	248
	Plasma	15 children	μmol/L	1.9	0.9	–	251
	Plasma	77 subjects	μmol/L	3	1	–	80
N^{ε}-Methyllysine	Plasma	77 subjects	μmol/L	7	6	–	80
Pipecolic acid	Serum	55 children	μmol/L	–	–	(0–20)	78
Sarcosine	Serum	13 subjects	μmol/L	–	–	(<0.5)	197

Table 6 *Amino-acid concentrations in plasma and erythrocytes in some hereditary diseases of amino-acid metabolism*[81]

Amino acid	Metabolic disease	Diseased subjects			6 control subjects		
		Plasma (μmol/L)	Erythrocytes (μmol/L)	P/Erys ratio	Plasma (μmol/L)	Erythrocytes (μmol/L)	P/Erys ratio
Glycine	Nonketotic hyperglycinemia	733	703	1.05	192	264	0.73
Histidine	Histidinemia	588	529	1.11	117	115	1.02
Cysteine homocysteine disulfide	Homocystinuria	48	77	0.63	0	0	–
Isoleucine	Maple syrup disease (under treatment)	306	260	1.18	49	43	1.14
Leucine	Maple syrup disease (under treatment)	871	700	1.24	114	100	1.14
Methionine	Homocystinuria	475	304	1.57	24	11	2.06
Ornithine	Hyperornithinemia	204	260	0.78	129	149	0.86
Phenylalanine	Phenylketonuria	1281	1314	0.97	60	61	0.98
Tyrosine	Tyrosinosis	1401	1431	0.98	75	78	0.96
Valine	Maple syrup disease (under treatment)	609	551	1.10	164	137	1.19

However, besides free amino acids, α-amino groups of peptides and other substances also react, and in some procedures the results are affected by ammonia. The α-amino nitrogen should be determined in the plasma, for upon coagulation various amino acids are liberated from the platelets so that the serum concentration is about 15% higher than the plasma concentration[52,54,56]. The α-amino nitrogen values are also affected by the type of deproteinization[56,57].

The *individual amino acids* can be determined quantitatively by microbiological techniques[58] or after separation in an ion-exchange column[59,60]. Paper chromatography[61,62] and thin-layer chromatography[62,63] are suitable methods for the detection of

Table 7a *Total and free tryptophan in plasma or serum*

	Total tryptophan		Free tryptophan		Total tryptophan		Free tryptophan		Reference
	Mean	s	Mean	s	Mean	s	Mean	s	
	µmol/L				mg/L				
Plasma									
8 mothers (labor established)	48.7	11.6	12.9	4.7	9.95	2.37	2.63	0.96	252
8 newborn, cord blood	101.5	27.2	20.5	6.3	20.7	5.55	4.19	1.29	252
Serum									
21 subjects	69.8	10.0	6.2	1.5	14.3	2.0	1.3	0.3	253
11 subjects	67.6	28.9	4.5	2.0	13.8	5.9	0.91	0.41	254

Table 7b *Hydroxyproline fractions (fasting values)*

	Free		Peptide-bound		Protein-bound		Free		Peptide-bound		Protein-bound		Reference
	Mean	(Extreme range)	Mean	(Extreme range)	Mean	(Extreme range)	Mean	(Extreme range)	Mean	(Extreme range)	Mean	(Extreme range)	
	µmol/L						mg/L						
Plasma													
Young adults	11	(9.9–13.7)	4.6	(3.1–6.1)	61	(42–74)	1.5	(1.3–1.8)	0.6	(0.4–0.8)	8.0	(5.5–9.7)	83
8 subjects	5.9	s 2.3	4.0	s 1.8	–	–	0.78	s 0.30	0.53	s 0.24	–	–	84
Serum													
10 newborn, cord	24	s 8.4	trace	–	27	s 4.6	3.14	s 1.1	trace	–	3.5	s 0.6	85
10 women	15	s 1.5	5.9	–	55	s 21	1.95	s 0.2	0.78	–	7.2	s 2.8	85
10 pregnant women	62	s 18	0.3	–	49	s 27	8.12	s 2.3	0.04	–	6.4	s 3.5	85

aminoacidopathies. Specific chemical-assay methods are available for certain amino acids. The amino acids should be determined in plasma rather than serum because individual amino acids are liberated in varying amounts upon coagulation[56]. See SCRIVER et al.[64] and also PERRY and HANSEN[65] on pretreatment of the samples.

Reference plasma and serum concentrations of amino acids are shown in Tables 2 and 3. Table 4 compares plasma and blood-cell values. Reference values of amino acids not shown in Tables 2–4 are given in Table 5. For other reference values see SOUPART[60] and SCRIVER et al.[64]; for reference values of umbilical cord plasma see e.g. GHADIMI and PECORA[66] and POHLANDT[247].

Physiological variations of plasma amino acids: The concentrations of most amino acids are lower in women – particularly those using oral contraceptives – than in men[51,67]. The effect of estrogen is also reflected in variations in the course of the cycle. Individual amino acids, notably taurine and tyrosine, are present in higher concentrations in premature infants than in newborn infants of normal body mass[68,69,196]. In children, the concentrations of most amino acids are lower than in adults, particularly during phases of intensive growth[51,64]. During pregnancy, most amino acids show a tendency to lower values and increase in the last month of pregnancy[70]. Variations of amino-acid concentrations during the course of the day are quite pronounced in some cases and the cause is not known[71]. After several days of fasting, the concentrations of the branched-chain amino acids – valine, leucine, isoleucine – are increased, while the concentration of alanine, an important substrate for gluconeogenesis, is decreased[72].

Pathological variations of plasma amino acids: The concentrations of most amino acids are increased in hepatic failure[213]. The tyrosine level is raised in hyperthyroidism; the histidine level is lowered in rheumatoid arthritis[62]. In kwashiorkor, the concentrations of the essential amino acids decrease, while those of the nonessential amino acids show little change[73]. A specific increase of individual amino-acid concentrations is seen in hereditary diseases of amino-acid metabolism (Table 6).

Bound amino acids. In the plasma, tryptophan is transported mostly together with albumin (Table 7a). – The major portion of hydroxyproline in the plasma is a constituent of protein; small amounts are in peptides or are free (Table 7b). 10–25% of aspartic acid and glutamic acid are present in the plasma in the form of peptides and conjugates[94]. – Glutathione is a component of the erythrocytes, in which it normally occurs almost exclusively in reduced form (glutathione accounts for approximately 30% of the reducing nonsugar substances in whole blood).

Table 8 *Polyamines in blood and blood cells*

Material	Subjects	Unit	Diaminopropane		Putrescine		Spermidine		Spermine		Reference
			Mean	s	Mean	s	Mean	s	Mean	s	
Blood	14 men	µmol/L	–	–	–	–	10.3	3.78	9.97	3.26	97
	13 women	µmol/L	–	–	–	–	8.47	2.02	7.25	2.96	97
	17 subjects	µmol/L	–	–	0.214	0.08	6.56	1.61	3.92	1.48	216
Plasma	17 subjects	µmol/L	–	–	0.08	0.04	0.08	0.08	0.03	0.04	216
	20 subjects	µmol/L	0.017	0.009	0.085	0.035	0.095	0.035	0.040	0.029	98
Erythrocytes	7 subjects	nmol/L	–	–	–	–	1.02	0.21	0.89	0.74	214
	17 subjects	µmol/10¹²	–	–	0.065	0.04	0.815	0.29	0.48	0.16	216
Lymphocytes + monocytes	17 subjects	µmol/10¹²	–	–	220	206	226	115	440	251	216
Granulocytes	17 subjects	µmol/10¹²	–	–	410	330	207	186	493	230	216
Leukocytes	3 subjects	nmol/L	–	–	18	14	30	9	129	38	103
Platelets	17 subjects	µmol/10¹²	–	–	0.21	0.12	0.44	0.21	–	–	216

↓See text on next page	B Blood, P Plasma, S Serum, Erys Erythrocytes, Grcs Granulocytes, Lkcs Leukocytes, Plts Platelets	Amount of substance				Mass				Reference
		Unit	Mean	*s*	95% range (extreme range in brackets)	Unit	Mean	*s*	95% range (extreme range in brackets)	
↓Carnitine										
– total	P 27 children, 11–15 years	µmol/L	38.8	6.2	–	mg/L	6.25	1.0	–	275
	P 16 men	µmol/L	57.3	12.8	–	mg/L	9.24	2.06	–	198
	P 45 women	µmol/L	46.5	12.4	21.7–71.3	mg/L	7.50	2.00	3.50–11.5	198
– free	P 27 children, 11–15 years	µmol/L	33.6	6.2	–	mg/L	5.42	1.0	–	275
	S Cord blood, 22 newborn	µmol/L	34	5	–	mg/L	5.5	0.8	–	255
	S 15 women	µmol/L	38.2	5.4	(25.0–48.1)	mg/L	6.16	0.87	(4.03–7.75)	256
	S 30 subjects	µmol/L	43.1	8.9	–	mg/L	6.9	1.4	–	86
↓Ergothioneine	Erys 94 adults	µmol/L	420	140	150–700	mg/L	96	31	34–158	87
	Relative to water:									
	P 15 adults	µmol/kg	–	–	(<10)	mg/kg	–	–	(<2.3)	89
	Erys Cord blood, 4 newborn	µmol/kg	162	68	–	mg/kg	37.1	15.6	–	88
	Erys 10 children, 4 days to 1 year	µmol/kg	125	54	–	mg/kg	28.6	12.3	–	88
	Erys 15 children, 1–12 years	µmol/kg	200	105	–	mg/kg	45.9	24.1	–	88
	Erys 13 adults	µmol/kg	458	184	–	mg/kg	105	42.2	–	89
	Lkcs 15 adults	µmol/kg	–	–	(<300)	mg/kg	–	–	(<70)	89
↓Aliphatic amines (as N)	B 35 subjects	µmol/L	21.4	7.9	–	mg/L	0.30	0.11	–	95
Ethanolamine	P 25 newborn	µmol/L	52.3	–	(26.2–91.7)	mg/L	3.2	–	(1.6–5.6)	74
	P 8 adults	µmol/L	1.6	–	(trace–11.5)	mg/L	0.1	–	(trace–0.7)	74
	Relative to water:									
	P 15 adults	µmol/kg	–	–	<10	mg/kg	–	–	<0.6	89
	Erys 15 adults	µmol/kg	–	–	(<10)	mg/kg	–	–	(<0.6)	89
	Lkcs 15 adults	µmol/kg	–	–	(<250)	mg/kg	–	–	(<15)	89
Phosphoethanolamine	P Cord blood, 22 newborn	µmol/L	19	9.9	–	mg/L	2.7	1.4	–	66
	P 22 women, post partum	µmol/L	4	2	–	mg/L	0.6	0.3	–	66
	P 9 children	µmol/L	–	–	(trace–11)	mg/L	–	–	(trace–1.6)	77
	P 20 adults	µmol/L	–	–	(trace–3)	mg/L	–	–	(trace–0.4)	65
	Erys 7 adults	µmol/kg	4	4	–	mg/kg	0.6	0.6	–	215
	Relative to water:									
	Lkcs 8 adults	mmol/kg	2.65	1.1	–	mg/kg	374	155	–	89
Cystamine	B	µmol/L	19	–	–	mg/L	2.9	–	–	96
↓Choline										
– total	S 38 men	mmol/L	2.94	–	(2.01–4.47)	mg/L	356	–	(244–542)	100
– free	P Cord blood, 3 newborn	µmol/L	27.5	3.3	–	mg/L	3.33	0.40	–	101
	P 23 children, adults	µmol/L	10.6	1.9	–	mg/L	1.28	0.23	–	101
	P	µmol/L	15.5	2.3	–	mg/L	1.89	0.28	–	258
	Erys	µmol/L	40	4	–	mg/L	4.8	0.48	–	258
↓Acetylcholine	P 14 subjects	nmol/L	78	74	(20–294)	µg/L	12.8	12.0	(3.2–48.0)	99
↓Polyamines	…	…	…	…	…	…	…	…	…	…
Aromatic and heterocyclic amines										
Phenylethylamine	P 15 subjects	nmol/L	5.2	1.6	(4.1–9.1)	µg/L	0.64	0.19	(0.5–1.1)	259
Phenylethanolamine	P 7 subjects	nmol/L	7.9	2.3	–	µg/L	1.08	0.32	–	260
***p*-Tyramine**	P 15 subjects	nmol/L	5.0	2.6	(2.9–14)	µg/L	0.68	0.35	(0.4–1.9)	259
	P 8 adults	nmol/L	9.5	2.1	–	µg/L	1.3	0.3	–	221
***p*-Hydroxyphenylethanolamine** (octopamine)	P 14 subjects	nmol/L	2.6	1.4	–	µg/L	0.40	0.22	–	200
	S 10 adults	nmol/L	11.4	3.9	–	µg/L	1.75	0.60	–	222
	Relative to protein:									
	Plts 17 subjects	nmol/g	0.5	0.1	–	µg/g	0.07	0.02	–	201

↓ See text below	B Blood, P Plasma, S Serum, Erys Erythrocytes, Grcs Granulocytes, Lkcs Leukocytes, Plts Platelets	Amount of substance				Mass				Reference
		Unit	Mean	*s*	95% range (extreme range in brackets)	Unit	Mean	*s*	95% range (extreme range in brackets)	
↓ Catecholamines										
Epinephrine										
– total	P 7 adults (a)	nmol/L	2.1	–	(0.82–4.5)	ng/L	380	–	(150–820)	199
– free	P 4 men (a)	nmol/L	0.72	–	(0.49–1.3)	ng/L	130	–	(90–240)	199
	P 15 adults (b)	nmol/L	0.13	0.10	(0–0.34)	ng/L	23	19	(0–62)	102
Norepinephrine										
– total	P 4 adults (a)	nmol/L	6.0	–	(4.9–7.2)	ng/L	1000	–	(830–1200)	199
– free	P 2 men (a)	nmol/L	1.4	–	–	ng/L	240	–	–	199
	P 15 adults (b)	nmol/L	1.65	1.00	(0.66–3.56)	ng/L	279	169	(111–603)	102
Dopamine										
– total	P 9 adults (a)	nmol/L	17	–	(7.7–27)	ng/L	2600	–	(1200–4100)	199
– free	P 5 adults (a)	nmol/L	2.0	–	(0.78–3.8)	ng/L	310	–	(120–580)	199
	P 15 adults (b)	nmol/L	0.22	0.20	(0–0.54)	ng/L	34	31	(0–83)	102
Metanephrine										
– total	P 5 adults (a)	nmol/L	2.6	–	(1.8–3.7)	ng/L	510	–	(360–730)	200
– free	P 4 adults (a)	nmol/L	1.6	–	(0.18–2.5)	ng/L	320	–	(35–490)	200
Normetanephrine										
– total	P 5 adults (a)	nmol/L	4.0	–	(3.1–4.9)	ng/L	730	–	(570–900)	200
– free	P 4 adults (a)	nmol/L	1.3	–	(0.55–1.9)	ng/L	240	–	(100–350)	200
	P 9 adults (b)	nmol/L	0.35	0.16	(0.17–0.67)	ng/L	64	30	(31–122)	262
3-Methoxytyramine										
– total	P 5 adults (a)	nmol/L	5.5	–	(2.5–10)	ng/L	920	–	(420–1700)	200
– free	P 4 adults (a)	nmol/L	2.5	–	(1.6–2.9)	ng/L	420	–	(270–480)	200
↓ Histamine	B Umbilical vein, 10 newborn	µmol/L	0.57	0.27	(0.22–1.20)	µg/L	63	30	(25–130)	104
	B 15 children	µmol/L	0.44	0.18	(0.18–0.72)	µg/L	49	20	(20–80)	104
	B 11 adults	µmol/L	0.50	0.21	(0.11–0.94)	µg/L	56	23	(12–105)	105
	P 16 subjects	nmol/L	6.3	1.8	–	µg/L	0.7	0.2	–	223
	P 17 subjects	nmol/L	3.4	0.69	(0.82–4.7)	µg/L	0.38	0.08	(0.09–0.52)	108
N^{τ}-Methylhistamine	P 10 adults	nmol/L	11	3	(6–16)	µg/L	1.4	0.4	(0.8–2.0)	276
↓ N,N-Dimethyltryptamine	B 50 subjects	µmol/L	0.21	0.03	(0.14–0.27)	µg/L	39	6	(27–51)	109
↓ 3-Indoxylsulfuric acid (urinary indican)	P 56 men	µmol/L	14	4.2	5.6–22	mg/L	3	0.9	1.2–4.8	111
	P 44 women	µmol/L	14	5.6	2.8–25	mg/L	3	1.2	0.6–5.4	111
6-Sulfatoxyskatole	P	µmol/L	–	–	(0–4)	mg/L	–	–	(0–1)	113

Carnitine. A fraction of carnitine is esterified with short- and long-chain fatty acids. Fasting leads to a decrease of the concentration of free carnitine but to an increase in the concentration of short-chain acylcarnitine[257]. In pregnancy, the concentration of free carnitine is reduced[256].

Ergothioneine. The blood level of ergothioneine depends on the ergothioneine content of the diet. Pathological changes have been described[87,90].

Aliphatic amines. Dimethylamine and trimethylamine are formed in the small intestine by bacterial action. Their serum concentrations are increased in uremia[217].

Choline. The choline in the serum is almost entirely in the form of phospholipids.

Acetylcholine. The acetylcholine concentration in the plasma is increased in asthmatic patients.

Polyamines. See Table 8 for normal values. The polyamines are found mainly as constituents of the leukocytes but the absolute magnitude of their concentration is not precisely known owing to the difficulty of isolating the white blood cells. The concentration of polyamines is higher in young erythrocytes than in old ones[216]. Cadaverine is not detectable in plasma of healthy persons. Increased plasma concentration of polyamines including cadaverine has been found in some patients with severe liver insufficiency[98].

Catecholamines. Values determined (a) by gas chromatography or mass fragmentography; (b) by radioenzymatic assay. The concentration of free norepinephrine in the plasma increases in adults with advancing age[201]. The levels of catecholamines – especially that of normetanephrine – are elevated in patients with pheochromocytoma[200,261].

Histamine. Histamine is found predominantly in the leukocytes[106] (µmol/10^{12}): Neutrophils 30, basophils 9700, eosinophils 1400, lymphocytes 5, monocytes 11 but platelets only 0.08. The histamine concentration in the blood is increased in the carcinoid syndrome[107] and particularly in chronic myeloid leukemia owing to an increase in basophils[106].

N,N-Dimethyltryptamine. Other authors have been unable to detect this compound in the blood of normal individuals[110].

3-Indoxylsulfuric acid. Increased in nephrotic syndrome[112].

↓See text below	B Blood, P Plasma, S Serum, Erys Erythrocytes, Grcs Granulocytes, Lkcs Leukocytes, Plts Platelets	Amount of substance				Mass				Reference
		Unit	Mean	s	95% range (extreme range in brackets)	Unit	Mean	s	95% range (extreme range in brackets)	
3-Indoleacetic acid	P	µmol/L	–	–	(6–12)	mg/L	–	–	(1–2)	113
3-Indolelactic acid	P	µmol/L	–	–	(0.5–5)	mg/L	–	–	(0.1–1)	113
Kynurenine	P 8 men	µmol/L	2.4	0.49	–	µg/L	504	101	–	194
↓**Melatonin** (N-acetyl-5-methoxytrypt-amine)	P 11 boys, 1 day to 3 months (a)	pmol/L	190	150	–	pg/L	44.1	34.8	–	273
	P 15 boys, 3–12 months (a)	pmol/L	2560	1680	–	pg/L	595	390	–	273
	S 45 men (b)	pmol/L	63	26	–	ng/L	14.6	6.0	–	204
	S 50 women (b)	pmol/L	60	15	–	ng/L	13.9	3.5	–	204
	S 47 men (c)	pmol/L	211	112	–	ng/L	49.1	26.1	–	204
	S 50 women (c)	pmol/L	285	161	–	ng/L	66.1	37.5	–	204
↓**Serotonin** (5-hydroxytrypt-amine)	B Umbilical vein, 10 newborn	µmol/L	0.07	–	(0–0.15)	µg/L	12	–	(0–27)	104
	B 11 children	µmol/L	0.70	0.32	(0.09–1.4)	µg/L	124	56	(16–245)	104
	B 6 adults	µmol/L	0.43	0.12	(0.15–0.53)	µg/L	76	22	(27–94)	104
	B 31 men	µmol/L	0.74	0.28	–	µg/L	131	50	–	202
	B 27 women	µmol/L	0.97	0.28	–	µg/L	171	50	–	202
	P 10 adults	µmol/L	0.04	–	(0.03–0.07)	µg/L	7.1	–	(5–12)	116
	Plts Umbilical vein, 10 newborn	µmol/10^{12}	0.30	0.27	(0–0.74)	µg/10^{12}	53	47	(0–130)	104
	Plts 11 children	µmol/10^{12}	2.40	0.89	(0.91–4.00)	µg/10^{12}	423	157	(160–710)	104
	Plts 6 adults	µmol/10^{12}	1.80	0.65	(0.85–2.60)	µg/10^{12}	317	115	(150–460)	104
	Plts 10 adults	µmol/10^{12}	2.61	–	(1.67–3.74)	µg/10^{12}	461	–	(295–659)	116
Porphyrins										
↓**5(δ)-Aminolevulinic acid**	P Umbilical vein, 25 newborn	µmol/L	0.35	0.09	(0.20–0.56)	µg/L	46	12	(26–74)	118
	S 18 subjects	µmol/L	0.39	0.22	(0–0.76)	µg/L	51	28.3	(0–100)	119
	Erys Umbilical vein, 40 newborn	µmol/L	5.67	2.67	(2.83–13.4)	µg/L	743	350	(371–1762)	118
	Erys Adults	µmol/L	–	–	(1.9–3.4)	µg/L	–	–	(250–450)	120
Aminoacetone	P 28 subjects	µmol/L	60	20	–	mg/L	4.4	1.5	–	274
↓**Porphobilinogen**	S 20 subjects	nmol/L	66	67	(0–190)	µg/L	15	15.2	(0–44)	119
	Erys Umbilical vein, 40 newborn	µmol/L	2.00	0.53	(1.0–3.1)	µg/L	452	120	(230–710)	118
	Erys Adults	µmol/L	–	–	(0.7–1.8)	µg/L	–	–	(150–400)	120
Pentacarboxy-porphyrin	Erys Umbilical vein	–	–	–	(0–trace)	–	–	–	(0–trace)	118
↓**Protoporphyrin**	P Umbilical vein, 41 newborn	nmol/L	5.9	3.0	(1.8–16)	µg/L	3.3	1.7	(1–8.9)	118
	S Adults	–	–	–	0	–	–	–	0	119
	Erys Umbilical vein, 50 newborn	µmol/L	1.09	0.57	(0.35–3.18)	µg/L	614	320	(197–1790)	118
	Erys Umbilical vein, 20 newborn	µmol/L	0.96	0.44	(0.57–2.40)	µg/L	540	250	(320–1350)	122
	Erys 8 children, 1–2 years	µmol/L	0.57	–	–	µg/L	320	–	–	122
	Erys 20 men	µmol/L	0.53	0.13	(0.28–0.92)	µg/L	300	75	(160–520)	122
	Erys 20 women	µmol/L	0.66	0.18	(0.32–0.91)	µg/L	370	100	(180–510)	122
	Erys 19 adults	µmol/L	0.519	0.200	(0.22–0.93)	µg/L	292	113	(120–530)	123

Melatonin. Values determined by radioimmunoassay (a) between 5 and 6 a.m., (b) at noon, (c) at midnight. – In women the melatonin level changes in the course of the menstrual cycle[205].

Serotonin. The serotonin in the blood is contained in specific organelles in the platelets[203]. The metabolites 5-hydroxylindoleacetic acid and/or 5-hydroxytryptophol account for about 5% of total platelet hydroxyindoles[115]. In the carcinoid syndrome the platelet serotonin concentration is increased[117], for example to 105 µmol/10^{12} in one study[114].

5(δ)-Aminolevulinic acid. Serum concentration increased in acute intermittent porphyria. During the biosynthesis of δ-aminolevulinic acid, aminoacetone too is formed in the erythrocytes[121].

Porphobilinogen. Serum concentration increased in acute intermittent porphyria.

Protoporphyrin. The protoporphyrin in the serum is bound mostly to albumin[127]. The protoporphyrin values are increased in congenital erythropoietic protoporphyria[124]. – The protoporphyrin concentration in the erythrocytes is not as closely correlated with the reticulocyte count as is the coproporphyrin concentration[125]. The highest values are found in lead poisoning (Fig. 2) and in congenital erythropoietic protoporphyria[124]. The concentration in the erythrocytes is also increased in iron deficiency anemia and hemolytic anemias; it is within normal limits in pernicious anemia[125].

↓See text below	B Blood, P Plasma, S Serum, Erys Erythrocytes, Grcs Granulocytes, Lkcs Leukocytes, Plts Platelets	Amount of substance				Mass				Reference
		Unit	Mean	s	95% range (extreme range in brackets)	Unit	Mean	s	95% range (extreme range in brackets)	
↓Uroporphyrin	S	–	–	–	0	–	–	–	0	119
	Erys Umbilical vein, 25 newborn	nmol/L	–	–	(<1.2)	µg/L	–	–	(<1)	118
	Erys Adults	nmol/L	–	–	(0–24)	µg/L	–	–	(0–20)	120
↓Coproporphyrin	P Umbilical vein, 41 newborn	nmol/L	7.3	3.5	(3.7–20.1)	µg/L	4.8	2.3	(2.4–13.2)	118
	P Umbilical vein, 16 newborn	nmol/L	23	11	(11–49)	µg/L	15	7	(7–32)	122
	P 11 adults	nmol/L	12	5	(6–23)	µg/L	8	3	(4–15)	122
	Erys Umbilical vein, 50 newborn	nmol/L	23	6.9	(13–52)	µg/L	15	4.5	(8.7–34)	118
	Erys Umbilical vein, 20 newborn	nmol/L	43	24	(17–110)	µg/L	28	16	(11–72)	122
	Erys 20 men	nmol/L	20	6	(11–35)	µg/L	13	4	(7–23)	122
	Erys 20 women	nmol/L	18	11	(5–35)	µg/L	12	7	(3–23)	122
	Erys 19 adults	nmol/L	14.5	7.8	(2.2–30.1)	µg/L	9.5	5.1	(1.4–19.7)	123
↓Myoglobin	S 92 adults	...	...	...	...	µg/L	28.9	17.3	(6–85)	206
	S 17 men	...	...	...	...	µg/L	37	13	–	224
	S 32 women	...	...	...	...	µg/L	21	10	–	224
	S 12 adults	...	...	...	...	µg/L	30.2	10.7	(14–47)	270
	S 45 children	...	...	...	...	µg/L	11.5	15.2	(0–93)	270
↓Hemoglobin	B 200 adults	...	...	...	...	g/L	159	–	134–173	129
	P Cord blood	...	...	...	...	mg/L	80	–	–	130
	P Newborn	...	...	...	...	mg/L	–	–	(1000–1310)	130
	P 25 adults	...	...	...	...	mg/L	3.1	–	(1.6–5.8)	131
	P 31 adults	...	...	...	...	mg/L	4.15	2.06	(0.3–8.9)	132
	Erys 200 adults	...	...	...	...	g/L	328	–	299–357	129

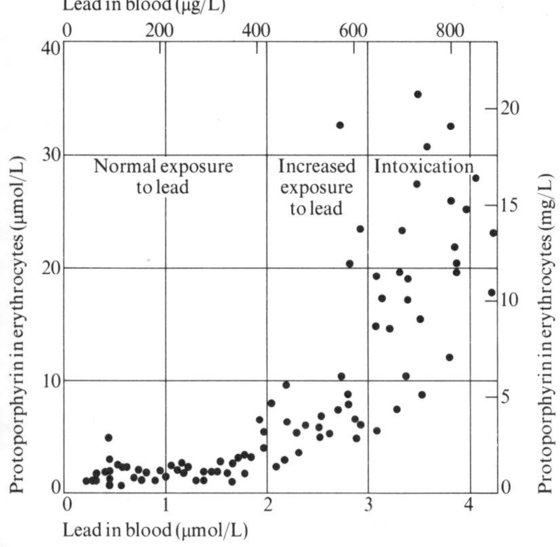

Fig. 2. Relation between protoporphyrin concentration in erythrocytes and lead concentration in whole blood[126].

Uroporphyrin. Increased erythrocyte values (uroporphyrin I) are found in congenital erythropoietic porphyria[124].

Coproporphyrin. The coproporphyrin in the serum is bound mainly to hemopexin[127]. The coproporphyrin values are increased in congenital erythropoietic porphyria[124]. – The coproporphyrin concentration in the erythrocytes is closely correlated with the reticulocyte count[125]. It is often markedly elevated in congenital erythropoietic porphyria (coproporphyrin I)[124] and in sideroachrestic anemia[128], increased in hemolytic anemias, and slightly increased in iron deficiency anemia, but nil in untreated pernicious anemia[125].

Myoglobin. Increased serum concentrations of myoglobin are found after damage to the heart and skeletal muscle[207]. In acute myocardial infarction, maximal values are recorded 8–12 hours after hospitalization[206].

Hemoglobin. For details see page 205 on hemoglobin concentrations in whole blood and erythrocytes.

Individual hemoglobin pigments: Normal values are presented in Table 9. – *Carboxyhemoglobin.* The catabolism of 1 mol of heme yields 1 mol of carbon monoxide[135]. The proportion of carboxyhemoglobin is therefore increased with increased hemolysis (Tables 10a and b). In addition, the proportion increases as exposure to external carbon monoxide increases (Table 10a). Carbon monoxide has approximately 250 times as great an affinity for hemoglobin as oxygen and influences the oxygen-binding curve (page 77). Clinical symptoms appear when the proportion of carboxyhemoglobin to total hemoglobin is 15–25%, and death threatens at a proportion of 65%[136]. – *Hemiglobin (methemoglobin).* Increased values are found when reduction of hemiglobin is impaired (hereditary methemoglobinemia) and when production is increased to such a point that the reduction cannot keep pace with it (acquired methemoglobinemia due to oxidizing agents such as nitrite, aniline, etc.)[137,138]. Clinical symptoms (cyanosis) manifest themselves when the proportion of hemiglobin to total hemoglobin reaches 20%[136], and death threatens when it reaches 70%[137]. – *Sulfhemoglobin.* Elevated values are seen at times in methemoglobinemias and hemolytic anemias[138].

Glycosylated hemoglobins. Glucose and some phosphorylated sugars can combine, in a nonenzymatic irreversible reaction, with the NH_2-terminal amino group in valine of the β chain of the hemoglobin molecule[233]. The predominant fraction of these glycosylated hemoglobins is HbA_{1c} (Table 11), which results from the reaction with glucose. This product reflects the time-averaged level of the blood glucose concentration for the preceding weeks and an estimation of HbA_{1c} is considered to be useful for the diagnosis and follow-up of diabetes mellitus[239,240]. These glycosylated hemoglobins are also known as 'fast' hemoglobins, because they are

Table 9 *Hemoglobin pigments in capillary blood*[139]

	Number	Adult nonsmokers			Adult smokers			Premature infants (age 24–72 hours)		
		Mean	*s*	(Extreme range)	Mean	*s*	(Extreme range)	Mean	*s*	(Extreme range)
		Fraction relative to total hemoglobin (%)								
Oxyhemoglobin (HbO_2)	12	95.55	0.86	(93.8–97.1)	95.7	0.85	(94.2–97.0)	89.83	3.2	(81.0–94.5)
Carboxyhemoglobin (HbCO)	12	0.51	0.32	(0–0.9)	4.2	2.0	(1.3–7.8)	1.92	0.61	(1.3–4.5)
Methemoglobin (Hi)	12	0.30	0.23	(−0.1–0.6)	1.15	0.62	(0.1–2.7)	1.11	0.23	(0.7–1.5)
Sulfmethemoglobin (SHb)	12	0.02	0.14	(−0.1–0.2)	0.04	0.14	(−0.1–0.2)	0.08	0.16	(−0.1–0.3)

Table 10a *Fraction of carboxyhemoglobin relative to total hemoglobin as a function of carbon monoxide exposure*

	%	Reference
Presence in CO-free atmosphere	0.45	140
Nonsmoking taxi drivers in London	1.4–3.0	141
Hemolytic diseases	1.0–3.0	141
Smoking	1–20	141
Carbon-monoxide poisoning	20–80	141

Table 10b *Fraction of carboxyhemoglobin relative to total hemoglobin in first few postnatal days*[241]

	Mean	(Extreme range)
	%	
Healthy newborn	0.42	(0.1–1.8)
AB0 incompatibility	–	(1.9–6.6)
Rh incompatibility	–	(2.6–11.9)

Table 11 *Fraction of glycosylated hemoglobins relative to total hemoglobin*

	Subjects	Mean	*s*	95% range	Reference
		%			
Glycosylated hemoglobins, total	140 subjects	8.1	–	6.5–9.0	234
	75 children	6.1	0.6	4.9–7.3	235
HbA_{1c}	16 subjects, 4–24 years	4.33	1.56	–	236
	92 adults	4.66	1.05	–	237
	40 subjects	5.2	0.7	–	238

eluted from cation exchange column ahead of HbA_0, the unmodified hemoglobin.

Hemoglobin in plasma: Serum is unsuited for assay since hemoglobin is liberated upon coagulation[133]. To avoid hemolysis, blood sampling has to be done very carefully. In the plasma, hemoglobin is bound to haptoglobin (maximal binding capacity up to 1.4 g/L[134]). The hemoglobin concentration is increased after physical exertion; in the plasma of soccer players, values varied between 18 mg/L and 132 mg/L after 90 minutes of play[132]. *Pathological* hemoglobinemia is encountered in intravascular hemolysis, for example upon transfusion of incompatible blood or in paroxysmal hemoglobinuria[133].

Bilirubin

Methods. Bilirubin is generally determined by means of a modified diazo reaction according to VAN DEN BERGH (Table 12). The values obtained vary, depending on the method. Use of a perfect bilirubin standard is of prime importance[12]. Recently, several methods for evaluation of the bilirubin-albumin interactions have been developed[148, 149].

Metabolism[150–152]. In the adult, approximately 85% of bilirubin is a metabolite of the hemoglobin of aging erythrocytes; the remaining 10–20% stems from other sources (predominantly, heme proteins of the microsomes and mitochondria). The proportion of bilirubin that is not formed from the hemoglobin of the erythrocytes is 2–3 times greater in the newborn[161]. The bilirubin transported in the plasma is bound to albumin; before uptake in the liver, it is split off again and is probably carried to the site of metabolism in the liver by means of specific cytosol proteins. The esterification with carbohydrates (mostly glucuronic acid) is effected with the aid of microsomal enzymes. The esterified bilirubin is excreted with the bile.

Physiologic variations. Albumin has 3 binding sites for nonesterified bilirubin - one of high affinity and two others of low affinity. Only when the binding sites are fully taken up does nonesterified

Table 12 *Determination of bilirubin as azo dye by the van den Bergh method*

Direct-reacting bilirubin	Indirect-reacting bilirubin
Bilirubin esters (mainly bilirubin monoglucuronide and bilirubin diglucuronide)	Nonesterified bilirubin (mainly bilirubin–albumin and bilirubin–phospholipid–albumin complexes) (a) By denaturation with methanol[162, 163] (b) By displacement with acetate, benzoate, caffeine, diphylline[12, 164, 165]

bilirubin appear in the plasma in a concentration surpassing that involved in the equilibrium reaction[153, 154]. At birth, all the bilirubin in the plasma is nonesterified; with increasing maturity of the bilirubin-UDP glucuronosyltransferase esterified bilirubin appears in the plasma several days after birth (Fig. 3). Factors influencing the concentration of bilirubin in the serum are indicated in Tables 13 and 14. However, no esterified bilirubin was demonstrable in the serum of healthy adults by specific methods (Table 15).

Physiologic jaundice of the newborn[12, 142, 155, 156]. This is found in 30–80% of newborn. In full-term infants, the maximum serum concentration of bilirubin appears between the 3rd and 6th days. Premature infants have higher average bilirubin values than infants born at term (Fig. 3).

Pathologic variations. A classification of hyperbilirubinemias is presented in Table 16. Inferences from the concentration of nonesterified plasma bilirubin are summarized in Table 17. The highest bilirubin values (up to 1900 µmol/L) are found in cases of biliary cirrhosis and concomitant renal insufficiency[157, 158].

Pathological forms of jaundice in the newborn[156]: *Icterus neonatorum praecox.* Rise of serum bilirubin to more than 120 µmol/L

(Continued on page 102)

↑ See text on previous page	B Blood, P Plasma, S Serum, Erys Erythrocytes, Grcs Granulocytes, Lkcs Leukocytes, Plts Platelets	Amount of substance				Mass				Reference
		Unit	Mean	s	95% range (extreme range in brackets)	Unit	Mean	s	95% range (extreme range in brackets)	
Cytochrome b_5	Erys Cord blood, 8 newborn	µmol/L	0.48	0.15	–	mg/L	7.7	2.4	–	263
	Erys 30 men	µmol/L	0.70	0.17	–	mg/L	11.2	2.7	–	263
	Erys 20 women	µmol/L	0.52	0.11	–	mg/L	8.3	1.8	–	263
↑ Bilirubin										
– total	P(S) Cord blood, 49 premature infants	µmol/L	31.6	13.3	5.0–58.3	mg/L	18.5	7.8	2.9–34.1	142
	– Cord blood, 150 newborn	µmol/L	25.8	11.5	2.8–48.8	mg/L	15.1	6.7	1.7–28.5	142
	– 11 newborn, 1st day	µmol/L	45.8	28.4	–	mg/L	26.8	16.6	–	143
	– 10 newborn, 3rd day	µmol/L	100	47.9	–	mg/L	58.5	28.0	–	143
	– 11 newborn, 5th day	µmol/L	104	51.0	–	mg/L	60.6	29.8	–	143
	– 6 newborn, 7th day	µmol/L	85.5	41.6	–	mg/L	50.0	24.3	–	143
	– 63 adults	µmol/L	8.5	4.3	–	mg/L	5.0	2.5	–	144
	– 100 adults	µmol/L	–	–	3–14	mg/L	–	–	2–8	145
– indirect-reacting	S 61 men	µmol/L	6.8	–	2.6–18.0	mg/L	4.0	–	1.5–10.5	146
	S 53 women	µmol/L	4.8	–	1.9–12	mg/L	2.8	–	1.1–7.0	146
– direct-reacting	S 110 adults	µmol/L	1.7	–	(0.9–4.1)	mg/L	1.0	–	(0.5–2.4)	144
	S 100 adults	µmol/L	–	–	<1.7	mg/L	–	–	<1	145
Urobilinoids	P(S)	...	...	...	...	mg/L	–	–	(0–0.3)	147
Urobilinogen	P(S)	µmol/L	–	–	(0.17–1.7)	mg/L	–	–	(0.1–1.0)	147

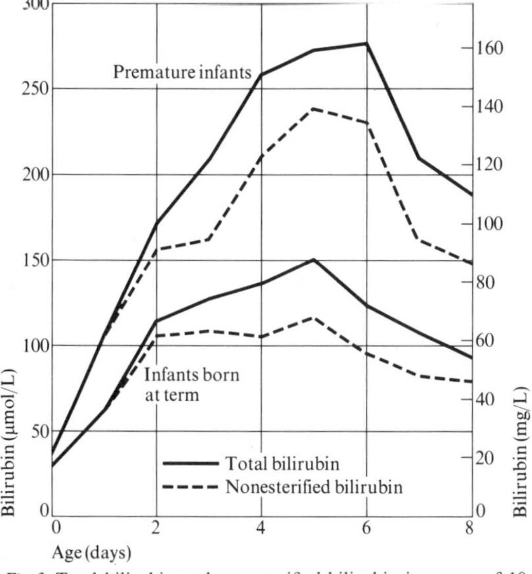

Fig. 3. Total bilirubin and nonesterified bilirubin in serum of 10 infants born at term and 23 premature infants[155]. The difference between total bilirubin and nonesterified bilirubin corresponds to esterified bilirubin.

Table 13 *Factors affecting the serum concentration of nonesterified bilirubin*[151]

Increase	Decrease*
Fasting◊	Ultraviolet rays
Physical activity	Cortisol
Pregnancy	Sulfonamides
Estrogens, oral contraceptives	Phenobarbital
Alcoholic beverages	Cholestyramine (man?)
Sepsis	

* Either through migration into tissue (creating hazard of kernicterus in the newborn, e.g. after administration of sulfonamides[168]), or through intensification of bilirubin metabolism in the liver (e.g. due to phenobarbital).
◊ Particularly in Gilbert's syndrome[167].

Table 14 *Factors affecting the serum concentration of esterified bilirubin*[151]

Increase	Decrease
Pregnancy	Cortisol
Menstruation	Surgical removal of a biliary tract obstruction
Estrogens, oral contraceptives	
Anabolic steroids	
Hemolysis	
Renal failure	

Table 15 *Total and esterified bilirubin in serum of healthy adults*[264]

Method	Nonesterified bilirubin	Mono-esterified bilirubin	Di-esterified bilirubin	Total bilirubin
	µmol/L			
Alkaline methanolysis plus high-performance liquid chromatography	8.1	n.d.	n.d.	8.1
Automatic diazo method	–	–	8.0	11.9

n.d. = Not detectable.

Table 16 *Disorders of bilirubin metabolism*[150]

Predominant form of pigment in blood	Disorder: Localization	Disorder: Type	Disorder: Etiology
Nonesterified ('unconjugated')	Prehepatic	Increased bilirubin production	Hemolysis Ineffective erythropoiesis Heme catabolism in liver (?)
	Hepatic	Hepatic uptake impaired	Gilbert's syndrome (?)* Flavaspidic acid
		Low UDP-glucuronosyl transferase activity	Newborn Crigler-Najjar syndrome (Type I)
		Absence of UDP-glucuronosyl transferase activity	Crigler-Najjar syndrome (Type II)
		UDP-glucuronosyl transferase activity inhibited	3α,20β-Pregnanediol (breast milk) Lucey-Driscoll syndrome◊
Esterified ('conjugated')	Hepatic	Impaired bilirubin secretion	Dubin-Johnson syndrome Rotor's syndrome
		Intrahepatic cholestasis	Primary biliary cirrhosis Intrahepatic atresia Recurrent familial cholestasis (?) Recurrent icterus in pregnant women Drugs (e.g. steroids, chlorpromazine)
		Damage to liver cells	Hepatitis (viral or drug-induced) Cirrhosis
	Posthepatic	Extrahepatic cholestasis	Biliary calculi Carcinoma (pancreas or bile ducts)

* Constitutional hyperbilirubinemia. ◊ Transitory familial neonatal hyperbilirubinemia.

Table 17 *Interpretation of values of nonesterified plasma bilirubin (indirect-reacting fraction)*[166]

Bilirubin concentration μmol/L	Bilirubin concentration mg/L	Bilirubin clearance of liver	Bilirubin production rate
<17	<10	Usually normal	Usually normal
17–60	10–35	Normal or reduced	Increased or normal
>60	>35	Usually reduced	Increased or normal

in the first 24 hours after birth due to hemolytic processes. – *Icterus neonatorum gravis.* Serum bilirubin in the first week above 240 μmol/L. Causes: Blood-group incompatibility between mother and child; hereditary spherocytosis; nonspherocytic hemolytic anemia; maternal diabetes; infections (sepsis, toxoplasmosis); Crigler-Najjar syndrome. – *Icterus prolongatus.* Hyperbilirubinemia lasting beyond the second postnatal week. Causes: Increased steroid intake with breast milk; congenital myxedema; pyloric stenosis; Crigler-Najjar syndrome. – *Kernicterus.* If nonesterified bilirubin is present in the serum in a concentration exceeding the binding capacity of albumin, free bilirubin can pass into the central nervous system[153,154]. Although the binding capacity amounts to more than 270 μmol/L in most newborn[153], cases of kernicterus have been seen at bilirubin levels between 160 μmol/L and 265 μmol/L[159,160]. Particularly at risk are underweight newborn infants, premature infants, children with hypoalbuminemia, with hypoglucosemia, hypoxia or with ketoacidosis[159–161]. In infants born at term with no hemolytic disease, there is very little danger of kernicterus at a bilirubin concentration of less than 340 μmol/L[153,160].

Hydroxypurines. Concentrations are high in plasma and erythrocytes after exercise[279]. Elevated levels in cord plasma are found in perinatal asphyxia[280].

Uric acid. Values determined with the use of urate oxidase. – In the United States and in most European countries, 420 μmol/L for men and 360 μmol/L for premenopausal women may be considered the upper limits of normal levels of serum uric acid[17]. In post-

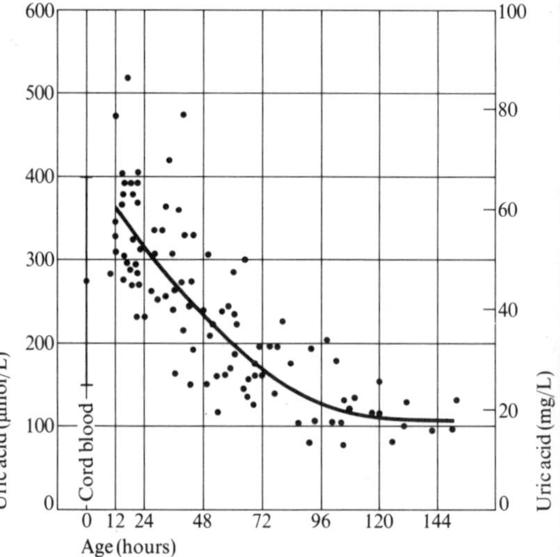

Fig.4. Serum uric-acid levels at birth (cord blood values: $\bar{x} \pm 2s$) and on first few postnatal days[177].

menopausal women, the values approach those common in men. They are increased on the first day after birth but drop to a low level in the succeeding days (Fig.4) The uric-acid level remains low until approximately the 10th year. It reaches adult values with the beginning of puberty. – The uric-acid level is *raised* in cases of excessive intake of dietary purines, increased de novo synthesis (primary gout, Lesch-Nyhan syndrome), increased endogenous nucleic-acid catabolism (particularly in chronic myeloid leukemia, polycythemia vera), and restricted renal excretion (renal diseases, ketoacidosis, lactacidosis, diuretics); it is *lowered* when renal excretion is increased (owing to uricosuric drugs, renal-tubular defects)[17,176].

(Continued on page 104)

↑↓ See text on pages 102–105	B Blood, P Plasma, S Serum, Erys Erythrocytes, Grcs Granulocytes, Lkcs Leukocytes, Plts Platelets	Amount of substance				Mass				Reference
		Unit	Mean	s	95% range (extreme range in brackets)	Unit	Mean	s	95% range (extreme range in brackets)	
Purines, pyrimidines										
↑ **Hydroxypurines**										
– total	P 4 subjects	µmol/L	8.0	–	(4.8–12.5)	...	...	...	...	174
	P Cord blood, 61 newborn	µmol/L	5.7	5.8	(0–18.3)	...	...	...	...	280
	S Cord blood, 17 newborn	µmol/L	26.9	9.6	–	...	...	...	...	265
	S 13 women	µmol/L	8.1	3.5	–	...	...	...	...	265
Xanthine	P	µmol/L	0.40	0.27	–	mg/L	0.060	0.041	–	266
	P 10 men	µmol/L	4.9	1.5	(3.0–7.3)	mg/L	0.75	0.23	(0.46–1.1)	267
	P 5 women	µmol/L	4.5	–	(2.7–8.0)	mg/L	0.68	–	(0.41–1.22)	175
	P 19 subjects	µmol/L	0.827	0.434	(0.270–2.01)	mg/L	0.125	0.066	(0.041–0.306)	277
	Erys 5 women	µmol/L	11.4	–	(4.9–17.8)	mg/L	1.74	–	(0.75–2.70)	175
Hypoxanthine	P	µmol/L	0.46	0.21	–	mg/L	0.063	0.029	–	266
	P 10 men	µmol/L	1.0	0.9	(0.5–3.5)	mg/L	0.14	0.12	(0.068–0.48)	267
	P 5 women	µmol/L	5.6	–	(3.1–7.1)	mg/L	0.76	–	(0.42–0.96)	175
	P 19 subjects	µmol/L	3.98	1.42	(2.36–7.34)	mg/L	0.542	0.193	(0.321–1.00)	277
	Erys 5 women	µmol/L	15.6	–	(6.3–22.7)	mg/L	2.12	–	(0.86–3.09)	175
Inosine	P 19 subjects	µmol/L	0.604	0.453	(0.102–1.81)	mg/L	0.162	0.122	(0.027–0.485)	277
Adenine	P 5 children, adults	µmol/L	0.64	0.15	–	µg/L	86	20	–	183
	Erys 18 children, adults	µmol/L	13	7	–	mg/L	1.8	0.9	–	183
Adenosine	P 4 children, adults	µmol/L	0.31	0.29	–	µg/L	83	78	–	183
	Erys 2 subjects	µmol/L	–	–	(0.9–1.5)	µg/L	–	–	(240–400)	183
	Plts 9 adults	nmol/10^{12}	165	57	–	µg/10^{12}	44	15	–	225
Guanosine	P 19 subjects	µmol/L	0.258	0.174	(0.106–0.618)	µg/L	73.01	49.3	(30.0–0.175)	277
	Plts 9 adults	µmol/10^{12}	1.31	0.88	–	µg/10^{12}	370	250	–	225
S-Adenosylmethionine	B 15 subjects	µmol/L	2.2	0.38	–	mg/L	0.88	0.15	–	195
	P 10 adults	µmol/L	–	–	(1.9–3.9)	mg/L	–	–	(0.76–1.6)	268
	Erys 10 adults	µmol/L	7.9	1.9	(5–11)	mg/L	3.2	0.76	(2.0–4.4)	268
↑ **Uric acid**	P(S) Cord blood, 15 newborn	µmol/L	329	129	(142–569)	mg/L	55.3	21.7	(23.9–95.7)	265
	– 139 children, 0–13 years	µmol/L	–	–	120–400	mg/L	–	–	20–67	170
	– 1269 men	µmol/L	302	60	182–422	mg/L	50.7	10.1	30.5–70.7	171
	– 457 women	µmol/L	234	52	130–338	mg/L	39.4	8.7	22.0–56.8	171
	– 88 men	µmol/L	332	–	208–456	mg/L	55.8	–	35–76.7	172
	– 39 women, 20–40 years	µmol/L	253	–	140–360	mg/L	42.6	–	24–61	172
	– 32 women, 50–70 years	µmol/L	316	–	180–461	mg/L	53.1	–	30–77.5	172
	Erys	µmol/L	149	–	–	mg/L	25	–	–	173
Allantoin	P 3 subjects	µmol/L	–	–	(19–38)	mg/L	–	–	(3–6)	169
Uridine	P	µmol/L	4.50	1.70	–	mg/L	1.10	0.42	–	266
	P 7 adults	µmol/L	21.1	8.4	–	mg/L	5.15	2.05	–	271
	P 19 subjects	µmol/L	3.66	1.24	(2.02–6.23)	mg/L	0.894	0.303	(0.493–1.52)	277
Deoxyuridine	P 7 adults	µmol/L	0.62	0.39	–	mg/L	0.15	0.09	–	271
↓ **Nucleotides, nucleic acids**										
↓ **Cyclic nucleotides**										
Adenosine 3′,5′-phosphate	P	nmol/L	–	–	(10.6–21.8)	µg/L	–	–	(3.49–7.18)	178
	P 23 subjects	nmol/L	11.1	2.4	–	µg/L	3.65	0.79	–	179
	P 7 men	nmol/L	15.8	2.8	(11.8–20.4)	µg/L	5.20	0.92	(3.88–6.72)	188
	Plts	nmol/L	4.5	–	–	µg/L	1.5	–	–	211
Guanosine 3′,5′-phosphate	P	nmol/L	–	–	(4–11)	µg/L	–	–	(1.4–3.8)	178
	P 13 men	nmol/L	9.9	2.4	(5.9–14.3)	µg/L	3.4	0.83	(2.0–4.9)	191
	P 11 women	nmol/L	9.5	2.1	(6.9–12.7)	µg/L	3.3	0.72	(2.4–4.4)	191
Ribonucleic acid	Lkcs	...	...	...	...	g/10^{12}	8.19	3.64	–	190
Deoxyribonucleic acid	P 5 subjects	...	...	...	...	µg/L	–	–	(3–11)	180
	Lkcs	...	...	...	...	g/10^{12}	6.86	1.17	–	190

↓See text on next page	B Blood, P Plasma, S Serum, Erys Erythrocytes, Grcs Granulocytes, Lkcs Leukocytes, Plts Platelets	Amount of substance				Mass				Reference
		Unit	Mean	*s*	95% range (extreme range in brackets)	Unit	Mean	*s*	95% range (extreme range in brackets)	
↓Protein	B	...	...	...	...	g/L	205	–	–	226
	P 60 men	...	...	...	...	g/L	75.2	–	(66.3–88.6)	227
	P 55 women	...	...	...	...	g/L	73.8	–	(63.0–81.6)	227
	S 30 subjects	...	...	...	...	g/L	73	3.7	(68–82)	228
	Erys	...	...	...	...	g/L	335	–	(300–400)	226
	Lkcs	...	...	...	...	$g/10^{12}$	100	–	–	229
	Plts	...	...	...	...	g/kg	119	–	–	230
	Plts 23 subjects	...	...	...	...	$g/10^{12}$	2.31	0.23	–	231
	– 14 subjects	...	...	...	...	$g/10^{12}$	1.58	–	(1.32–1.90)	232

Table 18 *Nucleotides in erythrocytes*

	Subjects	Mean	*s*	95% range (extreme range in brackets)	Mean	*s*	95% range (extreme range in brackets)	Reference
		µmol/L			$µmol/10^{12}$			
Adenosine monophosphate	30 adults	51	–	10–92	...	...	...	182
	26 adults	24	7	–	...	...	...	183
	12 men	14	3	–	...	...	...	278
Adenosine diphosphate	30 adults	279	–	162–396	...	...	...	182
	26 adults	201	29	–	...	...	...	183
	10 adults	...	...	...	17	36	–	184
	10 newborn	...	...	...	19	63	–	184
	12 men	160	14	–	...	...	...	278
Adenosine triphosphate	30 adults	1280	–	1030–1530	–	–	–	182
	26 adults	1390	170	–	–	–	–	183
	10 adults	...	...	...	135	9	–	184
	10 newborn	...	...	...	158	28	–	184
	20 adults	1140	140	(777–1483)	103	10	(76–130)	185
	21 newborn	1077	210	(533–1449)	117	19	(70–146)	185
	12 men	1552	161	–	...	...	...	278
Cytidine diphosphates*	26 adults	36	12	–	...	...	...	183
Uridine diphosphates◊	26 adults	41	12	–	...	...	...	183
Guanosine monophosphate	12 men	0	3	–	...	...	...	278
Guanosine diphosphate	26 adults	18	8	–	...	...	...	183
	12 men	15	2	–	...	...	...	278
Guanosine triphosphate	26 adults	108	35	–	...	...	...	183
	12 men	56	7	–	...	...	...	278
Nicotinamide adenine dinucleotide NAD	14 subjects	42	–	(30–63)	...	...	...	186
NADH	14 subjects	22	–	(14–40)	...	...	...	186
Nicotinamide adenine dinucleotide phosphate NADP	14 subjects	24	–	(20–32)	...	...	...	186
NADPH	14 subjects	51	–	(34–81)	...	...	...	186

*Cytidine and deoxycytidine diphosphate cholin, cytidine and deoxycytidine diphosphate ethanolamine.

◊Uridine diphosphate glucose and uridine diphosphate N-acetylglucosamine.

Table 19 *Nucleotides in platelets*

	Number	Mean	*s*	(Extreme range)	Reference		Number	Mean	*s*	(Extreme range)	Reference
		$µmol/10^{12}$						$µmol/10^{12}$			
Adenosine monophosphate	13	4.8	–	–	187	Cytidine monophosphate	9	15.3	0.70	–	225
	9	4.90	1.29	–	225	Cytidine triphosphate	9	1.41	0.86	–	225
Adenosine diphosphate	13	25	–	(19–31)	115	Uridine triphosphate	9	2.04	0.77	–	225
	9	19.3	4.02	–	225	Guanosine monophosphate	9	2.68	1.55	–	225
Adenosine triphosphate	13	47	–	(39–55)	115	Guanosine diphosphate	9	4.57	1.12	–	225
	9	31.9	6.82	–	225	Guanosine triphosphate	9	4.82	1.42	–	225

Nucleotides. See Tables 18–20 for normal values. The variability of the data in the literature probably is of methodologic origin (the pyridine nucleotide concentration in the erythrocytes, for example, depends on the extraction method[209]). The adenine nucleotides have also been found in plasma in a concentration of about 15 µmol/L (ATP + ADP + AMP)[279].

Table 20 *Nucleotides in leukocytes*[189]

	Number	Mean	s
		µmol/10¹²	
Nicotinamide adenine dinucleotide ... NAD	14	32	7.5
NADH	14	25	8.6
Nicotinamide adenine dinucleotide phosphate .... NADP	14	8	5.6
NADPH	14	24	15

Nucleic acids. The concentration of ribonucleic acid in the plasma is below a detection limit of 600 µg/L[208].

Cyclic nucleotides. The plasma concentration of cyclic adenosine monophosphate (adenosine 3′,5′-phosphate) changes during the course of the day[202]. It is increased after several days of fasting[210], in chronic kidney diseases[179], and in hyperthyroidism[181].

Protein. The protein of whole blood is mainly hemoglobin of erythrocytes. Plasma proteins are discussed on pages 135–162, proteins of the blood cells on pages 166–199.

References

[1] GRAM, H.C., *Amer. J. med. Sci.*, **168**, 511 (1924).
[2] HINSBERG and BERENDT, in FLASCHENTRÄGER and LEHNARTZ (Eds.), *Physiologische Chemie*, volume II/1a, Springer, Berlin, 1954, page 416.
[3] VALBERG et al., *J. clin. Invest.*, **44**, 379 (1965).
[4] DENNES et al., *Biochem. J.*, **78**, 578 (1961).
[5] NOUR-ELDIN, F., *Nature*, **196**, 1219 (1962).
[6] ARCHIBALD, R.M., *Stand. Meth. clin. Chem.*, **2**, 91 (1958).
[7] JOSEPHSON et al., *Acta paediat. (Uppsala)*, **51**, suppl. 135, 111 (1962).
[8] BJÖRNESJÖ, K.B., *Scand. J. clin. Lab. Invest.*, **15**, suppl. 69, 25 (1963).
[9] EASTHAM, R.D., *Biochemical Values in Clinical Medicine*, 6th ed., Wright, Bristol, 1978, page 142.
[10] ADDIS et al., *J. clin. Invest.*, **26**, 869 (1947).
[11] SCHALES, O., *Stand. Meth. clin. Chem.*, **1**, 118 (1953); Südhof et al., *Klin. Wschr.*, **40**, 208 (1962).
[12] RICHTERICH, R., *Klinische Chemie*, 3rd ed., Karger, Basle, 1971.
[13] KAPLAN, A., *Stand. Meth. clin. Chem.*, **5**, 245 (1965).
[14] SEARCY et al., *Lancet*, **2**, 1114 (1962).
[15] GOLDBERG et al., *Clin. Chem.*, **19**, 395 (1973).
[16] KEATING et al., *J. Lab. clin. Med.*, **73**, 825 (1969).
[17] LENTNER and EGGSTEIN, Leading Symptoms: Laboratory Values, CIBA-GEIGY Ltd., Basle, 1976.
[18] HYTTEN and LIND, Diagnostic Indices in Pregnancy, CIBA-GEIGY Ltd., Basle, 1974.
[19] GALLAGHER and SELIGSON, *New Engl. J. Med.*, **266**, 492 (1962).
[20] RUDMAN et al., *J. clin. Invest.*, **52**, 2241 (1973).
[21] BERLET, H.H., *Clin. chim. Acta*, **20**, 149 (1968).
[22] EMERY and BURT, *Clin. chim. Acta*, **39**, 361 (1972).
[23] SANDBERG et al., *Metabolism*, **2**, 22 (1953).
[24] VALERI and FORTIER, *New Engl. J. Med.*, **281**, 1452 (1969).
[25] KNOLL and STAMM, *Z. klin. Chem.*, **8**, 582 (1970).
[26] SCHWARTZ et al., *J. Pediat.*, **88**, 828 (1976).
[27] DITZEL et al., *Scand. J. clin. Lab. Invest.*, **20**, 360 (1967).
[28] TALAFANT et al., *Pediat. Res.*, **11**, 880 (1977).
[29] MENICHINI and GIOVANNETTI, *Experientia (Basel)*, **29**, 506 (1973).
[30] COHEN, B.D., *Arch. intern. Med.*, **126**, 846 (1970).
[31] SHAINKIN et al., *Clin. chim. Acta*, **60**, 45 (1975).
[32] HUTCHINSON and LABBY, *J. Lab. clin. Med.*, **60**, 170 (1962).
[33] MÜTING et al., *Clin. chim. Acta*, **19**, 391 (1968).
[34] PROELSS and WRIGHT, *Clin. Chem.*, **19**, 1162 (1973).
[35] MÜTING, D., *Diagnostik*, **8**, 475 (1975).
[36] SPOONER et al., *Clin. chim. Acta*, **65**, 47 (1975).
[37] KINGSLEY and TAGER, *Stand. Meth. clin. Chem.*, **6**, 115 (1970).
[38] BESSMAN, S.P., *Advanc. clin. Chem.*, **2**, 135 (1959); GABUZDA, G.J., *Advanc. intern. Med.*, **11**, 11, (1962).
[39] BATSHAW and BRUSILOW, *Pediat. Res.*, **12**, 221 (1978).
[40] MÜTING et al., *Dtsch. med. Wschr.*, **95**, 1390 (1970).
[41] OBERHOLZER et al., *Clin. Chem.*, **22**, 1976 (1976).
[42] ENGLHARDT et al., *Dtsch. med. Wschr.*, **95**, 1601 (1970).
[43] SINNIAH et al., *J. clin. Path.*, **23**, 720 (1970); IMLER et al., *Schweiz. med. Wschr.*, **101**, 1161 (1971).
[44] MÜTING et al., *Med. Welt (Stuttg.)*, **17**, 2288 (1966).
[45] RUBALTELLI et al., *Biol. Neonat. (Basel)*, **15**, 129 (1970).
[46] REZZONICO et al., *Experientia (Basel)*, **24**, 28 (1968).
[47] GLASGOW et al., *Amer. J. Dis. Child.*, **124**, 827 (1972).
[48] ATTILI et al., *Biochem. Med.*, **14**, 109 (1975).
[49] MALMQUIST et al., *New Engl. J. Med.*, **284**, 997 (1971).
[50] LEVIN, B., *Advanc. clin. Chem.*, **14**, 65 (1971).
[51] ARMSTRONG and STAVE, *Metabolism*, **22**, 561 (1973).
[52] RUSKIN and SUNDERMAN, in SUNDERMAN and SUNDERMAN (Eds.), *The Clinical Pathology of Infancy*, Thomas, Springfield, 1967, page 132.
[53] LACY and CROFFORD, *J. Lab. clin. Med.*, **64**, 828 (1964).
[54] GOODWIN, J.F., *Clin. Chem.*, **14**, 1080 (1968), and *Stand. Meth. clin. Chem.*, **6**, 89 (1970).
[55] ANDREWS et al., *J. Pediat.*, **60**, 201 (1962).
[56] ARMSTRONG and STAVE, *Metabolism*, **22**, 549 (1973).
[57] OEPEN and OEPEN, *Klin. Wschr.*, **41**, 921 (1963).
[58] JOHNSON and BERGEIM, *J. biol. Chem.*, **188**, 833 (1951); BLACKMORE and PARRY, *J. clin. Path.*, **25**, 171 (1972).
[59] STEIN and MOORE, *J. biol. Chem.*, **211**, 915 (1954); SPACKMAN et al., *Analyt. Chem.*, **30**, 1190 (1958).
[60] SOUPART, P., in HOLDEN, J.T. (Ed.), *Amino Acid Pools*, Elsevier, Amsterdam, 1962, page 220.
[61] EFRON et al., *New Engl. J. Med.*, **270**, 1378 (1964); SCRIVER et al., *Lancet*, **2**, 230 (1964).
[62] SAIFER, A., *Advanc. clin. Chem.*, **14**, 145 (1971).
[63] SUNDERMAN, F.W., in SUNDERMAN and SUNDERMAN (Eds.), *The Clinical Pathology of Infancy*, Thomas, Springfield, 1967, page 145.
[64] SCRIVER et al., *Amer. J. clin. Nutr.*, **24**, 876 (1971).
[65] PERRY and HANSEN, *Clin. chim. Acta*, **25**, 53 (1969).
[66] GHADIMI and PECORA, *Pediatrics*, **33**, 500 (1964).
[67] LIAPPIS, N., *Z. klin. Chem.*, **10**, 132 (1972).
[68] VALMAN et al., *Brit. med. J.*, **4**, 789 (1971).
[69] DICKINSON et al., *Pediatrics*, **45**, 606 (1970).
[70] REID et al., *Amer. J. Obstet. Gynec.*, **111**, 251 (1971).
[71] WURTMAN et al., *New Engl. J. Med.*, **279**, 171 (1968).
[72] FELIG et al., *J. clin. Invest.*, **48**, 584 (1969).
[73] WHITEHEAD, R.G., *Lancet*, **1**, 250 (1964).
[74] DICKINSON et al., *Pediatrics*, **36**, 2 (1965).
[75] BRODEHL and GELLISSEN, *Pediatrics*, **42**, 395 (1968).
[76] LIAPPIS and JÄKEL, *Mschr. Kinderheilk.*, **122**, 6 (1974).
[77] SCRIVER and DAVIES, *Pediatrics*, **36**, 592 (1965).
[78] GATFIELD et al., *Canad. med. Ass. J.*, **99**, 1215 (1968).
[79] WILCKEN and GUPTA, *Clin. Sci.*, **57**, 211 (1979).
[80] PERRY et al., *J. Neurochem.*, **24**, 587 (1975).
[81] LEVY and BARKIN, *J. Lab. clin. Med.*, **78**, 517 (1971).
[82] BRIGHAM et al., *J. clin. Invest.*, **39**, 1633 (1960).
[83] LEROY, E.C., *Advanc. clin. Chem.*, **10**, 213 (1967).
[84] DUBROVSKÝ et al., *Clin. chim. Acta*, **19**, 387 (1968).
[85] AMMA et al., *Indian J. med. Res.*, **59**, 1312 (1971).
[86] BÖHMER et al., *Clin. chim. Acta*, **57**, 55 (1974).
[87] FRASER, R., *J. Lab. clin. Med.*, **35**, 960 (1950). and **37**, 199 (1951).
[88] NICOLAIDOU et al., *Arch. Biochem.*, **96**, 613 (1962).
[89] MCMENAMY et al., *J. clin. Invest.*, **39**, 1675 (1960).
[90] MELVILLE, D.B., *Vitam. and Horm.*, **17**, 155 (1959).
[91] VETRELLA et al., *Klin. Wschr.*, **48**, 85 (1970).
[92] WALLER et al., *Klin. Wschr.*, **48**, 79 (1970).
[93] BUSCH and BOIE, *Klin. Wschr.*, **47**, 1172 (1969).
[94] PETERS et al., *Proc. Soc. exp. Biol. (N.Y.)*, **131**, 281 (1969).
[95] SIMENHOFF et al., *Clin. Sci.*, **25**, 65 (1963).
[96] MONDOVÌ et al., *Ital. J. Biochem.*, **10**, 42 (1961).
[97] LUNDGREN et al., *Clin. chim. Acta*, **62**, 357 (1975).
[98] DESSER et al., *J. clin. Chem.*, **19**, 159 (1981).
[99] SCUDAMORE et al., *J. Lab. clin. Med.*, **37**, 860 (1951).
[100] COHEN, L., *J. Lab. clin. Med.*, **53**, 629 (1959).
[101] ECKERNÄS and AQUILONIUS, *Scand. J. clin. Lab. Invest.*, **37**, 183 (1977).
[102] PEULER and JOHNSON, *Life Sci.*, **21**, 625 (1977).
[103] DESSER et al., *Clin. chim. Acta*, **63**, 243 (1975).
[104] MITCHELL and CASS, *J. clin. Invest.*, **38**, 595 (1959).
[105] HORAKOVA et al., *Clin. chim. Acta*, **79**, 447 (1977).
[106] GRAHAM et al., *Blood*, **10**, 467 (1955).
[107] HAVERBACK et al., *J. clin. Invest.*, **41**, 1364 (1962).
[108] BROWN et al., *Analyt. Biochem.*, **109**, 142 (1980).
[109] GROSS and FRANZEN, *Z. klin. Chem.*, **3**, 99 (1965).
[110] BIDDER et al., *Lancet*, **1**, 165 (1974).
[111] MÜTING et al., *Z. klin. Med.*, **157**, 538 (1963).
[112] MÜTING et al., *Z. klin. Med.*, **157**, 544 (1963).
[113] RODNIGHT, R., *Int. Rev. Neurobiol.*, **3**, 251 (1961).
[114] GIRARD, J.P., *Schweiz. med. Wschr.*, **93**, 1456 (1963).
[115] WEISS et al., *J. clin. Invest.*, **54**, 421 (1974).
[116] FRATTINI et al., *Clin. chim. Acta*, **92**, 353 (1979).
[117] DALGLIESH, C.E., *Advanc. clin. Chem.*, **1**, 193 (1958); RESNICK and GRAY, *Med. Clin. N. Amer.*, **44**, 1323 (1960).
[118] FIKENTSCHER et al., *Klin. Wschr.*, **47**, 919 (1969).
[119] MIYAGI et al., *J. Lab. clin. Med.*, **78**, 683 (1971); WATSON et al., *Arch. intern. Med.*, **131**, 698 (1973).
[120] HEILMEYER, L., *Schweiz. med. Wschr.*, **92**, 1285 (1962).
[121] DRUYAN and HAEGER-ARONSEN, *Scand. J. clin. Lab. Invest.*, **16**, 498 (1964).
[122] WRANNE, L., *Acta paediat. (Uppsala)*, **49**, suppl. 124 (1960).
[123] SALMI and TENHUNEN, *Clin. Chem.*, **26**, 1832 (1980).
[124] LEVERE and KAPPAS, *Advanc. clin. Chem.*, **11**, 133 (1968).
[125] WATSON, C.J., *Arch. intern. Med.*, **86**, 797 (1950).
[126] PIOMELLI, S., *J. Lab. clin. Med.*, **81**, 932 (1973).
[127] KOSKELO et al., *Clin. chim. Acta*, **29**, 559 (1970).
[128] VERLOOP et al., *Ser. Haematol.*, **5**, 76 (1965).
[129] DITTRICH, H., *Med. Klin.*, **58**, 1882 (1963).
[130] MICHAËLSSON and SJÖLIN, *Acta paediat. scand.*, **54**, 325 (1965).
[131] CHAPLIN et al., *J. Lab. clin. Med.*, **57**, 612 (1961).
[132] VANZETTI and VALENTE, *Clin. chim. Acta*, **11**, 442 (1965).
[133] JACOBS and FERNANDEZ, *Stand. Meth. clin. Chem.*, **6**, 107 (1970).
[134] JAYLE and MORETTI, *Progr. Hemat.*, **3**, 342 (1962).
[135] COBURN, R.F., *New Engl. J. Med.*, **282**, 207 (1970).
[136] SCHWERD, W., *Der rote Blutfarbstoff und seine wichtigsten Derivate*, Schmidt-Römhild, Lübeck, 1962, page 73.

[137] JAFFÉ and HELLER, *Progr. Hemat.*, **4**, 48 (1964).
[138] HARRIS and KELLERMEYER, *The Red Cell*, Harvard University Press, Cambridge (Mass.), 1970.
[139] SIGGAARD-ANDERSEN et al., *Clin. chim. Acta*, **42**, 85 (1972).
[140] STEWART et al., *J. Amer. med. Ass.*, **229**, 1187 (1974).
[141] ASTRUP and KJELDSEN, *Med. Clin. N. Amer.*, **58**, 323 (1974).
[142] VEST, M., *Bibl. paediat. (Basel)*, fascicle 69 (1959).
[143] OBRINSKY et al., *Amer. J. Dis. Child.*, **87**, 305 (1954).
[144] BEORCHIA et al., *Clin. chim. Acta*, **109**, 245 (1981).
[145] SIMMONS, N. A., *J. clin. Path.*, **21**, 196 (1968).
[146] BRODERSEN et al., *Scand. J. clin. Lab. Invest.*, **15**, 523 (1963).
[147] WITH, T. K., *Bile Pigments*, Academic Press, New York, 1968.
[148] CASHORE et al., *J. Pediat.*, **93**, 827 (1978).
[149] KARP, W. B., *Pediatrics*, **64**, 361 (1979).
[150] THOMPSON, R. P., *Brit. med. J.*, **1**, 223 (1970).
[151] FLEISCHNER and ARIAS, *Amer. J. Med.*, **49**, 576 (1970); ARIAS, I. M., *New Engl. J. Med.*, **285**, 1416 (1971).
[152] LESTER and TROXLER, *Gastroenterology*, **56**, 143 (1969).
[153] SCHIFF et al., *J. Lab. clin. Med.*, **80**, 455 (1972).
[154] GITZELMANN-CUMARASAMY and KUENZLE, *Pediatrics*, **64**, 375 (1979); LLOYD-STILL, J. D., *New Engl. J. Med.*, **303**, 1426 (1980).
[155] BAKKEN, A. F., *Acta paediat. scand.*, **59**, 148 and 153 (1970).
[156] SCHELLONG, G., *Med. Klin.*, **63**, 821 (1968).
[157] SCHRADER, Z. R., *New Engl. J. Med.*, **280**, 49 (1969).
[158] FULOP et al., *Arch. intern. Med.*, **127**, 254 (1971).
[159] GARTNER et al., *Pediatrics*, **45**, 906 (1970).
[160] ACKERMAN et al., *Pediatrics*, **45**, 918 (1970).
[161] THALER, M. M., *Advanc. Pediat.*, **19**, 215 (1972).
[162] MACDONALD, R. P., *Stand. Meth. clin. Chem.*, **5**, 65 (1965).
[163] DE LA HUERGA et al., in SUNDERMAN and SUNDERMAN (Eds.), *The Clinical Pathology of Infancy*, Thomas, Springfield, 1967, page 310.
[164] GAMBINO, R., *Stand. Meth. clin. Chem.*, **5**, 55 (1965).
[165] MICHAËLSSON et al., *Pediatrics*, **35**, 925 (1965).
[166] BLOOMER et al., *J. Amer. med. Ass.*, **218**, 216 (1971).
[167] FELSHER et al., *New Engl. J. Med.*, **283**, 170 (1970); OWENS and SHERLOCK, *Brit. med. J.*, **3**, 559 (1973).
[168] STERN, L., *Pediatrics*, **49**, 916 (1972).
[169] ARCHIBALD, R. M., *J. biol. Chem.*, **156**, 121 (1944).
[170] HARKNESS and NICOL, *Arch. Dis. Childh.*, **44**, 773 (1969).
[171] REMP, D. G., *Stand. Meth. clin. Chem.*, **6**, 1 (1970).
[172] OTT et al., *Schweiz. med. Wschr.*, **94**, 989 (1964).
[173] JØRGENSEN and NIELSEN, *Scand. J. clin. Lab. Invest.*, **8**, 108 (1956).
[174] KLINENBERG et al., *Clin. Chem.*, **13**, 834 (1967).
[175] HAYASHI et al., *Gynec. Invest.*, **3**, 221 (1972).
[176] MERTZ, D. P., *Gicht*, 2nd ed., Thieme, Stuttgart, 1973; SEEGMILLER, J. E., in BONDY and ROSENBERG (Eds.), *Duncan's Diseases of Metabolism*, 7th ed., Saunders, Philadelphia, 1974, page 655.
[177] MONKUS et al., *Amer. J. Obstet. Gynec.*, **108**, 91 (1970).
[178] BALL et al., *J. clin. Invest.*, **51**, 2124 (1972).
[179] SCHNEIDER and JUTZLER, *New Engl. J. Med.*, **291**, 155 (1974).
[180] DENNIN, R. H., *Klin. Wschr.*, **57**, 451 (1979).
[181] KARLBERG et al., *J. clin. Endocr.*, **39**, 96 (1974).
[182] BUSCH, D., *Klin. Wschr.*, **48**, 543 (1970).
[183] MILLS et al., *Proc. nat. Acad. Sci. (Wash.)*, **73**, 2867 (1976).
[184] WITT et al., *Klin. Wschr.*, **45**, 262 (1967).
[185] OSKI and NAIMAN, *Pediatrics*, **36**, 104 (1965).
[186] BUSCH and BOIE, *Klin. Wschr.*, **47**, 1172 (1969).
[187] MILLS and THOMAS, *Nature*, **222**, 991 (1969).
[188] LATNER and PRUDHOE, *Clin. chim. Acta*, **48**, 353 (1973).
[189] SILBER et al., *J. clin. Invest.*, **41**, 230 (1962).
[190] FREI et al., *Blood*, **18**, 317 (1961).
[191] LATNER et al., *Clin. chim. Acta*, **81**, 99 (1977).
[192] EKSBORG et al., *Clin. chim. Acta*, **82**, 141 (1978).
[193] KUO et al., *Clin. Chem.*, **24**, 1373 (1978).
[194] JOSEPH and RISBY, *Clin. chim. Acta*, **63**, 197 (1975).
[195] ANDREOLI and MAFFEI, *Lancet*, **2**, 922 (1975).
[196] ABITBOL et al., *J. Pediat.*, **86**, 766 (1975).
[197] VAN SANDE et al., *J. Neurochem.*, **17**, 125 (1970).
[198] CEDERBLAD, G., *Clin. chim. Acta*, **67**, 207 (1976).
[199] WANG et al., *Clin. chim. Acta*, **63**, 13 (1975).
[200] WANG et al., *Clin. chim. Acta*, **63**, 21 (1975).
[201] COULOMBE et al., *Metabolism*, **25**, 973 (1976).
[202] PUJOL-AMAT et al., *Lancet*, **1**, 489 (1977); HOLMES and HAMADAH, *Lancet*, **1**, 755 (1977).
[203] PLETSCHER and DA PRADA, *Ciba Found. Symp.*, NS **35**, 261 (1975).
[204] ARENDT and WILKINSON, in JAFFÉ and BEHRMAN (Eds.), *Methods of Hormone Radioimmunoassay*, 2nd ed., Academic Press, New York, 1979, page 101.
[205] WETTERBERG et al., *J. clin. Endocr.*, **42**, 185 (1976).
[206] STONE et al., *J. clin. Invest.*, **56**, 1334 (1975).
[207] KAGEN et al., *Amer. J. Med.*, **58**, 177 (1975); KAGEN, L. J., *Arch. intern. Med.*, **139**, 628 (1979).
[208] HAMILTON et al., *Clin. Chem.*, **25**, 1774 (1979).
[209] OMACHI et al., *Biochim. biophys. Acta (Amst.)*, **184**, 139 (1969).
[210] MJØS et al., *Scand. J. clin. Lab. Invest.*, **37**, 439 (1977).
[211] HASLAM, R. J., *Ciba Found. Symp.*, NS **35**, 121 (1975).
[212] HOUPERT et al., *Clin. chim. Acta*, **69**, 383 (1976).
[213] RECORD et al., *Europ. J. clin. Invest.*, **6**, 387 (1976).
[214] COHEN et al., *Blood*, **48**, 469 (1976).
[215] MARSTEIN et al., *New Engl. J. Med.*, **295**, 406 (1976).
[216] COOPER et al., *Clin. chim. Acta*, **82**, 1 (1978).
[217] SIMENHOFF et al., *Lancet*, **2**, 818 (1976).
[218] HAGENFELDT et al., *Clin. chim. Acta*, **85**, 167 (1978).
[219] KONRAD et al., *Acta haemat. (Basel)*, **48**, 193 (1972).
[220] DUBOVSKY and GEARY, *Clin. chim. Acta*, **76**, 41 (1977).
[221] FARAJ et al., *New Engl. J. Med.*, **294**, 1360 (1976).
[222] CHASE et al., *Europ. J. clin. Invest.*, **7**, 351 (1977).
[223] STOPIK et al., *Dtsch. med. Wschr.*, **102**, 932 (1977).
[224] ROSANO and KENNY, *Clin. Chem.*, **23**, 69 (1977).
[225] PROSS et al., *Proc. Soc. exp. Biol. (N. Y.)*, **154**, 508 (1977).
[226] ALBRITTON, E. C., *Standard Values in Blood*, Saunders, Philadelphia, 1952, page 94.
[227] LANGE, H. F., *Acta med. scand.*, **125**, suppl. 176 (1946).
[228] RIVA, G., *Das Serumeiweißbild*, Huber, Bern, 1957, page 257.
[229] HINSBERG and BERENDT, in FLASCHENTRÄGER and LEHNARTZ (Eds.), *Physiologische Chemie*, volume II/la, Springer, Berlin, 1954, page 416.
[230] KARPATKIN, S., *J. clin. Invest.*, **48**, 1073 (1969).
[231] SHATTIL et al., *J. Lab. clin. Med.*, **89**, 341 (1977).
[232] INGEBRETSEN et al., *Clin. chim. Acta*, **126**, 307 (1982).
[233] BUNN et al., *Science*, **200**, 21 (1978).
[234] LEV-RAN, A., *Arch. intern. Med.*, **141**, 747 (1981).
[235] DANEMAN et al., *J. Pediat.*, **99**, 847 (1981).
[236] TZE et al., *J. Pediat.*, **93**, 13 (1978).
[237] SCHOOS et al., *Clin. chim. Acta*, **86**, 61 (1978).
[238] WAJCMAN et al., *Clin. chim. Acta*, **92**, 33 (1979).
[239] JURY et al., *New Zeal. med. J.*, **95**, 105 (1982); MCFARLAND, K. F., *Arch. intern. Med.*, **141**, 712 (1981).
[240] MAYER and FREEDMAN, *Clin. chim. Acta*, **127**, 147 (1983).
[241] OSKI and ALTMAN, *J. Pediat.*, **61**, 709 (1962).
[242] JACOBSEN et al., *Lancet*, **1**, 319 (1980).
[243] CAPOCACCIA et al., *Clin. chim. Acta*, **75**, 99 (1977).
[244] GERRON et al., *Clin. Chem.*, **22**, 663 (1976).
[245] MOSES et al., *J. clin. Path.*, **31**, 1207 (1978).
[246] BACHMANN and COLOMBO, *Europ. J. Pediat.*, **134**, 109 (1980).
[247] POHLANDT, F., *J. Pediat.*, **92**, 617 (1978).
[248] POHLANDT, F., *J. Pediat.*, **92**, 614 (1978).
[249] HAGENFELDT and ARVIDSSON, *Clin. chim. Acta*, **100**, 133 (1980).
[250] ZÜRCHER and DA PRADA, *J. Neurochem.*, **33**, 631 (1979).
[251] BROYER et al., *Amer. J. clin. Nutr.*, **33**, 1396 (1980).
[252] TRICKLEBANK et al., *Acta paediat. scand.*, **68**, 199 (1979).
[253] YOSHIDA and HIRAYAMA, *Clin. chim. Acta*, **101**, 235 (1980).
[254] SAITO et al., *Amer. J. clin. Nutr.*, **33**, 1402 (1980).
[255] WARSHAW and CURRY, *J. Pediat.*, **97**, 122 (1980).
[256] SCHOLTE et al., *New Engl. J. Med.*, **299**, 1079 (1978).
[257] DI DONATO et al., *Clin. chim. Acta*, **100**, 209 (1980).
[258] JOPE et al., *New Engl. J. Med.*, **299**, 833 (1978).
[259] KAROUM et al., *J. Neurochem.*, **33**, 201 (1979).
[260] CANGIANO et al., *Europ. J. clin. Invest.*, **8**, 183 (1978).
[261] HANSSON et al., *Clin. chim. Acta*, **88**, 419 (1978).
[262] KOBAYASHI et al., *Life Sci.*, **26**, 567 (1980).
[263] TAKESHITA et al., *Analyt. Biochem.*, **107**, 305 (1980).
[264] BLANCKAERT et al., *J. Lab. clin. Med.*, **96**, 198 (1980).
[265] MANZKE et al., *Europ. J. Pediat.*, **133**, 157 (1980).
[266] WUNG and HOWELL, *Clin. Chem.*, **26**, 1704 (1980).
[267] MCBURNEY and GIBSON, *Clin. chim. Acta*, **102**, 19 (1980).
[268] HOBERG and HEMPEL, *Clin. chim. Acta*, **90**, 107 (1978).
[269] PERRY and HANSEN, *Clin. chim. Acta*, **117**, 7 (1981).
[270] HARGREAVES et al., *Brit. J. Haemat.*, **47**, 399 (1981).
[271] DUDMAN et al., *Analyt. Biochem.*, **115**, 428 (1981).
[272] KIKUCHI et al., *Clin. Chem.*, **27**, 1899 (1981).
[273] HARTMANN et al., *Clin. chim. Acta*, **121**, 37 (1982).
[274] PISANI et al., *Med. Lavoro*, **58**, 279 (1967).
[275] CEDERBLAD et al., *Clin. chim. Acta*, **125**, 207 (1982).
[276] KEYZER et al., *Clin. chim. Acta*, **113**, 165 (1981).
[277] ZAKARIA et al., *Clin. chim. Acta*, **126**, 69 (1982).
[278] ERICSON et al., *Clin. chim. Acta*, **127**, 47 (1983).
[279] HARKNESS et al., *Clin. Sci.*, **64**, 333 (1983).
[280] THIRINGER, K., *Acta paediat. scand.*, **72**, 231 (1983).

Nitrogen-free substances (for references see pages 110 and 111)

↓ See text below	B Blood, P Plasma, S Serum, Erys Erythrocytes, Plts Platelets	Amount of substance				Mass				Reference
		Unit	Mean	s	95% range (extreme range in brackets)	Unit	Mean	s	95% range (extreme range in brackets)	
Ethanol	B	µmol/L	–	–	(<33)	mg/L	–	–	(<1.5)	1
↓ **Acetaldehyde**	B	µmol/L	1.0	0.2	–	µg/L	44	9	–	2
↓ **Acetoin**	B 82 subjects	µmol/L	1.06	1.54	–	µg/L	93	136	–	3
↓ **2,3-Butylene glycol**	B 80 subjects	µmol/L	13.8	7.5	–	mg/L	1.24	0.68	–	3
↓ **Glycerol** (free)	B Umbilical artery, 22 newborn	µmol/L	44	17	–	mg/L	4.1	1.6	–	4
	B Umbilical vein, 22 newborn	µmol/L	40	19	–	mg/L	3.7	1.7	–	4
	B 10 men	µmol/L	43	9	(24–62)	mg/L	4.0	0.8	(2.2–5.7)	5
	B 33 women	µmol/L	50	16	(22–88)	mg/L	4.6	1.5	(2.0–8.1)	5
	P(S) Umbilical vein, 24 newborn	µmol/L	80	29	–	mg/L	7.4	2.7	–	72
	– 10 newborn, 1st day	µmol/L	175	32	–	mg/L	16.1	2.9	–	6
	– 10 newborn, 7th day	µmol/L	123	63	–	mg/L	11.3	5.8	–	6
	– 12 children, 8–14 years	µmol/L	60	18	–	mg/L	5.5	1.7	–	7
	– 57 adults	µmol/L	120	65	–	mg/L	11.1	6.0	–	8
	– 93 men	µmol/L	90	40	10–170	mg/L	8.3	3.7	0.9–15.7	9
	– 42 women	µmol/L	120	40	40–200	mg/L	11.1	3.7	3.7–18.5	9
↓ **Short-chain fatty acids**										
Acetic acid	B 39 subjects	µmol/L	47.7	50.6	–	mg/L	2.86	3.04	–	3
	P 10 subjects	µmol/L	60	–	(40–70)	mg/L	3.6	–	(2.4–4.2)	78
	P 27 adults	µmol/L	51	–	0–103	mg/L	3.1	–	0–6.2	79
	S 10 subjects	µmol/L	30.4	–	(22–40)	mg/L	1.83	–	(1.3–2.4)	80
Propionic acid	P 22 adults	µmol/L	–	–	0.7–1.9	mg/L	–	–	0.05–0.14	11
	S 24 children, 1 month to 4 years	µmol/L	1.6	1.2	(0–4.2)	mg/L	0.12	0.09	(0–0.31)	81
	S 17 adults	µmol/L	0.9	1.2	(0.1–5.1)	mg/L	0.07	0.09	(0.007–0.38)	81
	S 10 subjects	µmol/L	1.7	–	(1.0–2.4)	mg/L	0.13	–	(0.07–0.18)	80
Isobutyric acid	P 22 adults	µmol/L	–	–	2.1–5.3	mg/L	–	–	0.19–0.47	11
	S 10 subjects	µmol/L	2.3	–	(0.7–4.4)	mg/L	0.20	–	(0.06–0.39)	80
Butyric acid	P 22 adults	µmol/L	–	–	0–1.0	mg/L	–	–	0–0.09	11
	S 10 subjects	µmol/L	1.0	–	(0.3–1.5)	mg/L	0.09	–	(0.03–0.13)	80
2-Methylbutyric acid	P 22 adults	µmol/L	–	–	2.9–6.2	mg/L	–	–	0.30–0.63	11
Isovaleric acid	P 22 adults	µmol/L	–	–	3.9–8.8	mg/L	–	–	0.40–0.90	11
	S 10 subjects	µmol/L	1.6	–	(0.3–2.7)	mg/L				80
Valeric acid	P 22 adults	µmol/L	–	–	0–1.0	mg/L	–	–	0–0.10	11
	S 10 subjects	µmol/L	0.6	–	(0.3–1.2)	mg/L	0.06	–	(0.03–0.12)	80
Hexanoic acid	S 10 subjects	µmol/L	0.8	–	(0–1.6)	mg/L	0.09	–	(0–0.19)	80
Octanoic acid	S 24 subjects	µmol/L	1.5	–	<5	mg/L	0.22	–	<0.7	71

Acetaldehyde. Ethanol and possibly diethyl ether are metabolized to acetaldehyde in man[77]. When ethanol was given in an amount producing a blood ethanol level of about 22 mmol/L (1 g/L), the acetaldehyde concentration in the blood was approximately 20 µmol/L[77].

Acetoin and 2,3-butylene glycol. Elevated blood levels have been found in chronic renal failure, hepatic failure and diabetes.

Glycerol. About 10% of the total glycerol in the serum is free; the major portion is bound to fatty acids. The glycerol concentration is increased in obesity[10], hyperthyroidism[5], and after several days of fasting[10].

Short-chain fatty acids. Acetic acid normally accounts for the major portion of short-chain (volatile) acids, but the normal values cited in the literature vary considerably, probably owing to the different methods employed[76]. The serum level of octanoic acid is increased in liver cirrhosis and hepatic encephalopathy[71]. In hereditary metabolic disorders of the branched-chain amino acids, the propionic acid level may amount to 100–200 times[69], and the isovaleric acid level to more than 3000 times the normal value[70].

Long-chain fatty acids (nonesterified, 'free'). Approximately 3% and at most 10% of the fatty acids in the serum are not esterified[15]. They are bound to albumin, and less than 0.01% of the nonesterified fatty acids are present as anions in aqueous solution[16]. The mean serum concentrations of nonesterified fatty acids reported range from 266 µmol/L to 943 µmol/L, owing in part to the different methods employed[17]. Determination as copper soap following isolation by thin-layer chromatography may serve as the reference method[18]. The individual fatty acids are best determined by gas chromatography[19]. (See page 119 regarding the fatty acid pattern.) In cord blood, the concentration of free fatty acids is low but it increases sharply during the first few hours after birth[11]. In prepubertal children the concentration tends to be higher than in adults[20]. The values are increased toward the end of pregnancy – reaching a maximum during labor – but return to normal 2 days post partum[21]. The concentration is increased after several days of fasting[10,64]. A *pathological* increase of the concentration is found in diabetic coma (up to 4 mmol/L)[22], in cirrhosis of the liver[74] and, in connection with increased epinephrine secretion, after a myocardial infarction[23].

↑↓ See text on previous page and below	B Blood, P Plasma, S Serum, Erys Erythrocytes, Plts Platelets	Amount of substance				Mass				Reference
		Unit	Mean	s	95% range (extreme range in brackets)	Unit	Mean	s	95% range (extreme range in brackets)	
↑ **Long-chain fatty acids** (nonesterified, 'free')	P(S) Umbilical vein, 23 newborn	μmol/L	280	100	–	mg/L	79	28	–	72
	– Cord blood, 60 newborn	μmol/L	375	125	–	mg/L	106	36	–	12
	– 60 newborn, 12 hours	μmol/L	631	346	–	mg/L	178	98	–	12
	– 60 newborn, 3 days	μmol/L	750	210	–	mg/L	212	59	–	12
	– 62 adults, 20–35 years	μmol/L	405	80	240–570	mg/L	114	23	68–160	13
	– 10 men	μmol/L	380	–	(240–540)	mg/L	107	–	(68–152)	5
	– 33 women	μmol/L	520	190	(210–990)	mg/L	147	54	(59–279)	5
	Erys 8 adults	μmol/10^{12}	27	–	(10.6–38.0)	mg/10^{12}	7.6	–	(3.0–10.7)	14
	Plts 12 subjects	μmol/10^{12}	350	–	–	mg/10^{12}	100	–	–	73
↓ **Oxalic acid**	P 3 subjects (a)	μmol/L	–	–	(0.1–0.9)	mg/L	–	–	(0.01–0.08)	50
	P 22 subjects (b)	μmol/L	2.8	1.1	(1.3–5.3)	mg/L	0.25	0.10	(0.12–0.48)	51
	P 6 men (c)	μmol/L	10.7	2.7	(5.1–15.7)	mg/L	0.96	0.24	(0.46–1.41)	52
	S 9 men (c)	μmol/L	9.2	2.7	(5.3–14.0)	mg/L	0.83	0.24	(0.48–1.26)	52
Succinic acid	S 8 subjects	μmol/L	8.8	2.7	(4.1–12)	mg/L	1.04	0.32	(0.5–1.4)	38
Adipic acid	S 8 subjects	nmol/L	90	10	(<250)	μg/L	13	1.5	(<37)	38
↓ **Malonaldehyde**	P 14 subjects	μmol/L	2.36	0.55	–	mg/L	0.170	0.040	–	90
Glycolic acid	P 24 adults	μmol/L	170	50	(100–300)	mg/L	2.2	0.7	(1.3–3.9)	85
↓ **Lactic acid**	B Umbilical artery, 8 newborn	mmol/L	3.72	0.73	–	mg/L	335	66	–	24
	B Umbilical vein, 24 newborn	mmol/L	2.39	0.99	–	mg/L	215	89	–	24
	B Arterial:									
	10 newborn, 1st hour	mmol/L	2.5	1.6	(0.65–4.0)	mg/L	225	142	(59–360)	25
	69 adults	mmol/L	0.62	0.08	0.46–0.78	mg/L	56	7	42–70	26
	B Venous:									
	Adults	mmol/L	1.00	0.12	–	mg/L	90	11	–	26
	10 adults	mmol/L	0.92	0.26	–	mg/L	83	23	–	27
	9 adults	mmol/L	0.75	0.06	–	mg/L	68	5	–	28
	B Capillary:									
	158 boys, 8–10 years	mmol/L	1.12	0.34	0.44–1.80	mg/L	101	31	39–163	29
	123 girls, 8–10 years	mmol/L	1.14	0.36	0.42–1.86	mg/L	103	32	39–167	29
	P Venous, 15 subjects	mmol/L	0.76	0.34	(0.33–1.58)	mg/L	68	31	(30–142)	75
	Erys	mmol/L	0.84	0.25	–	mg/L	76	22	–	35
L-Lactic acid	P 7 men	mmol/L	1.51	–	(0.74–2.40)	mg/L	136	–	(67–216)	86
D-Lactic acid	P 7 men	mmol/L	0.023	–	(0.017–0.028)	mg/L	2.1	–	(1.5–2.5)	86
↓ **Pyruvic acid**	B Umbilical vein, 24 newborn	mmol/L	0.081	0.034	–	mg/L	7.1	3.0	–	24
	B 10 newborn, 1st hour	mmol/L	0.090	0.032	(0.07–0.12)	mg/L	7.9	2.8	(6.1–10.6)	25
	B 120 children, 2–13 years	mmol/L	0.076	0.01	0.056–0.096	mg/L	6.73	0.90	4.9–8.5	33
	B 10 adults	mmol/L	0.061	0.024	–	mg/L	5.37	2.11	–	27
	B 9 adults	mmol/L	0.068	0.008	–	mg/L	5.99	0.70	–	28
	B 21 adults	mmol/L	0.063	0.025	–	mg/L	5.6	2.2	–	34
	S 21 adults	mmol/L	0.073	0.022	–	mg/L	6.4	1.9	–	34
	P 15 subjects	mmol/L	0.032	0.019	(0.021–0.073)	mg/L	2.8	1.7	(1.8–6.4)	75
	Erys	mmol/L	0.093	0.032	–	mg/L	8.2	2.8	–	35

Oxalic acid. Values determined (a) in vivo with ^{14}C-oxalate infusion; (b) by gas chromatography; (c) radioenzymatically with isotope dilution. The plasma level of oxalate in health is still not known precisely, but elevations have been found in oxalic acid and ethylene glycol intoxications, in primary hyperoxaluria and in severe renal failure.

Malonaldehyde. Elevated levels in plasma were found after myocardial infarction indicating elevated platelet aggregation[90].

Lactic acid. All the data were obtained enzymatically (see Fleischer[30] for method). – Varying values are obtained, depending on the method of sample collection[28]. Arterial blood of fasting subjects collected at complete rest under hospital conditions contains only about 60% of the amount of lactate in venous blood[26]. The lactate concentration in cord blood is high but drops within 2 days to the characteristic value of children and adults[25,31]. Increased values are found after muscular work, emotional excitement, and toward the end of pregnancy[32]. Lactic acidosis can develop in hypoxia of poorly perfused tissues due to circulatory shock; extreme cases of lactic acidosis – with the lactate increasing more than the pyruvate (lactate levels up to 20–30 mmol/L) – have been described in connection with diabetes mellitus, renal failure, infections, and ethanol intoxication[33]. Genetic forms of lactic acidosis are known as well[91].

Pyruvic acid. All adult values were determined enzymatically (see Fleischer[30] for method). Pyruvic acid and other oxo acids have low stability and should therefore be determined in whole blood rather than in serum. – The pyruvic-acid concentration in the blood is increased in newborn and then declines in the first few

↓ See text below	B Blood, P Plasma, S Serum, Erys Erythrocytes, Plts Platelets	Amount of substance				Mass				Reference
		Unit	Mean	*s*	95% range (extreme range in brackets)	Unit	Mean	*s*	95% range (extreme range in brackets)	
Malic acid	B	µmol/L	34	–	(18–56)	mg/L	4.6	–	(2.4–7.5)	39
	P 14 subjects	µmol/L	3.2	0.9	–	mg/L	0.43	0.12	–	40
↓ **2-Oxoglutaric acid**	B Cord	µmol/L	14	–	–	mg/L	2	–	–	24
	B 120 children, 2–13 years	µmol/L	9.3	2.3	4.7–13.7	mg/L	1.36	0.33	0.70–2.02	33
	B 40 children, adults	µmol/L	8.9	2.7	3.5–14	mg/L	1.3	0.4	0.5–2.1	47
	P 17 newborn, 0–3 days	µmol/L	20.7	2.5	–	mg/L	3.02	0.37	–	82
2-Oxoisovaleric acid	B 9 subjects	µmol/L	12.9	2.0	–	mg/L	1.50	0.23	–	83
	B 40 children, adults	µmol/L	11	1.7	8–14	mg/L	1.3	0.2	0.9–1.7	47
	S 4 subjects	µmol/L	5.6	3.3	(3.4–10.3)	mg/L	0.65	0.38	(0.39–1.20)	48
2-Oxoisocaproic acid	B 9 subjects	µmol/L	33.5	8.2	–	mg/L	4.36	1.07	–	83
	S 4 subjects	µmol/L	27.8	14.1	(17–47)	mg/L	3.62	1.83	(2.2–6.1)	48
2-Oxo-3-methylvaleric acid	B 9 subjects	µmol/L	22.7	4.6	–	mg/L	2.95	0.60	–	83
	S 4 subjects	µmol/L	9.0	8.2	(3.0–21)	mg/L	1.2	1.1	(0.39–2.7)	48
Oxalacetic acid	B	µmol/L	9.1	–	–	mg/L	1.2	–	–	49
↓ **Citric acid**	B Umbilical artery	µmol/L	68	12	–	mg/L	13.0	2.4	–	24
	B Umbilical vein	µmol/L	88	33	–	mg/L	16.9	6.3	–	24
	B 31 adults	µmol/L	99	–	80–118	mg/L	19.0	–	15.4–22.6	41
	P(S) 32 children, 2–15 months	µmol/L	122	30	–	mg/L	23.5	5.8	–	44
	– 25 adults	µmol/L	99	–	67–142	mg/L	19.0	–	12.8–27.2	41
	– 50 men	µmol/L	90	–	49–131	mg/L	17.3	–	9.4–25.2	43
↓ **Ketone bodies** (as acetone)	B Umbilical artery, 18 newborn	µmol/L	316	348		mg/L	18.4	20.2	–	4
	B Umbilical vein, 22 newborn	µmol/L	396	389	–	mg/L	23.0	22.6	–	4
	B 19 adults, not fasting	µmol/L	107	70	–	mg/L	6.2	4.1	–	53
	B 94 adults, fasting	µmol/L	143	69	5–281	mg/L	8.3	4.0	0.3–16.3	53
Acetone	P 20 adults, not fasting	µmol/L	30	20	–	mg/L	1.7	1.2	–	54
	S 11 adults, fasting	µmol/L	50	5	(28–88)	mg/L	2.9	0.3	(1.6–5.1)	55
Acetoacetic acid	B 16 adults, not fasting	µmol/L	17	–	(5–45)	mg/L	1.7	–	(0.5–4.6)	56
	B 7 adults, fasting	µmol/L	31	–	(18–76)	mg/L	3.2	–	(1.8–7.8)	56
	P 8 newborn, 1–2 days, not fasting	µmol/L	249	106	–	mg/L	25.4	10.8	–	57
	P 10 newborn, 3 days, not fasting	µmol/L	279	116	–	mg/L	28.5	11.8	–	57
	P 10 newborn, 4–10 days, not fasting	µmol/L	161	131	–	mg/L	16.4	15.5	–	57
	P 13 adults, fasting	µmol/L	42	19	–	mg/L	4.3	1.9	–	57
	P 15 subjects, fasting	µmol/L	26	11	(16–43)	mg/L	2.7	1.1	(1.6–4.4)	75
3-Hydroxybutyric acid	B 16 adults, not fasting	µmol/L	36	–	(13–95)	mg/L	3.7	–	(1.4–9.9)	56
	B 7 adults, fasting	µmol/L	90	–	(56–164)	mg/L	9.4	–	(5.8–17.1)	56
	P Umbilical vein, 24 newborn	µmol/L	267	176	–	mg/L	27.8	18.3	–	72
	P 8 newborn, 1–2 days, not fasting	µmol/L	662	402	–	mg/L	68.9	41.9	–	57
	P 10 newborn, 3 days, not fasting	µmol/L	565	255	–	mg/L	58.8	26.5	–	57
	P 10 newborn, 4–10 days, not fasting	µmol/L	470	411	–	mg/L	48.9	42.8	–	57
	P 13 adults, fasting	µmol/L	82	54	–	mg/L	8.5	5.6	–	57
	P 15 subjects, fasting	µmol/L	36	20	(20–92)	mg/L	3.7	2.1	(2.1–9.6)	75

days of life[36]; it is also increased after glucose intake, muscular work, and emotional upsets. It is *pathologically* increased in vitamin B_1 deficiency, respiratory alkalosis, severe cardiovascular disorders, in arsenic and mercury intoxications, and in liver diseases. For review, see NORDMANN and NORDMANN[37].

2-Oxoglutaric acid. The physiological and pathological changes of the 2-oxoglutarate concentration in the blood closely match those of the pyruvic-acid concentration.

Citric acid. Approximately 80% of the citrate in whole blood is contained in the plasma and 20% in the erythrocytes[42]. – *Serum:* Citrate is for the most part complexed with calcium and magnesium; about 20% of it is free[46]. The citrate level is higher in young children than in adults. It increases after several days of fasting[45]. Increased values are also found in primary hyperparathyroidism, and decreased values are found in hypoparathyroidism and rickets. Elevation of the citrate level leads to a reduced concentration of ionized calcium (citrate intoxication). For review, see NORDMANN and NORDMANN[37].

Ketone bodies. One-third of the ketone bodies in the blood consist of acetoacetic acid plus acetone, and about two-thirds of 3-hydroxybutyric acid[58,59]. Most methods of ketone-body determination are unsatisfactory[57,60,61]. Acetoacetic acid and 3-hydroxy-

↓ See text below	B Blood, P Plasma, S Serum, Erys Erythrocytes, Plts Platelets	Amount of substance				Mass				Reference
		Unit	Mean	*s*	95% range (extreme range in brackets)	Unit	Mean	*s*	95% range (extreme range in brackets)	
Lipoic acid	S 10 adults	nmol/L	77	17	(55–106)	μg/L	15.8	3.5	(11.4–22.0)	67
Methylglyoxal	B 16 men	μmol/L	110	77	–	mg/L	7.9	5.5	–	88
Mevalonic acid ...	P 40 men	nmol/L	43	13	(12–102)	μg/L	6.4	1.9	(1.8–15.1)	89
Aromatic compounds										
↓ **Phenol, unconjugated**	S 10 subjects	μmol/L	0.86	0.63	–	μg/L	81	59	–	88
Phenylacetic acid										
– total	P 10 men	μmol/L	3.62	1.37	–	μg/L	493	187	–	92
– free	P 10 men	μmol/L	0.79	0.25	–	μg/L	107	34	–	92
↓ ***p*-Hydroxyphenylacetic acid**	P(S) 9 subjects	nmol/L	–	–	(70–390)	μg/L	–	–	(11–59)	84
4-Hydroxy-3-methoxyphenylglycol										
– total	S 10 men	nmol/L	90	24	(45–111)	μg/L	16.5	4.4	(8.2–20.4)	68
– free	S 10 men	nmol/L	25	5	(12–34)	μg/L	4.6	1.0	(2.2–6.3)	68
4-Hydroxy-3-methoxymandelic acid (vanillylmandelic acid)	S 10 men	nmol/L	35	8	(23–48)	μg/L	7.0	1.5	(4.5–9.6)	68

butyric acid can be determined enzymatically[56,57], while acetone can be determined by gas chromatography[54,55]. The concentration of ketone bodies is about 20% lower in whole blood than in plasma; the concentrations in arterial and venous blood are largely identical[61]. The values fluctuate considerably in the course of the day (maximum values about 500 μmol/L toward midnight)[62]. After a single day of fasting the ketone-body concentration increases markedly, and the increase persists with prolonged fasting[63,64]. The concentration of the ketone bodies is greatly increased during the first few weeks after birth[56,57,65]; in the course of childhood it approaches the adult values[65]. The ketone-body concentration is *pathologically* increased in untreated diabetes mellitus and, occasionally, after excessive consumption of ethanol: extreme values range up to about 8–12 mmol/L[66].

Phenol. Several phenols (*p*-cresol, benzyl alcohol etc.) which are normally undetectable in plasma, can be found in uremic plasma[87].

p-Hydroxyphenylacetic acid. Several hydroxylated phenylic acids can be found in very low concentrations in normal plasma; but the concentrations are increased in uremic plasma[84].

References

1 Review, *Nutr. Rev.*, **21**, 324 (1963).
2 Stowell et al., *Biochem. Med.*, **18**, 392 (1977).
3 Heierli and Thölen, *Klin. Wschr.*, **59**, 431 (1981).
4 Šabata et al., *Biol. Neonat. (Basel)*, **19**, 299 (1971).
5 Tibbling, G., *Clin. chim. Acta*, **24**, 121 (1969).
6 Stubbe and Wolf, *Horm. metab. Res.*, **3**, 175 (1971).
7 Öckerman, P.A., *Clin. chim. Acta*, **12**, 370 (1965).
8 Eggstein, M., *Klin. Wschr.*, **44**, 267 (1966).
9 Dyerberg and Hjørne, *Acta med. scand.*, **191**, 413 (1972).
10 Zimmer, G., *Nature*, **212**, 1201 (1966).
11 Bachmann et al., *Clin. chim. Acta*, **92**, 153 (1979).
12 Harris, R.J., *J. Pediat.*, **84**, 578 (1974).
13 Eggstein et al., *Klin. Wschr.*, **45**, 943 (1967).
14 Ways and Hanahan, *J. Lipid Res.*, **5**, 318 (1964).
15 Eggstein, M., *Z. klin. Chem.*, **4**, 12 (1966).
16 Hagenfeldt, L., *Clin. chim. Acta*, **32**, 471 (1971).
17 Falholt et al., *Clin. chim. Acta*, **46**, 105 (1973).
18 Regouw et al., *Clin. chim. Acta*, **31**, 187 (1971).
19 Sampson and Hensley, *Clin. chim. Acta*, **61**, 1 (1975).
20 Loeb et al., *Rev. franç. Etud. clin. biol.*, **5**, 916 (1960).
21 Burt, R.L., *Obstet. and Gynec.*, **15**, 460 (1960); Ogburn et al., *J. Lab. clin. Med.*, **95**, 943 (1980).
22 Foster, D.W., *Advanc. intern. Med.*, **19**, 159 (1974).
23 Reimann and Schwandt, *Dtsch. med. Wschr.*, **96**, 93 (1971); Editorial, *Lancet*, **1**, 843 (1971).
24 Räihä, N.C., *Pediatrics*, **32**, 1025 (1963).
25 Matthieu et al., *Helv. paediat. Acta*, **26**, suppl. 26, 3 (1971).
26 Huckabee, W.E., *J. clin. Invest.*, **37**, 244 (1958), and *Amer. J. Med.*, **30**, 833 (1961).
27 Marbach and Weil, *Clin. Chem.*, **13**, 314 (1967).
28 Niessner and Beutler, *Biochem. Med.*, **8**, 123 (1973).
29 Klimt et al., *Dtsch. Gesundh.-Wes.*, **72**, 1483 (1972).
30 Fleischer, W.R., *Stand. Meth. clin. Chem.*, **6**, 245 (1970).
31 Acharya and Payne, *Arch. Dis. Childh.*, **40**, 430 (1965).
32 Burt et al., *Obstet. and Gynec.*, **17**, 80 (1961); Editorial, *Lancet*, **2**, 27 (1973).
33 Versé, H., *Z. Kinderheilk.*, **86**, 347 (1962).
34 Tsirimbas and Stich, *Klin. Wschr.*, **38**, 1196 (1960).
35 Fornaini et al., *J. clin. Invest.*, **41**, 1446 (1962).
36 Boncompagni et al., *Minerva pediat.*, **13**, 176 (1961).
37 Nordmann and Nordmann, *Advanc. clin. Chem.*, **4**, 53 (1961).
38 Niwa et al., *Clin. chim. Acta*, **99**, 71 (1979).
39 Hummel, J.P., *J. biol. Chem.*, **180**, 1225 (1949).
40 Nordmann et al., *Clin. chim. Acta*, **12**, 304 (1965).
41 Tomisek et al., *Clin. Chem.*, **21**, 730 (1975).
42 Baruch et al., *Med. Clin. N. Amer.*, **59**, 569 (1975).
43 Zender, R., *Clin. chim. Acta*, **24**, 335 (1969).
44 Forfar et al., *Arch. Dis. Childh.*, **34**, 525 (1959).
45 Toftegaard Nielsen and Schwartz Sørensen, *Acta med. scand.*, **205**, 303 (1979).
46 Walser, M., *J. clin. Invest.*, **40**, 723 (1961).
47 Käser, H., *Clin. chim. Acta*, **6**, 337 (1961).
48 Lancaster et al., *Metabolism*, **23**, 257 (1974).
49 Gründig, E., *Clin. chim. Acta*, **6**, 331 (1961).
50 Prenen et al., *Acta med. scand.*, **209**, 87 (1981).
51 Wolthers and Hayer, *Clin. chim. Acta*, **120**, 87 (1982).
52 Bennett et al., *Clin. Chem.*, **25**, 1810 (1979).
53 Werk and Knowles, *Diabetes*, **10**, 22 (1961).
54 Trotter et al., *Clin. chim. Acta*, **35**, 137 (1971).
55 Levey et al., *J. Lab. clin. Med.*, **63**, 574 (1964).
56 Bergmeyer and Bernt, *Enzym. biol. clin.*, **5**, 65 (1965).
57 Persson, B., *Scand. J. clin. Lab. Invest.*, **25**, 9 (1970).
58 Williamson et al., *Biochem. J.*, **82**, 90 (1962).
59 Wakil and Bressler, *Metabolism*, **11**, 742 (1962).
60 Peden, V.H., *J. Lab. clin. Med.*, **63**, 332 (1964).
61 Gibbard and Watkins, *Clin. chim. Acta*, **19**, 511 (1968).
62 Wildenhoff, K.E., *Acta med. scand.*, **191**, 303 (1972).
63 Voigt and Apostolakis, *Klin. Wschr.*, **47**, 157 (1969); Owen et al., *J. clin. Invest.*, **48**, 574 (1969).
64 Göschke et al., *Klin. Wschr.*, **54**, 527 (1976).
65 Åkerblom et al., *Ann. Paediat. Fenn.*, **11**, 108 (1965).
66 Alberti and Hockaday, *Brit. med. J.*, **2**, 565 (1972); Cooperman et al., *Diabetes*, **23**, 433 (1974).
67 Shigeta et al., *J. Vitaminol.*, **7**, 48 (1961).

[68] TAKAHASHI et al., *Clin. chim. Acta*, **81**, 183 (1977).
[69] ANDO and NYHAN, in NYHAN, W. L. (Ed.), *Heritable Disorders of Amino Acid Metabolism*, Wiley, New York, 1974, page 37.
[70] LEVY and ERICKSON, in NYHAN, W. L. (Ed.), *Heritable Disorders of Amino Acid Metabolism*, Wiley, New York, 1974, page 81.
[71] RABINOWITZ et al., *Clin. Chem.*, **23**, 2202 (1977); STAEFFEN et al., *Nouv. Presse méd.*, **8**, 1663 (1979).
[72] PERSSON et al., *Acta paediat. scand.*, **62**, 465 (1973).
[73] RACCUGLIA, G., *Amer. J. Med.*, **51**, 818 (1971).
[74] LEINWEBER et al., *Med. Klin.*, **71**, 1043 (1976).
[75] HANSEN and FREIER, *Clin. Chem.*, **24**, 475 (1978).
[76] LENTNER, C., *Dtsch. med. Wschr.*, **103**, 1277 (1978).
[77] AUNE et al., *Lancet*, **2**, 97 (1978).
[78] KVEIM and BREDESEN, *Clin. chim. Acta*, **92**, 27 (1979).
[79] TOLLINGER et al., *Clin. Chem.*, **25**, 1787 (1979).
[80] DANKERT et al., *Clin. chim. Acta*, **110**, 301 (1981).
[81] HILLMAN, R. E., *Clin. Chem.*, **24**, 800 (1978).
[82] BATSHAW and BRUSILOW, *Pediat. Res.*, **12**, 221 (1978).
[83] SCHAUDER et al., *Klin. Wschr.*, **57**, 825 (1979).
[84] NIWA et al., *Clin. chim. Acta*, **96**, 247 (1979).
[85] KASIDAS and ROSE, *Clin. chim. Acta*, **96**, 25 (1979).
[86] BRANDT and SIEGEL, *Ciba Found. Symp.*, NS **67**, 211 (1979).
[87] NIWA et al., *Clin. chim. Acta*, **110**, 51 (1981).
[88] HARALAMBIE and MÖSSINGER, *Metabolism*, **29**, 1258 (1980).
[89] PARKER et al., *Proc. nat. Acad. Sci.* (Wash.) **79**, 3037 (1982).
[90] DOUSSET et al., *Clin. chim. Acta*, **129**, 319 (1983).
[91] LEONARD, J. V., *Ciba Found. Symp.*, **87**, 340 (1982).
[92] SANDLER et al., *Lancet*, **2**, 1269 (1978).

Carbohydrates (for references see page 115)

↓ See text below and on next page	B Blood, P Plasma, S Serum, Erys Erythrocytes, Grcs Granulocytes, Plts Platelets	Amount of substance				Mass				Reference
		Unit	Mean	s	95% range (extreme range in brackets)	Unit	Mean	s	95% range (extreme range in brackets)	
↓ **Glucose**	...	...	...	...	...	...	...	...	...	...
↓ **Galactose**	B Capillary:									
	Newborn	–	0	–	–	–	0	–	–	21
	113 children, 1 day to 12 years	µmol/L	210	92	(0–456)	mg/L	37.8	16.5	(0–82.1)	22
	100 adults	µmol/L	88.3	34.7	(0–241)	mg/L	15.9	6.25	(0–43.5)	23
	P 22 children	µmol/L	17	–	(0–39)	mg/L	3	–	(0.0–7)	87
	S 8 men	µmol/L	39	12	–	mg/L	7.0	2.2	–	10

Table 1 *Glucose in whole blood (fasting values)*

Age	Material	Method	Number	Mean	s	95% range	Mean	s	95% range	Reference
				mmol/L			mg/L			
Pregnant women ante partum	Capillary blood	HAGEDORN-JENSEN	19	5.17	0.148	–	931	26.7	–	1
		Glucose oxidase	19	4.81	0.219	–	867	39.5	–	1
Newborn	Cord blood	HAGEDORN-JENSEN	20	4.75	0.184	–	856	33.2	–	1
		Glucose oxidase	20	3.72	0.230	–	671	41.5	–	1
1st hour	Capillary blood	HAGEDORN-JENSEN	20	3.10	0.190	–	558	34.4	–	1
		Glucose oxidase	20	1.46	0.203	–	263	36.5	–	1
6th day	Capillary blood	HAGEDORN-JENSEN	16	3.93	0.153	–	708	27.5	–	1
		Glucose oxidase	16	2.48	0.182	–	447	32.8	–	1
Newborn	Cord blood	SOMOGYI-NELSON	14	4.05	0.938	–	730	169	–	2
1 hour	Capillary blood	SOMOGYI-NELSON	14	3.47	1.12	–	626	201	–	2
2 hours	Capillary blood	SOMOGYI-NELSON	14	3.27	1.05	–	589	190	–	2
9 hours	Capillary blood	SOMOGYI-NELSON	14	3.27	0.777	–	590	140	–	2
24 hours	Capillary blood	SOMOGYI-NELSON	14	3.21	0.772	–	579	139	–	2
48 hours	Capillary blood	SOMOGYI-NELSON	14	3.28	0.749	–	591	135	–	2
Children, 8–14 years	Venous blood	Glucose oxidase	12	4.44	–	–	800	–	–	3
Adults	Venous blood	Glucose oxidase	38	4.44	0.37	3.70–5.18	800	66	668–932	4
Adults	Blood	*o*-Toluidine	21	–	–	3.50–4.83	–	–	630–870	5
Men, <30 years	Capillary blood	Hexokinase	52	4.57	0.411	3.75–5.39	824	74.0	676–972	6
Men, >30 years	Capillary blood	Hexokinase	196	4.96	0.500	3.96–5.96	894	90.1	714–1074	6
Women, <30 years	Capillary blood	Hexokinase	106	4.47	0.346	3.77–5.16	806	62.4	681–931	6
Women, >30 years	Capillary blood	Hexokinase	146	4.68	0.341	4.00–5.36	844	61.5	721–967	6

Glucose. See Tables 1 and 2 for normal values.

Methods of determination: The reduction methods for the determination of 'blood sugar' – for example, those of HAGEDORN-JENSEN, HOFFMAN, FOLIN-WU, and SOMOGYI-NELSON – measure, in addition to glucose, other hexoses (fructose, mannose, galactose), pentoses, glucuronic acid, glutathione, uric acid, creatine, and creatinine, ascorbic acid as well as various drugs ('residual reduction'). Aldohexoses are assayed colorimetrically with *o*-toluidine[5,11] or with triphenyltetrazolium chloride[12]. The most specific methods are the enzymatic ones: reaction with glucose oxidase/peroxidase, and reaction with hexokinase/glucose-6-phosphate dehydrogenase[6,13,14].

Physiological variations: The glucose concentration is somewhat higher in arterial or capillary blood than in venous blood, particularly after meals[7,15]. Glucose values in serum and erythrocyte water are equal. However, since the erythrocytes contain less water than the serum, the glucose concentration in the serum, at normal hematocrit, is about 15% higher than that in whole blood[15]. The glucose concentration in the blood declines within the first few hours after birth and then increases slowly in the fol-

Table 2 *Glucose in plasma and serum (fasting values)*

Age	Material	Method	Number	Mean (mmol/L)	s (mmol/L)	95% range (mmol/L)	Mean (mg/L)	s (mg/L)	95% range (mg/L)	Reference
Newborn										
6 hours	Plasma, capillary	Glucose oxidase/peroxidase ..	20	1.79	0.727	–	322	131	–	7
5 days	Plasma, capillary	Glucose oxidase/peroxidase ..	20	2.45	0.866	–	441	156	–	7
Children										
1–2 years ..	Plasma, capillary	Glucose oxidase/peroxidase ..	20	4.00	1.10	–	720	198	–	7
3–4 years ..	Plasma, capillary	Glucose oxidase/peroxidase ..	20	4.17	0.638	–	751	115	–	7
5–6 years ..	Plasma, capillary	Glucose oxidase/peroxidase ..	20	4.38	0.275	–	789	49.6	–	7
7–9 years ..	Plasma, capillary	Glucose oxidase/peroxidase ..	20	4.54	0.415	–	818	74.8	–	7
10–12 years	Plasma, capillary	Glucose oxidase/peroxidase ..	20	4.45	0.512	–	802	92.2	–	7
13–15 years	Plasma, capillary	Glucose oxidase/peroxidase ..	20	4.34	0.426	–	782	76.8	–	7
16–20 years	Plasma, capillary	Glucose oxidase/peroxidase ..	20	4.57	0.276	–	824	49.7	–	7
Men										
21–30 years	Plasma, capillary	Glucose oxidase/peroxidase ..	20	4.41	0.281	–	795	50.6	–	7
31–50 years	Plasma, capillary	Glucose oxidase/peroxidase ..	20	4.64	0.419	–	836	75.5	–	7
51–80 years	Plasma, capillary	Glucose oxidase/peroxidase ..	20	4.68	0.476	–	843	85.8	–	7
Women										
21–30 years	Plasma, capillary	Glucose oxidase/peroxidase ..	20	4.63	0.289	–	834	52.0	–	7
31–50 years	Plasma, capillary	Glucose oxidase/peroxidase ..	20	4.65	0.426	–	838	76.8	–	7
51–80 years	Plasma, capillary	Glucose oxidase/peroxidase ..	20	4.63	0.455	–	835	81.9	–	7
Men										
20–49 years	Serum	Ferricyanide, automated		4.77	–	3.50–5.83	860	–	630–1050	8
>50 years	Serum	Ferricyanide, automated		4.61	–	3.22–6.22	830	–	580–1120	8
Women			1419							
20–49 years	Serum	Ferricyanide, automated		5.16	–	4.05–8.83	930	–	730–1590	8
>50 years	Serum	Ferricyanide, automated		5.05	–	3.77–7.22	910	–	680–1300	8
Adults	Serum	Gas chromatography..........	32	4.48	0.44	–	808	79	–	9
Men	Serum	High-pressure chromatography	8	4.16	0.683	–	749	123	–	10

Table 3 *Metabolites of glycolysis in erythrocytes*

	10 newborn[31]		10 adults[31]		9 adults[32]		30 adults[30]		20 adults[85]	
	Mean	s	Mean	s	Mean	s	Mean	s	Mean	s
	µmol/L									
Glucose 6-phosphate	4.52	8.7	24.8	9.8	27.8	7.5	29.1	6.8	35.7	6.6
Fructose 6-phosphate	9.9	2.3	5.4	1.0	9.3	2.0	10.2	1.8	13.6	2.5
Fructose 1,6-bisphosphate	3.8	0.7	4.6	1.0	1.9	0.6	1.2	0.4	5.1	1.7
Dihydroxyacetone phosphate	11.9	5.0	4.9	3.5	9.4	2.8			12.1	5.1
							}15.2	4.9		
Glyceraldehyde 3-phosphate	1.9	1.6	2.6	0.7	–	–			4.8	1.6
3-Phosphoglycerate	58.2	14.4	61.2	12.4	44.9	5.1	47.2	7.4	55	35
2-Phosphoglycerate	4.9	1.6	4.3	1.8	7.3	2.5	5.9	2.5	9.1	5.3
Phosphoenolpyruvate	7.6	2.9	8.8	2.6	12.2	2.2	17.4	3.8	13.4	8.0
2,3-Bisphosphoglycerate*	3610	800	4420	1910	–	–	4582	610	5250	400
Glucose 1,6-bisphosphate	–	–	–	–	–	–	98	17	–	–

*See also Table 4.

lowing days[1,2,16]. The hypoglucosemia of the newborn is particularly pronounced in premature infants, in children with intrauterine malnutrition, and in children of diabetic mothers[17,18]. During pregnancy, the glucose values in plasma are reduced by about 15% to 20%[19].

Pathological changes: A raised glucose level is found in diabetes mellitus (extreme values in hyperosmolar coma without ketoacidosis above 100 mmol/L) and in response to increased secretion of epinephrine (pheochromocytoma, stress situations), of growth hormone (acromegaly), glucocorticoids and corticotropin (Cushing's syndrome). The glucose level is *lowered* in overdosage of insulin and oral antidiabetics, in increased secretion of insulin (insulinoma), alcoholism, glucose-consuming tumors, acute liver diseases, some hereditary disorders of carbohydrate metabolism (fructose intolerance, fructose-1,6-bisphosphatase deficiency, glycogen-storage disease), in pituitary and adrenocortical insufficiency, as well as in ketotic hypoglucosemia of children. At elevated white blood cell counts, glycolysis in the leukocytes can simulate a hypoglucosemia[20].

Galactose. Values determined with the aid of galactose dehydrogenase. The blood level of galactose can be raised considerably in galactosemia. – Galactose tolerance test: Galactose is metabolized mainly in the liver. In normal individuals more than 90% of galactose intake is transformed; in the absence of liver function, 60% of intravenously administered galactose is excreted via the kidneys; 40% undergoes extrahepatic transformation[22]. The time course of the blood galactose level following oral or intravenous administration of galactose allows inferences to be drawn regarding the liver function. For details of the test and its interpretation, see the literature[24].

↓See text below	B Blood, P Plasma, S Serum, Erys Erythrocytes, Grcs Granulocytes, Plts Platelets	Amount of substance				Mass				Reference
		Unit	Mean	s	95% range (extreme range in brackets)	Unit	Mean	s	95% range (extreme range in brackets)	
↓**Fructose**	S 32 subjects................ (a)	µmol/L	31	3	(19–47)	mg/L	5.6	0.6	(3.5–8.5)	9
	S 8 men .... (b)	µmol/L	48	16	–	mg/L	8.7	2.8	–	10
↓**Mannose**..........	S 32 subjects................ (a)	µmol/L	39	7	(25–55)	mg/L	7.0	1.2	(4.5–9.9)	9
	S 8 men .... (b)	µmol/L	64	12	–	mg/L	11.5	2.2	–	10
Sucrose	S 8 men	µmol/L	1.8	1.2	–	mg/L	0.6	0.4	–	10
Raffinose	S 8 men	µmol/L	4.8	5.4	–	mg/L	2.4	2.7	–	10
↓**Pentoses**..........	P 28 subjects....................	µmol/L	44	21	–	mg/L	6.6	3.2	–	25
↓L-Xylulose........	S 36 subjects....................	µmol/L	9	12	–	mg/L	1.4	1.8	–	26
↓**Polyols**										
Erythritol.........	S 6 subjects.....................	µmol/L	0	–	–	mg/L	0	–	–	27
Arabitol	S 6 subjects.....................	µmol/L	0	–	–	mg/L	0	–	–	27
Mannitol	S 6 subjects.....................	µmol/L	34	18	–	mg/L	6.2	3.3	–	27
Sorbitol...........	S 6 subjects.....................	µmol/L	18	7	–	mg/L	3.3	1.3	–	27
	S 32 subjects....................	µmol/L	13	–	(4–24)	mg/L	2.4	–	(0.8–4.3)	9
myo-Inositol	S 18 subjects....................	µmol/L	27	6.8	–	mg/L	4.9	1.2	–	28
	S 32 subjects....................	µmol/L	17	–	(6–28)	mg/L	3.0	–	(1.0–5.0)	9
	P 50 subjects....................	µmol/L	24.0	7.8	–	mg/L	4.3	1.4	–	29
	P 37 children, adults	µmol/L	23	8	–	mg/L	4.1	1.4	–	33
	Erys 37 children, adults.........	µmol/L	20	16	–	mg/L	3.6	2.9	–	33
↓**Sugar phosphates**	....	...	...	...	...	...	...	...	...	...

Table 4
*2,3-Bisphosphoglycerate in erythrocytes at different ages**

Subjects	Mean	s	Mean	s	Reference
	mmol/L		µmol for 1 g hemoglobin		
7 newborn	4.88	0.72	–	–	34
8 newborn (intrauterine malnutrition)............................	3.51	0.47	–	–	34
62 children, 1–12 years...........	–	–	14.66	1.33	35
24 men	–	–	13.35	1.33	35
24 women	–	–	14.34	1.54	35
20 children, 1–12 years...........	4.41	0.67	12.98	1.90	36
15 adults.........................	4.40	1.1	13.00	1.93	36
20 men	4.07	0.68	–	–	37
20 women	4.19	0.53	–	–	37

* For additional data at different ages, see page 76.

Fructose, mannose. Values determined (a) by gas chromatography; (b) by high-pressure chromatography.

Pentoses. Values determined by means of orcin.

L-*Xylulose.* Increased in diabetes mellitus.

Polyols. Values determined by gas chromatography. – In chronic renal failure, erythritol and arabitol are detectable in the serum, and the concentrations of the other polyols are increased[27,29]; in diabetes mellitus the concentrations of sorbitol[9] and *myo*-inositol[33] are increased.

Sugar phosphates. Concentrations of various sugar phosphates in the blood cells are shown in Tables 3–5. 2,3-Bisphosphoglycerate is important for the oxygen affinity of hemoglobin (page 76). An increase of the 2,3-bisphosphoglycerate concentration in the erythrocytes by 1 mmol/L results in a decrease of oxygen affinity by about 0.3 kPa[46]. The 2,3-bisphosphoglycerate concentration is probably controlled genetically and is higher in women than in men. Protracted acidosis leads to a decrease, and tissue hypoxia to an increase of the 2,3-bisphosphoglycerate concentration. – *Galactose 1-phosphate in erythrocytes.* In children, postprandial values

Table 5 *Sugar phosphates in erythrocytes and leukocytes*

	Material	Subjects	Mean	s	(Extreme range)	Reference
			µmol/L			
Galactose 1-phosphate....................................	Erythrocytes..... (cord)	Newborn	65	31	–	38
	Erythrocytes.....	6 infants, 8 adults.....	14	–	(7–22)	39
	Erythrocytes.....	30 children	31	–	(0–57)	86
Sedoheptulose 1,7-bisphosphate	Erythrocytes.....	....	9	–	–	42
Octulose 1,8-bisphosphate	Erythrocytes.....	....	3	–	–	42
5-Phosphoribosyl 1-diphosphate	Erythrocytes.....	56 subjects...........	2.6	0.7	–	43
	Erythrocytes.....	12 children	5.72	0.86	–	44
	Erythrocytes.....	7 adults..............	13.2	2.34	–	44
	Erythrocytes.....	12 adults	4.9	2.1	–	41
	Leukocytes	Adults...............	3.84	1.7	–	82
Ribose 5-phosphate..	Erythrocytes.....	14 adults	13.2	4.8	–	41

↓ See text below	B Blood, P Plasma, S Serum, Erys Erythrocytes, Grcs Granulocytes, Plts Platelets	Amount of substance				Mass				Reference
		Unit	Mean	s	95% range (extreme range in brackets)	Unit	Mean	s	95% range (extreme range in brackets)	
↓ **Glycogen**	B Umbilical vein, 28 newborn ..	...	...	...	...	mg/L	11.4	–	–	48
	B 56 men	...	...	...	...	mg/L	26.1	2.1	23.9–30.3	49
	B 37 women	...	...	...	...	mg/L	28.9	2.3	24.3–33.5	49
	Grcs	...	...	...	...	g/10^{12}	7.5	–	(4.7–11.9)	50
	Relative to hemoglobin:									
	Erys Newborn, 1st day	...	...	...	...	µg/g	155	–	(48–361)	52
	Erys Children, 1–12 months ..	...	...	...	...	µg/g	86	–	(32–151)	52
	Erys Adults	...	...	...	...	µg/g	56	–	(26–105)	52
	As glucose equivalent:									
	Plts	µmol/10^{12}	433	–	–	...	...	...	...	51
	Plts 26 subjects	µmol/10^{12}	985	155	–	...	...	...	...	81
Isosaccharino-1,4-lactone	S 10 adults	µmol/L	10.5	9.3	(2.3–33.3)	mg/L	1.7	1.5	(0.38–5.4)	45
↓ **Glucuronic acid**										
– total	S Children .... (a)	µmol/L	335	–	–	mg/L	65	–	–	58
	S 58 men .... (b)	µmol/L	165	32	101–229	mg/L	32	6.2	19.6–44.4	59
	S 44 women .... (b)	µmol/L	165	23	119–211	mg/L	32	4.5	23–41	59
	Erys .... (b)	µmol/L	–	–	(0–103)	mg/L	–	–	(0–20)	60
↓ Glycosamino-glycans .... (as hexuronic acids)	P 6 children	...	...	...	...	mg/L	4.08	–	(3.36–5.04)	63
	P 16 men	...	...	...	...	mg/L	2.98	1.29	(1.12–5.19)	63
	P 22 women	...	...	...	...	mg/L	2.53	0.81	(0.98–4.04)	63
↓ **Sialic acid**										
– total	S 24 subjects	mmol/L	1.94	0.29	–	mg/L	600	90	–	83
– free	S 32 subjects	µmol/L	0.57	1.26	–	µg/L	176	390	–	84
↓ **Carbohydrates, protein-bound**	....	...	...	...	...	...	...	...	...	...

up to 75 µmol/L may be found[40]. The concentration is *pathologically* increased in galactosemia; values above 150 µmol/L point to a dietary indiscretion.

Glycogen. The granulocytes account for 45% and the platelets for 40% of the glycogen in whole blood[53,54]. Both the serum[47] and, probably, mature erythrocytes[56] contain no glycogen. Divergent reports on the glycogen content are attributable to the use of different methods. In women, the blood level of glycogen varies with the cycle[55]. It is sharply elevated during the first half of pregnancy but afterwards drops again[48,55]. The glycogen content of erythrocytes[53,56] and leukocytes[57] may be increased in glycogen-storage disease. In limit dextrinosis A, the erythrocyte values range up to more than 4000 µg/g (relative to hemoglobin)[53].

Glucuronic acid. Values determined (a) with carbazole; (b) with naphthoresorcinol. – In the serum, glucuronic acid is found mostly in glycoside linkage; a portion of it is present in free form[61] and a small amount as glycosaminoglycans. The glucuronic-acid concentration in the serum is reduced in the nephrotic syndrome[62].

Glycosaminoglycans. Values determined by the borate–carbazole method. The glycosaminoglycans (acid mucopolysaccharides) can be assayed via determination of hexuronic acids. Hexuronic acids are not contained in glycoproteins[64]. Except for hyaluronic acid, the glycosaminoglycans are covalently bonded to peptides (proteoglycans). The glycosaminoglycans of the serum are mainly chondroitin 4-sulfate and undersulfatized chondroitin 4-sulfate[65].

Sialic acid. Sialic acid is a constituent of glycoproteins and glycolipids.

Carbohydrates, protein-bound. Most of the proteins of the serum and the blood cells contain carbohydrates (glycoproteins)[64,67,68] (see pages 136–139 for the carbohydrate content of other serum proteins). The carbohydrates are hexoses (galactose and mannose), hexosamines (N-acetylglucosamine, N-acetylgalactosamine), sialic acid, fucose and xylose (Table 6). – Glycoproteins of high sialic-acid content are insoluble in 1% phosphotungstic acid but soluble in 0.6% perchloric acid and can thus be

Table 6 *Individual protein-bound carbohydrates in plasma*[66]

	Mean	s	Mean	s
	mmol/L		mg/L	
Total	13.9	–	2730	–
Hexoses	6.71	0.12	1210	21
Hexosamines	4.63	0.22	830	40
Sialic acid	2.0	0.12	600	37
Fucose	0.54	0.04	89	6

Table 7
Protein-bound and mucoprotein-bound hexose in serum of men[73]

Age	Number	Protein-bound hexose*		Mucoprotein-bound hexose*	
		Mean	s	Mean	s
		mg/L			
20–24 years	59	1165	120	148	37
25–29 years	100	1208	136	155	37
30–34 years	93	1194	174	168	93
35–39 years	85	1264	156	176	85
40–44 years	99	1221	135	163	37
45–49 years	88	1285	172	177	49
50–54 years	67	1264	179	172	47
55–59 years	65	1291	192	174	39
60–64 years	70	1279	145	168	34
≥65 years	73	1313	233	177	47

*Determined with orcin.

analytically determined in the mucoprotein (seromucoid) fraction[69]. This fraction contains mostly α_1-acid glycoprotein, haptoglobin, and α_2-macroglobulin. – There appear to be no age[70] or sex differences[80] in the serum concentration of protein-bound carbohydrates. The concentrations of protein-bound hexose[71–73], sialic acid, and mucoproteins[70,73,74] increase in adults with increasing age (see also Table 7). The concentrations of the protein-bound carbohydrates are increased toward the end of pregnancy[71,75], and those of sialic acid are lower in newborn than in their mothers[76,77] (they increase to adult values during the first 4 months of life[77]). – The glycoprotein concentration in the serum is increased in diseases associated with tissue breakdown as well as in collagen diseases and in inflammatory and degenerative diseases. See the literature on pathological changes of this type[67,71,78,79].

References

[1] WOLF, H., *Klin. Wschr.*, **38**, 87 (1960).
[2] ACHARYA and PAYNE, *Arch. Dis. Childh.*, **40**, 430 (1965).
[3] ÖCKERMAN, P.A., *Clin. chim. Acta*, **12**, 370 (1965).
[4] SUNDERMAN and SUNDERMAN, *Amer. J. clin. Path.*, **36**, 75 (1961).
[5] HYVÄRINEN and NIKKILÄ, *Clin. chim. Acta*, **7**, 140 (1962).
[6] SCHMIDT, F.H., *Klin. Wschr.*, **51**, 520 (1973).
[7] BÜRGI et al., *Schweiz. med. Wschr.*, **97**, 1721 (1967).
[8] REED et al., *Clin. Chem.*, **18**, 57 (1972).
[9] ALOIA, J.F., *J. Lab. clin. Med.*, **82**, 809 (1973).
[10] JOLLEY et al., *Amer. J. clin. Path.*, **53**, 793 (1970).
[11] ZENDER, R., *Clin. chim. Acta*, **8**, 351 (1963).
[12] LORENTZ, K., *Clin. chim. Acta*, **13**, 660 (1966).
[13] RICHTERICH, R., *Klinische Chemie*, 3rd ed., Karger, Basle, 1971.
[14] NEELEY, W.E., *Clin. Chem.*, **18**, 509 (1972).
[15] LENTNER and EGGSTEIN, *Leading Symptoms: Laboratory Values*, CIBA-GEIGY Ltd., Basle, 1976.
[16] CREERY and PARKINSON, *Arch. Dis. Childh.*, **28**, 134 (1953); FARQUHAR, J.W., *Arch. Dis. Childh.*, **29**, 519 (1954); PERSSON et al., *Acta paediat. scand.*, **62**, 465 (1973).
[17] ZETTERSTRÖM, R., in WOLSTENHOLME and O'CONNOR (Eds.), *Somatic Stability in the Newly Born*, Ciba Foundation Symposium, Churchill, London, 1961, page 59.
[18] CORNBLATH and SCHWARTZ, *Disorders of Carbohydrate Metabolism in Infancy*, Saunders, Philadelphia, 1966; NELIGAN, D., *J. clin. Path.*, **22**, suppl. 2, 51 (1969); CORNBLATH et al., *Advanc. metab. Disord.*, suppl. 1, 241 (1970); LUBCHENCO and BARD, *Pediatrics*, **47**, 831 (1971).
[19] HYTTEN and LIND, *Diagnostic Indices in Pregnancy*, CIBA-GEIGY Ltd., Basle, 1974.
[20] HANRAHAN et al., *Amer. J. clin. Path.*, **40**, 43 (1963).
[21] TENGSTRÖM and WRANNE, *Scand. J. clin. Lab. Invest.*, **22**, 137 (1968).
[22] KIELHORN and GLADTKE, *Dtsch. med. Wschr.*, **97**, 462 (1972).
[23] ROMMEL et al., *Klin. Wschr.*, **46**, 1042 (1968).
[24] BERNSTEIN et al., *Gastroenterology*, **39**, 293 (1960); ROMMEL et al., *Klin. Wschr.*, **46**, 936 (1968); MEHNERT et al., *Dtsch. med. Wschr.*, **93**, 1899 (1968); HENNECKE et al., *Dtsch. med. Wschr.*, **97**, 109 (1972).
[25] MCKAY, E., *Clin. Chim. Acta*, **10**, 320 (1964).
[26] WINEGRAD et al., *Diabetes*, **14**, 311 (1965).
[27] PITKÄNEN, E., *Clin. chim. Acta*, **38**, 221 (1972).
[28] PITKÄNEN, E., *Clin. chim. Acta*, **71**, 461 (1976).
[29] CLEMENTS et al., *Lancet*, **1**, 1137 (1973).
[30] BUC et al., *Clin. chim. Acta*, **95**, 83 (1979).
[31] OSKI, F.A., *Pediatrics*, **44**, 84 (1969).
[32] NIESSNER and BEUTLER, *Biochem. Med.*, **8**, 123 (1973).
[33] SERVO, C., *Acta med. scand.*, **201**, 59 (1977).
[34] FIORI and SCANLON, *Amer. J. Obstet. Gynec.*, **111**, 681 (1971).
[35] CARD and BRAIN, *New Engl. J. Med.*, **288**, 388 (1973).
[36] FREEDMAN and LEVISON, *New Engl. J. Med.*, **288**, 1026 (1973).
[37] LAPPIN et al., *Clin. chim. Acta*, **44**, 349 (1973).
[38] WOOLF, L.I., *Advanc. clin. Chem.*, **5**, 1 (1962).
[39] DAHLQVIST, A., *J. Lab. clin. Med.*, **78**, 931 (1971).
[40] DONNELL et al., *Pediatrics*, **31**, 802 (1963).
[41] BECHER et al., *Klin. Wschr.*, **58**, 1243 (1980).
[42] VANDERHEIDEN, B.S., *Biochem. biophys. Res. Commun.*, **21**, 265 (1965).
[43] FOX et al., *New Engl. J. Med.*, **283**, 1177 (1970).
[44] BORDEN et al., *Pediat. Res.*, **8**, 31 (1974).
[45] NIWA et al., *Chin. Chem.*, **26**, 1554 (1980).
[46] OSKI et al., *Med. Clin. N. Amer.*, **54**, 731 (1970).
[47] WAGNER, R., *Arch. Biochem.*, **11**, 249 (1946).
[48] FÖRSTER et al., *Klin. Wschr.*, **46**, 561 (1968).
[49] FÖRSTER et al., *Dtsch. med. Wschr.*, **91**, 1718 (1966).
[50] VALENTINE et al., *J. clin. Invest.*, **32**, 251 (1953).
[51] KARPATKIN, S., *J. clin. Invest.*, **48**, 1073 (1969).
[52] SIDBURY et al., *Helv. paediat. Acta*, **16**, 506 (1961).
[53] STEINITZ, K., *Advanc. clin. Chem.*, **9**, 227 (1967).
[54] BISERTE, G., *Actualités métab. Pédiat.*, **3**, 65 (1969).
[55] MUCK et al., *Arch. Gynäk.*, **211**, 311 (1971).
[56] SCHRÖTER, W., in DEUTSCH et al. (Eds.), *Stoffwechsel und Membranpermeabilität von Erythrozyten und Thrombozyten*, Thieme, Stuttgart, 1968, page 205.
[57] WAGNER et al., *Amer. J. Med.*, **51**, 685 (1971).
[58] VEST, M., *Bibl. paediat. (Basel)*, fascicle 69 (1959).
[59] MÜTING et al., *Z. klin. Med.*, **157**, 538 (1963).
[60] DEICHMANN and DIERKER, *J. biol. Chem.*, **163**, 753 (1946).
[61] GREEN et al., *Biochim. biophys. Acta (Amst.)*, **62**, 574 (1962).
[62] MÜTING et al., *Z. klin. Med.*, **157**, 544 (1963).
[63] CALATRONI et al., *J. clin. Invest.*, **48**, 332 (1969).
[64] SPIRO, R.G., *New Engl. J. Med.*, **281**, 991, 1043 (1969); HEIDE and SCHWICK, *Angew. Chem.*, **85**, 803 (1973).
[65] TANIGUCHI et al., *Clin. chim. Acta*, **50**, 319 (1974).
[66] WINZLER, R.J., in PUTNAM, F.W. (Ed.), *The Plasma Proteins*, volume 1, Academic Press, New York, 1960, page 309.
[67] STARY, Z., *Ergebn. Physiol.*, **50**, 174 (1959).
[68] MAGALINI and MASCIOLI, *J. Lab. clin. Med.*, **62**, 961 (1963).
[69] LANCHANTIN, G.F., *Stand. Meth. clin. Chem.*, **6**, 137 (1970).
[70] BÖTTIGER and HOLMSTRÖM, *J. Lab. clin. Med.*, **63**, 772 (1964).
[71] SHETLAR, M.R., *Ann. N.Y. Acad. Sci.*, **94**, 44 (1961).
[72] PEARCE et al., *Clin. Chem.*, **10**, 1066 (1964).
[73] ALLARD and GOULET, *Canad. med. Ass. J.*, **99**, 650 (1968).
[74] BÖTTIGER and CARLSON, *Clin. chim. Acta*, **5**, 664 (1960).
[75] HOROWITZ, R.N., *Amer. J. Obstet. Gynec.*, **105**, 216 (1969).
[76] LÖHR and PULLIG, *Klin. Wschr.*, **37**, 633 (1959).
[77] CABEZAS et al., *Clin. chim. Acta*, **7**, 406, 448 (1962).
[78] HEISKELL et al., *Ann. N.Y. Acad. Sci.*, **94**, 183 (1961).
[79] RUINEN et al., *Clin. chim. Acta*, **19**, 49 (1968).
[80] STRECKER and MONTREUIL, *Clin. chim. Acta*, **58**, 33 (1975).
[81] SCHNEIDER and GEAR, *Ciba Found. Symp.*, NS **35**, 225 (1975).
[82] BROSH et al., *J. clin. Invest.*, **58**, 289 (1976).
[83] SUGAHARA et al., *Clin. chim. Acta*, **108**, 493 (1980).
[84] RODRÍGUEZ-ITURBE et al., *New Engl. J. Med.*, **304**, 1506 (1981).
[85] STAAL et al., *Clin. chim. Acta*, **118**, 241 (1982).
[86] PESCE et al., *Clin. chim. Acta*, **118**, 177 (1982).
[87] PESCE and BODOURIAN, *Clin. Chem.*, **28**, 301 (1982).

Lipids* (for references see pages 124 and 125)

The blood lipids include free fatty acids, diglycerides (diacylglycerols) and triglycerides (triacylglycerols), phospholipids, sterols (cholesterol, bile acids, steroid hormones), carotenoids, and fat-soluble vitamins as well as traces of hydrocarbons and prostaglandins.

In *mature erythrocytes* virtually all of the lipids are contained in the membrane. The stroma – the insoluble portion of the cell remaining after hemolysis – is composed of about 40% lipid, 52% protein and 8% carbohydrate by mass[5].

In the *plasma*, the lipids are transported together with specific apolipoproteins as *lipoproteins*[7]. Their composition is variable. However, it is possible to define lipoprotein classes that encompass lipoproteins of similar composition, similar metabolic characteristics, and equal biological significance. The lipoprotein classes are named according to their behavior in the gravitational field of the ultracentrifuge or according to their electrophoretic mobility[8,9] (Table 1).

Apolipoproteins. Apolipoproteins are essential for the structure and function of the lipoprotein particles (Table 2). Each lipoprotein class has a typical apolipoprotein pattern (Table 3). Together with polar lipids, the apolipoproteins form the hydrophilic shell of the lipoprotein particles and ensure their stability in the aqueous milieu of the plasma[13]. The plasma concentrations of the apolipoproteins are indicated in Table 4.

Serum lipoproteins and lipids. Reference values for various age groups and subjects of varying origin are presented in Tables 5–10.

The lipid concentration in the serum is influenced by a number of factors, particularly age, sex, race, nutrition, hormonal status, stress, climate, occupation, and amount of physical exercise. Many studies have consistently shown that, except for the chylomicrons, the concentrations of all serum lipid fractions rise from low values in the newborn to high values at an advanced age (Tables 7–9). Toward the end of pregnancy, the total lipid concentration of the serum shows an average increase to about 8–10 g/L[14,15]. A positive correlation exists between the serum lipid levels or the serum concentrations of low-density lipoproteins, cholesterol and glycerides on one hand, and the risk of atherosclerosis on the other[17,18,51], although causal relations have not been conclusively demonstrated. However, dietary adjustments designed to prevent a high serum lipid level are desirable.

Glycerides. Mono- and diglycerides account for approximately 10% of the serum glycerides, and triglycerides for approximately 90%[19]. Small amounts of triglycerides, if any[5], are contained in the

* This chapter on 'Lipids' (pages 115–125) has been compiled in collaboration with H.H. Märki, Medizinische Poliklinik, Kantonsspital Winterthur, Winterthur, Switzerland.

See text and tables on pages 115–124	Fasting specimens (P Plasma, S Serum, Erys Erythrocytes, Lkcs Leukocytes, Plts Platelets)	Amount of substance				Mass				Reference
		Unit	Mean	s	(Extreme range)	Unit	Mean	s	(Extreme range)	
Total lipids	P(S)$^{\diamond}$	...	...	...	...	g/L	5.5–6	–	–	1
	Erys 14 adults	...	...	...	...	g/L	5.10	0.51	–	2
	Erys 7 adults	...	...	...	...	g/10^{12}	0.457	0.025	–	3
	Lkcs 4 adults	...	...	...	...	g/10^{12}	15.6	4.5	–	3
	Plts 12 subjects	...	...	...	...	mg/10^{12}	506	–	–	13
(Tri)glycerides*	P(S)$^{\diamond}$	mmol/L	1.1–1.5	–	–	g/L	1–1.3	–	–	1
	Erys 5 subjects	mmol/L	0.41	–	–	g/L	0.36	–	–	20
Cholesterol	P(S)$^{\diamond}$	mmol/L	4.5–5.5	–	–	g/L	1.7–2.1	–	–	1
	Erys 14 adults	mmol/L	3.1	0.23	–	g/L	1.20	0.09	–	2
	Erys 7 adults	mmol/10^{12}	0.341	0.015	–	g/10^{12}	0.132	0.006	–	3
	Lkcs 4 adults	mmol/10^{12}	5.21	1.06	–	g/10^{12}	2.02	0.41	–	3
	Plts 23 subjects	μmol/10^{12}	290	26	–	mg/10^{12}	112	10	–	4
	Plts 12 subjects	μmol/10^{12}	204	54	–	mg/10^{12}	79	21	–	13
Phospholipids*	P(S)$^{\diamond}$	mmol/L	2.6–3.2	–	–	g/L	2–2.5	–	–	1
	Erys 14 adults	mmol/L	3.85	0.26	–	g/L	2.98	0.20	–	2
	Erys 7 adults	mmol/10^{12}	0.354	–	–	g/10^{12}	~0.28	–	–	3
	Lkcs 4 adults	mmol/10^{12}	~9.0	–	–	g/10^{12}	~7.0	–	–	3
	Plts 23 subjects	μmol/10^{12}	444	43	–	mg/10^{12}	344	33	–	4
	Plts 12 subjects	μmol/10^{12}	451	80	–	mg/10^{12}	349	62	–	13
Fatty acids*										
– total	P(S)	mmol/L	12–14	–	–	g/L	3.5–4	–	–	1
	Erys 14 adults	mmol/L	7.0	–	–	g/L	2.0	–	–	2
– nonesterified	P(S)	mmol/L	0.5	–	–	g/L	0.15	–	–	1
	Erys 8 adults	μmol/10^{12}	27	–	(11–38)	mg/10^{12}	7.6	–	(3–11)	6

*Factors for conversion of mmol to g: triglycerides 0.885; phospholipids 0.774; fatty acids 0.282.

$^{\diamond}$Age-related values are presented in the tables which follow.

Table 1 *Physical properties of lipoproteins in plasma*[8,9]

	Electrophoretic migration (paper)	Density fraction*	Density rank	Mean density of hydrated lipoproteins	Relative molecular mass	$S_f^{\diamond}$	$F^{\diamond}$	Particle diameter
				g/cm^3	10^{-6}			nm
Chylomicrons	Start	–	0.92–0.95	0.94	20–5000	400–10000	–	750–12000
Pre-β-lipoproteins	Pre-β	VLDL	0.95–1.006	0.97	3–130	20–400	–	300–800
β-Lipoproteins	β	LDL	1.006–1.063	1.033	2.5	0–20	–	190–290
α-Lipoproteins	α	HDL_2	1.063–1.125	1.085	0.36	–	4.5–7.5	95–115
	α	HDL_3	1.125–1.21	1.145	0.18	–	1.7–3.5	55–95
	α	VHDL	>1.21	1.20	0.14	–	–	–

*VLDL: very-low-density lipoproteins; LDL: low-density lipoproteins; HDL: high-density lipoproteins; VHDL: very-high-density lipoproteins. Other lipoproteins: intermediate-density lipoproteins (IDL), density rank 1.006–1.019; Lp(a) lipoprotein, density rank 1.05–1.09.

$^{\diamond}S_f$: Svedberg flotation units ($-S \times 10^{-13}$ s) at a relative density of 1.063 and $t = 26\,°C$; F: Svedberg flotation units at a relative density of 1.210 and $t = 26\,°C$.

erythrocytes; in the leukocytes[20] they account for about 25%, and in the platelets[45] for about 2%, of total lipids.

The serum glyceride values cited in the literature should be interpreted in the light of the method used. The glyceride level, also termed 'neutral fat' or 'fat residue', is usually determined as a difference[21]:

Neutral fat (in mg/L) =
total lipid (in mg/L) − [free cholesterol (in mg/L) + ester cholesterol (1.68 × mg/L) + lipid phosphorus (25 × mg/L)]

More precise is the determination via the ester-bound fatty acids[21]:

Neutral fat (in mg/L) =
ester fatty acids (in mg/L) − [ester cholesterol (0.764 × mg/L) + lipid phosphorus (14.2 × mg/L)]

or via bound glycerol[21]:

Neutral fat (in mg/L) =
885 × [total glycerol (in mmol/L) − free glycerol (in mmol/L)] the glycerol being determinable by color reactions[22] or enzymatically[21].

The serum glyceride level in cord blood is low (Table 8); however, it begins to rise during the first day of life[30]. Perhaps owing to the type of nutrition, some studies have shown the serum triglyceride levels of children to be lower than the levels of young adults while other studies have shown them to be in approximately the same range (Tables 7, 8 and 9b). In adults (Table 10), there is a tendency to increasing values with increasing age; according to most studies, triglyceride levels are higher in men than in women[34–37]. Fluctuations over the course of the year need to be

Table 2 *Nomenclature and properties of apolipoproteins*

Apolipoprotein	Synonyms	Number of amino acids	Relative molecular mass	Sites of synthesis[11,129]	Function[10,11,129]
Apolipoprotein A					
Apo-A I	ApoHDL III, ApoLP-Gln I	243[10]	28300[11]	Intestine, liver	Cofactor for LCAT
Apo-A II	ApoHDL IV, ApoLP-Gln II	2 × 77 (dimer)[96]	17400[97]	Intestine, liver	Cofactor for lipoprotein lipase
Apo-A III	See Apo-D				
Apo-A IV	....	–	46000[107]	Intestine	?
Apolipoprotein B					
Apo-B	ApoLDL	Divergent data[99]	459000 (B 100)[11] 264000 (B 48)[11]	Liver (B 100) Intestine (B 48)	Binding protein for cell receptors
Apolipoprotein C					
Apo-C I	ApoVLDL VD1, ApoLP-Ser	57[96]	6500[10]	Liver	Cofactor for lipoprotein lipase
Apo-C II	ApoVLDL VD2, ApoLP-Glu	78[96]	~10000[10]	Liver	Cofactor for lipoprotein lipase
Apo-C III*	ApoVLDL VD3, ApoLP-Ala	79[10]	~10000[10]	Liver	?
Apolipoprotein D					
Apo-D	Apo-A III, 'thin-line' protein	–	22100[11]	?	Cholesterol ester exchange protein (?)
Apolipoprotein E					
Apo-E	Arginine-rich protein	299 (Apo-E 2)[121]	35000[109]	Liver	Binding protein for cell receptors
Apolipoprotein F					
Apo-F	....	–	26000–32000[108,110]	?	Receptors, inhibitor of lipoprotein lipase (?)

*Composed of 3 polymorphic forms C III-0, C III-1 and C III-2 according to a sialic-acid content of 0, 1 or 2 molecules per molecule peptide[106].

Table 3 *Composition of individual plasma lipoprotein classes*

Lipoprotein class	Lipoprotein composition[9]					Apolipoprotein composition[129]							Carbohydrate composition[98]		
	Protein*	Triglycerides	Cholesterol esters	Cholesterol, free	Phospholipids	A I	A II	A IV	B	C	D	E	Hexoses	Hexosamines	Sialic acid
	Mass fraction (relative to dry mass of total lipoprotein) as percent					Mass fraction (relative to dry mass of protein) as percent							Mass of carbohydrates relative to mass of protein as mg/g		
Chylomicrons◊	0.8–2.5	87–94	1–2.5	0.5–1	4–9	33	trace	14	5	32	–	10	–	–	–
VLDL	8–12	45–55	12–14	6–8	16–20	trace	trace	–	25	55	–	15	57.5	22.1	13.3
LDL	20–24	8–12	35–40	7–9	20–24	trace	trace	–	>90	2	–	3	42.9	20.0	6.3
HDL_2	40–44	4–5	8–10	5–7	35–37	65	10	–	3	13	2	3†	16.8 (HDL₂ and HDL₃)	9.9	5.5
HDL_3	54–57	2–4	7–9	4–6	21–23	62	23	trace	–	5	4	1			
VHDL	62–70	1–2	5–7	2–3	20–24	–	–	–	–	–	–	–	–	–	–

*Exclusive of bound carbohydrates.
◊In the lymph the major apolipoproteins of chylomicrons are A I and A II.

†A HDL_2 subclass contains apolipoprotein E; typical HDL_2 contains no apolipoprotein E.

taken into account in evaluating the data[39]. The use of oral contraceptives causes the triglyceride level to rise by about 50%[57]. Toward the end of pregnancy the serum triglyceride level shows a two- to threefold increase[15,38].

Cholesterol. Cholesterol accounts for about 85–90% of the total sterols in the serum. Other neutral sterols occurring in the serum are shown in Table 11. The cholesterol in the serum is made up of 20–30% free cholesterol, while 70–80% is esterified with fatty acids (the corresponding values in newborns are 20–40% and 60–80%, respectively)[30,43]. Small amounts (less than 10 μmol/L) are present in the form of cholesterol sulfate[44]. The cholesterol in the erythrocytes[5] and that in the platelets[45] is almost exclusively in free form. By contrast, the proportion of free cholesterol in the leukocytes is approximately 40%[20].

Various colorimetric methods have been developed for the determination of cholesterol, but none of them is very specific[46,47]. The multistage procedure of Abell et al.[48] using the Liebermann-Burchard reaction serves as reference method. It has recently become possible to determine cholesterol enzymatically with the aid of cholesterol oxidase[49] or by gas chromatography[50]. The method employed should be taken into consideration when evaluating the data. Enzymatically determined values are about 8%[33] and values obtained by gas chromatography 10–15% lower[50] than those obtained according to the procedure of Abell et al.[48].

The serum cholesterol level is determined by numerous factors (see page 115), nutrition and physical activity being of special significance. The cholesterol concentration in the serum is affected less by the cholesterol content of the diet (the major portion of the serum cholesterol is of endogenous origin) than by the fat content and fat composition of the diet. A diet in which the fat consists in large part of polyenoic fatty acids produces a low serum cholesterol level. The risk of atherosclerosis increases less with a rise in the total cholesterol level of the serum than with a low concentration of HDL-cholesterol and/or a high concentration of LDL-cholesterol[51].

The cholesterol concentration in the serum of neonates is low at birth (Tables 8 and 9a) but reaches about twice the baseline value after one week[52]. In the course of the first year of life the cholesterol level continues to rise[53], reaching values commonly found in

Table 4 *Apolipoproteins in plasma or serum*

Apolipoprotein	Subjects	Age	Number	Unit	Mean	s or 95% range	Method	Standard	Reference
Apo-A I	Men	13–58 years	37	g/L	1.00	s 0.34	RIA	Purified apo-A I	100
	Women	16–58 years	29	g/L	1.04	s 0.34	RIA	Purified apo-A I	100
	Men	18–35 years	15	g/L	1.13	s 0.24	RIA	Purified apo-A I	101
	Women	18–35 years	15	g/L	1.24	s 0.26	RIA	Purified apo-A I	101
	Adults	40–49 years	198	g/L	1.37	s 0.23	RID	Purified apo-A I	112
	Adults	...	146	g/L	1.38	s 0.12	EID	Purified apo-A I	111
	Newborn	Cord blood	80	g/L	0.70	0.47–0.93	N	Purified apo-A I	116
	Newborn	Cord blood	33	g/L	1.09	s 0.33	EID	...	123
Apo-A II	Men	18–35 years	15	g/L	0.35	s 0.14	RIA	Purified apo-A II	101
	Women	18–35 years	15	g/L	0.41	s 0.18	RIA	Purified apo-A II	101
	Newborn	Cord blood	80	g/L	0.18	0.13–0.32	N	Purified apo-A II	116
Apo-A IV	Adults	...	14	mg/L	157	s 34	EID	Purified apo-A IV	113
Apo-B	Adults	...	209	g/L	0.89	s 0.23	RID	...	102
	Adults	...	42	g/L	0.83	s 0.16	RIA	...	103
	Adults	20–40 years	64	g/L	0.91	s 0.16	RIA	Purified LDL_2 fraction	104
	Adults	...	146	g/L	0.98	s 0.19	EID	Purified lipoprotein B	119
	Newborn	Cord blood	80	g/L	0.25	0.11–0.42	N	Purified LDL_2 fraction	116
	Newborn	Cord blood	33	g/L	0.28	s 0.06	EID	...	123
Apo-C I	Adults	...	10	mg/L	69.2	s 20.1	RID	Purified apo-C I	117
	Adults	...	68	mg/L	60	s 15	EID	Purified apo-C I	118
	Adults	...	–	mg/L	70	s 20	EID	...	122
Apo-C II	Adults	...	47	mg/L	52	s 22	RIA	Purified apo-C II	105
	Adults	...	68	mg/L	40	s 20	EID	Purified apo-C II	118
	Adults	...	–	mg/L	37	s 20	EID	...	122
Apo-C III	Adults	...	–	mg/L	130	s 50	EID	...	122
Apo-D	Adults	...	51	mg/L	100	s 40	EID	Purified apo-D	114
	Men	...	48	mg/L	62	s 11	RID	Purified apo-D	108
	Women	...	26	mg/L	59	s 13	RID	Purified apo-D	108
Apo-E	Adults	20–62 years	26	mg/L	36	s 13	RIA	Purified apo-E	109
	Men	20–64 years	86	mg/L	49.4	s 17.1	RIA	Purified apo-E	115
	Women	20–64 years	86	mg/L	58.8	s 23.7	RIA	Purified apo-E	115
	Newborn	Cord blood	33	mg/L	52	s 23	EID	...	123
Apo-F	Adults	...	–	mg/L	19	s 7	EID	...	122

RIA: radioimmunoassay; RID: radial immunodiffusion; EID: electroimmunodiffusion; N: nephelometry.

Table 5 *Classes of lipoprotein in serum of employees of the University of California (determined with ultracentrifuge)*[12]

Age	Number	S_f 100–400		S_f 20–100		S_f 12–20		S_f 0–12		HDL_1		HDL_2		HDL_3	
		Mean	s	Mean	s	Mean	s	Mean	s	Mean	s	Mean	s	Mean	s
		g/L													
Men															
17–29 years	585	0.37	0.43	0.75	0.41	0.40	0.21	3.22	0.86	0.23	0.07	0.37	0.28	2.17	0.40
30–39 years	834	0.51	0.64	0.91	0.54	0.51	0.23	3.55	0.84	0.24	0.15	0.36	0.28	2.19	0.42
40–49 years	399	0.66	0.91	1.07	0.66	0.57	0.23	3.80	0.84	0.25	0.15	0.37	0.28	2.26	0.50
50–65 years	143	0.58	0.70	1.03	0.58	0.56	0.24	3.83	0.75	0.27	0.22	0.42	0.32	2.24	0.51
Women															
17–29 years	190	0.09	0.14	0.44	0.29	0.30	0.16	2.83	0.68	0.21	0.07	0.80	0.41	2.28	0.38
30–39 years	99	0.13	0.17	0.51	0.36	0.41	0.22	3.24	0.86	0.22	0.09	0.81	0.45	2.35	0.38
40–49 years	37	0.18	0.24	0.65	0.51	0.42	0.21	3.46	0.67	0.23	0.05	0.89	0.53	2.41	0.43
50–65 years	10	0.32	0.37	0.77	0.48	0.93	0.36	4.37	0.40	0.25	0.07	1.17	0.66	2.70	0.54

young adults even during childhood (Tables 7–9). In men the cholesterol level rises until about the age of 50; in women the rise continues after 50 (Tables 6 and 7); it tends to be lower in younger women than in men of the same age, and tends to be higher in older women than in men of the same age[10,17,34–37,54–56]. Fluctuations over the course of the year need to be taken into account when the data are being evaluated[39]. The use of oral contraceptives results in a rise in the cholesterol level by about 5%[55,57]. Toward the end of pregnancy, the cholesterol level is elevated by approximately 30%[15,38].

Phospholipids (phosphatides). Phospholipids are important constituents of the plasma membrane of the blood cells. They account for 60–65% of total lipids in the erythrocytes[2,3], for about 50% in the leukocytes[20], and for approximately 70% in the platelets[45,58]. In the plasma, the fraction of phospholipids relative to total lipids is 35–40%.

The phospholipid concentration can be determined by – generally colorimetric – assay of lipid phosphorus in a serum extract or a protein precipitate[7]. 1 mmol of phosphorus is equivalent to 1 mmol of phospholipid or 774 mg of phospholipid.

Table 6 *Serum lipids and serum lipoproteins* in a group of white English factory workers*[16]

Age	Number	Triglycerides Mean	Triglycerides s	Cholesterol Mean	Cholesterol s	Phospholipids Mean	Phospholipids s	β-Lipoproteins Mean	β-Lipoproteins s	Pre-β-lipoproteins Mean	Pre-β-lipoproteins s	α-Lipoproteins Mean	α-Lipoproteins s
		mmol/L						Mass fraction (relative to total lipoproteins) as percent					
Men													
18–29 years	195–213	1.09	0.54	4.95	1.01	2.63	0.47	49.0	6.8	20.3	7.3	30.5	7.6
30–39 years	173–182	1.25	0.64	5.52	1.11	2.83	0.49	50.8	7.2	20.6	7.8	28.4	7.2
40–49 years	249–267	1.51	0.80	6.01	1.12	3.01	0.48	50.0	7.4	23.0	9.2	26.8	6.6
50–59 years	227–237	1.31	0.60	5.96	1.10	3.03	0.47	51.5	6.6	19.9	7.8	28.5	7.1
60–64 years	92–97	1.41	0.76	6.10	1.20	3.01	0.48	52.6	6.8	21.3	9.0	26.4	6.4
Women◊													
18–29 years	48–50	0.75	0.33	4.78	0.74	2.63	0.45	49.0	5.1	13.1	5.6	37.8	6.2
30–39 years	50–54	0.88	0.45	5.16	0.93	2.69	0.45	49.7	6.5	15.2	5.5	35.0	6.6
40–49 years	135–142	1.07	0.48	5.87	0.99	3.01	0.42	50.2	6.1	16.4	6.6	33.3	7.6
50–59 years	191–203	1.24	0.56	6.39	1.13	3.24	0.50	50.7	7.5	17.7	7.6	31.4	7.2

* Determined by means of agarose gel electrophoresis. ◊ Women not using oral contraceptives.

Table 7 *Plasma lipids and plasma lipoproteins* in a Danish population*◊

Age	Number	Total lipids Mean	Total lipids s	Triglycerides Mean	Triglycerides s	Cholesterol Mean	Cholesterol s	Phospholipids Mean	Phospholipids s	Chylomicrons Mean	Chylomicrons s	β-Lipoproteins Mean	β-Lipoproteins s	Pre-β-lipoproteins Mean	Pre-β-lipoproteins s	α-Lipoproteins Mean	α-Lipoproteins s	Reference
		g/L		mmol/L						g/L								
Males																		
6–10 years	22	5.41	0.76	0.77	0.22	5.04	0.89	2.40	0.39	0.27	0.12	3.40	0.85	0.79	0.45	3.48	0.99	31
11–15 years	23	5.82	0.87	0.71	0.37	5.23	0.86	2.72	0.44	0.27	0.09	3.71	0.88	1.01	0.53	3.39	0.81	31
16–20 years	33	5.34	0.68	0.91	0.26	5.07	0.83	2.15	0.35	0.15	0.09	3.49	0.83	0.96	0.48	3.11	0.87	31
21–30 years	24	5.85	1.20	1.11	0.36	5.63	1.12	2.36	0.41	0.18	0.19	4.00	1.09	1.16	0.39	2.87	0.65	32
31–40 years	25	6.29	0.74	1.15	0.53	6.28	0.94	2.75	0.44	0.18	0.10	4.55	0.85	1.17	0.59	2.90	0.69	32
41–50 years	27	7.42	1.63	1.65	0.79	7.31	1.47	2.91	0.85	0.23	0.11	5.19	1.52	1.81	0.87	2.84	1.08	32
51–60 years	36	7.17	1.16	1.32	0.62	7.26	1.15	2.84	0.60	0.16	0.08	5.32	1.08	1.58	0.77	2.78	0.89	32
61–70 years	21	7.04	1.28	1.35	0.81	7.00	1.44	2.79	0.57	0.21	0.13	5.22	1.20	1.45	1.02	2.75	0.80	32
Females																		
6–10 years	21	5.90	0.62	0.83	0.23	5.59	0.75	2.61	0.51	0.29	0.12	3.79	0.58	0.99	0.41	3.43	1.01	31
11–15 years	33	5.74	0.70	0.80	0.28	5.28	0.76	2.54	0.46	0.20	0.08	3.63	0.79	1.06	0.53	3.43	1.13	31
16–20 years	21	5.94	0.64	1.07	0.39	5.70	0.84	2.78	0.61	0.26	0.19	3.99	0.84	1.13	0.49	3.00	0.92	31
21–30 years	23	5.41	0.81	0.75	0.26	5.63	1.12	2.53	0.44	0.16	0.14	3.80	0.78	0.78	0.46	3.06	0.87	32
31–40 years	20	6.32	0.97	0.95	0.40	6.44	1.18	2.83	0.62	0.16	0.10	4.29	1.23	0.99	0.54	3.71	0.92	32
41–50 years	21	6.77	1.05	1.02	0.43	7.09	1.32	2.98	0.40	0.15	0.09	4.86	1.22	1.11	0.49	3.57	1.10	32
51–60 years	20	8.02	1.29	1.10	0.41	8.32	1.24	3.28	0.47	0.19	0.10	6.02	1.45	0.98	0.55	4.35	1.04	32
61–70 years	22	8.19	1.26	1.30	0.47	8.45	1.58	3.30	0.54	0.23	0.08	6.26	1.52	1.23	0.68	3.78	0.97	32

* Determined by means of agarose gel electrophoresis. ◊ Not including overweight individuals and women using oral contraceptives.

In the newborn, the phospholipid concentration in the serum is low (Table 8)[59–61]; both reduced[61] and increased[62] values have been reported for the concentration in the erythrocytes of cord blood. In subsequent life phases, changes in the serum phospholipid level largely parallel those in the triglyceride level (the highest values being found in postmenopausal women)[17,63]. The serum phospholipid level is raised toward the end of pregnancy[15,38] as well as with the use of estrogen-containing ovulation inhibitors[57].

Individual phospholipids. They are determined on the basis of the phosphorus content of the individual fractions, obtained for example by thin-layer chromatographic separation. The phospholipid distribution in the plasma or the blood cells is shown in Tables 12–14. In the plasma more than half[64] of the phospholipids, and just under one-third in the erythrocytes, consist of phosphatidylcholine (lecithin)[3,65,67]. The lysolecithin concentration in the serum is lower in women of all ages than in men[63]. For the phospholipid distribution in the serum and erythrocytes of pregnant women, newborn infants, and children, refer to the pertinent literature[59–62].

The phosphorus-free glycosphingolipids, which represent a small fraction of the total lipids but are important for membrane stability, are also counted among the phospholipids. The serum concentration of glycosphingolipids amounts to approximately 5 mg/L[68]; the concentration in the erythrocytes is about ten times higher (Table 15). 8% of the total lipids in the platelets are glycosphingolipids[58]. Lactosylceramide predominates in the platelets[58] and leukocytes[72].

Fatty acids. About 3% and at most 10% of the fatty acids in the serum are present in nonesterified form (see page 107); they are for the most part components of glycerides, phospholipids and cholesterol esters. In contrast to the lipoprotein complexes of the other lipid fractions, the free fatty acids in the serum are loosely bound to albumin as anions. At most traces of free fatty acids are found in the erythrocytes[5] and leukocytes[20].

The fatty-acid pattern of the individual serum lipid fractions is presented in Tables 16, 17a, and 17b. The proportion of linoleic acid is lower in the neonate than in adults, whereas the proportion

(Continued on page 123)

Table 8 *Lipids and lipoproteins in serum of children*

	Origin	Number	Total lipids Mean	Total lipids s	Triglycerides Mean	Triglycerides s	Cholesterol Mean	Cholesterol s	Phospholipids Mean	Phospholipids s	β-Lipoproteins Mean	β-Lipoproteins s	Pre-β-lipoproteins Mean	Pre-β-lipoproteins s	α-Lipoproteins Mean	α-Lipoproteins s	Reference
			g/L		mmol/L						g/L						
Newborn, cord	USA	12	1.91	0.06	0.34	0.05	1.09	0.16	1.36	0.18	0.58	0.15	0.24	0.12	0.81	0.43	23
Boys, 28 days, breast-fed	USA, Whites	21	–	–	1.38	0.41	3.59	0.80	–	–	–	–	–	–	–	–	26
Girls, 28 days, breast-fed	USA, Whites	13	–	–	1.77	0.49	4.65	0.90	–	–	–	–	–	–	–	–	26
Mothers	USA	36	9.03	1.50	2.58	0.66	6.72	1.27	3.57	0.58	–	–	–	–	–	–	24
Newborn, cord	USA	21	2.91	0.70	0.78	0.23	1.94	0.46	1.27	0.31	–	–	–	–	–	–	24
Children, 6–8 weeks:																	
Milk–meat diet	USA	10	5.74	1.17	2.07	0.89	3.51	0.42	2.29	0.35	–	–	–	–	–	–	24
Soybean formula–vegetable diet	USA	10	3.83	0.51	1.24	0.47	2.30	0.43	1.71	0.31	–	–	–	–	–	–	24
Children, 3–16 years	USA, 75% Blacks	333	–	–	0.87	0.54	4.39	1.03	–	–	1.79	0.70	0.47	0.41	4.19	1.30	25
Adults, 20–25 years	USA, medical students	67	–	–	0.97	0.44	4.44	0.83	–	–	2.18	0.58	0.97	0.56	2.48	0.92	25
Children, 5–16 years	USA, rural community, 70% Blacks	430	–	–	0.55	0.32	4.86	0.90	–	–	2.37	0.63	0.40	0.32	4.02	1.41	29

Table 9a *Percentile values of serum cholesterol in infants*[116]

	Number	Total cholesterol P_5	P_{50}	P_{95}	P_5	P_{50}	P_{95}	VLDL–LDL cholesterol P_5	P_{50}	P_{95}	P_5	P_{50}	P_{95}	HDL cholesterol P_5	P_{50}	P_{95}	P_5	P_{50}	P_{95}
		mmol/L			g/L			mmol/L			g/L			mmol/L			g/L		
Newborn, cord blood	80	1.17	1.71	2.31	0.45	0.66	0.89	0.65	1.04	1.20	0.25	0.40	0.46	0.47	0.67	1.04	0.18	0.26	0.40
Infants, 7 days:																			
Breast-fed	30	2.18	2.85	3.52	0.84	1.10	1.36	1.56	2.07	2.48	0.60	0.80	0.96	0.49	0.78	1.27	0.19	0.30	0.49
Adapted commercial formula	25	2.33	2.82	3.77	0.90	1.09	1.46	1.70	2.00	2.55	0.66	0.77	0.99	0.53	0.83	1.21	0.20	0.32	0.47
Infants, 30 days:																			
Breast-fed	30	2.59	3.34	4.76	1.00	1.29	1.84	2.00	2.25	3.08	0.77	0.87	1.19	0.64	1.09	1.66	0.25	0.42	0.64
Adapted commercial formula	25	2.51	3.39	4.35	0.97	1.31	1.68	1.75	2.12	2.54	0.68	0.82	0.98	0.73	1.27	1.63	0.28	0.49	0.63

Table 9b *Percentile values of serum triglycerides and serum cholesterol in white children and young adults (USA)*[28]

Age	Number	Triglycerides P_5	P_{50}	P_{95}	P_5	P_{50}	P_{95}	Total cholesterol P_5	P_{50}	P_{95}	P_5	P_{50}	P_{95}	VLDL cholesterol P_5	P_{50}	P_{95}	LDL cholesterol P_5	P_{50}	P_{95}	HDL cholesterol P_5	P_{50}	P_{95}
		mmol/L			g/L			mmol/L			g/L			g/L								
Males																						
6–7 years	67	0.36	0.53	0.78	0.32	0.47	0.69	3.28	3.96	4.86	1.27	1.53	1.88	0	0.06	0.16	0.69	0.92	1.29	0.38	0.55	0.72
8–9 years	73	0.32	0.56	1.12	0.28	0.50	0.99	3.21	3.93	4.84	1.24	1.52	1.87	0	0.09	0.21	0.65	0.87	1.23	0.39	0.54	0.73
10–11 years	96	0.34	0.63	1.08	0.30	0.56	0.96	3.34	4.22	5.41	1.29	1.63	2.09	0.02	0.09	0.23	0.64	0.95	1.31	0.38	0.57	0.76
12–13 years	144	0.37	0.62	1.21	0.33	0.55	1.07	3.18	4.16	5.17	1.23	1.61	2.00	0.01	0.08	0.19	0.64	0.94	1.29	0.39	0.55	0.75
14–15 years	130	0.40	0.72	1.45	0.35	0.64	1.28	2.92	3.93	5.07	1.13	1.52	1.96	0	0.10	0.25	0.57	0.94	1.30	0.34	0.48	0.69
16–17 years	160	0.43	0.75	1.63	0.38	0.66	1.44	3.05	3.91	4.97	1.18	1.51	1.92	0.02	0.13	0.27	0.64	0.91	1.29	0.30	0.45	0.62
18–19 years	67	0.47	0.89	1.63	0.42	0.79	1.44	2.84	3.96	4.97	1.10	1.53	1.92	0.02	0.13	0.25	0.62	0.98	1.42	0.32	0.43	0.60
Females																						
6–7 years	59	0.27	0.64	1.60	0.24	0.57	1.42	3.39	4.22	4.94	1.31	1.63	1.91	0.01	0.08	0.23	0.66	1.05	1.24	0.28	0.49	0.68
8–9 years	61	0.38	0.66	1.31	0.34	0.58	1.16	3.28	4.29	5.17	1.27	1.66	2.00	0.01	0.09	0.25	0.67	0.96	1.42	0.37	0.56	0.75
10–11 years	101	0.44	0.77	1.28	0.39	0.68	1.13	3.26	4.22	5.25	1.26	1.63	2.03	0.02	0.10	0.23	0.70	0.95	1.40	0.34	0.50	0.72
12–13 years	102	0.41	0.77	1.38	0.36	0.68	1.22	3.23	4.14	5.38	1.25	1.60	2.08	0.01	0.09	0.23	0.68	0.95	1.33	0.37	0.53	0.69
14–15 years	122	0.41	0.75	1.38	0.36	0.66	1.22	2.95	3.96	5.12	1.14	1.53	1.98	0.02	0.10	0.23	0.60	0.93	1.29	0.34	0.49	0.70
16–17 years	167	0.38	0.66	1.37	0.34	0.62	1.21	3.16	4.03	5.35	1.22	1.56	2.07	0.03	0.11	0.26	0.57	0.92	1.38	0.35	0.52	0.77
18–19 years	53	0.44	0.80	1.39	0.39	0.71	1.23	2.92	4.16	5.51	1.13	1.61	2.13	0	0.12	0.24	0.58	1.01	1.43	0.37	0.52	0.74

Table 10 *Percentile values of serum triglycerides and serum cholesterol for black and white men and women (USA)*[27]

Age	Triglycerides						Total cholesterol						LDL cholesterol			HDL cholesterol		
	P_5	P_{50}	P_{95}	P_5	P_{50}	P_{95}	P_5	P_{50}	P_{95}	P_5	P_{50}	P_{95}	P_5	P_{50}	P_{95}	P_5	P_{50}	P_{95}
	mmol/L			g/L			mmol/L			g/L			g/L					
Men																		
Black, 20–39 years....	(0.58)	1.15	2.36	(0.51)	1.02	(2.09)	(3.59)	4.97	6.47	(1.39)	1.92	(2.50)	(0.63)	1.22	(1.79)	(0.34)	0.49	(0.71)
Black, 40–59 years....	0.68	1.13	(3.24)	(0.60)	1.00	(2.87)	3.98	5.53	7.03	1.54	2.14	2.72						
White, 20–39 years....	0.67	1.33	3.62	0.59	1.18	3.20	3.67	5.07	7.22	1.42	1.96	2.79	0.88	1.49	2.14	0.27	0.42	0.68
White, 40–59 years....	0.68	1.47	3.47	0.60	1.30	3.07	4.03	5.46	7.19	1.56	2.11	2.78						
Women not taking exogenous sex steroid hormones:																		
Black, 20–39 years....	0.50	0.81	1.63	0.44	0.72	1.44	3.10	4.81	6.34	1.20	1.86	2.45	(0.48)	1.10	(1.56)	0.39	0.53	0.82
Black, 40–59 years....	0.49	0.95	1.93	0.43	0.84	1.71	3.75	5.12	7.06	1.45	1.98	2.73	(0.79)	1.27	(1.85)			
White, 20–39 years....	0.49	0.84	2.08	0.43	0.74	1.84	3.39	4.55	6.13	1.31	1.76	2.37	0.75	1.29	1.93	0.35	0.52	0.78
White, 40–59 years....	0.59	1.07	2.60	0.52	0.95	2.30	3.91	5.20	6.91	1.51	2.01	2.67	0.77	1.36	2.14			
Women taking exogenous sex steroid hormones:																		
Black, 20–59 years....	(0.51)	1.04	(2.15)	(0.45)	0.92	(1.90)	(3.72)	4.58	(6.72)	(1.44)	1.77	(2.60)	–	1.10	–	–	0.60	–
White, 20–59 years....	0.68	1.24	2.77	0.60	1.10	2.45	3.83	5.02	6.70	1.48	1.94	2.59	0.78	1.33	2.01	0.39	0.56	0.82

Values presented in parentheses are based on sample sizes N < 100.

Table 11 *Sterols occurring in plasma or serum in traces*

	Mean	*s* or (extreme range)	Reference
	mg/L		
Dihydrocholesterol (5α-cholestan-3β-ol) .	~15	–	40
7-Dehydrocholesterol (5,7-cholestadien-3β-ol)........	~200	–	41
Δ^7-Cholestanol (5α-cholest-7-en-3β-ol)...	~50	–	41
Campesterol (children, any diet)	6.9	(0.1–35)	42
Stigmasterol (children, any diet)	4.6	(0.1–23)	42
β-Sitosterol (children, any diet)	8.3	(0.2–30)	42
Campesterol (35 subjects, any diet)			
– free	2	*s* 1	83
– esterified	4	*s* 1	83
β-Sitosterol (35 subjects, any diet)			
– free	2	*s* 1	83
– esterified	4	*s* 2	83

Table 12 *Phospholipids in plasma, erythrocytes, and erythrocyte membrane in 7 adults*[66]

	Plasma		Erythrocytes		Erythrocyte membrane	
	Mean	*s*	Mean	*s*	Mean	*s*
	µmol/L					
Lipid phosphorus..........	2062	156	3906	108	2540	167
Phospholipids						
Phosphatidylethanolamine	25	3	351	32	225	13
Phosphatidylcholine	1432	180	1472	66	951	101
Plasmalogens	83	11	415	45	272	24
Sphingomyelin	298	24	679	37	411	29
Phosphatidylserine........	11	3	182	13	138	11
Phosphatidic acid	9	0.8	156	8	95	13
Phosphatidylinositol	61	5	175	29	110	13
Phosphatidylglycerol	30	3	103	5	59	5
Cardiolipin	21	3	71	8	62	3
Alkyl ethers.............	32	5	149	13	90	19
Unknown................	39	8	73	13	55	11

Table 13 *Distribution of phospholipids in erythrocytes and platelets*

	Erythrocytes[67]		Platelets[67]		Platelets[45]	
	Mean	*s*	Mean	*s*	Mean	*s*
	Substance fraction (relative to lipid phosphorus) as percent					
Phosphatidylethanolamine... (cephalin)	15.2	0.3	13.6	0.4	25.4	0.8
Ethanolamine plasmalogen ..	13.1	0.8	14.0	0.4		
Phosphatidylcholine .... (lecithin)	32.6	0.4	39.8	0.7	39.8	1.6
Choline plasmalogen.........	1.2	0.2	<1	–		
Sphingomyelin	23.4	0.3	18.4	0.3	18.3	1.1
Phosphatidylserine..........	14.5	0.2	8.8	0.4	10.1	1.7
Phosphatidylinositol	<1	–	3.7	0.1	4.3	1.5
Lysophosphatidylcholine..... (lysolecithin)	–	–	1.7	0.2	0.8	0.7
Cardiolipin	–	–	–	–	0.5	0.4

Table 14 *Distribution of phospholipids in lymphocytes, granulocytes, and erythrocytes*[3]

	Lymphocytes		Granulocytes		Erythrocytes	
	Mean	*s*	Mean	*s*	Mean	*s*
	mmol/10^{12}					
Lipid phosphorus..........	4.73	0.93	9.67	1.11	0.354	0.010
	Substance fraction (relative to lipid phosphorus) as percent					
Phospholipids						
Phosphatidylethanolamine	28.7	1.8	33.4	1.1	29.3	0.9
Phosphatidylcholine	43.6	2.0	38.6	1.8	29.2	1.3
Sphingomyelin............	10.1	2.6	10.5	0.7	26.0	1.0
Phosphatidylserine....... Phosphatidylinositol	13.4	1.8	15.0	1.1	14.2	1.1
Cardiolipin*	3.2	2.4	1.3	0.3	0.9	0.6
Other phospholipids◊.....	1.0	1.1	1.1	1.0	0.4	0.1

* The fraction contains phosphatidic acid.
◊ The fraction contains lysolecithin.

Table 15 *Glycosphingolipids in serum, plasma, and erythrocytes*

	Serum		Plasma		Erythrocytes			
	4 subjects[69]		8–15 subjects[70]		8–15 subjects[70]		3 subjects*[71]	
	Mean	s	Mean	s	Mean	s	Mean	s
	μmol/L							
GL-1 (glucosylceramide)	6.0	2.0	9.8	0.9	4.5	0.8	7	3
GL-2 (lactosylceramide)	4.5	2.0	5.5	0.9	13.7	3.3	13	5
GL-3 (trihexosylceramide)	2.0	2.0	2.1	0.7	11.3	2.5	12	1
GL-4 (tetrahexosylceramide)◊	1.5	2.0	2.8	0.8	63.8	6.3	80	4
G_{M3} (hematoside)	4.5	2.0	–	–	–	–	–	–

* Values for erythrocyte membrane.
◊ Probably globoside.

Table 16 *Fatty acid pattern of serum lipid fractions of mothers, newborn, and children (mean values)*[74]

		6 mothers during delivery			5 newborn before first feeding			4 children, <6 months					
								Breast milk			Cow's milk		
		Triglycerides	Cholesterol esters	Phospholipids	Triglycerides	Cholesterol esters	Phospholipids	Triglycerides	Cholesterol esters	Phospholipids	Triglycerides	Cholesterol esters	Phospholipids
		mmol											
Fatty acid content of lipid fraction from 1 L of serum		8.97	4.86	6.10	0.89	0.99	1.84	3.36	2.59	3.69	3.40	2.55	3.19
Fatty acids		Substance fraction (relative to total fatty acids) as percent											
$C_{16:0}$	Palmitic acid	23.3	11.7	24.3	18.6	15.3	18.0	23.5	14.5	21.0	25.5	12.3	24.6
$C_{16:1}$	Palmitoleic acid	7.5	6.4	2.6	11.2	10.6	3.0	7.0	5.7	2.8	10.8	11.1	3.6
$C_{18:0}$	Stearic acid	3.1	0.7	10.4	3.4	2.5	11.5	5.1	1.6	15.1	3.9	2.1	11.3
$C_{18:1}$	Oleic acid	34.8	21.3	13.6	29.6	28.2	11.5	36.4	21.7	13.4	40.8	36.5	23.2
$C_{18:2}$	Linoleic acid	18.5	46.4	23.3	12.4	18.4	8.5	12.8	36.4	18.1	3.7	19.2	10.2
$C_{18:3}$	Linolenic acid	1.2	0.9	0.4	0.6	0.3	0.3	0.8	0.6	0.3	0.4	1.0	0.4
$C_{20:3}$	Icosatrienoic acid	0.2	0.1	0.2	0.9	0.3	1.0	0.3	0.1	0.1	0.6	1.4	3.3
$C_{20:4}$	Arachidonic acid	0.9	6.0	10.2	5.2	14.7	21.8	1.7	10.3	13.1	0.4	3.9	6.8
$C_{20:6}$	Clupanodonic acid	0.5	0.5	5.3	3.1	1.5	9.5	1.0	1.0	5.6	0.2	0.4	2.9
$C_{22:3}$	Docosatrienoic acid	0.3	0.7	3.4	1.2	1.4	5.9	0.4	0.9	2.9	0.2	0.7	2.9

Table 17a *Fatty acid pattern of serum lipid fractions of adults (mean values)*[73]

		15 men, 18–42 years				15 men, 46–71 years			
		Triglycerides	Cholesterol esters	Phospholipids	Nonesterified fatty acids	Triglycerides	Cholesterol esters	Phospholipids	Nonesterified fatty acids
		g							
Lipid fraction from 1 L of serum		1.78	2.20	2.02	0.27	2.59	2.43	2.19	0.28
Fatty acid content of lipid fraction from 1 L of serum		1.38	0.71	1.08	0.27	2.14	0.86	1.15	0.28
Fatty acids		Mass fraction (relative to total fatty acids) as percent							
$C_{14:0}$	Myristic acid	1.5	1.1	0.7	2.0	1.7	0.9	0.5	2.1
$C_{16:0}$	Palmitic acid	27.8	11.7	31.0	27.5	28.9	12.0	30.7	27.2
$C_{16:1}$	Palmitoleic acid	7.7	6.0	3.5	7.3	7.7	8.4	3.6	8.6
$C_{18:0}$	Stearic acid	3.6	2.5	12.5	15.3	4.3	3.1	12.1	13.1
$C_{18:1}$	Oleic acid	36.4	18.7	15.0	25.4	36.0	20.7	15.1	25.7
$C_{18:2}$	Linoleic acid	12.7	48.4	21.2	13.4	11.3	44.9	20.7	12.6
$C_{18:3}$, $C_{20:3}$	Trienoic acids	1.0	1.1	0.9	0.9	1.0	1.0	1.3	0.9
$C_{20:4}$	Arachidonic acid	3.0	5.0	8.1	2.4	2.4	3.9	8.7	2.4
$C_{20:5}$, $C_{22:5}$	Pentaenoic acids	1.2	1.3	2.1	1.3	1.4	1.4	2.3	1.3
$C_{22:6}$	Hexaenoic acids	1.8	2.0	3.0	1.8	2.0	1.7	2.8	1.9
Other fatty acids		3.3	2.2	2.0	2.7	3.3	2.0	2.2	4.2

Table 17b *Fatty acid pattern of the plasma nonesterified fatty-acid fraction*[120]

	103 males		94 females		134 males		61 females		45 males		42 females	
	8–10 years				15–17 years				20–25 years			
	Mean	s	Mean	s	Mean	s	Mean	s	Mean	s	Mean	s
	µmol											
Total nonesterified fatty-acid content of 1 L of plasma	442	249	499	282	308	149	424	197	251	114	293	151
Fatty acids	Substance fraction (relative to total nonesterified fatty acids) as percent											
$C_{14:0}$ Myristic acid	3.0	1.3	2.9	1.3	2.7	1.5	2.8	1.8	2.1	0.9	2.2	1.1
$C_{16:0}$ Palmitic acid	25.0	2.8	24.1	2.1	25.5	2.8	25.3	2.5	26.7	4.4	27.8	5.1
$C_{16:1}$ Palmitoleic acid	4.6	2.1	4.8	1.8	4.9	2.3	5.4	2.3	4.5	2.8	4.1	2.2
$C_{18:0}$ Stearic acid	12.2	3.2	10.6	2.4	11.4	3.0	10.4	2.3	11.0	2.3	10.7	2.8
$C_{18:1}$ Oleic acid	37.7	4.3	38.9	3.9	35.8	3.6	37.5	3.5	37.0	5.7	36.9	4.4
$C_{18:2}$ Linoleic acid	16.3	4.0	16.9	4.3	17.2	5.0	17.6	4.3	17.7	4.7	16.7	4.9
$C_{18:3}$ Linolenic acid	1.4	1.0	1.8	1.2	1.6	1.4	1.3	1.2	1.1	0.8	1.4	1.1

Table 18
Branched-chain hydrocarbons and fatty acids in plasma or serum

	Unit	Mean	s	(Extreme range)	Reference
Squalene, 26 subjects, any diet	mg/L	0.34	0.11	(0.19–0.74)	78
Squalene, 15 subjects	mg/L	0.85	0.22	(0.50–1.30)	79
Pristane	mg/kg	1.6	–	–	80
Phytane	mg/kg	0.17	–	–	80
Phytanic acid	mg/L	2.1	–	–	81
Phytenic acid	mg/L	0.73	–	–	81

of higher polyunsaturated fatty acids is higher (Table 16)[14,30,59,60]. The fatty-acid pattern of the plasma lipids is influenced by the diet. When fish consumption is high, fatty acids occurring in fish, for example, are also found in the plasma lipids[75]. The fatty-acid patterns of the erythrocyte lipids[67,76] and the platelet lipids [45,67,77] have also been studied. Besides straight-chain fatty acids, the plasma contains traces of branched-chain hydrocarbons and fatty acids (Table 18). The prostaglandins, which occur in very low concentrations in the plasma (10^{-10} mol/L), may also be counted among fatty acids[82].

Pathological changes in serum lipid level

Tables 19 and 20 summarize changes in the serum lipid level in primary and secondary hyperlipoproteinemias. The plasma of patients with intrahepatic or extrahepatic cholestasis contains an abnormal lipoprotein (LP-X) which consists of 66% phospholipids, 22% nonesterified cholesterol, 3% cholesterol esters, and 3% triglycerides[85].

Bile acids

Of the bile acids in the blood, 80% are found in the plasma and 20% in the blood cells[86]. In the plasma, the bile acids are bound to glycine or taurine; approximately 10–15% are present in the form of sulfates[87,88]. At most traces of free bile acids are normally found in the plasma.

Normal values of bile-acid concentrations are given in Table 21 on the next page. Postprandial values are higher than fasting values[89,90].

In most patients with liver diseases the bile-acid concentration in the serum is increased; in acute hepatitis and cirrhosis the values range up to 200 µmol/L and above[87,91,128]. The fraction of sulfated bile acids can reach 80%[87].

Table 19 *Primary hyperlipoproteinemias*[84]

Types according to FREDRICKSON	Appearance of serum	Laboratory findings: Density fraction (ultracentrifuge)	Triglycerides	Cholesterol	Lipoprotein lipase	Clinical findings
Fat-induced (Type I: hyperchylomicronemia)	Creamy-milky	S_f >400 observed	Greatly increased	Normal	Reduced	Lipemia retinalis, eruptive xanthomas, hepatosplenomegaly
Hypercholesterolemia (Type II: hyper-β-lipoproteinemia)	Clear	S_f 0–12 increased	Normal	Increased to greatly increased	Normal	Arcus lipoides corneae, tendon xanthomas, tuberous xanthomas
Hypercholesterolemia, hypertriglyceridemia (Type III: broad-β-disease)	Clear or turbid	S_f 12–400 increased	Increased	Increased	Normal	Palmar xanthomas, tuberous and eruptive xanthomas
Carbohydrate-induced (Type IV: hyperpre-β-lipoproteinemia)	Turbid to milky	S_f 20–400 increased	Increased	Slightly increased	Normal	Occasionally eruptive xanthomas, hepatosplenomegaly
Energy-induced (Type V: hyperchylomicronemia and hyperpre-β-lipoproteinemia)	Creamy-milky	S_f 20–400 increased S_f >400 observed	Very greatly increased	Increased	Normal or reduced	Overweight, eruptive xanthomas

Table 20 *Some secondary hyperlipoproteinemias in order of incidence*[84]

Underlying disease	Lipoprotein electrophoresis	Increase of concentration			
		Triglycerides	Cholesterol	Phospholipids	Free fatty acids
Diabetes mellitus	Pre-β-lipoproteins	Slight	Slight	Slight	Moderate
Ketoacidotic coma	Pre-β-lipoproteins	Moderate	None	None	Marked
Nephrotic syndrome	β-Lipoproteins	Marked	Moderate	Moderate	Slight
Chronic renal failure	Pre-β-lipoproteins	Slight	None	Slight	None
Primary biliary cirrhosis	'Obstructive' lipoprotein (LP-X)	Slight	Marked	Excessive	Slight
Intra- and extrahepatic cholestasis	'Obstructive' lipoprotein (LP-X)	Slight	Marked	Marked	Slight
Zieve syndrome	Pre-β-lipoproteins	Marked	Moderate	Moderate	Slight
Hypothyroidism	β-Lipoproteins and pre-β-lipoproteins	Moderate	Marked	Marked	Normal
Pancreatitis	Pre-β-lipoproteins	Marked	Slight	Moderate	Normal
Glycogenoses	Pre-β-lipoproteins	Marked	Moderate	Moderate	Normal

Table 21 *Bile acids in serum (fasting values)*

	Method	Subjects	Mean	s	(Extreme range)	Reference
			µmol/L			
Total bile acids	Enzymatic hydrolysis and fluorimetry	39 men	6.1	1.7	(1.6–9.2)	90
(3α-hydroxy bile acids)	Enzymatic hydrolysis and fluorimetry	21 women	5.9	1.7	(3.6–9.3)	90
	Enzymatic hydrolysis and fluorimetry	16 men	4.0	1.9	(1.3–7.2)	124
	Enzymatic hydrolysis and fluorimetry	30 women	3.0	1.1	(1.3–7.2)	124
Total bile acids	Thin-layer chromatography	12 subjects	3.11	0.69	(2.19–4.24)	92
Cholylglycine	Thin-layer chromatography	12 subjects	1.57	0.71	(0.26–2.79)	92
Chenodeoxycholylglycine	Thin-layer chromatography	12 subjects	0.86	0.30	(0.31–1.41)	92
Cholyltaurine	Thin-layer chromatography	12 subjects	0.38	0.20	(0.10–0.72)	92
Chenodeoxycholyltaurine	Thin-layer chromatography	12 subjects	0.30	0.08	(0.20–0.44)	92
Total bile acids	Gas chromatography	15 women	2.14	0.81	–	93
Cholic acid	Gas chromatography	15 women	0.58	0.50	–	93
Chenodeoxycholic acid	Gas chromatography	15 women	0.98	0.66	–	93
Deoxycholic acid	Gas chromatography	15 women	0.57	0.35	–	93
Total bile acids	Gas chromatography	10 adults	5.3	–	(1.1–16.4)	88
Nonsulfated bile acids	Gas chromatography	10 adults	4.6	–	(0.9–15.6)	88
Cholic acid	Gas chromatography	10 adults	2.1	–	(0.3–7.2)	88
Chenodeoxycholic acid	Gas chromatography	10 adults	1.2	–	(0.3–3.9)	88
Deoxycholic acid	Gas chromatography	10 adults	1.2	–	(0.3–4.5)	88
Lithocholic acid	Gas chromatography	10 adults	0.1	–	(0–0.3)	88
Sulfolithocholic acid	Gas chromatography	10 adults	0.6	–	(0–1.8)	88
Sulfochenodeoxycholic acid	Gas chromatography	10 adults	0.1	–	(0–1.0)	88
Cholic acid, conjugated	Radioimmunoassay	8 men	0.68	0.34	(0.18–1.25)	94
	Radioimmunoassay	80 adults	0.50	0.72	–	95
	Radioimmunoassay	11 men	1.12	0.29	(0.5–1.7)	125
	Radioimmunoassay	6 women	0.95	0.55	(0.4–1.9)	125
Cholylglycine	Radioimmunoassay	12 children, 7 weeks–10 months	1.99	0.50	–	126
	Radioimmunoassay	16 children, 1 year	0.27	0.09	–	126
	Radioimmunoassay	25 subjects	0.27	0.03	–	91
Chenodeoxycholylglycine	Radioimmunoassay	25 subjects	0.20	0.03	–	91
Deoxycholylglycine	Radioimmunoassay	25 subjects	0.06	0.01	–	91
Sulfolithocholylglycine	Radioimmunoassay	25 subjects	0.06	0.01	–	91
Ursodeoxycholic acid	Radioimmunoassay	24 subjects	0.19	0.19	(0.1–0.7)	127

References

[1] Mean values commonly cited in the literature.
[2] Farquhar, J.W., *Biochim. biophys. Acta (Amst.)*, **60**, 80 (1962).
[3] Gottfried, E.L., *J. Lipid Res.*, **8**, 321 (1967).
[4] Shattil et al., *J. Lab. clin. Med.*, **89**, 341 (1977).
[5] Wintrobe et al., *Clinical Hematology*, 8th ed., Lea & Febiger, Philadelphia, 1981, page 80.
[6] Ways and Hanahan, *J. Lipid Res.*, **5**, 318 (1964).
[7] Morrisett et al., *Ann. Rev. Biochem.*, **44**, 183 (1975); Jackson et al., *Physiol. Rev.*, **56**, 259 (1976).
[8] Havel et al., in Bondy and Rosenberg, *Metabolic Control and Disease*, 8th ed., Saunders, Philadelphia, 1980, page 393; Patsch and Gotto, *Expos. ann. Biochim. méd.*, **35**, 1 (1982).
[9] Scanu and Ritter, *Advanc. clin. Chem.*, **16**, 111 (1973); Kostner, G.M., in Schwiegk, H. (Ed.), *Handbuch der inneren Medizin*, 5th ed., volume 7, part 4, Springer, Berlin, 1976, page 125.

[10] BREWER, H.B., *Klin. Wschr.*, **59**, 1023 (1981).
[11] GREEN and GLICKMAN, *J. Lipid Res.*, **22**, 1153 (1981).
[12] LINDGREN and NICHOLS, in PUTNAM, F.W. (Ed.), *The Plasma Proteins*, volume 2, Academic Press, New York, 1960, page 1.
[13] HAMID et al., *Blood*, **55**, 124 (1980).
[14] OLEGÅRD and SVENNERHOLM, *Acta paediat. scand.*, **59**, 637 (1970).
[15] HYTTEN and LIND, *Diagnostic Indices in Pregnancy*, CIBA-GEIGY Ltd., Basle, 1974; JAISLE, F., *Med. Klin.*, **64**, 139 (1969).
[16] SLACK et al., *Brit. med. J.*, **2**, 353 (1977).
[17] KANNEL et al., *Hum. Path.*, **2**, 129 (1971); KANNEL, W.B., *Med. Clin. N. Amer.*, **58**, 363 (1974).
[18] KUO, P.T., *Med. Clin. N. Amer.*, **58**, 351 (1974); ENGLHARDT, A., *Dtsch. med. Wschr.*, **99**, 842 (1974); RHOADS et al., *New Engl. J. Med.*, **294**, 293 (1976).
[19] CARLSON and WADSTRÖM, *Clin. chim. Acta*, **4**, 197 (1959); ZÖLLNER et al., *Z. klin. Chem.*, **7**, 339 (1969); VOGELBERG and GRIES, *Klin. Wschr.*, **48**, 227 (1970).
[20] GIARDINI et al., *Clin. chim. Acta*, **42**, 15 (1972).
[21] EGGSTEIN, M., in ZÖLLNER and EBERHAGEN (Eds.), *Untersuchung und Bestimmung der Lipoide im Blut*, Springer, Berlin, 1965, page 289.
[22] RICE, E.W., *Stand. Meth. clin. Chem.*, **6**, 215 (1970).
[23] WILLE and PHILLIPS, *Clin. chim. Acta*, **34**, 457 (1971).
[24] SWEENEY et al., *Pediatrics*, **27**, 765 (1961).
[25] BERENSON et al., *Clin. chim. Acta*, **56**, 65 (1974).
[26] FOMON et al., *Acta paediat. scand.*, suppl. 202 (1970).
[27] MORRISON et al., *J. Amer. med. Ass.*, **245**, 939 (1981).
[28] TAMIR et al., *J. chron. Dis.*, **34**, 27 (1981).
[29] SRINIVASAN et al., *Clin. chim. Acta*, **60**, 293 (1975).
[30] ZEE, P., *Pediatrics*, **41**, 640 (1968).
[31] DYERBERG and HJÖRNE, *Scand. J. clin. Lab. Invest.*, **31**, 473 (1973).
[32] DYERBERG and HJÖRNE, *Acta med. scand.*, **191**, 413 (1972).
[33] KATTERMANN et al., *Dtsch. med. Wschr.*, **101**, 953 (1976).
[34] PEZOLD, F.A., *Lipide und Lipoproteide im Blutplasma*, Springer, Berlin, 1961.
[35] SCHAEFER, L.E., *Amer. J. Med.*, **36**, 262 (1964); SCHILLING et al., *Amer. J. clin. Nutr.*, **22**, 133 (1969).
[36] HARTMANN and WERNER, in HARTMANN and WYSS (Eds.), *Die Hyperlipidämien in Klinik und Praxis*, Huber, Berne, 1970, page 39.
[37] LEWIS et al., *Lancet*, **1**, 141 (1974).
[38] SAMSIOE et al., *Acta obstet. gynec. scand.*, **54**, 265 (1975).
[39] FULLER et al., *Clin. chim. Acta*, **52**, 305 (1974); WARNICK and ALBERS, *Lipids*, **11**, 203 (1976).
[40] CHATTOPADHYAY and MOSBACH, *Analyt. Biochem.*, **10**, 435 (1965).
[41] FRANEY and AMADOR, *Clin. chim. Acta*, **21**, 255 (1968).
[42] MELLIES et al., *Pediatrics*, **57**, 60 (1976).
[43] ZAK, B., *Stand. Meth. clin. Chem.*, **5**, 79 (1965).
[44] DRAYER and LIEBERMAN, *Biochem. biophys. Res. Commun.*, **18**, 126 (1965); MOSER et al., *Biochim. biophys. Acta (Amst.)*, **116**, 146 (1966).
[45] MARCUS et al., *J. Lipid Res.*, **10**, 108 (1969).
[46] KRITCHEVSKY et al., *J. Lab. clin. Med.*, **63**, 511 (1964); EBERHAGEN, D., *Z. klin. Chem.*, **7**, 167 (1969).
[47] RICHTERICH, R., *Klinische Chemie*, 3rd ed., Karger, Basle, 1971.
[48] ABELL et al., *Stand. Meth. clin. Chem.*, **2**, 26 (1958).
[49] RICHMOND, W., *Clin. Chem.*, **19**, 1350 (1973); RÖSCHLAU et al., *Z. klin. Chem.*, **12**, 403 (1974).
[50] MUNSTER et al., *Clin. chim. Acta*, **68**, 167 (1976).
[51] MILLER and MILLER, *Lancet*, **1**, 16 (1975); GORDON et al., *Amer. J. Med.*, **62**, 707 (1977); WILLIAMS et al., *Lancet*, **1**, 72 (1979); KANNEL and CASTELLI, *Lancet*, **2**, 950 (1979); MCSWEENY et al., *Arch. intern. Med.*, **142**, 473 (1982).
[52] DARMADY et al., *Brit. med. J.*, **2**, 685 (1972).
[53] FRIEDMAN and GOLDBERG, *J. Amer. med. Ass.*, **255**, 610 (1973),
[54] PINCHERLE, G., *J. chron. Dis.*, **24**, 289 (1971).
[55] WEISSHAAR, D., *Med. Welt (Stuttg.)*, **26**, 940 (1975).
[56] HAUG and LOCH, *Verh. dtsch. Ges. inn. Med.*, **81**, 1713 (1975).
[57] AURELL et al., *Lancet*, **1**, 291 (1966); WYNN et al., *Lancet*, **2**, 756 (1969).
[58] TAO et al., *J. Lipid Res.*, **14**, 16 (1973).
[59] ZÖLLNER et al., *Klin. Wschr.*, **44**, 380 (1966).
[60] ZEE, P., *Pediatrics*, **39**, 82 (1967).
[61] HÜRTER et al., *Pediatrics*, **46**, 259 (1970).
[62] NEERHOUT, R.C., *Pediat. Res.*, **6**, 736 (1972).
[63] BÖTTIGER, L.E., *Acta med. scand.*, **193**, 49 (1973).
[64] TURNER and ROUSER, *Analyt. Biochem.*, **38**, 437 (1970).
[65] TURNER and ROUSER, *Analyt. Biochem.*, **38**, 423 (1970).
[66] SCHWARZ et al., *Clin. Chem.*, **23**, 1548 (1977).
[67] COHEN and DERKSEN, *Brit. J. Haemat.*, **17**, 359 (1969).
[68] SUGITA et al., *J. Lipid Res.*, **15**, 223 (1974).
[69] DAWSON et al., *J. Lipid Res.*, **17**, 125 (1976).
[70] VANCE et al., *J. Lipid Res.*, **10**, 188 (1969).
[71] JOSEPH et al., *J. Lab. clin. Med.*, **85**, 34 (1975).
[72] KLIBANSKY et al., *Clin. chim. Acta*, **72**, 141 (1976).
[73] SCHRADE et al., *J. Atheroscler. Res.*, **1**, 47 (1961).
[74] PIKAAR and FERNANDES, *Amer. J. clin. Nutr.*, **19**, 194 (1966).
[75] DYERBERG et al., *Amer. J. clin. Nutr.*, **28**, 958 (1975).
[76] DODGE and PHILLIPS, *J. Lipid Res.*, **8**, 667 (1967); PHILLIPS and DODGE, *J. Lab. clin. Med.*, **71**, 629 (1968); KUNZE et al., *Clin. chim. Acta*, **43**, 333 (1973).
[77] SAFRIT et al., *Lipids*, **7**, 60 (1972).
[78] LIU et al., *J. Lipid Res.*, **17**, 38 (1976).
[79] YAMANISHI et al., *Clin. chim. Acta*, **88**, 105 (1978).
[80] AVIGAN et al., *Biochim. biophys. Acta (Amst.)*, **144**, 127 (1967).
[81] AVIGAN, J., *Biochim. biophys. Acta (Amst.)*, **116**, 391 (1966).
[82] SAMUELSSON et al., *Ann. Rev. Biochem.*, **47**, 997 (1978).
[83] KUKSIS et al., *Lipids*, **11**, 581 (1976).
[84] KATTERMANN, R., in HOLLMANN et al. (Eds.), *Biochemische Befunde in der Differentialdiagnose innerer Krankheiten*, Thieme, Stuttgart, 1975, page 164.
[85] SEIDEL, D., *Expos. ann. Biochim. méd.*, **31**, 17 (1972); SEIDEL, D., *Med. Welt (Stuttg.)*, **26**, 2131 (1975); MICHEL and RITTER, *Z. Gastroent.*, **14**, 556 (1976).
[86] ROOVERS et al., *Clin. chim. Acta*, **19**, 449 (1968).
[87] MAKINO et al., *Gastroenterology*, **68**, 545 (1975).
[88] CAMPBELL et al., *Clin. chim. Acta*, **63**, 249 (1975).
[89] KAPLOWITZ et al., *J. Amer. med. Ass.*, **225**, 292 (1973); LARUSSO et al., *Amer. J. dig. Dis.*, **23**, 385 (1978); WILDGRUBE, H.J., *Inn. Med.*, **8**, 50 (1981).
[90] SCHWARZ et al., *Schweiz. med. Wschr.*, **105**, 533 (1975).
[91] DEMERS and HEPNER, *Clin. Chem.*, **22**, 602 (1976).
[92] PANVELIWALLA et al., *J. clin. Path.*, **23**, 309 (1970).
[93] LAATIKAINEN and HESSO, *Clin. chim. Acta*, **64**, 63 (1975).
[94] MATERN et al., *Clin. chim. Acta*, **72**, 39 (1976).
[95] KORMAN et al., *Proc. Mayo Clin.*, **50**, 76 (1975).
[96] SPARROW and GOTTO, *Ann. N. Y. Acad. Sci.*, **348**, 187 (1980).
[97] REYNOLDS, J.A., *Ann. N. Y. Acad. Sci.*, **348**, 174 (1980).
[98] FONTAINE and MALMENDIER, *Clin. chim. Acta*, **64**, 91 (1975).
[99] BRADLEY et al., *Ann. N. Y. Acad. Sci.*, **348**, 87 (1980).
[100] SCHONFELD and PFLEGER, *J. clin. Invest.*, **54**, 236 (1974).
[101] ASSMANN et al., *J. clin. Invest.*, **59**, 565 (1977).
[102] HEUCK et al., *Ärztl. Lab.*, **23**, 143 (1977).
[103] SCHONFELD et al., *J. clin. Invest.*, **53**, 1458 (1974).
[104] DURRINGTON et al., *Clin. chim. Acta*, **82**, 151 (1978).
[105] KASHYAP et al., *J. clin. Invest.*, **60**, 171 (1977).
[106] VAITH et al., *Biochim. biophys. Acta (Amst.)*, **541**, 234 (1978).
[107] GREEN et al., *J. clin. Invest.*, **64**, 233 (1979).
[108] ALBERS et al., *Atherosclerosis*, **39**, 395 (1981).
[109] BLUM et al., *J. clin. Invest.*, **66**, 1240 (1980).
[110] OLOFSSON et al., *Biochemistry*, **17**, 1032 (1978).
[111] STAPRANS et al., *Clin. chim. Acta*, **93**, 135 (1979); LISCH et al., *Klin. Wschr.*, **60**, 337 (1982).
[112] REMAN and VERMOND, *Clin. chim. Acta*, **87**, 387 (1978).
[113] GREEN et al., *J. clin. Invest.*, **65**, 911 (1980).
[114] CURRY et al., *Biochim. biophys. Acta (Amst.)*, **491**, 232 (1977).
[115] HAVEL et al., *J. clin. Invest.*, **66**, 1351 (1980).
[116] VAN BIERVLIET et al., *Acta paediat. scand.*, **70**, 851 (1981).
[117] POLZ et al., *Biochem. Med.*, **24**, 229 (1980).
[118] CURRY et al., *Clin. Chem.*, **27**, 543 (1981).
[119] FRUCHART et al., *Clin. Chem.*, **28**, 59 (1982).
[120] ROGIERS, V., *J. Lipid Res.*, **22**, 1 (1981).
[121] RALL et al., *J. biol. Chem.*, **257**, 4171 (1982).
[122] NORUM et al., *New Engl. J. Med.*, **306**, 1513 (1982).
[123] DOLPHIN et al., *Arteriosclerosis*, **1**, 392a (1981).
[124] BRUUSGAARD et al., *Clin. chim. Acta*, **93**, 1 (1979).
[125] MINDER et al., *Clin. chim. Acta*, **92**, 177 (1979).
[126] HEUBI et al., *J. Lab. clin. Med.*, **100**, 127 (1982).
[127] HILL et al., *Clin. chim. Acta*, **127**, 327 (1983).
[128] SAMUELSON et al., *Scand. J. Gastroent.*, **16**, 225 (1981).
[129] ASSMANN, G., *Klin. Wschr.*, **61**, 169 (1983).

Vitamins (for references see pages 133 and 134)

Phytofluene. Carotene precursor (in tomatoes and other plants).

Carotenes. Values vary over a wide range, depending on intake (extreme value 55 μmol/L at high spinach consumption[9]). What effect pregnancy[10,11,39] and oral contraceptives[5,39] have on the serum carotene level is not clear. In cord blood it amounts to about 25% of the maternal value[11,12]. In infants the carotene level is often elevated, probably owing to a large intake of milk and vegetables (carotene jaundice).

Vitamin A. The values given were determined either colorimetrically with trifluoroacetic acid or fluorimetrically. – Vitamin A in serum is mostly in the form of retinol (Table 1), which is bound to the retinol-binding protein (RBP)[13]. The rise of the vitamin A concentration in the serum during childhood parallels that in RBP concentration[14]. The synthesis of RBP is increased by estrogens. The serum of women using estrogen-containing oral contraceptives[5,17,39,40] and of pregnant women[15] therefore has an increased vitamin A concentration provided intake is adequate. In newborn infants the values are lower than in the mothers[11,12]. As long as the body stores have not been exhausted, the serum level of vitamin A remains fairly constant. – It is increased, in conjunction with an increased RBP concentration, in kidney diseases[7]; it is reduced in dietary protein deficiency[2], liver diseases[7], cystic fibrosis[14], and infections[16].

↑↓ See text on previous page and below	B Blood, P Plasma, S Serum, Erys Erythrocytes, Grcs Granulocytes, Lkcs Leukocytes, Lycs Lymphocytes, Plts Platelets	Amount of substance				Mass				Reference
		Unit	Mean	s	95% range (extreme range in brackets)	Unit	Mean	s	95% range (extreme range in brackets)	
↑ **Phytofluene**	S 20 subjects	nmol/L	85	57	(2–180)	μg/L	46	31	(1–98)	1
↑ **Carotenes** (β-carotene)	P(S) Cord blood, 174 newborn	μmol/L	0.37	–	0.13–0.60	μg/L	200	–	70–320	11
	– 634 children, 10–13 years	μmol/L	2.70	–	1.12–4.34	μg/L	1450	–	600–2330	6
	– 76 women	μmol/L	1.23	–	(0.75–2.8)	μg/L	660	–	(400–1500)	11
	– 15 children, 1–2 years	μmol/L	0.82	0.58	–	μg/L	439	313	–	2
	– 133 adults	μmol/L	1.58	–	(0.37–3.71)	μg/L	850	–	(200–1990)	3
	– 156 men, 1–80 years	μmol/L	1.59	0.53	0.53–2.65	μg/L	856	286	284–1430	4
	– 216 women, 1–80 years	μmol/L	1.75	0.64	0.47–3.03	μg/L	940	343	254–1630	4
↑ **Vitamin A** (retinol)	P(S) Cord blood, 174 newborn	μmol/L	0.77	–	0.24–1.30	μg/L	220	–	70–370	11
	– 634 children, 10–13 years	μmol/L	1.54	–	0.70–2.30	μg/L	440	–	200–670	6
	– 76 women	μmol/L	1.15	–	(0.90–2.40)	μg/L	330	–	(250–700)	11
	– 15 children, 1–2 years	μmol/L	0.78	0.33	–	μg/L	224	93	–	2
	– 133 adults	μmol/L	1.13	–	(0.72–1.64)	μg/L	324	–	(207–471)	3
	– 109 adults	μmol/L	1.75	0.55	0.65–2.85	μg/L	501	157	187–815	7
	– 165 men, 1–80 years	μmol/L	1.84	0.46	0.92–2.76	μg/L	527	132	263–791	4
	– 216 women, 1–80 years	μmol/L	1.76	0.44	0.88–2.64	μg/L	505	127	251–759	4
↓ **Vitamin D**	P 24 subjects	nmol/L	5.7	2.9	(2.1–12)	μg/L	2.2	1.1	(0.8–4.7)	18
↓ 25-Hydroxy-vitamin D	P(S) Cord blood, 13 newborn	nmol/L	40.4	16.2	–	μg/L	16.2	6.5	–	23
	– 14 newborn	nmol/L	35.9	8.5	(14–44)	μg/L	14.4	3.4	(5.5–17.7)	19
	– 20 children, 1–18 years	nmol/L	87.9	23.0	(52–137)	μg/L	35.2	9.2	(21–54.8)	19
	– 40 adults	nmol/L	68.1	29.5	(27–137)	μg/L	27.3	11.8	(11–55)	21
	– 20 women	nmol/L	34.7	11.2	–	μg/L	19.3	4.5	–	23
	– 25 subjects	nmol/L	40	9.7	(23–60)	μg/L	16	3.9	(9.1–23.9)	18
25-Hydroxychole-calciferol	S 11 adults	nmol/L	24.5	23.0	(10.3–91.5)	μg/L	9.8	9.2	(4.1–36.8)	22
25-Hydroxyergo-calciferol	S 11 adults	nmol/L	6.5	2.5	(3.8–11.0)	μg/L	2.7	1.0	(1.6–4.6)	22
↓ 1,25-Dihydroxy-vitamin D	P(S) 7 children	pmol/L	120	7	(110–140)	ng/L	51	3	(44–57)	24
	– 20 adults	pmol/L	70	22	–	ng/L	29	9	–	25
	– 78 adults	pmol/L	79	14	51–107	ng/L	33	6	21–45	20
24,25-Dihydroxy-vitamin D	S 14 newborn	nmol/L	4.3	1.4	(2.3–5.9)	μg/L	1.8	0.6	(0.97–2.45)	19
	– 20 children, 1–18 years	nmol/L	7.9	3.1	(3.2–14.7)	μg/L	3.3	1.3	(1.34–6.14)	19
	– 4 adults	nmol/L	5.0	1.2	–	μg/L	2.1	0.5	–	29
25,26-Dihydroxy-vitamin D	S 4 adults	nmol/L	1.9	1.0	–	μg/L	0.8	0.4	–	29

Table 1 *Vitamin A components in serum (10 women)*[8]

	Mean	s	Mean	s
	nmol/L		μg/L	
Retinol*	312	85.2	89.5	24.4
Retinol ester◊	195	72.4	102.5	38.0
Retinal	155	232	44.1	66.1
Retinoic acid	207	180	62.1	54.1

* The extraction method employed gives low retinol values.
◊ Calculated as retinol palmitate.

Vitamin A stores may be assumed to be exhausted when the plasma retinol level has dropped to 100 μg/L or less[196].

Vitamin D. Insofar as no pharmacological doses of ergocalciferol are administered, vitamin D is present for the most part as cholecalciferol formed in the skin. The physiological effects are not exerted by vitamin D itself but by its hydroxylated metabolites. Vitamin D and its metabolites are bound in the plasma to a specific protein that is identical with Gc-globulin[26].

25-Hydroxyvitamin D. The concentration in the plasma is dependent on intake of vitamin D and on the degree to which the skin is irradiated by the sun. It varies, therefore, with the time of year and is frequently low in elderly individuals and institutionalized persons[27]. It shows no characteristic change during pregnancy[23] or childhood[188], and it is only slightly lower in cord serum than in maternal serum[23,28]. Increased values are found in vitamin D intoxication; reduced values occur in the nephrotic syndrome, advanced renal failure, chronic liver diseases, severe small-bowel diseases, and during treatment with anticonvulsants[189–191].

1,25-Dihydroxyvitamin D. Formation of the vitamin D hormone in the kidney is controlled by a feedback mechanism involving parathyroid hormone and the calcium and phosphate concentrations in the plasma. The concentration is high during pregnancy and lactation[192]. Very high values are found in the first two years of life, and the values are higher throughout childhood than those of adults[188]. No 1,25-dihydroxyvitamin D is detectable in the plasma of nephrectomized patients; low values are found in vitamin D deficiency, chronic renal failure, and pseudohypoparathyroidism. Increased values occur in primary hyperparathyroidism associated with hypophosphatemia[189–191].

Vitamin E. The major portion of the vitamin E present in the blood is in the form of α-tocopherol (Table 2); besides the tocoph-

↑↓ See text on previous page and below	B Blood, P Plasma, S Serum, Erys Erythrocytes, Grcs Granulocytes, Lkcs Leukocytes, Lycs Lymphocytes, Plts Platelets	Amount of substance				Mass				Reference
		Unit	Mean	s	95% range (extreme range in brackets)	Unit	Mean	s	95% range (extreme range in brackets)	
↑ **Vitamin E** .... (α-tocopherol)	P(S) Cord blood, 174 newborn ..	µmol/L	7	–	(2–14)	mg/L	3	–	(1–6)	11
	– 630 children, 10–13 years	µmol/L	21	–	7–35	mg/L	9	–	3–15	6
	– 76 women	µmol/L	16	–	(14–28)	mg/L	7	–	(6–12)	11
	– 240 children, 3 days	µmol/L	8.6	2.1	(3.3–22)	mg/L	3.7	0.9	(1.4–9.4)	42
	– 140 children, 6 months	µmol/L	18.6	5.6	(9.3–33.4)	mg/L	8.0	2.4	(4.0–14.4)	42
	– 104 children, 12 months	µmol/L	16.7	4.9	(10.2–32.0)	mg/L	7.2	2.1	(4.4–13.8)	42
	– 71 men	µmol/L	24.6	5.8	13.0–36.2	mg/L	10.6	2.5	5.6–15.6	30
	– 61 women	µmol/L	24.1	6.3	11.6–36.7	mg/L	10.4	2.7	5.0–15.8	30
Ubiquinone .... (as ubiquinone-10)	S 11 adults	µmol/L	0.85	–	(0.46–1.33)	mg/L	0.73	–	(0.40–1.15)	45
	– 5 men	µmol/L	1.17	0.12	–	mg/L	1.01	0.10	–	197
	– 7 women	µmol/L	0.65	0.18	–	mg/L	0.56	0.16	–	197
↓ **Phylloquinone** .... (vitamin K_1)	P 30 adults	nmol/L	0.58	–	(0.22–1.46)	µg/L	0.26	–	(0.10–0.66)	203
	S 40 adults	nmol/L	5.8	–	2.0–17	µg/L	2.6	–	0.9–7.8	204
↓ **Thiamine**	B Cord blood, 174 newborn (a)	nmol/L	340	–	140–790	µg/L	91	–	37–210	11
	– 634 children, 10–13 years .. (a)	nmol/L	160	–	60–410	µg/L	42	–	16–110	6
	– 76 women .... (a)	nmol/L	120	–	(94–280)	µg/L	32	–	(25–75)	11
	– 138 subjects .... (a)	nmol/L	110	–	(75–280)	µg/L	28	–	(20–75)	46
	– 11 subjects .... (b)	nmol/L	324	62	–	µg/L	85.9	16.4	–	48
	– 20 adults .... (c)	nmol/L	174	39	–	µg/L	46.2	10.3	–	201
	P(S) 128 subjects .... (a)	nmol/L	79	–	(68–230)	µg/L	21	–	(18–62)	46
	– 11 subjects .... (b)	nmol/L	146	18	(127–180)	µg/L	38.7	4.8	(33.7–47.8)	48
	Erys 11 subjects .... (b)	nmol/L	535	147	–	µg/L	142	39.1	–	48
	– 6 adults .... (b)	nmol/L	300	17	(250–350)	µg/L	80	4.4	(66–94)	49
	Lkcs 6 adults .... (b)	µmol/L	2.54	0.15	(2.10–2.92)	µg/L	675	41	(558–774)	49

Table 2 *Tocols in plasma and erythrocytes*

	Plasma				Erythrocytes				Reference
	Mean	s	Mean	s	Mean	s	Mean	s	
	µmol/L		mg/L		µmol/L		mg/L		
α-Tocopherol	24.3	8.1	10.5	3.5	5.46	1.3	2.35	0.54	32
	13.7	0.91	5.91	0.39	4.10	0.93	1.77	0.40	33
β-Tocopherol	0.65	0.014	0.27	0.006	0.45	0.05	0.19	0.02	33
γ-Tocopherol	7.80	0.33	3.25	0.14	3.17	0.29	1.32	0.12	33
δ-Tocopherol	5.94	0.25	2.39	0.10	1.57	0.32	0.63	0.13	33

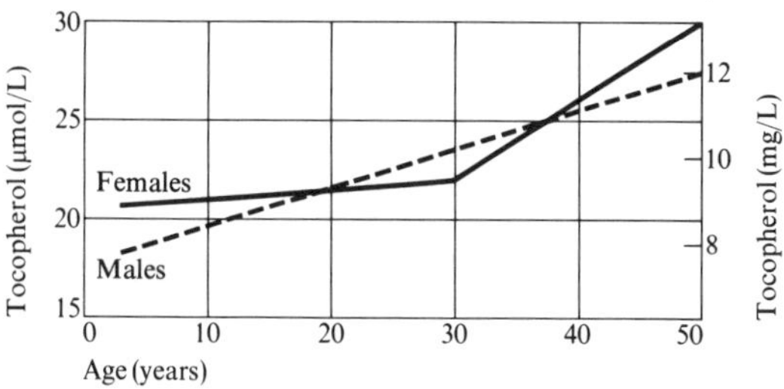

Fig. 1. Mean plasma tocopherol levels in males and females in relation to age[31].

erols, traces of tocotrienols are found[43]. In the plasma, α-tocopherol is partly associated with the β-lipoproteins; accordingly, variations in the tocopherol concentrations parallel the β-lipoprotein concentration[34,35]. During pregnancy the vitamin E level of the serum tends to rise[11,39]. It is low in the newborn, amounting to approximately 25% of the maternal value[11,41,200]. If there is adequate vitamin E intake, it rapidly rises during the first few months after birth[36] (see Fig. 1 for age-dependence). The effect of oral contraceptives on the vitamin E level is uncertain[5,39,40,44]. – The levels are lowered in abetalipoproteinemia[32], hyperthyroidism, cirrhosis of the liver, the malabsorption syndrome and cystic fibrosis[35], as also in hereditary spherocytosis[37] and β-thalassemia[38].

Phylloquinone. The values given were determined by high pressure liquid chromatography. Phylloquinone was not detected in cord plasma[203]. In adults no sex-dependence in plasma concentration was found[203].

Thiamine. The total thiamine values given were determined after hydrolysis of thiamine diphosphate with (a) *Ochromonas danica,* (b) by the thiochrome method, (c) by high pressure liquid chromatography. – The erythrocytes and leukocytes contain mainly thiamine diphosphate[49]; the plasma contains free thiamine as well (Table 3). Toward the end of pregnancy, the serum[50] or blood[11] level of thiamine is reduced; in the newborn it is about four times as high as the maternal value[11,50]. – A decrease of the thiamine diphosphate content of the erythrocytes – characteristic of thiamine deficiency – can be diagnosed by the transketolase test[51]. The blood level of thiamine is lowered in insulin-dependent diabetics[52].

Table 3 *Thiamine in blood*[47]

	Number	(Extreme range)
		nmol/L
Total	11	(150–260)
Free	11	(24–43)

Riboflavin. The total riboflavin values indicated were determined after hydrolysis of flavin adenine dinucleotide (FAD) and flavin mononucleotide (FMN) with (a) *Tetrahymena pyriformis*; (b) *Lactobacillus casei*; and (c) fluorimetrically. – Erythrocytes (Table 4) and leukocytes contain riboflavin mostly in the form of FAD and FMN. Neonatal serum has a higher concentration of free riboflavin and FMN but a lower concentration of FAD than maternal serum since the placenta is able to split FAD[58]. A decrease of the erythrocyte content of riboflavin – characteristic of riboflavin deficiency – can be diagnosed by the glutathione reductase test[54,59].

↑↓ See text on page 127 and on next page	B Blood, P Plasma, S Serum, Erys Erythrocytes, Grcs Granulocytes, Lkcs Leukocytes, Lycs Lymphocytes, Plts Platelets	Amount of substance				Mass				Reference
		Unit	Mean	s	95% range (extreme range in brackets)	Unit	Mean	s	95% range (extreme range in brackets)	
↑ **Riboflavin**	B Cord blood, 174 newborn . . (a)	nmol/L	845	–	361–1770	µg/L	318	–	136–665	11
	– 613 children, 10–13 years . . . (a)	nmol/L	385	–	150–960	µg/L	145	–	57–360	6
	– 76 women .... (a)	nmol/L	530	–	(265–1300)	µg/L	200	–	(100–500)	11
	– 798 subjects .... (a)	nmol/L	530	225	(265–1300)	µg/L	200	85	(100–500)	53
	S 798 subjects .... (a)	nmol/L	265	160	(100–640)	µg/L	100	60	(38–240)	53
	Erys 16 adults .... (b)	nmol/L	850	58	–	µg/L	320	22	–	54
	– 12 adults .... (c)	nmol/L	595	–	(478–697)	µg/L	224	–	(180–262)	55
	Lkcs 12 adults .... (c)	µmol/L	6.70	–	(6.03–7.78)	mg/L	2.52	–	(2.27–2.93)	55
	– 14 subjects .... (b)	µmol/10^{12}	7.17	1.38	(4.0–8.0)	mg/10^{12}	2.70	0.52	(1.5–3.0)	56
↓ **Vitamin B_6**	B 11 women .... (a)	...	...	...	...	µg/L	7.0	1.5	(5.9–11.5)	82
	– 11 women .... (b)	...	...	...	...	µg/L	10.2	3.0	(4.3–14.6)	82
	– 55 adults .... (c)	...	...	...	...	µg/L	37	6	(20–45)	61
	P(S) Cord blood, 174 newborn (c)	...	...	...	...	µg/L	45	–	21–96	11
	– 576 children, 10–13 years . . . (c)	...	...	...	...	µg/L	36	–	17–74	6
	– 76 women .... (c)	...	...	...	...	µg/L	41	–	(30–80)	11
	– 246 adults .... (c)	...	...	...	...	µg/L	44	16	(30–80)	61
	Erys 15 adults .... (c)	...	...	...	...	µg/L	20	3	(13–31)	61
Pyridoxal phosphate	B 3 children, 3 days	nmol/L	90	67	(34–164)	µg/L	22.2	16.5	(8.5–40.5)	205
	– 5 children, 10 days	nmol/L	108	87	(20–236)	µg/L	26.6	21.4	(4.9–58.3)	205
	– 13 children, 20–50 days	nmol/L	114	90	(24–286)	µg/L	28.1	22.2	(5.9–70.8)	205
	– 11 children, 1–10 years	nmol/L	61	52	(19–142)	µg/L	15.1	12.8	(4.7–35.2)	205
	– 9 subjects, 10–40 years	nmol/L	28	16	(14–62)	µg/L	7.0	4.0	(3.4–15.2)	205
	– 11 children, 3½–11 years	nmol/L	72	15	–	µg/L	17.8	3.6	–	62
	– 12 women	nmol/L	39.0	6.8	–	µg/L	9.63	1.67	–	68
	P(S) Cord blood, 10 newborn	nmol/L	56	42	–	µg/L	13.9	10.3	–	63
	– 10 children, 21 months	nmol/L	26	10	–	µg/L	6.35	2.51	–	64
	– 27 subjects	nmol/L	72	11	(55–93)	µg/L	17.8	2.71	(13.6–23.0)	198
	– 12 women, 20–34 years	nmol/L	68	15	–	µg/L	16.8	3.6	–	66
	– 7 women, 35–49 years	nmol/L	46	14	–	µg/L	11.4	3.4	–	66
	– 17 men, 20–34 years	nmol/L	75	22	–	µg/L	18.5	5.5	–	66
	– 7 men, 35–49 years	nmol/L	64	13	–	µg/L	15.8	3.3	–	66
	– 37 subjects, 1–73 years	nmol/L	47	61	–	µg/L	11.7	15.0	–	63
	Erys Cord blood, 9 newborn	nmol/10^{12}	5.9	3.8	–	µg/10^{12}	1.46	0.95	–	63
	– 37 subjects, 1–73 years	nmol/10^{12}	1.83	2.50	–	µg/10^{12}	0.452	0.617	–	63
	Lkcs Cord blood, 9 newborn	µmol/10^{12}	1.15	0.65	–	µg/10^{12}	285	160	–	63
	– 20 subjects, 1–73 years	µmol/10^{12}	1.09	0.78	–	µg/10^{12}	270	193	–	63
	– 20 adults	µmol/10^{12}	0.71	0.14	–	µg/10^{12}	176	35	–	67
	Lycs 20 adults	µmol/10^{12}	0.34	0.10	–	µg/10^{12}	84	25	–	67
	Grcs 20 adults	µmol/10^{12}	0.93	0.19	–	µg/10^{12}	229	46	–	67
	Plts 19 adults	nmol/10^{12}	13.0	2.9	–	µg/10^{12}	3.21	0.71	–	67
Pyridoxamine phosphate	S 27 subjects	nmol/L	15	5	(8–20)	µg/L	3.7	0.68	(2.1–4.9)	198
Pyridoxal	S 27 subjects	nmol/L	251	51	(170–364)	µg/L	42.0	8.45	(28.5–60.8)	198
Pyridoxamine	S 27 subjects	nmol/L	164	38	(93–203)	µg/L	27.6	6.36	(15.6–34.2)	198
Pyridoxic acid	P 6 adults	nmol/L	40	7	–	µg/L	7.3	1.3	–	193

Table 4 *Riboflavin in blood, serum, and erythrocytes*

	Blood[57]			Serum[55]			Erythrocytes[60]			
	Number	Mean	(Extreme range)	Number	Mean	(Extreme range)	Number	Mean	s	(Extreme range)
		nmol/L			nmol/L			nmol/L		
Total	18	177	(130–276)	13	87	(71–101)	–	–	–	–
Present as flavin adenine dinucleotide (FAD)	} 18	146	(114–189)	13	65	(49–82)	15	360	74	(237–478)
Present as flavin mononucleotide (FMN)	}			} 13	22	(8–35)	–	–	–	–
Free	–	–	–	}			–	–	–	–

↓See text below	B Blood, P Plasma, S Serum, Erys Erythrocytes, Grcs Granulocytes, Lkcs Leukocytes, Lycs Lymphocytes, Plts Platelets	Amount of substance				Mass				Reference
		Unit	Mean	s	95% range (extreme range in brackets)	Unit	Mean	s	95% range (extreme range in brackets)	
↓Nicotinic acid.....	B Cord blood, 174 newborn .. (a)	μmol/L	47	–	24–85	mg/L	5.8	–	3.0–10.5	11
	– 633 children, 10–13 years... (a)	μmol/L	23	–	15–38	mg/L	2.8	–	1.8–4.7	6
	– 76 women .... (a)	μmol/L	37	–	(28–57)	mg/L	4.5	–	(3.5–7.0)	11
	– 28 subjects .... (a)	μmol/L	–	–	(32–78)	mg/L	–	–	(3.9–9.6)	85
	– 46 women .... (b)	μmol/L	49.1	5.93	–	mg/L	6.05	0.730	–	84
	– 39 men.................... (b)	μmol/L	53.2	5.00	–	mg/L	6.55	0.615	–	84
	S 28 subjects .... (a)	μmol/L	–	–	(0.13–0.41)	μg/L	–	–	(16–50)	85
↓Pantothenic acid...............	B Cord blood, 174 newborn	μmol/L	3.6	–	1.8–6.8	μg/L	780	–	400–1480	11
	– 632 children, 10–13 years.......	μmol/L	1.3	–	0.66–2.6	μg/L	290	–	145–580	6
	– 76 women	μmol/L	1.1	–	(0.9–3.6)	μg/L	250	–	(200–800)	11
	– 367 adults	μmol/L	2.6	–	(1.0–8.7)	μg/L	560	–	(220–1900)	85
	– 14 women	μmol/L	2.86	0.94	–	μg/L	626	207	–	86
	– 20 adults	μmol/L	4.91	0.38	–	μg/L	1077	83	–	87
	P 9 women	μmol/L	0.90	0.52	–	μg/L	197	113	–	86
	Erys 9 women....................	μmol/L	5.62	1.12	–	μg/L	1232	246	–	86
Coenzyme A, total	Relative to protein: Plts 14 subjects..................	nmol/g	111	–	(94–159)	...	...	...	...	206

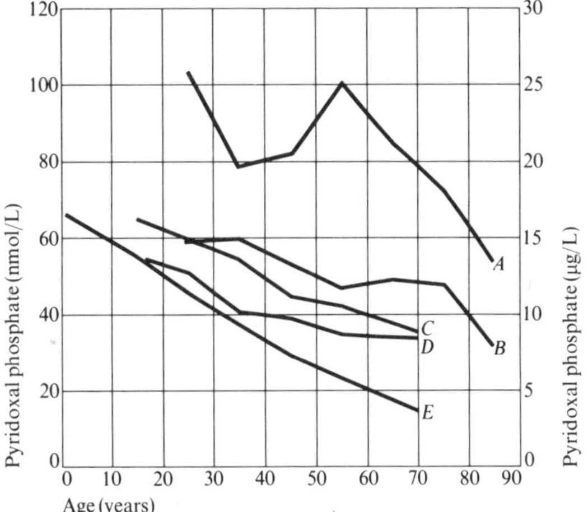

Fig. 2. Plasma pyridoxal phosphate in relation to age (*A* 203 men with vitamin B_6 supplement[69]; *B* 414 men without vitamin B_6 supplement[69]; *C* 194 men[83]; *D* 177 women[83]; *E* 59 subjects[70]).

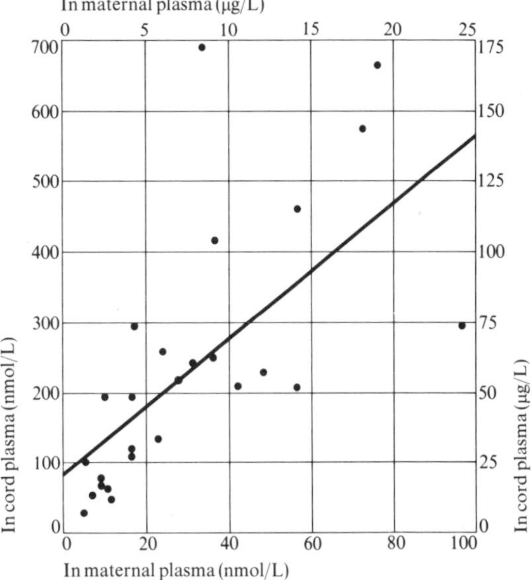

Fig. 3. Comparison of pyridoxal phosphate concentrations in plasma of mother and child[72].

Vitamin B_6. The values shown for total activity were determined with (a) *Saccharomyces uvarum (carlsbergensis)*; (b) *Streptococcus faecalis*; and (c) *Tetrahymena pyriformis*. The differences in total activity are due to the varying sensitivity of the microorganisms used for the determination. – The vitamin B_6 activity is reflected, above all, in pyridoxal[73], which is mostly present in the plasma as pyridoxal phosphate[74]. The pyridoxal phosphate in the plasma is bound to albumin and seems to be in equilibrium with a small amount of free pyridoxal[74]. The pyridoxal concentration in the plasma is strongly affected by the vitamin B_6 intake (Fig. 2). It decreases with increasing age (Fig. 2). It also decreases during pregnancy[68,71,75] insofar as the increased demand is not met by additional administration of vitamin B_6[72]. In cord blood the pyridoxal phosphate level is higher than in maternal blood (Fig. 3). According to most studies, the pyridoxal phosphate level is reduced in women using oral contraceptives[65,68,76]. – Pyridoxal phosphate deficiency is detectable in the aminotransferase test (transaminase test): aspartate aminotransferase or alanine aminotransferase activity in erythrocytes[63,69,77]. The pyridoxal phosphate concentration in the plasma is reduced in chronic uremia[78], chronic alcoholism[79,80], acute celiac disease[64,71], regional ileitis[71], rheumatoid arthritis[71,81], and during isoniazid therapy[79].

Nicotinic acid. The values shown for total activity were determined with (a) *Tetrahymena pyriformis*; (b) *Lactobacillus arabinosus*. – Nicotinic acid is almost exclusively a constituent of the erythrocytes, in which it is present in the form of nicotinamide adenine dinucleotides (NAD and NADP) (pages 104 and 105). The blood levels are slightly lowered toward the end of pregnancy[11].

Pantothenic acid. The values shown for total activity were determined – after hydrolysis – with the aid of *Lactobacillus plantarum*.

↓See text below	B Blood, P Plasma, S Serum, Erys Erythrocytes, Grcs Granulocytes, Lkcs Leukocytes, Lycs Lymphocytes, Plts Platelets	Amount of substance				Mass				Reference
		Unit	Mean	s	95% range (extreme range in brackets)	Unit	Mean	s	95% range (extreme range in brackets)	
↓**Biotin**	B Cord blood, 174 newborn .. (a)	nmol/L	3.4	–	2.0–5.1	ng/L	820	–	490–1240	11
	– 632 children, 10–13 years ... (a)	nmol/L	1.6	–	0.9–2.8	ng/L	380	–	220–680	6
	– 76 women .... (a)	nmol/L	2.4	–	(0.8–4.1)	ng/L	590	–	(200–1000)	11
	– 30 children, 2–27 months ... (b)	nmol/L	1.33	0.47	(0.60–2.27)	ng/L	324	114	(147–555)	90
	– 25 adults .... (b)	nmol/L	1.06	0.30	(0.49–1.73)	ng/L	258	74	(120–422)	90
	– 12 subjects .... (b)	nmol/L	6.0	2.6	(3.4–11)	ng/L	1470	630	(820–2700)	91
	P(S) 5 children, 6 months to 2 years .... (d)	nmol/L	1.26	0.50	(0.66–3.3)	ng/L	308	122	(160–810)	195
	– 30 adults .... (c)	nmol/L	35.6	3.7	–	ng/L	8690	900	–	199
↓**Vitamin B_{12}**	B Cord blood, 174 newborn .. (a)	pmol/L	370	–	87–1550	ng/L	500	–	118–2100	11
	– 635 children, 10–13 years ... (a)	pmol/L	136	–	40–500	ng/L	185	–	50–700	6
	– 76 women .... (a)	pmol/L	290	–	(70–600)	ng/L	390	–	(100–800)	11
	– 28 subjects .... (a)	pmol/L	–	–	(225–646)	ng/L	–	–	(305–875)	85
	– 28 subjects .... (b)	pmol/L	–	–	(343–1100)	ng/L	–	–	(465–1500)	85
	S Cord blood, 53 newborn.... (b)	pmol/L	231	–	(109–384)	ng/L	313	–	(148–521)	92
	– 15 children, 1–3 years ...... (b)	pmol/L	187	51	(74–310)	ng/L	253	69	(100–420)	93
	– 25 children, 3–14 years ..... (b)	pmol/L	275	74	(148–408)	ng/L	373	100	(201–553)	93
	– 36 women .... (b)	pmol/L	335	–	–	ng/L	454	–	–	92
	– 166 women .... (b)	pmol/L	284	125	–	ng/L	385	169	–	105
	– 30 women .... (c)	pmol/L	401	175	–	ng/L	543	237	–	105
	– 74 adults .... (c)	pmol/L	425	–	(162–907)	ng/L	576	–	(220–1230)	94
	– 165 men .... (c)	pmol/L	309	92	(136–753)	ng/L	419	125	(185–1020)	95
	– 55 women .... (c)	pmol/L	343	91	(155–668)	ng/L	465	124	(210–905)	95
	P 29 adults .... (a)	pmol/L	257	98	(140–520)	ng/L	349	133	(190–700)	96
	Erys 9 newborn .... (b)	pmol/L	136	27	(106–185)	ng/L	184	36	(144–250)	97
	– 256 subjects .... (b)	pmol/L	114	26	(60–210)	ng/L	155	35	(80–280)	97
	– 29 adults .... (a)	pmol/L	117	23	(77–170)	ng/L	158	31	(105–230)	96
	– 10 subjects .... (a)	pmol/L	143	–	(68–204)	ng/L	194	–	(92–276)	98
	– 10 subjects .... (c)	pmol/L	156	–	(81–218)	ng/L	211	–	(110–296)	98
	Lkcs 8 adults .... (a)	nmol/10^{12}	2.83	–	(0.75–5.68)	µg/10^{12}	3.84	–	(1.02–7.70)	99
	Plts 16 adults .... (a)	nmol/L	0.94	0.27	(0.4–1.5)	µg/L	1.27	0.37	(0.6–2.1)	100

Table 5 *Pantothenic acid in plasma and erythrocytes*[88]

	Number	Plasma		Erythrocytes	
		Mean	s	Mean	s
		µmol/L			
Total	18	0.59	0.05	7.80	0.40
Bound	18	0.36	0.05	7.50	0.40
Free	18	0.23	0.05	0.23	0.05

Table 6 *Normal range of individual cobalamins in plasma*[207]

	pmol/L	ng/L
Methylcobalamin	97–450	130–600
Hydroxocobalamin	15–74	20–100
Cyanocobalamin.....................	0–40	0–50
Deoxyadenosylcobalamin.............	25–130	40–210
Vitamin B_{12}, total	...	180–950

The differences in the normal values are probably due in part to the methods of hydrolysis employed. – In the erythrocytes pantothenic acid is predominantly present in bound form as coenzyme A (Table 5). During pregnancy the concentration in the blood does not change significantly; it is higher in neonatal blood than in maternal blood[11,86]. – Blood values are increased in cases of fatty liver and acute cirrhosis[89]; they are decreased in patients with rheumatoid arthritis[87].

Biotin. The values cited were determined with (a) *Ochromonas danica*; (b) *Lactobacillus plantarum*; (c) radioimmunoassay; and (d) radioisotope dilution. – During pregnancy, the concentration in the blood does not change appreciably; it is higher in neonatal than in maternal blood[11].

Vitamin B_{12}. The values given for total activity (calculated as cyanocobalamin) were determined (a) with *Euglena gracilis*; (b) with *Lactobacillus leichmannii*; and (c) radioisotopically by saturation analysis with ^{57}Co-cyanocobalamin. – *Escherichia coli* and *Ochromonas malhamensis* are likewise used for the determination of vitamin B_{12}[85]. The different microorganisms respond differently to individual substances possessing vitamin B_{12} activity[85]; moreover, their growth can be inhibited or promoted by certain substances in the blood (e.g. antibiotics)[104].

Values that have been obtained by the radioisotope methods in current use (in the form of assay kits[106]) are higher than those obtained by microbiological procedures since the serum contains vitamin B_{12} variants that are microbiologically inactive[94].

In the serum vitamin B_{12} is present mostly as methylcobalamin (Table 6). The serum cobalamins are transported in protein-bound form[107]. Transcobalamin I transports 70–90% of endogenous vitamin B_{12}, transcobalamin II 10–20%, and transcobalamin III 0 to 10%[108]; by contrast, vitamin B_{12} freshly absorbed from the intestine is at first transported mainly by transcobalamin II[109]. Free vitamin B_{12}-binding capacity (Table 7) is represented to the extent of 80% in the transcobalamin II concentration[108]. The vitamin B_{12} concentration in erythrocytes is lower than that in serum, and there is no relation between the two concentrations[97]. During pregnancy the blood[11], serum[92,110], and erythrocyte[111] values decline. They are higher in the blood[11], serum[92], and erythrocytes[97] of the newborn than in maternal blood. The serum concentration is reduced

↓ See text below	B Blood, P Plasma, S Serum, Erys Erythrocytes, Grcs Granulocytes, Lkcs Leukocytes, Lycs Lymphocytes, Plts Platelets	Amount of substance				Mass				Reference
		Unit	Mean	*s*	95% range (extreme range in brackets)	Unit	Mean	*s*	95% range (extreme range in brackets)	
↓ **Folic acid**	B 150 adults .... (a)	nmol/L	185	54	(104–352)	µg/L	85.2	25	(47.7–162)	115
	P(S) Cord blood, 174 newborn (a)	nmol/L	39	–	12–140	µg/L	18	–	5.5–66	11
	– 638 children, 10–13 years... (a)	nmol/L	11	–	4–28	µg/L	4.9	–	1.9–13.0	6
	– 76 women .... (a)	nmol/L	17	–	(11–52)	µg/L	8	–	(5–24)	11
	– 150 adults .... (a)	nmol/L	20	9.1	(5.0–61)	µg/L	9.2	4.2	(2.3–28.0)	115
	– 118 men .... (a)	nmol/L	9.6	–	(2.4–24)	µg/L	4.4	–	(1.1–11.0)	116
	– 120 women .... (a)	nmol/L	9.6	–	(2.6–26)	µg/L	4.4	–	(1.2–12.0)	116
	– 95 women .... (a)	nmol/L	11	–	5.20–23.2	µg/L	5.1	–	2.39–10.7	117
	– 81 subjects .... (a)	nmol/L	11	–	(4.6–28)	µg/L	4.9	–	(2.1–13)	118
	– 20 subjects .... (b)	nmol/L	17.9	4.2	–	µg/L	8.24	1.92	–	121
	– 135 adults .... (b)	nmol/L	13	8	(3.3–35)	µg/L	6.1	3.6	(1.5–16.0)	119
	– 59 subjects .... (b)	nmol/L	31	8	(15–57)	µg/L	14	3.7	(6.9–26)	120
	Erys Cord blood, 20 newborn (a)	nmol/L	735	202	–	µg/L	338	93	–	123
	– 107 adults .... (a)	nmol/L	453	131	(259–895)	µg/L	208	60	(118–411)	115
	– 114 men .... (a)	nmol/L	333	–	(67–870)	µg/L	153	–	(31–400)	116
	– 117 women .... (a)	nmol/L	320	–	(85–780)	µg/L	147	–	(39–360)	116
	– 95 women .... (a)	nmol/L	470	–	255–870	µg/L	216	–	117–400	117
	– 81 subjects .... (a)	nmol/L	418	–	(170–1020)	µg/L	192	–	(80–470)	118
	Lkcs 7 subjects .... (a)	µmol/L	1.19	–	(0.57–2.24)	µg/L	547	–	(263–1028)	124
	Plts 11 adults .... (a)	nmol/L	150	80	(90–370)	µg/L	67	36	(40–170)	100

Table 7 *Vitamin B_{12} concentration and free vitamin B_{12}-binding capacity of serum*

Subjects	Vitamin B_{12}			Free vitamin B_{12}-binding capacity			Reference
	Mean	*s*	(Extreme range)	Mean	*s*	(Extreme range)	
	pmol/L						
9 men	281	21.3	(192–387)	631	190	(401–947)	102
9 women	288	65.0	(184–392)	859	283	(451–1324)	102
28 adults	328	181	–	1184	285	–	103

under the action of oral contraceptives[40,105,110]. – The lower limit of normal serum concentrations of vitamin B_{12} is 150 pmol/L (200 ng/L)[112]. Values below 75 pmol/L (100 ng/L) point to a severe vitamin B_{12} deficiency such as occurs in intrinsic-factor deficiency (pernicious anemia, atrophy of gastric mucosa), in intestinal malabsorption, and on a diet lacking vitamin B_{12}[101,112]. Increased serum values are found in myeloproliferative diseases (myeloid leukemia, primary polycythemia)[101,103], in serious liver diseases[101], and in some children with kwashiorkor[113]. The vitamin B_{12} concentration in the erythrocytes is reduced in pernicious anemia, in untreated hypochromic anemia, in folic-acid deficiency and in primary polycythemia[96,97,114].

Folic acid. The values shown for total activity (calculated as methyltetrahydrofolic acid) were determined (a) with *Lactobacillus casei*; (b) radioisotopically by saturation analysis with ^{3}H-pteroylmonoglutamate or ^{3}H-methyltetrahydrofolate. – *Streptococcus faecalis* and *Pediococcus cerevisiae* are also used for folic-acid assays[125]. The different microorganisms react differently to the individual substances possessing folic-acid activity[85], in addition to which their growth can be inhibited by certain substances in the blood (e.g. antibiotics)[126]. Microbiological methods tend to yield higher values than the radioisotope techniques available as assay kits[127].

The predominant compound in the serum is methyltetrahydrofolic acid[128], while its conjugates (which need to be hydrolyzed by appropriate pretreatment of the sample before the assay[130]) predominate in erythrocytes[129]. In the serum, about one-half of the folic-acid activity is loosely bound to nonspecific proteins[131]. There is, in addition, a specific protein which strongly binds folic acid, having a binding capacity of 0.23–0.97 nmol/L (100 ng/L to 350 ng/L)[132]. The methyltetrahydrofolic acid conjugates in the erythrocytes are bound to protein[133]. More than 95% of the folic acid in the blood is contained in the erythrocytes. In the adult, sex and age do not affect the folic-acid concentrations in the serum[116,134] or in the erythrocytes[116]. During pregnancy the serum level of folic acid falls[11,122,135,136] unless adequate folic-acid supplements are supplied. The folic-acid concentration in the erythrocytes is also reduced in some pregnant women[158]. Both in the serum[11,50,122,137] and in the erythrocytes[122,137] of the newborn the folic-acid levels are appreciably higher than those in maternal blood. The decrease of the folic-acid concentration in the serum[137–139] and in the erythrocytes[137,138] during the first few postnatal months suggests a negative folic-acid balance. According to some studies, the folic-acid concentration in the serum and erythrocytes is reduced under the action of oral contraceptives[40,110,141], and is reduced further during an ensuing pregnancy[140]. In other studies oral contraceptives were not associated with any change in

Table 8 *Interpretation of serum folic acid levels**

nmol/L	µg/L	
<7	<3	Low
7–11	3–4.9	Probably low
11.5–15.5	5–6.9	Indeterminate
16–36	7–15.9	Normal
>36	>16	High

*For the Lactobacillus casei method[147] as well as for the radioassay[148].

↓ See text below	B Blood, P Plasma, S Serum, Erys Erythrocytes, Grcs Granulocytes, Lkcs Leukocytes, Lycs Lymphocytes, Plts Platelets	Amount of substance				Mass				Reference
		Unit	Mean	s	95% range (extreme range in brackets)	Unit	Mean	s	95% range (extreme range in brackets)	
↓ **Biopterin**	B 10 adults	nmol/L	17	2.5	–	μg/L	4.0	0.60	–	159
	S 114 adults	nmol/L	7.6	2.7	–	μg/L	1.81	0.64	–	159
	– 53 adults	nmol/L	6.8	2.4	–	μg/L	1.61	0.57	–	202
	Erys 10 adults	nmol/L	33	7.3	–	μg/L	7.8	1.73	–	159
Neopterin	S 53 adults	nmol/L	15.4	4.1	–	μg/L	8.76	1.04	–	202
↓ **Ascorbic acid**	B 284 children, 3–6 years	μmol/L	88.6	22.4	(21–171)	mg/L	15.6	3.95	(3.7–30.2)	161
	– 10 adults	μmol/L	60.8	15.9	–	mg/L	10.7	2.8	–	194
	– 11 men	μmol/L	28.8	–	(12.7–50.0)	mg/L	5.07	–	(2.24–8.80)	162
	– 7 women	μmol/L	50.2	–	(29.4–72.7)	mg/L	8.84	–	(5.17–12.8)	162
	P(S) Cord blood, 174 newborn	μmol/L	51	–	11–125	mg/L	9	–	2–22	11
	– 558 children, 10–13 years	μmol/L	34	–	0–85	mg/L	6	–	0–15	6
	– 76 women	μmol/L	45	–	(23–68)	mg/L	8	–	(4–12)	11
	– 96 children, 6 months	μmol/L	44	11	(23–87)	mg/L	7.7	1.9	(4.0–15.4)	42
	– 72 children, 1 year	μmol/L	41	12	(24–83)	mg/L	7.3	2.2	(4.2–14.6)	42
	– 11 men	μmol/L	27.0	–	(11.1–49.7)	mg/L	4.76	–	(1.96–8.76)	162
	– 7 women	μmol/L	50.9	–	(35.4–80.1)	mg/L	8.97	–	(6.24–14.1)	162
	Erys 65 women	μmol/L	68	43	–	mg/L	12.0	7.5	–	40
	– 30 children, 6 months to 14 years	μmol/10^{12}	5.84	1.07	–	mg/10^{12}	1.03	0.188	–	163
	Lkcs 63 women	mmol/kg	1.46	0.82	–	mg/kg	257	145	–	168
	– 30 children, 6 months to 14 years	mmol/10^{12}	1.44	0.26	–	mg/10^{12}	254	46.3	–	163
	– 18 men	mmol/10^{12}	0.56	0.14	–	mg/10^{12}	99	25	–	164
	– 26 women	mmol/10^{12}	0.79	0.29	–	mg/10^{12}	139	51	–	164
	– 31 women	mmol/10^{12}	2.2	1.6	–	mg/10^{12}	390	280	–	167
	– 25 subjects, 18–45 years	mmol/10^{12}	2.0	–	1.2–3.0	mg/10^{12}	350	–	210–530	165
	– 50 subjects, 60–91 years	mmol/10^{12}	0.76	–	0.11–2.0	mg/10^{12}	134	–	20–360	165
	Plts 10 women	mmol/kg	1.48	0.62	–	mg/kg	260	110	–	167
	– 18 men	μmol/10^{12}	19.5	6.5	–	mg/10^{12}	3.44	1.15	–	164
	– 26 women	μmol/10^{12}	18.5	6.6	–	mg/10^{12}	3.26	1.17	–	164

folic-acid concentration[142]. A diet of low folic-acid content causes the serum level of folic acid to decline within a few weeks, whereas the concentration in the erythrocytes changes more slowly[143]. The erythrocyte value is therefore a better indicator of the body stores of folic acid than the serum value[144,145]. The differences between the individual assay methods need to be taken into account[119,146] (Table 8). – The serum level of folic acid is lowered when the dietary folic-acid intake is inadequate, in iron deficiency[145,149,150], in idiopathic steatorrhea[151], and in patients being treated with anticonvulsants[151,152]; it is raised in vitamin B_{12} deficiency[150,151,153] and under the action of ethanol[154,155]. The folic-acid concentration in the erythrocytes is reduced after prolonged dietary folic-acid deficiency, in vitamin B_{12} deficiency[115,150,153] and in celiac disease[156]; it tends to be higher, on the other hand, in iron deficiency[150,157].

Biopterin. The values given were determined with the aid of *Crithidia fasciculata.* – Biopterin is presumed to be present in the serum as 7,8-dihydrobiopterin[159]. – The serum biopterin level is raised in children with phenylketonuria[158] and in patients with uremia[159,160].

Ascorbic acid. The values cited represent the total concentration (substances determined by the 2,4-dinitrophenylhydrazine method). In plasma, the major portion of these substances consists of ascorbic acid, besides which there is a small proportion of dehydroascorbic acid (~5%) and a variable proportion of 2,3-dioxogulonic acid[173,174]. As ascorbic-acid intake increases, the concentrations in blood[175,176], plasma (Fig. 4), and in the leukocytes[166] increase. At a content of 3.5 mmol/10^{12} (600 mg/10^{12}) the leukocytes are saturated with ascorbic acid (Fig. 5)[166]. There are indications that the ascorbic-acid concentration in the blood[162] as well as in the plasma[162,166,177,178] and in the leukocytes[177–179] of women is higher than that in the plasma or leukocytes of men, and that the

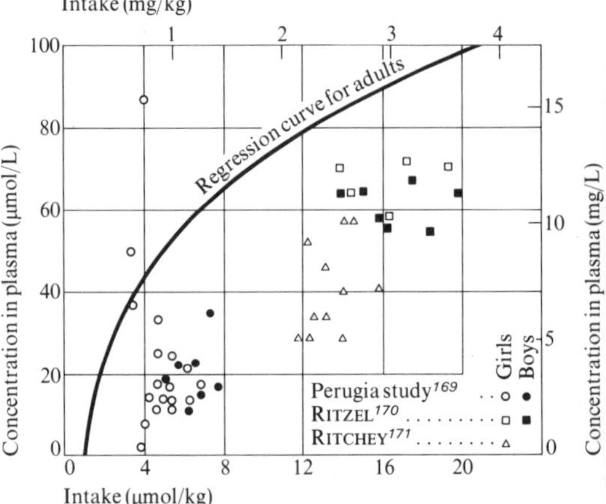

Fig. 4. Plasma levels of ascorbic acid in children and adults as a function of ascorbic-acid intake relative to body mass.

plasma concentration (and perhaps also the leukocyte concentration[165,179,180]) in the adult decreases with increasing age[166,177]. The diurnal fluctuations of the plasma ascorbic acid may be related to the fluctuations of the corticosteroid concentration[181]. In women, certain variations occur in the course of the cycle but they are difficult to interpret[174,182]. During pregnancy the plasma level of ascorbic acid[11] as well as the leukocyte level[167] tends to be low-

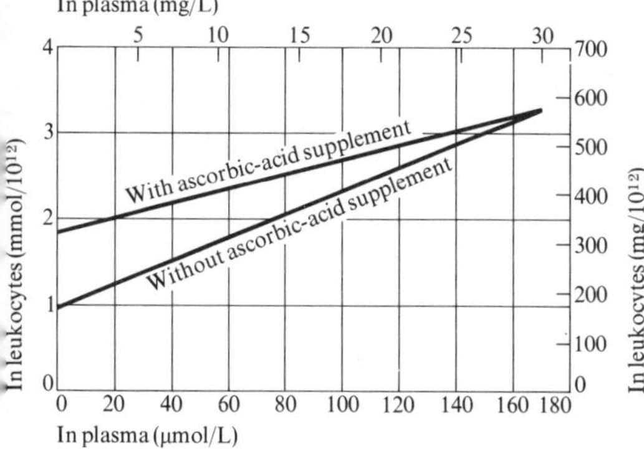

Fig. 5. Regression lines calculated from ascorbic-acid concentrations in plasma and in leukocytes of adults receiving, and adults not receiving, ascorbic-acid supplements[166].

ered. The concentration in the plasma[11,184] and leukocytes[184] of neonates is higher than that in the mothers. There have been reports of reduced ascorbic-acid concentrations in the blood[175,185], plasma[5,177,185], and leukocytes[5,177] of smokers as well as in the plasma[5,39,40,174,186], erythrocytes[40], and leukocytes[5,167,186], and platelets[167,186] of women using oral contraceptives. On a diet lacking ascorbic acid the plasma concentration drops to values below 3 μmol/L within 4 weeks, while the leukocyte content changes more slowly, reaching values around 0.1 mmol/kg after 20 weeks[187]. – In diseases affecting the leukocytes, the ascorbic-acid content of the leukocytes is frequently low[183].

References

[1] BUBB and MURPHY, *Clin. chim. Acta,* **48**, 329 (1973).
[2] SMITH et al., *Amer. J. clin. Nutr.,* **26**, 973 (1973).
[3] CAMPBELL and TONKS, *Brit. J. Ophthal.,* **46**, 151 (1962).
[4] KASPER, H., *Int. Z. Vitaminforsch.,* **38**, 142 (1968).
[5] YEUNG, D. L., *Amer. J. clin. Nutr.,* **29**, 1216 (1976).
[6] BAKER et al., *Amer. J. clin. Nutr.,* **20**, 850 (1967).
[7] SMITH and GOODMAN, *J. clin. Invest.,* **50**, 2426 (1971).
[8] ROBBOY et al., *Amer. J. clin. Nutr.,* **27**, 362 (1974).
[9] CRISP and STONEHILL, *Postgrad. med. J.,* **43**, 721 (1967).
[10] PULLIAM et al., *Proc. Soc. exp. Biol. (N. Y.),* **109**, 913 (1962).
[11] BAKER et al., *Amer. J. clin. Nutr.,* **28**, 59 (1975).
[12] LÜBKE and FINKBEINER, *Int. Z. Vitaminforsch.,* **29**, 45 (1958).
[13] GLOVER, J., *Vitam. and Horm.,* **31**, 1 (1973).
[14] SMITH et al., *J. Lab. clin. Med.,* **80**, 423 (1972).
[15] GAL and PARKINSON, *Amer. J. clin Nutr.,* **27**, 688 (1974).
[16] KAGAN and GOODHART, in WOHL and GOODHART (Eds.), *Modern Nutrition in Health and Disease,* 3rd ed., Lea & Febiger, Philadelphia, 1964, page 341.
[17] WYNN, V., *Lancet,* **1**, 561 (1975).
[18] JONES, G., *Clin. Chem.,* **24**, 287 (1978).
[19] WEISMAN et al., *J. Pediat.,* **91**, 904 (1977).
[20] HUGHES et al., *J. clin. Invest.,* **58**, 61 (1976).
[21] HADDAD and CHYU, *J. clin. Endocr.,* **33**, 992 (1971).
[22] POSKITT et al., *Brit. med. J.,* **1**, 221 (1979).
[23] DENT and GUPTA, *Lancet,* **2**, 1057 (1975).
[24] ROSEN et al., *J. clin. Endocr.,* **45**, 457 (1977).
[25] EISMAN et al., *Science,* **193**, 1021 (1976).
[26] IMAWARI and GOODMAN, *J. clin. Invest.,* **59**, 432 (1977).
[27] HADDAD and STAMP, *Amer. J. Med.,* **57**, 57 (1974); MCLAUGHLIN et al., *Lancet,* **1**, 536 (1974); MORRIS and PEACOCK, *Clin. chim. Acta,* **72**, 383 (1976); LESTER et al., *Lancet,* **1**, 979 (1977).
[28] HILLMAN and HADDAD, *J. Pediat.,* **84**, 742 (1974).
[29] HORST et al., *J. Lab. clin. Med.,* **93**, 277 (1979).
[30] BIERI et al., *Proc. Soc. exp. Biol. (N. Y.),* **117**, 131 (1964).
[31] LEWIS et al., *Amer. J. clin. Nutr.,* **26**, 136 (1973).
[32] BIERI et al., *J. Lipid Res.,* **11**, 118 (1970).
[33] LOVELADY, H. G., *J. Chromatogr.,* **85**, 81 (1973).
[34] DAVIES et al., *Clin. chim. Acta,* **24**, 431 (1969).
[35] KATER et al., *Amer. J. clin. Nutr.,* **23**, 913 (1970).
[36] GOLDBLOOM, R. B., *Pediatrics,* **32**, 36 (1963); HASHIM and ASFOUR, *Amer. J. clin. Nutr.,* **21**, 7 (1968).
[37] FUJII et al., *J. Vitaminol.,* **18**, 84 (1972).
[38] ZANNOS-MARIOLEA et al., *Brit. J. Haemat.,* **26**, 193 (1974).
[39] HORWITT et al., *Amer. J. clin. Nutr.,* **28**, 403 (1975).
[40] SMITH et al., *Amer. J. clin. Nutr.,* **28**, 371 (1975).
[41] LEONARD et al., *Amer. J. clin. Nutr.,* **25**, 480 (1972).
[42] VOBECKY et al., *Amer. J. clin. Nutr.,* **29**, 766 (1976).
[43] CHOW, C. K., *Amer. J. clin. Nutr.,* **28**, 756 (1975).
[44] BRIGGS and BRIGGS, *Amer. J. clin. Nutr.,* **28**, 436 (1975).
[45] BIERI, J. G., *Nutr. Rev.,* **21**, 129 (1963).
[46] BAKER et al., *Amer. J. clin. Nutr.,* **14**, 197 (1964).
[47] HAUGEN, H. N., *Scand. J. clin. Lab. Invest.,* **13**, 50 (1961).
[48] NIWA et al., *Amer. J. clin. Nutr.,* **28**, 1105 (1975).
[49] BURCH et al., *J. biol. Chem.,* **198**, 477 (1952).
[50] BAKER et al., *Proc. Soc. exp. Biol. (N. Y.),* **103**, 321 (1960).
[51] BRIN, M., *J. Amer. med. Ass.,* **187**, 762 (1964); SAUBERLICH, H. E., *Amer. J. clin. Nutr.,* **20**, 528 (1967); RITZEL, G., *Schweiz. med. Wschr.,* **98**, 1118 (1968).
[52] HAUGEN, H. N., *Scand. J. clin. Lab. Invest.,* **16**, 260 (1964).
[53] BAKER et al., *Amer. J. clin. Nutr.,* **19**, 17 (1966).
[54] BAMJI, M. S., *Clin. chim. Acta,* **26**, 263 (1969).
[55] BURCH et al., *J. biol. Chem.,* **175**, 457 (1948).
[56] PRAGER et al., *J. Lab. clin. Med.,* **53**, 926 (1959).
[57] KERPPOLA, W., *Acta med. scand.,* **153**, 33 (1955).
[58] LUST et al., *J. clin. Invest.,* **33**, 38 (1954).
[59] SAUBERLICH et al., *Amer. J. clin. Nutr.,* **25**, 756 (1972); TILLOTSON and BAKER, *Amer. J. clin. Nutr.,* **25**, 425 (1972); SCHORAH and MESSENGER, *Int. Z. Vitaminforsch.,* **45**, 39 (1974).
[60] FLATZ and SIMMERSBACH, *Klin. Wschr.,* **48**, 1071 (1970).
[61] BAKER et al., *Amer. J. clin. Nutr.,* **18**, 123 (1966).
[62] BHAGAVAN et al., *Pediatrics,* **55**, 437 (1975).
[63] HAMFELT, A., *Clin. chim. Acta,* **16**, 19 (1967).
[64] REINKEN et al., *Amer. J. clin. Nutr.,* **29**, 750 (1976).
[65] REINKEN and DAPUNT, *Int. Z. Vitaminforsch.,* **44**, 75 (1974).
[66] DEVITA et al., *Amer. J. clin. Nutr.,* **24**, 835 (1971).
[67] MAHUREN and COBURN, *Amer. J. clin. Nutr.,* **27**, 521 (1974).
[68] SHANE and CONTRACTOR, *Amer. J. clin. Nutr.,* **28**, 739 (1975).
[69] ROSE et al., *Amer. J. clin. Nutr.,* **29**, 847 (1976).
[70] HAMFELT, A., *Clin. chim. Acta,* **10**, 48 (1964).
[71] ANDERSON et al., *J. clin. Path.,* **23**, 232 (1970).
[72] LUMENG et al., *Amer. J. clin. Nutr.,* **29**, 1376 (1976).
[73] DURKÓ et al., *Clin. chim. Acta,* **49**, 407 (1973).
[74] ANDERSON et al., *Nature,* **250**, 502 (1974); LUMENG et al., *J. Lab. clin. Med.,* **84**, 334 (1974).
[75] HAMFELT and HAHN, *Clin. chim. Acta,* **25**, 91 (1979); HAMFELT and TUVEMO, *Clin. chim. Acta,* **41**, 287 (1972).
[76] LUMENG et al., *Amer. J. clin. Nutr.,* **27**, 326 (1974).
[77] JACOBS et al., *Amer. J. clin. Nutr.,* **21**, 502 (1968); SAUBERLICH et al., *Amer. J. clin. Nutr.,* **25**, 629 (1972).
[78] GÄNG et al., *Klin. Wschr.,* **53**, 335 (1975); STONE et al., *Amer. J. clin. Nutr.,* **28**, 950 (1975).
[79] HINES and LOVE, *J. Lab. clin. Med.,* **73**, 343 (1969).
[80] LUMENG and LI, *J. clin. Invest.,* **53**, 693 (1974).
[81] SCHUMACHER et al., *Amer. J. clin. Nutr.,* **28**, 1200 (1975).
[82] MILLER et al., *Amer. J. clin. Nutr.,* **28**, 846 (1975).
[83] DAVIS et al., *J. clin. Path.,* **26**, 871 (1973).
[84] KARLIN, R., *C. R. Soc. Biol. (Paris),* **153**, 1044 (1959).
[85] BAKER and SOBOTKA, *Advanc. clin. Chem.,* **5**, 173 (1962).
[86] SRINIVASAN and BELAVADY, *Int. Z. Vitaminforsch.,* **46**, 433 (1976).
[87] BARTON-WRIGHT and ELLIOTT, *Lancet,* **2**, 862 (1963).
[88] ELLESTAD-SAYED et al., *Amer. J. clin. Nutr.,* **29**, 1333 (1976).
[89] LEEVY et al., *J. clin. Invest.,* **39**, 1005 (1960).
[90] BHAGAVAN and COURSIN, *Amer. J. clin. Nutr.,* **20**, 903 (1967).
[91] BAUGH et al., *Amer. J. clin. Nutr.,* **21**, 173 (1968).
[92] TEMPERLEY et al., *J. Obstet. Gynaec. Brit. Cwlth,* **75**, 511 (1968).
[93] RUDOBIELSKA et al., *Helv. paediat. Acta,* **27**, 617 (1972).
[94] KOLHOUSE et al., *New Engl. J. Med.,* **299**, 785 (1978).
[95] WAGSTAFF and BROUGHTON, *Brit. J. Haemat.,* **21**, 581 (1971).
[96] OMER et al., *Blood,* **35**, 73 (1970).
[97] HARRISON, R. J., *J. clin. Path.,* **23**, 219 (1970).
[98] KELLY and HERBERT, *Blood,* **29**, 139 (1967).
[99] KIDD and THOMAS, *Brit. J. Haemat.,* **8**, 64 (1962).
[100] WEISS et al., *Blood,* **31**, 258 (1968).
[101] LINNELL et al., *Clin. Sci.,* **40**, 1 (1971).
[102] LOW-BEER et al., *Brit. med. J.,* **4**, 160 (1968).
[103] GILBERT et al., *Ann. intern. Med.,* **71**, 719 (1969).
[104] LIE et al., *J. clin. Path.,* **22**, 554 (1969).
[105] SHOJANIA and WYLIE, *Amer. J. Obstet. Gynec.,* **135**, 129 (1979).
[106] KAMPA and HUNDERTMARK, *Clin. chim. Acta,* **59**, 191 (1975).
[107] HALL, C. A., *Ann. intern. Med.,* **75**, 297 (1971); ALLEN, R. H., *Progr. Hemat.,* **9**, 57 (1975).
[108] ALLEN, R. H., *Brit. J. Haemat.,* **33**, 161 (1976).
[109] HALL, C. A., *J. clin. Invest.,* **56**, 1125 (1975).
[110] WERTALIK et al., *J. Amer. med. Ass.,* **221**, 1371 (1972).
[111] HARRISON, R. J., *J. Obstet. Gynaec. Brit. Cwlth,* **79**, 226 (1972).
[112] PIERCE and HILLMAN, *Blood,* **43**, 915 (1974).
[113] PEREIRA and BAKER, *Amer. J. clin. Nutr.,* **18**, 413 (1966); LEJEUNE-LENAIN and FONDU, *Clin. chim. Acta,* **59**, 81 (1975).
[114] HARRISON, R. J., *J. clin. Path.,* **24**, 698 (1971); HARRISON, R. J., *Brit. J. Haemat.,* **20**, 623 (1971).
[115] KARLIN, R., *Int. Z. Vitaminforsch.,* **39**, 44 (1969).
[116] GADE et al., *Ugeskr. Læg.,* **134**, 2473 (1972).
[117] FLEMING et al., *Amer. J. clin. Nutr.,* **24**, 1257 (1971).
[118] SPRAY, G. H., *J. clin. Path.,* **22**, 212 (1969).
[119] KAMEN and CASTON, *J. Lab. clin. Med.,* **83**, 164 (1974).
[120] LINDEMANS et al., *Clin. chim. Acta,* **65**, 15 (1975).
[121] ROTHENBERG et al., *New Engl. J. Med.,* **286**, 1335 (1972).
[122] AVERY and LEDGER, *Obstet. and Gynec.,* **35**, 616 (1970).
[123] EK, J., *J. Pediat.,* **97**, 288 (1980).
[124] SULLIVAN et al., *Clin. Res.,* **14**, 483 (1966).
[125] RACHMILEWITZ, M., *Ser. Haematol.,* **3**, 19 (1965); COOPERMAN, J. M., *Amer. J. clin. Nutr.,* **20**, 1015 (1967).
[126] REIZENSTEIN, P., *Acta med. scand.,* **178**, 133 (1965); SHOJANIA and HORNADY, *Amer. J. clin. Path.,* **52**, 454 (1969).

[127] WADDELL et al., *Amer. J. clin. Path.,* **66**, 746 (1976); SHANE et al., *Clin. chim. Acta,* **100**, 13 (1980).
[128] HERBERT et al., *J. clin. Invest.,* **41**, 1134 (1962).
[129] NORONHA and ABOOBAKER, *Arch. Biochem.,* **101**, 445 (1963).
[130] OMER, A., *J. clin. Path.,* **22**, 217 (1969).
[131] MARKKANEN et al., *J. clin. Path.,* **26**, 486 (1973); MARKKANEN et al., *Int. Z. Vitaminforsch.,* **44**, 81 (1974).
[132] COLMAN and HERBERT, *Blood,* **48**, 911 (1976).
[133] IWAI et al., *J. biol. Chem.,* **239**, 2365 (1964).
[134] GIRDWOOD et al., *Brit. med. J.,* **2**, 670 (1967).
[135] WILLOUGHBY and JEWELL, *Brit. med. J.,* **4**, 356 (1968).
[136] TEMPERLEY et al., *Brit. J. Haemat.,* **14**, 13 (1968); MARKKANEN et al., *Int. Z. Vitaminforsch.,* **39**, 37 (1969).
[137] HIBBARD, E.D., *Arch. Dis. Childh.,* **48**, 743 (1973); HIBBARD and KENNA, *J. Pediat.,* **84**, 750 (1974).
[138] EK and MAGNUS, *Acta paediat. scand.,* **68**, 239 (1979).
[139] VANIER and TYAS, *Arch. Dis. Childh.,* **41**, 658 (1966).
[140] MARTINEZ and ROE, *Amer. J. Obstet. Gynec.,* **128**, 255 (1977).
[141] SHOJANIA et al., *Lancet,* **1**, 1376 (1968); SHOJANIA et al., *Amer. J. Obstet. Gynec.,* **111**, 782 (1971); SHOJANIA, A.M., *Lancet,* **1**, 1198 (1975).
[142] STEPHENS et al., *Clin. Sci.,* **42**, 405 (1972); PAINE et al., *J. Amer. med. Ass.,* **231**, 731 (1975).
[143] HERBERT, V., *Trans. Ass. Amer. Phycns,* **75**, 307 (1962).
[144] HERBERT, V., *Ann. Rev. Med.,* **16**, 359 (1965).
[145] HERSHKO et al., *Amer. J. clin. Nutr.,* **28**, 1217 (1975).
[146] RUDZKI et al., *J. Lab. clin. Med.,* **87**, 859 (1976).
[147] HERBERT, V., *J. clin. Path.,* **19**, 12 (1966).
[148] LONGO and HERBERT, *J. Lab. clin. Med.,* **87**, 138 (1976).
[149] MICHOT, F., *Schweiz. med. Wschr.,* **100**, 1971 (1970).
[150] SARAYA et al., *Amer. J. clin. Nutr.,* **26**, 640 (1973).
[151] FORSHAW and HARWOOD, *J. clin. Path.,* **24**, 244 (1971).
[152] MILLER, D.R., *Pediatrics,* **41**, 630 (1968); REYNOLDS et al., *Lancet,* **1**, 1264 (1969).
[153] COOPER and LOWENSTEIN, *Blood,* **24**, 502 (1964).
[154] PAINE et al., *Amer. J. med. Sci.,* **266**, 135 (1973).
[155] CARNEY, M.W., *Brit. med. J.,* **4**, 512 (1967); CARNEY, M.W., *Quart. J. Stud. Alcohol,* **31**, 816 (1970).
[156] MCNEISH and WILLOUGHBY, *Lancet,* **1**, 442 (1969).
[157] OMER et al., *Blood,* **35**, 821 (1970).
[158] VARADI et al., *J. clin. Path.,* **19**, 33 (1966).
[159] LEEMING et al., *J. clin. Path.,* **29**, 444 (1976).
[160] BAKER et al., *Amer. J. clin. Nutr.,* **27**, 1247 (1974).
[161] BRADLEY et al., *Lancet,* **2**, 201 (1973).
[162] SPATHIS and HALLPIKE, *Guy's Hosp. Rep.,* **110**, 148 (1961).
[163] BINGÖL et al., *J. Pediat.,* **86**, 902 (1975).
[164] ATTWOOD et al., *Clin. chim. Acta,* **54**, 95 (1974).
[165] DENSON and BOWERS, *Clin. Sci.,* **21**, 157 (1961).
[166] LOH and WILSON, *Brit. med. J.,* **3**, 733 (1971).
[167] BRIGGS and BRIGGS, *Nature,* **238**, 277 (1972).
[168] MCLEROY and SCHENDEL, *Amer. J. clin. Nutr.,* **26**, 191 (1973).
[169] FIDANZA and BALDESSERINI, *Int. Z. Vitaminforsch.,* **45**, 61 (1975).
[170] RITZEL and SCHLETTWEIN-GSELL, *Int. Z. Vitaminforsch.,* **40**, 548 (1970).
[171] RITCHEY, S.J., *Amer. J. clin. Nutr.,* **17**, 78 (1965).
[172] BRUBACHER et al., *Int. Z. Vitaminforsch.,* **40**, 199 (1970).
[173] COX and WHICHELOW, *Biochem. Med.,* **12**, 183 (1975).
[174] RIVERS and DEVINE, *Amer. J. clin. Nutr.,* **25**, 684 (1972).
[175] PELLETIER, O., *Amer. J. clin. Nutr.,* **23**, 520 (1970).
[176] BRAMKAMP and WIRTHS, *Int. Z. Vitaminforsch.,* **43**, 479 (1973).
[177] BROOK and GRIMSHAW, *Amer. J. clin. Nutr.,* **21**, 1254 (1968).
[178] BURR et al., *Amer. J. clin. Nutr.,* **27**, 144 (1974).
[179] MILNE et al., *Brit. med. J.,* **4**, 383 (1971).
[180] JACOBS et al., *J. clin. Path.,* **24**, 694 (1971).
[181] LOH and WILSON, *Int. Z. Vitaminforsch.,* **43**, 355 (1973).
[182] FUJINO et al., *Amer. J. clin. Nutr.,* **18**, 256 (1966).
[183] BARTON and ROATH, *Int. Z. Vitaminforsch.,* **46**, 271 (1976).
[184] DŁUŻNIEWSKA et al., *Rocz. państwowego Zakt. Hig.,* **14**, 443 (1963), quoted from *Nutr. Abstr. Rev.,* **34**, 1103 (1964).
[185] PELLETIER, O., *Amer. J. clin. Nutr.,* **21**, 1259 (1968).
[186] RIVERS, J.M., *Amer. J. clin. Nutr.,* **28**, 550 (1975).
[187] KNOX and GOSWAMI, *Advanc. clin. Chem.,* **4**, 121 (1961).
[188] LUND et al., *Acta endocr. (Kbh.),* **94**, 426 (1980).
[189] FAVUS, M.J., *Med. Clin. N. Amer.,* **62**, 1291 (1978).
[190] STANBURY and MAWER, in LAWSON, D.E. (Ed.), *Vitamin D,* Academic Press, London, 1978, page 343.
[191] MAWER, E.B., *Clin. Endocr. Metab.,* **9**, 63 (1980).
[192] KUMAR et al., *J. clin. Invest.,* **63**, 342 (1979).
[193] LUMENG et al., *J. clin. Invest.,* **66**, 688 (1980).
[194] BRADLEY et al., *Clin. Chem.,* **18**, 968 (1972).
[195] HORSBURGH and GOMPERTZ, *Clin. chim. Acta,* **82**, 215 (1978).
[196] HODGES et al., *Amer. J. clin. Nutr.,* **31**, 876 (1978).
[197] OGURA et al., *Horm. Metab. Res.,* **12**, 537 (1980).
[198] CHAUHAN and DAKSHINAMURTI, *Clin. chim. Acta,* **109**, 159 (1981).
[199] ROTH et al., *Clin. chim. Acta,* **109**, 337 (1981).
[200] SLOAN and LAPPIN, *Clin. chim. Acta,* **119**, 197 (1982).
[201] KIMURA et al., *Clin. Chem.,* **28**, 29 (1982).
[202] DHONDT et al., in WACHTER et al., (Eds.), *Biochemical and Clinical Aspects of Pteridines,* de Gruyter, Berlin, 1982, page 133.
[203] SHEARER et al., *Lancet,* **2**, 460 (1982).
[204] LEFEVERE et al., *J. Lipid Res.,* **23**, 1068 (1982).
[205] SHIN et al., *Clin. Chim. Acta,* **127**, 77 (1983).
[206] INGEBRETSEN et al., *Clin. Chim. Acta,* **126**, 307 (1982).
[207] HOEY et al., *J. roy. Soc. Med.,* **75**, 656 (1982).

Plasma proteins* (for references see pages 160–162)

Table 1 *Functional classification of plasma proteins*

Protein	Main function	Electrophoretic fraction
Transport proteins		
Prealbumin	Binding of thyroxine (T_4) and triiodothyronine (T_3)	Prealbumin
Albumin	Binding of water, ions, bilirubin, fatty acids, hormones, drugs	Albumin
Transcortin	Binding of cortisol, corticosterone and progesterone	α_1
9.5 S-α_1-Glycoprotein	Binding of metal ions	α_1
α_1-Acid glycoprotein	Binding of progesterone and some drugs	α_1
Thyroxine-binding globulin	Binding of thyroxine (T_4) and triiodothyronine (T_3)	α_1
Retinol-binding protein	Binding of vitamin A	α_2
Gc-Globulin	Binding of 25-hydroxycholecalciferol, 1α,25-dihydroxycholecalciferol, vitamin D_2 and D_3	α_2
Haptoglobin	Binding of hemoglobin	α_2
α_2-Macroglobulin	Complexing with proteinases and removing them from circulation	α_2
Transcobalamins I, II, III	Binding of vitamin B_{12}	α_1 to β
Lipoproteins	Transport of lipids (see page 115)	α to β
Hemopexin	Binding of heme	β
Transferrin	Binding of iron	β
Sex-hormone-binding globulin	Binding of testosterone, dihydrotestosterone and estradiol	β
Immunoglobulins		
IgG	Late antibodies	γ
IgA	Mucosal-protective antibodies	β/γ
IgM	Early antibodies	β/γ
IgD	B-lymphocyte receptors	β/γ
IgE	Reagins	β/γ
β_2-Microglobulin	Constituent (light chain) of HLA antigens (see page 245)	β_2
Complement factors (see pages 236–244)		
Proteins of coagulation and fibrinolysis (see pages 222–235)		
Enzymes		
Cholinesterase	Cleavage of choline esters	α_2
Ceruloplasmin	Iron metabolism (ferroxidase I)	α_2
Plasminogen	Precursor of plasmin (see page 228)	β_1
Protein C	Precursor of a serine proteinase (see page 227)	–
β_2-Glycoprotein I	Proteinase (?)	β_2
Enzyme inhibitors		
$C\bar{1}$ inhibitor	Inhibitor of $C\bar{1}$ (see page 227)	α_2
α_1-Antitrypsin	Trypsin and chymotrypsin inhibition	α_1
α_1-Antichymotrypsin	Chymotrypsin inhibition	α_1
Inter-α-trypsin inhibitor	Trypsin inhibition	α_1/α_2
Antithrombin III	Thrombin inhibition (see page 227)	α_2
α_2-Macroglobulin	Binding and inactivation of endoproteinases (e.g. trypsin and plasmin)	α_2
α_2-Antiplasmin	Plasmin inhibition (see page 228)	α_2
Proteins with unknown function		
α_1B-Glycoprotein		α_1
α_1T-Glycoprotein		α_1
α_1-Microglobulin		α_1
Histidine-rich 3.8 S-α_2-glycoprotein		α_2
Zn-α_2-Glycoprotein		α_2
α_2HS-Glycoprotein		α_2
Leucine-rich 3.1 S-α_2-glycoprotein		α_2
Cold-insoluble globulin		α_2
β_2-Glycoprotein III		β
Protein S (page 227)		β_2
		–
Pregnancy-associated and oncofetal proteins (see Table 43 on page 158)		

*This chapter on 'Plasma Proteins' (pages 135–162) has been compiled in collaboration with H. H. MÄRKI, Medizinische Poliklinik, Kantonsspital, Winterthur, Switzerland.

Table 2 *Physicochemical and biological properties of plasma proteins**

	Protein	Structure	Mass of carbohydrates relative to mass of total protein	Sedimentation coefficient (S_{20w})	Diffusion coefficient (D_{20w})	Relative molecular mass (M_r)	Specific partial volume	Frictional ratio	Limiting viscosity number	Electrophoretic mobility◊	Iso-electric point (pI)
			%	10^{-13} s	10^{-7} $cm^2 s^{-1}$		cm^3/g			$10^{-5} cm^2 V^{-1} s^{-1}$	
1	Prealbumin (transthyretin, high-tryptophan prealbumin, thyroxine-binding prealbumin)	Tetramer of identical subunits, each consisting of 127 amino acids[6]	?[1]	4.2[2]	–	50000–66000[1]	0.74[6]	1.16[6]	–	7.6[2]	4.7[2]
2	Albumin	1 polypeptide chain consisting of 585 amino acids[7]	0[2]	4.6[2]	6.1[2]	66500[7]	0.733[2]	1.28[2]	0.042[2]	5.92[2]	4.9[2]
3	Transcortin (corticosteroid-binding globulin)	1 polypeptide chain consisting of 290–295 amino acids[12]	35.1[13]	3.6[13]	5.6[13]	50700[13]	0.690[13]	1.5[13]	–	–	–
4	9.5 *S*-α_1-Glycoprotein	....	12.8[15]	9.5[15]	–	308000[15]	0.7301[15]	–	–	–	–
5	α_1-Acid glycoprotein (orosomucoid)	204 amino acids[2]	41.4[16]	3.1[2]	5.27[2]	44000[16]	0.675[2]	1.78[2]	0.069[2]	5.2[2]	2.7[16]
6	α_1-Antitrypsin (α_1-proteinase inhibitor)	1 polypeptide chain consisting of 394 amino acids[18]	12.2[19]	3.5[19]	5.2[2]	51000[18]	0.728[20]	–	0.068[2]	5.42[2]	4.0[16]
7	α_1-Antichymotrypsin (α_1X-glycoprotein)	....	26[27]	3.9[2]	–	58000–68000[27]	–	–	–	–	–
8	α_1B-Glycoprotein (easily precipitable glycoprotein)	~400 amino acids[2]	13.3[2]	3.8[2]	–	50000[2]	–	–	–	–	–
9	α_1T-Glycoprotein (tryptophan-poor glycoprotein)	....	13.7[2]	3.3[2]	–	~60000[2]	–	–	–	–	–
10	α_1-Microglobulin	~175 amino acids[23]	20[24]	2.35[24]	7.5[24]	25000–31000[24] 33000[25]	0.704[24]	1.45[24]	–	–	–
11	Thyroxine-binding globulin	1 polypeptide chain with 4 oligosaccharide chains[337]	13[26]	3.4[26]	–	63000[26] 54000[337]	–	–	–	–	3.8[26]
12	Inter-α-trypsin inhibitor	1 polypeptide chain[27]	8.4[27]	6.4[2]	–	~180000[27]	–	–	–	–	–
13	Gc-Globulin (vitamin D plasma binding protein, transcalciferin)	....	–	3.49[28]	–	52000[28]	–	–	–	–	4.8[28]
14	Retinol-binding protein	1 polypeptide chain consisting of 182 amino acids[6]	0[1]	2.3[6]	–	21200[6]	0.72[6]	1.28[6]	–	–	–
15	Haptoglobin	$\alpha_2\beta_2$ α: 84 amino acids[33] β: 275–300 amino acids[33] Phenotypes: Hp 1-1, Hp 2-1, Hp 2-2 (see also page 269)	19.3[2]	Hp 1–1: 4.4[17] Hp 2–1: 4.3–6.5[17] Hp 2–2: 7.5[17]	Hp 1–1: 4.7[2]	Hp 1–1: 100000[2]	Hp 1–1: 0.766[2]	–	–	–	Hp 1–1: 4.1[2]
16	Ceruloplasmin	1 polypeptide chain consisting of 1065 amino acids[36]	8[2]	7.08[2]	3.76[2]	135000[36]	0.713[2]	–	0.044[2]	4.6[2]	4.4[2]
17	α_2-Macroglobulin	Tetramer of identical subunits (M_r ~ 179000), each consisting of 1451 amino acids[38]	8–11[27]	18.1[39]	2.41[2]	725000[39]	0.735[2]	1.57[39]	0.068[2]	4.2[2]	5.4[2]
18	Histidine-rich 3.8 *S*-α_2-glycoprotein	478 amino acids[42] (~ 10% histidine)	14[42]	3.8[42]	–	58500[42]	0.7205[42]	–	–	–	–
19	α_2-Antiplasmin (α_2-plasmin inhibitor)	1 polypeptide chain[50]	11.7[51]	3.43[51]	–	63000–67000[52]	0.72[50]	–	–	–	–
20	Cholinesterase (serum cholinesterase, pseudocholinesterase)	Multiple forms	24.5[166]	11.1[166]	–	345000–371000[167]	–	–	–	–	4.0[167]
21	C$\bar{1}$ inhibitor (C1-esterase inhibitor, C1s inactivator, α_2-neuraminoglycoprotein)	....	35[27]	3.7[2]	–	96000–104000[27]	–	–	–	–	–

*For properties of apolipoproteins see page 117, for those of the blood clotting factors see pages 222 and 226, for those of the components of the complement system see page 238.

◊pH 8.6, barbital-Na buffer (ionic strength 0.1 mol/kg).

o Table 2)

xtinction E_{280}†	Concentration in plasma	Fraction of the intravascular pool in total body pool	Rate of synthesis	Site of synthesis	Half-life in plasma	Function
		%	mg d⁻¹ kg⁻¹		d	
4.1[1]	♀ 200–360 mg/L[5] ♂ 240–360 mg/L[5]	49 (47–52)[4]	9.74 (7.48–11.6)[4]	–	1.9[4]	Binding and transport of T_4 and T_3 under physiological conditions; 3% (s = 0.4%) of T_3 and 17% (s = 1%) of T_4 are bound to prealbumin[3]). Formation of an equimolar protein complex with retinol-binding protein[6]
.8[2]	♀ 38–51 g/L[5] ♂ 40–52 g/L[5]	42 (36–53)[2]	200 (120–260)[2] 239 (s 40.5)[8]	Liver parenchymal cells[9]	19 (17–23)[2]	The most important protein for maintaining oncotic pressure. Binding and transport of bile acids, bilirubin, porphyrins, uric acid, acetylcholine, fatty acids, copper, calcium, zinc, drugs, vitamins, hormones (T_3 and T_4, cortisol, progesterone, testosterone, aldosterone, estrone), etc.[1,11]
.5[1]	24–44 mg/L[13]	–	–	–	5.3–6[14]	Binding and transport of corticosteroids (high affinity for cortisol, corticosterone, progesterone, 17α-hydroxyprogesterone, less close affinity for aldosterone and testosterone). 1 binding site per molecule
8.2[15]	36–83 mg/L[15]	–	–	–	–	Binding and transport of calcium, barium, strontium, nickel and other metal ions[15]
.9[2]	♀ 0.50–1.00 g/L[5] ♂ 0.55–1.15 g/L[5]	–	10[17]	Liver[16]	5.2[16]	Binding and inactivation of progesterone (?)[17]. Acute-phase protein
.3[2]	♀ 0.95–1.85 g/L[5] ♂ 0.85–1.85 g/L[5]	–	–	Liver[16]	3.9 (without sialic acid)[16]	Inhibitor of tissue proteinases including trypsin, chymotrypsin, elastase, collagenase, renin[22] (92% of trypsin-inhibiting capacity of plasma). Acute-phase protein
.0[2]	300–600 mg/L[21]	–	–	–	–	Chymotrypsin inhibition[27]. Acute-phase protein
.0[2]	150–300 mg/L[21]	–	–	–	–	?
.0[2]	50–120 mg/L[21]	–	–	–	–	?
–	54 mg/L[24]	–	–	–	–	?
.9–8.4[1]	21.5 mg/L (s 5.1 mg/L)[14]	–	0.25 (s 0.03)[14]	–	5.01 (s 1.21)[14]	Binding and transport of T_3 and T_4 (67% of T_3- and 53% of T_4-binding capacity)[3]
.1[2]	200–700 mg/L[21]	–	–	–	–	Trypsin inhibition
.1[28]	250–350 mg/L[30]	–	–	Liver[29]	–	Binding of 25-hydroxycholecalciferol, 1α,25-dihydroxycholecalciferol, vitamin D_2 and D_3; 1 sterol-binding site per molecule[29]
9.4[1]	33–96 mg/L[31]	–	–	Liver[6]	0.5[6]	Binding and transport of vitamin A (equimolar) in a complex with thyroxine-binding prealbumin[32]
2[2]	Hp 1-1: 1.45 g/L (s 0.34 g/L)[34] Hp 2-1: 2.06 g/L (s 0.67 g/L)[34] Hp 2-2: 1.74 g/L (s 0.70 g/L)[34]	Hp 1-1: ~50[16] Hp 2-2: ~75[16]	14–23[16]	Liver[33]	Haptoglobin: 2–4[16] Hemoglobin–haptoglobin complex: ~9 min[33]	Equimolar binding of hemoglobin [½ hemoglobin molecule (αβ-dimer) per ½ αβ-haptoglobin molecule][35] that protects the organism against renal loss of iron. Acute-phase protein
4.9[2] .68§[2]	♀ 250–550 mg/L[5] ♂ 200–450 mg/L[5]	40[16]	5.9–6.2[16]	Liver[16]	4.25[16]	Copper binding (7 Cu atoms per molecule of ceruloplasmin)[37]. Participation in iron metabolism
.1[2]	♀ 2.05–4.30 g/L[5] ♂ 1.80–3.40 g/L[5]	92–94[40]	18.4 (14.4–25.0)[41]	Liver[16]	7.8[41]	Elimination of free proteolytic activity (e.g. trypsin and plasmin activity). Zinc transport
.85[42]	92 mg/L (s 45 mg/L)[42]	–	–	–	–	Regulation of fibrinolysis[43]
.03[51]	69 mg/L (s 6 mg/L)[52]	–	–	Liver[52]	–	Inhibitor of various serine proteinases including trypsin, chymotrypsin, and proteinases participating in blood coagulation, fibrinolysis and the kinin-forming system[52]
4.5[167]	5–14 mg/L[103]	–	–	Liver[167]	3.4[167]	Hydrolysis of acylcholines
.0[2]	150–350 mg/L[21]	–	–	–	–	Inhibitor of C$\bar{1}$ (page 227)

†E_{280}: extinction of a solution with protein concentration of 10 g/L at 280 nm.
§E_{610}: extinction of a solution with protein concentration of 10 g/L at 610 nm.

Table 2 *Physicochemical and biological properties of plasma proteins* (*continued*)

	Protein	Structure	Mass of carbohydrates relative to mass of total protein	Sedimentation coefficient (S_{20w})	Diffusion coefficient (D_{20w})	Relative molecular mass (M_r)	Specific partial volume	Frictional ratio	Limiting viscosity number	Electrophoretic mobility◇	Iso-electri point (pI)
			%	10^{-13} s	10^{-7} $cm^2 s^{-1}$		cm^3/g			$10^{-5} cm^2 V^{-1} s^{-1}$	
22	Zn-α_2-Glycoprotein	287 amino acids[2]	18.2[2]	3.2[2]	–	41000[2]	0.706[2]	–	–	4.2[2]	3.8[2]
23	α_2HS-Glycoprotein	402 amino acids[2]	13.4[2]	3.3[45]	–	49000[45]	–	–	–	4.2[2]	4.1[45]
24	Leucine-rich 3.1 *S*-α_2-glycoprotein	...	23[46]	3.1[46]	–	49600[46]	0.702 5[46]	–	–	–	4[46]
25	Cold-insoluble globulin (cryoprecipitable protein, soluble fibronectin)	2 similar polypeptide chains connected by disulfide bonds[53]	~5[53]	–	–	450000[53]	–	–	–	–	–
26	Sex-hormone-binding globulin (testosterone-estradiol-binding globulin)	Polypeptide consisting of 4 identical subunits[47]	12.6[47]	4.1[47]	–	65000[47] 94100[48]	–	–	–	–	–
27	Hemopexin	1 polypeptide chain consisting of ~410 amino acids[56]	23[21]	4.8[2]	–	57000[56]	0.702[56]	–	–	3.1[2]	5.8[57]
28	Transferrin	1 polypeptide chain consisting of 678 amino acids[59]	5.9[2]	5.54[60]	5.0[2]	79600[59]	0.758[60]	1.37[2]	0.055[2]	3.1[2]	5.9[2]
29	C-reactive protein	Aggregates of 5 identical subunits (M_r 21500)[171]. 1 subunit contains 187 amino acids[172] in a single chain	0[171]	7.5[168] 6.5[169]	–	110000[171]	–	–	–	–	4.8[168]
30	β_2-Glycoprotein I	1 polypeptide chain consisting of 326 amino acids[61]	19[61]	2.7[62]	–	50000[61]	–	–	–	1.6[2]	–
31	β_2-Glycoprotein II	...	6[62]	3.7[62]	–	93000[21]	–	–	–	–	–
32	β_2-Glycoprotein III	...	10[63]	2.14[63]	–	35000[63]	–	–	–	–	–
33	β_2-Microglobulin	1 polypeptide chain consisting of 100 amino acids. Amino-acid sequence homologous with constant domains of IgG (especially C_H3)[64]	0[65]	1.6[65]	13.3[65]	11800[65]	0.727[65]	1.16[65]	–	–	5.8[65]
34	Fibrinogen	6 polypeptide chains of 1482 amino acids altogether[67]: 2 α-chains (M_r 67000) 2 β-chains (M_r 56000) 2 γ-chains (M_r 47000)	2.5[2]	7.63[68]	1.97[68]	340000[67]	0.723[68]	2.34[2]	–	2.1[2]	5.5[68]
35	Transcobalamin II	347 amino acids[10]	0[10]	–	–	38000[10]	–	–	–	–	–
36	IgG	Corresponds to the basic structure of the immunoglobulin molecule (page 143). Subclasses: IgG_1, IgG_2, IgG_3, IgG_4	2.97[2]	6.6[73]	4.0[2]	150000[73]	0.739[2]	1.38[2]	0.060[2]	1.2[2]	5.8–7.3
37	IgA	Corresponds to the basic structure of the immunoglobulin molecule (page 143). Dimer joined by a J chain ('joining chain'). Dimers with secretory component (SC) in mucosal secretions. H chain consisting of 475 amino acids[77]. Subclasses: IgA_1, IgA_2	7.5[76]	Monomer: 6.3–6.9[76]	3.0–3.6[76]	Monomer: 162000[76]	0.725[76]	–	–	2.1[76]	–
38	IgM	Pentamer consisting of 5 basic structures, joined by a J chain[79]. H chain consisting of ~570 amino acids with 5 homologous regions[80]	12[82]	19.0[73]	–	900000[73] 935000[80]	0.724[81]	–	–	2.1[2]	–
39	IgD	Corresponds to the basic structure of the immunoglobulin molecule (page 143)	11.3[83]	7.0[83]	–	172000[83]	0.717[83]	–	–	–	4.7–6.1
40	IgE	Like the basic structure of the immunoglobulin molecule (page 143), except for the H chain which has 5 homologous regions	10.7[173]	7.9[173]	–	196000[173]	–	–	–	–	–

◇pH 8.6, barbital-Na buffer (ionic strength 0.1 mol/kg).

Table 2)

xtinction E_{280}†	Concentration in plasma	Fraction of the intravascular pool in total body pool	Rate of synthesis	Site of synthesis	Half-life in plasma	Function
		%	$mg\,d^{-1}\,kg^{-1}$		d	
[2]	104 mg/L (s 40 mg/L)[44]	–	–	–	–	?
5[2]	400–850 mg/L[21]	–	–	–	–	?
)[46]	21 mg/L[46]	–	–	–	–	?
–	170 mg/L (s 40 mg/L)[54]	–	–	Fibroblasts	–	Mediating cell attachment to various matrix substances including fibrin and collagen[55]
–	♀ 3–15 mg/L[47] ♂ 1–12 mg/L[47]	–	–	–	–	Binding and transport of testosterone, dihydrotestosterone and estradiol[49]
.7[56]	721 mg/L (s 83 mg/L)[58]	32[58]	6.9 (s 1.23)[58]	Liver[58]	9.52 (s 1.91)[58]	Equimolar binding of heme to hemopexin. Elimination of heme in hemolysis
oo: 11.2[1] : 13.8[1]	♀ 1.65–2.90 g/L[5] ♂ 1.54–2.75 g/L[5]	45[2]	25[2]	Liver[2]	8.5 (7–10)[2]	Binding and transport of Fe^{3+} in the plasma (2 binding sites per molecule)
–	0.8 mg/L (90% < 3mg/L)[170]	–	–	Liver[171]	–	Complement activation (classical pathway). Phagocytosis-promoting activity
4[62]	150–350 mg/L[21]	–	–	–	–	Associated with lipoproteins
.0[62]	100–400 mg/L[21]	–	–	–	–	Proenzyme of C3 activator (factor B of the complement system; see page 243)
.2[63]	50–150 mg/L[21]	–	–	–	–	?
–	0.58–2.24 mg/L[66]	–	–	–	–	?
.6[2]	♀ 1.90–4.70 g/L[5] ♂ 1.80–4.50 g/L[5]	81[16]	31[16] 18.0 (s 1.21)[69]	Liver[16]	3.1–3.4[16] 3.84 (s 0.1)[69]	Coagulation; acute-phase protein
–	0.5–1.5 μg/L[71]	–	–	Liver	–	Equimolar binding and transport of vitamin B_{12}
.8[2]	♀ 7.2–15.5 g/L[5] ♂ 6.7–14.7 g/L[5] IgG_1: 5.3–14.5 g/L[72] IgG_2: 1.9–6.5 g/L[72] IgG_3: 0.18–1.1 g/L[72] IgG_4: 0.12–1.8 g/L[72]	45[74]	33[74] IgG_1: 25.4[72] IgG_3: 3.4[72]	Plasma cells	23[74] IgG_1, IgG_2, IgG_3: 20–21 IgG_4: 7–8[72]	Late antibodies in primary and secondary immunization. Biological activities[75]: (see below)

Biological activities[75]	IgG_1	IgG_2	IgG_3	IgG_4
Complement fixation	++	+	+++	0
Passive cutaneous anaphylaxis	+++	0	+++	+++
Placental passage	+++	+++	+++	+++
Binding to macrophage receptors	+++	0	+++	0

xtinction E_{280}†	Concentration in plasma	Fraction of the intravascular pool in total body pool (%)	Rate of synthesis ($mg\,d^{-1}\,kg^{-1}$)	Site of synthesis	Half-life in plasma (d)	Function
.4[76]	0.5–3.0 g/L[5] IgA_1: 0.5–2 g/L[78] IgA_2: 0–0.2 g/L[78]	40–42[76]	24–30§[70]	Plasma cells	5–6.5[76]	Local immunity in mucosae[78]. Complement activation (alternative pathway). Cytophilia for neutrophilic granulocytes[78]
.3[2]	♀ 0.20–2.10 g/L[5] ♂ 0.15–1.20 g/L[5]	76[74]	6.7[74]	Plasma cells	5.1[74]	Cell-surface receptor. Early antibodies in primary and secondary immunization. Complement activation[78]
.5[82]	3–400 mg/L[82]	75[74]	0.4[74]	Plasma cells	2.8[74]	Cell-surface receptor on immature B lymphocytes[85]. Role in triggering the proliferation and differentiation of B lymphocytes which results in a specific antibody response[86]. Antibody function of serum IgD (?)[175]
.0[174]	111 μg/L[74]	41[74]	0.0038[74]	Plasma cells	2.7[74]	Reagins. Cytophilia for basophilic granulocytes with subsequent secretion of histamine, serotonin and bradykinin from cells. Anti-parasite immune response

E_{280}: extinction of a solution with protein concentration of 10 g/L at 280 nm. §Only IgA entering the circulation.

Plasma contains more than 100 identified proteins with special functions (Table 1) and with varying physicochemical and biological properties (Table 2). Changes in the concentration of one or more plasma proteins may be detected by determining the erythrocyte sedimentation rate (page 162). The determination of total protein, and the electrophoretic fractionation of serum proteins into the 5 fractions, albumin, α_1-, α_2-, β-, and γ-globulins, provide information on characteristic changes in the concentration of serum protein groups usually sufficient for diagnostic purposes. Measurements of the concentration of individual serum proteins yield additional diagnostically relevant information only in the case of special problems.

Method of investigation

Total protein concentration. The results to a large extent depend on the procedural details and on the standard used. Currently, the Doumas biuret method[95] and – as material for reference – the bovine serum albumin standard of the National Committee for Clinical Laboratory Standards (NCCLS) of the USA are recommended (IFCC Expert Panel on Proteins, Mexico City, 1978).

Electrophoretic fractionation of serum proteins. In a slightly alkaline medium (e.g. pH 8.6), serum proteins migrate in 5 groups toward the anode in an electrical direct-current field. The analysis system is placed in a porous carrier material (filter paper, acetate foils, agar or agarose gel) for easier handling. Then the separated protein fractions are stained (usually with the red azo dye Ponceau S or with Amido Black 10B), and the relative concentrations of the individual fractions are measured by densitometry.

The result depends on the carrier material and the buffer system[96]; an influence is to be expected even by minor variations in the carrier material (e.g. variations from one production batch to another). A dependence of the results on the dye used has been supposed[97]. The standardization of the procedure is difficult. Therefore, the omission of the densitometric assay, i.e. its substitution by a qualitative assessment of the picture presented by the stained streak, and the supplementation by a selected spectrum of individual quantitative determinations, has been recommended[98].

Immunoelectrophoresis. In the first of the 2 steps, the serum proteins are separated by electrophoresis in an agar gel, agarose gel, or cellulose acetate carrier. In the second step, the serum proteins are diffused against univalent or multivalent anti-human-protein serum perpendicularly to the electrophoretic track. The individual proteins show up as precipitation arches. The most important individual proteins may be evaluated semiquantitatively. However, the main role of immunoelectrophoresis lies in the detection and identification of paraproteins (monoclonal immunoglobulins).

Determination of the concentration of individual serum proteins. Immunological and, if the concentration is very low, radioimmunological methods (radioimmunoassay: RIA) are used. Frequently used immunological methods are electroimmunodiffusion (EID), single radial immunodiffusion (RID), and nephelometrically assessed immunoprecipitation. Reference standards are available for immunoglobulins (page 149), and a US National Reference preparation[99] for some other human serum proteins.

Reference values

Total protein concentration (Table 3). This increases in children until the 10th year[89], and in adults it decreases between the ages of 20 and 70 (Fig. 1)[92, 100]. It decreases earlier in women than in men. The values show a wider range in women taking ovulation inhibitors, and are lower, on the average, than in a comparison group[92]. The protein concentration decreases during pregnancy, reaching a level in mid-pregnancy that is on the average roughly 10 g/L lower than in nonpregnant women[101].

Electrophoretic fractionation (Table 4). The albumin concentration in the newborn is distinctly lower than in adults; the adult level is reached in the 1st year of life[89]. The α_1-globulin concentration remains roughly constant throughout childhood, while that of α_2-globulin reaches a peak between the 1st and the 3rd year, after which it decreases to the adult level. The β-globulin concentration shows a distinct rise during the first months of life, but thereafter the increase is slower. The depression in IgG concentration during the first months of life, as discussed on page 150, is evident in the behavior of γ-globulins[89]. In women taking ovulation inhibitors, the albumin concentration was 3.0 g/L lower than in a control group, while the α_1-, α_2-, and β-globulin levels were 0.56, 0.72, and 0.87 g/L higher, respectively, and the γ-globulin concentration decreased by 0.54 g/L[94]. In women without ovulation inhibitors, the albumin level decreases by 0.069 mg/L yearly between t[h] ages of 20 and 50. The β-globulin level undergoes its main increa[se] after the age of 40[94]. The α_1- and α_2-globulin concentrations sh[ow] a slight decline to the age of 30, after which they remain constant. During pregnancy, the albumin concentration decreases mar[k]edly, this constituting the main factor responsible for the decrea[se] in total proteins[101]. Most studies have shown that the concentr[a]tions of the α_1-, α_2-, and β-globulin fractions increase slight[ly] while that of the γ-globulin fraction declines slightly[101].

Individual proteins. In the period 1970–1974, reference valu[es] were determined principally by electroimmunodiffusion, but sin[ce] 1974 radial diffusion has been the most frequently used meth[od] (see Tables). For proteins present in very low concentrations, r

Table 3
Total protein concentration in the serum of children and adults

Subjects	Age	Number	Mean	s	95% range	Year
			g/L			
Men	20 years	–	–	–	62.5–76.6	1969
Women	20 years	–	–	–	60.4–74.8	1969
Men	30 years	–	–	–	61.8–75.9	1969
Women	30 years	–	–	–	60.0–74.4	1969
Men	40 years	–	–	–	61.1–75.2	1969
Women	40 years	–	–	–	59.5–73.9	1969
Men	50 years	–	–	–	60.4–74.5	1969
Women	50 years	–	–	–	59.0–73.4	1969
Men	60 years	–	–	–	59.7–73.8	1969
Women	60 years	–	–	–	58.5–73.0	1969
Men	70 years	–	–	–	59.0–73.1	1969
Women	70 years	–	–	–	58.1–72.5	1969
Adults		54	74.6	3.7	–	1971
Children	≤ 14 days	20	57.2	5.1	–	1972
Children	14 days to 13 months	17	65.8	5.1	–	1972
Children	1–3 years	20	70.2	3.3	–	1972
Children	3–7 years	75	69.8	4.4	–	1972
Children	7–10 years	59	72.5	4.6	–	1972
Children	10–14 years	37	73.1	5.5	–	1972
Cord blood		130	59.4	5.4	–	1977
Black men		92	72.3	4.1	–	1980
Black women		108	72.5	4.8	–	1980
White men		92	70.8	4.6	–	1980
White women		137	69.7	3.7	–	1980

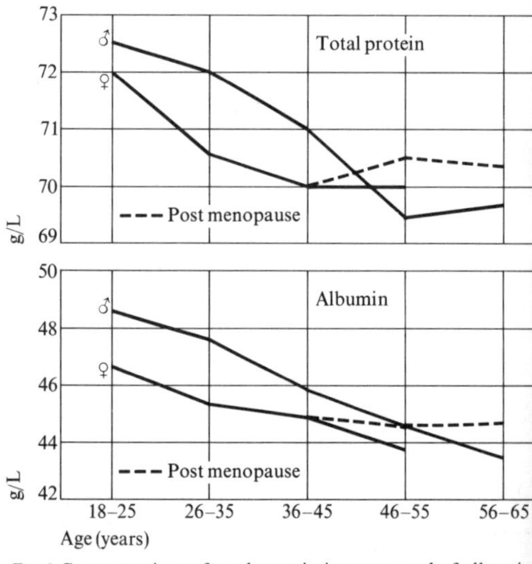

Fig. 1. Concentrations of total protein in serum and of albumin [in] plasma as a function of sex and age[92].

Table 4 *Electrophoretic fractionation of serum proteins in children and adults*

Subjects	Age	Number	Albumin		α_1-Globulin		α_2-Globulin		β-Globulin		γ-Globulin		Carrier	Dye	Year	Reference
			Mean	s	Mean	s	Mean	s	Mean	s	Mean	s				
			g/L													
Children	≤ 14 days .	20	34.8	3.09	1.97	0.36	4.86	0.77	5.53	0.56	10.10	1.72	Cellulose acetate	....	1972	89
Children	14 days to 13 months .	17	41.59	4.32	2.12	0.60	7.32	1.49	7.33	1.11	7.63	2.34	Cellulose acetate	....	1972	89
Children	1–3 years ..	20	43.65	3.40	2.09	0.43	8.34	1.53	7.79	1.23	8.26	1.75	Cellulose acetate	....	1972	89
Children	3–7 years ..	75	42.63	3.39	2.07	0.45	7.47	1.18	7.33	1.15	10.34	2.38	Cellulose acetate	....	1972	89
Children	7–10 years .	59	43.61	2.93	2.14	0.50	7.49	1.41	8.10	1.14	11.17	1.77	Cellulose acetate	....	1972	89
Children	10–14 years	37	43.72	3.38	2.12	0.45	7.14	1.34	7.78	1.31	12.36	2.34	Cellulose acetate	....	1972	89
Adults	....	15	47.5	3.1	2.25	0.15	7.43	0.46	8.48	0.54	10.13	0.66	Cellulose acetate	Ponceau S ..	1975	93
Women	20–54 years	9255	41.02	3.05	2.40	0.56	6.96	1.19	9.32	1.35	12.56	2.39	Cellulose acetate	Ponceau S ..	1977	94
Cord blood ..	....	130	35.7	4.3	2.6	1.1	4.2	1.1	4.5	1.1	12.0	2.5	Filter paper	Acid fuchsin	1977	90
Black men ...	....	92	41.8	2.9	1.46	0.36	5.49	1.34	8.17	1.41	15.45	3.17	....	....	1980	91
Black women	....	108	41.4	3.3	1.33	0.36	6.01	1.19	8.59	1.32	15.02	3.18	....	....	1980	91
White men ...	....	92	42.6	3.7	1.46	0.45	6.09	1.28	7.99	1.38	12.60	3.39	....	....	1980	91
White women	....	137	43.0	3.2	1.32	0.40	5.98	1.00	8.01	1.44	11.35	2.81	....	....	1980	91

Table 5 *Prealbumin concentration in the serum of children and adults*

Subjects	Age	Number	Mean	s	95% range	Method	Standard	Year	Ref.
			mg/L						
Adults	20–95 years	232	–	–	180–370*	EID	Behringwerke standard serum	1971	102
Children	≤ 14 years	58	170	–	80–250	EID	Behringwerke standard serum	1972	103
Adults	18–93 years	150	250	–	120–390	EID	Behringwerke standard serum	1972	103
Men	....	30	340	50.1	–	RID	Behringwerke standard serum	1974	104
Women	....	32	295	38.1	–	RID	Behringwerke standard serum	1974	104
Adults	....	11	293	97	–	RID	Behringwerke standard serum	1977	105
Adults◊	....	19	286	48	–	RID	....	1978	106
Adults	....	87	194	56	–	EID	....	1981	107
Adults	19–72 years	50	272	–	181–375	EID	....	1982	31

*Calculation with logarithmic-normal distribution. ◊Plasma. EID: electroimmunodiffusion; RID: radial immunodiffusion.

Table 6 *Albumin concentration in the serum of children and adults*

Subjects	Age	Number	Mean	s	95% range	Method	Standard	Year	Ref.
			g/L						
Boys	8–19 years	17	46.8	3.89	–	EID	Behringwerke standard serum	1971	102
Girls	8–19 years	11	44.1	2.27	–	EID	Behringwerke standard serum	1971	102
Men	20–39 years	62	45.0	4.86	36.2–55.3*	EID	Behringwerke standard serum	1971	102
Women	20–39 years	36	43.9	4.63	36.2–55.3*	EID	Behringwerke standard serum	1971	102
Men	40–59 years	44	43.4	4.24	36.2–55.3*	EID	Behringwerke standard serum	1971	102
Women	40–59 years	35	41.2	4.02	36.2–55.3*	EID	Behringwerke standard serum	1971	102
Men	60–95 years	26	42.1	4.44	36.2–55.3*	EID	Behringwerke standard serum	1971	102
Women	60–95 years	29	39.6	3.16	36.2–55.3*	EID	Behringwerke standard serum	1971	102
Children	≤ 14 years	58	45.2	–	34.3–56.0	EID	Behringwerke standard serum	1972	103
Adults	18–93 years	150	46.3	–	37.6–54.9	EID	Behringwerke standard serum	1972	103
Adults	....	62	45.57	3.467	–	RID	Behringwerke standard serum	1974	104
Adults	....	30	46.25	3.43	–	HABA-binding◊	....	1977	108
			46.37	3.61	–	Biuret	....	1977	108

*Calculation with logarithmic-normal distribution.
EID: electroimmunodiffusion; RID: radial immunodiffusion.

◊2-(4′-Hydroxyphenylazo)benzoic acid.

lioimmunoassay is the method of choice. The most frequently ised standard (as far as it is mentioned at all) has been the human tandard serum of the Behringwerke. Evaluation of the distribu-ion of serum protein concentrations in healthy persons yielded livergent results. Thus a logarithmic-normal distribution was ound for albumin, α_1-acid glycoprotein, α_1-antitrypsin, haptoglo-oin, α_2-macroglobulin, α_2HS-glycoprotein, ceruloplasmin, hemo-exin, transferrin, and C3[102,103,139]. On the other hand, normal listributions have been reported for prealbumin, albumin, α_1-antitrypsin, Gc-globulin, α_2HS-glycoprotein, α_2-macroglobulin, cholinesterase, transferrin (in women), and C3[103,139].

In children, lower concentrations of prealbumin, α_1-antitrypsin, α_1-antichymotrypsin, Gc-globulin, haptoglobin, and hemopexin were found as compared with adult levels, while ceruloplasmin, α_2-macroglobulin, cholinesterase, C3, and transferrin levels were higher[103].

In adults, the concentrations of α_1-acid glycoprotein, α_1-antitrypsin, haptoglobin, hemopexin, and C3 increase with ageing, the

Table 7 *Transcortin concentration in the serum or plasma of children and adults*

Subjects	Age	Number	Mean	s	Method	Standard	Year	Ref.
			mg/L					
Men	....	5	41.5	4.7	RID	Purified transcortin	1973	109
Women	....	5	41.5	3.6	RID	Purified transcortin	1973	109
Cord blood	....	5	17.3	2.8	RID	Purified transcortin	1973	109
Men	20–45 years	36	39.7	3.6	EID	Purified transcortin	1976	110
Women	18–42 years	36	42.1	3.9	EID	Purified transcortin	1976	110
Adults	....	40	34	5	RIA	....	1979	13

RID: radial immunodiffusion; EID: electroimmunodiffusion; RIA: radioimmunoassay.

Table 8 *Concentration of α_1-acid glycoprotein in the serum of children and adults*

Subjects	Age	Number	Mean	s	95% range	Method	Standard	Year	Ref.
			g/L						
Boys	8–19 years	17	0.74	0.227	–	EID	Behringwerke standard serum	1971	102
Girls	8–19 years	11	0.70	0.141	–	EID	Behringwerke standard serum	1971	102
Men	20–39 years	62	0.82	0.166		EID	Behringwerke standard serum	1971	102
Women	20–39 years	36	0.74	0.183		EID	Behringwerke standard serum	1971	102
Men	40–59 years	44	0.87	0.184	0.50–1.17*	EID	Behringwerke standard serum	1971	102
Women	40–59 years	35	0.76	0.220		EID	Behringwerke standard serum	1971	102
Men	60–95 years	26	0.84	0.150		EID	Behringwerke standard serum	1971	102
Women	60–95 years	29	0.90	0.240		EID	Behringwerke standard serum	1971	102
Children	≤ 14 years	58	0.77	–	0.38–1.58*	EID	Behringwerke standard serum	1972	103
Adults	18–93 years	150	0.78	–	0.48–1.26*	EID	Behringwerke standard serum	1972	103
Adults	....	62	0.888	0.2354	–	RID	Behringwerke standard serum	1974	104
Adults	....	16	0.70	0.096	–	RID	Behringwerke standard serum	1975	111
Cord blood	....	79	0.37	–	0.12–1.06*	EID	....	1979	112
Men◊	....	16	0.77	0.23	–	ELISA	....	1979	113
Women◊	Premenopausal†	10	0.74	0.16	–	ELISA	....	1979	113
Women◊	Postmenopausal	10	0.86	0.16	–	ELISA	....	1979	113
Men	....	79	0.69	0.15	–	RID	....	1981	114
Women	....	41	0.72	0.15	–	RID	....	1981	114

* Calculation with logarithmic-normal distribution.
◊ Plasma.
† Without ovulation inhibitors.

EID: electroimmunodiffusion.
RID: radial immunodiffusion.
ELISA: enzyme-linked immunosorbent assay.

Table 9 *Concentration of α_1-antitrypsin in the serum of children and adults*

Subjects	Age	Number	Mean	s	95% range	Method	Standard	Year	Ref.
			g/L						
Boys	8–19 years	17	1.65	0.308	–	EID	Behringwerke standard serum	1971	102
Girls	8–19 years	11	1.81	0.54	–	EID	Behringwerke standard serum	1971	102
Men	20–39 years	62	1.70	0.355		EID	Behringwerke standard serum	1971	102
Women	20–39 years	36	1.88	0.670		EID	Behringwerke standard serum	1971	102
Men	40–59 years	44	1.80	0.334	1.10–2.50*	EID	Behringwerke standard serum	1971	102
Women	40–59 years	35	1.84	0.309		EID	Behringwerke standard serum	1971	102
Men	60–95 years	26	1.83	0.390		EID	Behringwerke standard serum	1971	102
Women	60–95 years	29	1.95	0.292		EID	Behringwerke standard serum	1971	102
Children	≤ 14 years	58	1.41	–	0.39–2.43	EID	Behringwerke standard serum	1972	103
Adults	18–93 years	150	1.71	–	0.98–2.45	EID	Behringwerke standard serum	1972	103
Adults	....	62	2.154	0.3991	–	RID	Behringwerke standard serum	1974	104
Adults	....	16	2.360	0.44	–	RID	Behringwerke standard serum	1975	111
Cord blood	....	75	1.40	–	0.64–2.13	EID	....	1979	112
			1.77	–	0.91–2.63	Nephelometry	....	1979	112
Men	18–50 years	1296	2.68	0.76	–	RID	Behringwerke standard serum	1979	115

* Calculated with logarithmic-normal distribution.

EID: electroimmunodiffusion; RID: radial immunodiffusion.

α_2-macroglobulin concentration also beginning to rise later on in life[102,153]. The albumin concentration decreases after the 40th year (Fig. 1). The α_2-macroglobulin concentration falls markedly until the age of 40 to 50, after which it begins to rise again[102]. The concentrations of albumin and α_1-acid glycoprotein are higher in men than in women[102]. Women have higher concentrations of transcortin[110], of sex-hormone-binding globulin[138] and of ceruloplasmin α_1-antitrypsin and, during the period of sexual maturity, of transferrin as well[102].

Ovulation inhibitors cause increases in the concentrations of transcortin, α_1-antitrypsin, ceruloplasmin, α_2-macroglobulin, thyroxine-binding globulin, sex-hormone-binding globulin (Table 11

Table 10 *Concentration of α_1-microglobulin in the serum of children and adults*

Subjects	Age	Number	Mean (mg/L)	s (mg/L)	(Extreme range) (mg/L)	Method	Standard	Year	Reference
Adults		20	32	5	–	EID	Purified α_1-microglobulin	1976	23
Cord blood		27	40.6	11.3	–	RID	Purified α_1-microglobulin	1980	116
Adults	20–40 years	67	44.2	14.6	(25–83)	RID	Purified α_1-microglobulin	1980	116
Adults	20–40 years	60	8.8	2.9	(4.2–20.4)	ELISA	Purified α_1-microglobulin	1980	117

EID: electroimmunodiffusion; RID: radial immunodiffusion; ELISA: enzyme-linked immunosorbent assay.

Table 11 *Comparison of some plasma proteins in women on contraception with oral estrogens for 6 months and in pregnant women in their third trimester*[160]

Protein	On estrogens Mean	On estrogens s	Pregnant Mean	Pregnant s
	as percent of the mean concentration in untreated nonpregnant women			
Sex-hormone-binding globulin	202	28	763	172
Transcortin	202	21	290	56
Thyroxine-binding globulin	167	27	247	35
Ceruloplasmin	203	28	209	10
Transferrin	163	31	170	27
α-Lipoproteins	130	15	126	23
Plasminogen	127	12	129	20
Albumin	80.4	13	68.4	6.5
Haptoglobins	79	(Skew)	80	(Skew)

bove), fibrinogen, plasminogen, α_2HS-glycoprotein, transferrin, realbumin, and C3, whereas the concentrations of albumin, α_1-cid glycoprotein, and haptoglobin decrease[103, 110, 113, 120, 128, 58, 159].

During pregnancy, the serum protein changes correspond to that roduced by ovulation inhibitors (Table 11). The concentrations of ranscortin, α_1-antitrypsin, thyroxine-binding globulin, sex-hormone-binding globulin, Gc-globulin, fibrinogen, plasminogen, nd transferrin are increased[110, 118, 120, 126, 160], that of prealbumin, lbumin, haptoglobin, and α_1-acid glycoprotein are reduced, while hose of α_2-macroglobulin, hemopexin, C3, and C4 remain unchanged[157].

mmunoglobulins

tructure

The immunoglobulin molecule consists of 4 peptide chains: 2 lentical long or heavy chains (H chains) with about 450 (IgG, IgA, gD) or 576 (IgM, IgE) amino acids and 2 short or light chains (L hains) with about 217 amino acids[201].

One H chain and one L chain together form a half-molecule. he 2 halves join symmetrically together to form a whole Ig molecule (Table 12, below). The 2 half-molecules and 2 chains in each half are held together by disulfide bridges and noncovalent bonds. Chain segments of about 110 amino acids are folded into globular domains held together within the chains by disulfide bridges. The L chain consists of 2 and the H chain of 4 domains or homologous regions. The domains of the immunoglobulin polypeptide chains

(Continued on page 146)

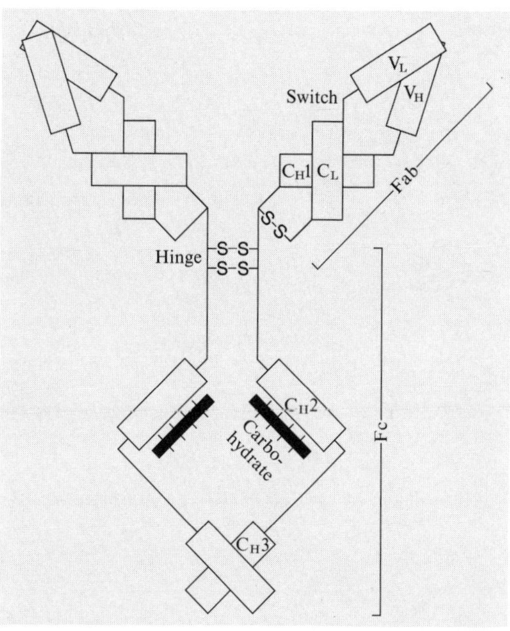

Fig. 2. Schematic drawing of an IgG_1 molecule. The arms and the stem of the Y-shaped molecule are formed by the Fab parts and the Fc part, respectively. The light chains are linked to the heavy chains by a disulfide bridge close to the carboxy terminus. The 2 heavy chains are covalently connected by 2 disulfide bridges located in the hinge region[200].

Table 12 *Types, classes and subclasses of immunoglobulins*

Chains H / L	γ: κ	γ: λ	α: κ	α: λ	δ: κ	δ: λ	ε: κ	ε: λ	μ: κ	μ: λ
Molecular type	K	L	K	L	K	L	K	L	K	L
Chain combination	$\kappa_2\gamma_2$	$\lambda_2\gamma_2$	$[\kappa_2\alpha_2]_n$	$[\lambda_2\alpha_2]_n$	$\kappa_2\delta_2$	$\lambda_2\delta_2$	$\kappa_2\varepsilon_2$	$\lambda_2\varepsilon_2$	$[\kappa_2\mu_2]_n$	$[\lambda_2\mu_2]_n$
			$n = 1, 2, 3$						$n = 5$	
Classes	IgG		IgA		IgD		IgE		IgM	
Subclasses	IgG_1, IgG_2, IgG_3, IgG_4		IgA_1, IgA_2				IgE_1, IgE_2		IgM_1, IgM_2	

Table 13 *Concentration of thyroxine-binding globulin (TBG) in the serum of children and adults*

Subjects	Age	Number	Mean	s	Method	Standard	Year	Ref.
			mg/L					
Adults		5	21.5	5.1	RIA	Purified TBG	1975	14
Children*	1 week	–	13.4	1.3	RIA	Purified TBG	1976	119
Adults*	Young	34	9.7	1.4	RIA	Purified TBG	1976	119
Children	0–4 weeks	13	34.3	4.1	RIA	Purified TBG	1977	118
Children	5 weeks to 1 year	19	29.4	6.9	RIA	Purified TBG	1977	118
Children	1–15 years	105	25.5	5.4	RIA	Purified TBG	1977	118
Adults	16–49 years	50	20.1	4.4	RIA	Purified TBG	1977	118
Adults	>49 years	30	22.9	6.0	RIA	Purified TBG	1977	118
Cord blood		25	21.7	3.5	RIA	Purified TBG	1980	120
Men	18–54 years	34	15.3	2.11	RIA	Purified TBG	1980	120
Women◊	19–62 years	32	18.4	2.72	RIA	Purified TBG	1980	120
Adults		20	21.2	3.7	RIA	Purified TBG	1982	154

* Plasma. ◊ Without ovulation inhibitors. RIA: radioimmunoassay.

Table 14 *Concentration of Gc-globulin in the serum of children and adults*

Subjects	Age	Number	Mean	s	95% range	Method	Standard	Year	Ref.
			mg/L						
Children	≤ 14 years	58	250	–	150–350	EID	Behringwerke standard serum	1972	103
Adults	18–93 years	150	270	–	170–380	EID	Behringwerke standard serum	1972	103
Adults		16	272	28	–	RID	Behringwerke standard serum	1975	111
Adults	14–70 years	35	422	27	–	RID	Purified Gc-globulin	1977	124
Adults*	18–45 years	17	292	33	–	RID	Behringwerke standard serum	1979	125
Men		28	379	280	–	EID	Purified Gc-globulin	1982	126
Women		19	414	331	–	EID	Purified Gc-globulin	1982	126

* Plasma. EID: electroimmunodiffusion; RID: radial immunodiffusion.

Table 15 *Concentration of retinol-binding protein in plasma or serum*

Material	Subjects	Age	Number	Mean	s	95% range	Method	Standard	Year	Ref.
				mg/L						
Plasma	Adults		8	48.3	3.61	–	RID	Purified retinol-binding protein	1974	121
Serum	Adults		31	47.2	10.9	–	RID		1976	122
Plasma	Adults	38–68 years	19	45.3	8.3	–	RID		1978	106
Plasma	Adults		20	57	15	–	RID	Behringwerke standard serum	1982	123
Serum	Adults	19–72 years	50	62.4	–	32.6–96.3	EID		1982	31

RID: radial immunodiffusion; EID: electroimmunodiffusion.

Table 16 *Haptoglobin concentration in the serum of children and adults*

Subjects	Age	Number	Mean	s	95% range	Method	Standard	Year	Ref.
			g/L						
Boys	8–19 years	17	1.28	0.776	–	EID	Behringwerke standard serum	1971	102
Girls	8–19 years	11	1.23	0.774	–	EID	Behringwerke standard serum	1971	102
Men	20–39 years	62	1.34	0.621		EID	Behringwerke standard serum	1971	102
Women	20–39 years	36	1.57	0.785		EID	Behringwerke standard serum	1971	102
Men	40–59 years	44	1.67	1.09	0.55–3.57*	EID	Behringwerke standard serum	1971	102
Women	40–59 years	35	1.56	0.757		EID	Behringwerke standard serum	1971	102
Men	60–95 years	26	1.82	0.635		EID	Behringwerke standard serum	1971	102
Women	60–95 years	29	1.71	1.05		EID	Behringwerke standard serum	1971	102
Children	≤ 14 years	58	1.03	–	0.18–5.9*	EID	Behringwerke standard serum	1972	103
Adults	18–93 years	150	1.47	–	0.58–3.73*	EID	Behringwerke standard serum	1972	103
Adults		16	1.42	0.28	–	RID	Behringwerke standard serum	1975	111
Men◊		734	1.06†	0.38	–	Peroxidase activity		1976	127
Women◊		82	0.94†	0.29	–	Peroxidase activity		1976	127
Men		79	1.56	0.84	–	RID		1981	114
Women		41	1.69	0.66	–	RID		1981	114

* Calculation with logarithmic-normal distribution. ◊ Plasma. EID: electroimmunodiffusion; RID: radial immunodiffusion.
† Geometric mean.

Table 17 *Ceruloplasmin concentration in the serum of children and adults*

Subjects	Age	Number	Mean	s	95% range	Method	Standard	Year	Ref.
			g/L						
Boys	8–19 years	17	0.15	0.039	–	EID	Behringwerke standard serum	1971	102
Girls	8–19 years	11	0.20	0.062	–	EID	Behringwerke standard serum	1971	102
Men	20–39 years	62	0.18	0.049	0.18–0.40*	EID	Behringwerke standard serum	1971	102
Women	20–39 years	36	0.24	0.108		EID	Behringwerke standard serum	1971	102
Men	40–59 years	44	0.20	0.063		EID	Behringwerke standard serum	1971	102
Women	40–59 years	35	0.23	0.093		EID	Behringwerke standard serum	1971	102
Men	60–95 years	26	0.21	0.064		EID	Behringwerke standard serum	1971	102
Women	60–95 years	29	0.28	0.066		EID	Behringwerke standard serum	1971	102
Children	≤ 14 years	58	0.27	–	0.10–0.70*	EID	Behringwerke standard serum	1972	103
Adults	18–93 years	150	0.21	–	0.09–0.51*	EID	Behringwerke standard serum	1972	103
Women◇	19–30 years	30	0.28	0.034	–	*p*-Phenylenediamine oxidation	...	1972	128
Newborn	...	45	0.17	0.067	–	*p*-Phenylenediamine oxidation	...	1974	129
Men	Mean 51 years	180	0.321	0.079	–	RID	...	1974	130
Adults	...	16	0.291	0.108	–	RID	Behringwerke standard serum	1975	111
Men	22–59 years	64	0.287	0.057	–	*p*-Phenylenediamine oxidation	...	1975	131
Adults	16–52 years	25	0.326	0.077	–	RID	Behringwerke standard serum	1977	132
Cord blood	...	79	0.135	–	0.005–0.265	EID	...	1979	112
Men	...	83	0.333	0.061	–	Dimethyl *p*-phenylene-diamine oxidation	...	1979	133
Women	...	112	0.410	0.130	–	Dimethyl *p*-phenylene-diamine oxidation	...	1979	133

◇Without ovulation inhibitors.
*Calculation with logarithmic-normal distribution.
EID: electroimmunodiffusion; RID: radial immunodiffusion.

Table 18 *Concentration of α_2-macroglobulin in the serum of children and adults*

Subjects	Age	Number	Mean	s	95% range	Method	Standard	Year	Ref.
			g/L						
Boys	8–19 years	17	3.17	0.770	–	EID	Behringwerke standard serum	1971	102
Girls	8–19 years	11	2.91	0.780	–	EID	Behringwerke standard serum	1971	102
Men	20–39 years	62	2.17	0.598	0.90–3.00*	EID	Behringwerke standard serum	1971	102
Women	20–39 years	36	2.32	0.681		EID	Behringwerke standard serum	1971	102
Men	40–59 years	44	1.50	0.473		EID	Behringwerke standard serum	1971	102
Women	40–59 years	35	2.07	0.604		EID	Behringwerke standard serum	1971	102
Men	60–95 years	26	1.91	0.476		EID	Behringwerke standard serum	1971	102
Women	60–95 years	29	2.28	0.732		EID	Behringwerke standard serum	1971	102
Children	≤ 14 years	58	4.07	–	2.25–5.89	EID	Behringwerke standard serum	1972	103
Adults	18–93 years	150	2.94	–	1.45–4.43	EID	Behringwerke standard serum	1972	103
Men	22–53 years	10	1.59	0.25	–	RID	Behringwerke standard serum	1973	134
Women	25–57 years	10	1.78	0.30	–	RID	Behringwerke standard serum	1973	134
Men	...	30	2.595	0.764	–	RID	Behringwerke standard serum	1974	104
Women	...	32	3.226	0.453	–	RID	Behringwerke standard serum	1974	104
Adults	...	16	2.52	0.72	–	RID	Behringwerke standard serum	1975	111
Cord blood	...	71	2.73	–	0.86–4.60	Nephelometry	...	1979	112

*Calculation with logarithmic-normal distribution.
EID: electroimmunodiffusion; RID: radial immunodiffusion.

Table 19 *Concentration of histidine-rich glycoprotein in the serum or plasma of children and adults*

	Age	Number	Mean	s	Method	Standard	Year	Ref.
			mg/L					
Cord blood	...	566	34	11	RID	Purified histidine-rich glycoprotein	1978	135
Men	21–57 years	55	128	35	RID	Purified histidine-rich glycoprotein	1978	135
Women	21–57 years	45	120	27	RID	Purified histidine-rich glycoprotein	1978	135
Adults*	24–65 years	20	118	27	RID	...	1982	136

*Plasma.
RID: radial immunodiffusion.

Table 20 *Cholinesterase concentration in the serum of children and adults*

Subjects	Age	Number	Mean (mg/L)	95% range (mg/L)	Method	Standard	Year	Ref.
Children	≤ 14 years	58	11	4–18	EID	Behringwerke standard serum	1972	103
Adults	18–93 years	150	9	5–14	EID	Behringwerke standard serum	1972	103

EID: electroimmunodiffusion.

Table 21 *Concentration of Zn-α_2-glycoprotein in the serum of children and adults*

	Age	Number	Mean (mg/L)	*s* (mg/L)	Method	Standard	Year	Ref.
Cord blood		33	48	16	EID	Purified Zn-α_2-glycoprotein	1974	44
Children	7 days to 1 year	24	90	28	EID	Purified Zn-α_2-glycoprotein	1974	44
Children	2–5 years	17	94	28	EID	Purified Zn-α_2-glycoprotein	1974	44
Children	6–10 years	14	91	26	EID	Purified Zn-α_2-glycoprotein	1974	44
Children	11–15 years	11	94	26	EID	Purified Zn-α_2-glycoprotein	1974	44
Youth	16–20 years	9	89	22	EID	Purified Zn-α_2-glycoprotein	1974	44
Adults	21–40 years	16	93	22	EID	Purified Zn-α_2-glycoprotein	1974	44
Adults	41–60 years	26	98	26	EID	Purified Zn-α_2-glycoprotein	1974	44
Adults	>60 years	18	104	40	EID	Purified Zn-α_2-glycoprotein	1974	44

EID: electroimmunodiffusion.

Table 22 *Concentration of α_2HS-glycoprotein in the serum of children and adults*

Subjects	Age	Number	Mean (g/L)	*s* (g/L)	95% range (g/L)	Method	Standard	Year	Ref.
Boys	8–19 years	17	0.62	0.074	–	EID	Behringwerke standard serum	1971	102
Girls	8–19 years	11	0.58	0.136	–	EID	Behringwerke standard serum	1971	102
Men	20–39 years	62	0.54	0.113	0.39–0.76* (Men 20–39 to Women 60–95)	EID	Behringwerke standard serum	1971	102
Women	20–39 years	36	0.55	0.074		EID	Behringwerke standard serum	1971	102
Men	40–59 years	44	0.55	0.095		EID	Behringwerke standard serum	1971	102
Women	40–59 years	35	0.51	0.135		EID	Behringwerke standard serum	1971	102
Men	60–95 years	26	0.51	0.091		EID	Behringwerke standard serum	1971	102
Women	60–95 years	29	0.52	0.097		EID	Behringwerke standard serum	1971	102
Children	≤ 14 years	58	0.59	–	0.23–0.95	EID	Behringwerke standard serum	1972	103
Adults	18–93 years	150	0.60	–	0.30–0.90	EID	Behringwerke standard serum	1972	103
Adults		16	0.598	0.088	–	RID	Behringwerke standard serum	1975	111
Adults		38	0.595	0.120	–	RID	Behringwerke standard serum	1979	137

*Calculation with logarithmic-normal distribution. EID: electroimmunodiffusion; RID: radial immunodiffusion.

subdivide the molecule into structural units with different functions. The N-terminal domains of 1 heavy and 1 light chain together form an antigen-recognizing and -binding site. Since – in terms of amino-acid sequence – the individual molecules show variability in this region, due to deletions and insertions of a small number of amino-acid residues or to substitution of single amino acids, the N-terminal domains of the H and L chains are referred to as variable domains (V_H: variable segment of the H chain; V_L: variable segment of the L chain). Variations in the primary structure are concentrated in 3 hypervariable regions: around position 30 (amino-acid residues: 23–36), between positions 50 and 60 (amino-acid residues: 50–56), and around the position 100 (amino-acid residues: 91–100) of the 2 implicated chains. These hypervariable segments form the wall of the cavity in which the haptene is bound[201].

The other domains of the immunoglobulin chains are for the most part constant within one Ig class or Ig type, and are therefore referred to as constant domains (C_L: constant domain in the L chain; C_H1, C_H2, C_H3: constant domains in the H chain). In the Ig molecule, the 2 C_H2 domains are each linked with a carbohydrate chain.

The entire Ig molecule is in the shape of a Y, the arms of which are formed by the domains V_H, V_L, C_H1, and C_L (Fig. 2, p. 143). The antigen recognition site is at the furthermost end of the arms. The stem is formed from 2 C_H2 and C_H3 domains each. A flexible peptide (hinge region) is situated at the attachment site of the arms, i.e. between domains C_H1 and C_H2, to permit variations in the arms' angle of attachment. Switch peptides with the same function are located between the constant and variable segments of the H and L chains. These peptides lend the Ig shape a broad flexibility, enabling it to accommodate geometrically to polyvalent antigens.

The IgG and IgD molecules, as well as the monomeric IgA molecule, conform to the described basic structure. The monomers of the IgM molecule and the IgE molecule have an additional 5th domain in the constant segments of their H chains. The IgA dimers are held together by a J chain. There is another secretory component in secretions. The IgM molecule is a pentamer, held together by a J chain.

Function

Immunoglobulins are antibodies with 2 functions:

1. They recognize and bind cells and macromolecules alien to the body (antigens). This function entails the specific recognition of the antigen by means of complementary surface structures. These are built up out of the variable segments of the L chains and H chains, which together form the antibody-binding sites of the immunoglobulin[202].

(Continued on page 149)

Table 23 *Concentration of sex-hormone-binding globulin in the serum of adults*

	Number	Mean	s	Method	Standard	Year	Ref.
		nmol/L					
Men	12	18	9	RID	Purified sex-hormone-binding globulin	1983	138
Women	8	54	13	RID	Purified sex-hormone-binding globulin	1983	138
Pregnancy:							
10–15 weeks	4	115	48	RID	Purified sex-hormone-binding globulin	1983	138
20–25 weeks	4	212	35	RID	Purified sex-hormone-binding globulin	1983	138
35–40 weeks	6	374	55	RID	Purified sex-hormone-binding globulin	1983	138

RID: radial immunodiffusion.

Table 24 *Hemopexin concentration in the serum of children and adults*

	Age	Number	Mean	s	95% range	Method	Standard	Year	Ref.
			g/L						
Cord blood		120	0.317	0.075	–	RID	Behringwerke standard serum	1970	151
Children	≤ 14 years	58	0.65	–	0.35–1.25*	EID	Behringwerke standard serum	1972	103
Adults	18–93 years	150	0.80	–	0.53–1.21*	EID	Behringwerke standard serum	1972	103
Men		48	0.84	–	0.56–1.11	RID	Behringwerke standard serum	1973	152
Women		53	0.95	–	0.58–1.31	RID	Behringwerke standard serum	1973	152
Men	21–30 years	17	0.84	–	0.64–1.05	RID	Behringwerke standard serum	1974	153
Women	21–30 years	23	0.90	–	0.56–1.24	RID	Behringwerke standard serum	1974	153
Men	31–40 years	18	0.78	–	0.53–1.03	RID	Behringwerke standard serum	1974	153
Women	31–40 years	14	0.94	–	0.60–1.28	RID	Behringwerke standard serum	1974	153
Men	41–60 years	8	0.85	–	0.64–1.05	RID	Behringwerke standard serum	1974	153
Women	41–60 years	11	0.99	–	0.40–1.40	RID	Behringwerke standard serum	1974	153
Men	61–80 years	5	0.98	–	0.62–1.35	RID	Behringwerke standard serum	1974	153
Women	61–80 years	5	1.09	–	0.86–1.32	RID	Behringwerke standard serum	1974	153
Adults		16	0.746	0.052	–	RID	Behringwerke standard serum	1975	111

*Calculation with logarithmic-normal distribution. RID: radial immunodiffusion; EID: electroimmunodiffusion.

Table 25 *Transferrin concentration in the serum of children and adults*

Subjects	Age	Number	Mean	s	95% range	Method	Standard	Year	Ref.
			g/L						
Boys	8–19 years	17	2.83	0.43	–	EID	Behringwerke standard serum	1971	102
Girls	8–19 years	11	2.69	0.33	–	EID	Behringwerke standard serum	1971	102
Men	20–39 years	62	2.51	0.33	1.79–3.35*	EID	Behringwerke standard serum	1971	102
Women	20–39 years	36	2.68	0.54		EID	Behringwerke standard serum	1971	102
Men	40–59 years	44	2.42	0.34		EID	Behringwerke standard serum	1971	102
Women	40–59 years	35	2.42	0.56		EID	Behringwerke standard serum	1971	102
Men	60–95 years	26	2.42	0.27		EID	Behringwerke standard serum	1971	102
Women	60–95 years	29	2.42	0.43		EID	Behringwerke standard serum	1971	102
Children	3 days to 14 years	58	2.43	–	1.46–4.05*	EID	Behringwerke standard serum	1972	103
Adults	18–93 years	150	2.26	–	1.52–3.36*	EID	Behringwerke standard serum	1972	103
Men	19–46 years	507	2.55	0.26	2.07–3.10*	RID		1973	139
Women	19–46 years	102	2.59	0.31	2.02–3.27*	RID		1973	139
Adults		52	2.43	0.39	–	RID	Behringwerke standard serum	1974	34
Children	1st week	7	1.24	0.18	–	RID		1974	140
Children	2nd week	18	1.34	0.24	–	RID		1974	140
Children	3rd week	10	1.46	0.29	–	RID		1974	140
Children	4th week	6	1.46	0.26	–	RID		1974	140
Children	2nd month	23	1.67	0.38	–	RID		1974	140
Children	3rd month	13	2.07	0.46	–	RID		1974	140
Children	4th month	8	2.12	0.58	–	RID		1974	140
Children	5th–6th month	6	2.15	0.45	–	RID		1974	140
Children	7th–10th month	7	2.16	0.31	–	RID		1974	140
Adults		16	2.29	0.36	–	RID	Behringwerke standard serum	1975	111
Cord blood		75	1.79	–	0.63–2.95	Nephelometry		1979	112

*Calculation with logarithmic-normal distribution. EID: electroimmunodiffusion; RID: radial immunodiffusion.

Table 26 *Concentration of β_2-microglobulin and post-γ-globulin in the serum of children and adults*

	Subjects	Age	Number	Mean (mg/L)	s (mg/L)	(Extreme range) (mg/L)	Method	Year	Reference
β_2-Microglobulin	Men	17–36 years	19	1.37	0.20	–	RIA	1972	141
	Men	37–56 years	20	1.57	0.31	–	RIA	1972	141
	Men	57–76 years	19	1.83	0.41	–	RIA	1972	141
	Women	17–36 years	21	1.40	0.26	–	RIA	1972	141
	Women	37–56 years	20	1.65	0.36	–	RIA	1972	141
	Women	57–76 years	20	1.75	0.30	–	RIA	1972	141
	Cord blood	...	29	3.00*	0.64	–	RID	1973	142
	Children	0–6 months	15	2.33*	0.74	–	RID	1973	142
	Children	6–12 months	11	2.25*	0.80	–	RID	1973	142
	Children	1–3 years	21	1.90*	0.55	–	RID	1973	142
	Children	3–6 years	67	1.82*	0.54	–	RID	1973	142
	Children	6–12 years	38	1.70*	0.40	–	RID	1973	142
	Adults	...	10	1.71*	0.37	–	RID	1973	142
	Adults	70–102 years	414	2.30*	–	1.99–3.20◊	RIA	1980	143
	Adults	19–71 years	63	1.44	0.39	–	RIA	1981	144
	Adults	...	100	1.52	0.29	(0.65–2.24)	RIA	1983	164
Post-γ globulin	Adults	...	100	0.96	0.20	(0.6–1.7)	RIA	1983	164

*Geometric mean. ◊ 1st–3rd quartile. RIA: radioimmunoassay; RID: radial immunodiffusion.

Table 27 *Fibrinogen concentrations in the plasma of children and adults*

	Subjects	Age	Number	Mean (g/L)	s (g/L)	95% range (g/L)	Method	Year	Ref.
Fibrinogen	...	...	–	–	–	1.90–3.65	Isolation as fibrin; phenol reagent	1971	145
	Men	16–40 years	15	2.93	0.79	–	Coagulation test	1973	146
	Women*	18–43 years	15	2.95	1.38	–	Coagulation test	1973	146
	Newborn	...	21	2.71	0.87	–	Automatic coagulometer	1976	147
	Children, adults	13–85 years	150	2.8	–	1.2–4.4	Nephelometry after $(NH_4)_2SO_4$ precipitation	1977	148
	Adults	23–30 years	12	2.02	0.45	–	...	1977	69
	Umbilical artery	...	33	1.92	0.46	–	Amidolytic assay	1979	149
	Umbilical vein	...	33	2.18	0.57	–	Amidolytic assay	1979	149
	Adults	18–45 years	22	2.00	0.60	–	Clotting by thrombin	1979	150
Cryofibrinogen	Adults	18–45 years	22	0.23	0.22	–	...	1979	150
Fibrin(ogen) degradation products	Adults	18–45 years	22	–	–	<0.005	...	1979	150
				µg/L					
Fibrinopeptide A	Adults	...	37	1.5	0.5	–	RIA	1980	327

*Without ovulation inhibitors. RIA: radioimmunoassay

Table 28 *Concentrations of prothrombin, plasminogen, α_2-antiplasmin, and antithrombin III in the plasma of adults*

	Subjects	Age	Number	Mean (mg/L)	s (mg/L)	Method	Year	Ref.
Prothrombin	Adults	Mean 37 years	11	140	10	EID	1978	161
	Adults	...	12	79	9	RIA	1983	163
Plasminogen	Adults	Mean 38 years	12	208	19	EID	1978	161
	Adults	...	28	172	26	Caseinolytic test	1979	162
α_2-Antiplasmin	Adults	...	50	61.3	8.8	RID	1979	162
Antithrombin III	Adults	...	–	300	80	RID	1979	328
	Adults	...	7	230	23	RIA	1981	329

EID: electroimmunodiffusion; RIA: radioimmunoassay; RID: radial immunodiffusion.

Table 29 *Concentration of transcobalamins in serum or plasma*

	Material	Subjects	Age	Number	Mean	s	Year	Ref.
					ng/L			
Transcobalamin I	Serum	Men	23–48 years	10	59	27	1977	155
	Plasma	Men	23–48 years	10	44	22	1977	155
	Serum	Women	22–58 years	10	52	13	1977	155
	Plasma	Women	22–58 years	10	40	11	1977	155
		Whites:						
	Serum	Cord blood		33	108	33	1982	156
	Serum	Men		40	84	26	1982	156
	Serum	Women		40	77	24	1982	156
		Blacks:						
	Serum	Cord blood		13	125	43	1982	156
	Serum	Men		37	97	30	1982	156
	Serum	Women		42	99	30	1982	156
Transcobalamin II	Serum	Men	23–48 years	10	612	122	1977	155
	Plasma	Men	23–48 years	10	522	85	1977	155
	Serum	Women	22–58 years	10	697	188	1977	155
	Plasma	Women	22–58 years	10	608	186	1977	155
		Whites:						
	Serum	Cord blood		33	588	159	1982	156
	Serum	Men		40	558	105	1982	156
	Serum	Women		40	641	123	1982	156
		Blacks:						
	Serum	Cord blood		13	999	162	1982	156
	Serum	Men		37	881	205	1982	156
	Serum	Women		42	1059	231	1982	156
Transcobalamin III	Serum	Men	23–48 years	10	199	43	1977	155
	Plasma	Men	23–48 years	10	133	34	1977	155
	Serum	Women	22–58 years	10	182	38	1977	155
	Plasma	Women	22–58 years	10	135	36	1977	155
		Whites:						
	Serum	Cord blood		33	106	39	1982	156
	Serum	Men		40	166	37	1982	156
	Serum	Women		40	151	41	1982	156
		Blacks:						
	Serum	Cord blood		13	200	60	1982	156
	Serum	Men		37	273	67	1982	156
	Serum	Women		42	208	71	1982	156

2. Immunoglobulins activate the body's intrinsic defense systems which commence the elimination of the antigen. This function is common to all immunoglobulins, and resides in their constant domains. It comprises, for example, the activation of the complement system and the binding capacity to phagocytes and other blood cells. Class-specific variants of the immunoglobulin functions are shown in Table 1 (page 135).

Reference values

Immunochemical methods (single radial immunodiffusion according to MANCINI, electroimmunodiffusion, and immunoprecipitation with nephelometric evaluation, etc.) are used for the determination of IgG, IgA, IgM and IgD, radioimmunological methods for the determination of IgD and IgE.

Published reference values and intervals (Tables 34–40, pages 152–156) reflect the differences attributable to biological and technical peculiarities of determination.

Calibration of standards. The WHO has provided reference material for standard calibrations for determining the concentration of immunoglobulins; the Ig concentrations in this standard are given in IU/mL[203] (IU: international units). Later, officially recognized conversion factors to calculate mass concentrations for IgG, IgA, and IgM were published[204]. The conversion factors for IgD and IgE are still a subject of debate[174,184,198,205]. The concentrations given in Table 34 (page 152) were calculated from data in IU/mL, using these factors. They are, therefore, affected by any error in the conversion factor.

The *distribution of the reference values* varies depending on the Ig concerned, the population studied and the statistical methods used[206]. Normal distributions have been reported for IgG, IgA, and IgM concentrations[176], but more commonly the distributions are more or less logarithmic-normal (Table 34).

The *antibody spectrum of the anti-immunoglobulin sera* influences the results of immunochemical concentration determinations. The antisera contain antibodies to antigens specific to classes, subclasses and types and, in addition, antibodies to individual antigens in the variable domains of the immunoglobulin chains. The antigen spectrum of immunoglobulins varies in the patients and normal subjects under investigation, especially for the variable segments. Variable subclass concentrations may also cause considerable variations in the antigen spectrum. Differences in the antigen composition may lead to divergent results mainly when mass concentrations are determined[207]. An elimination of antibodies to the variable regions in the Ig molecule may improve the results[208].

IgM determinations are further distorted by the variable percentage of monomer IgM in patients' and in normal sera. A nephelometric evaluation of immunoprecipitation eliminates this source of error, but cannot remove the difficulties arising from divergent antibody and antigen spectra.

Influence of age, sex, race, and the selection of a reference population. The fetal production of immunoglobulins is very low, but since IgG passes from the mother on to the fetus through the pla-

Table 30 *Concentration of the complement factors C3 and C4 in the serum of children and adults*

Subjects	Age	Number	C3 Mean	C3 s	C3 95% range	C4 Mean	C4 s	C4 95% range	Method	Year	Ref.
			g/L								
Boys	8–19 years	17	0.81	0.118	–	...	...	...	EID*	1971	102
Girls	8–19 years	11	0.92	0.179	–	...	...	...	EID*	1971	102
Men	20–39 years	62	0.83	0.167		...	...	...	EID*	1971	102
Women	20–39 years	36	0.81	0.217		...	...	...	EID*	1971	102
Men	40–59 years	44	0.89	0.149	0.54–1.17◇	...	...	...	EID*	1971	102
Women	40–59 years	35	0.84	0.161		...	...	...	EID*	1971	102
Men	60–95 years	26	0.92	0.136		...	...	...	EID*	1971	102
Women	60–95 years	29	0.96	0.145		...	...	...	EID*	1971	102
Children	≤14 years	58	0.82	–	0.57–1.07	...	...	...	EID*	1972	103
Adults	18–93 years	150	0.75	–	0.35–1.15	...	...	...	EID*	1972	103
Adults		62	0.875	0.2043	–	...	...	...	RID*	1974	104
Adults		16	0.77	0.088	–	0.259	0.064	–	RID*	1975	111
Adults		11	...	...	...	0.35	0.10	–	RID	1977	105
Cord blood		50	0.83	–	0.57–1.16†	0.13	–	0.066–0.23†	Rate nephelometry	1982	165
Children	1 month	50	0.83	–	0.53–1.24†	0.14	–	0.070–0.25†	Rate nephelometry	1982	165
Children	2 months	50	0.96	–	0.59–1.49†	0.15	–	0.074–0.28†	Rate nephelometry	1982	165
Children	3 months	50	0.94	–	0.64–1.31†	0.16	–	0.087–0.27†	Rate nephelometry	1982	165
Children	4 months	50	1.07	–	0.62–1.75†	0.19	–	0.083–0.38†	Rate nephelometry	1982	165
Children	5 months	50	1.07	–	0.64–1.67†	0.18	–	0.071–0.36†	Rate nephelometry	1982	165
Children	6 months	50	1.15	–	0.74–1.71†	0.21	–	0.086–0.42†	Rate nephelometry	1982	165
Children	7–9 months	50	1.13	–	0.75–1.66†	0.20	–	0.095–0.37†	Rate nephelometry	1982	165
Children	10–12 months	50	1.26	–	0.73–1.80[e]	0.22	–	0.12–0.39†	Rate nephelometry	1982	165
Children	1 year	50	1.29	–	0.84–1.74[e]	0.23	–	0.12–0.40†	Rate nephelometry	1982	165
Children	2 years	50	1.20	–	0.81–1.70†	0.19	–	0.092–0.34†	Rate nephelometry	1982	165
Children	3 years	50	1.17	–	0.77–1.71†	0.20	–	0.097–0.36†	Rate nephelometry	1982	165
Children	4–5 years	50	1.21	–	0.86–1.66†	0.21	–	0.13–0.32†	Rate nephelometry	1982	165
Children	6–8 years	50	1.18	–	0.88–1.55†	0.20	–	0.12–0.32†	Rate nephelometry	1982	165
Children	9–10 years	50	1.34	–	0.89–1.95†	0.22	–	0.10–0.40†	Rate nephelometry	1982	165
Adults		120	1.25	–	0.83–1.77†	0.28	–	0.15–0.45†	Rate nephelometry	1982	165

* Behringwerke standard serum.
◇ Calculation with logarithmic-normal distribution.
† Calculation with logarithmic-normal distribution except ranges indicated ([e]), which were distributed in a gaussian fashion.

EID: electroimmunodiffusion; RID: radial immunodiffusion.

centa, the IgG concentration in the blood of the newborn corresponds to that of healthy adults or is even higher, as a result of the postnatal contraction of the plasma volume[209] (Tables 36 and 37). The IgG concentration decreases rapidly during the first 3 months of life (Tables 36 and 37), since the maternal immunoglobulins are broken down, whereas the synthesis within the infant's body increases only slowly. The IgG concentration reaches adult levels at the age of 4[199,210] or somewhere between the age of 6 to 8[165,193,196,209], depending on the study.

The IgA concentration in the healthy newborn is so low that it often cannot be detected by radial immunodiffusion[193,196,209]. It rises in infancy[211] and in later childhood, reaching adult levels not before puberty[165,193].

The IgM concentration is low in the newborn, reaching adult levels somewhere between the age of 4 to 16, depending on the population studied and the method used[165] (Tables 36 and 37).

IgD is detected in the newborn by radioimmunoassay (Table 34) but not easily by radial immunodiffusion[209]. Adult levels are reached somewhere in childhood[186,209].

The IgE concentration is very low in the newborn[189,212], but increases steadily from infancy[190] up to the age of 5 to 15[190,213]. After this age, the IgE level tends to decrease[187,190,213]. The interindividual variation in children is distinctly more pronounced than in adults[196].

The IgG and IgA concentrations increase steadily with age in healthy adults (Table 35)[192,214,215], while the IgM concentration remains constant[192].

IgM concentrations are higher in women than in men (Table 34), whereas in the case of IgG and IgA concentrations no significant differences between the sexes have been observed. Blacks show higher IgG, IgA, and IgM concentrations than Whites even in the same environments (for example hospital personnel)[177]. The IgE concentration also seems to be higher in Blacks than in Whites[213].

Apart from age, sex, and race, the Ig concentrations in an individual are contingent first and foremost on the influx of antigens from the environment. Since the individual environment is difficult to define, divergent settings of reference intervals for the concentrations of Ig classes must be accepted, according to the population concerned.

During pregnancy, the IgG, IgA, and IgM concentrations decrease slightly[216]. As to the IgD concentration, no univocal alteration has been reported[217].

Role of aberrations in serum protein levels (dysproteinemias)

Many of the components of the complex serum protein pattern display parallel disease-related changes constituting typical reaction constellations[247] (Table 31).

Reactive dysproteinemias

Acute inflammatory dysproteinemia[247], *acute phase plasma protein response*[236,237]. An acute inflammatory dysproteinemia occurs in cases of tissue damage and tissue inflammation. It can be initiated, for example, by operations, myocardial infarction, necrotic tumor tissue, bacterial infections, and active collagen diseases. The extent of the change in protein level is parallel with the extent and the intensity of the precipitating process. Acute inflammatory dysproteinemia is manifested in a proliferation of fibrinogen, α_1-antitrypsin, α_1-antichymotrypsin, α_1-acid glycoprotein, ceruloplasmin, haptoglobin, C2, C3, C4, and a massive increase in C-reactive protein as well as in serum amyloid A protein *(positive reaction of the acute phase)*[237] (Table 32). The concentrations of albumin, prealbumin, transferrin, and α_2HS-glycoprotein are diminished *(negative reaction of the acute phase)*[249]. The reaction of C-reactive protein and α_1-antichymotrypsin begins during the first hours, while the rest of the proteins of the acute phase do not react until after 1–2 days[237,249]. α_2-Macroglobulin, Gc-globulin, and hemopexin

Table 31 *Disease-related changes in serum protein levels (reaction constellations)*[235]

Reactive dysproteinemias
Acute inflammation (acute phase reaction)
Chronic inflammation
Liver disease
Disturbances in plasma protein balance
Plasma protein depletion syndrome:
Nephrotic syndrome (selective plasma protein depletion)
Enteral protein depletion syndrome (global plasma protein depletion syndrome)
Disorders in plasma protein synthesis:
Defect-related dysproteinemias (defect-related pathoproteinemias)
Paraproteinemias (monoclonal gammopathies)

Table 32 *The positive acute-phase response*[246]

Concentration may increase by about 50%
Ceruloplasmin
C3
Concentration may increase 2-fold to 3-fold
α_1-Acid glycoprotein
α_1-Antitrypsin
α_1-Antichymotrypsin
Haptoglobin
Fibrinogen
Concentration may increase up to 1000-fold
C-reactive protein
Serum amyloid A protein

remain unimplicated[237,250,251] as do the immunoglobulins in the initial stage[92]. The total plasma protein concentration remains within the normal range, while the total serum protein concentration tends toward lower levels as a result of the larger fibrinogen fraction. A distinct hypoproteinemia may develop in cases of very severe tissue lesions. Electrophoresis shows an elevation in α_1- and α_2-globulin levels at the expense of albumins. β-Globulin levels may also be elevated. Acute inflammatory dysproteinemia can be reliably detected by electrophoretic serum protein fractionation. Determinations of the concentration of individual proteins yield no additional information.

Chronic inflammatory dysproteinemia is characterized by the combination of the acute-phase reaction with a proliferation of immunoglobulins[249]. The activity of the tissue process is lower in this chronic form than with acute inflammatory dysproteinemia, and accordingly the acute phase is in general notably milder and in some instances detectable only through the decrease in the albumin, prealbumin and transferrin concentrations. The increase in Ig is based on stimulation by endogenous and exogenous antigens, in some cases known (as in infections), in others presumed (as in autoimmune diseases), and in still others difficult to identify (as in granulomatous diseases and malignant tumors)[252]. Chronic inflammatory dysproteinemia is in general easy to identify in the electrophoretic diagram by virtue of the decrease in albumin, slight rise in α_2-globulin, and increase in the concentration of the γ fraction. The total protein concentration usually remains within the normal range. However, potent stimulation of Ig synthesis, with high Ig concentrations, can result in definite hyperproteinemia (with serum levels up to 100 g/L).

Dysproteinemia secondary to diseases of the liver. In *hepatic cirrhosis,* electrophoresis results in an unmistakable protein pattern. The concentration of the γ fraction is markedly increased and merged with the β fraction wave. The α_1 and α_2 fractions show a tendency to fall, and the albumin fraction is decreased. The total protein concentration may be normal, low, or elevated. It is the resultant of opposing influences, such as an enhancement of Ig synthesis, a diminution in albumin and α-globulin synthesis in the liver, fluctuations in plasma volume, and a loss of plasma proteins in the peritoneal space[247]. Decreases of the prealbumin and prothrombin concentrations are sensitive indicators of liver disease.

The pattern of increases in the concentration of the Ig classes in hepatobiliary diseases are very variable[253,254], and its evaluation is

(Continued on page 154)

Table 33 *Defect-related dysproteinemias*[236–238]

Defect-related dysproteinemia	Consequences
Analbuminemia	Tendency toward edema[239]; in some cases disorders in transport of hormones, enzymes and calcium
α_1-Antitrypsin deficiency	Bronchopulmonary disease, hepatopathy (page 269)
Thyroxine-binding globulin deficiency	Normal thyroid function but reduced T_3 and T_4 levels in plasma; in some cases retarded growth[240]
Sex-hormone-binding globulin deficiency	Slight hirsutism[241]
Haptoglobin deficiency:	
Primary	None
Secondary	None
Hypoceruloplasminemia:	
Wilson's disease	Copper deposits in tissue
Secondary to severe chronic hepatopathy, protein depletion syndrome	None
Cholinesterase deficiency (or cholinesterase variants with altered substrate specificity)	Increased sensitivity to succinylcholin (page 274)
Deficiency of complement components	Increased susceptibility to infection (page 241)
Deficiency of C$\bar{1}$ inhibitor:	
Primary	Angioneurotic edema (Quincke)
Secondary to B-lymphocyte tumors[242]	None
Hypotransferrinemia:	
Primary	Iron-refractory sideropenic anemia, hemosiderin deposits in the tissue (liver cirrhosis)
Secondary to infections, tumors, protein depletion syndrome	Only in severe forms of distinct anemia
Transcobalamin II deficiency (or variants with altered function)[243]	Disturbed maturation of B lymphocytes with antibody-deficiency syndrome, megaloblastic anemia[244]
Fibrinogen deficiency (or variants with altered function)[245]	Clotting disorder (page 231)
Antithrombin III deficiency (or variants with altered function)[262]	Tendency toward thromboembolic disorders (page 232)

Table 34 *Ig concentrations in the serum*

Subjects	Age	Number	Mean (IU/mL)	*s* or 95% confidence interval (IU/mL)	Mean (g/L)	*s* or 95% confidence interval (g/L)	Method	Standard	Remarks	Year	Reference
IgG concentration											
German men	20–70 years	54	...	...	12.37	*s* 1.59	RID	Hyland standard serum	Normal distribution	1972	176
German women	20–70 years	25	...	...	12.95	*s* 2.11	RID	Hyland standard serum		1972	176
American black men	...	50	...	...	11.14	*s* 2.27	RID	...	Significantly higher concentrations in Blacks than in Whites	1973	177
American white men	...	50	...	...	9.59	*s* 1.83	RID	...		1973	177
American black women	...	50	...	...	10.53	*s* 1.69	RID	...		1973	177
American white women	...	50	...	...	9.25	*s* 1.38	RID	...		1973	177
Bulgarian men and women	21–50 years	60	129.4	*s* 28.6	10.40	*s* 2.30	RID	Calibrated with WHO reference preparation 67/97	No sex difference[179]	1973	178
German men and women	20–30 years	106	136.8	*s* 33.7	11.00	*s* 2.71	RID	Behringwerke standard serum	Normal distribution	1974	180
German men	...	292	...	...	12.51	*s* 2.9	Nephelometry	Behringwerke standard serum	No sex difference; logarithmic-normal distribution	1974	181
German women	...	261	...	...	11.52	*s* 2.8	Nephelometry	Behringwerke standard serum		1974	181
American white men and women	18–80 years	508	125	70–195	10.05	5.63–15.68	RID	Calibrated with WHO reference preparation 67/95	No sex difference; distribution skewed to the right	1977	182
IgA concentration											
German men	20–70 years	54	...	...	2.44	*s* 0.45	RID	Hyland standard serum	Normal distribution	1972	176
German women	20–70 years	25	...	...	2.54	*s* 0.53	RID	Hyland standard serum		1972	176
American black men	...	50	...	...	2.75	*s* 0.73	RID	...	Significantly higher concentrations in Blacks than in Whites	1973	177
American white men	...	50	...	...	2.33	*s* 0.53	RID	...		1973	177
American black women	...	50	...	...	2.67	*s* 0.63	RID	...		1973	177
American white women	...	50	...	...	2.34	*s* 0.52	RID	...		1973	177
Bulgarian men and women	21–50 years	60	114.3	*s* 40.5	1.62	*s* 0.58	RID	Calibrated with WHO reference preparation 67/97	No sex difference[179]	1973	178
German men	20–30 years	60	114.5*	*s* 56.4	1.63*	*s* 0.86	RID	Behringwerke standard serum	Logarithmic-normal distribution	1974	180
German women	20–30 years	37	114.5*	*s* 52.4	1.63*	*s* 0.74	RID	Behringwerke standard serum		1974	180
German men	...	292	...	...	2.12	*s* 0.81	Nephelometry	Behringwerke standard serum	No sex difference; logarithmic-normal distribution	1974	181
German women	...	261	...	...	1.82	*s* 0.76	Nephelometry	Behringwerke standard serum		1974	181
American white men	18–80 years	352	125	40–250	1.78	0.57–3.55	RID	Calibrated with WHO reference preparation 67/95	Distribution skewed to the right	1977	182
American white women	18–80 years	212	107	40–215	1.52	0.57–3.05	RID	Calibrated with WHO reference preparation 67/95		1977	182
IgM concentration											
German men	20–70 years	54	...	...	1.20	*s* 0.39	RID	Hyland standard serum	Higher concentrations in women than in men; normal distribution	1972	176
German women	20–70 years	25	...	...	1.51	*s* 0.50	RID	Hyland standard serum		1972	176
American black men	...	50	...	...	1.39	*s* 0.50	RID	...	Significantly higher concentrations in Blacks than in Whites	1973	177
American white men	...	50	...	...	1.03	*s* 0.39	RID	...		1973	177
American black women	...	50	...	...	1.48	*s* 0.42	RID	...		1973	177
American white women	...	50	...	...	1.01	*s* 0.32	RID	...		1973	177
Bulgarian men	21–50 years	30	114.7	*s* 51.5	0.97	*s* 0.45	RID	Calibrated with WHO reference preparation 67/97	Higher concentrations in women than in men	1973	178
Bulgarian women	21–50 years	30	147.0	*s* 34.4	1.25	*s* 0.29	RID	Calibrated with WHO reference preparation 67/97		1973	178

Subjects	Age	Number	Mean (IU/mL)	95% confidence interval (IU/mL)	Mean (mg/L)	95% confidence interval (mg/L)	Method	Standard	Remarks	Year	Reference
IgM concentration (continued)											
German men	20–30 years	68	133.1*	33.0–293.7	1.13*	0.28–2.49	RID	Behringwerke standard serum	Higher concentrations in women than in men; logarithmic-normal distribution	1974	180
German women	20–30 years	43	173.4*	81.2–299.1	1.47*	0.69–2.53	RID	Behringwerke standard serum		1974	180
German men	...	292	...	...	1.09	s 0.49	Nephelometry	Behringwerke standard serum	No sex difference; logarithmic-normal distribution	1974	181
German women	...	261	...	...	1.21	s 0.50	Nephelometry	Behringwerke standard serum		1974	181
American white men	18–80 years	308	160	50–350	1.36	0.42–2.96	RID	Calibrated with WHO reference preparation 67/95	Distribution skewed to the right	1977	182
American white women	18–80 years	219	201	60–460	1.70	0.51–3.90	RID	Calibrated with WHO reference preparation 67/95		1977	182

Subjects	Age	Number	Mean (IU/mL)	95% confidence interval (IU/mL)	Mean (mg/L)	95% confidence interval (mg/L)	Method	Standard	Remarks	Year	Reference
IgD concentration											
American children	6 weeks to 19 months	23	...	...	1*	0–6	RID	Calibrated with WHO research standard 67/37	(Multimodal) logarithmic-normal distribution	1975	183
American children	3–14 years	105	...	...	16*	Z0–700	RID	Calibrated with WHO research standard 67/37		1975	183
American men and women	21–55 years	57	...	...	24*	0–610	RID	Calibrated with WHO research standard 67/37		1975	183
American white men and women	19–59 years	112	13.0*	0.19–156	18.3*	0.27–220	RIA	Purified myeloma protein, calibrated with WHO research standard 67/37	No sex difference. (Multimodal) logarithmic-normal distribution with familial aggregation of the values[185]	1977	184
American children	Newborn	16	0.14*	0.09–0.22	...	...	RIA	Calibrated with WHO research standard 67/37	...	1980	186
American children	1–20 years	82	13.7*	0.54–340	...	...	RIA	Calibrated with WHO research standard 67/37	Logarithmic-normal distribution, skewed to the right	1980	186
American men and women	21–70 years	80	11.8*	0.72–194	...	...	RIA	Calibrated with WHO research standard 67/37		1980	186

Subjects	Age	Number	Mean (IU/mL)	95% confidence interval (extreme range in brackets) (IU/mL)	Mean (μg/L)	95% confidence interval (μg/L)	Method	Standard	Remarks	Year	Reference
IgE concentration											
American children	2–19 months	12	18*	1–222	105*	2.4–537	RIA	Calibrated with WHO research standard 68/341	(Multimodal) logarithmic-normal distribution	1975	183
American children and adults	2–55 years	106	55*	5–621	133*	12–1502	RIA	Calibrated with WHO research standard 68/341		1975	183
German children and adults	11–70 years	355	55*	< 672	...	...	RIST	Calibrated with WHO research standard 68/341	No sex difference. (Multimodal) logarithmic-normal distribution, skewed to the right	1977	187
Swiss men and women	...	93	47*	< 195	...	...	RIST	...	Logarithmic-normal distribution	1979	188
Swiss men and women	...	93	36*	< 331	...	...	PRIST	...		1979	188
Dutch newborn (cord blood)	...	20	0.54	(0.05–2.85)	...	...	PRIST	...		1979	189
Dutch men and women	...	31	38.6*	< 664	...	...	PRIST	...	Logarithmic-normal distribution	1981	190
French men and women	18–59 years	138	152	(< 10–1260) 80% < 200	...	...	ELISA	Calibrated with WHO research standard 68/341	Values very dispersed	1983	191

*Geometric mean. RID: radial immunodiffusion; RIA: radioimmunoassay; RIST: radioimmunosorbent test; PRIST: paper radioimmunosorbent test; ELISA: enzyme-linked immunosorbent assay.

Table 35 *Ig concentrations in the serum of 3213 white American children and adults*[192]

Age	IgG				IgA				IgM*			
	Men		Women		Men		Women		Men		Women	
	Geometric mean	95% confidence interval	Geometric mean	95% confidence interval	Geometric mean	95% confidence interval	Geometric mean	95% confidence interval	Geometric mean	95% confidence interval	Geometric mean	95% confidence interval
	g/L											
5–9 years ...	10.28	6.34–16.65	11.05	6.82–17.92	1.09	0.47–2.49	1.10	0.48–2.51				
10–14 years .	10.41	6.42–16.88	11.13	6.87–18.04	1.16	0.51–2.65	1.15	0.50–2.64				
15–19 years .	10.55	6.51–17.10	11.20	6.91–18.16	1.23	0.54–2.83	1.21	0.53–2.78				
20–24 years .	10.69	6.60–17.33	11.28	6.96–18.28	1.32	0.57–3.01	1.28	0.56–2.93				
25–29 years .	10.83	6.68–17.56	11.35	7.00–18.40	1.40	0.61–3.21	1.35	0.59–3.08				
30–34 years .	10.98	6.77–17.79	11.43	7.05–18.52	1.50	0.65–3.42	1.42	0.62–3.25				
35–39 years .	11.12	6.86–18.03	11.50	7.10–18.65	1.59	0.70–3.65	1.49	0.65–3.42				
40–44 years .	11.27	6.95–18.27	11.58	7.14–18.77	1.70	0.74–3.89	1.57	0.69–3.60	0.77	0.30–2.01	1.06	0.41–2.77
45–49 years .	11.42	7.04–18.50	11.66	7.19–18.90	1.81	0.79–4.15	1.65	0.72–3.79				
50–54 years .	11.57	7.14–18.75	11.74	7.24–19.02	1.93	0.84–4.42	1.74	0.76–3.99				
55–59 years .	11.72	7.23–19.00	11.81	7.29–19.15	2.06	0.90–4.72	1.83	0.80–4.20				
60–64 years .	11.88	7.33–19.25	11.89	7.34–19.28	2.20	0.96–5.03	1.93	0.84–4.42				
65–69 years .	12.04	7.43–19.51	11.97	7.39–19.41	2.34	1.02–5.36	2.03	0.89–4.66				
70–74 years .	12.20	7.52–19.77	12.05	7.44–19.54	2.49	1.09–5.71	2.14	0.94–4.91				
75 and over .	12.36	7.62–20.03	12.13	7.49–19.67	2.66	1.16–6.09	2.26	0.98–5.16				

Method: radial immunodiffusion.
*The IgM concentrations show no age dependence.

Standard: purified immunoglobulins, calibrated with WHO reference preparation 67/95.

Table 36 *Ig concentrations in the serum of American children* and adults*[193]

Age	Number	IgG				IgA				IgM			
		Mean	95% confidence interval	Mean	95% confidence interval	Mean	95% confidence interval	Mean	95% confidence interval	Mean	95% confidence interval	Mean	95% confidence interval
		IU/mL		g/L		IU/mL		g/L		IU/mL		g/L	
Cord blood	29	135.9	92.7–199.2	10.93	7.45–16.02	0.4	0.03–5.3	0.006	0.0004–0.075	12.5	5.0–31.1	0.106	0.042–0.263
½–3 months.....	7	60.5	36.5–100.2	4.86	2.93–8.06	9.2	2.1–40.2	0.131	0.030–0.571	60.5	18.9–193.9	0.512	0.160–1.642
3–6 months	9	44.8	17.3–116.2	3.60	1.39–9.34	12.9	3.0–54.8	0.183	0.043–0.778	58.0	23.7–141.7	0.491	0.201–1.200
6–12 months	13	82.8	51.0–134.4	6.66	4.10–10.81	22.8	9.1–57.6	0.324	0.129–0.818	123.0	56.1–268.9	1.042	0.475–2.278
1–2 years	22	78.4	43.4–141.7	6.30	3.49–11.39	25.0	8.8–71.7	0.355	0.125–1.018	121.4	47.5–270.2	1.028	0.402–2.289
2–3 years	16	94.6	60.0–149.3	7.61	4.82–12.00	35.7	15.4–82.8	0.507	0.219–1.176	125.2	63.7–246.2	1.060	0.540–2.085
3–6 years	74	105.7	68.8–162.5	8.50	5.53–13.07	54.2	23.2–126.7	0.770	0.329–1.799	131.0	66.5–257.9	1.110	0.563–2.184
6–9 years	32	120.4	80.3–180.5	9.68	6.46–14.51	70.8	19.6–156.1	1.005	0.278–2.217	133.6	65.1–274.3	1.132	0.551–2.323
9–12 years	20	119.7	76.2–188.0	9.62	6.13–15.12	85.1	40.3–180.0	1.208	0.572–2.556	166.7	82.9–335.1	1.412	0.702–2.838
12–16 years	14	123.0	83.0–182.1	9.89	6.67–14.64	90.4	53.9–154.4	1.284	0.765–2.192	133.6	57.9–308.4	1.131	0.490–2.612
Adults	22	136.7	81.8–228.5	10.99	6.58–18.37	113.0	50.3–253.8	1.605	0.714–3.604	157.0	47.5–310.2	1.330	0.402–2.627

Method: radial immunodiffusion.
Standard: pooled serum, calibrated with WHO reference preparation 67/95.
Mean value and 95% confidence interval calculated assuming a logarithmic-normal distribution.

Conversion factor for IgG: 1 IU = 80.4 μg; for IgA: 1 IU = 14.2 μg; for IgM: 1 IU = 8.47 μg[197].
* 106 boys and 101 girls, including 96 Whites and 68 Blacks.

usually not of help in differential diagnosis. The IgG level appears to provide some measure of the mesenchymal activity in the diseased liver, which is inaccessible to the usual plasma enzyme diagnostic. High IgA levels or a high IgA/transferrin ratio indicate alcoholic hepatopathy[255].

In *acute hepatitis* there is a limited acute inflammatory dysproteinemia. All globulin fractions, but especially the γ fraction, show a rise[100]. As to the proteins of the positive acute-phase response, the concentrations of α_1-antitrypsin and C3 rise, while haptoglobin and α_1-acid glycoprotein scarcely respond at all[256].

Disturbed plasma protein balance

Disease-specific serum protein patterns may be observed, but such conditions are much rarer than reactive dysproteinemias.

Plasma-protein depletion syndrome

Plasma proteins may be lost via the kidneys (in nephrotic syndromes), through the intestinal mucosa, through the skin (in extensive, weeping dermatitis and burns), and as a result of effusions from the body cavities[247]. One characteristic feature of the plasma-protein depletion syndrome is a pronounced hypoproteinemia, the plasma protein concentration in the nephrotic syndrome and in the enteral protein depletion falling often far below 50 g/L.

Nephrotic syndrome. When hypoproteinemia is pronounced, electrophoresis shows a marked relative increase in the α_2- and β-globulin fractions. The albumin fraction is distinctly reduced in both absolute and relative terms, while in relative terms the α_1 fraction is slightly increased. In most cases, the γ-globulin fraction is reduced in both absolute and relative terms, although a strong stimulation of Ig synthesis by the underlying disease (as in lupus nephritis) can bring about an increase or a return to normal values in the γ fraction. Usually the nephrotic syndrome is unmistakably identifiable by electrophoretic fractionation. Where hypoproteinemia is equivocal, an increase of proteins of high molecular mass (α_2-macroglobulins, β-lipoproteins, and haptoglobin polymers) indicates nephrotic syndrome[237,250]. The typical electrophoretic pattern develops mainly as a result of the loss of plasma proteins of

Table 37 *Ig concentrations in the serum of American children and adults*[165]

	Number	IgG				IgA				IgM			
		Mean	95% range	Mean	95% range	Mean	95% range	Mean	95% range	Mean	95% range	Mean	95% range
		IU/mL		g/L		IU/mL		g/L		IU/mL		g/L	
Cord blood ..	50	139.4	79.1–199.8	11.21	6.36–16.06	1.62	0.99–2.54	0.023	0.014–0.036	15.3	7.44–29.5	0.13	0.063–0.25
1 month	50	62.6	31.2–112.7	5.03	2.51–9.06	9.15	0.92–37.3	0.13	0.013–0.53	53.1	23.6–102.7	0.45	0.20–0.87
2 months	50	45.4	25.6–74.8	3.65	2.06–6.01	10.6	1.97–33.1	0.15	0.028–0.47	54.3	20.1–124.0	0.46	0.17–1.05
3 months	50	41.5	21.9–72.3	3.34	1.76–5.81	12.0	3.24–32.4	0.17	0.046–0.46	57.9	28.3–105.1	0.49	0.24–0.89
4 months	50	42.7	24.4–69.4	3.43	1.96–5.58	16.2	3.10–51.4	0.23	0.044–0.73	64.9	31.9–119.2	0.55	0.27–1.01
5 months	50	50.1	21.4–101.2	4.03	1.72–8.14	21.8	5.70–59.2	0.31	0.081–0.84	73.2	39.0–127.5	0.62	0.33–1.08
6 months	50	50.6	26.7–87.6	4.07	2.15–7.04	17.6	5.70–47.9	0.25	0.081–0.68	73.2	41.3–120.4	0.62	0.35–1.02
7–9 months ..	50	59.1	27.0–112.4	4.75	2.17–9.04	25.4	7.75–63.4	0.36	0.11–0.90	94.5	40.1–148.8	0.80	0.34–1.26[e]
10–12 months	50	73.9	36.6–133.0	5.94	2.94–10.69	28.2	11.3–59.2	0.40	0.16–0.84	96.8	48.4–175.9	0.82	0.41–1.49
1 year........	50	84.5	42.9–150.9	6.79	3.45–12.13	31.0	9.86–74.6	0.44	0.14–1.06	109.8	50.8–204.3	0.93	0.43–1.73
2 years.......	50	85.3	52.7–130.7	6.86	4.24–10.51	33.1	9.86–86.6	0.47	0.14–1.23	112.2	56.7–198.3	0.95	0.48–1.68
3 years.......	50	90.5	54.9–141.2	7.28	4.41–11.35	46.5	15.5–112.0	0.66	0.22–1.59	122.8	55.5–236.1	1.04	0.47–2.00
4–5 years	50	97.0	57.6–153.7	7.80	4.63–12.36	47.9	17.6–108.5	0.68	0.25–1.54	116.9	50.8–231.4	0.99	0.43–1.96
6–8 years	50	113.8	78.7–159.2	9.15	6.33–12.80	63.4	23.2–142.3	0.90	0.33–2.02	126.3	56.7–244.4	1.07	0.48–2.07
9–10 years ...	50	125.2	75.6–195.5	10.07	6.08–15.72	79.6	31.7–166.2	1.13	0.45–2.36	142.9	61.4–285.7	1.21	0.52–2.42
Adults	120	123.6	79.5–167.8	9.94	6.39–13.49	120.4	49.3–219.7	1.71	0.70–3.12	184.2	66.1–415.6	1.56	0.56–3.52

Method: rate nephelometry.
Ranges based on a logarithmic transformation of the data to eliminate skewness except range indicated ([e]), which is distributed in a gaussian fashion.

Conversion factor for IgG: 80.4 µg = 1 IU; for IgA: 14.2 µg = 1 IU; for IgM: 8.47 µg = 1 IU[197].

Table 38 *Ig concentration in the serum of Dutch children and adults*[196]

	Number	IgG				IgA				IgM				IgD				IgE			
		Mean	*s*	Mean	*s*	Mean	*s*	Mean	*s*	Mean	*s*	Mean	*s*	Mean	*s*	Mean	*s*	Mean	*s*	Mean	*s*
		IU/mL		g/L		IU/mL		g/L		IU/mL		g/L		IU/mL		mg/L		IU/mL		µg/L	
Boys																					
4–5 years	15	96	16	7.7	1.3	66	32	0.94	0.45	98	31	0.83	0.26	39	53	55	75	134	169	324	409
5–6 years	15	97	20	7.8	1.6	44	21	0.62	0.30	83	28	0.70	0.24	21	130	30	183	390	530	944	1280
6–7 years	15	105	19	8.4	1.5	59	24	0.84	0.34	114	41	0.97	0.35	40	38	56	54	309	685	748	1660
7–8 years	15	91	25	7.3	2.0	56	27	0.80	0.38	94	40	0.80	0.34	29	20	41	28	418	737	1010	1780
8–9 years	15	99	12	8.0	1.0	59	27	0.84	0.38	91	37	0.77	0.31	22	16	31	23	119	149	288	361
9–10 years	15	102	26	8.2	2.1	68	35	0.97	0.50	92	35	0.78	0.30	28	31	39	44	167	242	404	585
10–11 years	15	107	32	8.6	2.6	69	37	0.98	0.53	102	35	0.86	0.30	35	41	49	58	275	589	666	1430
11–12 years	15	109	21	8.8	1.7	70	24	0.99	0.34	116	51	0.98	0.43	43	30	61	42	272	625	658	1510
12–13 years	15	101	25	8.1	2.0	59	28	0.84	0.40	85	30	0.72	0.25	41	25	58	35	128	199	310	482
Men	15	107	22	8.6	1.8	109	45	1.55	0.64	144	47	1.22	0.40	21	14	30	20	68	72	165	174
Girls																					
4–5 years	15	99	25	8.0	2.0	56	28	0.80	0.40	144	60	1.22	0.51	36	46	51	65	309	941	748	2280
5–6 years	15	104	24	8.4	1.9	57	25	0.81	0.36	140	60	1.19	0.51	29	29	41	41	382	676	924	1640
6–7 years	15	101	26	8.1	2.1	52	24	0.74	0.34	125	57	1.06	0.48	27	24	38	34	188	176	455	426
7–8 years	15	107	17	8.6	1.4	44	19	0.62	0.27	134	54	1.13	0.46	34	31	48	44	143	155	346	375
8–9 years	15	118	20	9.5	1.6	62	34	0.88	0.48	129	32	1.09	0.27	27	27	38	38	248	392	600	949
9–10 years	15	111	23	8.9	1.8	63	24	0.89	0.34	130	38	1.10	0.32	19	16	27	23	185	248	448	600
10–11 years	15	114	23	9.2	1.8	57	17	0.81	0.24	134	48	1.13	0.41	40	34	56	48	712	970	1720	2350
11–12 years	15	115	25	9.2	2.0	77	36	1.09	0.51	134	47	1.13	0.40	50	43	71	61	331	595	801	1440
12–13 years	15	109	19	8.8	1.5	60	17	0.85	0.24	141	69	1.19	0.58	30	23	42	32	197	275	477	666
Women	15	117	32	9.4	2.6	94	40	1.33	0.57	168	62	1.42	0.53	24	20	34	28	88	96	213	232

Methods: IgG, IgA, IgM, IgD with radial immunodiffusion, IgE with radioimmunoassay.
Standard: calibrated with WHO reference preparation.

Conversion factor for IgG: 1 IU = 80.4 µg; for IgA: 1 IU = 14.2 µg; for IgM: 1 IU = 8.47 µg[197]; for IgD: 1 IU = 1.41 µg[198]; for IgE: 1 IU = 2.42 ng[174].

low molecular mass (α_1-globulins, albumin, IgG) through the enlarged pores of the glomerular filter[236]. Measurement of the concentrations of individual serum proteins (e.g. the IgG/transferrin ratio) gives some idea of pore size and is of prognostic significance. A reduction in C3, which, being a large molecule, is lost only slowly through a damaged glomerular filter, indicates an attenuating antigen – antibody reaction and is prognostically inauspicious[236].

Enteral protein-depletion syndrome. This condition may occur in many diseases accompanying injury to the intestinal epithelium, by increased pressure in the lymph drainage system of the intestine, and on rare occasions, by increased pressure in the venous branch of the intestinal circulation[236]. The syndrome is characterized by pronounced hypoproteinemia. Electrophoretic fractionation in some instances shows a relative decrease in the albumin and γ fractions. The α_1- and α_2-globulin fractions may show a rela-

(Continued on page 158)

Table 39 *Ig concentration in the serum of 132 Swedish children*[199]

Age	IgG				IgA		IgM				IgD		IgE	
	Boys		Girls		Mean	*s*	Boys		Girls		Mean	*s*	Mean	*s*
	Mean	*s*	Mean	*s*			Mean	*s*	Mean	*s*				
	g/L										mg/L		µg/L	
2–2½ years	–	–	–	–	–	–	–	–	–	–	–	–	137	47
2½–3½ years	8.96	2.76	8.76	1.43	0.626	0.327	0.729	0.088	0.926	0.430	9.5	6.3	140	58
3½–4½ years	8.53	1.12	10.33	1.92	0.730	0.228	0.662	0.331	1.202	0.665	11.4	8.3	178	93
4½–6½ years	9.60	3.11	10.31	2.41	1.010	0.615	0.762	0.336	0.909	0.186	11.1	6.7	209	119
6½–8½ years	10.06	2.21	10.68	1.63	0.952	0.310	0.732	0.246	0.861	0.235	21.4	14.7	251	167
8½–10½ years	9.72	1.34	10.54	0.90	1.025	0.311	0.780	0.248	0.941	0.324	27.8	24.2	256	158
10½–12½ years	11.69	2.46	13.35	0.75	1.131	0.492	0.792	0.371	1.081	0.429	29.6	16.5	239	169
12½–15½ years	14.70	3.86	15.62	4.09	1.327	0.866	0.839	0.302	1.021	0.395	36.2	37.1	330	212

Methods: IgG, IgA, IgM, IgD with radial immunodiffusion; IgE with radioimmunoassay.

Table 40 *Concentration of IgG subclasses in the serum of children and adults*

	Number	IgG_1		IgG_2		IgG_3		IgG_4		Method	Standard	Reference
		Mean	*s*	Mean	*s* or 95% confidence interval	Mean	*s* or 95% confidence interval	Mean	*s* or 95% confidence interval			
		g/L										
Mothers	38	5.14	1.28	2.70	*s* 0.63	0.48	*s* 0.26	0.19	*s* 0.14	RIA	WHO reference preparation 67/97	194
Cord blood	38	5.59	1.55	2.69	*s* 0.89	0.51	*s* 0.36	0.20	*s* 0.20	RIA	WHO reference preparation 67/97	194
10 days	7	5.94	2.11	2.56	*s* 0.52	0.56	*s* 0.14	0.29	*s* 0.24	RIA	WHO reference preparation 67/97	194
20 days	12	5.21	2.15	2.27	*s* 0.36	0.39	*s* 0.08	0.18	*s* 0.09	RIA	WHO reference preparation 67/97	194
30 days	13	4.25	1.27	1.75	*s* 0.58	0.30	*s* 0.10	0.21	*s* 0.14	RIA	WHO reference preparation 67/97	194
2 months	11	3.83	1.72	1.53	*s* 0.53	0.31	*s* 0.12	0.11	*s* 0.05	RIA	WHO reference preparation 67/97	194
3 months	12	3.32	1.81	0.91	*s* 0.44	0.45	*s* 0.18	0.13	*s* 0.08	RIA	WHO reference preparation 67/97	194
4 months	10	4.24	2.07	1.10	*s* 0.39	0.47	*s* 0.17	0.10	*s* 0.06	RIA	WHO reference preparation 67/97	194
8 months	10	6.59	2.77	1.47	*s* 0.56	0.51	*s* 0.27	0.12	*s* 0.09	RIA	WHO reference preparation 67/97	194
12 months	6	6.53	1.90	1.60	*s* 0.75	0.53	*s* 0.26	0.07	*s* 0.04	RIA	WHO reference preparation 67/97	194
24 months	14	6.52	1.82	1.66	*s* 0.41	0.45	*s* 0.10	0.25	*s* 0.20	RIA	WHO reference preparation 67/97	194
20 years	108	6.63	1.70	3.22	*s* 1.08	0.58	*s* 0.30	0.46	–	RIA	WHO reference preparation 67/97	194
Adults	111	8.01	1.71	2.17	0.81–3.89	0.94	0.28–1.94	0.08	0.025–0.16	RID	Purified myeloma proteins	195

RIA: radioimmunoassay; RID: radial immunodiffusion.

Table 41 *Defects in Ig synthesis*[236,238,247,271,272]

Ig system	Consequences
Primary agammaglobulinemias and hypogammaglobulinemias	
Transient hypogammaglobulinemia in infancy	Transient antibody-deficiency sydrome
X-linked agammaglobulinemia	Antibody-deficiency syndrome
Variable late-onset agammaglobulinemia	Defect in T- and B-cell systems; antibody-deficiency syndrome and impairment of cellular immunodefenses
Selective primary immunoglobulin disorders	
IgA deficiency (IgA concentration <0.1 g/L)	Respiratory-tract infections, atopic diseases, autoimmune diseases
IgM deficiency	Bacterial infections
Reduced IgG level and marked increase of IgM level (autoantibodies against IgG?)	Antibody-deficiency syndrome
Dysgammaglobulinemias	
Variable changes in the ratios between concentrations of the various Ig classes	In some cases antibody-deficiency syndrome
Secondary hypogammaglobulinemias	
Neoplasms of the lymphoreticular tissue (chronic lymphatic leukemia, plasmocytoma, macroglobulinemia, reticulosarcoma, lymphosarcoma), immunosuppressants, ionizing radiation	Moderate to pronounced antibody-deficiency syndrome

Table 42 *Concentrations of tissue proteins in serum or plasma*

Protein	Material	Subjects	Age	Number	Mean	95% range (extreme range in brackets) or *s*	Method	Year	Reference
					µg/L				
Ferritin	Serum	Men		78	131*	52–334	IRMA	1977	218
	Serum	Women		92	67*	21–213	IRMA	1977	218
	Serum	Cord blood		54	144	(46–400)	RIA	1980	219
	Serum	Men	14–60 years	27	96	(25–245)	ELISA	1981	220
	Serum	Women	14–60 years	51	39	(10–168)	ELISA	1981	220
	Serum	Pregnant women	3rd trimester	22	18.4	(8–39)	RIA	1982	221
	Plasma	Boys	11–18 years	91	38.9*	28–43	RIA	1982	222
	Plasma	Girls	11–18 years	67	33.8*	19–36	RIA	1982	222
	Serum	Men		79	98*	21–447	IRMA	1982	223
	Serum	Women	Menstruating	63	29*	8–110	IRMA	1982	223
	Serum	Women	Postmenopausal	39	85*	26–279	IRMA	1982	223
Lactoferrin	Plasma	Men		15	150	(30–280)	RIA	1982	224
	Plasma	Women		13	100	(<200)	RIA	1982	224
	Plasma	Children		16	60	(40–140)	RIA	1982	224
Ligandin	Serum			12	–	(<5.3)	RIA	1978	225
Osteocalcin (bone Gla protein, BGP)	Plasma	Men		47	7.89	*s* 0.32	RIA	1980	226
	Plasma	Women		62	4.85	*s* 0.36	RIA	1980	226
	Serum	Men		25	6.8	*s* 0.5	RIA	1983	227
	Serum	Women		26	5.8	*s* 0.5	RIA	1983	227
	Serum	Children	1 year	–	–	(25–30)	RIA	1983	227
Thyroglobulin	Serum	Adults		39	–	(0–44)	RIA	1979	228
	Serum			146	13.3	*s* 10.3	ELISA	1979	229
	Serum	Cord blood		56	37	*s* 3	RIA	1982	230
	Serum	Newborn	0–14 days	44	55	*s* 4	RIA	1982	230
	Serum	Adults	15–87 years	74	16.0	(4.8–89.6)	RIA	1983	335
Group I pepsinogens (Pg I)	Serum	Newborn	1st week	33	39.1	(22–140)	RIA	1979	231
	Serum	Adults		38	104	*s* 30	RIA	1979	231
	Serum	Men		–	122	*s* 34 (60–216)	RIA	1982	232
	Serum	Women		–	85	*s* 27 (33–171)	RIA	1982	232
	Serum	Men		162	44.0	*s* 24.6	RIA	1982	233
	Serum	Women		52	42.1	*s* 25.9	RIA	1982	233
Group II pepsinogens (Pg II)	Serum	Men		162	16.3	*s* 11.6	RIA	1982	233
	Serum	Women		52	12.6	*s* 8.8	RIA	1982	233
Pancreas-specific antigen (PaA)	Serum	Adults		51	–	<21.5 (<4–34)	ELISA	1981	234
Platelet factor 4 (PF-4)	Plasma	Children, adults	12–75 years	220	5.0	*s* 2.5	RIA	1980	330
	Plasma	Adults		30	2.98	*s* 1.04 (1.86–6.77)	RIA	1980	331
	Plasma	Adults	23–35 years	67	4.8	*s* 3.4 (0–30)	RIA	1981	332
β-Thromboglobulin	Plasma	Children		–	29	*s* 6 (0–71)	RIA	1980	333
	Plasma	Adults		30	25.8	*s* 11.7 (13.1–57.7)	RIA	1980	331
	Plasma	Adults	22–44 years	24	27	*s* 12 (8–54)	RIA	1980	334
'Tamm-Horsfall-like' glycoprotein	Serum	Adults		34	158	*s* 76 (58–341)	RIA	1983	336

*Geometric mean. IRMA: immunoradiometric assay; RIA: radioimmunoassay; ELISA: enzyme-linked immunosorbent assay.

tive increase, but the increase in α_2-globulin always remains much smaller than in the case of nephrotic syndrome and is accompanied by an increase in the α_1-globulin fraction. Measurements of individual protein concentrations show that the loss of protein takes place independently of molecular size[257]. In contrast to the pattern accompanying the nephrotic syndrome, IgM and IgA levels are reduced along with the IgG concentration. The concentrations of proteins of the positive acute-phase reaction may lie within the normal range. These findings reveal an equilibrium between depletion and intensified synthesis[235].

Disturbed plasma protein synthesis in protein malnutrition. Plasma protein synthesis is inhibited, as may be shown by the reduced prealbumin[258] and albumin levels[259,260]. The levels of prealbumin and also retinol-binding protein reflect a protein deficiency at an earlier stage than the albumin level[261].

Disorders in plasma protein synthesis

Defect-related dysproteinemias (defect-related pathoproteinemias). These conditions arise as a result of inherited or secondary disturbances in the synthesis of plasma proteins (Table 33 [page 151] and Table 41 [page 156]). Disorders in the synthesis of albumin, IgG and α_1-antitrypsin are detectable by electrophoretic fractionation (in the latter case, however, not reliably), while other disturbances in synthesis can be detected only by immunoelectrophoresis or by quantitative measurement of the specific proteins. The most frequent form of defect-related dysproteinemia is lack or extreme diminution of IgA. Its frequency among the population is about 1 : 700.

Immunoglobulin proliferation. Several classes of Ig and both Ig types are involved when plasma immunoglobulins proliferate as a result of stimulation by antigens. The result is surplus synthesis of immunoglobulins differing from one another in the structure of the variable segment of their H and L chains. The heterogenous (polyclonal) hypergammaglobulinemia shows up as a broad band in electrophoretic fractionation and on the diagram as a broad-based peak.

In monoclonal gammopathies, the proliferation of a single clone of plasma cells produces a homogenous, monoclonal immunoglobulin (paraprotein)[263]. Each paraprotein consists of 2 heavy chains of the same class and subclass and 2 light chains of the same type. These immunoglobulins are easily detected by electrophoresis: as a narrow band on the strip and as a narrow-based spike on the diagram. Class (and type) must be determined by immunoelectrophoresis, whereby the reduction in physiological immunoglobulins that is typical for all B-cell tumors is manifest at the same time. Bence-Jones proteins* are best detected by immunofixation[264]. Paraproteins of classes G and A occur in multiple myelomas, while those of class M are found in Waldenström's macroglobulinemia. Multiple myelomas with class D paraproteins are rare, and those with class E paraproteins are very rare. The uncontrolled intensification of synthesis in many cases results in marked hyperproteinemia (reaching levels far above 100 g/L). Paraproteins may also occur in other tumors of the B-lymphocyte system, in particular in chronic lymphatic leukemia. Usually their concentration remains low (around 10–20 g/L). Paraproteins may have the properties of cryoglobulins◊[265] or pyroglobulins†[266].

Paraproteins (usually an IgG or IgA globulin) also occur in about 1% of the otherwise normal, asymptomatic population; in persons older than 70 years, the incidence increases to 3%[267]. Usually the monoclonal immunoglobulins are present in a concentration of 10–20 g/L which remains constant for years. At the same time, there is no demonstrable reduction in the concentration of physiological immunoglobulins, and no Bence-Jones protein is found in the urine. The benign monoclonal gammopathy seems to

* These proteins are light-chain dimers.

◊ These proteins reversibly precipitate at low temperatures and redissolve on warming. They seem to differ from non-cryoimmunoglobulins in not having carbohydrate groups (most probably sialic-acid residues)[270].

† These proteins precipitate at temperatures of 45–60 °C.

Table 43 *Pregnancy-associated and oncofetal proteins*

	Protein	Structure	Mass of carbohydrates relative to mass of total protein	Sedimentation coefficient S_{20W}	Diffusion coefficient D_{20W}	Relative molecular mass	Electrophoretic fraction	Iso-electric point pI
			%	10^{-13} s	10^{-7} cm² s⁻¹			
Pregnancy-associated proteins	Pregnancy-specific β_1-glycoprotein.... (SP_1)	Glycoprotein	29.3[278]	4.5[278]	–	90000[278] 110000[279]	β_1[278]	4.1[278]
	Pregnancy-associated α_2-glycoprotein. (SP_3, pregnancy-zone protein)	Glycoprotein consisting of 2 identical subunits[283]	12.1[284]	11.5[284]	–	360000[284]	α_2[284]	4.7[284]
	Pregnancy-associated plasma protein A (PAPP-A)	Glycoprotein	–	–	–	750000– 820000[286]	α_2[286]	4.4[279]
	Pregnancy-associated plasma protein B (PAPP-B)	–	–	–	–	1000000[279]	β_1[279]	4.6–5.0[279]
	Placental protein 5.................. (PP5)	Glycoprotein	19.8[278]	2.8[278]	–	36000[278]	β_1[278]	4.6[278]
Oncofetal protein	Carcinoembryonic antigen............ (CEA)	Glycoprotein consisting of a single polypeptide chain[299]	50[300]	6.9–8.5[300]	–	200000– 250000[300]	β[301]	4.8[301]
	α-Fetoprotein........................ (α_1-fetoprotein)	1 polypeptide chain consisting of 590 amino acids[292]	3–4.3[293]	4.5–5.5[293]	6.18[293]	70000[292]	α_1[293]	4.7[293]
	α_2H-Fetoprotein......................	Iron-containing[304,305]	–	17[304]	–	600000[306]	α_2[304]	–
	βS-Fetoprotein	Glycoprotein[306]	–	–	–	200000[306]	β	–

be a biochemical abnormality; in long-term follow-ups only less than 10% of the subjects show a progression to overt myeloma[267].

Not only paraproteins, but also fibrinogen[268] (e.g. in the serum of heparin-treated patients) and C-reactive protein[152,268] (in acute dysproteinemias) may form additional fractions leading erroneously to suspicion of multiple myeloma or a related disease. The double paraprotein spikes which very occasionally occur on the electrophoretic diagram may be due to 2 different paraproteins, a complete paraprotein and a Bence-Jones protein, a paraprotein and its polymers, a paraprotein and its degradation products, and in some cases to an accumulation of lysozyme in the serum as well[251,268,269].

The significance of changes in the concentrations of individual proteins

Haptoglobin. The haptoglobin level falls in hemolytic anemias, and disappears from the serum of patients who have suffered intravascular or intramedullary hemolysis of serious degree[273,274].

Hemopexin. In certain intravascular hemolyses, the hemopexin level may decrease if a high heme level is found in the plasma, as in sickle-cell anemia[273]. In addition, the hemopexin level falls in porphyria cutanea tarda, although not in other disorders of porphyrin metabolism[248].

Transferrin. A rise in the transferrin level is evidence of iron deficiency[237], but it may also occur under the influence of ovulation inhibitors or during pregnancy, even though the iron reserves are not depleted[157].

Ferritin. The concentration in the plasma reflects the iron content of the body; low levels are found in childhood and during pregnancy (Table 42). Values below 12 µg/L are common in iron deficiency anemia; in the presence of an iron overload they can range up to 10000 µg/L[275].

IgE. Atopic allergy is characterized by the development of antibody responses of IgE[276]. Atopic persons show increased IgE levels, ranging from less than a 2- or 3-fold increase in asthma, in allergic rhinitis and in urticaria up to a 10- to more than a 100-fold increase in various parasitic infestations (Table 44)[188,190,277]. The highest IgE levels are found in the very rare cases of IgE myeloma.

Table 44 *Causes of increased IgE concentrations in the serum*[277]

Allergic diseases: asthma, allergic rhinitis, urticaria

Dermatologic diseases: atopic dermatitis, bullous pemphigus, dermatitis herpetiformis

Parasitic diseases: ascariasis, visceral larva migrans (*Toxocara*), capillariasis, echinococcosis, ancylostomiasis, amebiasis

Allergic bronchopulmonary aspergillosis

Immunodeficiency diseases: Wiskott-Aldrich syndrome, DiGeorge's syndrome, Nezelof's syndrome, selective IgA deficiency, hyperimmunoglobulin-E syndrome

Immunosuppressive therapy

Hypereosinophilic syndrome

IgE myeloma

The significance of plasma proteins for tumor diagnosis

Tumor markers (Table 45) are antigens (because they are chiefly detected by immunological methods) found in plasma or serum mainly or entirely in association with a tumor. Carcinoembryonic antigen and tissue polypeptide antigen can be observed in tissues which contain rapidly-dividing cells. The production of these proteins in normal tissues is low or completely blocked, except in connection with cell division. Carcinoembryonic antigen has an immunological similarity to α_1-acid glycoprotein[313]. Tissue polypeptide is a nonconjugated membrane protein containing no carbohydrate[314]. α-Fetoprotein is the main serum protein during intrauterine life, at first synthesized by the yolk sac, afterwards by the endoderm and the fetal liver. The disappearance of α-fetopro-

(to Table 43)

Concentration in plasma of adults (pregnant women excepted)	Site of synthesis	Half-life in plasma	Occurrence	Function
≤5 µg/L (in 46% below the limit of detection of 1 µg/L)[280]	Placenta	30–40 h[281]	In serum of pregnant women rising to 80–350 mg/L at end of pregnancy[282]	(?)
Men: <5 mg/L[285] Women (30 years): <30 mg/L[285] Women (75 years): <60 mg/L[285]	Liver (?)	7–21 d[279]	In serum of pregnant women rising to about 850 mg/L in 3rd trimester[279]	Immunosuppressive effect (?)[284]
0.1–0.5 mg/L[287]	Placenta	3–4 d[279]	In serum of pregnant women rising to 10 mg/L at 13th week[288] and to 36 mg/L at end of pregnancy[289]	Involved in regulation of fibrinolysis[286]
–	Placenta	<1 d[279]	Peak level in 3rd trimester of pregnancy (?)[279]	–
Not detectable[290]	Placenta	~0.3 h[279]	In serum of pregnant women rising to 20–140 µg/L at end of pregnancy; disappears rapidly post partum[290]	Proteinase inhibitor. Involved in the coagulation system[291]
≤5.0 µg/L (in 89% ≤2.5 µg/L)[302] Men: <5.2 µg/L[303] Women: <3.6 µg/L[303]	Fetal colonic mucosa[300,301]	–	–	–
2.6 µg/L (*s* 1.6 µg/L)[294] <5 µg/L[295]	Yolk sac, fetal liver, fetal intestine[293]	6 d[293] 3.5 d (at birth)[296]	In fetal serum from the 4th week of pregnancy onward; highest concentration around 13th–15th week of pregnancy (3–4 g/L); disappears 2–3 weeks after birth almost completely[293]	Albumin substitute; estrogen binding[293]; immunoregulatory effect[297,298]
≤1.5 µg/L[306]	Fetal liver[304,306]	–	In fetal serum to end of 2nd month of life[304]	–
–	–	–	In fetal serum up to 5th–7th month of life[304]	–

Table 45 *Tumor markers*[306–309]

Protein	Tumor marked
Carcinoembryonic antigen (CEA)	Cancer of colon and rectum, but also many other malignant and benign tumors
Tissue polypeptide antigen (TPA)	Several types of cancer
Tennessee antigen	Cancer of lung and stomach; colorectal and pancreatic cancer
B-protein	All common types of cancer
α-Fetoprotein (AFP)	Cancer of liver and testes
α_2H-Fetoprotein	Several types of cancer
Pregnancy-associated α_2-glycoprotein	Several types of cancer
Embryonic prealbumin[311]	Several types of cancer
Prostatic acid phosphatase	Cancer of prostate
Human chorionic gonadotropin (HCG)	Cancer of the uterus, testicular tumors
Thyroglobulin	Thyroid cancer
Calcitonin	Thyroid cancer
Breast-cyst fluid protein (BCFP)	Breast cancer
Colon mucoprotein antigen (CMA)	Cancer of colon
Colon-specific antigen (CSA)	Cancer of colon
Pancreas-specific antigen (PaA)[234]	Pancreatic cancer
Galactosyltransferase isoenzyme II[312]	Pancreatic cancer
Creatinekinase isoenzyme BB[310]	Several types of cancer, particularly adenocarcinoma of the prostate

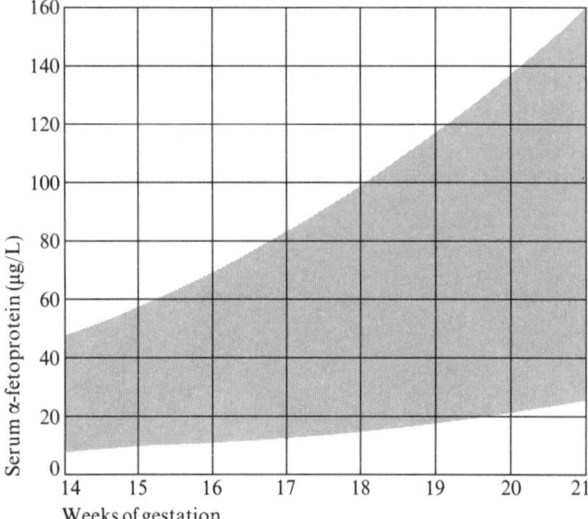

Fig. 3. Concentrations of maternal serum α-fetoprotein between 14 and 21 weeks of gestation. The shaded zone represents the upper (2.5 × median) and lower (0.4 × median) limits of normal[325].

tein at birth is accompanied by an increase in albumin production, so that α-fetoprotein can be considered to be expressed by fetal hepatocytes and albumin by mature hepatocytes[315]. In the adult organism, production of small amounts of α-fetoprotein occurs during hepatocyte regeneration. Other tumor markers – e.g. prostatic acid phosphatase – are normal products of the organ involved but, due to the lesion, released in abnormally high quantities.

Carcinoembryonic antigen (CEA). The serum level is markedly increased in 35–40% of patients with carcinoma of the colon, rectum, or pancreas (to levels exceeding 10 µg/L)[300,301,316]. Concentrations of this order of magnitude may also occur in esophageal, gastric, liver, lung, or breast carcinoma; they are rare in nonmalignant diseases of the liver and gastrointestinal tract[300,301]. The frequency of levels between 2.5 and 10 µg/L in the aforementioned nonmalignant diseases and in lung emphysema is 25% to 65%[300,301,317]. These concentrations are also found in smokers, the frequency increasing with duration of tobacco consumption[318]. Thus, the informative value of an increased CEA level for diagnosis is not very specific; it is unsuited for mass screening and the early diagnosis of malignant tumors[319]. On the other hand, CEA determination can yield useful information for controlling the course of colon or rectal carcinoma under treatment, since the CEA concentration returns to normal values after total tumor resection, decreases after incomplete resection, and rises again in the case of relapse.

α-Fetoprotein[293,320]. Serum levels above 400 µg/L are found in a high percentage of patients with primary hepatocellular carcinoma. Elevations of the serum α-fetoprotein level are also associated with germ-cell tumors; in patients with teratocarcinomas containing yolk-sac elements, serum levels of 360–169000 µg/L have been found[320]. The determination of the α-fetoprotein level provides useful information for therapeutic control.

In the serum of pregnant women, the α-fetoprotein level rises from undetectable amounts to a median peak of 200 µg/L at 32 weeks of pregnancy[321]. An increase beyond the physiological level (initial testing is recommended at about 16 weeks of gestation) is of significance for the prenatal diagnosis of spina bifida and anencephaly[321–324]. Corrections for maternal body mass and race should be applied when values in maternal serum are being interpreted[326].

References

1 Cederblad, G., in Blombäck and Hanson (Eds.), *Plasma Proteins,* Wiley, New York, 1979, page 94.
2 Schultze and Heremans, *Molecular Biology of Human Proteins,* volume 1, Elsevier, Amsterdam, 1966.
3 Hagen and Elliott, *J. clin. Endocr.,* **37**, 415 (1973).
4 Oppenheimer et al., *Science,* **149**, 748 (1965).
5 Johansson, B.G., in Blombäck and Hanson (Eds.), *Plasma Proteins,* Wiley, New York, 1979, page 309.
6 Rask et al., *Scand. J. clin. Lab. Invest.,* **40**, suppl. 154, 45 (1980).
7 Meloun et al., *FEBS Lett.,* **58**, 134 (1975); McLachlan and Walker, *J. molec. Biol.,* **112**, 543 (1977).
8 Mayer and Schomerus, *Acta hepato-gastroenterol. (Stuttg.),* **24**, 82 (1976).
9 Birke et al., in Blombäck and Hanson (Eds.), *Plasma Proteins,* Wiley, New York, 1979, page 54.
10 Allen, R.H., *Progr. Hemat.,* **9**, 57 (1975).
11 Vallner, J.J., *J. pharm. Sci.,* **66**, 447 (1977).
12 Le Gaillard et al., *Biochimie (Paris),* **57**, 559 (1975).
13 Bernutz et al., *Acta endocr. (Kbh.),* **92**, 370 (1979).
14 Cavalieri, R.R., *J. clin. Invest.,* **56**, 79 (1975).
15 Haupt et al., *Hoppe-Seylers Z. physiol. Chem.,* **353**, 1841 (1972).
16 Koj, A., in Allison, A.C. (Ed.), *Structure and Function of Plasma Proteins,* volume 1, Plenum Press, London, 1974, page 73.
17 Turner and Hulme, *The Plasma Proteins,* Pitman, London, 1971.
18 Carrell et al., *Nature,* **298**, 329 (1982).
19 Horng and Gan, *Tex. Rep. Biol. Med.,* **32**, 489 (1974).
20 Crawford, I.P., *Arch. Biochem.,* **156**, 215 (1973).
21 *Table of Human Blood Plasma Proteins,* Hoechst AG, Frankfurt, 1976.
22 Bagdasarian et al., *J. clin. Invest.,* **67**, 281 (1981).
23 Svensson and Ravnskov, *Clin. chim. Acta,* **73**, 415 (1976).
24 Ekström and Berggård, *J. biol. Chem.,* **252**, 8048 (1977).
25 Takagi et al., *J. clin. Invest.,* **63**, 318 (1979).
26 Refetoff et al., *J. clin. Invest.,* **56**, 177 (1975).
27 Travis and Salvesen, *Ann. Rev. Biochem.,* **52**, 655 (1983).
28 Imawari et al., *J. clin. Invest.,* **58**, 514 (1976).
29 Haddad et al., *J. clin. Invest.,* **67**, 1550 (1981).

[30] BROWN et al., *J. clin. Path.,* **33**, 966 (1980).
[31] MOODY, B.J., *Clin. chim. Acta,* **118**, 87 (1982).
[32] GOODMAN, D.S., *Vitam. and Horm.,* **32**, 167 (1974).
[33] GIBLETT, E., in ALLISON, A.C. (Ed.), *Structure and Function of Plasma Proteins,* volume 1, Plenum Press, London, 1974, page 55.
[34] DOUMA and VAN DALEN, *Z. klin. Chem.,* **12**, 474 (1974).
[35] PASTEWKA et al., *Biochim. biophys. Acta (Amst.),* **386**, 530 (1975).
[36] NOYER et al., *Analyt. Biochem.,* **102**, 450 (1980).
[37] LAURIE and MOHAMMED, *Coord. Chem. Rev.,* **33**, 279 (1980).
[38] SOTTRUP-JENSEN et al., *J. biol. Chem.,* **259**, 8318 (1984).
[39] JONES et al., *Biochem. J.,* **127**, 187 (1972).
[40] NORBERG et al., in ROTHSCHILD and WALDMANN (Eds.), *Plasma Protein Metabolism,* Academic Press, New York, 1970, page 427.
[41] FARROW and BAAR, *Clin. chim. Acta,* **46**, 39 (1973).
[42] HEIMBURGER et al., *Hoppe-Seylers Z. physiol. Chem.,* **353**, 1133 (1972).
[43] SAITO et al., *Amer. J. Med.,* **73**, 179 (1982).
[44] JIRKA et al., *Clin. chim. Acta,* **56**, 31 (1974).
[45] SCHMID and BÜRGI, *Biochim. biophys. Acta (Amst.),* **47**, 440 (1961).
[46] HAUPT and BAUDNER, *Hoppe-Seylers Z. physiol. Chem.,* **358**, 639 (1977).
[47] BOHN, H., *Blut,* **29**, 17 (1974).
[48] VIGERSKY et al., *J. clin. Invest.,* **58**, 1061 (1976).
[49] VIGERSKY et al., *J. clin. Endocr.,* **49**, 899 (1979).
[50] ANDERSSON et al., in BLOMBÄCK and HANSON (Eds.), *Plasma Proteins, Wiley, New York, 1979, page 305.*
[51] MOROI and AOKI, *J. biol. Chem.,* **251**, 5956 (1976).
[52] SAKATA and AOKI, *J. clin. Invest.,* **69**, 536 (1982).
[53] MOSESSON, M.W., *Ann. N.Y. Acad. Sci.,* **312**, 11 (1978).
[54] RENNARD and ABE, *New Engl. J. Med.,* **300**, 368 (1979).
[55] HÖRMANN, H., *Klin. Wschr.,* **60**, 1265 (1982).
[56] MULLER-EBERHARD and LIEM, in ALLISON, A.C. (Ed.), *Structure and Function of Plasma Proteins,* volume 1, Plenum Press, London, 1974, page 35.
[57] MULLER-EBERHARD and MORGAN, *Ann. N.Y. Acad. Sci.,* **244**, 624 (1975).
[58] WOCHNER et al., *New Engl. J. Med.,* **290**, 822 (1974).
[59] MACGILLIVRAY et al., *Proc. nat. Acad. Sci. (Wash.),* **79**, 2504 (1982).
[60] LUNDH, S., *Int. J. Pept. Protein Res.,* **5**, 309 (1973).
[61] LOZIER et al., *Proc. nat. Acad. Sci. (Wash.),* **81**, 3640 (1984).
[62] HAUPT and HEIDE, *Clin. chim. Acta,* **12**, 419 (1965).
[63] SCHWICK et al., *Klin. Wschr.,* **46**, 981 (1968).
[64] CUNNINGHAM et al., *Biochemistry,* **12**, 4811 (1973).
[65] BERGGÅRD et al., *Scand. J. clin. Lab. Invest.,* **40**, suppl. 154, 13 (1980).
[66] PLESNER et al., *Scand. J. clin. Lab. Invest.,* **35**, 729 (1975).
[67] DOOLITTLE, R.F., *Sci. Amer.,* **245**, December, 126 (1981).
[68] KRANTZ and LOBER, *Folia haemat. (Lpz.),* **98**, 1 (1972).
[69] COLLEN et al., *J. appl. Physiol.,* **42**, 865 (1977).
[70] SKVARIL and MORELL, *Advanc. exp. Med. Biol.,* **45**, 433 (1974).
[71] JAKOB et al., *Physiol. Rev.,* **60**, 918 (1980).
[72] SCHUR, P.H., *Progr. clin. Immunol.,* **1**, 71 (1972).
[73] MATTIOLI and TOMASI, *DM (Chic),* April, 1 (1970).
[74] IIO et al., *J. clin. Invest.,* **59**, 743 (1977).
[75] NATVIG and KUNKEL, *Advanc. Immunol.,* **16**, 1 (1973).
[76] TOMASI and GREY, *Progr. Allergy,* **16**, 81 (1972).
[77] KRATZIN et al., *Hoppe-Seylers Z. physiol. Chem.,* **356**, 1337 (1975).
[78] SPIEGELBERG, H.L., *Advanc. Immunol.,* **19**, 259 (1974).
[79] RICARDO and INMAN, *Biochem. J.,* **131**, 677 (1973).
[80] WATANABE et al., *Hoppe-Seylers Z. physiol. Chem.,* **354**, 1505 (1973).
[81] FILITTI-WURMSER and TEMPÊTE-GAILLOURDET, *Biochimie (Paris),* **56**, 1183 (1974).
[82] STEVENSON, G.T., in ALLISON, A.C. (Ed.), *Structure and Function of Plasma Proteins,* volume 1, Plenum Press, London, 1974, page 223.
[83] SPIEGELBERG et al., *Biochemistry,* **9**, 2115 (1970).
[84] JOHNSON et al., *FEBS Lett.,* **49**, 310 (1975).
[85] FRANKLIN, E.C., *New Engl. J. Med.,* **294**, 531 (1976).
[86] JEFFERIS, R., *Trends biochem. Sci.,* **6**, 111 (1981); CALVERT and JEFFERIS, *Trends biochem. Sci.,* **6**, 125 (1981).
[87] KEATING et al., *J. Lab. clin. Med.,* **73**, 825 (1969).
[88] DOUMAS et al., *Clin. chim. Acta,* **31**, 87 (1971).
[89] LIAPPIS, N., *Mschr. Kinderheilk.,* **120**, 265 (1972).
[90] HEVÉR et al., *Biol. Neonat. (Basel),* **31**, 32 (1977).
[91] KOH et al., *Amer. J. clin. Nutr.,* **33**, 1828 (1980).
[92] MCPHERSON et al., *Clin. chim. Acta,* **84**, 373 (1978).
[93] THOMAS and EVANS, *Clin. chim. Acta,* **60**, 237 (1975).
[94] WINGERD and SPONZILLI, *Clin. Chem.,* **23**, 1310 (1977).
[95] DOUMAS, B.T., *Clin. Chem.,* **21**, 1159 (1975).
[96] MILLER et al., *Clin. chim. Acta,* **31**, 427 (1971).
[97] SIEGERT et al., *Clin. chim. Acta,* **73**, 423 (1976).
[98] LAURELL, C.B., *Scand. J. clin. Lab. Invest.,* **30**, 233 (1972) and *Clin. Chem.,* **19**, 99 (1973).
[99] REIMER et al., *Amer. J. clin. Path.,* **77**, 12 (1982).
[100] GRABNER et al., *Ärztl. Lab.,* **16**, 193 (1970).
[101] HYTTEN and LIND, *Diagnostic Indices in Pregnancy,* CIBA-GEIGY Ltd., Basle, 1973.
[102] LYNGBYE and KRØLL, *Clin. Chem.,* **17**, 495 (1971).
[103] WEEKE and KRASILNIKOFF, *Acta med. scand.,* **192**, 149 (1972).
[104] AGOSTONI et al., *Clin. Chem.,* **20**, 428 (1974).
[105] NILIUS et al., *Z. ges. inn. Med.,* **32**, 265 (1977).
[106] VAHLQUIST et al., *Scand. J. clin. Lab. Invest.,* **38**, 301 (1978).
[107] HUTCHINSON et al., *Clin. chim. Acta,* **114**, 69 (1981).
[108] BERGERON et al., *Clin. chim. Acta,* **75**, 49 (1977).
[109] VAN BAELEN and DE MOOR, *J. clin. Endocr.,* **39**, 160 (1974).
[110] RACADOT et al., *Clin. chim. Acta,* **66**, 171 (1976).
[111] SNYDER et al., *Amer. Heart J.,* **90**, 582 (1975).
[112] FREER et al., *Clin. Chem.,* **25**, 565 (1979).
[113] WANG and CHU, *Clin. Chem.,* **25**, 546 (1979).
[114] CHAPELLE et al., *Clin. chim. Acta,* **115**, 199 (1981).
[115] LELLOUCH et al., *Clin. chim. Acta,* **95**, 337 (1979).
[116] TAKAGI et al., *J. clin. Path.,* **33**, 786 (1980).
[117] TAKAGI et al., *Clin. chim. Acta,* **108**, 277 (1980).
[118] HORN et al., *Klin. Wschr.,* **55**, 881 (1977).
[119] HESCH et al., *Clin. chim. Acta,* **70**, 33 (1976).
[120] RAOUF et al., *Clin. chim. Acta,* **104**, 25 (1980).
[121] GLOVER et al., *Clin. chim. Acta,* **50**, 371 (1974).
[122] SCARPIONI et al., *Clin. chim. Acta,* **68**, 107 (1976).
[123] STEWART and FLEMING, *Nephron,* **30**, 15 (1982).
[124] IMAWARI and GOODMAN, *J. clin. Invest.,* **59**, 432 (1977).
[125] BROWN et al., *Clin. chim. Acta,* **95**, 75 (1979).
[126] WALSH and HADDAD, *Clin. Chem.,* **28**, 1781 (1982).
[127] HARDUIN et al., *Ann. Biol. clin.,* **34**, 411 (1976).
[128] SCHENKER et al., *Int. J. Fertil.,* **17**, 28 (1972).
[129] HILDERBRAND et al., *Amer. J. Obstet. Gynec.,* **118**, 950 (1974).
[130] YUNICE et al., *J. Geront.,* **29**, 277 (1974).
[131] HOHNADEL et al., *Ann. clin. Lab. Sci.,* **5**, 65 (1975).
[132] GOLLAN et al., *J. clin. Path.,* **30**, 81 (1977).
[133] GIBBS and WALSHE, *Quart. J. Med.,* **48**, 447 (1979).
[134] MCBEAN et al., *Clin. chim. Acta,* **50**, 43 (1974).
[135] MORGAN et al., *Proc. Soc. exp. Biol. (N.Y.),* **158**, 647 (1978).
[136] SAITO et al., *Amer. J. Med.,* **73**, 179 (1982).
[137] LEBRETON et al., *J. clin. Invest.,* **64**, 1118 (1979).
[138] CHENG et al., *J. clin. Endocr.,* **56**, 68 (1983).
[139] WEIPPL et al., *Blut,* **27**, 376 (1973).
[140] GEKLE et al., *Z. Kinderheilk.,* **117**, 19 (1974).
[141] EVRIN and WIBELL, *Scand. J. clin. Lab. Invest.,* **29**, 69 (1972).
[142] ČEJKA et al., *Clin. chim. Acta,* **47**, 59 (1973).
[143] MERRETT et al., *Clin. chim. Acta,* **104**, 119 (1980).
[144] BEORCHIA et al., *Clin. chim. Acta,* **109**, 245 (1981).
[145] *Mayo Clinic Laboratory Manual of Hemostasis,* Saunders, Philadelphia, 1971.
[146] LACKNER and JAVID, *Amer. J. clin. Path.,* **60**, 175 (1973).
[147] MUNTEAN and MÜLLER, *Helv. paediat. Acta,* **31**, 149 (1976).
[148] STAKENBURG and NEUMANN, *Clin. chim. Acta,* **80**, 141 (1977).
[149] JÜRGENS et al., *Europ. J. Pediat.,* **131**, 199 (1979).
[150] RICHARDSON et al., *Brit. J. Haemat.,* **42**, 469 (1979).
[151] PANTLITSCHKO et al., *Ärztl. Lab.,* **16**, 214 (1970).
[152] MEIERS et al., *Dtsch. med. Wschr.,* **98**, 2243 (1973).
[153] MEIERS et al., *Klin. Wschr.,* **52**, 453 (1974).
[154] MIYAI et al., *Clin. Chem.,* **28**, 2408 (1982).
[155] JACOB et al., *J. Lab. clin. Med.,* **89**, 1145 (1977).
[156] FERNANDES-COSTA and METZ, *Amer. J. clin. Nutr.,* **35**, 83 (1982).
[157] GANROT, P.O., *Scand. J. clin. Lab. Invest.,* **29**, suppl. 124, 83 (1972).
[158] BACHMANN and GLEICHMANN, *Verh. dtsch. Ges. inn. Med.,* **77**, 573 (1971).
[159] WEINDLING and HENRY, *J. Amer. med. Ass.,* **229**, 1762 (1974).
[160] LAURELL and RANNEVIK, *J. clin. Endocr.,* **49**, 719 (1979).
[161] COLLEN et al., *Eur. J. clin. Invest.,* **8**, 185 (1978).
[162] AOKI et al., *J. clin. Invest.,* **63**, 877 (1979).
[163] BLANCHARD et al., *J. Lab. clin. Med.,* **101**, 242 (1983).
[164] POULIK et al., *Clin. chim. Acta,* **128**, 249 (1983).
[165] JOLLIFF et al., *Clin. Chem.,* **28**, 126 (1982).
[166] MUENSCH et al., *Europ. J. Biochem.,* **70**, 217 (1976).
[167] BROWN et al., *Advanc. clin. Chem.,* **22**, 1 (1981).
[168] WOOD et al., *J. exp. Med.,* **100**, 71 (1954).
[169] VOLANAKIS et al., *J. immunol. Meth.,* **23**, 285 (1978).
[170] SHINE et al., *Clin. chim. Acta,* **117**, 13 (1981).
[171] GEWURZ et al., *Advanc. intern. Med.,* **27**, 345 (1982).
[172] OLIVEIRA et al., *J. biol. Chem.,* **254**, 489 (1979).
[173] TURNER, K.J., *Med. J. Aust.,* **2**, 846 (1974).
[174] BAZARAL and HAMBURGER, *J. Allergy clin. Immunol.,* **49**, 189 (1972).
[175] OLSON and LESLIE, in THORBECKE and LESLIE (Eds.), *Immunoglobulin D: Structure and Function,* New York Academy of Sciences, New York, 1982, page 97.
[176] GRABNER et al., *Clin. chim. Acta,* **39**, 59 (1972).
[177] KARAYALCIN et al., *N.Y. St. J. Med.,* **73**, 751 (1973).
[178] ŠINKOV et al., *Bull. Wld Hlth Org.,* **49**, 217 (1973).
[179] TOSHKOV et al., *Folia haemat. (Lpz.),* **101**, 269 (1974).
[180] CEGLA, U.H., *Z. klin. Chem.,* **12**, 207 (1974).
[181] PRELLWITZ et al., *Z. klin. Chem.,* **12**, 427 (1974).
[182] BUTTS et al., *Clin. Chem.,* **23**, 511 (1977).
[183] BUCKLEY and FISCUS, *J. clin. Invest.,* **55**, 157 (1975).
[184] DUNNETTE et al., *J. Immunol.,* **119**, 1727 (1977).
[185] DUNNETTE et al., *J. clin. Invest.,* **82**, 248 (1978).
[186] JOSEPHS and BUCKLEY, *J. Pediat.,* **96**, 417 (1980).
[187] BARSOUM and KUWERT, *Z. Immun.-Forsch.,* **152**, 388 (1977).
[188] WÜTHRICH and WYSS, *Schweiz. med. Wschr.,* **109**, 315 (1979).
[189] BRUYNZEEL et al., *Clin. chim. Acta,* **91**, 67 (1979).
[190] BRUYNZEEL and HOUBEN, *Clin. chim. Acta,* **112**, 315 (1981).
[191] BEAUDONNET, A., *Clin. chim. Acta,* **129**, 215 (1983).
[192] CASSIDY et al., *J. chron. Dis.,* **27**, 507 (1974).
[193] ČEJKA et al., *Clin. Chem.,* **20**, 656 (1974).
[194] MORELL et al., *J. Pediat.,* **80**, 960 (1972).
[195] SHAKIB et al., *J. immunol. Meth.,* **8**, 17 (1975).
[196] ZEGERS et al., *Clin. chim. Acta,* **65**, 319 (1975).
[197] HUMPHREY and BATTY, *Clin. exp. Immunol.,* **17**, 708 (1974).
[198] ROWE et al., *Bull. Wld Hlth Org.,* **43**, 607 (1970).
[199] BERG and JOHANSSON, *Acta paediat. scand.,* **58**, 513 (1969).
[200] HUBER, R., *Klin. Wschr.,* **58**, 1217 (1980).
[201] DAVIES et al., *Ann. Rev. Biochem.,* **44**, 639 (1975).

202 Leder, P., *Sci. Amer.*, **246** (5), 72 (1982).
203 *Bull. Wld Hlth Org.*, **45**, 255 (1971).
204 Humphrey and Batty, *Int. Arch. Allergy*, **47**, 795 (1974).
205 Gunson and Thomas, *Lancet*, **1**, 162 (1979).
206 Hapke and Patil, *Hum. Path.*, **12**, 1011 (1981).
207 Soothill, J.F., *Lancet*, **1**, 39 (1975).
208 Ward and Lea, *Lancet*, **1**, 456 (1975).
209 Rauer and Freund, *Mschr. Kinderheilk.*, **117**, 559 (1969).
210 Uffelman et al., *Clin. chim. Acta*, **28**, 185 (1970).
211 Saarinen et al., *J. Pediat.*, **95**, 410 (1979).
212 Gordon et al., *Lancet*, **1**, 72 (1982).
213 Grundbacher, F.J., *J. Allergy clin. Immunol.*, **56**, 104 (1975).
214 Buckley et al., *Fed. Proc.*, **33**, 2036 (1974).
215 Lamy et al., *Ann. Biol. clin.*, **32**, 529 (1974).
216 Tatra et al., *Arch. Gynäk.*, **217**, 113 (1974).
217 Kretschmer et al., *Clin. Immunol. Immunopath.*, **4**, 9 (1975).
218 Kaltwasser et al., *Dtsch. med. Wschr.*, **102**, 1150 (1977).
219 Bratlid and Moe, *Europ. J. Pediat.*, **134**, 125 (1980).
220 Anderson and Kelly, *Clin. chim. Acta*, **116**, 405 (1981).
221 Entman et al., *Amer. J. Obstet. Gynec.*, **144**, 418 (1982).
222 Bailey et al., *J. Pediat.*, **101**, 774 (1982).
223 Oertel, J., *Klin. Wschr.*, **60**, 571 (1982).
224 Sykes et al., *Clin. chim. Acta*, **122**, 385 (1982).
225 Tsuru et al., *Clin. chim. Acta*, **84**, 251 (1978).
226 Price et al., *J. clin. Invest.*, **66**, 878 (1980).
227 Gundberg et al., *Clin. chim. Acta*, **128**, 1 (1983).
228 Merkelbach and Burger, *Schweiz. med. Wschr.*, **109**, 1606 (1979).
229 Endo et al., *Clin. chim. Acta*, **95**, 325 (1979).
230 Black et al., *Clin. Endocr.*, **16**, 267 (1982).
231 Liebman and Samloff, *J. Pediat.*, **94**, 132 (1979).
232 Axelsson et al., *Clin. chim. Acta*, **121**, 309 (1982).
233 Ichinose et al., *Clin. chim. Acta*, **126**, 183 (1982).
234 Loor et al., *Clin. chim. Acta*, **117**, 251 (1981).
235 Märki, H.H., *Dtsch. med. J.*, **23**, 217 (1972).
236 Hitzig, W.H., *Plasmaproteine; Pathophysiologie und Klinik*, 2nd ed., Springer, Berlin, 1977.
237 Alper, C.A., *New Engl. J. Med.*, **291**, 287 (1974).
238 Märki, H.H., in Siegenthaler, W. (Ed.), *Klinische Pathophysiologie*, 4th ed., Thieme, Stuttgart, 1979, page 101.
239 Dammacco et al., *Vox Sang. (Basel)*, **39**, 153 (1980).
240 Barragry and Burr, *Brit. med. J.*, **2**, 742 (1977).
241 Ahrentsen et al., *Lancet*, **2**, 377 (1982).
242 Oberling et al., *Nouv. Presse méd.*, **4**, 2705 (1975).
243 Fràter-Schröder et al., *Schweiz. med. Wschr.*, **112**, 1435 (1982).
244 Hakami et al., *New Engl. J. Med.*, **285**, 1163 (1971).
245 Flute, P.T., *Brit. med. Bull.*, **33**, 253 (1977).
246 Kushner et al., *J. Lab. clin. Med.*, **97**, 739 (1981).
247 Wuhrmann and Märki, *Dysproteinämien und Paraproteinämien; Grundlagen, Klinik und Therapie*, 4th ed., Schwabe, Basle, 1963.
248 Muller-Eberhard et al., *Proc. Soc. exp. Biol. (N.Y.)*, **146**, 694 (1974).
249 Wandall, J.H., *Acta chir. scand.*, **140**, 171 (1974).
250 Wewalka, F.G., *Med. Klin.*, **70**, 488 (1975).
251 Bichler et al., *Urol. int. (Basel)*, **29**, 329 (1974).
252 Heremans and Masson, *Clin. Chem.*, **19**, 294 (1973).
253 Vittal et al., *Amer. J. Med.*, **57**, 546 (1974).
254 Nilius et al., *Z. ges. inn. Med.*, **28**, 541 (1973).
255 Fruchart et al., *Nouv. Presse méd.*, **3**, 1751 (1974).
256 Bostian et al., *J. Lab. clin. Med.*, **87**, 577 (1976).
257 Märki, H.H., *Öst. Ärzteztg.*, **25**, 237 (1970).
258 Ingenbleek et al., *Lancet*, **2**, 106 (1972); Young et al., *Amer. J. clin. Nutr.*, **31**, 429 (1978).
259 Shakir et al., *Lancet*, **2**, 143 (1972).
260 Bistrian et al., *J. Amer. med. Ass.*, **230**, 858 (1974).
261 Shetty et al., *Lancet*, **2**, 230 (1979); Frey et al., *Metabolism*, **28**, 363 (1979).
262 Schramm, W., *Internist (Berl.)*, **25**, 88 (1984).
263 Kyle and Greipp, *Mayo Clin. Proc.*, **53**, 719 (1978).
264 Marshall, M.O., *Clin. chim. Acta*, **104**, 1 (1980).
265 Tomaszewski et al., *Clin. chim. Acta*, **75**, 331 (1977).
266 Invernizzi et al., *Acta haemat. (Basel)*, **50**, 65 (1973).
267 Bloch and Franklin, *J. Amer. med. Ass.*, **248**, 2670 (1982).
268 Hood, W., *Clin. Chem.*, **23**, 1192 (1977).
269 Villiaumey et al., *Nouv. Presse méd.*, **3**, 2707 (1974).
270 Levo, Y., *Lancet*, **1**, 285 (1980).
271 Belohradsky et al., *Klin. Wschr.*, **54**, 1109 (1976).
272 Cooper and Buckley, *J. Amer. med. Ass.*, **248**, 2658 (1982).
273 Muller-Eberhard, U., *New Engl. J. Med.*, **283**, 1090 (1970).
274 Marchand et al., *J. Amer. med. Ass.*, **243**, 1909 (1980).
275 Munro and Linder, *Physiol. Rev.*, **58**, 317 (1978).
276 Marsh et al., *New Engl. J. Med.*, **305**, 1551 (1981).
277 *Amer. J. Med.*, **74**, 887 (1983).
278 Bohn, H., in Klopper and Chard (Eds.), *Placental Proteins*, Springer, Berlin, 1979, page 71.
279 Halbert and Lin, in Klopper and Chard (Eds.), *Placental Proteins*, Springer, Berlin, 1979, page 89.
280 Würz, H., *Arch. Gynec.*, **277**, 1 (1979).
281 Searle et al., *Lancet*, **1**, 579 (1978).
282 Horne et al., in Klopper and Chard (Eds.), *Placental Proteins*, Springer, Berlin, 1979, page 143.
283 Bauer and Bohn, *Klin. Wschr.*, **56**, 531 (1978).
284 Bohn and Winckler, *Blut*, **33**, 377 (1976).
285 Wood et al., *J. clin. Path.*, **31**, 1065 (1978).
286 Bischof, P., *Arch. Gynec.*, **227**, 315 (1979).
287 Bischof et al., *Amer. J. Obstet. Gynec.*, **143**, 379 (1982).
288 Bischof et al., *Brit. J. Obstet. Gynaec.*, **88**, 973 (1981).
289 Sinosich et al., *Clin. Chem.*, **28**, 50 (1982).
290 Nisbet et al., *Brit. J. Obstet. Gynaec.*, **88**, 484 (1981).
291 Siiteri et al., *Life Sci.*, **30**, 1885 (1982).
292 Morinaga et al., *Proc. nat. Acad. Sci. (Wash.)*, **80**, 4604 (1983).
293 Lamerz and Fateh-Moghadam, *Klin. Wschr.*, **53**, 147 (1975).
294 Masseyeff et al., *Digestion*, **10**, 17 (1974).
295 Bellet et al., *Proc. nat. Acad. Sci. (Wash.)*, **81**, 3869 (1984).
296 Adinolfi et al., *J. med. Genet.*, **12**, 138 (1975).
297 Bernaudin, F., *Nouv. Presse méd.*, **5**, 643 (1976).
298 Gassner and Grob, *Schweiz. med. Wschr.*, **104**, 557 (1974).
299 Wagener and Breuer, *J. clin. Chem.*, **20**, 705 (1982).
300 Wagener and Breuer, *J. clin. Chem.*, **15**, 529 (1977).
301 Lamerz and Fateh-Moghadam, *Klin. Wschr.*, **53**, 193 (1975).
302 Amino et al., *J. clin. Endocr.*, **52**, 457 (1981).
303 Beaudonnet et al., *Clin. Chem.*, **27**, 771 (1981).
304 Laurence and Munro Neville, *Brit. J. Cancer*, **26**, 335 (1972).
305 Nørgaard-Pedersen and Gaede, *Acta obstet. gynec. scand.*, **53**, suppl. 29, 37 (1974).
306 Lamerz and Fateh-Moghadam, *Klin. Wschr.*, **53**, 403 (1975).
307 Maugh, T.H., *Science*, **211**, 909 (1981).
308 Klee and Go, *Mayo Clin. Proc.*, **57**, 129 (1982).
309 Bohn, H., *Klin. Wschr.*, **58**, 489 (1980).
310 Silverman et al., *Clin. Chem.*, **25**, 1432 (1979).
311 Tatarinov et al., *Lancet*, **2**, 1122 (1978).
312 Podolsky et al., *New Engl. J. Med.*, **304**, 1313 (1981).
313 Ochi et al., *Clin. chim. Acta*, **122**, 145 (1982).
314 Björklund, B., *Tumordiagnostik*, **1**, 9 (1980).
315 Jacob, F., *Ciba Found. Symp.*, **96**, 4 (1983).
316 Fateh-Moghadam et al., *Klin. Wschr.*, **56**, 267 (1978).
317 Hirai, H., *Antibiot. and Chemother. (Basel)*, **22**, 67 (1978).
318 Persijn and Korsten, *J. clin. Chem.*, **14**, 377 (1976).
319 Moertel, C.G., *J. Amer. med. Ass.*, **228**, 156 (1974).
320 Sell, S., *Hum. Path.*, **12**, 959 (1981).
321 Council on Scientific Affairs, *J. Amer. med. Ass.*, **247**, 1478 (1982).
322 Brock et al., *Lancet*, **1**, 1281 (1979).
323 Davidson and Walker, *Clin. chim. Acta*, **105**, 1 (1980).
324 Mennuti, M.T., *Clin. chim. Acta*, **105**, 5 (1980).
325 Milunsky et al., *Amer. J. Obstet. Gynec.*, **142**, 1030 (1982).
326 Crandall et al., *Clin. Chem.*, **29**, 531 (1983).
327 Peuscher et al., *J. Lab. clin. Med.*, **96**, 5 (1980).
328 Benoit et al., *Nouv. Presse méd.*, **8**, 528 (1979).
329 Chan et al., *Clin. Sci.*, **60**, 681 (1981).
330 Green et al., *New Engl. J. Med.*, **302**, 193 (1980).
331 Brown et al., *Clin. chim. Acta*, **101**, 225 (1980).
332 White and Marouf, *J. Lab. clin. Med.*, **97**, 369 (1981).
333 Mehta, P., *J. Pediat.*, **97**, 941 (1980).
334 Green et al., *J. Lab. clin. Med.*, **95**, 679 (1980).
335 Hegedüs et al., *Clin. Endocr.*, **19**, 231 (1983).
336 Hartmann et al., *Clin. chim. Acta*, **133**, 215 (1983).
337 Crimaldi et al., *J. clin. Endocr.*, **57**, 1186 (1983).

Erythrocyte sedimentation rate* (for references see page 164)

Mechanism

The mechanism of the erythrocyte sedimentation is only partly understood. 3 phases can be distinguished[7]:

1. *Aggregation phase.* In the first phase, erythrocytes aggregate. The sedimentation rate is low (initial retention).
2. *Precipitation phase* (phase with fastest fall). The red cell aggregates are precipitated in the plasma. The sedimentation rate increases with increasing size of the aggregates.
3. *Packing phase.* The sedimentation rate slows down as a result of mutual interference of the closely packed aggregates.

The size of the aggregates formed in the aggregation phase is critical for the outcome of the sedimentation rate. Aggregation and sedimentation rate are manifestations of the suspension instability of the blood, which is based on a reciprocal effect between the structures of the erythrocyte membrane (glycolipids[8]) and certain plasma proteins, i.e. agglomerins.

Agglomerins are plasma proteins which, on the one hand, have a high affinity for the erythrocyte membrane and, on the other, are of sufficient molecular size to form bridges between erythrocytes. For very large molecules, only a slight erythrocyte membrane af-

*This chapter on 'Erythrocyte Sedimentation Rate' (pages 162–164) has been compiled by H. H. Märki, Medizinische Poliklinik, Kantonsspital, Winterthur, Switzerland.

finity is sufficient; for a very high affinity, the critical limit of the size of the agglomerin molecule is lower[9].

Fibrinogen[10], IgM, and α_2-macroglobulin[9] all possess agglomerin properties. The products of fibrinogen cleavage have a sedimentation activity that decreases with decreasing molecular size[11]. The sedimentation activity of the glycoproteins α_1-acid glycoprotein, α_1-antitrypsin, ceruloplasmin, and haptoglobin has not yet been ascertained. Although there is a positive correlation between their concentration and erythrocyte sedimentation[9], they are, like fibrinogen, acute-phase proteins, and the plasma concentrations rise or fall with the fibrinogen concentration. The correlation may thus be a manifestation of this parallelism.

An increase in the IgG concentration accelerates the sedimentation rate of erythrocytes only at very high concentrations[12]. The apparent sedimentation activity of moderately elevated IgG concentrations is probably the result of a parallel increase in IgM.

Macromolecules not normally found in the blood may also behave as agglomerins. Thus, erythrocyte aggregation and sedimentation take place in solutions of gum arabic, pectin, DNA, gelatin, and hyaluronic acid[7].

Erythrocytes affect the sedimentation rate primarily through changes in their number and shape. Anemia accelerates sedimentation. Megaloblastic anemia is much more sedimentation-active than iron-deficiency anemia. A close correlation between the hematocrit, the mean corpuscular hemoglobin (MCH), and mean corpuscular hemoglobin concentration (MCHC) on the one hand, and acceleration of sedimentation, on the other, has not been demonstrated[12]. Pronounced polycythemia inhibits sedimentation.

A good number of variations in erythrocyte shape, such as spherocytosis, acanthocytosis, and sickle-cell formation inhibit aggregation and sedimentation. Pronounced anisocytosis gives rise to aggregates of different sizes and hence to the formation of an erythrocyte veil in the supernatant plasma column (veil sedimentation)[12,13]. This occurs especially when a large number of reticulocytes is present (reticulocytes have low aggregation activity)[12].

Human blood plasma, which accelerates sedimentation, loses this property after several hours of incubation at 37 °C[14]. *Inhibition* of sedimentation is due to an increase in lysolecithin in the plasma as a result of the effect of lecithin acyltransferase on the lecithin of α_1-lipoproteins[14]. The increase in lysolecithin results in the formation of acanthocytes and spherocytes, which inhibit sedimentation. These relationships demonstrate the importance of the lysolecithin concentration for the outcome of the sedimentation rate. Fatty acids, sodium salicylate, phenylbutazone, thiosemicarbazone, and cinchophen also inhibit sedimentation[8,12]. The sedimentation-inhibiting effect of albumin is disputed[15]. It may be related to fatty-acid transport by the albumin fraction[2].

Procedure

The conditions in the test tube have a considerable influence on the erythrocyte sedimentation rate. If undiluted blood and EDTA as anticoagulant are used, exaggerations in the readings can occur[16]. EDTA may be used in place of citrate when the same blood dilution is maintained[8]. A 5–10% greater quantity of added citrate will inhibit the sedimentation considerably, while an insufficient amount results in a substantially enhanced sedimentation[17]. An increase of 10 °C in the temperature seems to double the sedimentation rate[18].

Standardization of the tests has been achieved. The International Committee for Standardization in Haematology (ICSH) recommended in 1973 the Westergren method as a reference method[19] and in 1977 as the standard method[20]. The recommendation includes the following procedures:

Anticoagulation and dilution: 1 part by volume of sodium citrate solution to 4 parts by volume of blood (concentration: 109 mmol/L or 32.8 g/L). – *Sedimentation tube:* 300 ± 1.5 mm in length, outer diameter 5.5 ± 0.5 mm, inner diameter 2.55 ± 0.15 mm, position perpendicular ± 1°. – *Commencement of test:* at most 2 hours after taking the blood sample; for blood stored at 4 °C, at most 6 hours after taking the sample. – *Temperature:* 18–25 °C. – *Reading:* after the 1st hour.

Reference values

The sedimentation rate is higher in women than in men. The difference may in part be attributed to the lower hematocrit value in women[2]. The sedimentation rate accelerates with age. The increase is especially marked in women of 50 years and over[1,2,22]. The conjecture that the rise in sedimentation rate with age is the result of some occult inflammatory or neoplastic process has so far not been refuted[21].

Table 1 *Erythrocyte sedimentation rate (Westergren method)*

Subjects	Age	Number	Sedimentation after 1 hour: Mean (mm)	s (mm)	Reference range (mm)	Reference
Men	18–30 years	117	3.1	2.0	<7.1	1
Women	18–30 years	43	5.1	2.8	<10.7	1
Men	31–40 years	115	3.4	2.2	<7.8	1
Women	31–40 years	37	5.6	2.7	<11	1
Men	41–50 years	79	4.6	3.0	<10.6	1
Women	41–50 years	61	6.2	3.5	<13.2	1
Men	51–60 years	71	5.6	3.3	<12.2	1
Women	51–60 years	55	9.4	4.6	<18.6	1
Men	>60 years	13	5.3	3.7	<12.7	1
Women	>60 years	12	9.4	5.4	<20.2	1
Men	20–49 years	940	5.0	4.0	0–13	2
Women	20–49 years	733	8.8	6.1	0–21	2
Men	50–70 years	507	7.0	5.8	0–19	2
Women	50–70 years	278	11.8	8.0	0–28	2
Men, Women	....	520*	–	–	<20◇	3
Men	....	–	–	–	4–20	4
Women	....	–	–	–	10–25	4
Men	21–60 years	49	5.47	5.24	–	5
Women	21–60 years	55	14.29	11.43	–	5
Men	20–30 years	50	–	–	<15	6
Women	20–30 years	50	–	–	<20	6

* Unselected subjects.
◇ For criteria defining the upper limit of the reference range, consult the original publication[3].

The International Committee for Standardization in Haematology[19,20] gives no reference values. The upper limit of reference values published originally by WESTERGREN (men 3 mm, women 7 mm after the 1st hour) are most certainly too low for practical purposes, especially in older persons[2], as shown by studies on carefully selected healthy persons (Table 1).

The setting of an upper limit of reference values is problematic because of the wide interindividual variations. The lower the upper limit is set, the greater is the frequency of false-positive results. Conversely, the frequency of false-negative results increases the higher the upper limit is set.

Evaluation of the sedimentation rate[7]

In principle, this blood *plasma* test cannot be expected to yield more information than would be expected from such a simple, nonspecific routine method. A thorough examination of the patient must be carried out even if the sedimentation rate is normal. In contrast to the rapid response to disease shown by the differential leukocyte count, 20–30 hours usually elapse before a change in the sedimentation rate is observed.

Daily fluctuations in the sedimentation rate may be related to the intake of meals[23]. Because of the individual differences, knowledge of the sedimentation rate when the person in question is in full health would be helpful in distinguishing a deviation from a pathological state. Values show marked differences in any one individual, so that a knowledge of his minimal values when in good health is important.

A marked increase in the sedimentation rate is an objective indication of a pathological process but cannot be interpreted as direct evidence of the presence of disease (it may, for instance, persist during convalescence). When there is a marked increase that cannot be explained, further examination of the patient is essential.

An exceptionally large and rapid increase in the sedimentation rate reaching the maximum in 15–20 minutes points strongly to a plasmacytoma or to macroglobulinemia.

A marked and persistent increase in the sedimentation rate that cannot be otherwise accounted for in the middle-aged and elderly should raise suspicion of a carcinoma. In these circumstances the patient should continue to be examined at intervals until the cause of the increase is revealed.

A normal sedimentation rate never excludes the possibility of disease, even a severe progressive one such as cancer; particularly in hemodynamic disorders, an increase in the rate often appears very late. In these circumstances, electrophoresis will reveal a clear dysproteinemia.

In rare cases, a marked increase in the sedimentation rate is accompanied by a completely normal plasma protein pattern, for instance in decompensated pernicious anemia. There is no correlation, however, between the sedimentation rate and the fibrinogen, globulin or total protein content of the blood.

The full significance of a sedimentation rate measured at the climax of an illness is apparent only when it is compared with later measurements, so that in an acute illness there should be no unnecessary delay in making the test.

The sedimentation rate is often less affected by the disease itself than by the secondary complications, such as pneumonia, thrombophlebitis, infarction of the lung, intercurrent infection, etc. Anticoagulant therapy often delays normalization of the sedimentation rate for a considerable time. While drugs in general have no direct effect on the sedimentation rate, they may have a secondary effect due to damage to the liver parenchyma.

Measurement of the sedimentation rate provides an opportunity of examining the plasma for color and clarity (golden-yellow in hemolysis, unusually clear in iron deficiency, straw-colored in pernicious anemia, cloudy in lipemia). Pathological increases in the leukocyte count (over 50000/µL in leukemia) may also be visible to the naked eye.

Veil sedimentation is observed primarily in acute anemia, particularly in hemolysis-related anemia with elevated reticulocyte counts, and in severe dys- and paraproteinemias, especially in cases with incomplete cold and heat antibodies.

References

[1] Hilder and Gunz, *J. clin. Path.*, **17**, 292 (1964).
[2] Böttiger and Svedberg, *Brit. med. J.*, **2**, 85 (1967).
[3] Hargreaves et al., *Brit. J. prev. soc. Med.*, **27**, 63 (1973).
[4] Pickup et al., *Ann. rheum. Dis.*, **40**, 272 (1981).
[5] Bucher et al., *Amer. J. clin. Path.*, **64**, 613 (1975).
[6] Morris et al., *Amer. J. clin. Path.*, **64**, 254 (1975).
[7] Wuhrmann and Märki, *Dysproteinämien und Paraproteinämien; Grundlagen, Klinik und Therapie*, 4th ed., Schwabe, Basle, 1963.
[8] Mücke et al., *Z. med. Labortech.*, **14**, 116 (1973).
[9] Scherer et al., *Klin. Wschr.*, **53**, 265 (1975).
[10] Holdstock and Mitchell, *Lancet*, **2**, 1314 (1977).
[11] Hörmann and Ruhenstroth-Bauer, *Blut*, **30**, 51 (1975).
[12] Jeannet, M., *Schweiz. med. Wschr.*, **94**, 465 (1964).
[13] Marsh, N.A., *Thrombos. Haemostas.*, **42**, 757 (1979).
[14] Scherer and Ruhenstroth-Bauer, *Klin. Wschr.*, **52**, 208 (1974).
[15] Davis and Musselman, *J. Trauma*, **14**, 963 (1974).
[16] Lane and Gill, *Brit. med. J.*, **3**, 577 (1974).
[17] Weicker and Kuhn, *Dtsch. med. Wschr.*, **91**, 1656 (1966).
[18] Nöller, H.G., *Med. Klin.*, **58**, 960 (1963).
[19] International Committee for Standardization in Haematology, *Brit. J. Haemat.*, **24**, 671 (1973).
[20] International Committee for Standardization in Haematology, *Amer. J. clin. Path.*, **68**, 505 (1977).
[21] Brücher, H., *Dtsch. med. Wschr.*, **102**, 1362 (1977).
[22] Rafnsson et al., *Acta med. scand.*, **206**, 207 (1979).
[23] Mallya et al., *Lancet*, **1**, 389 (1982).

Blood-cell proteins (for references see page 166)

Quantitative data on the concentration of individual proteins in blood cells are scarce; some are given in Table 1. Hemoglobin is dealt with in the chapter on 'Blood cells' (pages 205–213).

Erythrocytes

The erythrocyte consists of a membrane surrounding a solution of proteins and electrolytes. More than 95% of the protein is hemo-

Table 1 *Protein in blood cells* (for hemoglobin see pages 205–208)

Protein	Material	Subjects	Number	Mean	s	(Extreme range)	Method	Year	Ref.
				fg (for 1 cell)					
Ferritin	Erythrocytes	Men	11	~0.045	–	–	RIA	1980	1
	Leukocytes	Men	11	~10	–	–	RIA	1980	1
	Erythrocytes	Adults	37	0.123	0.058	(0.065–0.357)	IRMA (antibody to heart ferritin)	1983	2
	Erythrocytes	Adults	37	0.012	0.006	(0.005–0.034)	IRMA (antibody to spleen ferritin)	1983	2
	Erythrocytes	....	32	0.013	0.010	(0.004–0.047)	RIA (antibody to hepatic ferritin)	1983	3
	Granulocytes	....	5	4.6	2.2	(1.7–7.9)	RIA (antibody to hepatic ferritin)	1983	3
	Mononuclear cells	....	5	4.2	1.8	(1.6–6.8)	RIA (antibody to hepatic ferritin)	1983	3
IgG	Platelets	Adults	20	4.4	1.75	–	RIA	1981	4
	Platelets (intact)	Adults	18	1.5	1.0	(0.4–3.3)	MSPRIA	1983	5
	Platelets (sonicated)	Adults	18	3.3	1.0	(1–5)	MSPRIA	1983	5
Fibrinogen	Platelets	....	10	71	10	–	RIA	1980	6
High-molecular-weight kininogen	Platelets	Men	9	0.60	0.24	(0.27–1.01)	CELISA	1983	7
Platelet factor 4	Platelets	Adults	25	21.8	6.1	–	RIA	1983	11
β-Thromboglobulin	Platelets	Adults	25	63.2	19.1	–	RIA	1983	11
				pg (for 1 cell)					
Lactoferrin	Neutrophils	Men	31	17.8	5.3	–	RIA	1978	8
	Neutrophils	Women, <50 years	19	10.0	4.4	–	RIA	1978	8
	Neutrophils	Women, >50 years	10	20.8	6.5	–	RIA	1978	8
Lysozyme	Neutrophils	Adults	60	11.1	6.3	–	Turbidimetric	1978	8
Actin	Lymphocytes	....	20	2.2	0.4	–	IEF	1982	9
				mg/g (relative to hemoglobin)					
Calmodulin	Erythrocytes	Adults	11	0.179	0.030	(0.140–0.228)	Stimulation of cAMP phosphodiesterase	1982	10

RIA: radioimmunoassay; IRMA: immunoradiometric assay; MSPRIA: microtiter solid-phase radioimmunoassay; CELISA: competitive enzyme-linked immunosorbent assay; IEF: isoelectric focusing.

Table 2 *Proteins of the erythrocyte membrane*[14,15]

Band	Relative molecular mass	Mass fraction of total protein (%)	Nomenclature	Relation to membrane
Pattern by SDS-gel electrophoresis, stained with Coomassie blue				
1..........	240000	15	Spectrin α subunit*	Peripheral
2..........	220000	15	Spectrin β subunit*	Peripheral
2.1........	215000	–	Ankyrin; syndein	Peripheral
3..........	88000	24	Component a; anion transport protein	Integral
4.1........	78000	4.2	–	Peripheral
4.2........	72000	5.0	Protein kinase	Integral
4.5........	–	–	–	Integral
4.9........	60000	–	–	Integral
5..........	43000	4.5	Actin	Peripheral
6..........	35000	5.5	Glyceraldehyde-phosphate dehydrogenase	Peripheral
7..........	3 components[16]: 30000 28000 26000	3.4	–	Classification not possible
8..........	18000	–	–	–
Pattern by SDS-gel electrophoresis, stained by PAS reaction				
PAS-1..... PAS-2.....	55000	6.7	Glycophorin A; sialoglycoprotein α	Integral
PAS-3.....	–	–	Glycophorin B; sialoglycoprotein δ	Integral
Glycoconnectin.....	–	–	Glycophorin C; sialoglycoprotein β	Integral

*Membrane spectrin contains a heterodimere composed of 2 subunits, α and β.

Table 3 *Proteins of platelets*[25,36]

Band	Apparent relative molecular mass
Cytoskeletal proteins	
Actin-binding protein (ABP)........................	260000
Myosin heavy chain (M)..........................	200000
Actin (A)..	43000
Profilin...	16000
Membrane glycoproteins	
GP Ia..	150000
GP Ib*...	205000
GP IIa...	150000
GP IIb...	130000
GP III...	105000
GP IV..	110000
Other proteins	
Thrombospondin (TSP)............................	380000
Fibrinogen (Fib).................................	250000
230K...	230000

*The external portion of the α chain is referred to as glycocalcin[37].

globin[12], the remainder consisting of free globin and various enzymes (page 200). Information about the composition of the membrane is derived from studies on the insoluble portion of the cell after hemolysis. This material is known as 'stroma' or, if the membrane remains intact, as 'red-cell ghosts'. The stroma consists of about 52% protein, 40% lipid and 8% carbohydrate (by mass)[12]. The carbohydrates are mainly constituents of glycoproteins. The membrane proteins can be solubilized with the help of the detergent sodium dodecyl sulfate (SDS). The individual polypeptides can be separated by electrophoresis in polyacrylamide gel. The bands are designated by arabic numerals (the main fractions being given in Table 2). Provided a careful technique is used, as many as 40 different membrane polypeptides can be demonstrated[13]. Four bands can be detected by periodic acid-Schiff's base (PAS) staining for glycoproteins. The membrane proteins can be divided into 2 classes: the integral and the peripheral proteins. The integral proteins are strongly bound to the membrane. They penetrate the lipid bilayer and produce functionally important interactions with the lipids. The peripheral proteins are only weakly bound to the membrane and presumably do not interact with the lipid matrix. The spectrin–actin complex accounts for about 35% by mass of the membrane protein[12]. Glycophorin A is the principal integral protein. It consists of 40% protein and 60% carbohydrate, the latter accounting for most of the membrane sialic acid. The sialic-acid-rich oligosaccharide chains, which are attached to the N-terminal domain of the protein, project into the erythrocyte environment. Blood-group antigens are assigned to these chains (page 261). Several specific defects of membrane proteins have been described in certain hemolytic anemias, including hereditary spherocytosis, hereditary elliptocytosis, hereditary pyropoikilocytosis, and sickle-cell anemia[34]. The defect can exist as a deficiency of a specific protein (spectrin, protein 4.1) or as a defective protein–protein interaction (e.g. spectrin–protein 4.1).

Leukocytes

Except for enzymes, the proteins of the various types of leukocytes are only poorly characterized. Several plasma proteins are associated with leukocytes[23]: prealbumin, albumin and transferrin have been detected in lymphocytes, monocytes and granulocytes, whereas cellular variants of α_1-acid glycoprotein and haptoglobin have been found in granulocytes only. Different variants of α_1-antitrypsin are differently distributed among the various cells. Granulocytes contain transcobalamin III[17] and lactoferrin[8]. This latter protein has also been detected in monocytes[8]. From neutrophils actin and myosin resembling other cytoplasmic actins and myosins have been isolated [18]. In the cytoskeleton of lymphocytes, actin accounts for 32% by mass of total protein[33]. Using monoclonal antibodies, specific antigens have been demonstrated on the surface of lymphocytes[19], granulocytes[20] and monocytes[21]. The absence of specific glycoproteins in the membrane of granulocytes has been found to be associated with recurrent bacterial infections[22].

Platelets

Platelets are capable of synthesizing proteins, but also of adsorbing various proteins from the plasma. In platelet homogenates, at least 20 different proteins can be identified by electrophoresis in polyacrylamide gel[24]. Prominent proteins as identified by electrophoresis in agarose–polyacrylamide gels are given in Table 3. Platelet actomyosin (thrombosthenin) is a contractile protein complex accounting for 15–20% by mass of total platelet protein[26]. It consists of platelet actin (thrombosthenin A) and platelet myosin (thrombosthenin M). In platelet homogenates, actomyosin is found almost entirely in the membrane and granule fraction. Platelets contain gesolin – a protein that binds reversibly to actin in the presence of calcium, thereby regulating the length of actin filament[27] – as well as tubulin, the major structural protein of various platelet tubular systems, which also exhibits protein kinase activity[28]. Depending on the technique used, as many as 10 individual glycoproteins have been isolated from human platelet membranes[29]. Specific deficiency of membrane glycoproteins has been demonstrated in thromboasthenia and in the Bernard-Soulier syndrome[35]. The platelets contain significant amounts of plasma coagulation factors. Most of them are more or less firmly adsorbed from the plasma. Fibrinogen occurs in both an adsorbed and an α-granule-bound form[29,38]. Factor VIII-related antigen is concentrated in the α-granule fraction[30]. These granules also contain the platelet-specific proteins platelet factor 4 and β-thromboglobulin[6,31] as well as thrombospondin, which is also termed 'thrombin-sensitive protein'[6]. Factor XIII seems to be synthesized by the megakaryocytes[32]. The λ granules of platelets contain lysosomal enzymes[31].

References

[1] BIRGEGÅRD, G., *Clin. chim. Acta,* **103**, 277 (1980).
[2] PETERS et al., *Brit. J. Haemat.,* **53**, 211 (1983).
[3] VAN DER WEYDEN et al., *Clin. chim. Acta,* **127**, 397 (1983).
[4] PFUELLER et al., *Brit. J. Haemat.,* **49**, 293 (1981).
[5] CHEUNG et al., *J. Lab. clin. Med.,* **101**, 392 (1983).
[6] GERRARD et al., *J. clin. Invest.,* **66**, 102 (1980).
[7] SCHMAIER et al., *J. clin. Invest.,* **71**, 1477 (1983).
[8] BENNETT and KOKOCINSKI, *Brit. J. Haemat.,* **39**, 509 (1978).
[9] STARK et al., *Blood,* **59**, 536 (1982).
[10] MONZON et al., *Brit. J. Haemat.,* **51**, 261 (1982).
[11] SCHARF et al., *Klin. Wschr.,* **61**, 703 (1983).
[12] WINTROBE et al., *Clinical Hematology,* 8th ed., Lea & Febiger, Philadelphia, 1981, page 75.
[13] NEVILLE and GLOSSMANN, *J. biol. Chem.,* **246**, 6335 (1971).
[14] GRATZER, W. B., *Biochem. J.,* **198**, 1 (1981).
[15] TANNER, M. J., *Ciba Found. Symp.,* **94**, 3 (1983).
[16] LANDE et al., *J. clin. Invest.,* **70**, 1273 (1982).
[17] DE VET and TEN HOOPEN, *Acta med. scand.,* **203**, 197 (1978).
[18] BOXER and STOSSEL, *J. clin. Invest.,* **57**, 964 (1976).
[19] MORETTA et al., *Semin. Hemat.,* **19**, 273 (1982).
[20] SKUBITZ et al., *Blood,* **61**, 19 (1983).
[21] TODD and SCHLOSSMAN, *Blood,* **59**, 775 (1982).
[22] CROWLEY et al., *New Engl. J. Med.,* **302**, 1163 (1980); Arnaout et al., *New Engl. J. Med.,* **306**, 693 (1982).
[23] ANDERSEN, M. M., *Scand. J. clin. Lab. Invest.,* **43**, 49 (1983).
[24] NIEWIAROWSKI, S., *Thrombos. Haemostas.,* **38**, 924, (1977).
[25] DAVIES and PALEK, *Blood,* **59**, 502 (1982).
[26] POLLARD et al., *Ann. N. Y. Acad. Sci.,* **283**, 218 (1977).
[27] LIND et al., *J. clin. Invest.,* **69**, 1384 (1982).
[28] IKEDA and STEINER, *J. biol. Chem.,* **254**, 66 (1977).
[29] WINTROBE et al., *Clinical Hematology,* 8th ed., Lea & Febiger, Philadelphia, 1981, page 355.
[30] ZUCKER et al., *J. Lab. clin. Med.,* **94**, 675 (1979).
[31] SHATTIL and BENNETT, *Ann. intern. Med.,* **94**, 108 (1980).
[32] MCDONAGH et al., *J. clin. Invest.,* **48**, 940 (1969).
[33] OWENS and CRUMPTON, *Biochem. Soc. Trans.,* **11**, 156 (1983).
[34] PALEK and LUX, *Semin. Hemat.,* **20**, 189 (1983).
[35] WINTROBE et al., *Clinical Hematology,* 8th ed., Lea & Febiger, Philadelphia, 1981, page 1135.
[36] NACHMIAS, V. T., *Semin. Hemat.,* **20**, 261 (1983).
[37] OKUMURA et al., *J. biol. Chem.,* **251**, 5950 (1976).

Enzymes – Fundamentals of enzyme diagnostics (for references see pages 174–176)

Enzymes are proteins with specific catalytic functions. They are identified and measured in terms of their activity, i.e. their capacity to convert a specific substrate. The more substrate that is converted per unit of time, the higher is the enzyme activity.

Enzyme units. Since many enzymes have not yet been isolated in pure form, neither amount of substance nor mass can as a rule be used as basic unit. Instead, catalytic activity is used. According to the Committee for Biochemical Nomenclature[1] set up by the International Union of Pure and Applied Chemistry (IUPAC) and the International Union of Biochemistry (IUB), 1 µmol of substrate is changed by 1 enzyme unit (U) in 1 min under standard conditions. The International Federation of Clinical Chemistry (IFCC)[2] recommends the katal (kat) as basic unit of enzyme activity: 1 kat is defined as the amount of catalyst which catalyzes the conversion of 1 mol in 1 s under given conditions. 1 U/L corresponds to 16.67 nkat/L. The catalytic activity in body fluids is expressed as volume activity (usually referred to 1 L).

*This chapter on 'Enzymes in Plasma' (pages 166–199) has been compiled in collaboration with E. and F. W. SCHMIDT, Zentrum für innere Medizin und Dermatologie, Medizinische Hochschule Hannover, Hannover, FRG.

With the exception of the IFCC recommendation for reference methods of 30.00 °C[3], there is no international agreement on the choice of temperature at which activity is measured. Table 1 shows the influence of temperature on the activity of the more important enzymes.

The various organs and tissues have different *enzyme patterns* in accordance with their diverse functions. These differences are essentially quantitative: the functional interplay of different enzymes is reflected in 'constant-proportion groups'. In the principal cycles of energy-yielding metabolism, these enzymes form a basic enzyme pattern surrounded by the more variable enzymes. The latter – lactate dehydrogenase, glycerol-3-phosphate dehydrogenase, the enzymes of hexose monophosphate cycle, etc. – are present in quite different proportions with regard to the basic metabolic structure depending on the metabolic type to which the tissue in question belongs. Their activities may vary by several orders of magnitude from organ to organ[32–35] (Table 2).

All enzymes which support specific organ functions (and which are found primarily in the parenchymatous organs) are of course variable enzymes. In some cases, their activities are so different that they are called 'organ-specific' or 'tissue-specific' enzymes.

Table 1 *Factors for conversion of enzyme activities in serum at 25 °C (factor = 1.00) to activity at 30 °C and 37 °C*

Enzyme	Conversion of enzyme activity at 25 °C: to activity at 30 °C (Factor)	to activity at 37 °C (Factor)	Reference	Enzyme	Conversion of enzyme activity at 25 °C: to activity at 30 °C (Factor)	to activity at 37 °C (Factor)	Reference
L-Iditol dehydrogenase	1.23	1.63	6	Creatine kinase activated with GSH	1.47	2.52	18
Lactate dehydrogenase	1.33	1.67	7	– activated with N-acetylcysteine	1.62	2.72	19
– LDH-1, rabbit	1.08	1.19	8	Phosphoglucomutase	1.60	2.70	20
– LDH-2, rabbit	1.10	1.24	8	Arylesterase (paraoxonase)	1.10	1.20	21
– LDH-3, rabbit	1.14	1.33	8	Triacylglycerol lipase (lipase)	1.25	1.44	22
– LDH-4, rabbit	1.16	1.38	8	Cholinesterase*	1.05	1.15	23
– LDH-5, rabbit	1.19	1.44	8		1.29	1.83	24
'2-Hydroxybutyrate dehydrogenase'	1.19	1.37	9	Alkaline phosphatase◇	1.19	1.45	25
Malate dehydrogenase	1.47	2.50	10	Acid phosphatase◇	1.49	2.08	25
Isocitrate dehydrogenase ($NADP^+$)	1.49	2.78	11	5′-Nucleotidase	1.67	2.27	26
Phosphogluconate dehydrogenase	1.32	1.89	12	Aminopeptidase (amino-acid arylamidase)	1.54	2.63	27
Xanthine oxidase	1.38	2.08	13	Cystyl aminopeptidase (oxytocinase)	1.05	1.10	28
Glutamate dehydrogenase [$NAD(P)^+$]	1.23	1.61	14	Carboxypeptidase A	1.18	1.70	29
Ornithine carbamoyltransferase	1.41	2.46	15	Carboxypeptidase B	1.32	1.79	29
γ-Glutamyltransferase	1.25	1.59	16	Urease	1.28	1.56	30
Aspartate aminotransferase	1.38	2.13	17	Guanine deaminase	1.50	2.30	31
Alanine aminotransferase	1.38	2.13	17	Adenosine deaminase	1.35	2.18	32

*Substrate: benzoylcholine.
◇Substrate: 4-nitrophenyl phosphate.

Table 2 *Enzyme activities in tissues[33] and blood cells[36] measured at 25 °C*

	Hexokinase	L-Iditol dehydrogenase	Fructose-bisphosphate aldolase	Glycerol-3-phosphate dehydrogenase	Alcohol dehydrogenase	Glyceraldehyde-phosphate dehydrogenase	Enolase	Pyruvate kinase	Lactate dehydrogenase	Malate dehydrogenase	Isocitrate dehydrogenase	Glutamate dehydrogenase	Aspartate aminotransferase	Alanine aminotransferase	Glucose-6-phosphate dehydrogenase	Phosphogluconate dehydrogenase	Phosphoglycerate kinase	Phosphoglyceromutase	Creatine kinase[37]
	U/g																		
Liver	25.2	71.9	5.7	14.8	30.5	75.2	22.2	15.5	156	202	36.2	60.2	96.0	58.7	0.93	1.39	217	134	4
Skeletal muscle	3.5	0.01	98.1	2.3	0.01	175	21.4	67.6	148	93.8	6.8	0.5	36.7	3.4	0.01	0.01	33.8	35.0	2588
Myocardium	2.0	0.01	5.0	0.6	0.01	62.6	1.7	29.0	125	482	5.2	1.1	52.5	3.0	0.2	0.1	0	0	379
Uterus	2.2	0.01	0.9	0.01	0.01	37.5	2.7	11.1	25.6	33.8	1.1	1.1	4.1	0.9	0.9	0.01	15.0	23.1	38
Gastric smooth muscle	2.3	0.3	2.6	0.05	0.01	57.4	5.2	17.6	54.1	49.8	2.8	0.7	4.3	0.05	0.5	0.1	0	0	122 (gastric smooth muscle and mucosa)
Gastric mucosa	1.1	1.2	1.1	0.1	0.9	69.8	6.4	22.2	65.7	113	11.0	3.0	28.9	1.1	0.7	0.3	0	0	
Pancreas	0.4	0.2	0.04	0.04	0.1	37.7	3.5	9.8	50.8	47.7	1.8	0.5	3.0	0.7	0.4	0.2	0	0	3
Renal cortex	2.1	3.6	1.8	2.4	0.01	108	9.1	15.6	114	105	6.1	6.7	10.6	2.0	0.7	0.5	0	0	18 (renal cortex and medulla)
Renal medulla	1.1	0.6	0.7	0.2	0.05	57.8	3.3	23.5	101	49.2	4.4	2.2	8.2	0.7	0.3	0.3	0	0	
Cerebral cortex (gray matter)	3.2	0.2	5.3	0.09	0.01	69.3	10.5	28.5	54.6	117	0.8	4.1	20.3	0.1	0.3	0.3	0	0	157 (cerebral cortex and medullary brain substance)
Medullary brain substance (white matter)	1.0	0.2	2.5	0.2	0.01	69.1	7.7	27.9	40.1	61.8	0.9	2.3	9.3	0.01	0.2	0.1	0	0	
Cerebellar hemisphere	1.8	0.1	4.7	0.01	0.01	69.7	12.4	34.9	64.7	78.4	0.2	1.5	21.6	0.07	0.3	0.3	0	0	–
Lungs	1.6	1.6	0.5	0.1	0.3	27.3	2.6	8.6	27.4	27.3	1.1	2.5	1.1	0.3	0.6	0.5	0	0	23
Adipose tissue	0.7	0.01	1.6	4.3	0.2	19.4	1.6	3.8	52.8	72.7	1.7	1.3	5.2	1.9	1.5	1.2	0	0	1
Lymph nodes	3.7	0.2	3.4	0.1	0.2	75.3	10.8	30.4	84.0	69.7	4.1	2.7	7.4	0.07	0.9	0.5	0	0	1
	$U/10^{10}$																		
Erythrocytes	0.2	0	1.03	0	0	19.8	1.89	3.28	17.1	12.5	0.12	0	0.68	0.14	1.32	0.71	28.9	6.42	0.1
– fetal	0.15	0	1.49	0.19	0	28.4	3.03	2.33	35.7	30.4	0.27	0	1.43	0.13	2.85	0.82	60.0	7.54	–
Platelets	0.45	0	0.82	0.12	0	3.9	2.36	12.0	9.77	3.72	0.33	0.07	0.16	0.08	0.69	0.09	8.27	3.94	–
Granulocytes	17.4	0	40.6	15.9	0	529	338	36.8	922	243	16.6	2.38	27.1	8.23	92.6	34.2	1170	416	–

On the basis of these organ-specific enzymes (the liver enzymes L-iditol dehydrogenase or glutamate dehydrogenase, for example, or the muscle and brain enzyme creatine kinase) it is possible – provided the varying proportions of the ubiquitous key-pathway enzymes are taken into account – to identify the enzyme pattern specific to a given organ using only a small segment, indeed, as few as 3 or 4 enzymes if appropriately chosen[38, 39].

Enzyme variants

The molecular enzyme variants[40, 41] are subdivided into 3 groups: isoenzymes, heteroenzymes, and alloenzymes.

Table 3
Distribution of lactate dehydrogenase isoenzymes in human tissues[44]

	Isoenzyme				
	LDH-1	LDH-2	LDH-3	LDH-4	LDH-5
	Structure				
	H_4	H_3M	H_2M_2	HM_3	M_4
	Percent of total activity				
Heart muscle	60	30	5	3	2
Kidney	28	34	21	11	6
Cerebrum	28	32	19	16	5
Liver	0.2	0.8	1	4	94
Skeletal muscle	3	4	8	9	76
Epidermis (skin)	0	0	4	17	79
Lung	10	18	28	23	21
Spleen	5	15	31	31	18

Isoenzymes are enzymes with the same function but with different structures. Therefore, their reactions in activation and inactivation processes, and their specificity for chemically similar substrates differ from one another. The isoenzyme patterns of tissues, organs, or cell organelles are genetically determined, and often differ so much from one another that an assignment can be made on the basis of the proportions present in the serum.

In addition to their systematic names, the isoenzymes are designated with arabic numerals. These numerals describe their electrophoretic mobility, beginning with 1 at the anode. So far, isoenzymes of more than 100 enzymes of the human body have been found. The isoenzymes of lactate dehydrogenase (Table 3), creatine kinase (Table 4), acid phosphatase, alkaline phosphatase (Table 5), and α-amylase, in particular, are of practical importance.

Heteroenzymes are species-specific enzymes with the same function. They differ in their molecular structures and, because of their different antigenic properties, can be separated by immunological procedures.

Alloenzymes are genetically determined variants of enzymes and isoenzymes. Every human being may be presumed to be the carrier of at least one alloenzyme formed by mutation. The majority of alloenzymes have no bearing on pathological phenomena, although more and more metabolic disorders caused by enzyme defects are being discovered[45].

Enzyme defects may assume 3 forms:

1. *Changes in enzyme structure.* In these cases, the enzyme activity is usually diminished, but its molecular concentration in the tissues or in serum is normal. A point mutation in the structural gene is assumed to be the cause of the structural aberration.
2. *Changes in enzyme structure and concentration.* In these cases, mutation in the structural gene gives rise to abnormal enzymes with a reduced rate of synthesis or increased rate of breakdown. The extreme case is the complete absence of an enzyme.

Table 4 *Creatine kinase isoenzymes*[42]

Isoenzyme	Structure*	Occurrence
	Cytoplasmic forms	
CK-1	BB	Brain (smooth muscle, stomach, intestine, kidney, prostate, uterus, placenta)
CK-2	MB	Heart muscle (skeletal muscle)
CK-3	MM	Skeletal muscle, heart muscle
	Mitochondrial forms	
CK-4	MtMt (?)	Heart muscle, liver, brain
	Macro forms	
Macro CK, type I	Aggregates of BB and immunoglobulins	Plasma
Macro CK, type II	Oligomeres of CK-4	Plasma
	Inactive forms	
CK-Bi	Glycosylated derivatives of BB (?)	–

*B for brain-derived, M for skeletal-muscle-derived, Mt for mitochondria-derived.

Table 5 *Properties of alkaline phosphatases of human tissues*[43]

	Unit	Alkaline phosphatase			
		Intestine	Placenta	Bone	Liver
Anodal migration on starch gel	cm	3.0	3.8–4.2	4.0–6.0	4.4–5.0
Inhibition by L-phenylalanine	%	75	75	0–10	0–10
Inhibition by L-homoarginine	%	5	5	78	78
Heat inactivation	%	50–60	0	90–100	50–70
Effect of pretreatment with neuraminidase	–	0	+	+	+
Reaction with dilute antiserum to placental isoenzyme	–	0	+	0	0
Reaction with dilute antiserum to liver isoenzyme	–	0	0	+	+
Reaction with dilute antiserum to intestinal isoenzyme	–	+	0	0	0

Table 6 *Classification of enzymes on the basis of site of action*[47]

Site of action	Enzyme	Enzyme activity in plasma when cell of origin is damaged	Causes of change in activity
Cell	Lactate dehydrogenase, aspartate aminotransferase, alanine aminotransferase, creatine kinase, etc.	Rise	Increased release from the damaged cell into the extracellular space
Cell membrane	γ-Glutamyltransferase, alkaline phosphatase, aminopeptidase (leucine aminopeptidase), etc.	Rise	Increased synthesis and increased release into the extracellular space
Plasma	Cholinesterase, coagulation factors, etc.	Decline	Decreased secretion due to impaired synthesis or diminished number of cells
Gastrointestinal tract	α-Amylase, lipase, trypsin	Rise	Increased release from the damaged cells into the extracellular space (in cases of acute cell damage only)

3. *Changes in enzyme concentration.* Here, the enzyme is structurally normal, but its rate of synthesis is reduced or – far more rarely – increased. These defects are attributed to mutations in the control gene.

Enzyme localization

Within the cell, the enzymes are localized in different cell compartments: in the cytosol, in mitochondria, in lysosomes, in the cell membranes, and in the cell nucleus. For practical purposes, a distinction can be made between enzymes of type I, which can be quite readily extracted and are probably very loosely bound in cytosol (for example lactate dehydrogenase and alanine aminotransferase), and type II enzymes, which become soluble only when the cell structure has been severely damaged (for example the mitochondrial enzyme glutamate dehydrogenase). Aspartate aminotransferase, malate dehydrogenase, and isocitrate dehydrogenase must be classified separately as type III, since their cytosol isoenzymes have a high solubility while their mitochondrial isoenzymes have low solubility. Other enzymes, such as those of the electron transfer system, are so firmly a part of the structure that they lose their activity when attempts are made to bring them into solution[34,46].

Enzymes in plasma (for normal values see pages 176–196)

From the diagnostic standpoint, the enzymes circulating in the plasma are defined proteins of which the quantity parameter can be specifically and sensitively determined on the basis of their catalytic function, i.e. their activity. For enzyme diagnostics it is advantageous to classify enzymes on the basis of their sites of action[38] rather than on the basis of the reactions they catalyze or their place in metabolism, since this is what governs their behavior in the plasma when their organ of origin is damaged (Table 6).

Comment to Table 6: Except in a few genetically determined metabolic diseases (e.g. hypophosphatasemia), no reduced activities of *cell enzymes* in the plasma have so far been observed. Elevated activities of *plasma-specific enzymes* have been found to accompany increased synthesis and secretion. In the case of chronic lesions with reduced mass or reduced synthesizing function of the cells of the digestive tract, *secretory enzymes* diminish at the site of function, i.e. the intestinal lumen, and even reduced activities in the plasma may ensue.

Practically all cell enzymes of diagnostic importance can also be found in the plasma of 'normal healthy' persons in very low activities (between 1‰ and 0.01‰ of their activity in the cells). This steep activity gradient (Table 7), which can be maintained only through a continuous expenditure of energy, renders the physiological activities of cell enzymes in the plasma comprehensible, even though their most essential sources are still disputed. Most probably numerous organs contribute to the normal enzyme content of the plasma[48,49].

Table 7 *Organ/serum activity gradients*[33]

Enzyme	Skeletal muscle/serum	Liver/serum
Fructose-bisphosphate aldolase	21800:1	2700:1
Pyruvate kinase	6200:1	1400:1
Lactate dehydrogenase	1400:1	1400:1
Malate dehydrogenase	2000:1	2600:1
Aspartate aminotransferase	5700:1	9000:1
Alanine aminotransferase	750:1	7600:1

An intensification of cell function as, for example, during muscle work or as a reaction to cell damage, is made possible through the enhancement of cell metabolism. Increased conversion of substrate results in increased exchange through the boundary surfaces of the cells, that is, a greater permeability of the plasma membranes. It is not known whether the mere increase in substrate permeation of the boundary surfaces is itself sufficient to enable an 'incidental' escape of cell enzymes or whether a reduction – even only relative – in the energy potential is necessary for the cells to begin to 'leak'[50,51]. The distinction between 'borderline physiological' and 'borderline pathological' is blurred here, and can probably only be evaluated in terms of the cause and extent of the enzyme release[48,49,52].

Experimental studies have shown that with oxidative phosphorylation impaired, glycolysis alone is sufficient to prevent greater enzyme efflux from the liver, provided that sufficient glycogen stores are present[53,54].

The dependence of the rate of efflux of an enzyme not only on its binding to the cell structure, on its intracellular localization, and on its concentration, but also on its relative molecular mass shows that the plasma membranes form diffusion barriers even when cells are considerably damaged. Cell damage must be extremely severe before the activity ratios prevailing in the cell are reflected roughly in the extracellular space[35,52,54].

The loss of cell enzymes into the extracellular space is a sensitive indicator of cell damage. It can be demonstrated experimentally – and clinical experience has confirmed this – that considerable enzyme efflux may already be taking place even though the light or electron microscope may be unable to detect with certainty any changes in cell structure. Whether enzymes continue to be released after cell death depends on the type of necrosis. However, necrotic cells contribute very little, if anything at all, to a pathological increase of enzyme activity in serum, the major share of which is attributable to cells that are still living, and – as, e.g. in the case of acute viral hepatitis – cells that, though damaged, will survive.

Enzyme elimination from the plasma

The release of enzymes from the cells results in modifications of their activity. The 'instantaneous' effect[55], which may be manifested in either a decrease or an increase of enzyme activity, depending on the enzyme, results from changes in the enzyme molecule as it passes from its site of synthesis or of action through the boundary layers into the alien milieu of the extracellular space. Experimental studies have shown that by partial spreading of enzymes, changes in the Michaelis constant can be demonstrated, and that reversible dissociations may be brought about by dilution as well as by reversible oxidation of SH groups at the active site. These changes can be partly reversed by 'reactivation'. An example of this is the activation of creatine kinase by addition of sulfhydryl-containing reagents[56,57].

After release from the cells, enzymes are distributed in parts of the extracellular space. Enzymes from most organs pass into the circulation primarily via the lymph system[49]. An exception is the liver, where parenchymal cells have direct contact with the plasma. This is – in addition to the key role played by the liver in metabolism, its specific functions, and its high enzyme content – the most important reason for the special significance of enzyme diagnostics in liver disease.

The distribution of an enzyme in the various extracellular compartments (interstitial, lymphatic, intravascular) is a matter of minutes or a few hours, diffusion from the intravascular to the extravascular space occurring more quickly than vice versa. Studies with radioactively labelled enzymes have shown that no changes occur in an enzyme's activity as it passes from one fluid compartment to another[52].

The spread of an enzyme throughout a part of the extracellular space is evidenced with particular clarity by the primary rapid decrease of enzyme activity after intravenous injection of enzymes[58,59], which is followed by the phase of true enzyme elimination, reflected by a slow fall of enzyme activity in the plasma. The elimination rate is independent of the absolute value of enzyme activity; it is an exponential function, which means that the half-life of individual enzymes can be easily calculated. Activity half-lives in plasma are specific and characteristic properties of the individual enzymes. They are independent of age and sex, and vary from hours to days (Table 8). Interestingly, considerable differences also exist between isoenzymes. The practical import of the different half-lives is made clear by the LDH isoenzymes: while isoenzymes 1 and 2 (myocardial type) are diagnostically quite useful because of their long half-lives, LDH-5 (liver and skeletal muscle type) has hardly any relevance for the diagnosis of liver diseases: it is eliminated so rapidly that significant increases in activity are likely only in cases of acute and severe liver damage.

As a rule, the decrease of enzyme activities in the plasma is not a consequence of a loss of specific activity due, e.g., to ageing of enzyme proteins in the extracellular space. Furthermore, there is no specific organ of elimination. Experiments with radioactively labelled enzymes have shown that almost all cells are capable of reabsorbing enzyme proteins from the circulation and breaking them down. However, the greatest portion is absorbed by the liver, kidneys, and lungs. Less than 3% are eliminated into the gastrointestinal tract[61,84,85]. The participation, at least potential, of all cells in enzyme elimination explains the constancy of the elimination rate even in serious illnesses. In animal experiments, diminished elimination rates were observed only in the severest cases of poisoning. In summary, one of the most important results of the studies of enzyme elimination for practical enzyme diagnostics is the constancy of the elimination rate. This means that in the equilibrium between influx and efflux of enzymes, it is the *influx* which is the crucial parameter. Thus, the extent by which enzyme activity increases in the serum becomes an indicator of cell damage.

Determination of enzyme activity in serum

With the exception of coagulation factors, the majority of diagnostically useful enzymes can be determined in the serum or plasma. When plasma is used, enzyme inhibition as a result of addition of citrate, oxalate, heparin, fluoride, etc., must be taken into consideration[5]. Release of enzymes from platelets during clotting is relatively minor in humans (in contrast to small laboratory animals) and interferes to any notable degree only with the determination of acid phosphatase[49]. However, even slight hemolysis disturbs the determination of enzymes present in high activities in erythrocytes, such as lactate dehydrogenase, glucose-6-phosphate dehydrogenase, phosphogluconate dehydrogenase, fructose-bisphosphate aldolase, etc. (see pages 200–204). For other enzymes with much smaller differences of activity between erythrocytes and serum, such as aspartate aminotransferase, alanine aminotransferase, glutamate dehydrogenase, etc., slight hemolysis is acceptable. Nevertheless, blood cells should be separated from serum or plasma within 1 hour.

Because of their varying stability in serum, enzyme activities should be determined as soon as possible after the serum has been obtained. The majority of enzymes used diagnostically, however, show no notable losses of activity for 24 hours when stored at

Table 8 *Apparent half-life of activity in plasma of diagnostically useful enzymes*

Enzyme	Mean	*s* or range	Reference
	h		
Lactate dehydrogenase	116	–	60
– LDH-1	113	*s*30	61
	72	–	62
	59	–	63
– LDH-5	10	*s*1	61
	14.4	–	64
	8	–	63
Malate dehydrogenase	16	*s*2.5	61
	18	*s*7	65
– mitochondrial	18.4	*s*6	65
Glutamate dehydrogenase [NAD(P)$^+$]	18	*s*0.5	61
	–	11–18	66
γ-Glutamyltransferase	98	–	67
Aspartate aminotransferase	17	*s*2.5	61
	22	–	68
	40	–	60
	12.5	–	69
– cytosolic	–	12–17	70
– mitochondrial	6	–	70
Alanine aminotransferase	47	*s*5	61
	32	–	68
	43	–	71
	–	25–67	66
Creatine kinase	15	–	61
	24	–	60
	17	*s*4	65
	15	–	42
– isoenzyme MB	13.4	*s*4	65
	12	–	42
– isoenzyme BB	3	–	42
– isoenzyme Bi	108	–	42
Adenylate kinase	0.28	*s*0.05	72
Triacylglycerol lipase (lipase)	15	–	73
Cholinesterase	~240	–	74
	288	–	75
	82	–	76
Alkaline phosphatase	~144	–	77
– biliary	233	*s*24	67
– liver	52	*s*8	78
– placenta	168	–	79
– small intestine, slow-moving component	7.5	–	80
– – fast-moving component	1.3	–	80
– bones	–	27–52	81
Acid phosphatase, prostate	~4	–	82
α-Amylase	~4	–	82
	–	3–6	83
Aminopeptidase (amino-acid arylamidase)	209	*s*24	67
Fructose-bisphosphate aldolase	21	–	61

Table 9
Mean losses of enzyme activity during the storage of serum[86]

Enzyme	Temperature	Duration of storage				
		1 day	2 days	3 days	5 days	7 days
		Loss of activity (%)				
L-Iditol dehydrogenase	4 °C	22	–	38	–	–
	25 °C	24	31	58	69	78
Lactate dehydrogenase	4 °C	0	4	8	9	12
	25 °C	0	1	2	10	15
'2-Hydroxybutyrate dehydrogenase'	4 °C	0	0	0	3	5
Glutamate dehydrogenase	4 °C	0	2	5	13	26
	25 °C	0	0	0	0	5
	25 °C	10	12	15	24	30
γ-Glutamyltransferase	4 °C	0	0	0	0	0
	20 °C	0	0	0	0	0
Aspartate aminotransferase	4 °C	2	5	8	10	12
	25 °C	2	6	10	11	13
Alanine aminotransferase	4 °C	2	5	10	14	20
	25 °C	8	12	17	19	39
Creatine kinase*	4 °C	0	0	0	0	0
	25 °C	0	0	1	4	6
Triacylglycerol lipase (lipase)	4 °C	0	0	0	0	0
	25 °C	0	0	0	0	0
Cholinesterase	4 °C	0	0	0	0	0
	25 °C	0	0	0	0	0
Alkaline phosphatase	4 °C	0	0	0	0	0
	25 °C	0	2	3	6	10
Acid phosphatase◊	4 °C	0	0	0	0	0
	25 °C	0	0	0	0	0
α-Amylase	4 °C	0	0	0	0	0
	25 °C	0	0	0	0	0
'Leucine aminopeptidase'	4 °C	0	0	0	0	0
	25 °C	0	0	0	0	0
Fructose-bisphosphate aldolase	4 °C	0	0	0	8	12
	25 °C	0	0	0	15	20

*After reactivation by SH compounds. ◊In acidified serum (pH 5.5–6.0).

+4 °C and even at room temperature (Table 9). Exceptions are glucose-6-phosphate dehydrogenase, phosphogluconate dehydrogenase, creatine kinase, and acid phosphatase. Often the original activity can be maintained or restored by means of preservatives or reactivating additives. For enzyme determination procedures see the relevant literature[4] and the data on pages 176–196.

Physiological variations in enzyme activity

Sex-related differences

Demonstrable, although not always significant differences between the sexes exist for the majority of enzymes occurring in the plasma of normal persons. The normal values (reference intervals) of the following enzymes are lower in women than in men: aspartate aminotransferase and alanine aminotransferase[90,91], creatine kinase[18,92–94], γ-glutamyltransferase[53,95], acid phosphatase[87], cholinesterase[88] and β-D-glucuronidase[89]. Differences have also been found in the activity ratios of LDH isoenzymes[96].

Age-dependence

Numerous enzymes show higher normal values (reference intervals) in the serum of children, especially in the newborn and in early infancy. However, between the 2nd and 3rd years of life, only the distinctly elevated levels of alkaline phosphatase retain major practical interest. During the accelerated growth period, the activity of alkaline phosphatase in the plasma (Fig. 1) shows a close correlation with bone growth[98]. The reason for the age-dependence in the case of acid phosphatase is less clear but can be referred to osteoclast activity (Fig. 2). γ-Glutamyltransferase activity is high in cord blood, but stays low in the serum of children (page 181). In the newborn high activities of creatine kinase in serum are often found during the first few days of life; infants after the 2nd month of life show activities almost identical to that of adults (page 184). Elevated normal values for malate dehydrogenase, aspartate aminotransferase, and alanine aminotransferase in advanced age have also been reported[97]. However, the elevated average values are probably rather due to subclinical illnesses which are more frequent in this period of life.

Race-related differences

Differences have been reported for activities in the serum for creatine kinase (page 184), α-amylase (page 190), and β-N-acetyl-D-glucosaminidase (page 191).

Circadian variations

Data on circadian variations in enzyme activity vary. If rhythms do exist, they do not seem to be of any significance for practical purposes[100].

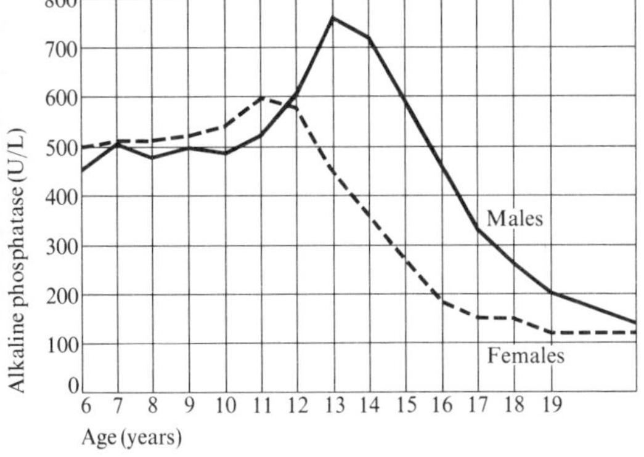

Fig. 1. Activity of alkaline phosphatase in the plasma (geometric mean) in children and adolescents measured at 37 °C[97].

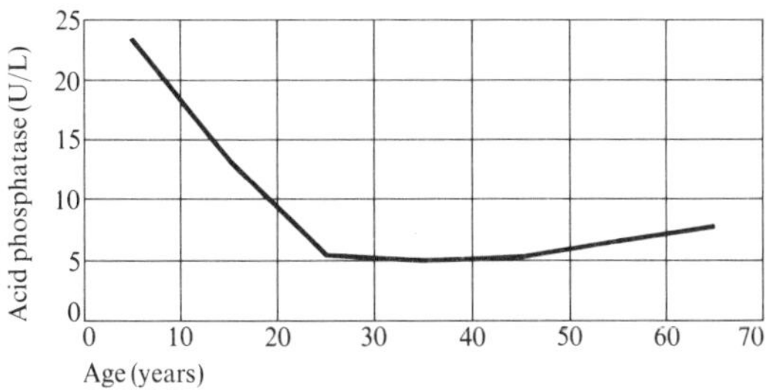

Fig. 2. Activity of acid phosphatase in the plasma as a function of age measured at 37 °C[99].

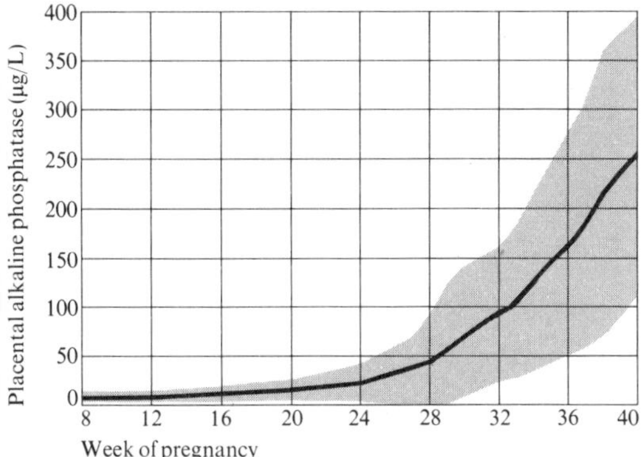

Fig. 3. Concentration of placental alkaline phosphatase in the serum during pregnancy (mean and 95% range)[109].

Muscle activity

Heavy muscular work gives rise to a distinct elevation of enzyme activities in the serum. Clear increases of the activities of creatine kinase, aspartate aminotransferase, alanine aminotransferase, lactate dehydrogenase, fructose-bisphosphate aldolase, malate dehydrogenase, and pyruvate kinase have been demonstrated after prolonged exertions, particularly in untrained subjects[101–105]. Creatine kinase showed the most sensitive response: Its activity may rise considerably even after moderate physical exercise[102, 106]. Alkaline phosphatase, acid phosphatase and α-amylase show no changes[5].

Pregnancy

The changes of the individual serum enzyme activities vary during normal pregnancy (Table 10). However, these changes, if they occur at all, remain slight for the majority of diagnostically important enzymes. The increase of alkaline phosphatase activity in the 2nd, and especially in the 3rd trimester, caused by the isoenzyme

Table 10 *Enzyme activity in serum during pregnancy*[38, 107, 108]

EC number	Recommended name
	Activity unchanged
1.1.1.14	L-Iditol dehydrogenase
1.1.1.27	Lactate dehydrogenase
1.1.1.37	Malate dehydrogenase
1.1.1.42	Isocitrate dehydrogenase ($NADP^+$)
1.1.1.44	Phosphogluconate dehydrogenase (decarboxylating) (page 178)
1.4.1.3	Glutamate dehydrogenase [$NAD(P)^+$]
2.1.3.3	Ornithine carbamoyltransferase
2.6.1.1	Aspartate aminotransferase
2.6.1.2	Alanine aminotransferase
3.1.3.5	5′ Nucleotidase (page 189)
3.2.1.1	α-Amylase
3.4.15.1	Dipeptidyl carboxypeptidase (ACE) (page 193)
4.1.2.13	Fructose-bisphosphate aldolase
	Activity at lower limit of normal or slightly subnormal
2.3.2.2	γ-Glutamyltransferase (page 181)
2.7.3.2	Creatine kinase (page 184)
3.1.1.3	Triacylglycerol lipase (lipase) (page 185)
3.1.1.8	Cholinesterase (page 186)
	Activity above normal
1.4.3.6	Amine oxidase (diamine oxidase) (page 179)
1.16.3.1	Ferroxidase (page 180)
3.1.3.1	Alkaline phosphatase (page 187)
3.1.27.5	Ribonuclease (pancreatic) (page 189)
3.2.1.23	β-D-Galactosidase (page 190)
3.2.1.30	β-N-Acetyl-D-glucosaminidase (page 191)
3.2.1.31	β-D-Glucuronidase (page 191)
3.4.11.2	Aminopeptidase (amino-acid arylamidase) (page 192)
3.4.11.3	Cystyl aminopeptidase (oxytocinase) (page 192)

from the placenta, must be taken into account in differential diagnosis (Fig. 3).

Enzymes and diagnosis

The use of the determination of enzyme activities in the plasma or serum for diagnostic purposes is based essentially on the fact that, in cell injury, enzymes leak out into the extracellular space as a consequence of the increased permeability of the cell membrane. The extent by which the activity in the serum increases is a direct measure of the extent and severity of cell damage, provided the following conditions are met:

1. The cell damage must be of a type that results in impairment of permeability and hence in efflux of enzymes.
2. The damaged cells must not be cut off from the intravascular space.
3. The damaged organ must be large enough, and/or have a high enough enzyme content (e.g. the liver) for even slight to moderate damage to cause an increase of enzyme activity.
4. If the damaged organ is not large, and/or does not have a high enzyme content, the damage must be so severe and acute that it results in a detectable increase of enzyme activity (e.g. acute myocardial infarction).
5. If the damaged organ is small, its content of a specific enzyme can nevertheless be high enough for even moderate damage to lead to a detectable rise in the activity of this specific enzyme (e.g. carcinoma of the prostate).

The purpose of determining the activities of organ- or tissue-specific enzymes in the serum is to ascertain which organ or tissue is damaged. Because of differences in the activities of most enzymes in the various organs, organ diagnosis can also be made by assessing the activity ratios between these enzymes (Table 2). Activity ratios also make it possible to ascertain the site of the damage in the organ itself and, if the different elimination rates from the plasma as well as the pathological activity changes in tissue are known, to assess the stage of the disease[52,110,111].

Although a great many enzymes can be detected in the serum, the determination of only a few of them has proved useful for diagnostic purposes and has become routine. These are the following, ranked in order of their practical importance (the abbreviations used hereafter in the text are given in parentheses): *aspartate aminotransferase* (AST), *γ-glutamyltransferase* (γ-GT), *creatine kinase* (CK) and its isoenzymes, *alanine aminotransferase* (ALT), *α-amylase, alkaline phosphatase* (ALP), *glutamate dehydrogenase* (GLDH), *lactate dehydrogenase* (LDH) and its isoenzymes such as '*2-hydroxybutyrate dehydrogenase*' (HBDH), *acid phosphatase* (ACP), *cholinesterase* (CHE), *triacylglycerol lipase* (lipase), *leucine arylamidase* (LAP), *leucine aminopeptidase* (LAP), *isocitrate dehydrogenase* (ICDH), and *L-iditol dehydrogenase* (SDH). Enzyme determinations have become indispensable in the diagnosis of diseases of the heart, liver, muscle, and pancreas[112].

Heart disease

The rise of activity of some enzymes in the serum is a constant and reliable symptom in the diagnosis of *myocardial infarction* and can be demonstrated in 95–100% of cases[113,114]. Since the cell damage is acute, localized and shortlived, and since, furthermore, a distortion of the enzyme pattern owing to an overlaying by enzymes from other organs can occur later from the possible consequences of the infarction (shock, cardiac insufficiency), early and timely determination of the enzyme activities is of crucial significance for diagnosis (Table 11)[38,115,116].

The principal enzyme is the muscle-specific CK. To differentiate myocardial infarction from damage of the skeletal musculature, simultaneous determination of AST has proven a reliable measure. In the early stage of myocardial infarction, the rising CK and AST activities stand in a proportion of approximately 5 : 1 to one another; thus, the CK/AST ratio is around 5 (2–9) in the case of myocardial infarction, whereas it is around 27 (13–56) in the case of damage to the skeletal musculature (methods: AST, optimized, 25 °C; CK, N-acetylcysteine activated, 25 °C). Using the value 10 for discrimination, the diagnostic reliability of the CK/AST ratio is 90% if the CK activity is higher than 160 U/L and if the rise of the AST activity cannot be attributed to disease in some other organ[117,118].

If the CK/AST ratio cannot be used, determination of the CK isoenzyme MB is recommended[119–126]. The myocardium contains more than a 20% portion of CK-MB[122] (almost 80% CK-MM), most skeletal muscles less than 3% CK-MB. Since CK-MB is also not heart-specific, detection of CK-MB in the serum is not itself of decisive diagnostic significance, but the CK-MB fraction of total CK activity, which must be more than 6%[125–128].

Since the LDH activity in the serum remains elevated longer than the activities of CK and AST, an increase of LDH activity with an HBDH/LDH ratio of more than 0.8 in the late stage (to the 20th day) may be taken as an indication of an infarction that has run its course[38,129].

An *extension of the infarction* results in a renewed rise of enzyme activity, with the same pattern as has been observed in the first episode; in acute *right-ventricular insufficiency with liver congestion and in shock,* an especially high increase with a 'liver pattern' is to be expected[38,130]. If other organs with different enzyme patterns are involved in the pathological process, the activity ratios of the enzymes in the serum also change, and are thus useful for differential diagnosis (Table 12).

In over 50% of cases of *pulmonary embolism,* there is no detectable rise of the activity of aminotransferases in the serum, and in over 80% of cases there is no detectable rise of CK activity as long as shock does not occur. If, however, a rise of enzyme activities is observed without shock having occurred, the enzyme pattern is that of right-ventricular insufficiency with acutely congested liver[38,116].

The principal enzyme in the differential diagnosis of myocardial infarction from *acute pancreatitis* is α-amylase, the activity of which is as a rule considerably increased in the latter (slight rises also accompany myocardial infarction), whereas CK activity is only slightly elevated (exception: shock!). In pancreatitis with acute occlusion of the common bile duct, the pattern of acute biliary obstruction is present in addition to a rise of α-amylase activity[38,130].

In *biliary colic* with acute obstruction, there is no rise of CK activity, in contrast to the situation with myocardial infarction; on the other hand, a rise of the activity of aminotransferases does occur, with the AST/ALT quotient less than 1, the (AST+ALT)/GLDH quotient less than 20, and the HBDH/LDH quotient less than 0.6[130].

Since the *prognosis of a myocardial infarction* depends not only on the area of myocardium involved, but also on the site of damage as well as on the complications, the extent of increase of enzyme activities in serum is only a crude prognostic index[126,131,132]. A rise of LDH activity beyond 1000 U/L, an increase of AST activity beyond 200 U/L, and a CK/AST quotient of more than 10 (cardiogenic shock) or less than 1 (right-ventricular insufficiency with acute liver congestion) are unfavorable (mortality over 50%).

In *angina pectoris,* as a rule no changes of enzyme activities in the serum are found. The same may be said of *tachycardia* and *pericarditis*. If increases of enzyme activities are found, damage to the myocardium or liver are likely[133,134].

In *myocarditis,* CK activity can rise to above 440 U/L[135]. The increase is less considerable in *radiation damage to the myocardium*[136]. A rise of the activities of CK and CK-MB in the serum – as indeed can be expected – is observed after *heart operations*[125,137], as well as in *blunt injuries to the heart.*

In most patients with *myogenic cardiac insufficiency* the activities of the aminotransferases in serum are nearly normal. If a rise of enzyme activity occurs, congestion-related hypoxic liver-cell damage is likely. However, other organs – the skeletal musculature, for example – most probably contribute to changes in the enzyme level as well. Where right-ventricular insufficiency predominates, the activity ratios in the serum resemble more those attendant on liver conditions than in the case of left-ventricular insufficiency[138].

Muscle disease

The principal enzymes in the diagnosis of diseases of the skeletal muscles are CK (and its isoenzymes) and fructose-bisphosphate aldolase.

Table 11
Enzyme activities in serum after myocardial infarction[86,115]

Enzyme	Lag period	Peak activity	Length of interval with elevated activity	Relative size of peak (in relation to upper reference value)
	Time since onset of symptoms h		d	
Creatine kinase	2–4	12–36	4–6	3- to 30-fold
Aspartate aminotransferase	4–6	24–48	4–6	1.5- to 12-fold
Lactate dehydrogenase	6–10	36–72	10–14	2- to 6-fold
'2-Hydroxybutyrate dehydrogenase'	6–10	36–96	10–20	2.5- to 8-fold

Table 12 *Differential diagnosis between myocardial infarction and right-ventricular insufficiency with acute liver congestion on the basis of enzyme activity ratios in serum*

Ratio	Infarction or 2nd infarction	Right-ventricular insufficiency with acute liver congestion
	Activity ratio	
CK/AST	>1 (~5–10)	<1
AST/ALT	>2	<2 (usually <1)
LDH/GLDH	>100	<100

Table 13 *Causes of the rise of creatine kinase activity in serum*

Physical stress
Sports and enlargement of skeletal muscle mass[139–141]
Acute psychosis and delirious states[142–144]
Convulsions (e.g. in epilepsy and tetanus)[145]
Childbirth labor[108,146,147]
Traumatic muscle damage
Direct injuries[108,148]
Extensive burns[149]
Surgical interventions[108,150–152]
Intramuscular injections[153–155]
Diagnostic and therapeutic interventions[108,156–158]
Hypoxic muscle damage
Shock[108,116,157,159]
Myocardial infarction[113–129]
Intoxications[108,157,160]
Toxic muscle damage
Alcoholism[108,161–163]
(Local) intoxications (intramuscular injections)[153–155]
Drugs (anesthetics, bronchodilators, clofibrate?)[108,164,165]
Degenerative and inflammatory muscle diseases
Myopathy[108,166–172]
Myositis[108,173,174]
Myocarditis[135]
Erysipelas (?)[108]
Trichinosis[175]
Metabolic muscle damage
Hyperthyroidism[108,176–178]
Myoglobinuria[179]
Glycogenosis[180]
Hyperosmolar diabetic coma[108,181]
Malignant hyperpyrexia[169,182–185]

The skeletal musculature is implicated in a multitude of exertions, injuries, or diseases, with associated rises of the activity of muscle enzymes in the serum (Table 13).

In addition to differences in the activity ratios of enzymes and isoenzymes, the extent of increase of CK activity also provides diagnostically useful clues. Very high activities (10 times the normal) are found in polymyositis (less frequently in dermatomyositis), in paroxysmal myoglobinuria, in tetanus, in strychnine poisoning, and during shock. Enzyme activities increase to 5–10 times the normal in the *early* stages of Duchenne muscular dystrophy, in acute severe trichinosis, in severe trauma, in hypoxia of muscle tissue, and in acute alcoholic myopathy. Moderately high activities (2–5 times the normal) are found in the *later* stages of Duchenne muscular dystrophy (as well as in some female carriers), in other types of muscular dystrophy, in myotonia, in progressive neuromuscular disease, in moderately severe trauma, and in hypoxia of muscle tissue. The CK activity in the serum is normal or only slightly elevated (up to twice the normal) in the terminal stages of all forms of neuromuscular disease and of Duchenne muscular dystrophy (but also in some female carriers). In muscular dystrophy, the CK activities in the serum fluctuate over a wide range. Physical stress or injury lead to transitory sharp rises. The activity ratio of the CK isoenzymes in muscle tissue changes during the course of the disease. CK-MB can increase to as much as 75% of total CK activity. As a rule, therefore, CK-MB can be found in the serum as well, although the relative activities are less marked than in the case of myocardial infarction.

Diseases of the pancreas

The enzymes of choice for determination continue to be α-amylase and lipase[186–190]. In acute pancreatitis, as well as during acute episodes of chronic pancreatitis, an increase of α-amylase activity is observed commonly after 3–6 hours (1–12 hours), a peak of 10–50 times the normal level being reached after 20–30 hours. The activity of lipase increases in parallel with that of α-amylase[191]. It generally returns to normal after 2 weeks, but in some cases it may do so even later[192]. Whereas α-amylase clearance is increased in pancreatitis[193], lipase cannot be detected in the urine on account of its high relative molecular mass. In acute necrotizing pancreatitis, the rise of α-amylase activity is often an especially marked and lasting one, although it declines as the clinical condition deteriorates further, while at the same time cholinesterase activity falls and LDH activity rises. Depending on the extent and acuteness of cholestasis secondary to pancreatitis, the enzyme pattern in the serum can also disclose obstructive jaundice[130]. Only distinct, pronounced rises of α-amylase activity may be taken as a sign of primary pancreatitis. Slight rises occur as a secondary reaction in perforated ulcer and in ulcer penetration into the pancreas, in ileus, peritonitis, mesenteric infarction, ruptured spleen, parotitis, and renal insufficiency (in the latter case without a rise of the α-amylase activity in the urine, as in macroamylasemia)[194].

In chronic pancreatitis, cystic fibrosis, and pancreatic cysts, changes of enzyme activities may be expected only in the case of acute episodes or complications. Provocation tests with determination of enzymes in the serum yield no more than uncertain results[195]. Determinations of the conversion of synthetic substrates in the intestine[196], determination of the chymotrypsin concentration in the feces[197], or quantitative determination of exocrine pancreatic secretion in the duodenal fluid after stimulation[198] give positive information on the impairment of pancreatic function.

In carcinoma of the tail and body of the pancreas, α-amylase and lipase activities are almost always normal; in rare cases, the values are borderline. In carcinoma of the head of the pancreas, transitory rises of lipase activity, and more rarely of α-amylase activity, are occasionally observed; rises of γ-GT activity are more frequent. Constriction or occlusion of the papilla will result in a rise of the activities of the aminotransferases, GLDH, and the 'cholestasis-indicating' enzymes. Their activity ratios will exhibit the pattern of obstructive jaundice[130].

Diseases of the liver

The abundance and diversity of enzymes in the liver[35] and its unique anatomical structure (no basal membranes in the sinusoids) render this organ and its diseases especially amenable to enzyme diagnostics. 3 groups of enzymes are accessible for the differential diagnosis of liver disorders:

1. Cell enzymes with different localization in the liver lobules and within the liver cells (AST, ALT, GLDH, LDH, ICDH, etc.).
2. Membrane-associated or 'cholestasis-indicating' enzymes (ALP, γ-GT, LAP).
3. Plasma-specific enzymes (formed in the liver): cholinesterase, coagulation factors.

Changes of the activities of these enzymes in the serum depend on the type, severity, course, and stage of the liver damage. Every liver disease has a more or less typical enzyme pattern in the serum which undergoes regular changes over time (Table 14)[199–202].

Acute viral hepatitis, a liver disease that can be diagnosed on the basis of a rise of the activity of so-called 'liver-specific' enzymes (SDH, ALT), typically implicates the entire organ (sharp rise of the activities of aminotransferases: 200–3000 U/L)[203]. The average single-cell damage is moderate, with single-cell or focal necrosis only; therefore, the activities of cytosolic enzymes (ALT) increase more markedly than those of mitochondrial enzymes (GLDH)[54,204]. The liver lobules suffer diffuse damage, so that there are no activity ratios indicative of the preferential involvement of a specific area (as ALT/ICDH, for instance). After the illness has passed its peak, the de Ritis quotient (AST/ALT)[205] falls gradually as a result of the longer half-life of ALT in the plasma, thereby indicating the stage of the illness. The extent of cholestasis (principal enzymes ALP, γ-GT) exhibits wide variations. The cholestatic forms of acute hepatitis are accompanied by pronounced rises of activity. In uncomplicated viral hepatitis, the impairment of the 'functional liver mass' is minor: a brief fall of the activities of cholinesterase and coagulation factors occurs only at the height of the illness.

Corresponding to the various forms of acute viral hepatitis, enzyme activities in the serum show qualitatively and quantitatively different changes: minor changes are indicative of the anicteric form[200,206], somewhat more pronounced changes, with a marked increase of the activities of 'cholestasis-indicating' enzymes, suggest hepatitis with a cholestatic component[130], while high activities, including that of mitochondrial GLDH, are indicative of the acute necrotizing form, in which the enzyme activities may de-

Table 14 *Interpretation of changes of enzyme activities in the serum or plasma in liver diseases*[111]

Parameter	Information
Organ-specificity of enzymes with changed activity	Diseased organ (involvement of other organs)
Extent of the rise of activity of cell enzymes	Extent and acuteness of cell damage
Ratio between the activity of cytosolic enzymes (LDH, ALT) and the activity of partially or entirely mitochondrial enzymes (AST, GLDH)	Severity of damage to individual cells
Ratio between the activity of enzymes with predominantly periportal localization (ALT, SDH) and that of enzymes with predominantly centrilobular localization (ICDH, GLDH)	Main site of damage within the liver lobule
Ratio between the activity of enzymes with a long half-life (ALT, LDH-1) and that of enzymes with a short half-life (AST, LDH-5) in plasma	Phase of an acute illness
Ratio between the activity of enzymes which are changed in the liver by the disease and the activity of enzymes which are not changed	Stage of a chronic illness
Ratio between the activity of cell enzymes and that of membrane-associated enzymes ('cholestasis-indicating' enzymes)	Extent of cholestasis or - more generally - the reaction to damage of the liver
Activity of plasma-specific enzymes	Degree of impairment of the functional liver mass (both qualitative and quantitative)

crease sharply in the preterminal stages, despite deterioration of the clinical picture[207]. Differences in the activity ratios can also be noted in etiologically diverse forms of hepatitis (e.g. between viral hepatitis A, B on the one hand, and non-A, non-B forms of viral hepatitis on the other hand) which, however, may run the same course[208].

In *chronic viral diseases of the liver,* the changes of enzyme activities are considerably less pronounced[209]. As disease progresses, the advancing alterations of the enzyme pattern in the liver cells modify the enzyme pattern in the plasma as well. More and more commonly the AST activity is higher than the ALT activity, and a rise of GLDH activity can also be observed. These activity ratios, which differ from the picture of acute viral hepatitis, are indicative of the 'necrotic type' of cell damage which preponderates in these cases. The reduction in the liver-cell mass caused by the increasing formation of connective tissue results in a progressive restriction of the formation and secretion of plasma-specific enzymes (cholinesterase, coagulation factors)[130].

Toxic liver lesions go along with a wide variety of changes of enzyme activity ratios in the plasma corresponding to their various etiologies and effects on the liver[210–212]. A characteristic of chronic alcoholic hepatitis is a distinct rise of γ-GT activity, with usually only slightly increased aminotransferase activities[199,209]. The relative increase of the γ-GT activity permits etiological differentiation between the various forms of cirrhosis as well (γ-GT/AST quotient less than 2 in the case of post-hepatitic cirrhosis, and above 2 in alcohol-related cirrhosis)[130,199,202]. The most prominent finding in delirium tremens is a very marked rise of γ-GT activity - often over 1000 U/L - and an increase of CK activity, with only a moderate increase of the activities of aminotransferases, GLDH, and ALP.

Chronic nonsuppurative destructive cholangitis, the early forms of which are often difficult to distinguish from chronic forms of hepatitis with relatively severe cholestasis, exhibit strikingly high activities for ALP, γ-GT, and GLDH during these stages, while the activities of aminotransferases show only slight to moderate rises. As jaundice appears and deepens, the activity of cell enzymes increases to approximately the 5-fold, and the activity of ALP to about the 10-fold of normal, while γ-GT activity can reach levels exceeding 1000 U/L[130,199].

Liver cell carcinoma arising in a cirrhotic liver leads initially to very subtle changes in the enzyme pattern; later, however, these changes differ distinctly from the pattern characteristic of the primary disease. AST activity rises slowly, while ALT activity even declines. As a consequence, the AST/ALT quotient reaches values of 2 or even >3. GLDH activity also rises, with levels sometimes reaching 50 times the normal. Furthermore, the activities of ALP and LAP, and especially of γ-GT, show a rise[130,213]. The exceptionally marked increase of γ-GT activity to 15–20 times the normal (such high activities are otherwise observed only in alcoholic delirium and biliary cirrhosis) is also characteristic of *liver metastases,* in which activity ratios in the serum otherwise resemble those in hepatocellular carcinoma[130,214].

In *obstructive jaundice,* an acute rise in pressure in the bile ducts leads to a brief, mainly centrilobular parenchymal cell damage, as a result of which the aminotransferase activities rise markedly to levels also observed in mild forms of viral hepatitis. In this phase, an indicative rise of the activity of 'cholestasis-indicating' enzymes in the serum is usually not yet observed. The activities of these do not begin to increase notably until the aminotransferase activities have fallen again. The (AST + ALT)/GLDH ratio is diagnostically quite useful in that it is over 30 in inflammatory icteric liver diseases and under 20 in obstructive jaundice[215].

In addition to the diseases and syndromes discussed above, enzyme activity determinations in the serum are valuable aids to the diagnosis, differential diagnosis, and monitoring of many other diseases as well[4,5,39,40,48,52,54,111,115,116,130,186,189]. The major practical advantage of enzyme diagnostics becomes especially evident if not only the activity of *one* enzyme is measured, but if a selected pattern of 2, 3, or even more enzymes is brought together with the other symptoms of a disease process to form a composite pathophysiological picture.

References

1 International Union of Pure and Applied Chemistry and International Union of Biochemistry, *Enzyme Nomenclature,* Recommendations 1972, Elsevier, Amsterdam, 1973, page 26.
2 BOWERS et al., *Clin. chim. Acta,* **61**, F11 (1975).
3 International Federation of Clinical Chemistry, *Clin. chim. Acta,* **98**, 163F (1979).
4 BERGMEYER, H. U. (Ed.), *Methoden der enzymatischen Analyse,* 2nd ed., Verlag Chemie, Weinheim, 1970.
5 KING, J., *Practical Clinical Enzymology,* Van Nostrand, London, 1965.
6 GERLACH and HIBY, in BERGMEYER[4], page 527.
7 *Temperature Conversion Tables,* Boehringer Mannheim Corporation, New York, 1970.
8 PLAGEMANN et al., *Biochem. Z.,* **334**, 37 (1961).
9 WILKINSON, J. H., in BERGMEYER[4], page 564.
10 KING[5], page 93.
11 KING[5], page 75.
12 KING[5], page 99.
13 FRIED and FRIED, in BERGMEYER[4], page 624.
14 SCHMIDT, E., in BERGMEYER[4], page 607.
15 CERIOTTI, G., in Bergmeyer[4], page 654.
16 SZASZ, G., *Clin. Chem.,* **15**, 124 (1969).
17 KING[5], page 121.
18 ROSALKI, S. B., *J. Lab. clin. Med.,* **69**, 696 (1967).
19 SZASZ et al., *Clin. Chem.,* **22**, 650 (1976).
20 KING, J., in BERGMEYER[4], page 764.
21 PILZ, W., in BERGMEYER[4], page 772.
22 NÄHER, G., in BERGMEYER[4], page 781.
23 PILZ, W., in BERGMEYER[4], page 792.
24 KING[5], page 174.
25 WALTER and SCHÜTT, in BERGMEYER[4], page 818.
26 GERLACH and HIBY, in BERGMEYER[4], page 833.
27 APPEL, W., in BERGMEYER[4], page 911.
28 TUPPY and WINTERSBERGER, *Mh. Chem.,* **91**, 1001 (1960).
29 APPEL, W., in BERGMEYER[4], page 941.
30 SCHLEGEL and KALTWASSER, in BERGMEYER[4], page 1039.
31 GIUSTI, G., in BERGMEYER[4], page 1044.
32 GIUSTI, G., in BERGMEYER[4], page 1049.
33 SCHMIDT and SCHMIDT, *Klin. Wschr.,* **38**, 957 (1960); SCHMIDT and SCHMIDT, *Enzym. biol. clin.,* **2**, 201 (1962).

[34] PETTE, D., in SCHMIDT, F.W. (Ed.), *Praktische Enzymologie*, Huber, Berne, 1968, page 15.
[35] SCHMIDT and SCHMIDT, *Enzym. biol. clin.*, **11**, 67 (1970).
[36] LÖHR, G.W., *Folia haemat. (Frankfurt)*, NS **6**, 49 (1961); LÖHR and WALLER, *Z. Geburtsh. Gynäk.*, **159**, suppl. (1962).
[37] TSUNG, S.H., *Clin. Chem.*, **22**, 173 (1976).
[38] SCHMIDT and SCHMIDT, *Enzym-Fibel*, Boehringer, Mannheim, 1966.
[39] HENLEY et al., *Enzymes in Serum*, Thomas, Springfield, 1966.
[40] LATNER and SKILLEN, *Isoenzymes in Biology and Medicine*, Academic Press, London, 1968; WILKINSON, J.H., *Isoenzymes*, 2nd ed., Chapman & Hall, London, 1970.
[41] RATTAZZI et al. (Eds.), *Isoenzymes*, 2 volumes, Liss, New York, 1977/1978.
[42] LANG and WÜRZBURG, *Clin. chim. Acta*, **28**, 1439 (1982).
[43] FISHMAN, W.H., *Amer. J. Med.*, **56**, 617 (1974).
[44] PFLEIDERER et. al., in SCHMIDT et al. (Eds.), *Advances in Clinical Enzymology*, Karger, Basle, 1979, page 17.
[45] STANBURY et al. (Eds.), *The Metabolic Basis of Inherited Disease*, 5th ed., McGraw-Hill, New York, 1983.
[46] REITH, A., in SCHMIDT et al. (Eds.), *Advances in Clinical Enzymology*, Karger, Basle, 1979, page 53.
[47] BÜCHER et al., *Transactions of the 9th Middle East Medical Assembly*, Beirut, 1959, page 85.
[48] SCHMIDT, E., in SCHMIDT, F.W. (Ed.), *Praktische Enzymologie*, Huber, Berne, 1968, page 93.
[49] FRIEDEL et al., in SCHMIDT et al. (Eds.), *Advances in Clinical Enzymology*, Karger, Basle, 1979, page 70.
[50] WILKINSON and ROBINSON, *Nature*, **249**, 662 (1974).
[51] WILKINSON and ROBINSON, *Clin. Chem.*, **20**, 1331 (1974).
[52] SCHMIDT and SCHMIDT, *FEBS Lett.*, **62**, suppl. E62 (1976).
[53] SWEETIN and THOMSON, *Clin. chim. Acta*, **48**, 403 (1973).
[54] SCHMIDT et al., in KEPPLER, D. (Ed.) *Pathogenesis and Mechanisms of Liver Cell Necrosis*, MTP Press, Lancaster, 1975, page 147.
[55] SCHMIDT et al., *Enzym. biol. clin.*, **7**, 53 (1966).
[56] WIESMANN et al., *Enzym. biol. clin.*, **7**, 266 (1966).
[57] VÉLEZ-GARCÍA et al., *J. Lab. clin. Med.*, **68**, 636 (1966).
[58] AMELUNG et al., *Klin. Wschr.*, **36**, 963 (1958); AMELUNG, D., *Z. physiol. Chem.*, **318**, 219 (1960).
[59] FLEISHER and WAKIM, *J. Lab. clin. Med.*, **61**, 76 and 98 (1963).
[60] KONTTINEN and HALONEN, *Cardiologia (Basel)*, **43**, 56 (1963).
[61] BÄR and OHLENDORF, *Klin. Wschr.*, **48**, 776 (1970).
[62] FLEISHER et al., *Mayo Clin. Proc.*, **40**, 300 (1965).
[63] FRÖHLICH and KURRLE, *Klin. Wschr.*, **47**, 903 (1969).
[64] FRIEDEL and MATTENHEIMER, *Clin. chim. Acta*, **30**, 37 (1970).
[65] MÜHLHAUS, K., personal communication.
[66] DONATH, R., *Dtsch. Gesundh.-Wes.*, **26**, 2319 (1971).
[67] KLEIN et al., *Verh. dtsch. Ges. inn. Med.*, **81**, 1327 (1975).
[68] AMELUNG, D., in SCHMIDT, F.W. (Ed.), *Praktische Enzymologie*, Huber, Berne, 1968, page 149.
[69] PRAETORIUS and KÖRTGE, *Angiology*, **17**, 640 (1970).
[70] GRUBER, W., *J. mond. Pharm. (La Haye)*, **12**, 203 (1969).
[71] LAUBINGER, G., *Med. Klin.*, **61**, 753 (1966).
[72] SACHSENHEIMER et al., *Klin. Wschr.*, **53**, 617 (1975).
[73] RICK, W., in SCHMIDT, F.W. (Ed.), *Praktische Enzymologie*, Huber, Berne, 1968, page 159.
[74] JENKINS et al., *Science*, **156**, 1748 (1967).
[75] ALTLAND and GOEDDE, quoted by GÜNTHER et al., *Med. Klin.*, **66**, 785 (1971).
[76] GARRY et al., *Res. Commun. chem. Pathol. Pharmacol.*, **8**, 371 (1974).
[77] ARMSTRONG et al., *Canad. med. Ass. J.*, **31**, 14 (1934).
[78] MASSARRAT and MASSARRAT, *Verh. dtsch. Ges. inn. Med.*, **77**, 1210 (1971).
[79] CLUBB et al., *J. Lab. clin. Invest.*, **66**, 493 (1965).
[80] KOMODA et al., *Clin. chim. Acta*, **117**, 167 (1981).
[81] POSEN and GRUNSTEIN, *Clin. Chem.*, **28**, 153 (1982).
[82] POSEN, S., *Clin. Chem.*, **16**, 71 (1970).
[83] SCHMIDT and SCHMIDT, in SIEGENTHALER, W. (Ed.), *Klinische Pathophysiologie*, 4th ed., Thieme, Stuttgart, 1979, page 189.
[84] BÄR and OHLENDORF, *Z. ges. exp. Med.*, **154**, 140 (1971).
[85] BÄR et al., *Enzyme (Basel)*, **14**, 133 (1972/1973).
[86] SCHMIDT and SCHMIDT, *Kleine Enzym-Fibel*, Boehringer, Mannheim, 1976.
[87] RICHTERICH et al., *Schweiz. med. Wschr.*, **92**, 1496 (1962).
[88] REINHOLD et al., *Amer. J. clin. Path.*, **23**, 645 (1953); BREUER and SCHÖNFELDER, *Clin. chim. Acta*, **6**, 515 (1961).
[89] COHEN and HUSEBY, *Cancer Res.*, **11**, 52 (1951); GOLDBARG et al., *Gastroenterology*, **36**, 193 (1959); PRICE, C.H., *J. clin. Path.*, **14**, 661 (1961).
[90] SIEKERT and FLEISHER, *Proc. Mayo Clin.*, **31**, 459 (1956).
[91] LAUDAHN et al., *Klin. Wschr.*, **48**, 838 (1970).
[92] HUGHES, B.P., *Clin. chim. Acta*, **7**, 597 (1962).
[93] SZASZ et al., *Dtsch. med. Wschr.*, **95**, 829 (1970).
[94] GOLDBERG and WINFIELD, *Clin. chim. Acta*, **54**, 357 (1974).
[95] ADLERCREUTZ et al., *Scand. J. Gastroent.*, **3**, 273 (1968).
[96] COHEN et al., *Proc. Soc. exp. Biol. (N.Y.)*, **126**, 55 (1967).
[97] FLEISHER et al., *Clin. Chem.*, **23**, 469 (1977).
[98] CLARK and BECK, *J. Pediat.*, **36**, 335 (1950).
[99] ERIKSSON et al., *Clin. chim. Acta*, **40**, 181 (1972).
[100] WISSER and BREUER, *J. clin. Chem.*, **19**, 323 (1981).
[101] OTTO et al., *Klin. Wschr.*, **42**, 75 (1964).
[102] BAUMANN et al., *Schweiz. Z. Sportmed.*, **10**, 33 (1962).
[103] BUHL and HÄCKER, in FRIEDMANN and WINTER (Eds.), *Diagnostische Enzymologie*, Verlag Volk und Gesundheit, Berlin, 1973, page 86.
[104] HOFFMANN et al., in Friedmann and WINTER (Eds.), *Diagnostische Enzymologie*, Verlag Volk und Gesundheit, Berlin, 1973, page 92.
[105] DORAN and WILKINSON, *Clin. chim. Acta*, **35**, 115 (1971); RILEY et al., *Clin. chim. Acta*, **65**, 83 (1975).
[106] COLOMBO et al., *Klin. Wschr.*, **40**, 37 (1962).
[107] CAROL and BONOW, *Zbl. Gynäk.*, **87**, 426 (1965).
[108] CHEMNITZ et al., in LANG, H. (Ed.), *Creatine Kinase Isoenzymes: Pathophysiology and Clinical Applications*, Springer, Berlin, 1981, page 224.
[109] HOLMGREN et al., *Clin. chim. Acta*, **83**, 205 (1978).
[110] SCHMIDT and SCHMIDT, *Laboratoriumsblätter*, **26**, 89 (1976).
[111] SCHMIDT and SCHMIDT, in SIEGENTHALER, W. (Ed.), *Klinische Pathophysiologie*, 5th ed., Thieme, Stuttgart, 1982, page 182.
[112] SCHMIDT and SCHMIDT, *Diagnostik*, **8**, 427 (1975).
[113] KATTUS et al., *Circulation*, **15**, 502 (1957); SNODGRASS et al., *New Engl. J. Med.*, **261**, 1259 (1959); AGRESS, C.M., *Amer. J. Cardiol.*, **3**, 74 (1959).
[114] WEST et al., *Med. Clin. N. Amer.*, **50**, 171 (1966); LEHMANN et al., *Enzym. biol. clin.*, **6**, 36 (1966); LEHMANN and SCHNEIDER, *Enzym. biol. clin.*, **6**, 66 (1966); COHEN and MORGAN, *Med. Clin. N. Amer.*, **57**, 105 (1973).
[115] AMELUNG, D., *Fermentdiagnostik interner Erkrankungen*, Thieme, Stuttgart, 1964.
[116] WILKINSON, J.H., *The Principles and Practice of Diagnostic Enzymology*, Arnold, London, 1976.
[117] SZASZ and BUSCH, in KAISER, E. (Ed.), *Fortschritte der klinischen Chemie*, Verlag Medizinische Akademie, Wien, 1972, page 163.
[118] CHEMNITZ et al., in GOLDBERG and WILKINSON (Eds.), *Enzymes in Health and Disease*, Karger, Basle, 1978.
[119] KONTTINEN and SOMMER, *Amer. J. Cardiol.*, **29**, 817 (1972); KLEIN et al., *Cardiovasc. Res.*, **7**, 412 (1973).
[120] ROBERTS and SOBEL, *Ann. intern. Med.*, **79**, 741 (1973); ROBERTS et al., *Amer. J. Cardiol.*, **33**, 650 (1974).
[121] MERCER, D.W., *Clin. Chem.*, **20**, 36 (1974); MERCER and VARAT, *Clin. Chem.*, **21**, 1088 (1975).
[122] JOCKERS-WRETOU and PFLEIDERER, *Clin. chim. Acta*, **58**, 223 (1975).
[123] NEALON and HENDERSON, *Clin. Chem.*, **21**, 392 (1975); YASMINEH and HANSON, *Clin. Chem.*, **21**, 381 (1975); MORIN, L.G., *Clin. Chem.*, **22**, 92 (1976).
[124] NEUMEIER et al., *Clin. chim. Acta*, **73**, 445 (1976); WÜRZBURG et al., *Z. klin. Chem.*, **15**, 131 (1977).
[125] CHEMNITZ et al., in BURLINA and GALZIGNA (Eds.), *Clinical Enzymology Symposium 1*, Piccin Medical Books, Padua, 1977, page 307.
[126] KUPPER and BLEIFELD, in SCHMIDT et al. (Eds.), *Advances in Clinical Enzymology*, Karger, Basle, 1979, page 106.
[127] NEUMEIER et al., *Klin. Wschr.*, **52**, 329 (1975); KLAPDOR et al., *Dtsch. med. Wschr.*, **102**, 1309 (1977); KLAPDOR and HARM, *Dtsch. med. Wschr.*, **103**, 1665 (1978); NEUMEIER et al., *Klin. Wschr.*, **56**, 449 (1978); VON ARNIM et al., *Verh. dtsch. Ges. inn. Med.*, **84**, 1408 (1978).
[128] CHEMNITZ et al., *Verh. dtsch. Ges. inn. Med.*, **84**, 1587 (1978).
[129] SZASZ et al., *Dtsch. med. Wschr.*, **96**, 980 (1971).
[130] WALLNÖFER et al. (Eds.), *Synopsis der Leberkrankheiten*, Thieme, Stuttgart, 1974.
[131] SHELL and SOBEL, *Amer. J. Cardiol.*, **31**, 474 (1973); SHELL et al., *J. clin. Invest.*, **50**, 2614 (1971); SOBEL et al., *Circulation*, **46**, 640 (1972).
[132] BLEIFELD et al., *Verh. dtsch. Ges. Kreisl.-Forsch.*, **40**, 449 (1974); KUPPER et al., *Dtsch. med. Wschr.*, **103**, 550 (1978).
[133] AMELUNG and HORN, *Dtsch. med. Wschr.*, **81**, 1701 (1956); GOBLE and O'BRIEN, *Lancet*, **2**, 873 (1958); RESNIK, W.H., *Amer. Heart J.*, **63**, 290 (1962); EVERS, C., *Med. Klin.*, **58**, 1260 (1963).
[134] ELLIOTT and WILKINSON, *Lancet*, **2**, 71 (1962); THÜRMER and LÜBCKE, *Dtsch. med. Wschr.*, **98**, 1568 (1973); DALE and RUNDE, *Acta med. scand.*, **180**, 671 (1966).
[135] KINDERMANN et al., *Dtsch. med. Wschr.*, **98**, 1609 (1973).
[136] MUGGIA et al., *J. Amer. med. Ass.*, **211**, 1345 (1970).
[137] VOGEL and WINTZER, *Med. Klin.*, **71**, 653 (1976); SMITH et al., *Brit. Heart J.*, **38**, 225 (1976).
[138] WEST et al., *Amer. J. med. Sci.*, **241**, 350 (1961).
[139] HALONEN and KONTTINEN, *Nature*, **193**, 942 (1962); GRIFFITHS, P.D., *Clin. chim. Acta*, **13**, 413 (1966); NUTTALL and JONES, *J. Lab. clin. Med.*, **71**, 847 (1968).
[140] SCHMIDT and SCHMIDT, *Med. and Sport*, **3**, 216 (1969); KIEF et al., *Med. Klin.*, **67**, 195 (1972); CRITZ and CUNNINGHAM, *J. Sport Med. (Torino)*, **12**, 143 (1972).
[141] SCHAPIRO et al., *Canad. J. Physiol. Pharmacol.*, **51**, 271 (1973); GARCIA, W., *J. Amer. med. Ass.*, **228**, 1395 (1974).
[142] SCHIAVONE and KALDOR, *Med. J. Aust.*, **2**, 790 (1965); MELTZER, H., *Science*, **159**, 1368 (1968); MELTZER, H., *Arch. gen. Psychiat.*, **21**, 102 (1969); MELTZER et al., *Arch. gen. Psychiat.*, **21**, 731 (1969); MELTZER et al., *Comprehens. Psychiat.*, **11**, 552 (1970).
[143] MELTZER et al., *Psychopharmacologia (Berl.)*, **16**, 419 (1970); ENGEL and MELTZER, *Science*, **168**, 273 (1970); MELTZER et al., *Arch. gen. Psychiat.*, **24**, 568 (1971).
[144] GOSLING et al., *Brit. J. Psychiat.*, **121**, 351 (1972).
[145] BRODY and HATCHER, *Arch. Neurol. (Chic.)*, **16**, 89 (1967); KING and ZAPF, *Med. J. Aust.*, **1**, 699 (1972); MOHR et al., *Med. Klin.*, **69**, 1112 (1974).
[146] KONTTINEN and PYÖRÄLÄ, *Scand. J. clin. Lab. Invest.*, **15**, 429 (1963); FRANZA and PALMIERI, *Arch. Ostet. Ginec.*, **69**, 724 (1964).
[147] RUDOLPH and GROSS, *Pediatrics*, **38**, 1039 (1966); MCNEELY et al., *Clin. Chem.*, **23**, 1878 (1977).
[148] DUBO et al., *Lancet*, **2**, 743 (1967).
[149] LAFARGUE et al., *Biomedicine (Express)*, **27**, 244 (1977).
[150] SØRENSEN et al., *Ugeskr. Laeg.*, **127**, 1431 (1965); ZELDER, O., *Chirurg*, **41**, 278 (1970); MOSTERT et al., *J. surg. Oncol.*, **2**, 189 (1970).
[151] CATTOLICA, E.V., *J. Urol.*, **106**, 262 (1971); DIXON et al., *Arch. Surg.*, **103**, 66 (1971); MAHON et al., *J. Urol.*, **107**, 88 (1972).
[152] HOBSON et al., *Amer. J. Surg.*, **124**, 625 (1972); KRAFFT et al., *Ann. clin. Biochem.*, **14**, 294 (1977); BRISSE et al., *Herz/Kreislauf*, **10**, 12 (1978).
[153] HESS and MACDONALD, *J. Mich. med. Soc.*, **62**, 1095 (1963); BATSAKIS et al., *Clin. Biochem.*, **2**, 125 (1968); MELTZER et al., *Amer. J. med. Sci.*, **259**, 42 (1970).

154 KNIRSCH and GRALLA, *New Engl. J. Med.*, **282**, 1081 (1970); COHEN, L., *J. Amer. med. Ass.*, **219**, 625 (1972); GREENBLATT et al., *New Engl. J. Med.*, **288**, 689 (1973).

155 KÜSTER, J., *Med. Welt (Stuttg.)*, **24**, 1328 (1973); GLOOR et al., *Schweiz. med. Wschr.*, **107**, 948 (1977).

156 CROWLEY and ALTON, *Amer. J. clin. Path.*, **53**, 948 (1970); MICHIE et al., *Amer. J. med. Sci.*, **260**, 11 (1970); ROBERTS et al., *Brit. Heart J.*, **37**, 1144 (1975).

157 PRELLWITZ et al., *Dtsch. med. Wschr.*, **101**, 983 (1976).

158 RETTIG et al., *Münch. med. Wschr.*, **118**, 997 (1976); REIFFEL et al., *J. Amer. med. Ass.*, **239**, 122 (1978).

159 PRELLWITZ and NEUMEIER, *Internist (Berl.)*, **17**, 436 (1976).

160 OSSENBERG et al., *Münch. med. Wschr.*, **112**, 1730 (1970); FROTSCHER et al., *Med. Klin.*, **67**, 1442 (1972); GRABENSEE, B., *Dtsch. med. Wschr.*, **101**, 976 (1976).

161 NYGREN, A., *Acta med. scand.*, **179**, 623 (1966), and **182**, 383 (1967); DIMBERG et al., *Acta med. scand.*, **181**, 227 (1967).

162 LAFAIR and MYERSON, *Arch. intern. Med.*, **122**, 417 (1968); MYERSON and LAFAIR, *Med. Clin. N. Amer.*, **54**, 723 (1970).

163 MARTIN et al., *Neurology (Minneap.)*, **21**, 1160 (1971); SONG and RUBIN, *Science*, **175**, 327 (1972).

164 TAMMISTO and AIRAKSINEN, *Brit. J. Anaesth.*, **38**, 510 (1966); LANGER and LEVY, *New Engl. J. Med.*, **279**, 856 (1968); SMITH et al., *Brit. med. J.*, **2**, 86 (1970).

165 MELTZER, H., *Biochem. Pharmacol.*, **20**, 1739 (1971); PHORNPHUTKUL et al., *Clin. Chem.*, **20**, 340 (1974); SCHMIDT et al., *Arzneimittel-Forsch.*, **26**, 1455 (1976).

166 DREYFUS and SCHAPIRA, in GIGON and LUDWIG (Eds.), *Enzymatische Regulation in der Klinik*, Schwabe, Basle, 1961, page 145; DREYFUS and SCHAPIRA, *Biochemistry of Hereditary Myopathies*, Thomas, Springfield, 1962.

167 SHAW et al., *Enzym. biol. clin.*, **6**, 10 (1966); CAO et al., *Riv. Clin. pediat.*, **81**, 504 (1968).

168 HEYCK and LAUDAHN, in MILHORAT, A.T. (Ed.), *Exploratory Concepts in Muscular Dystrophy and Related Disorders*, Excerpta Medica Foundation, New York, 1967, page 232; LAUDAHN et al., in SCHMIDT, F.W. (Ed.), *Praktische Enzymologie*, Huber, Berne, 1968, page 249.

169 DEMOS, J., *Ann. Génét.*, **12**, 191 (1969).

170 HUGHES, B.P., *Brit. med. J.*, **3**, 464 (1971); SOMER et al., *Arch. Neurol. (Chic.)*, **29**, 343 (1973); MUNSAT et al., *J. Amer. med. Ass.*, **226**, 1536 (1973); MOSER and VOGT, *Lancet*, **2**, 661 (1974).

171 ROSALKI, S.B., in WILKINSON, J.H., *The Principles and Practice of Diagnostic Enzymology*, Arnold, London, 1976, page 263.

172 BECKMANN and SCHEUERBRANDT, *Diagnostik*, **10**, 802 (1977); GOEDDE et al., *Klin. Wschr.*, **55**, 215 (1977); RICKER and SCHIMRIGK, in SCHMIDT et al., (Eds.), *Advances in Clinical Enzymology*, Karger, Basle, 1979, page 124.

173 DEBRECZENI and LADANYI, *Hautarzt*, **21**, 81 (1970); MIDDLETON et al., *Lancet*, **2**, 533 (1970).

174 VIGNOS and GOLDWYN, *Amer. J. med. Sci.*, **263**, 291 (1972); WOLF and MAGORA, *Harefuah*, **84**, 534 (1973).

175 GENTILINI et al., *Bull. Soc. Path. exot.*, **69**, 525 (1976).

176 GRIFFITHS, P.D., *J. clin. Path.*, **18**, 660 (1965); GRAIG and SMITH, *J. clin. Endocr.*, **25**, 723 (1965); KRÜSKEMPER et al., *Dtsch. med. Wschr.*, **93**, 1099 (1968).

177 ITELSON et al., *Rev. franç. Etud. clin. biol.*, **13**, 905 (1968); CAO et al., *J. Pediat.*, **78**, 134 (1971); SLIWA et al., *Pol. Tyg. lek.*, **29**, 1247 (1974).

178 SMITH, D.P., *Clin. chim. Acta*, **68**, 333 (1976); DORAN, G.R., *J. roy. Soc. Med.*, **71**, 189 (1978).

179 ZINGANELL et al., *Z. prakt. Anästh. Wiederbeleb.*, **7**, 161 (1972); BERNHARDT and HÖRDER, *Med. Klin.*, **72**, 1967 (1977).

180 BLOOM et al., *Circulation*, **50**, suppl. 3, 56 (1974); GERSON et al., *Arch. Path. Lab. Med.*, **101**, 213 (1977).

181 KNIGHT et al., *Diabetes*, **23**, 126 (1974).

182 DENBOROUGH et al., *Lancet*, **1**, 1138 (1970); STEERS et al., *Brit. med. J.*, **2**, 341 (1970); REINECKE, R.D., *Amer. J. Ophthal.*, **70**, 858 (1970).

183 ALDRETE et al., *J. Amer. med. Ass.*, **215**, 1465 (1971); BRITT, B.A., *Anesth. Analg. (Cleveland)*, **51**, 841 (1972); KELSTRUP et al., *Acta anaesth. scând.*, **17**, 283 (1973).

184 THOMPSON and TALLACK, in GORDON et al. (Eds.), *Malignant Hyperthermia*, Thomas, Springfield, 1973, page 309.

185 KYEI-MENSAH et al., *Proc. roy. Soc. Med.*, **66**, 63 (1973); BERNHARDT and SCHILLER, *Anaesthesist*, **22**, 367 (1973); MOULDS and DENBOROUGH, *Brit. med. J.*, **2**, 245 (1974).

186 RICHTERICH, R., *Enzymopathologie; Enzyme in Klinik und Forschung*, Springer, Berlin, 1958.

187 WOLF and WILLIAMS, *Practical Clinical Enzymology*, Wiley, New York, 1973.

188 GOWENLOCK, A.H., in WILKINSON, J.H., *The Principles and Practice of Diagnostic Enzymology*, Arnold, London, 1976, page 361.

189 ADOLPH and LORENZ, *Enzyme Diagnosis in Diseases of the Heart, Liver, and Pancreas*, Karger, Basle, 1982.

190 BRUNNER, G., in SCHMIDT et al. (Eds.), *Advances in Clinical Enzymology*, Karger, Basle, 1979, page 208.

191 LIFTON et al., *J. Amer. med. Ass.*, **229**, 47 (1974).

192 SCHOLZ and APPEL, *Med. Klin.*, **74**, 145 (1979).

193 LEVITT et al., *Ann. intern. Med.*, **71**, 919 (1969); MULHAUSEN et al., *Metabolism*, **18**, 669 (1969).

194 WILDING et al., *Ann. intern. Med.*, **60**, 1053 (1964); BERK et al., *New Engl. J. Med.*, **277**, 941 (1967); LEVITT et al., *Lancet*, **1**, 957 (1968).

195 GOEBELL, H., in SCHWIEGK, H. (Ed.), *Handbuch der inneren Medizin*, 5th ed., volume 3, part 6, Springer, Berlin, 1976, page 473.

196 DEBENEVILLE et al., *J. med. Chem.*, **15**, 1098 (1972); IMONDI et al., *Gut*, **13**, 726 (1972); HOFMANN and SCHMIDT, *Verh. dtsch. Ges. inn. Med.*, **84**, 1036 (1978).

197 VON GREGORY and OPITZ, *Verh. dtsch. Ges. inn. Med.*, **84**, 1040 (1978); THIENHAUS et al., *Verh. dtsch. Ges. inn. Med.*, **84**, 1043 (1978).

198 RICK, W., in SCHWIEGK, H. (Ed.), *Handbuch der inneren Medizin*, 5th ed., volume 3, part 6, Springer, Berlin, 1976, page 326.

199 SCHMIDT and SCHMIDT, *Scand. J. Gastroent.*, **8**, suppl. 19, 13 (1972).

200 ROSALKI, S.B., in WILKINSON, J.H., *The Principles and Practice of Diagnostic Enzymology*, Arnold, London, 1976, page 303.

201 SCHMIDT and SCHMIDT, *Diagnostik*, **10**, 348 (1977); SCHMIDT and SCHMIDT, *Therapiewoche*, **28**, 1788 (1978).

202 SCHMIDT and SCHMIDT, in SCHMIDT et al. (Eds.), *Advances in Clinical Enzymology*, Karger, Basle, 1979, page 239.

203 WROBLEWSKI, F., *Amer. J. Med.*, **27**, 911 (1959); ROSALKI, S.B., *Proc. roy. Soc. Med.*, **53**, 199 (1960).

204 GUDER et al., *Z. klin. Chem.*, **13**, 311 (1975).

205 DE RITIS et al., *Minerva med.*, **47**, 167 (1956).

206 DE RITIS et al., *Bull. Wld Hlth Org.*, **32**, 59 (1965).

207 SCHMIDT and SCHMIDT, *Bibl. gastroent. (Basel)*, **4**, 15 (1961); SCHMIDT and SCHMIDT, *Enzym. biol. clin.*, **3**, 1 (1963).

208 SCHMIDT and SCHMIDT, in DEINHARDT and DEINHARDT (Eds.), *Viral Hepatitis: Laboratory and Clinical Science*, Decker, New York, 1983, page 411.

209 SCHMIDT et al., in LINDNER, H. (Ed.), *Die chronische Hepatitis*, Witzstrock, Baden-Baden, 1974, page 108.

210 SCHMIDT and SCHMIDT, *Dtsch. med. Wschr.*, **98**, 1572 (1973); THALER, H., *Z. allg. Med.*, **49**, 300 (1973).

211 BIANCHI and OHNACKER, *Praxis*, **61**, 829 (1972); DÖLLE, W., *Dtsch. med. J.*, **23**, 643 (1972).

212 ERLINGER and PRANDI, *Nouv. Presse méd.*, **4**, 1651 (1975); FERNANDES and GIRARD, *Méd. et Hyg. (Genève)*, **34**, 1118 (1976).

213 SCHMIDT and SCHMIDT, *Dtsch. med. Wschr.*, **93**, 1153 (1968).

214 SCHMIDT and SCHMIDT, *Dtsch. med. Wschr.*, **93**, 1198 (1968).

215 SCHMIDT and SCHMIDT, *Klin. Wschr.*, **40**, 962 (1962); FILIPPA, G., *Enzym. biol. clin.*, **3**, 97 (1963).

Normal values (reference intervals) for enzyme activities in plasma or serum (for references see page 196–199)

↓ See text on next page Normal values (reference intervals) in plasma or serum of adults, unless otherwise stated

EC number **Recommended name** (Other names) Abbreviation	Method (substrate in brackets)	Number	μmol min⁻¹ L⁻¹ (U/L) Mean	s	95% range (extreme range in brackets)	nmol s⁻¹ L⁻¹ (nkat/L) Mean	s	95% range (extreme range in brackets)	Reference
1.1.1.1 ↓**Alcohol dehydrogenase**..... (Aldehyde reductase) ADH	UV test[7], modified, 25 °C	7	1.8	–	–	30	–	–	2
1.1.1.8 ↓**Glycerol-3-phosphate dehydrogenase (NAD⁺)**....... (Glycerophosphate dehydrogenase, polyol dehydrogenase)	UV test[5], modified, 25 °C	19	2.7	–	(1.6–6.6)	45	–	(27–110)	2

↓ See text below — Normal values (reference intervals) in plasma or serum of adults, unless otherwise stated

EC number **Recommended name** (Other names) Abbreviation	Method (substrate in brackets)	Number	µmol min⁻¹ L⁻¹ (U/L) Mean	s	95% range (extreme range in brackets)	nmol s⁻¹ L⁻¹ (nkat/L) Mean	s	95% range (extreme range in brackets)	Reference
1.1.1.14									
↓ **L-Iditol dehydrogenase**	UV test[6], modified, 24 °C	16	0.9	–	–	15	–	–	7
(Sorbitol dehydrogenase)	UV test[7], modified, 25 °C	91	0.06	0.1	(0–0.4)	1.0	1.7	(0–6.7)	8
SDH	UV test[7], modified, 37 °C	32	0.08	–	(0–0.6)	1.3	–	(0–10)	9
	UV test[7], modified, 25 °C:								
	Cord blood	–	–	–	0–4.5	–	–	0–75	10
	Children	–	–	–	0–6.0	–	–	0–100	10
	Adults	–	–	–	0–3.0	–	–	0–50	10
	UV test, optimized, 37 °C:								
	Men	30	–	–	0–2.8	–	–	0–47	11
	Women	147	–	–	0–2.4	–	–	0–40	11
1.1.1.27									
↓ **Lactate dehydrogenase**	UV test[12], modified, 25 °C	209	100	22	–	1670	370	–	8
LDH, LD	UV test[12], modified, 25 °C	175	144	28.8	–	2400	480	–	13
	UV test[12], modified, 25 °C:								
	Cord blood	29	306	118	–	5100	1970	–	10
	1st month	6	306	89	–	5100	1480	–	10
	2nd and 3rd months	13	221	44	–	3680	730	–	10
	4th–6th month	12	217	41	–	3620	680	–	10
	6th–12th month	14	197	44	–	3280	730	–	10
	2nd year	12	230	57	–	3830	950	–	10
	2nd–16th year	24	145	45		2420	750	–	10
	Adults	100	140	45	–	2330	750	–	10
	UV test[12], modified, 25 °C:								
	Cord blood	202	–	–	(87–580)	–	–	(1450–9670)	14
	UV test[12], modified, 37 °C	20	158	51.4	(96–241)	2630	857	(1600–4020)	16
	UV test, optimized, 37 °C:								
	Men	113	331	55	240–525	5520	920	4000–8750	17
	Women	167	346	65		5770	1080		17
	UV test, optimized (Boehringer test kit), 25 °C:								
	Men	33	131	17.7	(94.2–164)	2180	295	(1570–2730)	18
	Women	33	129	24.5	(51.6–186)	2150	408	(860–3100)	18
	UV test[19], optimized, 30 °C	205	205	35	135–275	3420	580	2260–4580	20
	UV test, optimized[398], 37 °C:								
	Cord blood	68	–	–	433–1224	–	–	7220–20400	399

1.1.1.1 *Alcohol dehydrogenase.* Slight hemolysis does not interfere with the determination. Highest activities in the liver. Rise of activity in the serum in acute, diffuse liver injuries[2–4] – however, of no clinical significance.

1.1.1.8 *Glycerol-3-phosphate dehydrogenase (NAD⁺).* Slight hemolysis does not interfere with the determination. Rise of activity in the serum in acute, diffuse liver injuries – however, of no clinical significance[2].

1.1.1.14 *L-Iditol dehydrogenase.* Slight hemolysis does not interfere with the determination. Present in high activity only in the liver, but measurable activity also found in seminal vesicles and kidneys; thus, a rise of activity in the serum is a specific indication of marked acute liver damage[7,9,11]. Activities lie within normal range in milder forms of liver damage.

1.1.1.27 *Lactate dehydrogenase.* Hemolysis leads to a rise of the activity in the serum. The enzyme is present in high activity in all organs; hence, increased total lactate dehydrogenase activity is nonspecific[21]. The lowest serum LDH activities are to be found in 20- to 30-year-olds[22]. Increased activity has been found in childhood and advanced age[17,22,23] (although normal values are found in 100-year-olds[366]). In women, lactate dehydrogenase activity varies little with the menstrual cycle[18].

Isoenzymes of lactate dehydrogenase (Table 1). In almost all tissues and in the plasma, lactate dehydrogenase is present in 5 fractions, designated either LDH-1 to LDH-5 in order of decreasing anodic migration rate, or H_4, H_3M, H_2M_2, HM_3 and M_4 in accordance with the subunit composition of the tetrameric molecule[24] (Table 3, page 167). A further isoenzyme, LDH-X, is found in spermatozoa. The different isoenzyme distribution patterns in tissues – LDH-1 and LDH-2 mainly in heart, kidneys and erythrocytes, LDH-5 mainly in skeletal muscle and liver, and the intermediate isoenzymes mainly in mesenchymal and malignant tissue – constitute a basis for the diagnostic use of LDH isoenzymes[21,24], which is limited by the very short half-life of LDH-5 in the circulation (Table 8, page 170). In myocardial infarction, the activity ratio LDH-1/LDH-2 is usually above the reference range of 0.45–0.74 and often above 1.0 ('flipped ratio')[15].

Table 1 *Activity of lactate dehydrogenase isoenzymes in serum of 'healthy' adults*

Temperature	Total lactate dehydrogenase	LDH-1	LDH-2	LDH-3	LDH-4	LDH-5	Reference
	U/L						
25 °C	–	111.1 (s22.1)				16.7 (s7.9)	26
37 °C	117	47 (33–64)			54 (38–75)		25
	Activity fraction (relative to total activity) as percent						
37 °C	100	20.3 (s2.8)	34.0 (s2.3)	22.8 (s1.6)	11.8 (s1.8)	11.0 (s2.5)	15

↓ See text below — Normal values (reference intervals) in plasma or serum of adults, unless otherwise stated

EC number **Recommended name** (Other names) Abbreviation	Method (substrate in brackets)	Number	μmol min^{-1} L^{-1} (U/L) Mean	s	95% range (extreme range in brackets)	nmol s^{-1} L^{-1} (nkat/L) Mean	s	95% range (extreme range in brackets)	Reference
↓('2-Hydroxybutyrate dehydrogenase')	UV test[27,28], 25 °C	42	90	38	–	1500	630	–	29
HBDH, HBD	UV test[27,28], 25 °C	175	108	23.5	–	1800	390	–	13
	UV test[27,28], 25 °C:								
	Cord blood	15	211	164	–	3520	2730	–	30
	Adults	152	76	30	–	1270	500	–	30
	UV test, optimized, 37 °C:								
	Men	113	148	26	80–440 (Men and Women)	2470	430	1300–7300 (Men and Women)	17
	Women	167	174	57		2900	950		17
	UV test, optimized, 30 °C	144	166	29.4	107–225	2770	490	1780–3750	20
	UV test, optimized, 25 °C	21	75	19	–	1250	317	–	365
1.1.1.29 ↓**Glycerate dehydrogenase**	UV test, optimized, 37 °C:								
	Men	113	499	85	–	8320	1420	–	17
	Women	167	545	112	–	9090	1870	–	17
1.1.1.37 ↓**Malate dehydrogenase**	UV test[35], modified, 25 °C:								
MDH, MD	Cord blood	202	–	–	(93.4–265)	–	–	(1560–4420)	14
	Adults	88	71	17	–	1180	280	–	8
	UV test (malate), 37 °C:								
	Men	124	15	–	5–36	250	–	83–600	36
1.1.1.38(40) **Malate dehydrogenase (oxaloacetate-decarboxylating)** ('Malic' enzyme) ME	UV test[38], 25 °C	30	–	–	(0–0.5)	–	–	(0–8)	39
1.1.1.42 ↓**Isocitrate dehydrogenase (NADP$^+$)**	UV test, 25 °C	44	2.0	–	(0.86–4.8)	33	–	(14–80)	40
ICDH, ICD, IDH	UV test[41], modified, 25 °C:								
	Cord blood	30	3.7	2.6	–	62	43	–	42
	UV test[40], modified, 37 °C	24	2.91	0.65	(1.61–3.86)	49	11	(27–64)	16
	Colorimetric[43], modified, 37 °C:								
	Cord blood	–	12.7	–	(3.7–25.4)	212	–	(62–423)	44
	Adults	–	4.75	1.65	(2.0–8.7)	79	28	(33–145)	44
1.1.1.44 ↓**Phosphogluconate dehydrogenase (decarboxylating)**	UV test, 25 °C	26	2.5	–	(0.7–4.0)	42	–	(12–67)	40
PGDH, PGD	UV test[40], modified, 37 °C	15	1.98	0.46	(0.96–3.22)	33	8	(16–54)	16
	UV test[40], modified, 25 °C	–	–	–	1.5–7.5	–	–	25–125	44

'*2-Hydroxybutyrate dehydrogenase*'. When 2-oxobutyrate is substituted for pyruvate as substrate, the reduction is termed '2-hydroxybutyrate dehydrogenase' activity and represents the activity of lactate dehydrogenase isoenzymes with fast electrophoretic mobility (especially LDH-1)[27]. Practically speaking, the HBDH/LDH ratio corresponds to the ratio of 'heart-specific' isoenzymes to total lactate dehydrogenase. Normal range for the ratio for adults (optimized method): 0.68–0.94 (30 °C)[20] and 0.63–0.81 (25 °C)[31]. A simultaneous rise of LDH activity and of the HBDH/LDH ratio is characteristic of myocardial infarction[32–34].

1.1.1.29 *Glycerate dehydrogenase.* A rise of activity in the serum with age is found in adults[17].

1.1.1.37 *Malate dehydrogenase.* Because of the high activity of this enzyme in erythrocytes, even slight hemolysis results in misleadingly high values. In the neonatal period, the upper limit of normal is 100 U/L[37]. The diagnostic significance of this enzyme is but slight. Because it is present in high activities in all organs, a rise of activity in the serum is discernible in all severe forms of organ damage, as, for example, in myocardial infarction, in liver damage, and in diseases of the blood. In the serum, the cytosol isoenzyme is found in considerable preponderance. A reduced ratio of cytosolic MDH to mitochondrial MDH is used as an indicator of cell destruction[26,367].

1.1.1.42 *Isocitrate dehydrogenase (NADP$^+$).* Slight hemolysis does not interfere with the determination. An increase of isocitrate dehydrogenase activity in the serum is found in liver diseases[2,45] and in Duchenne muscular dystrophy[16]. Only a slight and transitory[47] rise occurs, if at all[46], in myocardial infarction. Since the 'slow' – mainly mitochondrial – isoenzyme is very unstable, virtually only 'rapid' cytosol isocitrate dehydrogenase is found in the serum[368].

1.1.1.44 *Phosphogluconate dehydrogenase (decarboxylating).* Because the activity of this enzyme is high in the erythrocytes, its determination in the serum is rendered useless by even the slightest hemolysis. During pregnancy, activities are normal; the level is somewhat higher in cord blood than in adults. The enzyme has little diagnostic importance. Rises of activity have been observed in acute hepatitis[2,3] and in diseases of the blood[48].

1.1.1.49 *Glucose-6-phosphate dehydrogenase.* Determination in the serum is rendered useless by even the slightest hemolysis. In acute hepatitis[2], myocardial infarction and other severe tissue lesions, the activity in the serum rises.

↑↓ See text on previous page and below — Normal values (reference intervals) in plasma or serum of adults, unless otherwise stated

EC number **Recommended name** (Other names) Abbreviation	Method (substrate in brackets)	Number	μmol min^{-1} L^{-1} (U/L)			nmol s^{-1} L^{-1} (nkat/L)			Reference
			Mean	s	95% range (extreme range in brackets)	Mean	s	95% range (extreme range in brackets)	
1.1.1.49 ↑ **Glucose-6-phosphate dehydrogenase**	UV test[49], modified, 25 °C	38	0.24	0.29	–	4.0	4.8	–	8
G-6-PDH, G-6-PD	UV test[49], modified, 37 °C	15	1.73	0.59	(1.12–2.89)	29	10	(19–48)	16
	UV test, 25 °C	–	–	–	(0–0.18)	–	–	(0–3)	50
1.2.1.12 ↓ **Glyceraldehyde-phosphate dehydrogenase** (Triosephosphate dehydrogenase) GAPDH	UV test[51], modified, 37 °C: Men	200	–	–	23–41	–	–	380–680	52
1.2.3.2 ↓ **Xanthine oxidase**	Spectrophotometric[369], 25 °C	36	–	–	0–10	–	–	0–167	370
XO	Spectrophotometric[369], 37 °C	30	5.7	–	0–18	95	–	0–300	371
1.4.1.3 ↓ **Glutamate dehydrogenase [NAD(P)$^+$]**	UV test (Boehringer test kit), 25 °C	243	0.39	0.28	<0.8	6.5	4.7	<13	8
GLDH, GDH, GD	UV test, optimized standard method[54,55], 25 °C:								
	Men	362	–	–	≤4	–	–	≤67	56
	Women	373	–	–	≤3	–	–	≤50	56
	UV test, optimized standard method[54,55], 25 °C:								
	Men	–	–	–	0.3–4.1	–	–	5–68	57
	Women	–	–	–	0.4–3.9	–	–	7–65	57
1.4.3.6 ↓ **Amine oxidase (copper-containing)** (Monoamine oxidase, diamine oxidase, histaminase)	Colorimetric [(4-aminomethylphenyl) azo-2-naphthol], 37 °C	126	0.48	0.26	–	8.0	4.3	–	63
1.6.4.2 ↓ **Glutathione reductase [NAD(P)H]**	UV test, NADH, 25 °C	10	7.0	–	(3.3–10.2)	120	–	(55–170)	67
GR	UV test, NADPH, 25 °C	10	12.6	–	(4.3–17.4)	210	–	(72–290)	67
	UV test[68], NADPH, 37 °C:								
	Children, 4 months to 18 years	64	29	8	–	480	130	–	69
	Adults	60	21	8	–	350	130	–	69
1.6.4.3 **Dihydrolipoamide reductase (NAD$^+$)** (Lipoamide dehydrogenase, diaphorase)	UV test, optimized, 30 °C	–	–	–	3000–19000	–	–	50×10^3 to 320×10^3	72

1.2.1.12 *Glyceraldehyde-phosphate dehydrogenase.* Even slight hemolysis interferes considerably with the determination. The clinical significance of the determination is minimal. Rises of activity in the serum have been found in acute hepatitis[2], in infectious mononucleosis[53], in tumors[39] and after myocardial infarction[52].

1.2.3.2 *Xanthine oxidase.* Rises of activity in the serum occur in acute lesions of the liver parenchyma and especially in acute viral hepatitis, but also in EPH gestosis, immediately after operations and in ulcerative colitis and regional ileitis[370–372].

1.4.1.3 *Glutamate dehydrogenase [NAD(P)$^+$].* Slight hemolysis does not interfere with the determination. This enzyme is a largely liver-specific enzyme of the mitochondrial matrix, and above all of the centrilobular liver cells. Rises of activity in the serum occur in all acute liver lesions, and are particularly high in centrilobular liver necrosis after intoxications and in acute circulatory disorders[59–61]. In conjunction with aminotransferases, this enzyme is of major importance for the differential diagnosis of jaundice[61]. The activity is elevated in fatty liver (including the alcohol-related form)[58,62].

1.4.3.6 *Amine oxidase (copper-containing).* This enzyme is found in many tissues[64], including nervous tissue, platelets, lymphocytes, and granulocytes. It occurs in several forms which differ in their substrate specificity. The relationship between the activity in platelets or in the serum, on the one hand, and schizophrenia and other mental disorders, on the other hand, is unclear[65]. Elevated activities of this enzyme in the serum, referred to as 'histaminase', have been found in a number of patients with medullary thyroid carcinoma and small-cell carcinoma of the lung[346]. The activity of the enzyme from the placenta, referred to as 'diamine oxidase', is elevated in the serum of pregnant women as early as the first trimester. Regular control determinations provide information on the state of the fetus[66].

1.6.4.2 *Glutathione reductase [NAD(P)H].* An elevated activity is found in the serum of many patients with neoplastic diseases and acute hepatitis, megaloblastic anemia, and sickle-cell anemia[69,70].

↓ See text below	Normal values (reference intervals) in plasma or serum of adults, unless otherwise stated								
EC number **Recommended name** (Other names) Abbreviation	Method (substrate in brackets)	Number	µmol min⁻¹ L⁻¹ (U/L)			nmol s⁻¹ L⁻¹ (nkat/L)			Reference
			Mean	s	95% range (extreme range in brackets)	Mean	s	95% range (extreme range in brackets)	
1.11.1.9 **Glutathione peroxidase**	UV test[402], 25 °C:								
	Adults	40	151.3	34.8	–	2520	580	–	403
	UV test[402], modified, 37 °C:								
	Women	38	424	40	–	7070	670	–	404
1.14.17.1 ↓ **Dopamine β-monooxygenase** (Dopamine β-hydroxylase)	Colorimetric[73], 37 °C	82	31	30	(2–100)	520	500	(33–1670)	74
	Colorimetric[73], modified, 37 °C:								
	Men	32	53.9	33.8	(10.7–141)	899	563	(178–2350)	75
	Women	38	47.4	25.0	(0.9–114)	790	417	(15–1900)	75
	Colorimetric[73], 37 °C:								
	Men	114	35	–	7–85	580	–	120–1420	76
	Colorimetric[73], modified, 37 °C	127	68	36	3–138	1130	600	50–2300	77
1.16.3.1 ↓ **Ferroxidase** (Ceruloplasmin)	Colorimetric (4-phenylene diamine)[78], 37 °C:								
	Cord blood	–	–	–	3.3–16.7	–	–	55–278	10
	1st to 3 month	–	–	–	12.1–39	–	–	202–650	10
	Children	–	–	–	19.2–60	–	–	320–1000	10
	Adults	–	–	–	19–45	–	–	317–750	10
	Colorimetric (o-dianisidine), 30 °C:								
	Men	78	–	–	62–140	–	–	1030–2330	79
2.1.3.3 ↓ **Ornithine carbamoyltransferase** OCT	Microdiffusion[80], 37 °C	15	0.39	0.28	(0.10–0.70)	6.5	4.7	(1.7–11.7)	16
	Colorimetric[81], modified, 37 °C	40	–	–	0.63–4	–	–	11–67	82
	Colorimetric, optimized, 37 °C	200	5.0	–	0.5–10.5	83	–	8.3–175	83
2.2.1.1 ↓ **Transketolase** (Glycolaldehydetransferase)	Colorimetric (sedoheptulose 7-phosphate assay)[87], 37 °C	15	0.82	–	(0.38–1.42)	14	–	(6.3–24)	87
		21	0.29	–	(0.17–0.60)	4.8	–	(2.8–10)	88
2.3.1.23 **Lysolecithin acyltransferase** LAT	Isotope method (1-^{14}C-palmitoyl glyceryl phosphoryl choline)[405], 37 °C	6	0.120	0.025	–	2.00	0.42	–	406
2.3.1.43 ↓ **Lecithin-cholesterol acyltransferase** (Lecithin acyltransferase) LCAT	Isotope method (7-^{3}H-cholesterol)[89], 37 °C	20	1.00	0.14	–	16.7	2.3	–	90
	Enzymatic cholesterol assay, 37 °C	15	1.31	0.08	–	21.8	1.3	–	91
	Enzymatic cholesterol assay, 37 °C:								
	Men	18	1.52	0.25	(1.27–2.22)	25	4.2	(21–37)	375
	Women	10	1.03	0.20	(0.73–1.28)	17	3.3	(12–21)	375
	Isotope method[89], modified (7-^{3}H-cholesterol), 37 °C	6	1.24	0.16	–	20.7	2.7	–	406

1.14.17.1 *Dopamine β-monooxygenase*. The activity in the serum is low in 1- to 5-year-olds[347]. It is highest in 15- to 19-year-olds[348]. The enzyme is released together with noradrenaline when sympathetic nerves are stimulated; thus the activity in the serum is elevated on the first days after a myocardial infarction[76]. The relationship between the activity in the serum and the blood pressure cannot be regarded as certain[71]. Elevated activities are found in patients with pheochromocytoma[349], while patients with renal failure exhibit reduced activities[373].

1.16.3.1 *Ferroxidase*. This is a plasma-specific enzyme and a transport protein for copper (page 137). Rise of activity in the serum during pregnancy, after myocardial infarction, in infections, and in leukemia; diminished activity in Wilson's disease (diagnostically important!), but also in nephrotic syndrome and in sprue[374].

2.1.3.3 *Ornithine carbamoyltransferase*. Because of the high activity of this enzyme in the liver, its determination in the serum is suited for the specific detection of liver lesions[84,85]; however, the test is not very sensitive, since this is a mitochondrial enzyme. Its activity in the serum is also elevated in alcohol-related liver lesions[62,86], although only in the more severe forms of liver damage when compared with γ-glutamyltransferase.

2.2.1.1 *Transketolase*. A rise of activity in the serum is found in uremia and, irregularly, in acute hepatitis. Activity is normal in myocardial infarction, liver cirrhosis, and obstructive jaundice[87].

2.3.1.43 *Lecithin-cholesterol acyltransferase*. This plasma-specific enzyme is deficient in hereditary absence of cholesterol esteri-

↓ See text below — Normal values (reference intervals) in plasma or serum of adults, unless otherwise stated

EC number **Recommended name** (Other names) Abbreviation	Method (substrate in brackets)	Number	μmol min⁻¹ L⁻¹ (U/L) Mean	s	95% range (extreme range in brackets)	nmol s⁻¹ L⁻¹ (nkat/L) Mean	s	95% range (extreme range in brackets)	Reference
2.3.2.2 ↓ **γ-Glutamyltransferase** (γ-Glutamyltranspeptidase) γ-GT, GGT, GT, GGTP	Colorimetric[92] (γ-L-glutamyl-4-nitroanilide), 25 °C:								
	Men	61	–	–	4.5–24.8	–	–	75–413	93
	Women	57	–	–	3.2–13.5	–	–	53–225	93
	Cord blood	32	54.0	–	11.2–96.8	900	–	187–1610	94
	Children, 2nd–15th year	–	7.3	–	3.0–11.5	12	–	50–192	94
	Colorimetric[95], modified (γ-L-glutamyl-4-nitroanilide), 37 °C:								
	Men	60	12	–	5–19	200	–	83–320	96
	Women	52	9	–	4–14	150	–	67–230	96
	Colorimetric[97] (γ-L-glutamyl-4-nitroanilide), 37 °C:								
	Men	–	–	–	≤ 60	–	–	≤ 1000	98
	Women	–	–	–	≤ 50	–	–	≤ 830	98
	Colorimetric (γ-L-glutamyl-4-nitroanilide) (Boehringer test kit), 25 °C:								
	Men	33	13.1	7.6	(5.2–37.3)	218	127	(87–622)	18
	Women	33	7.5	3.5	(2.8–18.8)	125	58	(47–313)	18
	Colorimetric[92] (γ-L-glutamyl-4-nitroanilide), 25 °C:								
	Men	53	–	–	6–28	–	–	100–470	99
	Women	39	–	–	6–18	–	–	100–300	99
	Male blood donors, normal mass	–	–	–	5–23	–	–	83–380	100
	Female blood donors, normal mass	–	–	–	4–14	–	–	67–230	100
	Colorimetric[92], modified (γ-L-glutamyl-4-nitroanilide), 25 °C:								
	Women	89	10.5	–	6.0–37.0	175	–	100–617	101
	Pregnancy, mens X	68	7.1	–	3.8–14.3	118	–	63–238	101
	Colorimetric (γ-L-glutamyl-4-nitroanilide) (Roche test kit), 25 °C:								
	Men	–	–	–	5.2–22.2	–	–	87–370	102
	Women	–	–	–	4.7–14.5	–	–	78–242	102
	Colorimetric[92] (γ-L-glutamyl-4-nitroanilide), 37 °C:								
	Men, 20–30 years, normal mass, fasting	–	22.9	–	11.4–72.3	382	–	190–1210	103
	Women, 20–30 years, normal mass, fasting	–	15.6	–	7.2–38.5	260	–	120–642	103
	Colorimetric[400] (γ-L-glutamyl-4-nitroanilide), 37 °C:								
	Cord blood	111	–	–	17–209	–	–	283–3480	399

fication[407]. The relationship between activity changes in the serum, on the one hand, and lipoprotein metabolism, lesions of the liver parenchyma, and cholestasis, on the other hand, is not completely clear; this also explains the contradictory views which have been presented on the diagnostic significance of this enzyme for diseases of the liver and disorders in lipid metabolism[376,377].

The mass concentration of the enzyme in normolipidemic subjects, determined by radioimmunoassay, is 6.14 (*s* 0.98) mg/L[408].

2.3.2.2 *γ-Glutamyltransferase.* This is a membrane-associated enzyme with its highest activity in the renal tubules, where it is 12 times higher than in the pancreas, and 25 times higher than in the liver. Low activities are also found in the small intestine, the spleen, and other organs. Electrophoretically separable fractions occur in the serum as a result of complex formation with lipoproteins, but are of no diagnostic importance[104,105]. There are also true isoenzymes, which are separable by means of affinity chromatography on concanavalin A[378].

In the serum, activities exhibit a roughly logarithmic-normal distribution[101,103]. The activity is high in cord blood[94,399], declines rapidly during the first 6 months[409], and stays low in children[103,107] (median for boys about 30% lower than for young men, and for girls about the same level as for young women). In assessing the upper limit of normal for adults, the sex- and age-dependence must be taken into account[101,103]. The activity in the serum is an extremely sensitive indicator of even subclinical liver lesions. The median value rises by 38% in men and by 39% in women between the 3rd and 6th decades of life[103]. It is also higher in overweight persons[101,103], and is slightly elevated in women taking ovulation inhibitors[101,103]. Furthermore, a rise directly after (15 hours after) alcohol consumption[98,103,108] as well as during anticonvulsant therapy[103] and therapies with numerous other drugs[109,379] has been found. A rise of γ-glutamyltransferase activity is an indicator of diseases of the liver, the bile ducts and the pancreas[104,109,110]. With few exceptions[379], a normal activity rules out liver disease[111]. Very high activities indicate cholestasis, although further differentiation, as to the site and etiology, is not possible[112,113]. In anicteric patients, determination of γ-glutamyltransferase activity is an aid in the detection of diseases of the liver and bile[107,111,114], and in the early detection of primary and secondary malignancies of the liver[110,114]. If no neoplastic processes or obstructions to the bile flow are in evidence, high γ-glutamyltransferase activity is a characteristic indicator of toxic (especially alcohol-related) liver lesions[104,109,110]. Since – in contrast to 'leucine aminopeptidase' and alkaline phosphatase activities – the activity of γ-glutamyltransferase does not rise in pregnant women[112], it is a major aid in the detection of liver diseases during pregnancy[110]. The liver is

↓ See text below — Normal values (reference intervals) in plasma or serum of adults, unless otherwise stated

EC number **Recommended name** (Other names) Abbreviation	Method (substrate in brackets)	Number	μmol min⁻¹ L⁻¹ (U/L) Mean	s	95% range (extreme range in brackets)	nmol s⁻¹ L⁻¹ (nkat/L) Mean	s	95% range (extreme range in brackets)	Reference
2.4.99.1 ↓**CMP-N-acetylneuraminate-galactosyl-glycoprotein sialyltransferase** (Sialyltransferase)	Isotope method, 37 °C:								
	Children, 6–15 years	115	0.0033	–	(0.002 to 0.0045)	0.055	–	(0.033 to 0.075)	380
	Adults	39	0.0032	–	(0.0024 to 0.0042)	0.054	–	(0.041 to 0.071)	380
2.5.1.18 **Glutathione transferase** (Glutathione S-aralkyl-transferase) GST	UV test[410], modified (1-chloro-2,4-dinitrobenzene), 37 °C	158	5.2	2.4	–	86.7	40.0	–	411
2.6.1.1 ↓**Aspartate aminotransferase** (Glutamic-oxaloacetic transaminase) AST, ASAT, AspAT, GOT	UV test[116], 38 °C	160	16.6	0.4	–	277	7	–	117
	UV test (Boehringer test kit), 25 °C	577	7.67	1.8	–	128	30	–	8
	UV test[116], 25 °C:								
	Cord blood	44	21.3	9.5	–	355	158	–	10
	≤ 30th day	12	20.4	9.7	–	340	162	–	10
	2nd–3rd month	13	22.6	6.3	–	377	105	–	10
	4th–6th month	12	24.3	5.5	–	405	92	–	10
	7th–12th month	16	19.3	5.4	–	322	90	–	10
	2nd year	6	15.7	4.8	–	262	80	–	10
	2nd–16th year	58	14.1	3.9	–	235	65	–	10
	16th year	49	14.4	4.0	–	240	67	–	10
	Adults	100	13.6	3.2	–	228	53	–	10
	UV test[116], 25 °C:								
	Cord blood	15	12.6	9.0	–	210	150	–	30
		202	–	–	(0–29)	–	–	(0–480)	14
	UV test[118], modified, 37 °C	20	26.9	5.65	(13.3–33.3)	448	94	(222–555)	16
	UV test, optimized, 25 °C:								
	Men	2384	11.3	–	6.2–20.8	188	–	103–347	119
	Women	1595	9.4	–	5.1–17.5	157	–	85–292	119
	UV test, optimized (Boehringer test kit), 25 °C:								
	Men	33	10.6	2.2	(6.4–16.2)	177	37	(107–270)	18
	Women	33	9.3	1.5	(7.6–13.1)	155	25	(127–218)	18
	UV test, optimized standard method[54], 25 °C:								
	Men	708	11.1	–	≤ 19	185	–	≤ 320	120
	Women	668	9.2	–	≤ 15	153	–	≤ 250	120
	UV test, optimized (Boehringer test kit), 25 °C:								
	Male blood donors, normal mass	–	–	–	8–19	–	–	130–320	100
	Female blood donors, normal mass	–	–	–	7–15	–	–	120–250	100
	UV test, optimized standard method[54], 25 °C:								
	Men	442	–	–	5–17	–	–	83–280	56
	Women	469	–	–	5–15	–	–	83–250	56
	UV test, optimized standard method[54], 37 °C:								
	Men, 20–30 years, normal mass, fasting	452	20.9	–	13.0–31.0	348	–	217–517	121
	UV test, optimized[398], 37 °C:								
	Cord blood	68	–	–	22–58	–	–	367–967	399

probably implicated in the increase of γ-glutamyltransferase activity after myocardial infarction, in diabetes, and in many neurological diseases[104] (e.g. multiple sclerosis[113]). Despite high activity in kidneys[115], renal diseases are, as a rule, not accompanied by increased γ-glutamyltransferase activities in the serum[104, 109].

2.4.99.1 *CMP-N-acetylneuraminate-galactosyl-glycoprotein sialyltransferase.* The activity in the serum is decreased in α_1-antitrypsin deficiency[381], and elevated in tumor patients[380, 382]. However, the practical significance in tumor diseases is still unclear.

2.6.1.1 *Aspartate aminotransferase.* Slight hemolysis does not interfere notably with the determination. The activity is high in the liver, heart, and skeletal muscle, and low in erythrocytes. The enzyme occurs in 2 principal forms (isoenzymes), one of which originates in the cytosol (c-AST), and the other in mitochondria

↓ See text below — Normal values (reference intervals) in plasma or serum of adults, unless otherwise stated

EC number **Recommended name** (Other names) Abbreviation	Method (substrate in brackets)	Number	µmol min⁻¹ L⁻¹ (U/L) Mean	s	95% range (extreme range in brackets)	nmol s⁻¹ L⁻¹ (nkat/L) Mean	s	95% range (extreme range in brackets)	Reference
2.6.1.2 ↓**Alanine aminotransferase** (Glutamic-pyruvic transaminase) ALT, ALAT, GPT	UV test (Boehringer test kit), 25 °C:								
	Cord blood	202	–	–	(0.5–9.6)	–	–	(8–160)	14
	Cord blood	44	5.0	2.3	–	83	38	–	10
	1st month	11	4.0	3.0	–	67	50	–	10
	2nd and 3rd months	11	7.5	1.6	–	125	27	–	10
	4th–12th month	14	6.2	2.7	–	103	45	–	10
	> 1st year	31	6.8	3.3	–	113	55	–	10
	Adults	722	5.54	1.7	–	92	28	–	8
	UV test[118], modified, 37 °C	20	22.7	4.99	(13.3–30.0)	378	83	(222–500)	16
	UV test, optimized, 25 °C:								
	Men	2384	14.7	–	6.4–33.3	245	–	110–555	119
	Women	1595	10.4	–	5.2–21.0	173	–	87–350	119
	UV test, optimized (Boehringer test kit), 25 °C:								
	Men	33	11.8	5.1	(4.8–32.1)	197	85	(80–535)	18
	Women	33	8.9	3.4	(3.6–22.4)	148	57	(60–373)	18
	UV test, optimized standard method[54], 25 °C:								
	Men, normal mass	395	11.1	–	≤ 22.3	185	–	≤ 372	120
	Men, overweight	313	14.0	–	–	233	–	–	120
	Women	686	9.1	–	≤ 18	152	–	≤ 300	120
	UV test, optimized (Boehringer test kit), 25 °C:								
	Male blood donors, normal mass	–	–	–	6–23	–	–	100–380	100
	Female blood donors, normal mass	–	–	–	6–17	–	–	100–280	100
	UV test, optimized standard method[54], 25 °C:								
	Men	464	–	–	5–23	–	–	83–380	56
	Women	470	–	–	5–19	–	–	83–320	56
	UV test, optimized standard method[54], 37 °C:								
	Men, 20–30 years, normal mass, fasting	452	22.0	–	12.7–40.0	367	–	212–667	121
	UV test, optimized[398], 37 °C:								
	Cord blood	96	–	–	6–24	–	–	100–400	399

Table 2 *Activity of aspartate aminotransferase isoenzymes in serum measured at 37 °C*[412]

Subjects	Age	c-AST Mean (U/L)	c-AST s (U/L)	m-AST Mean (U/L)	m-AST s (U/L)
116 men	18–81 years	17.4	4.15	4.94	1.05
114 women	16–82 years	16.9	4.85	4.43	1.02

Table 3 *Reference intervals for aspartate aminotransferase activity in serum of children measured at 30 °C*[413]

Age	Males Number	Males P_5 (U/L)	Males P_{95} (U/L)	Females Number	Females P_5 (U/L)	Females P_{95} (U/L)
5–6 years	67	16	27	68	17	28
7–8 years	68	16	27	80	16	26
9–10 years	70	16	26	66	15	23
11–12 years	76	15	23	79	13	22
13–14 years	75	14	22	77	11	20
15–16 years	67	13	23	58	11	19
17–20 years	92	12	24	90	10	23

Method: UV test[116], optimized (Boehringer test kit).

(m-AST)[122]. Normally the cytosol enzyme predominates in the serum (Table 2). In children, activities are higher than in young adults[22,23,121] (Table 3). There are reports that the upper limit of normal rises with age[121]; however, activities within the normal range for younger persons have been found in 100-year-olds[366]. Determination of aspartate aminotransferase activity is of major clinical significance for the diagnosis of myocardial infarction[21,33,34], as well as of liver disease[45,60,61], especially when conjoined with determinations of the activities of other enzymes[34,61].

2.6.1.2 *Alanine aminotransferase.* Slight hemolysis does not interfere with the determination. Alanine aminotransferase is a cytosol enzyme. It is not present in erythrocytes; its activity is highest in the liver. Only slight differences exist between the activities in the serum of children and of young adults[23,121]. The highest activities have been found in 30- to 40-year-old men and 50- to 60-year-old women[121]. Pathological rises of activity occur especially in liver lesions, and accordingly alanine aminotransferase plays an important role in the detection of liver diseases[45,60,61]. The AST/ALT ratio (de Ritis quotient), which is important for diagnosis, varies depending on whether the activities are determined with formerly customary or with optimized methods[123].

2.7.1.40 *Pyruvate kinase.* 3 tetrameric isoenzymes with the structure K_4 (PK-1), L_4 (PK-2), and M_4 (PK-3) arise from the association of identical subunits. The isoenzyme PK-1 is present in all embryonal cells; PK-2 is found in liver, kidneys and erythrocytes; PK-3 occurs in the muscle only[130]. In acute hepatitis, a nonsignificant decrease of the activity in the serum (due to bed rest?[2]) has been observed, while a rise has been found in tumor patients[39].

↑↓ See text on previous page and below — Normal values (reference intervals) in plasma or serum of adults, unless otherwise stated

EC number **Recommended name** (Other names) Abbreviation	Method (substrate in brackets)	Number	µmol min⁻¹ L⁻¹ (U/L) Mean	s	95% range (extreme range in brackets)	nmol s⁻¹ L⁻¹ (nkat/L) Mean	s	95% range (extreme range in brackets)	Reference
2.7.1.40									
↑**Pyruvate kinase**	UV test[124], modified, 25 °C	30	15.8	6.0	–	263	100	–	39
PK	UV test (Boehringer test kit), 25 °C:								
	Men	24	17.6	4.1	(9.4–25.2)	293	68	(157–420)	125
	Women	24	15.5	3.2	(9.4–19.4)	258	53	(157–323)	125
	UV test[126], modified, 30 °C	34	32	–	≤50	530	–	≤830	127
	UV test[128], modified, 30 °C:								
	Children	9	44.6	9.1	–	743	152	–	129
	Adults	10	22.0	4.8	–	367	80	–	129
2.7.3.2									
↓**Creatine kinase**	UV test[131], modified, 37° C:								
(Creatine phosphokinase)	Men	50	42	21	≤80	700	350	≤1330	132
CK, CPK	Women	50	23	11	≤50	380	180	≤830	132
	UV test[131], modified, converted from 37 °C to 30 °C:								
	Men	50	–	–	≤50	–	–	≤830	132
	Women	50	–	–	≤30	–	–	≤500	132
	UV test, optimized (Boehringer test kit), 25 °C:								
	Men	33	32.6	12.7	(11.7–60.4)	543	212	(195–1010)	18
	Women	33	20.6	8.5	(10.5–41.4)	343	142	(175–690)	18
	UV test, optimized, NAC-activated[133], 37 °C:								
	Cord blood	117	–	–	71–567	–	–	1180–9450	399
	UV test, optimized standard method, NAC-activated[134], 25 °C:								
	Males, 11–90 years	388	–	–	10–80	–	–	167–1330	383
	Females, 11–90 years	410	–	–	10–70	–	–	167–1170	383
	UV test, optimized, NAC-activated[133], 37 °C:								
	Women	143	71	–	<170 (27–247)	1180	–	<2830 (450–4120)	401

Table 4 *Activity of creatine kinase isoenzymes in serum measured at 30 °C*

Subjects	Age	Number	Total CK Mean (U/L)	s	CK-MM Mean	s	CK-MB Mean	s	CK-BB Mean	s	Reference
Infants*	Cord blood	45	185	73	173	71	3	3	9	9	415
	5–8 hours	45	536	236	468	218	25	18	43	22	415
	24–33 hours	45	494	254	450	240	18	14	25	12	415
	71–100 hours	45	288	163	252	152	11	9	25	15	415
Men◊	17–79 years	81	–	–	43.3	14.9	1.32	0.70	0.15	0.20	416
Women◊	14–85 years	63	–	–	32.4	9.7	1.40	0.99	0.22	0.31	416

* UV test[132], optimized (Boehringer test kit, NAC-activated). ◊ UV test[132] (Worthington Diagnostics test kit).

The activity is increased in all patients with Duchenne muscular dystrophy and in some female carriers as well[127].

2.7.3.2 *Creatine kinase.* Determination of creatine kinase activity can be interfered with by adenylate kinase or glutathione reductase, which pass into the serum from erythrocytes, platelets, or the liver[139–141]. The enzyme is a dimer consisting of the 2 subunits M (muscle) and B (brain). The combinations MM, MB, and BB are characteristic for skeletal muscle, myocardium, and brain, respectively[136]. Isoenzyme MM is, however, also found in the myocardium and many other organs, while isoenzyme BB also occurs in the stomach, intestine, kidney, prostate, uterus, and placenta[137,138]. Creatine kinase activity in liver and erythrocytes is low. Normal adult serum contains mostly the MM isoenzyme (Table 4). Considerable amounts of the BB isoenzyme occur in the serum of infants[396,415,417] (Tables 4 and 5) and in the serum of women during labor[147]. The BB and MB isoenzymes are relatively labile compounds, compared with the MM isoenzyme. Losses of creatine kinase activity in serum samples due to oxidation of the sulfhydryl groups present at the active sites of the enzyme may occur. Full activity, however, can be regained by the addition of a reducing agent, such as N-acetylcysteine (NAC), dithiothreitol, or glutathione. Only methods allowing for the above-mentioned interferences yield reproducible results[133,134].

Levels of activity in the serum show a roughly logarithmic-normal distribution[142,401,415]. In the newborn high activities of creatine kinase in serum are often found during the first few days of life; infants after the 2nd month of life show activities almost identical to that of adults[135,143]. High levels have been observed in 15- to 16-year-old boys (Table 6). Activities are higher for men than for women, and higher for Blacks than for Whites[144,418]. No clear influence of age is discernible in adults[142,145,401]. Creatine kinase activity in the serum of women is not influenced by the menstrual

↓ See text below — Normal values (reference intervals) in plasma or serum of adults, unless otherwise stated

EC number **Recommended name** (Other names) Abbreviation	Method (substrate in brackets)	Number	$\mu mol\,min^{-1}L^{-1}$ (U/L) Mean	s	95% range (extreme range in brackets)	$nmol\,s^{-1}L^{-1}$ (nkat/L) Mean	s	95% range (extreme range in brackets)	Reference
2.7.4.3 ↓**Adenylate kinase**	UV test[159], 25 °C	25	8.7	3.1	–	145	52	–	160
(Myokinase)	UV test[159], 25 °C	50	17.8	6.3	–	297	105	–	161
ADK, MK	UV test[131], optimized, 25 °C:								
	Men	184	–	–	8–53	–	–	133–883	140
	Women	204	–	–	8–47	–	–	133–783	140
	UV test[131], optimized, 30 °C	–	25	–	10–70	420	–	17–1170	141
2.7.5.1 ↓**Phosphoglucomutase**	Fructose 6-phosphate assay[162], 37 °C	30	9.8	5.2	–	163	87	–	39
(Glucose phosphomutase)	Glucose 1-phosphate assay, 37 °C	–	9.2	3.4	(4–17)	153	57	(67–280)	163
PGM, PGluM	UV test, 25 °C	–	–	–	(0.5–6.3)	–	–	(8–105)	164
3.1.1.3 ↓**Triacylglycerol lipase**	Titrimetric (olive oil), 37 °C:								
(Lipase)	Children	20	57	24	–	950	400	–	166
	Adults	68	78	29	–	1300	480	–	166
	Titrimetric[167], modified (olive oil), 37 °C	146	–	–	0–80	–	–	0–1300	168
	Colorimetric (olive oil), 37 °C	100	–	–	2–40	–	–	30–670	169
	Photometric[170] (olive oil), 25 °C	156	–	–	0–80	–	–	0–1300	171
	Titrimetric[172], modified (olive oil), 25 °C	1458	59	–	5–130	980	–	80–2170	173
	UV test (Boehringer test kit), 25 °C:								
	Adults	632	65	–	22–193	1080	–	367–3220	422

Table 5
Age-related reference intervals for creatine kinase BB in serum[417]

Age	Number	95% reference interval µg/L
Newborn	49	14–550
4 days	47	1.4–43
1 year	49	0–22
8 years	32	3.0–10
14 years	50	0–16
25 years	37	0–5.1
40 years	50	0–3.5
65 years	50	0–3.5

Method: radioimmunoassay.

Table 6 *Reference intervals for creatine kinase activity in serum of children measured at 30 °C*[413]

Age	Males Number	P_5 (U/L)	P_{95} (U/L)	Females Number	P_5 (U/L)	P_{95} (U/L)
5–6 years	67	35	108	68	33	101
7–8 years	68	32	103	80	29	91
9–10 years	70	33	109	66	32	88
11–12 years	76	33	108	79	28	87
13–14 years	75	30	130	77	26	85
15–16 years	67	45	247	58	21	74
17–20 years	92	30	180	90	18	66

Method: UV test[132], optimized (Boehringer test kit).

cycle or by ovulation inhibitors[145]. It is low during the first half of pregnancy[146,419], but elevated *post partum*[147,148]. If the person has engaged in physical exercise before the sample is taken, the levels of activity show a marked elevation[149,150]. A rise in activity is also observed after intramuscular injection of a number of drugs[139].

Creatine kinase is the most sensitive of the enzymes used in the diagnosis of heart[21,33,34,139,158] and muscle lesions[149,151] (Table 11, page 172, and Table 13, page 173). In practically all cases, the activity is elevated 18–36 hours after myocardial infarction[34,158] and in Duchenne muscular dystrophy[145,149,151,401]. Elevated levels are also found in about ⅔ of female carriers of Duchenne muscular dystrophy[149,151,401]. Subnormal levels may occur in connective tissue diseases[420]. The quality of the diagnosis can be improved with the isoenzymes: namely, with vast predominance of the MM type in muscular dystrophy[152] and with a higher fraction of the MB type in myocardial infarction[153–155]. Elevated concentrations of the MB type are also found in hyperthyroidism[152]. The significance of the occurrence of isoenzyme BB in the serum is less clear[156]. It has been definitely detected in cases of malignant hyperthermia[157], in some carcinomas[138,421], and in kidney failure[138].

2.7.4.3 *Adenylate kinase.* In striated muscle, the absolute activity of adenylate kinase is higher than that of creatine kinase[131]. Relatively high activities are also found in leukocytes and platelets. The usefulness of adenylate kinase determination in serum for the detection of diseases of the heart and muscles is limited because the half-life is extremely short and completely hemolysis-free serum must be used[72,160,161].

2.7.5.1 *Phosphoglucomutase.* Slight hemolysis does not interfere with the determination. Compared with adult levels, activities in cord blood are elevated[164]. The enzyme is of little clinical significance. Rises of activity occur in liver lesions[165].

3.1.1.3 *Triacylglycerol lipase.* Although activity in the serum is inhibited by hemoglobin, slight hemolysis does not interfere with the determination[174]. Levels of activity in the serum show a roughly logarithmic-normal distribution[172,173]. No sex-related differences have been found[173,175]. Activity in the serum may be reduced during pregnancy[176]. The high rise of activity in acute pancreatitis is of decisive diagnostic significance[174,177,178,183]. The changes in chronic pancreatitis and in pancreatic carcinoma are, however, of no diagnostic value; better results may be obtained after provocation with pancreozymin and secretin[179,180,183], although the reliability is still only 60%. Slight rises of activity occur in inflammatory diseases of the liver[181], in nephropathies[182], and in secondary reactions of the pancreas.

3.1.1.8 *Cholinesterase.* Because of the high serum levels of this plasma-specific enzyme, slight hemolysis does not interfere with the determination. The enzyme occurs in many variants[187,189], most of which are of no practical significance. The dibucaine-

↑↓ See text on previous page and below — Normal values (reference intervals) in plasma or serum of adults, unless otherwise stated

EC number **Recommended name** (Other names) Abbreviation	Method (substrate in brackets)	Number	μmol min⁻¹ L⁻¹ (U/L)			nmol s⁻¹ L⁻¹ (nkat/L)			Reference
			Mean	s	95% range (extreme range in brackets)	Mean	s	95% range (extreme range in brackets)	
3.1.1.8									
↑ **Cholinesterase**	Colorimetric (acetylcholine), 37 °C	250	1.53	0.333	–	25.5	5.55	–	184
(Pseudocholinesterase)	Colorimetric (benzoylcholine), 37 °C	250	1.56	0.333	–	26.0	5.55	–	184
CHE, BuCHE	Colorimetric (α-naphthyl propionate), 37 °C	250	3.05	0.466	–	50.8	7.77	–	184
	Colorimetric (β-naphthyl propionate), 37 °C	250	1.75	0.383	–	29.2	6.38	–	184
	Colorimetric (phenyl acetate), 37 °C	250	16.6	3.83	–	277	63.8	–	184
	Colorimetric (monosuccinylcholine), 37 °C	250	–	–	< 0.02	–	–	< 0.33	184
	Colorimetric (disuccinylcholine), 37 °C	250	–	–	< 0.02	–	–	< 0.33	184
	UV test (α-naphthyl acetate), 25 °C:								
	Children, < 13 years	10	1.65	0.35	–	27.5	5.83	–	185
	Blood donors	100	1.07	0.21	0.65–1.49	17.8	3.50	10.8–24.8	185
	Colorimetric (acetylthiocholine iodide), 25 °C:								
	Men	226	2.43	0.68	1.30–3.70	40.5	11.3	21.7–61.7	186
	Women	198	2.20	0.51	1.22–3.20	36.7	8.5	20.3–53.3	186
	Colorimetric (butyrylthiocholine iodide), 25 °C:								
	Men	226	4.74	1.34	2.27–7.40	79.0	22.3	37.8–123	186
	Women	198	4.31	1.22	2.05–6.70	71.8	20.3	34.2–112	186
	Colorimetric (propionylthiocholine iodide), 25 °C:								
	Men	221	5.30	1.12	3.10–7.50	88.4	18.7	51.7–125	186
	Women	173	4.95	1.06	2.90–6.90	82.5	17.7	48.3–115	186
	Colorimetric (butyrylthiocholine iodide), 25 °C:								
	Children, 1–15 years	309	5.75	–	3.61–8.53	95.8	–	60.2–142	393
	Men, 16–94 years	715	5.63	–	3.20–8.53	93.8	–	53.3–142	393
	Women, 16–39 years	147	4.69	–	2.82–7.41	78.2	–	47.0–124	393
	Women, 40–99 years	473	5.41	–	3.52–8.80	90.2	–	58.7–147	393
			μmol min⁻¹ L⁻¹ (U/L)			nmol s⁻¹ L⁻¹ (nkat/L)			
3.1.1.34									
↓ **Lipoprotein lipase** (Diacylglycerol lipase, clearing factor lipase, postheparin lipase)	Titrimetric (olive oil), 25 °C, 10 min after heparin injection	–	–	–	(200–530)	–	–	(3330–8840)	191
	Titrimetric (1-monoolein), 25 °C, 10 min after heparin injection	–	–	–	(270–570)	–	–	(4500–9500)	191
	Isotope method (acyl-1-¹⁴C-triolein), 28 °C, 15 min after heparin injection								
	Protamine-inactivated lipoprotein lipase:								
	Men	12	362	98	–	6030	1630	–	192
	Protamine-resistant lipoprotein lipase:								
	Men	12	463	196	–	7720	3270	–	192

resistant and the fluoride-resistant variants are clinically important (page 274); if they are present (along with a reduced total activity of the enzyme), the breakdown of muscle relaxants is delayed. There are also variants with elevated activity and no clinical symptoms, but the enzyme may be totally lacking. Activity is slightly diminished in cord blood, but reaches adult levels within the 1st month of life[10]. Serum activity is reduced by about 30% in the 2nd half of pregnancy[188] and in some women on ovulation inhibitors[393]. More or less reduced activities are found in acute and chronic liver diseases[21,187], in malnutrition and under cytostatic therapy, while elevated levels are found in fatty infiltration of the liver[61] and other disturbances of lipid metabolism, such as in the nephrotic syndromes. The determination of cholinesterase activity is also important for the detection of poisoning with organic phosphoric acid esters (insecticides[189,190]). For the formal genetics of cholinesterase variants see page 274.

3.1.1.34 *Lipoprotein lipase.* The activity in the serum after intravenous administration of heparin (maximal activity 7–10 minutes after injection[193]) seems to derive from several organs: lipoprotein lipase itself in part from adipose tissue, and another lipase from the liver[194]. In contrast to lipoprotein lipase, liver lipase is resistant to protamine. Krauss et al.[195] as well as Burton and Nadler[196] published values found in children. In women, the activity of lipoprotein lipase increases with age[195].

3.1.3.1 *Alkaline phosphatase.* This enzyme constitutes a system of multiple molecular forms in which heterogeneity is partly due to genetic factors and partly to posttranslational modifications[200]. In the serum, 4 major fractions may be distinguished. These may, in order of increasing electrophoretic mobility, be ascribed to the intestine, the placenta, the bones, and the liver[21,199]. Properties of the fractions are listed in Table 5 on page 168. The substrate most frequently used for activity measurements is 4-nitrophenyl phos-

↑ See text on previous page — Normal values (reference intervals) in plasma or serum of adults, unless otherwise stated

EC number **Recommended name** (Other names) Abbreviation	Method (substrate in brackets)	Number	μmol min⁻¹ L⁻¹ (U/L) Mean	s	95% range (extreme range in brackets)	nmol s⁻¹ L⁻¹ (nkat/L) Mean	s	95% range (extreme range in brackets)	Reference
3.1.3.1 ↑ **Alkaline phosphatase** ALP, AP, APh	Colorimetric (4-nitrophenyl phosphate), 37 °C:								
	Cord blood	15	60	19	–	1000	320	–	197
	1st month	3	59	–	–	980	–	–	197
	2nd–3rd month	17	98	29	–	1630	480	–	197
	4th–6th month	14	98	32	–	1630	530	–	197
	7th–12th month	15	92	29	–	1530	480	–	197
	2nd–15th year	142	88	26	–	1470	430	–	197
	Adults	100	29	8	–	480	130	–	197
	Colorimetric (4-nitrophenyl phosphate), 37 °C	92	37	10	–	617	167	–	99
	Colorimetric (4-nitrophenyl phosphate), optimized standard method[54], 25 °C:								
	Men*	708	115	–	≤ 180	1920	–	≤ 3000	120
	Women*	668	95.5	–	≤ 170	1590	–	≤ 2830	120
	Colorimetric (4-nitrophenyl phosphate), optimized standard method[54], 25 °C:								
	Men	332	–	–	50–190	–	–	830–3200	56
	Women	363	–	–	40–190	–	–	670–3200	56
	Colorimetric (4-nitrophenyl phosphate), optimized standard method[54], 25 °C:								
	Boys, 3–15 years	37	310	79	–	5170	1320	–	23
	Girls, 3–14 years	26	311	81	–	5180	1520	–	23
	Boys, 0–18 years	50	344	119	164–574◊	5730	1980	2730–9570◊	198
	Girls, 0–17 years	50	327	104	123–502◊	5450	1730	2050–8370◊	198
	Men	80	111	33.5	62.1–176◊	1850	558	1035–2930◊	198
	Women	105	100	32.9	55.6–155◊	1670	548	927–2580◊	198
	Colorimetric (4-nitrophenyl phosphate), optimized[398], 37 °C:								
	Cord blood	116	–	–	108–420	–	–	1800–7000	399

* Values for persons over 30; upper limit of normal for young adults: 200 U/L. ◊ 90% range.

Table 7 *Reference intervals for alkaline phosphatase activity in serum of children measured at 30 °C*[413]

Age	Males Number	P_5 U/L	P_{95} U/L	Females Number	P_5 U/L	P_{95} U/L
5–6 years	67	146	291	68	155	345
7–8 years	68	149	289	80	160	358
9–10 years	70	145	389	66	165	355
11–12 years	76	159	355	79	121	372
13 years	75	162	497	46	80	334
14 years				31	69	203
15–16 years	67	92	365	58	57	140
17–20 years	92	70	174	90	40	97

Method: colorimetric (4-nitrophenyl phosphate as substrate)[414].

hate; the enzyme is about equally as effective against α-naphthyl phosphate and phenyl phosphate, and much less effective against phenolphthalein monophosphate[201]. In interpreting serum activities, it should be borne in mind that conventional methods are not comparable with optimized methods[202,423]. The distribution of activity values in the serum is skewed to the right[423].

Serum levels in the newborn are slightly higher than in adults[10,203], and are considerably elevated during childhood[22,23,98,203]; they are highest at the beginning of the 1st year of life[10,201,203] and in 10- to 12-year-old girls and 12- to 15-year-old boys, respectively[201,204,205] (Fig. 1, page 171; Table 7). From about the 50th year onward, the values tend to be higher than in young adults[22,206,207]; however, in a study of enzyme activities in 100-year-old subjects, alkaline phosphatase was within the normal range for younger persons[366]. The serum of normal adults contains liver-cell phosphatase and bone phosphatase as the principal fractions, but also intestinal phosphatase, especially in Lewis-positive AB0 secretors and after meals[208–210]. During childhood, the bone enzyme accounts for 90% of the activity[208]; the liver enzyme appears to be responsible for a rise of activity in later years[209,424]. The activity increases gradually during pregnancy. The rise of activity is due to the placental isoenzyme and can be determined on the basis of the heat-stability of that isoenzyme[211] or by immunological methods[212,213] (Fig. 3, page 171).

The most important diagnostic use of alkaline phosphatase is its determination in cases of liver[45,214] and bone disease[214,215]. When alkaline phosphatase activity is high, normal values for glutamate dehydrogenase or γ-glutamyltransferase suggest bone disease, while high levels for glutamate dehydrogenase, γ-glutamyltransferase and 5′-nucleotidase indicate liver disease. The quality of the diagnosis can be improved by determination of organ-specific enzyme fractions[200].

High activities in the serum are found in intra- and extrahepatic cholestasis; in these cases, an isoenzyme specific to the bile duct and normally not occurring in the serum may be found [216–218]. High activities are also found in Paget's disease, bone tumors, and bone metastases with intensified osteoblastic activity, in rickets, and also, though less pronounced, in osteomalacia of the elderly. Many tumors produce an oncofetal isoenzyme similar to the placental variant of alkaline phosphatase[200,219] (Regan enzyme).

Low activities for alkaline phosphatase are found in hypophosphatasia[215].

↓ See text below — Normal values (reference intervals) in plasma or serum of adults, unless otherwise stated

EC number **Recommended name** (Other names) Abbreviation	Method (substrate in brackets)	Number	µmol min⁻¹ L⁻¹ (U/L) Mean	s	95% range (extreme range in brackets)	nmol s⁻¹ L⁻¹ (nkat/L) Mean	s	95% range (extreme range in brackets)	Reference
3.1.3.2 ↓**Acid phosphatase** .... ACP, AcP	Colorimetric[221] (α-naphthyl phosphate), 37 °C:								
	Men	36	1.60	0.43	–	26.7	7.1	–	222
	Colorimetric (phenyl phosphate), 37 °C								
	Total ACP:								
	Men	25	4.5	1.4	(2.6–8.3)	75	23	(43–140)	223
	Women	25	4.0	1.4	(1.4–7.7)	67	23	(23–130)	223
	Tartrate-labile ACP:								
	Men	25	0.9	0.6	(0.2–2.2)	15	10	(3–37)	223
	Women	25	1.1	0.6	(0.2–2.9)	18	10	(3–48)	223
	Colorimetric (thymolphthalein monophosphate), 37 °C:								
	'Prostate ACP', men	85	0.28	0.09	0.13–0.56	4.7	1.5	2.2–9.3	224
	Colorimetric (4-nitrophenyl phosphate), 37 °C:								
	Children	13	22.4	10.5	–	373	175	–	225
	Adults	22	6.02	1.69	–	100	28.2	–	225
	Colorimetric (α-naphthyl phosphate), 37 °C:								
	Children	4	7.4	1.6	–	123	27	–	225
	Adults	22	2.14	0.66	–	35.7	11.0	–	225
	Colorimetric (α-naphthyl phosphate), 37 °C								
	Formaldehyde-stable ACP:								
	Men	82	–	–	0.8–3.9	–	–	13–65	425

Table 8 *Age-dependence of acid phosphatase activity in serum measured at 37 °C*[220]

Subjects	Age	Number	Total ACP Mean	Total ACP s	Tartrate-resistant ACP Mean	Tartrate-resistant ACP s
			U/L			
Males........	Newborn to 12 years	31	6.1	1.5	5.6	1.5
	13–18 years	7	2.9	0.7	2.3	0.8
	> 18 years	28	1.6	0.5	1.1	0.4
Females	Newborn to 12 years	18	5.9	1.8	5.3	1.7
	13–18 years	22	2.1	1.4	1.7	1.4
	> 18 years	23	1.6	0.5	1.1	0.4

Method: fluorimetry (α-naphthyl phosphate as substrate).

Table 9
Prostate-specific acid phosphatase concentration in serum of men

Age	Number	Unit	Upper limit of normal	Method	Year	Reference
> 40 years	–	µg/L	2.2	RIA	1982	426
> 40 years	–	µg/L	2.0	ELISA	1982	426
> 40 years	42	µg/L	2.2	RIA	1982	427
30–85 years	151	U/L	0.65	IEA	1982	428
Men	10	µg/L	2.0	IEA*	1983	429

* With monoclonal antibody.
RIA: radioimmunoassay; ELISA: enzyme-linked immunosorbent assay; IEA: immunoenzymatic assay.

3.1.3.2 *Acid phosphatase.* Its activity in the serum is derived from several sources (erythrocytes, leukocytes, platelets, prostate, bones)[21,227,228]. The findings in prostate carcinoma are of some diagnostic importance; the rise of activity, however, in the majority of cases does not occur until bone metastases have formed. The isoenzymes originating in the prostate and in platelets are inhibited by L-tartrate, while the erythrocytic isoenzyme is inhibited by formaldehyde. Of the various substrates, thymolphthalein monophosphate is most probably specific for the prostate enzyme[229]. However, no methodological modification improves the quality of early diagnosis of prostate carcinoma any more than slightly[230]. Acid phosphatase can be separated into several fractions by different separation procedures[228,231]. One of these fractions is characteristic for the prostatic isoenzyme[226,231], while another, which migrates rapidly in electrophoresis and is tartrate-resistant, is characteristic for isoenzymes from the spleen and/or the osteoclasts[231,232]. This latter enzyme fraction is responsible for the elevated activity of acid phosphatase in the serum of children (Fig. 2, page 171; Table 8)[225]; it reaches high levels in Gaucher's disease[231,233] and in some bone metastases[231]. Improved detection of prostatic disease has been claimed to be possible by determination of the prostate isoenzyme with special immunological techniques[234]. However, more extensive studies challenge the assumption. For upper limits of normal see Table 9. According to results obtained with such a method, the prostate isoenzyme is responsible for 10–25% of total activity in normal serum[229].

3.1.3.5 *5′-Nucleotidase.* This enzyme is found in many tissues including the liver and bones[21,240]. In contrast to alkaline phosphatase, the activity of 5′-nucleotidase in the serum is not elevated during childhood[241] or pregnancy[242]. Like alkaline phosphatase activity, that of 5′-nucleotidase can rise in all liver diseases, the highest values being found in intra- and extrahepatic cholestasis[45,243]. In contrast to alkaline phosphatase, no rise of activity, or at most only a slight one, is observed in bone disease[45,99]. Determination of this enzyme is helpful in the differentiation between liver and bone disease, and in the diagnosis of liver disease in childhood and pregnancy[45].

↑↓ See text on previous page and below — Normal values (reference intervals) in plasma or serum of adults, unless otherwise stated

EC number **Recommended name** (Other names) Abbreviation	Method (substrate in brackets)	Number	μmol min^{-1} L^{-1} (U/L)			nmol s^{-1} L^{-1} (nkat/L)			Reference
			Mean	s	95% range (extreme range in brackets)	Mean	s	95% range (extreme range in brackets)	
3.1.3.5 ↑**5′-Nucleotidase**	Colorimetric[235], 37 °C	92	–	–	3.5–11.0	–	–	58–183	99
	Colorimetric[236], 37 °C: Children, 2–24 weeks	24	4.0	2.4	–	67	40	–	237
	UV test, 37 °C	65	5.0	1.35	–	83	22.5	–	238
	UV test, optimized, 37 °C	35	–	–	2.1–10.6	–	–	35–177	239
	Colorimetric, 37 °C: Adults, 18–60 years	309	–	–	2.9–8.7	–	–	48–145	430
3.1.3.9 ↓**Glucose-6-phosphatase**	Colorimetric, 37 °C	–	8	–	–	130	–	–	224
3.1.6.1 ↓**Arylsulfatase** (Sulfatase)	Fluorimetric (4-methylumbelliferone sulfate), 37 °C	56	0.052	0.014	–	0.87	0.23	–	246
	Colorimetric (4-nitrocatechol sulfate), 37 °C	26	0.035	0.008	–	0.58	0.13	–	247
3.1.21.1 **Deoxyribonuclease I** DNase I	Colorimetric, 37 °C	–	0.65	–	(0–1.8)	11	–	(0–30)	245
3.1.22.1 **Deoxyribonuclease II** DNase II	Colorimetric, 37 °C	–	0.56	–	(0–1.2)	9.3	–	(0–20)	245
3.1.27.5 ↓**Ribonuclease (pancreatic)** RNase I	UV test [poly(C)], pH 6.5, 37 °C: Males and females, 11–20 years	15	9.48	3.07	–	158	51	–	431
	Males and females, 81–90 years	23	34.7	5.88	–	578	98	–	431
3.2.1.1 ↓**α-Amylase**	Amyloclastic (amylose)[250], modified, 37 °C	145	–	–	60–300	–	–	1000–5000	168
	Chromogenic (cross-linked and colored starch), 37 °C: Male blood donors	80	–	–	88–282	–	–	1470–4700	251
	Female blood donors	34	–	–	86–226	–	–	1430–3770	251
	Saccharogenic (starch), 37 °C	50	62	–	24–163	1030	–	400–2720	252
	Saccharogenic (starch), 37 °C	–	–	–	90–270	–	–	1500–4500	253
	Saccharogenic (maltoheptaose), 25 °C	251	–	–	30–100	–	–	500–1670	254
	Saccharogenic (maltoheptaose), 30 °C	251	–	–	40–130	–	–	670–2170	254

3.1.3.9 *Glucose-6-phosphatase.* On account of the rise it causes in the activity of nonspecific phosphatases, hemolysis interferes with the determination. The elevated activity in the serum observed in acute hepatitis and in chronic liver diseases[244] is of no diagnostic value because of the instability of the enzyme.

3.1.6.1 *Arylsulfatase.* This enzyme occurs in lysosomes in 2 forms (A and B); another form (C) is found in microsomes[248]. The ratio of activities A to B in the serum is about 5 : 1. The activity of A increases, while that of B decreases during pregnancy. There is no B activity in homozygotes for the Maroteaux-Lamy syndrome; in colorectal carcinoma it is elevated[391].

3.1.27.5 *Ribonuclease (pancreatic).* This enzyme occurs in a series of isoenzymes differing on the basis of charge[432]. Activity in the serum increases with age[431], and slightly during pregnancy[433]. Increased levels have been observed in patients with renal failure, leukemia and pancreatic disorders, but the enzyme does not seem to be a useful marker for pancreatic carcinoma[434].

The mass concentration of the enzyme in the serum, determined by radioimmunoassay, is 99.4 μg/L (s 66.3 μg/L)[435].

3.2.1.1 *α-Amylase.* The principal sources of serum amylase are the pancreas and the salivary glands, although this enzyme is also detectable in other organs, such as lungs, muscles, adipose tissue,

Table 10 *Activities of total amylase and amylase isoenzymes in serum measured at 37 °C*

Subjects	Age	Number	Total amylase	S-type amylase	P-type amylase	Reference
			95% range			
			U/L			
Children	0.06–0.8 years	16	–	0–45◊	0–64◊	436
	0.9–1.9 years	17	–	7–151◊	11–124◊	436
	2–4.9 years	32	–	1–140◊	13–89◊	436
	5–7.9 years	42	–	3–196◊	22–169◊	436
	8–13 years	59	–	5–166◊	31–151◊	436
Men		72	56–270*	9–172◊	37–162◊	437
Women		69	75–277*	9–196◊	52–175◊	437
Men		82	110–309†	24–186◊	52–213◊	478
Women		87	121–365†	31–276◊	36–260◊	478

* Chromogenic technique.
† α-4-Nitrophenylmaltoheptaosid as substrate.
◊ Inhibition of the S-type isoenzyme by wheat protein inhibitor.

↓See text below and on next page	Normal values (reference intervals) in plasma or serum of adults, unless otherwise stated									
EC number **Recommended name** (Other names) Abbreviation	Method (substrate in brackets)	Number	μmol min^{-1} L^{-1} (U/L)			nmol s^{-1} L^{-1} (nkat/L)			Reference
			Mean	*s*	95% range (extreme range in brackets)	Mean	*s*	95% range (extreme range in brackets)	
3.2.1.3 **Exo-1,4-α-D-glucosidase**.... (Glucoamylase, γ-amylase)	Saccharogenic, after inactivation of α-amylase[384] (starch), 37 °C.........	32	32	19	–	533	317	–	385
3.2.1.17 ↓**Lysozyme**.................. (Muramidase)	....	...	...	...	...	...	...	...	...
3.2.1.20 α-D-**Glucosidase**	Fluorimetric (4-methylumbelliferyl-α-D-glucoside), 37 °C	33	0.195	0.048	(0.12–0.312)	3.25	0.80	(2.0–5.20)	267
3.2.1.22 ↓α-D-**Galactosidase**	Fluorimetric (4-methylumbelliferyl-α-D-galactoside), 37 °C..............	38	0.308	0.113	(0.175–0.663)	5.13	1.88	(2.92–11.1)	267
3.2.1.23 ↓β-D-**Galactosidase**	Fluorimetric (4-methylumbelliferyl-β-D-galactoside), 37 °C..............	45	0.398	0.227	(0.12–1.12)	6.63	3.78	(2.0–18.7)	267

and small intestine[21,255,256]. It can be separated into several isoenzymes by different separation procedures; some of the isoenzymes may be ascribed to the pancreas (P type) and others to the salivary glands (S type)[255,257] (Table 10). The amylase activity in the serum of the newborn is low (P type activity 32%, S type activity 3% of the values of adults[479]), but by the second year of life it reaches adult levels[10,258]. Increased activities (chiefly due to the S-type isoenzyme) have been found in Asians and West Indians[438].

Determination of activities in serum and urine is of crucial significance for the diagnosis of acute pancreatitis or an acute flare-up in chronic pancreatitis; on the other hand, determination of serum levels during remissions of chronic pancreatitis and in pancreatic tumors is of no diagnostic value[176,255]. Determinations in the serum after provocation are a complement to the lipase determination[179,181], although they do not improve reliability. Elevated activities are also found in diseases of the salivary glands (e.g. mumps), in ectopic amylase production by a tumor, and as a consequence of secondary reactions of the pancreas in many acute illnesses of the abdomen and, less often, of the thorax[255,256]. A rise of activity in the serum without increased elimination with the urine is observed in renal insufficiency and in macroamylasemia. In macroamylasemia, the high-molecular-mass complexes of amylase with IgA or IgG cannot pass through the glomerular filter[255,259]. In defective enzyme formation in the pancreas, the P isoenzyme is sometimes lacking in the serum[260].

Table 11 *Lysozyme concentration in serum*

Subjects	Number	Mean	95% range or *s*	Method	Year	Reference
		mg/L				
Adults (blood donors)	60	6.9	4–11	Bacteriolytic	1974	354
Adults	20	4.6	*s* 0.8	RIA........	1978	353
Men	30	8.8	*s* 1.6	EID........	1979	439
Women.............	30	6.6	*s* 2.2	EID........	1979	439
Newborn	43	2.65	*s* 0.82	Bacteriolytic	1980	440
Adults, <35 years ...	18	1.47	*s* 0.4	RIA........	1981	441

RIA: radioimmunoassay; EID: electroimmunodiffusion.

3.2.1.17 *Lysozyme.* This enzyme is a cationic protein with a known amino-acid sequence and a relative molecular mass of 14500[351,352]. It is found in many tissues, and especially in the blood cells. Activity in the serum is normally dependent on the turnover of neutrophilic granulocytes and monocytes. (For normal values of the mass concentration see Table 11.) Elevated serum levels are found in myeloid, myelomonocytic and monocytic leukemias, in reactive neutrophilia, in polycythemia vera, and in Crohn's disease; diminished levels are found in stem-cell lymphatic leukemias, in panmyelopathies, and in lymphosarcomatosis[351,352,355–358]. Elevated levels have also been observed in patients with diabetes mellitus and chronic liver diseases[356]. Despite statistically significant differences between patient groups, lysozyme determination in the serum is of no use either for differential diagnosis or for assessing the level of activity of chronic inflammatory intestinal diseases[359].

Table 12 *Age-dependence of lysosomal glycohydrolase activities in serum measured at 37 °C*[264]

Subjects	Age	Number	β-D-Galactosidase		α-D-Mannosidase		β-N-Acetyl-D-glucosaminidase		β-D-Glucuronidase		α-L-Fucosidase	
			Mean	*s*	Mean	*s*	Mean	*s*	Mean	*s*	Mean	*s*
			U/L									
Boys........................	Cord blood	113	0.57	0.34	1.20	0.59	23.0	6.1	3.25	1.07	11.5	5.8
Girls........................	Cord blood	118	0.48	0.29	1.10	0.62	21.1	5.2	3.13	1.12	12.7	6.0
Boys........................	10–14 years	50	0.14	0.04	0.20	0.11	8.1	1.5	0.95	0.28	3.13	1.85
Girls........................	10–14 years	48	0.16	0.06	0.22	0.07	8.0	1.4	1.03	0.32	3.55	1.57
Men	25–49 years	232	0.25	0.12	0.32	0.17	14.5	3.3	1.93	0.80	8.03	4.10
Women.....................	25–49 years	110	0.26	0.13	0.29	0.14	12.4	2.4	1.25	0.42	7.08	3.43

Fluorimetric method (substrates: 4-methylumbelliferyl-β-D-galactoside, 4-methylumbelliferyl-α-D-mannoside, 4-methylumbelliferyl-β-N-acetyl-D-glucosaminide, 4-methylumbelliferyl-β-D-glucuronide, 4-methylumbelliferyl-α-L-fucoside, respectively).

↓ See text below — Normal values (reference intervals) in plasma or serum of adults, unless otherwise stated

EC number **Recommended name** (Other names) Abbreviation	Method (substrate in brackets)	Number	µmol min⁻¹ L⁻¹ (U/L) Mean	s	95% range (extreme range in brackets)	nmol s⁻¹ L⁻¹ (nkat/L) Mean	s	95% range (extreme range in brackets)	Reference
3.2.1.24 ↓ **α-D-Mannosidase**	Fluorimetric (4-methylumbelliferyl-α-D-mannoside), 37 °C	46	3.16	1.11	(1.54–5.50)	52.7	18.5	(25.7–91.7)	262
	Fluorimetric (4-methylumbelliferyl-α-D-mannoside), pH 5.2, 37 °C	45	2.48	0.37	(1.52–3.63)	41.3	6.2	(25.3–60.5)	267
	Fluorimetric (4-methylumbelliferyl-α-D-mannoside), pH 4.0, 37 °C	30	0.57	0.10	(0.47–0.73)	9.5	1.7	(7.8–12.2)	267
3.2.1.30 ↓ **β-N-Acetyl-D-glucosaminidase** (Hexosaminidase) β-NAG	Colorimetric (4-nitrophenyl-N-acetyl-β-D-glucosaminide), 37 °C	26	14.3	2.1	–	238	35	–	247
	Colorimetric (4-nitrophenyl-N-acetyl-β-D-glucosaminide), 37 °C	87	21	5.4	10–32	350	90	170–530	443
	Fluorimetric (4-methylumbelliferyl-N-acetyl-β-D-glucosaminide), 37 °C	41	13.7	3.9	(6.5–23.3)	228	65	(108–388)	267
3.2.1.31 ↓ **β-D-Glucuronidase** β-Gc	Colorimetric (4-nitrophenyl-β-D-glucuronate), 25 °C:								
	Men	52	–	–	0.35–1.32	–	–	5.8–22.0	266
	Women	53	–	–	0.22–0.99	–	–	3.7–16.5	266
	Colorimetric (phenolphthalein-β-D-glucuronate), 37 °C	26	0.92	0.25	–	15.3	4.2	–	247
	Fluorimetric (4-methylumbelliferyl-β-D-glucuronide), 37 °C	42	0.56	0.34	(0.16–1.03)	9.3	5.7	(2.7–17.2)	267
3.2.1.50 ↓ **α-N-Acetyl-D-glucosaminidase**	Colorimetric (4-nitrophenyl-N-acetyl-α-D-glucosaminide), 37 °C	40	0.44	0.15	–	7.3	2.5	–	270
	Colorimetric (phenyl-α-D-glucosaminide), 37 °C	142	0.70	0.21	–	11.7	3.5	–	270
	Colorimetric (UDP-N-acetylglucosamine), 37 °C	172	0.88	0.24	–	14.7	4.0	–	270
	Colorimetric (4-nitrophenyl-N-acetyl-α-D-glucosaminide), 37 °C	32	0.33	0.07	(0.16–0.48)	5.5	1.2	(2.7–8.0)	267

3.2.1.22 α-D-*Galactosidase*. Activity in the serum is for the most part lacking in homozygotes for Fabry's disease. Activity is subnormal in heterozygotes[261].

3.2.1.23 *β*-D-*Galactosidase*. Activity in the serum is elevated in early childhood[264,272] (Table 12). In pregnant women, the β-D-galactosidase activity at the end of pregnancy rises up to 3 times the normal level[444].

3.2.1.24 α-D-*Mannosidase*. This enzyme occurs in at least 2 forms in the serum[263]. For the age-dependence of activity see Table 12. In mannosidosis, acid α-D-mannosidase from lysosomes is lacking. Activity in the serum is increased in patients with I-cell disease[397].

3.2.1.30 *β-N-Acetyl*-D-*glucosaminidase*. The serum contains several forms of β-NAG. These can be separated into the heat-labile form, β-NAG A, and several heat-stable enzymes. Separation in chromatographic systems reveals the heat-stable forms, including β-NAG B, and a series of enzymes with intermediate mobility which have been labeled β-NAG I. Activity in the serum is determined primarily by the activity of β-NAG A (Table 13). In Blacks, the activity in the serum is higher than in Whites[268]. Low levels have been found in adolescence[264,272] (Table 12). In pregnant women, the β-NAG activity at the end of pregnancy rises up to 3 times the normal level[444], the rise being mostly due to an increase in β-NAG I[444]. An increase of activity in the serum occurs in polymyositis, in systemic lupus erythematosus[386], in chronic liver diseases[269,443], and in diabetes mellitus[269]. In homozygotes for Tay-Sachs disease, there is no isoenzyme A activity in the serum. In homozygotes for Sandhoff's disease, neither isoenzyme A nor isoenzyme B activity is found in the serum.

Table 13 *β-N-Acetyl*-D-*glucosaminidase isoenzyme activities in serum measured at 37 °C*

Subjects	Number	Isoenzyme A Mean	s	Isoenzyme I Mean	s	Isoenzyme B Mean	s	Reference
		U/L						
Adults	21	8.73	1.14	1.82	0.7	0.37	0.17	265
		Activity fraction (relative to total activity) as percent						
Nonpregnant women	5	65.7	2.2	16.7	3.8	17.5	4.8	442
Pregnancy, 10–20 weeks	6	44.5	11.2	39.8	8.7	14.9	3.2	442

Separation of isoenzymes by DEAE-cellulose chromatography.

3.2.1.31 *β*-D-*Glucuronidase*. Slight hemolysis does not interfere with the determination. Activity in the serum is elevated in early childhood[264] (Table 12) and in advanced age[272]. In pregnant women, the β-D-glucuronidase activity at the end of pregnancy rises up to 4 times the normal level[444]. Elevated activities can be found in hepatic cirrhosis[269].

3.2.1.50 α-*N-Acetyl*-D-*glucosaminidase*. In homozygotes for Sanfilippo B disease, activity in the serum is virtually lacking, while in heterozygotes it is about ⅓ the normal level[270].

↓ See text on next page — Normal values (reference intervals) in plasma or serum of adults, unless otherwise stated

EC number **Recommended name** (Other names) Abbreviation	Method (substrate in brackets)	Number	μmol min⁻¹ L⁻¹ (U/L) Mean	s	95% range (extreme range in brackets)	nmol s⁻¹ L⁻¹ (nkat/L) Mean	s	95% range (extreme range in brackets)	Reference
3.2.1.51 ↓ **α-L-Fucosidase**	Colorimetric (4-nitrophenyl-α-L-fucoside), 37 °C	10	8.14	2.55	(4.69–11.0)	136	43	(78–183)	271
	Fluorimetric (4-methylumbelliferyl-α-L-fucoside), 37 °C	41	6.38	2.97	–	106	50	–	350
	Colorimetric (4-nitrophenyl-α-L-fucoside), 37 °C	38	4.17	1.43	(1.5–6.5)	70	24	(25–108)	267
3.4.11.1 ↓ **Aminopeptidase (cytosol)** (Leucine aminopeptidase) LAP	Colorimetric (L-leucylglycine), 37 °C	82	16.4	0.67	–	273	11	–	273
	Titrimetric (L-leucinamide), 37 °C: Children	11	105	113	–	1750	1880	–	275
	Adults	–	–	–	(80–130)	–	–	(1300–2170)	274
	Fluorimetric[276] (L-leucyl-β-naphthylamide), 37 °C	32	–	–	20–50	–	–	330–830	277
3.4.11.2 ↓ **Aminopeptidase (microsomal)** (Amino-acid arylamidase, leucine arylamidase, nitroanilidase) LAP, 'LAP', AAP	Colorimetric (L-leucine-4-nitroanilide), 25 °C: Men	50	–	–	9.8–20.5	–	–	163–342	278
	Women	51	–	–	11.9–22.9	–	–	198–382	278
	Colorimetric (L-leucine-4-nitroanilide), 25 °C: Men	25	16.9	3.11	–	282	52	–	279
	Colorimetric (L-leucine-4-nitroanilide), optimized[389], 25 °C	–	–	–	5–35	–	–	183–583	390
	Colorimetric (L-phenylalanine-4-nitroanilide), 25 °C: Men	25	5.3	2.05	–	88	34	–	279
	Colorimetric (L-alanine-4-nitroanilide), 25 °C: Men	25	18.9	3.40	–	315	57	–	279
	Colorimetric (L-alanine-4-nitroanilide), optimized, 25 °C	100	–	–	15–45	–	–	250–750	280
3.4.11.3 ↓ **Cystyl aminopeptidase** (Oxytocinase)	Colorimetric (S-benzyl-L-cysteine -4-nitroanilide), 25 °C: Men	27	2.8	1.3	–	47	22	–	284
	Women	21	3.9	1.2	–	65	20	–	284
	Colorimetric (S-benzyl-L-cysteine-4-nitroanilide), 25 °C: Men	25	1.25	0.50	–	20.8	8.3	–	279
	Fluorimetric (S-benzyl-L-cysteinyl-4-methylcoumarinylamide), 37 °C: Pregnancy, 1st trimester	48	3.08	1.57	–	51	26	–	285
	Pregnancy, 2nd trimester	40	10.3	3.92	–	171	65	–	285
	Pregnancy, 3rd trimester	46	29.6	5.52	–	493	92	–	285
3.4.11.4 **Tripeptide aminopeptidase** (Aminotripeptidase)	Colorimetric (glycylglycylglycine), 37 °C	39	64.7	4.2	–	1080	70	–	273
3.4.11.5 **Proline iminopeptidase**	Colorimetric[297], modified, 25 °C: Children, < 1 year	12	1.11	0.23	(0.65–1.43)	18.5	3.8	(11–24)	298
	Children, 2–6 years	15	0.77	0.15	(0.55–1.13)	12.8	2.5	(9–18)	298
	Adults	44	0.53	0.10	(0.33–0.72)	8.8	1.7	(5.5–12)	298
3.4.13.3 ↓ **Aminoacyl-histidine dipeptidase** (Carnosinase)	Fluorimetric (carnosine), 37 °C	–	–	–	(42–117)	–	–	(700–1950)	445
3.4.13.11 **Dipeptidase** (Glycylglycine dipeptidase)	Titrimetric, 37 °C: Children	–	160	120	–	2670	2000	–	289
	Adults	24	240	130	–	4000	2170	–	288

↓ See text below	Normal values (reference intervals) in plasma or serum of adults, unless otherwise stated								
EC number **Recommended name** (Other names) Abbreviation	Method (substrate in brackets)	Number	µmol min⁻¹ L⁻¹ (U/L) Mean	s	95% range (extreme range in brackets)	nmol s⁻¹ L⁻¹ (nkat/L) Mean	s	95% range (extreme range in brackets)	Reference
3.4.14.1 ↓**Dipeptidyl peptidase I** (Glycylproline dipeptidyl-aminopeptidase, glycyl-prolyl-4-nitroanilidase)	Colorimetric[448] (glycyl-L-proline 4-nitroanilide tosylate), 37 °C:								
	Children, 2–9 years	10	126	22	(100–178)	2100	367	(1670–2970)	449
	Adults, 15–65 years	1117	70.1	11.4	(47.1–93.1)	1170	190	(785–1550)	449
	Colorimetric[448] (glycyl-L-proline 4-nitroanilide tosylate), 37 °C	40	37.8	8.4	–	630	140	–	450
3.4.15.1 ↓**Dipeptidyl carboxypeptidase** (Angiotensin converting enzyme, kinase II) ACE	Fluorimetric (hippuryl-L-histidyl-L-leucine), 37 °C	58	32.2	9.9	–	537	165	–	451
	Fluorimetric (4-nitrobenzyloxycarbonylglycyl-L-tryptophylglycine), 37 °C	–	16.5	5.0	–	275	83	–	452
	Colorimetric (hippuryl-L-histidyl-L-leucine), 37 °C:								
	Children, 4–19 years	36	51.8	19.3	–	863	322	–	453
	Men, 21–82 years	117	46.5	15.3	22–82	775	255	336–1370	453
	Women, 20–92 years	112	45.5	10.7	25–69	758	178	417–1150	453
	Fluorimetric (hippuryl-L-histidyl-L-leucine), 37 °C:								
	Children, < 15 years	164	46.7	11.9	–	778	198	–	454
	Adults, > 18 years	32	32.1	8.5	–	535	142	–	454
	Colorimetric (hippuryl-L-histidyl-L-leucine), 37 °C:								
	Men, 21–59 years	85	30.2	7.4	–	503	123	–	455
	Women, 21–70 years	50	26.2	6.4	–	437	107	–	455
3.4.17.1 **Carboxypeptidase A** (Carboxypolypeptidase)	Fluorimetric (N-carbobenzoxy-glycyl-L-phenylalanine), 37 °C:	15	0.74	0.465	–	12.3	7.8	–	287
3.4.21.4 ↓**Trypsin**	...	...	...	...	...	...	...	...	...

3.2.1.51 *α-L-Fucosidase.* Activity is high in cord blood[264]; then, until the 20th year of life, in the serum it is lowered[264,272] (Table 12, page 190). An enzyme variant with low activity occurs in the serum of some normal persons[350]. There is no discernible α-L-fucosidase activity in fucosidosis.

3.4.11.1, 3.4.11.2 *Aminopeptidase (cytosol), (microsomal).* Both enzymes are referred to as 'leucine aminopeptidase' in the medical literature. Slight hemolysis does not interfere with the determination. Sex-related differences of activity in the serum found in some studies are of no diagnostic importance[23,281]. The levels in children do not differ from those found in adults[10,23]. A rise of activity in the serum occurs during the second half of pregnancy (to 5 to 8 times the initial levels by the end of pregnancy)[112,282], but this is due to the elevated cystyl aminopeptidase activity (3.4.11.3)[392]. The rises of activity are considerable in extrahepatic and intrahepatic cholestasis, and are less marked in inflammatory liver diseases, and in acute pancreatitis[45,114,283]. The levels are normal in carcinoma of the head of the pancreas without occlusion of the common bile duct and without liver metastases. Activity is usually normal in bone diseases[112,283]. Today, however, determination of γ-glutamyltransferase is preferred for differential diagnosis[45].

3.4.11.3 *Cystyl aminopeptidase.* During pregnancy, the activity in the serum rises to several times the normal value[282,284–286]. According to one study[284], this rise describes an exponential curve with the equation $\log y = 0.2104 + 0.0497x$ (y: U/L; x: week of pregnancy).

3.4.13.3 *Aminoacyl-histidine dipeptidase.* The enzyme is not detectable in cord blood[445]. Activity in the serum rises gradually during the first 16 years of life[446]. A low level of activity has been reported in some persons with the phenotype characterized by carnosinuria[446]. Absence of activity has been observed in patients with urea cycle defects[447].

3.4.14.1 *Dipeptidyl peptidase I.* Activity in the serum is increased in hepatobiliary diseases[448,450].

3.4.15.1 *Dipeptidyl carboxypeptidase.* The enzyme is mainly present on the surface of the capillary endothelial cells of the lung. It converts angiotensin I to angiotensin II and inactivates bradykinin. Activity in the serum of children is increased[453,454]. It does not change during pregnancy[456]. Elevated levels have been found in sarcoidosis[454,457,459], in Gaucher's disease[451,458], in acute hepatitis and liver cirrhosis[460,461], in leprosy[462], in histoplasmosis[463], in silicosis and asbestosis[464], in hyperthyroidism[455], and in diabetic retinopathy[465]. In sarcoidosis, activity in the serum reflects the granulomatous activity[459]. Activity is decreased in various types of chronic lung disease[457].

The mass concentration of the enzyme in normal plasma, determined by radioimmunoassay, is 400 µg/L (s 131 µg/L)[466].

3.4.21.4 *Trypsin.* The mass concentration of immunoreactive trypsin in the serum, which includes cathodic trypsin and trypsinogen, can be determined by radioimmunoassay (Table 14). However, no active trypsin is found in the serum[290], as the trypsin-inhibitor capacity in 1 mL serum is sufficient to inhibit 0.4–1.9 mg trypsin[291]. In adults, the concentration of immunoreactive trypsin in the serum increases with age[468,469]. It is increased in acute pancreatitis, but decreased in chronic pancreatitis[295,470]. In newborns and infants with cystic fibrosis, the level of immunoreactive trypsin is increased during the 1st month of life[471]; but in later life, when pancreatic insufficiency is pronounced, low levels are characteristic[295].

↓ See text below — Normal values (reference intervals) in plasma or serum of adults, unless otherwise stated

EC number **Recommended name** (Other names) Abbreviation	Method (substrate in brackets)	Number	µmol min^{-1} L^{-1} (U/L) Mean	s	95% range (extreme range in brackets)	nmol s^{-1} L^{-1} (nkat/L) Mean	s	95% range (extreme range in brackets)	Reference
3.4.21.8 **Kallikrein** (Kininogenin)	Colorimetric [α-N-(4-toluolsulfonyl)-L-arginine, methyl ester], 37 °C:								
	Children	20	0.69	0.13	(0.51–0.92)	11.5	2.2	(8.5–15.3)	292
	Adults	15	0.72	0.30	(0.34–1.23)	12.0	5.0	(5.7–20.5)	292
3.4.99.19 ↓ **Renin**	...		...	...	...	...	...	...	...
3.5.1.12 **Biotinidase**	Radioassay, 37 °C	8	6.0	0.8	–	100	13	–	479
3.5.1.14 **Aminoacylase**	Colorimetric (trifluoroacetyl-L-methionine), optimized, 25 °C	33	–	–	(0–21)	–	–	(0–350)	345
	Colorimetric (chloroacetyl-L-methionine), optimized, 25 °C	33	–	–	(0–27)	–	–	(0–450)	345
3.5.3.1 ↓ **Arginase**	Isotope method, 37 °C	50	6.5	3.2	–	108	53	–	299
	Colorimetric, 37 °C	66	4.0	1.8	–	67	30	–	300
3.5.4.3 ↓ **Guanine deaminase** (Guanase)	UV test[304], 37 °C	–	–	–	0–3	–	–	0–50	305
	Colorimetric, 37 °C	102	0.70	–	≤3	12	–	≤50	306
	UV test, 37 °C	500	–	–	≤2.5	–	–	≤42	307
	UV test[308], 37 °C	>100	2.1	2.0	(0–7.0)	35	33	(0–120)	309
	UV test, 30 °C	25	0.44	0.29	–	7.3	4.8	–	472

Table 14 *Immunoreactive trypsin in serum*

Subjects	Origin	Number	Mean (µg/L)	s or 95% range (µg/L)	Year	Reference
Adults, 21–56 years	England	76	273	s 67	1977	293
Adults	Switzerland	144	150	s 77	1978	294
Adults	FRG	62	212	115–350	1979	295
Adults	England	46	273	117–637	1981	296
Children:						
Cord blood	Switzerland	18	394	s 173	1981	467
1–4 days	Switzerland	7	380	s 180	1981	467
5 days	Switzerland	21	312	s 100	1981	467
6 days	Switzerland	36	317	s 165	1981	467
7 days	Switzerland	9	336	s 161	1981	467
15 days to 6 months	Switzerland	6	79	s 19	1981	467
6 months to 18 years	Switzerland	70	144	s 93	1981	467
Adults:						
17–29 years	Switzerland	21	210	s 81	1982	468
30–59 years	Switzerland	40	310	s 119	1982	468
60–84 years	Switzerland	63	470	s 197	1982	468

Method: radioimmunoassay.

Table 15
Reference interval of plasma renin activity (122 normotensive adults) measured at 37 °C[361]

	Angiotensin I (µg h^{-1} L^{-1})
Supine	0.5–5.0
Erect	0.9–10.7
Stimulated with furosemide	1.8–19.0

Table 16
Plasma renin activity in supine position (free intake of sodium) measured at 37 °C[362]

Subjects	Number	Angiotensin I Mean (µg h^{-1} L^{-1})	$s_{\bar{x}}$ (µg h^{-1} L^{-1})
Men, 21–37 years	14	1.26	0.14
Men, 45–55 years	470	0.96	0.16
Women, before ovulation	37	0.74	0.08
Women, after ovulation	34	1.18	0.13

3.4.99.19 *Renin.* This enzyme is formed in the juxtaglomerular apparatus of the kidneys and released into the plasma, where it is involved in the release of angiotensin. Renin release is dependent on a number of factors, such as sodium intake, the activity of the sympathetic nervous system, age, and sex[360,361]. Renin determination is important for the differentiation of hypertensive diseases[363,364]. For normal values see Tables 15 and 16.

3.5.3.1 *Arginase.* By far the highest activity is found in the mitochondria of the liver, while lower activities are also found in other tissues, including erythrocytes (hemolysis interferes with the determination). Activity in the serum is elevated in acute and chronic lesions of the liver parenchyma; it is normal in obstructive jaundice[301]. A rise of activity has also been observed after myocardial infarction[303], in typhoid fever, and in severe secondary liver lesions[302].

3.5.4.3 *Guanine deaminase.* Hemolysis does not interfere with the determination. The activity is markedly elevated in the serum in acute virus hepatitis[308,473], and less clearly elevated in liver cirrhosis, hepatoma, and obstructive jaundice[309,473].

↓ See text below and on next page — Normal values (reference intervals) in plasma or serum of adults, unless otherwise stated

EC number **Recommended name** (Other names) Abbreviation	Method (substrate in brackets)	Number	μmol min⁻¹ L⁻¹ (U/L)			nmol s⁻¹ L⁻¹ (nkat/L)			Reference
			Mean	*s*	95% range (extreme range in brackets)	Mean	*s*	95% range (extreme range in brackets)	
3.5.4.4									
↓**Adenosine deaminase**	Colorimetric[310], 25 °C	70	2.6	0.54	(1.4–4.7)	43	9	(23–78)	311
	UV test, 37 °C	500	–	–	≤33	–	–	≤550	307
	Colorimetric[310], modified, 37 °C	>100	17.1	3.8	–	285	63	–	312
3.5.4.5									
Cytidine deaminase (Cytidine aminohydrolase)	Colorimetric (cytidine), 22 °C:								
	Men	30	0.27	0.06	–	4.5	1.0	–	326
	Women	30	0.27	0.065	–	4.5	1.1	–	326
3.5.4.6									
↓**AMP deaminase** ADA	Colorimetric (adenosine monophosphate), optimized, 37 °C	36	2.7	–	(0–6.2)	45	–	(0–103)	314
4.1.2.13									
↓**Fructose-bisphosphate aldolase**	Colorimetric[315], modified, 37 °C	21	3.3	–	(1.8–4.9)	55	–	(30–82)	316
(Aldolase)	UV test[124], 25 °C	48	1.8	0.65	–	30	11	–	8
ALD	UV test[124], 25 °C	30	5.0	2.5	–	83	42	–	39
	Colorimetric[317], 37 °C:								
	Children	–	6.4	0.5	–	107	8	–	318
	Adults	–	3.2	0.4	–	53	7	–	318
	UV test[124], 25 °C:								
	Infants	50	5.3	1.3	–	88	22	–	10
	Children	43	3.6	1.5	–	60	25	–	10
	Adults	100	6.4	2.4	–	107	40	–	10
	UV test[124], 37 °C	20	11.0	4.12	(4.86–18.6)	183	69	(81–310)	16
	UV test, optimized (Boehringer test kit), 25 °C:								
	Men	33	1.70	0.32	(1.14–2.32)	28.3	5.3	(19–39)	18
	Women	33	1.54	0.36	(0.84–2.32)	25.7	6.0	(14–39)	18
4.2.1.11									
↓**Enolase**	UV test[124], 25 °C	30	10.5	3.3	–	175	55	–	39
(Phosphopyruvate hydratase)	UV test[325], modified, 37 °C	10	11.7	3.54	(6.75–16.9)	195	59	(113–282)	16
ENO	UV test, 37 °C	61	13	4	–	220	70	–	394

Table 17 *Enolase isoenzymes in serum*

Type	Subjects	Number	Mean (μg/L)	*s* (μg/L)	(Extreme range) (μg/L)	Method	Year	Reference
'Neuron-specific'	Adults	30	5.2	–	(2.4–9.6)	RIA	1982	474
'Nervous-system-specific' (γ subunit)	Children	20	5.76	2.42	–	EIA	1982	475
	Adults, 20–40 years	20	2.87	1.18	–	EIA	1982	475
αα dimer	Adults	33	59	27	–	EIA	1983	476
αγ dimer	Adults	33	8.0	3.1	–	EIA	1983	476
γγ dimer	Adults	33	2.0	0.9	–	EIA	1983	476
β subunit	Adults	59	5.6	3.1	(1.6–16.7)	EIA	1983	477

RIA: radioimmunoassay; EIA: enzyme immunoassay.

3.5.4.4 *Adenosine deaminase.* Hemolysis interferes with the determination on account of the activity in erythrocytes. Activity in the serum is elevated in liver diseases, in hemoblastosis, in malignant lymphomas, in acute kidney diseases, and in typhoid fever[311,313]. The importance of this enzyme for differential diagnosis and for the diagnosis of tumors is disputed and probably slight[312].

3.5.4.6 *AMP deaminase.* This enzyme is present mainly in the skeletal muscles. Muscle damage should show up in an increase of activity of this enzyme in the serum[314].

4.1.2.13 *Fructose-bisphosphate aldolase.* Hemolysis interferes with the determination on account of the activity in erythrocytes. The highest activity is found in the skeletal muscles, where it comprises about 10% of the total water-soluble protein[319]. After physical exercise, a moderate rise of activity in the serum is observed[320]. The rises of activity in diseases of the skeletal muscle[149], of the myocardium and of the liver can be diagnostically useful[21]. High levels are found in particular in patients with Duchenne muscular dystrophy; mothers and sisters of such patients also frequently exhibit high levels[321].

↓ See text below	Normal values (reference intervals) in plasma or serum of adults, unless otherwise stated								
EC number **Recommended name** (Other names) Abbreviation	Method (substrate in brackets)	Number	µmol min⁻¹ L⁻¹ (U/L)			nmol s⁻¹ L⁻¹ (nkat/L)			Reference
			Mean	*s*	95% range (extreme range in brackets)	Mean	*s*	95% range (extreme range in brackets)	
4.3.2.1 ↓**Argininosuccinate lyase** (Argininosuccinase)	Colorimetric (argininosuccinic acid), 37 °C	48	0.23	0.18	0–0.60	3.8	3.0	0–10.0	343
5.3.1.1 ↓**Triosephosphate isomerase** TIM	UV test[124], 25 °C	30	42.8	15	–	713	250	–	39
	UV test[124], modified, 25 °C	26	234	58	(100–400)	3900	970	(1670–6670)	327
	UV test[124], modified, 37 °C	20	198	52.5	(190–251)	3300	875	(3170–4180)	16
5.3.1.6 ↓**Ribosephosphate isomerase** (Phosphoriboisomerase)	Colorimetric, 37 °C	11	58.4	–	(33.4–90.2)	974	–	(557–1500)	329
5.3.1.9 ↓**Glucosephosphate isomerase** (Phosphohexose isomerase, hexosephosphate isomerase) GPI, PHI	Colorimetric[330], 37 °C	–	50.8	24.2	–	847	403	–	39
	Colorimetric, 37 °C: Cord blood	–	–	–	(45–170)	–	–	(750–2800)	331
	Adults	–	–	–	(13–80)	–	–	(220–1300)	331
	Colorimetric[332], modified, 37 °C: Men	52	74.2	31	–	1240	520	–	333
	Women	48	46.5	27	–	775	450	–	333
	UV test[334], modified (Behringwerke test kit), 25 °C	418	–	–	13–69	–	–	220–1150	335

The enzyme occurs as a series of isoenzymes. Aldolase A is a homopolymer of 4 A subunits and is found predominantly in muscles. Aldolase B is a homopolymer of 4 B subunits and found in the liver. Aldolase C is composed of various combinations of A and C subunits with the homomeric C_4 predominately found in brain. Aldolase A acts primarily on fructose 1,6-bisphosphate, and only minimally on fructose 1-phosphate, thus resulting in an activity ratio of 50; for aldolase B, the activity ratio is about 1, and for aldolase C, it is 10[322]. The properties of aldolase in the serum correspond widely to those of the muscle isoenzyme. Rises of activity in the serum, when using fructose 1-phosphate as substrate, indicate a liver lesion: marked elevations indicate acute hepatitis, while slight rises point to chronic diseases of the liver and to obstructive jaundice[324]. In the serum, differences can be found between the isoenzyme patterns in liver and muscle diseases, in various liver diseases and tumors, and even in various forms of viral hepatitis[387,388].

The normal mass concentration of aldolase A in the serum, determined by radioimmunoassay, has been reported to be 124–212 µg/L[323].

4.2.1.11 *Enolase.* A rise of activity in the serum occurs in liver diseases, in myocardial infarction, in metastatic carcinoma, and in Duchenne muscular dystrophy[2,29,395]. The enzyme occurs in tissues and in the serum as several dimers (Table 17, page 195), composed of 3 immunologically distinct subunits; α, β, and γ[475,476]. The γγ and αγ enolases predominate in nervous tissue and have been designated 'nervous-system-specific' or 'neuron-specific' enolases[476]. High levels of these types have been found in neuroendocrine cells and tumors; increased levels in the serum occur in neuroblastoma and small-cell carcinoma of the lung[474,475].

Since 'nervous-system-specific' enolase also occurs in platelets and in lymphocytes, its concentration in serum is higher than in plasma[476]. The ββ and αβ enolases are mainly distributed in the skeletal muscle and heart; increased levels of the β unit in the serum occur in Duchenne muscular dystrophy and after myocardial infarction[477].

4.3.2.1 *Argininosuccinate lyase.* Hemolysis interferes with determination on account of the activity in erythrocytes. A rise of activity in the serum is specific to liver lesions[343,344].

5.3.1.1 *Triosephosphate isomerase.* A rise of activity in the serum occurs in viral hepatitis and in Duchenne muscular dystrophy[16,327,328]. High activities are also found in generalized neoplastic diseases, especially with liver metastases[327].

5.3.1.6 *Ribosephosphate isomerase.* In liver diseases, nephritis, and lymphosarcoma, activity rises in the serum[329].

5.3.1.9 *Glucosephosphate isomerase.* During the first days of life, activity in the serum is higher than in adults. A rise occurs in myocardial infarction[336,337] and in acute hepatitis[337,338]. Only a slight rise occurs in chronic liver diseases and in obstructive jaundice[337,338]. Elevated values are also found in leukemia[339], in megaloblastic anemia[340], in Duchenne muscular dystrophy[318], in severe thyrotoxicosis[341], and in carcinoma[335,338,341,342].

References

1 NEGELEIN and WULFF, *Biochem. Z.*, **293**, 351 (1937).
2 SCHMIDT et al., *Klin. Wschr.*, **36**, 280 (1958).
3 WOLFSON et al., *Ann. N. Y. Acad. Sci.*, **75**, 260 (1958/59).
4 MEZEY et al., *New Engl. J. Med.*, **279**, 241 (1968).
5 BÜCHER, T., in COLOWICK and KAPLAN (Ed.), *Methods in Enzymology*, volume 1, Academic Press, New York, 1955, page 415.
6 HOLZER et al., *Biochem. Z.*, **326**, 451 (1955).
7 GERLACH, U., *Klin. Wschr.*, **37**, 93 (1959).
8 FEISSLI et al., *Klin. Wschr.*, **44**, 390 (1966).
9 WÜST and SCHÖN, *Klin. Wschr.*, **39**, 280 (1961).
10 GAUTIER et al., *Helv. paediat. Acta*, **17**, 415 (1962).
11 ROSE and HENDERSON, *Clin. Chem.*, **21**, 1619 (1975).
12 KUBOWITZ and OTT, *Biochem. Z.*, **314**, 94 (1943).
13 SCHNEIDER et al., *Med. Klin.*, **60**, 6 (1965).
14 HAUG and KLUGE, *Klin. Wschr.*, **43**, 680 (1965).
15 MCKENZIE and HENDERSON, *Clin. Chem.*, **29**, 189 (1983).
16 GIUSTI et al., *Klin. Wschr.*, **45**, 292 (1967).
17 MCQUEEN et al., *Clin. chim. Acta*, **46**, 5 (1973).
18 SWEETIN and THOMSON, *Clin. chim. Acta*, **48**, 49 (1973).
19 GAY et al., *Clin. Chem.*, **14**, 740 (1968).
20 SHAW and GRAY, *Clin. Chem.*, **20**, 494 (1974).
21 WILKINSON, J. H., *The Principles and Practice of Diagnostic Enzymology*, Arnold, London, 1976.
22 WERNER et al., *Z. klin. Chem.*, **8**, 105 (1970).
23 SZASZ and RAUTENBURG, *Z. Kinderheilk.*, **111**, 233 (1971).
24 WIEME, R. J., in BERGMEYER, H. U. (Ed.), *Methoden der enzymatischen Analyse*, 3rd ed., Verlag Chemie, Weinheim, 1974, page 627; DIETZ et al., *Stand. Meth. clin. Chem.*, **7**, 49 (1972).
25 MERCER, D. W., *Clin. Chem.*, **21**, 1102 (1975).
26 SCHMIDT et al., *Clin. chim. Acta*, **15**, 283 (1967).
27 ROSALKI and WILKINSON, *Nature*, **188**, 1110 (1960); LEUNG and HENDERSON, *Clin. chim. Acta*, **115**, 145 (1981).
28 ELLIOTT and WILKINSON, *Lancet*, **1**, 698 (1961).
29 ELLIOTT et al., *Clin. Sci.*, **23**, 305 (1962).
30 KONTTINEN and PYÖRÄLÄ, *Scand. J. clin. Lab. Invest.*, **15**, 429 (1963).
31 WILKINSON, J. H., *Isoenzymes*, Spon, London, 1965, page 76.
32 ROSALKI and WILKINSON, *J. Amer. med. Ass.*, **189**, 61 (1964); KONTTINEN et al., *Clin. chim. Acta*, **52**, 245 (1974).

33 Gerlach, U., in Bergmeyer, H.U. (Ed.), *Methoden der enzymatischen Analyse,* 3rd ed., Verlag Chemie, Weinheim, 1974, page 30.
34 Koch, C.D., *Dtsch. med. Wschr.,* **99**, 127 (1974).
35 Mehler et al., *J. biol. Chem.,* **174**, 961 (1948).
36 Wong and Smith, *Clin. chim. Acta,* **72**, 409 (1976).
37 King and Morris, *Arch. Dis. Childh.,* **36**, 604 (1961).
38 Ochoa et al., *J. biol. Chem.,* **174**, 979 (1948).
39 Merten and Solbach, *Klin. Wschr.,* **39**, 222 (1961).
40 Wolfson and Williams-Ashman, *Proc. Soc. exp. Biol. (N.Y.),* **96**, 231 (1957).
41 Ochoa, S., *J. biol. Chem.,* **174**, 133 (1948).
42 Pehrson, S.L., *Acta obstet. gynec. scand.,* **43**, 69 (1964).
43 Bell and Baron, *Clin. chim. Acta,* **5**, 740 (1960).
44 King, J., in Bergmeyer, H.U. (Ed.), *Methoden der enzymatischen Analyse,* 3rd ed., Verlag Chemie, Weinheim, 1974, page 664.
45 Rosalki, S.B., in Wilkinson, J.H., *The Principles and Practice of Diagnostic Enzymology,* Arnold, London, 1976, page 303.
46 Bowers and MacDuffee, *Clin. Chem.,* **5**, 369 (1959).
47 Strandjord et al., *J. clin. Invest.,* **38**, 2111 (1959).
48 Heller et al., *J. Lab. clin. Med.,* **55**, 425 (1960).
49 Kornberg and Horecker, in Colowick and Kaplan (Eds.), *Methods in Enzymology,* volume 1, Academic Press, New York, 1955, page 323.
50 Löhr and Waller, in Bergmeyer, H.U. (Ed.), *Methoden der enzymatischen Analyse,* 3rd ed., Verlag Chemie, Weinheim, 1974, page 673.
51 Duggleby and Dennis, *J. biol. Chem.,* **249**, 167 (1974).
52 Griffiths and Shaw, *Clin. Chem.,* **23**, 245 (1977).
53 Kalk et al., *Klin. Wschr.,* **38**, 421 (1960).
54 Deutsche Gesellschaft für klinische Chemie, *Z. klin. Chem.,* **10**, 182 (1972).
55 Deutsche Gesellschaft für klinische Chemie, *Z. klin. Chem.,* **12**, 391 (1974).
56 Schlebusch et al., *Dtsch. med. Wschr.,* **99**, 765 (1974).
57 Schmidt, E., in Bergmeyer, H.U. (Ed.), *Methoden der enzymatischen Analyse,* 3rd ed., Verlag Chemie, Weinheim, 1974, page 689.
58 Wahls and Arndt-Hanser, *Ärztl. Lab.,* **14**, 397 (1968).
59 Wallnöfer et al. (Eds.), *Synopsis der Leberkrankheiten,* Thieme, Stuttgart, 1974: Schmidt and Schmidt, *Klin. Wschr.,* **40**, 962 (1962); Guder et al., *Z. klin. Chem.,* **13**, 311 (1975).
60 Schmidt and Schmidt, in Bergmeyer, H.U. (Ed.), *Methoden der enzymatischen Analyse,* 3rd ed., Verlag Chemie, Weinheim, 1974, page 14.
61 Schmidt and Schmidt, *Diagnostik,* **8**, 427 (1975).
62 van Waes and Lieber, *Brit. med. J.,* **2**, 1508 (1977).
63 Ono et al., *J. Lab. clin. Med.,* **85**, 1022 (1975).
64 Bond and Cundall, *Clin. chim. Acta,* **80**, 317 (1977).
65 Murphy et al., *Psychol. Med.,* **7**, 149 (1977); Joseph et al., *Psychol. Med.,* **7**, 159 (1977).
66 Weingold and Southern, *Obstet. and Gynec.,* **32**, 593 (1968); Weingold et al., *Int. J. Fertil.,* **16**, 24 (1971).
67 Horn and Bruns, *Biochem. Z.,* **331**, 58 (1958).
68 Racker, E., in Colowick and Kaplan (Eds.), *Methods in Enzymology,* volume 2, Academic Press, New York, 1955, page 722.
69 West et al., *J. Lab. clin. Med.,* **57**, 946 (1961).
70 Manso and Wróblewski, *J. clin. Invest.,* **37**, 214 (1958); Kerppola et al., *Acta med. scand.,* **164**, 357 (1959).
71 Cubeddu et al., *Hypertension,* **3**, 448 (1981).
72 Pelley et al., *Clin. Chem.,* **22**, 275 (1976).
73 Nagatsu and Udenfriend, *Clin. Chem.,* **18**, 980 (1972).
74 Schanberg et al., *Science,* **183**, 523 (1974).
75 Spohr et al., *Klin. Wschr.,* **55**, 1089 (1977).
76 Gutteberg et al., *Clin. chim. Acta,* **69**, 61 (1976).
77 Grant et al., *Clin. chim. Acta,* **69**, 333 (1976).
78 Ravin H.A., *Lancet,* **1**, 726 (1956).
79 Schosinsky et al., *Clin. Chem.,* **20**, 1556 (1974).
80 Reichard and Reichard, *J. Lab. clin. Med.,* **52**, 709 (1958).
81 Brown and Grisolia, *J. Lab. clin. Med.,* **54**, 617 (1959).
82 Lorentz and Wrabetz, Z. *klin. Chem.,* **9**, 220 (1971).
83 Ceriotti, G., *Clin. chim. Acta,* **47**, 97 (1973).
84 Reichard, H., *J. Lab. clin. Med.,* **57**, 78 (1961).
85 Reichard, H., *Enzym. biol. clin.,* **1**, 47 (1961).
86 Konttinen et al., *Acta med. scand.,* **188**, 257 (1970).
87 Bruns et al., *Biochem. Z.,* **330**, 497 (1958).
88 Englhardt-Gölkel and Withöft, *Klin. Wschr.,* **40**, 642 (1962).
89 Stokke and Norum, *Scand. J. clin. Lab. Invest.,* **27**, 21 (1971).
90 Ritland et al., *Clin. chim. Acta,* **49**, 251 (1973).
91 Nagasaki and Akanuma, *Clin. chim. Acta,* **75**, 371 (1977).
92 Szasz G., *Z. klin. Chem.,* **7**, 213 (1969).
93 Szasz et al., *Dtsch. med. Wschr.,* **94**, 1911 (1969).
94 Bartels and von Kleist, *Mschr. Klinderheilk.,* **119**, 334 (1971).
95 Jacobs, W.L., *Clin. chim. Acta,* **31**, 175 (1971).
96 Haesen et al., *Clin. chim. Acta,* **37**, 463 (1972).
97 Rosalki et al., *Ann. clin. Biochem.,* **7**, 143 (1970).
98 Rosalki and Rau, *Clin. chim. Acta,* **39**, 41 (1972).
99 Dingjan et al., *Z. klin. Chem.,* **11**, 167 (1973).
100 Weisshaar et al., *Med. Welt (Stuttg.),* **25**, 351 (1974).
101 Feldmann et al., *Dtsch. med. Wschr.,* **99**, 1171 (1974).
102 Rieder et al., *Clin. chim. Acta,* **79**, 211 (1977).
103 Schiele et al., *Clin. Chem.,* **23**, 1032 (1977).
104 Rosalki, S.B., *Advanc. clin. Chem.,* **17**, 53 (1975).
105 Freise et al., *Z. klin. Chem.,* **14**, 589 (1976); Freise et al., *Clin. chim. Acta,* **73**, 267 (1976).
106 Thefeld and Möller, *Z. klin. Chem.,* **15**, 205 (1977).
107 Mayr, K., *Wien. klin. Wschr.,* **85**, 83 (1973).
108 Freer and Statland, *Clin. Chem.,* **23**, 830 (1977).
109 Schmidt and Schmidt, *Dtsch. med. Wschr.,* **98**, 1572 (1973).
110 Kokot and Sledzinski, *Z. klin. Chem.,* **12**, 374 (1974).
111 Rutenburg et al., *Gastroenterology,* **45**, 43 (1963).
112 Lum and Gambino, *Clin. Chem.,* **18**, 358 (1972).
113 Rieder et al., *Clin. chim. Acta,* **79**, 211 (1977).
114 Szasz et al., *Dtsch. med. Wschr.,* **94**, 1911 (1969).
115 Szasz, G., in Bergmeyer, H.U. (Ed.), *Methoden der enzymatischen Analyse,* 3rd ed., Verlag Chemie, Weinheim, 1974, page 757.
116 Karmen, A., *J. clin. Invest.,* **34**, 131 (1955).
117 Fleisher et al., *Proc. Mayo Clin.,* **32**, 188 (1957).
118 de Ritis et al., *Ann. Sanità pubbl.,* **18**, 637 (1957).
119 Laudahn et al., *Klin. Wschr.,* **48**, 838 (1970).
120 Thefeld et al., *Dtsch. med. Wschr.,* **99**, 343 (1974).
121 Siest et al., *Clin. Chem.,* **21**, 1077 (1975).
122 Wieme, R.J., in Bergmeyer, H.U. (Ed.), *Methoden der enzymatischen Analyse,* 3rd ed., Verlag Chemie, Weinheim, 1974, page 778.
123 Schmidt and Schmidt, *Diagnostik,* **8**, 447 (1975).
124 Beisenherz et al., *Z. Naturforsch.,* **8b**, 555 (1953).
125 Smith and Thomson, *Clin. chim. Acta,* **78**, 439 (1977).
126 Harano et al., *Metabolism,* **22**, 493 (1973).
127 Weinstock et al., *Clin. chim. Acta,* **80**, 415 (1977).
128 Alberts and Samaha, *Neurology (Minneap.),* **24**, 462 (1974).
129 Yamuna et al., *Clin. chim. Acta,* **79**, 277 (1977).
130 Jacobasch, G., *Advanc. clin. Enzymol.,* **2**, 158 (1982).
131 Oliver, I.T., *Biochem. J.,* **61**, 116 (1955).
132 Rosalki, S.B., *J. Lab. clin. Med.,* **69**, 696 (1967).
133 Committee on Enzymes of the Scandinavian Society for Clinical Chemistry and Clinical Physiology, *Scand. J. clin. Lab. Invest.,* **36**, 711 (1976), and **39**, 1 (1979).
134 Deutsche Gesellschaft für klinische Chemie, *J. clin. Chem.* **15**, 255 (1977).
135 Kupke et al., *Klin. Pädiat.,* **192**, 348 (1982).
136 Forster et al., in Bergmeyer, H.U. (Ed.), *Methoden der enzymatischen Analyse,* 3rd ed., Verlag Chemie, Weinheim, 1974, page 812.
137 Jockers-Wretou and Pfleiderer, *Clin. chim. Acta,* **58**, 223 (1975).
138 van Lenten and Galen, *Clin. chim. Acta,* **87**, 211 (1978).
139 Cohen and Morgan, *Med. Clin. N. Amer.,* **57**, 105 (1973).
140 Szasz et al., *Clin. Chem.,* **22**, 1806 (1976).
141 Szasz et al., *Clin. Chem.,* **23**, 1888 (1977).
142 Szasz et al., *Dtsch. med. Wschr.,* **95**, 829 (1970).
143 Bodensteiner and Zellweger, *J. Lab. clin. Med.,* **77**, 853 (1971).
144 Meltzer and Holy, *Clin. chim. Acta,* **54**, 215 (1974).
145 Perry and Fraser, *Neurology (Minneap.),* **23**, 1316 (1973).
146 King et al., *Clin. chim. Acta,* **36**, 267 (1972).
147 Laboda and Britton, *Clin. Chem.,* **23**, 1329 (1977).
148 McNeely et al., *Clin. Chem.,* **23**, 1878 (1977).
149 Rosalki, S.B., in Wilkinson, J.H., *The Principles and Practice of Diagnostic Enzymology,* Arnold, London, 1976, page 263.
150 Ledwich, J.R., *Canad. med. Ass. J.,* **109**, 273 (1973).
151 Munsat et al., *J. Amer. med. Ass.,* **226**, 1536 (1973).
152 Fang et al., *Clin. Chem.,* **23**, 1898 (1977).
153 Neumeier et al., *Klin. Wschr.,* **53**, 329 (1975); Fiolet et al., *Clin. chim. Acta,* **80**, 23 (1977).
154 Blomberg et al., *Amer. J. Med.,* **59**, 464 (1975); Roberts and Sobel, *Amer. Heart J.,* **95**, 521 (1978); Grande et al., *Scand. J. clin. Lab. Invest.,* **39**, 607 (1979).
155 Klapdor et al., *Dtsch. med. Wschr.,* **102**, 1309 (1977); Klapdor and Harm *Dtsch. med. Wschr.,* **103**, 1665 (1978); von Arnim et al., *Verh. dtsch. Ges. inn. Med.,* **84**, 1408 (1978); Neumeier et al., *Klin. Wschr.,* **56**, 449 (1978).
156 Prellwitz et al., *Dtsch. med. Wschr.,* **101**, 981 (1976); Lang et al., *Klin. Wschr.,* **56**, 641 (1978).
157 Henry et al., *Clin. Chem.,* **21**, 1845 (1975).
158 Szasz et al., *Dtsch. med. Wschr.,* **96**, 980 (1971).
159 Schmidt F.H., *Klin. Wschr.,* **42**, 476 (1964).
160 Schreiber F.K., *Klin. Wschr.,* **42**, 478 (1964).
161 Madritsch, K., *Schweiz. med. Wschr.,* **98**, 646 (1968).
162 Noltmann and Bruns, *Hoppe-Seylers. Z. physiol. Chem.,* **313**, 194 (1958).
163 Bodansky, O., *Cancer (Philad.),* **10**, 859 (1957).
164 King, J., in Bergmeyer, H.U. (Ed.), *Methoden der enzymatischen Analyse,* 3rd ed., Verlag Chemie, Weinheim, 1974, page 826.
165 de Ritis et al., *Boll. Soc. ital. Biol. sper.,* **32**, 386 (1956); de Ritis et al., *G. Mal. infett.,* **9**, 240 (1957).
166 Weber, H., *Dtsch. med. Wschr.,* **90**, 1170 (1965).
167 Tietz et al., *Amer. J. clin. Path.,* **31**, 148 (1959).
168 van Riet and Hoeke, *Clin. chim. Acta,* **19**, 459 (1968).
169 Fried and Hoeflmayr, *Z. klin. Chem.,* **11**, 189 (1973).
170 Shihabi and Bishop, *Clin. Chem.,* **17**, 1150 (1971).
171 Verduin et al., *Clin. chim. Acta,* **46**, 11 (1973).
172 Rick, W., *Z. klin. Chem.,* **7**, 530 (1969).
173 Appel and Scholz, *J. clin. Chem.,* **15**, 339 (1977).
174 Tietz and Fiereck, *Stand. Meth. clin. Chem.,* **7**, 19 (1972).
175 Comfort and Osterberg, *Proc. Mayo Clin.,* **15**, 427 (1940).
176 Fabian et al., *Amer. J. Obstet. Gynec.,* **100**, 904 (1968).
177 Brooks, F.P., *New Engl. J. Med.,* **286**, 300 (1972).
178 Gowenlock, A.H., in Wilkinson, J.H., *The Principles and Practice of Diagnostic Enzymology,* Arnold, London, 1976, page 361.
179 Goebell et al., *Dtsch. med. Wschr.,* **94**, 2086 (1969).
180 Olbermann et al., *Dtsch. med. Wschr.,* **98**, 8 (1973).
181 Cummins and Bockus, *Gastroenterology,* **18**, 518 (1951).
182 Ticktin et al., *Gastroenterology,* **48**, 12 (1965).
183 Schultis et al., *Dtsch. med. Wschr.,* **98**, 364 (1973).
184 Pilz, W., *Z. klin. Chem.,* **3**, 89 (1965).
185 Zapf and Coghlan, *Clin. chim. Acta,* **44**, 237 (1973).
186 Prellwitz et al., *Z. klin. Chem.,* **14**, 93 (1976).
187 Pilz, W., in Bergmeyer, H.U. (Ed.), *Methoden der enzymatischen Analyse,* 3rd ed., Verlag Chemie, Weinheim, 1974, page 862.
188 Evans, R.T., *Advanc. clin. Enzymol.,* **2**, 67 (1982).

189 Brown et al., *Advanc. clin. Chem.*, **22**, 1 (1981).
190 O'Brien, R.D., *Insecticides, Action and Metabolism,* Academic Press, New York, 1967.
191 Fritsch and Rick, in Bergmeyer, H.U. (Ed.), *Methoden der enzymatischen Analyse,* 3rd ed., Verlag Chemie, Weinheim, 1974, page 854.
192 Huttunen et al., *Clin. chim. Acta,* **63**, 335 (1975).
193 Hansen, W., *Z. klin. Chem.*, **14**, 433 (1976).
194 Nilsson-Ehle, P., *Clin. chim. Acta,* **54**, 283 (1974).
195 Krauss et al., *J. clin. Invest.*, **54**, 1107 (1974).
196 Burton and Nadler, *J. Pediat.*, **90**, 777 (1977).
197 Richterich and Gautier, *Schweiz. med. Wschr.*, **92**, 781 (1962).
198 Eastman and Bixler, *Clin. Chem.*, **23**, 1769 (1977).
199 Fishman and Ghosh, *Advanc. clin. Chem.*, **10**, 255 (1967).
200 Fishman, W.H., *Amer. J. Med.*, **56**, 617 (1974); Moss, D.W., *Clin. Chem.*, **28**, 2007 (1982).
201 Bowers and McComb, *Clin. Chem.*, **21**, 1988 (1975).
202 Richter and Ohlen, *Z. klin. Chem.*, **12**, 432 (1974).
203 Sitzmann and Wendler, *Tägl. Prax.*, **13**, 105 (1972).
204 Fleisher et al., *Clin. Chem.*, **23**, 469 (1977).
205 Bennett et al., *J. Pediat.*, **88**, 633 (1976).
206 Sharland, D.E., *Clin. chim. Acta,* **56**, 187 (1974).
207 Fenuku and Foli, *Clin. chim. Acta,* **60**, 303 (1975).
208 Statland et al., *Clin. Chem.*, **18**, 1468 (1972).
209 Whitaker et al., *Clin. chim. Acta,* **80**, 209 (1977).
210 Klein, U.E., *Untersuchungen zu Herkunft, diagnostischer Bedeutung und Elimination einiger Isoenzyme der alkalischen Phosphatase des Menschen,* thesis, Kiel, 1971; Kaplan, M., *Gastroenterology,* **62**, 452 (1972).
211 Curzen and Morris, *J. Obstet. Gynaec. Brit. Cwlth,* **75**, 151 (1968); Oesterling et al., *Amer. J. clin. Nutr.*, **30**, 182 (1977).
212 Sussman et al., *Nature,* **218**, 359 (1968).
213 Holmgren et al., *Clin. chim. Acta,* **83**, 205 (1978).
214 Kaplan, M.M., *New Engl. J. Med.*, **286**, 200 (1972).
215 Moss, D.W., in Wilkinson, J.H., *The Principles and Practice of Diagnostic Enzymology,* Arnold, London, 1976, page 399.
216 Sundblad et al., *Clin. chim. Acta.*, **45**, 219 (1973); Brohult et al., *Clin. chim. Acta,* **76**, 205 (1977).
217 Fritsche and Adams-Park, *Clin. chim. Acta,* **52**, 81 (1974).
218 Hosenfeld, D., *Dtsch. med. Wschr.*, **103**, 286 (1978).
219 Lehmann, F.G., *Antibiot. and Chemother. (Basel),* **22**, 105 (1978).
220 Chen et al., *Clin. Chem.*, **25**, 719 (1979).
221 Babson and Phillips, *Clin. chim. Acta,* **13**, 264 (1966).
222 Amador et al., *Amer. J. clin. Path.*, **51**, 202 (1969).
223 Dow and Whitaker, *Brit. med. J.*, **4**, 470 (1970).
224 Roy et al., *Clin. Chem.*, **17**, 1093 (1971).
225 Lam et al., *Clin. Chem.*, **24**, 1105 (1978).
226 Mercer, D.W., *Clin. Chem.*, **23**, 653 (1977).
227 Bodansky, O., *Advanc. clin. Chem.*, **15**, 43 (1972).
228 Yam, L.T., *Amer. J. Med.*, **56**, 604 (1974).
229 Foti et al., *Clin. Chem.*, **23**, 95 (1977).
230 Gittes, R., *New Engl. J. Med.*, **297**, 1398 (1977).
231 Li et al., *J. Lab. clin. Med.*, **82**, 446 (1973).
232 Lam et al., *Clin. Chem.*, **28**, 467 (1982).
233 Mercer et al., *Clin. Chem.*, **23**, 631 (1977).
234 Foti et al., *New Engl. J. Med.*, **297**, 1357 (1977); Gittes, R., *New Engl. J. Med.*, **297**, 1398 (1977).
235 Persijn et al., *Z. klin. Chem.*, **8**, 398 (1970).
236 Campbell, D.M., *Biochem. J.*, **82**, 34P (1962).
237 Yeung, C.Y., *Pediatrics.* **50**, 812 (1972).
238 Goldberg and Ellis, *J. clin. Path.*, **25**, 907 (1972).
239 Arkesteijn, C.L., *J. clin. Chem.*, **14**, 155 (1976).
240 Bodansky and Schwartz, *Advanc. clin. Chem.*, **11**, 277 (1968).
241 Belfield and Goldberg, *Arch. Dis. Childh.*, **46**, 842 (1971).
242 Seitanidis and Moss, *Clin. chim. Acta,* **25**, 183 (1969).
243 Belfield and Goldberg, *Clin. Chem.*, **15**, 931 (1969).
244 Koide and Oda, *Clin. chim. Acta,* **4**, 554 (1959).
245 Gavosto et al., *Clin. chim. Acta,* **4**, 192 (1959).
246 Geokas and Rinderknecht, *Clin. chim. Acta,* **46**, 27 (1973).
247 Niebes, P., *Clin. chim. Acta,* **42**, 399 (1972).
248 Farooqui and Mandel, *Clin. chim. Acta,* **74**, 93 (1977).
249 Gniot-Szulżycka, J., *Clin. chim. Acta,* **32**, 17 (1971).
250 Close and Street, *Clin. chim. Acta,* **3**, 476 (1958).
251 Ceska et al., *Clin. chim. Acta,* **26**, 445 (1969).
252 Schiwara, H.W., *Z. klin. Chem.*, **10**, 12 (1972).
253 Scharpé, S., *Clin. chim. Acta,* **37**, 301 (1972).
254 Weisshaar et al., *Dtsch. med. Wschr.*, **106**, 936 (1981).
255 Salt and Schenker, *Medicine (Baltimore),* **55**, 269 (1976).
256 Flood et al., *Clin. Chem.*, **24**, 1207 (1978).
257 Otsuki et al., *Clin. Chem.*, **22**, 439 (1976).
258 Kamarýt and Fintajslová, *Z. klin. Chem.*, **8**, 564 (1970); Warshaw, A.L., *J. Lab. clin. Med.*, **90**, 1, (1977); Levitt et al., *J. Lab. clin. Med.*, **90**, 141 (1977).
259 Kanno and Sudo, *Clin. chim. Acta,* **76**, 67 (1977).
260 Taussig et al., *Pediatrics,* **54**, 229 (1974).
261 Desnick et al., *J. Lab. clin. Med.*, **81**, 157 (1973).
262 Öckerman, P.A., *Clin. chim. Acta,* **23**, 479 (1969).
263 Hirani et al., *Clin. chim. Acta,* **81**, 135 (1977).
264 Lombardo et al., *Clin. chim. Acta,* **113**, 141 (1981).
265 Nakagawa et al., *Clin. chim. Acta,* **75**, 181 (1977).
266 Szasz, G., *Clin. chim. Acta,* **15**, 275 (1967).
267 Griffiths et al., *Clin. chim. Acta,* **90**, 129 (1978).
268 Singh and Gyorkey, *Biochem. Med.*, **20**, 336 (1978).
269 Reglero et al., *Clin. chim. Acta,* **103**, 155 (1980).
270 von Figura et al., *Z. klin. Chem.*, **13**, 285 (1975).
271 Zielke et al., *J. Lab. clin. Med.*, **79**, 164 (1972).
272 Eriksson et al., *Clin. chim. Acta,* **40**, 181 (1972).
273 Fleisher et al., *Ann. N. Y. Acad. Sci.*, **75**, 363 (1958/59).
274 Appel, W., in Bergmeyer H.U. (Ed.), *Methoden der enzymatischen Analyse,* 3rd ed., Verlag Chemie, Weinheim, 1974, page 991.
275 Appel et al., *Z. klin. Chem.*, **7**, 576 (1969).
276 Roth, M., *Clin. chim. Acta,* **9**, 448 (1964).
277 Rockerbie and Rasmussen, *Clin. chim. Acta,* **18**, 183 (1967).
278 Szasz, G., *Amer. J. clin. Path.*, **47**, 607 (1967).
279 Haralambie and Berg, *Clin. chim. Acta,* **69**, 433 (1976).
280 Schlaeger, R., *Z. klin. Chem.*, **11**, 326 (1973).
281 Miller and Worsley, *Brit. med. J.*, **2**, 1419 (1960).
282 Miller et al., *Obstet. and Gynec.*, **24**, 707 (1964).
283 Weber, H., *Dtsch. med. Wschr.*, **94**, 181 (1969).
284 van Oudheusden, A.P., in Bergmeyer, H.U. (Ed.), *Methoden der enzymatischen Analyse,* 3rd ed., Verlag Chemie, Weinheim, 1974, page 1008.
285 Suzuki et al., *Clin. chim. Acta,* **115**, 223 (1981).
286 Durham, B.H., *Chin. Chem.*, **22**, 79 (1976).
287 Roth and Rohner, *Clin. chim. Acta,* **135**, 65 (1983).
288 Appel et al., *Anästhesist,* **17**, 95 (1968).
289 Appel, W., in Bergmeyer, H.U. (Ed.), *Methoden der enzymatischen Analyse,* 3rd ed., Verlag Chemie, Weinheim, 1974, page 1015.
290 Roman and Favilla, *Enzymologia,* **26**, 249 (1963).
291 Fritz et al., in Bergmeyer, H.U. (Ed.), *Methoden der enzymatischen Analyse,* 3rd ed., Verlag Chemie, Weinheim, 1974, page 1105.
292 Rao et al., *Science,* **177**, 610 (1972).
293 Elias et al., *Lancet,* **2**, 66 (1977).
294 Gobelet et al., *Schweiz. med. Wschr.*, **108**, 1902 (1978).
295 Heinrich et al., *Klin. Wschr.*, **57**, 1237 (1979).
296 Ruddell et al., *Brit. med. J.*, **283**, 1429 (1981).
297 Gries et al., *Experientia (Basel),* **26**, 31 (1970).
298 Nakano et al., *Clin. chim. Acta,* **81**, 257 (1977).
299 Adlung et al., *Z. klin. Chem.*, **9**, 411 (1971).
300 Zapf, P.W., *Clin. chim. Acta,* **26**, 547 (1969).
301 Manning and Grisolia, *Proc. Soc. exp. Biol. (N. Y.),* **95**, 225 (1957); Ugarte et al., *J. Lab. clin. Med.*, **57**, 359 (1961); Pelikán et al., *Clin. chim. Acta,* **9**, 141 (1964).
302 Kumate et al., *J. infect. Dis.*, **103**, 25 (1958); Ugarte et al., *J. Lab. clin. Med.*, **55**, 522 (1960).
303 Porembska and Kedra, *Clin. chim. Acta,* **60**, 355 (1975).
304 Hue and Free, *Clin. Chem.*, **10**, 631 (1964).
305 Knights et al., *J. Lab. clin. Med.*, **65**, 355 (1965).
306 Nyssen and Dorche, *Clin. chim. Acta,* **22**, 363 (1968).
307 Ellis et al., *Clin. chim. Acta,* **47**, 75 (1973).
308 Giusti, G., in Bergmeyer, H.U. (Ed.), *Methoden der enzymatischen Analyse,* 3rd ed., Verlag Chemie, Weinheim, 1974, page 1128.
309 Mandel and Macalincag, *Amer. J. Gastroent.*, **54**, 255 (1970).
310 Martinek, R.G., *Clin. Chem.*, **9**, 620 (1963).
311 Müller-Beissenhirtz and Keller, *Dtsch. med. Wschr.*, **91**, 159 (1966).
312 Giusti, G., in Bergmeyer, H.U. (Ed.), *Methoden der enzymatischen Analyse,* 3rd ed., Verlag Chemie, Weinheim, 1974, page 1134.
313 Goldberg et al., *Clin. chim. Acta,* **14**, 720 (1966); Galanti and Giusti, *Minerva med.*, **59**, 5867 (1968); Bruttini et al., *Arch. ital. Urol.*, **42**, 215 (1969).
314 Pedersen and Berry, *Clin. Chem.*, **23**, 1726 (1977).
315 Sibley and Lehninger, *J. biol. Chem.*, **177**, 859 (1949).
316 Bruns and Puls, *Klin. Wschr.*, **32**, 656 (1954).
317 Meyerhof and Lohmann, *Biochem. Z.*, **271**, 89 (1934).
318 Schapira et al., *Amer. J. phys. Med.*, **34**, 313 (1955).
319 Bergmeyer and Bernt, in Bergmeyer, H.U. (Ed.), *Methoden der enzymatischen Analyse,* 3rd ed., Verlag Chemie, Weinheim, 1974, page 1142.
320 Cantone and Cerretelli, *Int. Z. angew. Physiol.*, **18**, 107 (1960); Baumann et al., *Schweiz. Z. Sportmed.*, **10**, 33 (1962); Fowler et al., *J. appl. Physiol.*, **17**, 943 (1962); Otto et al., *Klin. Wschr.*, **42**, 75 (1964).
321 Schapira and Schapira, *Ann. Biol. clin.*, **18**, 1 (1960); Chung et al., *Amer. J. hum. Genet.*, **12**, 52 (1960); Leyburn et al., *Ann. hum. Genet.*, **25**, 41 (1961).
322 Asaka et al., *Clin. chim. Acta,* **117**, 289 (1981).
323 Asaka et al., *Clin. chim. Acta,* **125**, 31 (1982).
324 Wolf et al., *Gastroenterologia (Basel),* **87**, 172 (1957); Rick and Oesterle, *Verh. dtsch. Ges. inn. Med.*, **65**, 692 (1959); Forster and Jenny, *Helv. med. Acta,* **26**, 673 (1959); Schneiderbaur and Rettenbacher, *Wien. med. Wschr.*, **111**, 322 (1961).
325 Coltorti and Giusti, *Boll. Soc. ital. Biol. sper.*, **34**, 964 (1958).
326 Jones et al., *Brit. J. Obstet. Gynaec.*, **89**, 314 (1982).
327 Robert et al., *Cancer (Philad.),* **14**, 1166 (1961).
328 Giusti, G., *Boll. Soc. ital. Biol. sper.*, **38**, 10 (1962).
329 Bruns, F.H., *Biochem. Z.*, **327**, 523 (1956).
330 Bruns and Hinsberg, *Biochem. Z.*, **325**, 532 (1954).
331 King, J., in Bergmeyer, H.U. (Ed.), *Methoden der enzymatischen Analyse,* 3rd ed., Verlag Chemie, Weinheim, 1974, page 1155.
332 German et al., *Clin. chim. Acta,* **22**, 551 (1968).
333 Brunelle and Pesquet, *Clin. chim. Acta,* **33**, 265 (1971).
334 Schwartz et al., *Clin. Chem.*, **17**, 656 (1971).
335 Hohenwallner, W., *Diagnostik,* **8**, 577 (1975).
336 Siegel and Bing, *Proc. Soc. exp. Biol. (N. Y.),* **91**, 604 (1956).
337 Bing et al., *J. Amer. med. Ass.*, **164**, 647 (1957).
338 Bruns and Jacob, *Klin. Wschr.*, **32**, 1041 (1954).
339 Blanchaer et al., *Blood,* **13**, 245 (1958).
340 Tanaka et al., *Blood,* **19**, 267 (1962).
341 White, L.P., *J. nat. Cancer Inst.*, **21**, 671 (1958).
342 Schwartz et al., *Cancer (Philad.),* **15**, 347 (1962).
343 Takahara and Natelson, *Amer. J. clin. Path.*, **47**, 693 (1967).
344 Chirillo et al., quoted by Wilkinson, J.H., *The Principles and Practice of Diagnostic Enzymology,* Arnold, London, 1976, page 192.

[345] LORENTZ et al., *Clin. chim. Acta,* **63**, 263 (1975).
[346] BAYLIN et al., *Amer. J. Med.,* **53**, 723 (1972); BAYLIN et al., *New Engl. J. Med.,* **293**, 1286 (1975).
[347] FREEDMAN et al., *J. Lab. clin. Med.,* **85**, 1008 (1975).
[348] OGIHARA et al., *J. Lab. clin. Med.,* **85**, 566 (1975).
[349] LAMPRECHT, F., *Dtsch. med. Wschr.,* **102**, 1128 (1977).
[350] WOOD, S., *J. Lab. clin. Med.,* **88**, 469 (1976).
[351] ZUCKER and WEBB, *Stand. meth. clin. Chem.,* **7**, 9 (1972).
[352] LABEDZKI et al., *Klin. Wschr.,* **55**, 677 (1977).
[353] PEETERS et al., *Clin. Chem.,* **24**, 2155 (1978).
[354] BARTHELEMY et al., *Clin. chim. Acta,* **50**, 257 (1974).
[355] PERILLIE et al., *J. Amer. med. Ass.,* **203**, 317 (1968).
[356] PANIZZON and SENN, *Klin. Wschr.,* **51**, 383 (1973).
[357] BRIERE et al., *Clin. chim. Acta,* **50**, 265 (1974).
[358] AFZAL, M., *Postgrad. med. J.,* **53**, 257 (1977).
[359] RÖLLINGHOFF et al., *Klin. Wschr.,* **55**, 225 (1977); FALCHUK et al., *New Engl. J. Med.,* **292**, 395 (1975); PEETERS et al., *Gut,* **17**, 300 (1976); NUGENT et al., *Gastroenterology,* **70**, 1014 (1976); MANIER et al., *Amer. J. Gastroent.,* **67**, 245 (1977).
[360] DAVIS and FREEMAN, *Physiol. Rev.,* **56**, 1 (1976).
[361] KARLBERG and TOLAGEN, *Scand. J. clin. Lab. Invest.,* **37**, 521 (1977).
[362] FYHRQUIST et al., *Clin. Chem.,* **22**, 250 (1976).
[363] LARAGH, J.H. (Ed.), *Hypertension Manual,* Yorke Medical Books, New York, 1973.
[364] WOODS et al., *New Engl. J. Med.,* **294**, 1137 (1976); WILLIAMS, G.H., *New Engl. J. Med.,* **294**, 1176 (1976); WEIDMANN et al., *Amer. J. Med.,* **62**, 209 (1977).
[365] BREUER and STUCKY, *Z. klin. Chem.,* **13**, 355 (1975); LARAGH et al., *J. Amer. med. Ass.,* **241**, 151 (1979).
[366] FRANKE et al., *Klin. Wschr.,* **51**, 183 (1973).
[367] GARBUS, J., *Clin. chim. Acta,* **35**, 502 (1971); IDÉO et al., *Z. klin. Chem.,* **10**, 74 (1972).
[368] CAMPBELL and MOSS, *Proc. Ass. clin. Biochem.,* **2**, 10 (1962).
[369] RAMBOER, C.R., *J. Lab. clin. Med.,* **74**, 828 (1969).
[370] RAMBOER et al., *Digestion,* **7**, 183 (1972).
[371] WOLKO and KRAWCZYNSKI, *Mater. med. Pol.,* **6**, 95 (1974).
[372] SHAMMA'A et al., *Gastroenterology,* **48**, 226 (1965).
[373] SPOHR et al., *Klin. Wschr.,* **55**, 1089 (1977); WANG et al., *Clin. chim. Acta,* **101**, 241 (1980).
[374] LENTNER and EGGSTEIN, *Leading Symptoms: Laboratory Values,* CIBA-GEIGY Limited, Basle, 1977; MONDORF et al., *Klin. Wschr.,* **49**, 61 (1971).
[375] PATSCH et al., *J. Lipid Res.,* **17**, 182 (1976).
[376] GLOMSET and NORUM, *Advanc. Lipid Res.,* **11**, 1 (1973); BLOMHOFF et al., *Clin. chim. Acta,* **53**, 197 (1974); WIELAND et al., *Inn. Med.,* **3**, 478 (1976).
[377] KAISER and PAULA, in BURLINA and GALZIGNA (Eds.), *Clinical Enzymology Symposium 1,* Piccin Medical Books, Padua, 1977, page 113; SABESIN et al., *Gastroenterology,* **72**, 510 (1977).
[378] KÖTTGEN and GEROK, *Klin. Wschr.,* **54**, 439 (1976); KÖTTGEN et al., *Verh. dtsch. Ges. inn. Med.,* **84**, 1062 (1978).
[379] SCHMIDT and VIDO, in WANNAGAT, L. (Ed.), *Toxische Leberschäden,* Thieme, Stuttgart, 1976, page 166.
[380] BERGE et al., *Klin. Wschr.,* **60**, 445 (1982).
[381] KUHLENSCHMIDT et al., *Lab. Invest.,* **31**, 413 (1974).
[382] KESSEL and ALLEN, *Cancer Res.,* **35**, 670 (1975).
[383] CHEMNITZ et al., *Dtsch. med. Wschr.,* **104**, 257 (1979).
[384] RUTTLOFF et al., *Acta biol. med. germ.,* **19**, 831 (1967).
[385] BERGMANN et al., *Dtsch. Z. Verdau.-u. Stoffwechselkr.,* **34**, 151 (1974).
[386] KAR and PEARSON, *Proc. Soc. exp. Biol. (N.Y.),* **140**, 1480 (1972).
[387] LEHMANN and KORNACHER, *Digestion,* **12**, 118 (1975).
[388] GEMPP-FRIEDRICH and PRELLWITZ, *Klin. Wschr.,* **53**, 44 (1975); CHEMNITZ et al., *Verh. Dtsch. Ges. inn. Med.,* **83**, 560 (1977).
[389] Deutsche Gesellschaft für klinische Chemie, *Z. klin. Chem.,* **8**, 658 (1970).
[390] VEIT et al., *Klin. Paediat.,* **187**, 244 (1975).
[391] BOSTICK et al., *Clin. Chem.,* **24**, 1305 (1978).
[392] TIDERSTRÖM and HEINEGÅRD, *Clin. chim. Acta,* **88**, 293 (1978).
[393] DEN BLAAUWEN et al., *J. clin. Chem.,* **21**, 381 (1983).
[394] HERRAEZ-DOMINGUEZ et al., *Enzyme (Basel),* **21**, 211 (1976).
[395] GOLDBERG et al., *Clin. chim. Acta,* **71**, 89 (1976); HERRAEZ-DOMINGUEZ et al., *Clin. chim. Acta,* **64**, 307 (1975).
[396] JUNG et al., *Clin. chim. Acta,* **91**, 165 (1979).
[397] VAN ELSEN and LEROY, *Clin. chim. Acta,* **112**, 159 (1981).
[398] Committee on Enzymes of the Scandinavian Society for Clinical Chemistry and Clinical Physiology, *Scand. J. clin. Lab. Invest.,* **33**, 291 (1974).
[399] KRISTENSEN et al., *Scand. J. clin. Lab. Invest.,* **39**, 777 (1979).
[400] Committee on Enzymes of the Scandinavian Society for Clinical Chemistry and Clinical Physiology, *Scand. J. clin. Lab. Invest.,* **36**, 119 (1976).
[401] MOSS et al., *Clin. chim. Acta,* **116**, 209 (1981).
[402] PAGLIA and VALENTINE, *J. Lab. clin. Med.,* **70**, 158 (1967).
[403] MATSUMOTO et al., *Clin. chim. Acta,* **110**, 121 (1981).
[404] PLEBAN et al., *Clin. Chem.,* **28**, 311 (1982).
[405] SUBBAIAH and BAGDADE, *Life Sci.,* **22**, 1971 (1978).
[406] SUBBAIAH, P.V., *Metabolism,* **31**, 294 (1982).
[407] FREDRICKSON et al., in STANBURY et al., (Eds.), *The Metabolic Basis of Inherited Disease,* 4th ed., McGraw-Hill, New York, 1978, page 643.
[408] ALBERS et al., *J. clin. Invest.,* **67**, 141 (1981).
[409] KNIGHT and HAYMOND, *Clin. Chem.,* **27**, 48 (1981).
[410] HABIG et al., *J. biol. Chem.,* **249**, 7130 (1974).
[411] ADACHI et al., *Clin. chim. Acta,* **106**, 243 (1980).
[412] BOYDE and KWONG, *Clin. chim. Acta,* **128**, 95 (1983).
[413] CHERIAN and HILL, *Amer. J. clin. Path.,* **70**, 783 (1978).
[414] CHERIAN and HILL, *Clin. Biochem.,* **6**, 326 (1973).
[415] JEDEIKIN et al., *Clin. Chem.,* **28**, 317 (1982).
[416] BONDAR et al., *Clin. Chem.,* **26**, 618 (1980).
[417] URDAL et al., *Scand. J. clin. Lab. Invest.,* **42**, 621 (1982).
[418] VAN STEIRTEGHEM et al., *Clin. chim. Acta,* **93**, 25 (1979).
[419] CHEMNITZ et al., in LANG, H. (Ed.), *Creatine Kinase Isoenzymes: Pathophysiology and Clinical Application,* Springer, Berlin, 1981, page 224.
[420] WEI et al., *J. Amer. med. Ass.,* **246**, 1921 (1981).
[421] FELD et al., *Clin. chim. Acta,* **100**, 267 (1980); THOMPSON et al., *Lancet,* **2**, 673 (1980).
[422] ALLNER et al., *Med. Welt (Stuttg.),* **32**, 1533 (1981).
[423] POSEN and DOHERTY, *Advanc. clin. Chem.,* **22**, 163 (1981).
[424] HITZ et al., *Clin. chim. Acta,* **107**, 203 (1980).
[425] COOPER et al., *Clin. chim. Acta,* **126**, 297 (1982).
[426] GRIFFITHS et al., *Clin. Chem.,* **28**, 183 (1982).
[427] BLICK et al., *Clin. Chem.,* **28**, 2373 (1982).
[428] DAVIES and GRIFFITHS, *Clin. chim. Acta,* **122**, 29 (1982).
[429] LIN et al., *Clin. chim. Acta,* **130**, 263 (1983).
[430] BERTRAND and BURET, *Clin. chim. Acta,* **119**, 275 (1982).
[431] FRANCESCONI et al., *J. clin. Chem.,* **19**, 17 (1981).
[432] THOMAS and HODES, *Clin. chim. Acta,* **111**, 185 (1981).
[433] BISWAS and HINDOCHA, *Clin. chim. Acta,* **51**, 285 (1974).
[434] HÖLBLING et al., *Klin. Wschr.,* **59**, 1201 (1981); Corbishley et al., *Clin. chim. Acta,* **124**, 225 (1982).
[435] OHTA et al., *Clin. chim. Acta,* **124**, 51 (1982).
[436] O'DONNELL and MILLER, *Clin. chim. Acta,* **104**, 265 (1980).
[437] KEOGH et al., *Gut,* **19**, 1125 (1978).
[438] TSIANOS et al., *Lancet,* **1**, 856 (1982).
[439] PLOUET and MADEC, *Clin. chim. Acta,* **93**, 51 (1979).
[440] DICK, W., *Mschr. Kinderheilk.,* **128**, 30 (1980).
[441] THOMAS et al., *Clin. Chem.,* **27**, 1223 (1981).
[442] LOWDEN, J.A., *Clin. chim. Acta,* **93**, 409 (1979).
[443] GRESSNER and ROEBRUCK, *Clin. chim. Acta,* **124**, 315 (1982).
[444] HULTBERG and ISAKSSON, *Clin. chim. Acta,* **113**, 135 (1981).
[445] MURPHEY et al., *Clin. chim. Acta,* **42**, 309 (1972).
[446] LENNEY et al., *Clin. chim. Acta,* **123**, 221 (1982).
[447] BURGESS et al., *Clin. chim. Acta,* **61**, 215 (1975).
[448] KOJIMA et al., *Clin. chim. Acta,* **93**, 181 (1979).
[449] NAGATSU et al., *Clin. Chem.,* **25**, 376 (1979).
[450] HUTCHINSON et al., *Clin. chim. Acta,* **109**, 83 (1981).
[451] SILVERSTEIN and FRIEDLAND, *Clin. chim. Acta,* **74**, 21 (1977).
[452] RUSSO et al., *Clin. Chem.,* **24**, 1539 (1978).
[453] HURST and LOVELL-SMITH, *Clin. Chem.,* **27**, 2048 (1981).
[454] RODRIGUEZ et al., *J. Pediat.,* **99**, 68 (1981).
[455] NAKAMURA et al., *J. clin. Endocr.,* **55**, 931 (1982).
[456] PARENTE et al., *Amer. J. Obstet. Gynec.,* **135**, 586 (1979).
[457] LIEBERMAN, J., *Amer. J. Med.,* **59**, 365 (1975).
[458] LIEBERMAN and BEUTLER, *New Engl. J. Med.,* **294**, 1442 (1976).
[459] ROHATGI et al., *Amer. J. Med.,* **70**, 44 (1981).
[460] SCHWEISFURTH and WERNZE, *Acta hepato-gastroent.,* **26**, 207 (1979).
[461] MATSUKI and SAKATA, *Amer. J. Med.,* **73**, 549 (1982).
[462] LIEBERMAN and REA, *Ann. intern. Med.,* **87**, 422 (1977).
[463] RYDER et al., *J. Amer. med. Ass.,* **249**, 1888 (1983).
[464] GRÖNHAGEN-RISKA et al., *Scand. J. resp. Dis.,* **59**, 228 (1978).
[465] LIEBERMAN and SASTRE, *Ann. intern. Med.,* **93**, 825 (1980).
[466] ALHENC-GELAS et al., *J. Lab. clin. Med.,* **101**, 83 (1983).
[467] CARREL et al., *Helv. paediat. Acta,* **36**, 405 (1981).
[468] AMMANN et al., *Klin. Wschr.,* **60**, 243 (1982).
[469] MØLLER-PETERSEN and PEDERSEN, *Clin. chim. Acta,* **124**, 31 (1982).
[470] FAHRENKRUG and MAGID, *Clin. Chem.,* **26**, 1573 (1980).
[471] CROSSLEY et al., *Lancet,* **1**, 472 (1979); TRAVERT et al., *Nouv. Presse méd.,* **10**, 2093 (1981).
[472] NISHIKAWA and FUKUMOTO, *Clin. Chem.,* **27**, 560 (1981).
[473] ITO et al., *Clin. chim. Acta,* **115**, 135 (1981).
[474] CARNEY et al., *Lancet,* **1**, 583 (1982).
[475] ISHIGURO et al., *Clin. chim. Acta,* **121**, 173 (1982).
[476] KATO et al., *Clin. chim. Acta,* **127**, 353 (1983).
[477] KATO et al., *Clin. chim. Acta,* **131**, 75 (1983).
[478] SOYAMA and ONO, *Clin. chim. Acta,* **131**, 149 (1983).
[479] GILLARD et al., *Clin. Chem.,* **29**, 1119 (1983).
[480] WOLF and SECOR MCVOY, *Clin. chim. Acta,* **135**, 275 (1983).

Erythrocyte enzymes (for references see pages 203 and 204)

Compared with other cells, the mature erythrocyte carries only a modest variety of enzymes[1]. It can synthesize neither RNA nor DNA and neither heme nor proteins. In all probability it is incapable of forming glycerides, phospholipids or cholesterol. There is no possibility of oxidative phosphorylation taking place, and the cytochrome system is lacking. The tricarboxylic acid cycle does not operate despite the presence in the erythrocyte of some of the enzymes involved. On the other hand, all the enzymes participating

Table 1 *Enzyme activity in young and old erythrocytes*

EC number	Name of enzyme	Measured at 28 °C [12]					Measured at 27 °C [35]			
		10 newborn		20 adults		Activity ratio* (young over old erythrocytes)	30 normal subjects		7 subjects with 15–20% reticulocytes	
		Mean	s	Mean	s		Mean	s	Mean	s
		kU/L					kU/L			
1.1.1.27	Lactate dehydrogenase	27.56	4.25	20.33	2.87	1.05	28.6	2.8	39.7	4.1
1.1.1.44	Phosphogluconate dehydrogenase (decarboxylating)	–	–	–	–	–	0.76	0.16	1.29	0.38
1.1.1.49	Glucose-6-phosphate dehydrogenase	3.28	0.40	2.15	0.18	1.65	1.45	0.26	3.04	0.60
1.2.1.12	Glyceraldehyde-phosphate dehydrogenase	8.84	2.45	8.85	1.27	1.21	18	4	23	9
1.6.4.2	Glutathione reductase [NAD(P)H]	–	–	–	–	–	0.66	0.16	0.90	0.20
2.6.1.1	Aspartate aminotransferase	–	–	–	–	3.81	–	–	–	–
2.7.1.1	Hexokinase	0.340	0.060	0.129	0.021	2.68	0.18	0.03	0.68	0.14
2.7.1.11	6-Phosphofructokinase	0.845	0.24	1.48	0.245	1.23	1.31	0.30	1.98	0.28
2.7.1.40	Pyruvate kinase	2.56	0.50	1.79	0.16	2.20	2.9	0.4	7.9	2.5
2.7.2.3	Phosphoglycerate kinase	39.26	5.28	27.95	1.44	1.06	28.6	3.5	42	10
2.7.4.3	Adenylate kinase	–	–	–	–	–	43.9	4.3	59.9	13
2.7.5.3	Phosphoglyceromutase	10.49	1.60	7.51	0.99	1.23	6.1	1.3	9.8	1.4
4.1.2.13	Fructose-bisphosphate aldolase	0.420	0.100	0.245	0.037	2.05	0.48	0.13	0.80	0.21
4.2.1.11	Enolase	5.17	1.21	2.52	0.54	1.08	2.7	0.4	4.8	1.5
5.3.1.1	Triosephosphate isomerase	291.1	41.0	263.2	32.4	1.10	293	55	418	65
5.3.1.9	Glucosephosphate isomerase	5.60	1.12	4.06	0.37	1.19	6.6	2.0	8.25	0.82

* Activity related to 10^{12} cells, separated by ultracentrifugation; reticulocytes 4.7% versus 0.05%.

Table 2 *Enzyme activity in erythrocytes of newborn and adults*

EC number	Name of enzyme	Measured at 37 °C [13]				Measured at 30 °C [36]			
		22 newborn (cord)		15–52 children and adults		16–20 newborn (cord)		16–20 men	
		Mean	s	Mean	s	Mean	s	Mean	s
		kU/10^{12}				Activity relative to hemoglobin U/g			
1.1.1.27	Lactate dehydrogenase	5.94	0.78	4.49	0.61	95.0	11.7	72.2	8.2
1.1.1.37	Malate dehydrogenase	–	–	–	–	81.3	11.9	75.4	7.8
1.1.1.44	Phosphogluconate dehydrogenase (decarboxylating)	0.27	0.04	0.18	0.03	1.73	0.45	1.82	0.35
1.1.1.49	Glucose-6-phosphate dehydrogenase	0.47	0.09	0.27	0.06	15.0	1.3	8.52	0.87
1.2.1.12	Glyceraldehyde-phosphate dehydrogenase	5.16	0.55	3.03	0.45	28.3	3.1	27.6	2.3
1.6.4.2	Glutathione reductase [NAD(P)H]	–	–	–	–	6.10	2.02	4.33	0.90
1.11.1.9	Glutathione peroxidase	0.40	0.11	0.72	0.18	20.2	1.7	20.2	2.5
2.6.1.1	Aspartate aminotransferase	–	–	–	–	8.30	1.73	5.05	1.62
2.7.1.1	Hexokinase	0.055	0.012	0.023	0.007	2.30	0.35	1.48	0.27
2.7.1.11	6-Phosphofructokinase	0.29	0.04	0.30	0.06	–	–	–	–
2.7.1.40	Pyruvate kinase	0.72	0.12	0.45	0.07	20.9	3.3	13.6	3.2
2.7.2.3	Phosphoglycerate kinase	4.20	0.28	2.55	0.37	180	12	126	8
2.7.4.3	Adenylate kinase	6.12	0.83	7.78	1.68	73.5	10.1	93.8	7.7
2.7.5.1	Phosphoglucomutase	–	–	–	–	3.67	0.57	4.47	0.47
2.7.5.3	Phosphoglyceromutase	0.95	0.11	0.78	0.15	–	–	–	–
2.7.6.1	Ribosephosphate pyrophosphokinase	2.19	0.47	3.05	0.38	–	–	–	–
3.1.2.6	Hydroxyacylglutathione hydrolase (25 °C)	1.75	0.27	1.68	0.21	–	–	–	–
4.1.2.13	Fructose-bisphosphate aldolase	0.14	0.03	0.10	0.02	–	–	–	–
4.2.1.11	Enolase	0.95	0.11	0.38	0.09	–	–	–	–
4.4.1.5	Lactoyl-glutathione lyase (25 °C)	6.32	0.66	4.94	1.00	–	–	–	–
5.3.1.1	Triosephosphate isomerase	16.5	1.20	16.3	2.15	1724	198	1423	177
5.3.1.9	Glucosephosphate isomerase	2.06	0.22	1.27	0.18	77.3	5.5	50.4	4.6
	Distal pentosephosphate shunt*	1.73	0.43	1.27	0.28	–	–	–	–

* Formation of fructose 6-phosphate from ribose 5-phosphate.

in glycolysis, glycogen synthesis and the pentose phosphate shunt are present. The breakdown of glucose furnishes the little energy required by the erythrocyte in the form of ATP, together with the necessary reducing capacity in the form of NADH and NADPH.

Other enzymes playing an important role in the functioning of the erythrocyte are glutathione peroxidase[2], catalase[3] and superoxide dismutase[4], the last-named a protein formerly known as erythrocuprein. These enzymes protect the tetrapyrrole ring of heme and

(Continued on page 203)

Table 3 *Enzyme activity in erythrocytes of adults at 37 °C and conversion factors for 30 °C and 25 °C*[7]

EC number	Name of enzyme	Activity* at 37°C, relative to hemoglobin Mean (U/g)	s (U/g)	Factor 30 °C/37 °C	Factor 25 °C/37 °C
1.1.1.27	Lactate dehydrogenase	200	26.5	0.670	0.440
1.1.1.44	Phosphogluconate dehydrogenase (decarboxylating)	8.78	0.78	0.668	0.486
1.1.1.49	Glucose-6-phosphate dehydrogenase	8.34	1.59	0.815	0.559
1.2.1.12	Glyceraldehyde-phosphate dehydrogenase	226	41.9	0.699	0.520
1.6.4.2	Glutathione reductase (without flavin adenine dinucleotide)	7.18	1.09	0.714	0.543
	– (with flavin adenine dinucleotide)	10.4	1.50	0.735	0.562
1.6.99.3	NADH dehydrogenase (25 °C)	2.60	0.71	◊	◊
1.11.1.9	Glutathione peroxidase	31.4	2.97	0.867	0.818
2.6.1.1	Aspartate aminotransferase (without pyridoxal phosphate)	3.02	0.67	0.867	0.601
	– (with pyridoxal phosphate)	5.04	0.90	0.789	0.561
2.7.1.1	Hexokinase	1.27	0.18	0.709	0.477
2.7.1.11	6-Phosphofructokinase	9.05	1.89	0.750	0.580
2.7.1.40	Pyruvate kinase	15.0	1.99	0.689	0.432
2.7.2.3	Phosphoglycerate kinase	320	36.1	0.735	0.604
2.7.4.3	Adenylate kinase	258	29.3	0.770	0.553
2.7.5.1	Phosphoglucomutase	5.50	0.62	0.643	0.416
2.7.5.3	Phosphoglyceromutase	24.9	2.52	0.583	0.307
2.7.5.4	Bisphosphoglyceromutase	4.78	0.65	0.710	0.504
3.1.1.7	Acetylcholinesterase	36.9	3.83	0.822	0.730
3.5.4.4	Adenosine deaminase	1.11	0.23	0.750	0.489
4.1.2.13	Fructose-bisphosphate aldolase	3.19	0.86	0.628	0.548
4.2.1.11	Enolase	5.39	0.83	0.700	0.445
5.3.1.1	Triosephosphate isomerase	2111	397	0.656	0.475
5.3.1.9	Glucosephosphate isomerase	60.8	11.0	0.760	0.590

*Enzyme saturated with the substrate. To detect variants of pyruvate kinase and hexokinase it may be necessary to use methods with low substrate concentration.
◊ Unstable at temperatures above 25 °C.

Table 4 *Catalase and superoxide dismutase in erythrocytes (mass relative to hemoglobin)*

EC number	Name of enzyme	Subjects	Mean (mg/g)	s (mg/g)	Reference
1.11.1.6	Catalase	9 men	2.20	0.30	8
1.15.1.1	Superoxide dismutase	9 men	0.488	0.084	8
		20 children, adults	0.471	0.067	9

Table 5 *Carbonate dehydratase (carbonic anhydrase) in erythrocytes*

EC number	Name of enzyme	Subjects	Isoenzyme B (CA I) Mean	s	(Extreme range)	Isoenzyme C (CA II) Mean	s	(Extreme range)	Reference
			g/L						
4.2.1.1	Carbonate dehydratase	109 adults	4.89	0.75	(3.39–6.39)	0.60	0.07	(0.46–0.74)	37
			Mass relative to hemoglobin mg/g						
		23 newborn (umbilical vein)	1.34	0.88	(0.12–4.0)	0.28	0.20	(0–0.58)	10
		13 adults	13.3	0.94	(11.9–15.2)	1.77	0.17	(1.44–2.02)	10
		25 children, 2–14 years	10.0	2.0	–	1.72	0.45	–	11
		10 adults, 20–40 years	13.5	2.5	–	1.76	0.19	–	11

Table 6 *Enzymes of galactose metabolism (activity relative to hemoglobin)*

EC number	Name of enzyme	Measured at	Subjects	Mean	s	(Extreme range)	Reference
				mU/g			
2.7.1.6	Galactokinase	37 °C	122 subjects	29.7	4.9	–	14
2.7.7.12	UDPglucose–hexose-1-phosphate uridylyltransferase (galactose-1-phosphate uridylyltransferase)	37 °C	66 subjects	472	87	(338–702)	17
		37 °C	20 subjects	505	47	(400–550)	18
		30 °C	Newborn, cord blood	983	200	–	36
		30 °C	Adults	883	83	–	36
5.1.3.2	UDPglucose 4-epimerase	37 °C	36 subjects	81.7	18.8	(45.3–132)	48

Galactokinase: Activity increased in children younger than 4 years[15]. (Lower values in Blacks than in Whites[16].) Galactose-1-phosphate uridylyltransferase: The Duarte variant of the enzyme shows lower activity[17].

Table 7 *Enzymes of purine metabolism*

EC number	Name of enzyme (substrate in brackets)	Measured at	Subjects	Mean	s	(Extreme range)	Reference
				U/g			
	Activity relative to hemoglobin						
2.4.2.1	Purine-nucleoside phosphorylase	25 °C	14 newborn, cord blood	17.2	3.6	(13.0–21.0)	49
		25 °C	50 adults	19.3	4.7	(12.1–23.7)	49
	Activity relative to protein						
2.4.2.1	Purine-nucleoside phosphorylase (inosine)	37 °C	65 subjects	39.5	10.2	–	19
2.4.2.7	Adenine phosphoribosyltransferase	37 °C	26 subjects	0.431	0.049	–	20
			32 subjects	0.518	0.100	–	21
2.4.2.8	Hypoxanthine phosphoribosyltransferase (hypoxanthine)	37 °C	26 subjects	2.14	0.15	–	20
			32 subjects	1.72	0.30	–	21
	– (guanine)	37 °C	26 subjects	2.49	0.24	–	20
			32 subjects	1.72	0.35	–	21
2.7.6.1	Ribosephosphate pyrophosphokinase	37 °C	28 subjects	1.1	0.3	(0.7–1.6)	46
3.6.1.19	Nucleosidetriphosphate pyrophosphatase (ITP)	37 °C	150 subjects	4.9	2.4	(0.3–12)	38

Table 8 *Adenosine deaminase in erythrocytes and lymphocytes*

EC number	Name of enzyme	Material	Measured at	Subjects	Mean	s	95% range (experimental range)	Reference
					U/g			
		Activity relative to hemoglobin						
3.5.4.4	Adenosine deaminase	Erythrocytes	25 °C	14 newborn, cord blood	0.58	0.08	(0.42–0.76)	49
		Erythrocytes	25 °C	50 adults	0.62	0.13	(0.35–0.91)	49
		Erythrocytes	37 °C	12 adults	1.38	0.26	(1.05–1.90)	33
		Erythrocytes	37 °C	46 subjects	1.14	0.52	–	39
		Activity relative to protein						
		Erythrocytes	37 °C	37 adults	1.22	0.25	–	44
		Lymphocytes	37 °C	19 adults	14.3	3.6	–	44

Table 9 *Enzymes of pyrimidine metabolism (measured at 37 °C)*

EC number	Name of enzyme	Subjects	Mean	s	(Extreme range)	Reference
			U/L			
2.4.2.10	Orotate phosphoribosyltransferase	20 adults	1.13	0.58	(0.45–2.5)	22
4.1.1.23	Orotidine-5′-phosphate decarboxylase	20 adults	4.4	2.1	(2.1–10.2)	22
			mU/g			
	Activity relative to hemoglobin					
3.1.3.5	Pyrimidine-specific 5′-nucleotidase (substrate CMP)	10 subjects	2.54	0.29	–	40

other structures from fission by H_2O_2 or O_2^-. All the enzymes so far mentioned, as well as carbonate dehydratase (carbonate hydro-lyase) – after hemoglobin the most plentiful protein in the erythrocyte – are intracellular components. A considerable number of other enzymes, such as cholinesterase, the glycoside hydrolases and also a few of those involved in glycolysis, are components of the erythrocyte membrane[5].

In young erythrocytes the activity of many enzymes is greater than in older cells (Table 2). It should be noted however that in the erythrocytes of the newborn the activity of some enzymes is greater than the proportion of young cells would lead one to expect[6]. The principal diagnostic advantage offered by the determination of enzyme activities in the erythrocytes lies in the recognition of hereditary enzyme defects. Reference values for the enzymes in question are given in Tables 1–12. The inhibition of porphobilinogen synthase (aminolevulinate dehydratase) by lead can be taken as evidence of excessive exposure to lead[28,29] (Fig. 1). The activity of some enzymes is dependent on an adequate intake of certain vitamins. Thus the activation of transketolase by thiamine[30] and of glutathione reductase by riboflavin[31] can be used to confirm the nutritional status in respect of these vitamins.

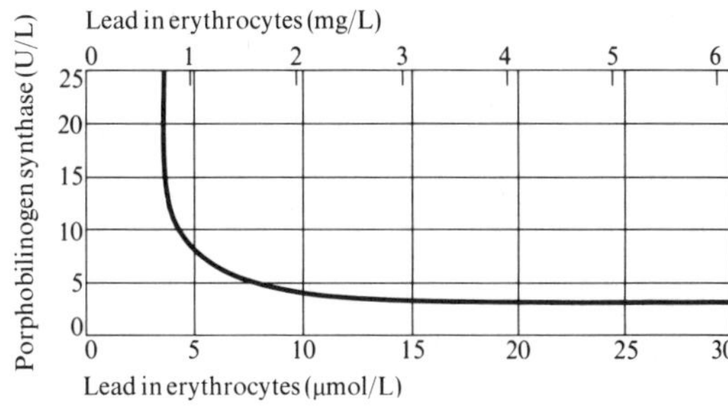

Fig. 1. Relationship between porphobilinogen synthase activity and concentration of lead in the erythrocytes[28].

Glutathione transferase catalyzes the conjugation of glutathione with several foreign compounds yielding easily excreted, water-soluble conjugates.

Table 10 *Enzymes of glutathione metabolism (activity relative to hemoglobin)*

EC number	Name of enzyme	Measured at	Subjects	Mean (U/g)	s (U/g)	Reference
2.3.2.4	γ-Glutamylcyclotransferase	37 °C	7 subjects	2.9	0.24	23
2.5.1.18	Glutathione transferase	25 °C	46 men	2.50	0.83	45
		25 °C	55 women	3.13	1.25	45
		25 °C	15 newborn, 1 week	3.42	0.98	47
		25 °C	67 adults, 15–60 years	1.62	0.36	47
6.3.2.2	γ-Glutamylcysteine synthetase	37 °C	25 subjects	0.43	0.04	24
6.3.2.3	Glutathione synthetase	37 °C	25 subjects	0.19	0.03	24

Table 11 *Enzymes of porphyrin metabolism (measured at 37 °C)*

EC number	Name of enzyme	Subjects	Mean	s	Reference
			U/L		
4.2.1.24	Porphobilinogen synthase	57 men	44.2	8.3	25
		49 women	48.2	8.7	25
		89 subjects	41.9	12.1	26
4.3.1.8	Uroporphyrinogen I synthase	59 subjects	0.513	0.093	26
		63 young men	0.633	0.078	41
		67 young women	0.667	0.085	41
	Activity relative to hemoglobin		mU/g		
4.1.1.37	Uroporphyrinogen decarboxylase	29 subjects	6	0.5	34

Uroporphyrinogen I synthase: Activity increased in the 1st month of life[27].

Table 12 *Catechol methyltransferase (measured at 37 °C)*

EC number	Name of enzyme	Subjects	Mean (U/L)	s (U/L)	Reference
2.1.1.6	Catechol methyltransferase (substrate 3,4-dihydroxybenzoic acid)	184 young men	197	78	42
		189 young women	182	65	42
	– (substrate 2-hydroxyesterone)	43 men	132	24	43
		57 women	142	28	43
		100 pregnant women	178	48	43

References

[1] HARRIS and KELLERMEYER, *The Red Cell*, Harvard University Press, Cambridge (Mass.), 1970; VALENTINE, W. N., *Arch. intern. Med.*, **135**, 1307 (1975).

[2] FLOHÉ, L., *Klin. Wschr.*, **49**, 669 (1971); PERONA et al., *Brit. J. Haemat.*, **39**, 399 (1978); SUNDE and HOEKSTRA, *Nutr. Rev.*, **38**, 265 (1980).

[3] AEBI and WYSS, in STANBURY et al. (Eds.), *The Metabolic Basis of Inherited Disease*, 4th ed., McGraw-Hill, New York, 1978, page 1792.

[4] WINTERBOURN et al., *J. Lab. clin. Med.*, **85**, 337 (1975); RISTER and BAEHNER, *Dtsch. med. Wschr.*, **103**, 977 (1978).

[5] Schrier, S.L., *Blood,* **50**, 227 (1977).
[6] Oski and Komazawa, *Semin. Hematol.,* **12**, 209 (1975).
[7] Beutler et al., *Brit.J. Haemat.,* **35**, 331 (1977).
[8] Hartz et al., *Clin.chim.Acta,* **48**, 117 (1973).
[9] Golse et al., *Nouv. Presse méd.,* **7**, 1952 (1978).
[10] Funakoshi and Deutsch, *J. Lab.clin. Med.,* **77**, 39 (1971).
[11] Kondo et al., *J.clin. Invest.,* **62**, 610 (1978).
[12] Oski, F.A., *Pediatrics,* **44**, 84 (1969).
[13] Konrad et al., *Acta haemat. (Basel),* **48**, 193 (1972).
[14] Beutler et al., *New Engl.J. Med.,* **288**, 1203 (1973).
[15] Ng et al., *J. Lab.clin. Med.,* **66**, 115 (1965); Shin-Buehring et al., *Clin. chim. Acta,* **74**, 1 (1977).
[16] Tedesco et al., *Science,* **178**, 176 (1972).
[17] Fensom et al., *Brit.med.J.,* **1**, 21 (1979).
[18] Shin-Buehring et al., *Clin.chim.Acta,* **70**, 371 (1976).
[19] Fox et al., *Science,* **197**, 1084 (1977).
[20] Chow et al., *J. Lab.clin. Med.,* **76**, 733 (1970).
[21] Kelley, W.N., *Arch. intern. Med.,* **130**, 199 (1972).
[22] Rogers et al., *J. Lab.clin. Med.,* **85**, 287 (1975).
[23] Board et al., *J. Lab.clin. Med.,* **91**, 127 (1978).
[24] Minnich et al., *J.clin. Invest.,* **50**, 507 (1971).
[25] Davis and Avram, *Clin.Chem.,* **24**, 726 (1978).
[26] Anderson et al., *Amer.J. Med.,* **63**, 359 (1977).
[27] Nordmann et al., *Lancet,* **2**, 201 (1976).
[28] Morgan and Burch, *J. Lab.clin. Med.,* **85**, 746 (1975).
[29] Nieburg et al., *Amer.J. Dis. Child.,* **127**, 348 (1974); Granick et al., *Advanc. clin. Chem.,* **20**, 287 (1978).
[30] Brin, M., *J.Amer.med.Ass.,* **187**, 762 (1964); Kjøsen and Seim, *Amer.J. clin. Nutr.,* **30**, 1591 (1977); Lonsdale et al., *Amer.J.clin.Nutr.,* **33**, 205 (1980).
[31] Bamji, M.S., *Clin.chim.Acta,* **26**, 263 (1969); Nichoalds, G.E., *Clin. Chem.,* **20**, 624 (1974); Garry and Owen, *Amer.J. clin. Nutr.,* **29**, 663 (1976).
[32] Scott et al., *J. clin. Invest.,* **53**, 1194 (1974).
[33] Körber et al., *Clin.chim.Acta,* **63**, 323 (1975).
[34] Felsher et al., *New Engl.J. Med.,* **299**, 1095 (1978).
[35] Buc et al., *Clin.chim.Acta,* **95**, 83 (1979).
[36] Fielek and Mohrenweiser, *Clin. Chem.,* **25**, 384 (1979).
[37] Mondrup et al., *Clin.chim.Acta,* **100**, 107 (1980).
[38] Holmes et al., *Clin.chim.Acta,* **97**, 143 (1979).
[39] Valentine et al., *Science,* **195**, 783 (1977).
[40] Torrance et al., *J. Lab.clin. Med.,* **90**, 563 (1977).
[41] Piepkorn et al., *Clin. Chem.,* **24**, 1751 (1978).
[42] Weinshilboum et al., *Nature,* **252**, 490 (1974).
[43] Bates et al., *Amer.J. Obstet. Gynec.,* **131**, 555 (1978).
[44] Müller et al., *Klin. Wschr.,* **60**, 317 (1982).
[45] Strange et al., *Clin.chim.Acta,* **120**, 251 (1982).
[46] Becker et al., *Amer.J. Med.,* **55**, 232 (1973).
[47] Carmagnol et al., *Clin.chim.Acta,* **117**, 209 (1981).
[48] Gitzelmann et al., *Helv.paediat.Acta,* **31**, 441 (1976).
[49] Glader et al., *New. Engl.J. Med.,* **309**, 1486 (1983).

Composition of the blood

Human blood, like the blood of all vertebrates, consists of a cellular fraction, and a fluid (plasma) fraction. The ratio between these two fractions varies even in normal persons among the different segments of the vascular system, and also depends on the basic conditions (orthostatic or supine position, ambient temperature, state of hydration, altitude of residence; see pages 65–67). In addition, the composition of a blood sample from the same individual will depend on the site from which it was drawn (finger tip or vein), as well as on the sampling technique (e.g. congestion, tissue compression). Unless otherwise indicated, the normal values given below apply to the following conditions: sampling without congestion from the brachial vein, supine position, room temperature of 20–25 °C, altitude less than 1000 m above sea level, and dry EDTA used to inhibit clotting.

The cellular fraction of the blood

In normal adults, blood cells are formed in the bone marrow and lymphatic organs; in children, until about the 3rd month of life, a small quantity is also formed in the liver. Blood cells survive for between a few hours (granulocytes) and several years (T lymphocytes) after leaving the hemopoietic tissues. Lymphocytes recirculate via the lymph nodes and the thoracic duct, while the other cells pass through the peripheral blood pool only once and, with the exception of monocytes, perish once they have left the vascular system. The relative constancy of the blood-cell concentration over prolonged periods of time reflects a subtly regulated equilibrium with by and large constant production and decomposition rates.

Table 1 *Cellular fractions in venous blood of adults*

Type of cell	Number concentration	Mean corpuscular volume	Volume fraction
	L^{-1}	fL	
Erythrocytes	5×10^{12}	87	0.4350
Granulocytes*	4.4×10^{9}	450	0.0020
Monocytes	0.5×10^{9}	470	0.0002
Lymphocytes	2.2×10^{9}	230	0.0005
Platelets	2.5×10^{11}	9	0.0225
Precursors, plasma cells	Sporadic	–	–
Total	5.26×10^{12}	–	0.4602

*Band and segmented neutrophils, eosinophils and basophils.

If blood treated with an anticlotting agent is centrifuged in narrow tubes or capillaries for about 5 minutes at 12000 *g*, the cellular fraction is separated as a result of the relative density of the blood cells, which exceeds 1.0. At such conditions, 1–2% of the plasma is trapped in the cell fraction. The cell volume, expressed as a fraction of whole-blood volume, is referred to as the hematocrit (Hct) or packed cell volume (PCV). Since erythrocytes normally make up 96% of the cellular fraction of the volume (Table 1), the designations Hct or PCV are as a rule used to refer only to the erythrocyte fraction.

*This chapter on 'Blood Cells' (pages 205–213) has been compiled in collaboration with H. Heimpel, Zentrum für innere Medizin, Universität Ulm, Ulm, FRG.

Erythrocytes

Erythrocytes are formed by extrusion of the nucleus from oxyphilic or orthochromatic erythroblasts of the bone marrow. Their main function is oxygen transport, while their main component is hemoglobin. Residues of ribosomes and other cell organelles are still detectable in young erythrocytes a few days after loss of the nucleus. These residues are responsible for the slight polychromatophilia in panoptic stains, and for the formation of substantia granulofilamentosa, which stains deeply with basic vital stains, whence the term 'reticulocytes' (cells having a net-like pattern). In contrast to other blood cells, erythrocytes circulating in the plasma are not spheroidal but disc-shaped, with a slight central depression. In determinations of size, it should be borne in mind that changes in the osmotic or colloid-osmotic pressure of the suspending fluid may give rise to reversible changes in shape and size. Table 2 presents some important parameters for erythrocytes.

Determination methods

Erythrocyte count (E). The classical method of optical counting under a microscope (counting chamber) is time-consuming and relatively imprecise (coefficient of variation up to 15%), and has been replaced in most laboratories by electronic counting, whereby the automated volume measurement reduces the pipetting error as well, so that the main source of error left is the uneven mixing of the blood sample before processing. If the procedure is carried out carefully, and if the instruments are technically in order, the coefficient of variation is 2%[1].

In most electronic counting instruments, the counting is based on changes in the electrical conductivity as a cell (or other particle) passes through a capillary of diameter 50–100 μm (the Coulter principle). Since the change in conductivity is approximately proportional to the cell volume, cells of different orders of volume (e.g. platelets, erythrocytes, leukocytes) can be counted separately. Less often, deflection or interruption of a beam of light as a cell passes through a capillary is used as the basis of measurement.

Hemoglobin concentration (Hb). Hemoglobin is determined photometrically after hemolysis and conversion of hemoglobin to cyanmethemoglobin. The details of the procedure, and the transformation and calibration solutions have been internationally standardized[2]. All hemoglobin compounds with the exception of sulfhemoglobin are detected by the cyanmethemoglobin method.

Hematocrit (Hct). The hematocrit (volume of erythrocytes in relation to the volume of whole blood) is determined by two fundamentally different methods:

1. Separation of cells from plasma by means of gravity. The sample is centrifuged at high speed in capillaries, and the segment of the total length of the filled capillary that is filled by the erythrocyte column is measured. The details of the procedure (especially the duration of centrifugation) have been standardized internationally[3]. The plasma trapped between the erythrocytes (1–2%) is not corrected for in routine determinations. In the case of pathologically reduced erythrocyte deformability (e.g. in sickle-cell anemia or in spherocytosis), this fraction may be elevated.
2. Determination of corpuscular volume distribution and calculation of hematocrit as a product of the mean corpuscular volume (MCV) and erythrocyte count. This procedure is used in most semi- or completely automated blood-cell counting instruments. Cell deformability is of no essential importance here, although absorption of plasma proteins in paraproteinemias or of anti-erythrocytic autoantibodies does play some role in so far as 'pseudomacrocytosis' may occur as a result. Since the plasma remaining in the erythrocyte fraction is taken into account with

Table 2 *Nomenclature and typical values of erythrocyte indices*

Parameter	Abbreviation	Unit	Example of a normal value
Erythrocyte count (number concentration of erythrocytes) in whole blood	E	L^{-1}	5×10^{12}
Hemoglobin concentration (mass concentration of hemoglobin) in whole blood	Hb	g/L	150
Hematocrit (volume fraction of erythrocytes in whole blood)	Hct	–	0.46
Mean corpuscular volume (volume of 1 erythrocyte)	MCV	fL	90
Mean corpuscular hemoglobin (mass of hemoglobin in 1 erythrocyte)	MCH (Hb_E)	pg	30
Mean corpuscular hemoglobin concentration (mass concentration of hemoglobin in erythrocytes)	MCHC	g/L	340

a 0.94 correction factor in calibrating against microhematocrit values in control blood samples, the hematocrit value calculated with the Coulter method is lower than the uncorrected macrohematocrit or microhematocrit values.

Mean corpuscular volume (MCV). This value is either calculated from the capillary hematocrit and the erythrocyte count:

$$MCV = \frac{Hct}{E} \times 10^{15}$$

or measured directly from the change in conductivity of a large number of individual cells. As a rule, the cell volumes show a logarithmic-normal distribution (skewed to the right)[4]. In anemias, abnormal distributions occur. The same applies to cellular hemoglobin contents measured directly by cytophotometry[5].

A reduction in the MCV is referred to as 'microcytosis', while an elevated MCV is designated 'macrocytosis'. The MCV is of particular diagnostic importance for the mechanism of the anemias since microcytosis is evidence of a disturbance in hemoglobinization (e.g. in iron deficiency), while macrocytosis indicates impaired cell formation (in vitamin B_{12} deficiency).

Mean corpuscular hemoglobin (MCH). This value normally correlates, and in almost all forms of anemia, with the mean corpuscular volume since the mean hemoglobin concentration is by and large constant. It is calculated from the hemoglobin concentration and the erythrocyte count:

$$MCH = \frac{Hb}{E} \times 10^{12}$$

Mean corpuscular hemoglobin concentration (MCHC). This value is calculated either from the hemoglobin content and the hematocrit

$$MCHC = \frac{Hb}{Hct}$$

or as the quotient MCH/MCV (e.g. with the Coulter counter). It is diminished only rarely (e.g. in extreme iron deficiency), and just as rarely elevated (in some forms of hemolytic anemia). Fluctuations beyond the normal usually indicate analytical errors in the measurement of one of the indices used in the calculation.

It should be noted that MCV, MCH, and MCHC are mean values derived from distribution curves which in pathological cases may have been obtained on the basis of distinct cell populations. Such distribution curves are available only for MCV values measured directly in automated cell counters.

Reference values of erythrocyte indices

The normal values for the various erythrocyte indices are interdependent and are therefore presented together. However, erythrocyte count, hemoglobin concentration and hematocrit do not correlate directly with one another, for MCV, MCH, and MCHC are biological variables and as such dependent on age, sex, and the incidence of iron deficiency in the reference population. In the newborn, erythrocytes are distinctly larger and richer in hemoglobin, and consequently MCV and MCH are higher than in normal adults. During the period of growth these values fall temporarily to below adult levels as a consequence of 'physiological' iron deficiency.

From among the numerous reference groups, two have been selected here (see Tables 3 and 4) which reproduce the statistical pattern of economically highly developed populations[1,6]. Almost identical values to those given have been found in an European study[7]. Hb, Hct, MCV and MCH are higher in smokers of both sexes in almost all age groups than in nonsmokers[8]. The distribution curves of the indices are usually roughly symmetrical with a tendency toward a 'skewness to the left' in nonselected reference groups derived from the fact that undiscovered moderate anemias are more frequent than polycythemia[6]. The distributions tend to have higher dispersion with age[9]. It is usually difficult to determine whether interracial differences exist since socioeconomic influences tend to predominate[1,10]. There is evidence, however, that some normal values for Whites and Blacks differ[11].

Morphological variations in erythrocytes and erythrocyte diameter

A clear distinction must be made between erythrocyte indices measured and calculated in whole blood, and indices determined in blood smears. The cells undergo changes in size and shape during the processing of the smear, its drying and fixation. The extent of these changes is dependent on a number of different factors which in turn may be themselves subject to divergent influences in cases of erythrocyte pathology.

An abnormally great and more frequent divergence from the normal disc shape is called poikilocytosis; a preponderance of oval shapes is referred to as ovalocytosis or elliptocytosis; an increased variation in the diameter is termed anisocytosis; while a heightened variability in staining is known as anisochromatophilia.

In technically well prepared smears from normal adults, the mean erythrocyte diameter is 7.2–7.9 µm; the value obtained by holography with the interference microscope is 7.82 µm (s0.62 µm)[12]. Measurements of the mean erythrocyte diameter or the plotting of diameter distribution curves (Price-Jones curves), however, are no longer of any diagnostic significance. The same applies to derived values such as 'erythrocyte thickness', or the 'spherical index'. The terms 'microcytosis' or 'macrocytosis', 'hypochromia' or 'hyperchromia' are often used in their morphological sense for erythrocytes in blood smears. They must not be considered as being identical with the parameters of the same name referring to whole blood (see section 'Mean corpuscular volume'), even if in many cases they may parallel them.

Hemoglobin F

During human ontogeny there is a switch from fetal hemoglobin (Hb F, $\alpha_2\gamma_2$) to adult hemoglobin (Hb A, $\alpha_2\beta_2$), due to a change in the non-α-globin synthesis[13]. For Hb F determination, the alkali-denaturation technique is recommended, at least for a Hb F fraction between 2% and 40%; for values below 2%, radioimmunoassay and for values above 40%, chromatographic procedures are more accurate[14]. Hb F is the predominant hemoglobin in fetal life and early infancy; in children and adults only traces can be found (Table 5).

Hemoglobin A_2

Hemoglobin A_2 (Hb A_2, $\alpha_2\delta_2$) can be separated from Hb A and Hb F by various electrophoretic or chromatographic methods. Hb A_2 is found in relatively small amounts in fetal erythrocytes[13], but the fraction increases after birth, reaching values of 2–3% in children and adults (Table 5).

Reticulocytes

After erythrocytes have escaped into the peripheral blood, the residues of the cell organelles remain detectable by vital staining for another 24–36 hours (brilliant cresyl blue or methylene blue are mainly used for staining). Since vital staining of very young erythrocytes results in the formation of net-like clumps of organelle residues, erythrocytes in this stage are called reticulocytes (also vital-granulated erythrocytes or proerythrocytes). Given a survival time of 115 days for all erythrocytes, reticulocytes account for about 1–2% of the total erythrocyte count. Elevated reticulocyte fractions, which may exceed 50% in the individual case, are an expression either of a cohort of immature erythrocytes in the regeneration phase of anemia (after acute hemorrhage or after administration of vitamin B_{12} in pernicious anemia) or of a lasting reduction in the erythrocyte survival time in the blood (chronic hemolysis, chronic hemorrhage). The reticulocyte count in 1 L of blood is termed 'absolute reticulocyte count' and serves as a measure of the number of erythrocytes emerging daily from the bone marrow ('effective erythrocyte production').

The normal values for the reticulocyte count (Tables 6–8) are dependent on age (up to the age of 1 year), sex (slightly higher values for women, probably because of menstrual blood loss), and above all on the staining and counting techniques. Reference values are determined with especially careful and thorough microscopical focusing, so that simple routine values tend to be lower.

When erythropoiesis is intensively stimulated (severe anemia, high erythropoietin concentration), younger, readily stainable types of reticulocytes enter into the peripheral blood. It used to be thought of value to classify reticulocytes into degrees 1 through 4 according to their maturity (Table 9); this classification is still utilized in certain pathophysiological contexts. Because of the earlier efflux of reticulocytes in severe anemia, the reticulocyte counts in this condition show a greater rise than might be expected from the decrease of erythrocyte life-span alone.

In normal panoptical staining of blood smears, the same young erythrocytes show a bluish coloration (due to RNA) and are therefore referred to as 'polychromatic erythrocytes'. However, identification by means of this coloration is difficult, as the difference is only slight, so reticulocyte staining is always used to count young erythrocytes.

(Continued on page 208)

Table 3 *Erythrocytometric values for 'apparently healthy' white and black subjects of different ages**

Subjects	Age	Erythrocytes: Number concentration in whole blood		Erythrocytes: Mean corpuscular volume		Hematocrit		Hemoglobin concentration in whole blood		Mean corpuscular hemoglobin concentration		Mean corpuscular hemoglobin	
		Mean	95% range	Mean	95% range	Mean	95% range	Mean	95% range	Mean	95% range	Mean	95% range
		10^{12}/L		fL				g/L				pg	
Men	Adults	5.1	4.3–5.9	90	80–100	0.47	0.39–0.55	151	139–163	340	310–370	30	25.4–34.6
Women	Adults	4.5	3.5–5.5	88	79–98	0.42	0.36–0.48	135	120–150	330	300–360	30	25.4–34.6
Boys	Newborn	5.6	5.0–6.3	105	95–115	0.59	0.53–0.65	200	185–215	330	320–340	36	30–42
	1 month	5.2	4.7–5.9	101	92–110	0.50	0.44–0.56	170	155–185	320	310–330	36	30–42
	3 months	4.5	3.8–5.2	100	92–110	0.45	0.39–0.52	150	135–165	330	320–340	33	28–38
	6 months	4.6	3.8–5.1	100	92–109	0.46	0.39–0.51	140	130–160	300	290–310	30	27–34
	9 months	4.6	3.7–5.2	97	90–104	0.45	0.39–0.52	130	120–140	280	270–300	28	24–32
	1 year	4.2	3.5–4.9	95	87–98	0.41	0.37–0.45	121	100–140	290	280–300	27	24–32
	2 years	4.2	3.5–4.9	88	80–95	0.40	0.36–0.47	123	105–142	300	280–310	28	24–32
	4 years	4.2	3.7–5.0	89	80–96	0.37	0.30–0.44	126	112–143	280	270–290	28	24–32
	8 years	4.6	4.0–5.1	87	80–94	0.41	0.37–0.45	134	120–148	290	280–300	29	23–34
	14 years	4.7	3.9–5.3	88	80–95	0.41	0.36–0.46	140	125–150	300	290–310	29	23–34
Girls	Newborn	5.6	5.0–6.3	103	94–114	0.58	0.51–0.65	195	180–210	340	330–350	34	28–40
	1 month	5.2	4.7–6.0	102	92–112	0.49	0.42–0.56	170	158–189	320	310–330	36	30–42
	3 months	4.4	3.8–5.2	104	92–112	0.44	0.39–0.51	148	133–164	330	320–340	33	27–39
	6 months	4.2	3.5–4.9	100	91–109	0.44	0.39–0.50	138	128–148	320	310–330	30	25–35
	9 months	4.2	3.5–4.9	98	90–105	0.43	0.37–0.50	128	117–139	300	290–310	28	23–34
	1 year	4.2	3.4–5.0	95	87–100	0.43	0.37–0.49	122	100–140	300	290–310	27	22–30
	2 years	4.2	3.5–5.0	94	86–101	0.43	0.36–0.50	122	105–142	300	290–310	27	22–30
	4 years	4.4	3.8–5.2	88	80–95	0.43	0.36–0.51	127	113–142	280	270–290	28	23–31
	8 years	4.5	3.9–5.1	89	80–96	0.40	0.36–0.46	130	115–145	280	270–290	29	23–33
	14 years	4.5	3.8–5.2	87	80–94	0.40	0.36–0.47	132	116–148	290	280–300	29	23–33

From MIALE, J. B., *Laboratory Medicine: Hematology*, 6th ed., The C.V. Mosby Co., St. Louis, Mo., 1982, page 378, with kind permission of the publishers.

Table 4 *Erythrocytometric values of a nonselected reference population*◊

Subjects	Age	Number	Erythrocytes: Number concentration in whole blood		Erythrocytes: Mean corpuscular volume		Hematocrit		Hemoglobin concentration in whole blood		Mean corpuscular hemoglobin concentration		Mean corpuscular hemoglobin	
			Mean	1.96 s	Mean	1.96 s	Mean	1.96 s	Mean	1.96 s	Mean	1.96 s	Mean	1.96 s
			10^{12}/L		fL				g/L				pg	
Males	All ages	1082	4.97	0.39	88.71	4.91	0.44	0.035	149.4	12.2	339.8	8.6	30.13	1.77
	10–14 years	145	4.84	0.34	83.88	3.43	0.40	0.025	137.2	8.8	339.0	7.3	28.42	1.20
	15–19 years	148	5.05	0.35	86.99	3.71	0.44	0.031	149.2	10.9	340.5	7.4	29.61	1.31
	20–24 years	101	5.05	0.32	88.97	3.72	0.45	0.026	152.6	9.6	340.5	7.3	30.27	1.27
	25–34 years	183	5.03	0.36	89.30	4.33	0.45	0.028	152.8	9.6	341.0	6.3	30.44	1.56
	35–44 years	134	5.03	0.34	89.73	3.97	0.45	0.028	152.9	10.4	344.0	7.0	30.56	1.45
	45–54 years	139	5.01	0.39	90.21	4.94	0.45	0.014	154.0	10.9	341.2	7.2	30.79	1.70
	55–64 years	101	4.93	0.42	90.54	4.96	0.45	0.036	151.2	12.8	339.4	7.2	30.71	1.88
	65–74 years	93	4.86	0.43	90.64	5.52	0.44	0.034	140.4	17.5	336.5	8.4	30.49	2.02
	≥75 years	38	4.60	0.53	91.45	5.50	0.42	0.045	147.8	12.1	338.4	8.7	30.55	1.92
Females	All ages	1279	4.52	0.36	88.26	4.72	0.40	0.031	133.7	10.8	335.4	9.6	29.60	1.79
	10–14 years	149	4.69	0.30	85.65	3.58	0.40	0.024	135.4	8.3	337.2	7.9	28.87	1.25
	15–19 years	159	4.58	0.31	87.80	3.95	0.40	0.026	134.6	9.3	335.3	8.9	29.45	1.52
	20–24 years	119	4.45	0.34	89.27	4.07	0.40	0.030	133.3	10.6	335.8	8.3	29.98	1.50
	25–34 years	218	4.47	0.33	88.57	4.30	0.40	0.028	132.7	10.0	335.4	7.5	29.69	1.53
	35–44 years	167	4.46	0.42	89.02	4.77	0.40	0.033	133.2	11.8	335.7	8.7	29.91	1.75
	45–54 years	190	4.50	0.38	88.15	5.93	0.40	0.035	132.5	12.9	335.0	10.3	29.52	2.30
	55–64 years	131	4.55	0.32	88.77	3.82	0.40	0.027	135.3	9.5	335.0	7.1	29.73	1.45
	65–74 years	105	4.55	0.40	88.44	5.63	0.40	0.036	134.1	12.3	334.2	9.5	29.56	2.22
	≥75 years	42	4.40	0.40	90.40	4.13	0.40	0.033	133.2	12.2	334.9	8.7	30.29	1.61

◊From KELLY, A., and MUNAN, L., *Brit. J. Haemat.*, **35**, 154 (1977), with kind permission of the authors and publishers.

Table 5 *Hemoglobin F and hemoglobin A_2 fractions*[15]

Age	Number	Hemoglobin F			Hemoglobin A_2		
		Mean	s	(Extreme range)	Mean	s	(Extreme range)
		Mass fraction (relative to total hemoglobin) as percent					
1–7 days	10	74.7	2.70	(61.0–79.6)	–	–	–
2 weeks	13	74.9	2.85	(66.0–80.5)	–	–	–
1 month	11	60.2	3.15	(45.7–67.3)	0.2	0.15	(0–0.8)
2 months	10	45.6	5.05	(29.4–60.8)	1.1	0.35	(0.4–2.2)
3 months	10	26.6	7.25	(14.8–55.9)	1.6	0.30	(0.4–2.3)
4 months	10	17.7	3.05	(9.4–28.5)	1.6	0.20	(0.8–2.1)
5 months	10	10.4	3.35	(2.3–22.4)	1.7	0.30	(0.6–2.5)
6 months	15	6.5	1.50	(2.7–13.0)	2.0	0.15	(1.4–2.5)
8 months	11	5.1	1.80	(2.3–11.9)	2.1	0.15	(1.4–2.6)
10 months	10	2.1	0.35	(1.5–3.5)	2.3	0.15	(1.9–2.8)
12 months	10	2.6	0.75	(1.3–5.0)	2.3	0.10	(2.0–2.7)
1–14 years and adults	100	0.6	0.2	–	1.3	0.1	–

Table 6 *Reticulocyte fraction in newborn*

Age	FAXÉN[16]	SEIP[17]
	Number relative to 1000 erythrocytes	
1 day	22	52
2 days	20.4	50
3 days	16.6	52
4 days	10.7	45
5 days	5.3	33
6 days	4.8	18
7 days	3.8	13

Table 7 *Reticulocyte fraction in children*

Age	Mean	s	95% range	Reference
	Number relative to 1000 erythrocytes			
Premature, <48 hours	54	19	–	18
Full-term, <48 hours	47	19	–	18
1–24 hours	39.2	–	–	19
1st–7th day	22.3	–	–	19
7th–10th day	10.6	–	–	19
10th–30th day	7.9	3.8	0.3–15.5	19
1st–2nd month	12.9	7.4	0–27.7	19
2nd–6th month	10.6	7.1	0–24.8	19
6th–12th month	7.5	4.9	0–17.3	19
1st year	7.5	4.4	0–16.3	19
2nd year	7.1	4.0	0–15.1	19
3rd year	7.2	4.1	0–15.4	19
4th year	8.1	5.0	0–18.1	19
5th year	8.2	4.5	0–17.2	19
6th year	7.5	4.0	0–15.5	19
7th year	7.6	3.5	0.6–14.6	19
8th year	6.8	3.2	0.4–13.2	19
9th year	7.5	3.3	0.9–14.1	19
10th year	7.6	3.2	1.2–14.0	19
11th–15th year	7.4	4.0	0–15.4	19

Nucleated erythrocytes (erythroblasts)

Normally, these are not found in the peripheral blood of adults and older children, but do occur sporadically in cord blood and in normal infants (Table 10)[23].

Table 8 *Reticulocyte fraction and concentration in adults*

Subjects	Mean	s	95% range	Mean	95% range	Reference
	Number relative to 1000 erythrocytes			10^9/L		
Men	16	–	8–25	88	18–158	20
Women	17	–	8–41	–	–	20
Men and women	8	4	–	–	–	18
	–	–	2–20	–	24–84	21

Table 9
Distribution of reticulocytes according to their degree of maturity[22]

	Mean	(Extreme range)
	Number relative to 1000 erythrocytes	
Degree of maturity 1	0.02	(0–0.2)
Degree of maturity 2	1.1	(0–2.6)
Degree of maturity 3	5.0	(1.8–10.8)
Degree of maturity 4	9.5	(5.8–12.0)

Table 10 *Erythroblast fraction in peripheral blood*[23]

Age	Mean	(Extreme range)
	Number relative to 1000 nucleated cells	
Newborn (cord blood)	32	(0–300)
Newborn (1–10 hours)	16	(0–160)
Newborn (2 days)	–	(0–10)
Adults	0	–

Erythrocyte fragility

Various resistance tests are used to determine primary and secondary changes in the erythrocyte membrane, although the importance of these tests has declined lately owing to the broader use of exact biochemical analyses. The end point of all resistance tests is the appearance or concentration of dissolved hemoglobin in the supernatant.

Osmotic resistance is tested with different concentrations of NaCl (Fig. 1); mechanical resistance is tested by mechanical alteration with, for example, rotating glass beads. The term 'autohemolysis' is used to refer to relative hemolysis (expressed as the fraction of hemoglobin dissolved in the supernatant relative to the total hemoglobin in the sample) after 24 or 48 hours of incubation at 37 °C. A characteristic feature of the various forms of hemolytic anemia is, in addition to a decrease in the baseline values, the inhibition of hemolysis by addition of glucose or ATP.

Erythrocyte life-span

ASHBY's method (differential agglutination of transfused donor erythrocytes) has been replaced by determination using ^{51}Cr- or ^{32}P-diisopropylfluorophosphate (page 215). For life-span and half-life of erythrocytes see Table 11.

Leukocytes

All nucleated cells normally occurring in the peripheral blood are called leukocytes. They are derived from two cell-renewal systems, that of the myeloid stem cell and that of the lymphoid stem cell which most probably originate from the same parent cell but are regulated independently of one another. Nucleated erythrocyte-precursor cells are found only sporadically in the peripheral blood after the first 3 months of life and are then immediately eliminated in the spleen: in pathological conditions with erythroblastosis, however, erythroblasts and all other nucleated cells are included in the 'total leukocyte count' as determined with today's counting techniques.

Although the total leukocyte count is the resultant of the dynamics of two different cell systems, it is useful to give reference

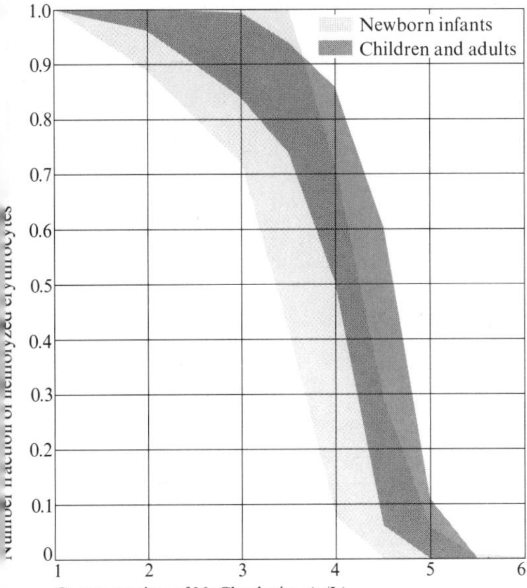

ig. 1. Osmotic fragility of erythrocytes[24].

alues. In clinical practice, when the total leukocyte count is nor-nal, microscopic determination of the fractions of the different ell forms (differential leukocyte count) is often dispensed with. ertain changes in the circulatory situation affect all nucleated ells in the blood and give rise to leukopenia (e.g. in hypersplen-sm) or leukocytosis (e.g. in release of epinephrine) without any hange in the differential blood count.

etermination of the total leukocyte count

With all methods, the erythrocytes are hemolyzed before the eukocytes are counted. The older counting-chamber methods are elatively imprecise (coefficients of variation may range between 5 nd 15% in counts from the same blood sample). Greater precision s achieved with automatic counters (coefficients of variation within 2%[7]). However, because it is impossible to eliminate other articles from the count, automatic counters are not suited for he precise determination of very low leukocyte concentrations $< 0.5 \times 10^9$/L).

eference values for the total leukocyte count

It should be borne in mind that when several leukocyte counts re made consecutively on the same individual, they show much roader variations within the normal range than do erythrocyte ounts[31]. This is due, first, to the fact that the granulocyte-storage ites in the bone marrow contain several times the number of ma-

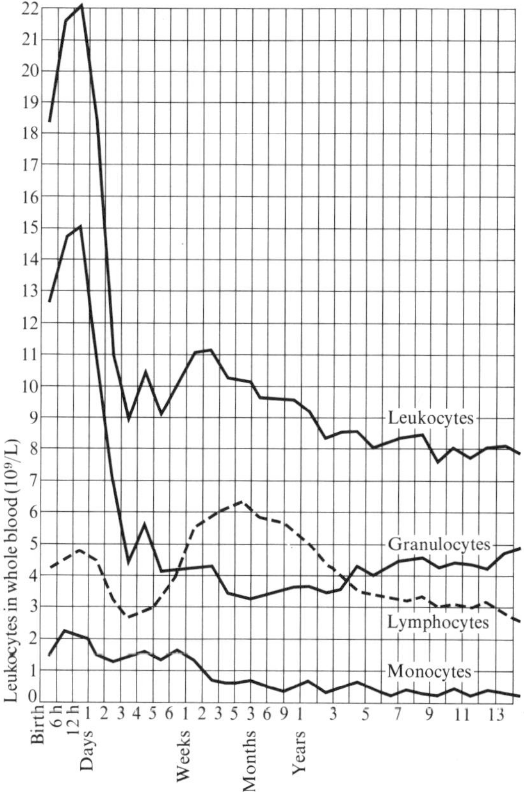

Fig. 2. Number concentration of leukocytes in whole blood from birth to 14 years[32].

ture granulocytes circulating in the peripheral blood and that they can be rapidly released, and, second, to the rapid and reversible relative changes between the circulating and marginal cell pools. The total leukocyte count is thus dependent on various external factors over the short term, e.g. on physical exertion, mental stress, or the intake of meals.

The total leukocyte count is highest in the newborn, decreasing to less than half this original level by the end of puberty (Fig. 2 and Table 12). There are no unequivocal sex differences. Somewhat higher counts are observed among smokers[8]. The total neutrophil count is lower in black adults and in black children than in white adults and in white children[37,38].

(Continued on page 211)

able 11 *Kinetic and metabolic data for erythrocytes*

Parameter	Age	Unit	Mean	s	(Extreme range)	Ref.
Mean life-span	Adults	d	103	–	(74–153)	25
	Adults	d	107	12	–	26
Apparent half-life (^{51}Cr)	Newborn (cord blood)	d	17.5	–	(14.5–20.5)	27
	1st–5th day	d	–	–	(21–35)	28
	3rd–9th week	d	–	–	(12–33)	28
	Adults	d	29	–	(25–40)	29
	Adults	d	25	2	–	27
Glucose consumption in 10^{12} cells	Premature infants, < 48 hours	µmol/h	424	106	(204–608)	18
	Full-term infants, < 48 hours	µmol/h	470	160	(216–714)	18
	Adults	µmol/h	268	62	(196–423)	18
O_2 uptake in 10^{12} cells		µmol/h	27	14	–	30
CO_2 formation in 10^{12} cells		µmol/h	25	11	–	30
Pyruvate formation in 10^{12} cells		µmol/h	19	4	–	30
Lactate formation in 10^{12} cells		µmol/h	384	59	–	30

Table 12 *Leukocyte concentrations in whole blood and distribution in different age groups*

Age	Total leukocyte concentration		Neutrophils: Total concentration			Neutrophils: Band		Neutrophils: Segmented		Eosinophils			Basophils			Lymphocytes			Monocytes			Neutrophilic myelocytes		Reference
	Mean	95% range (extreme range in brackets)	Mean	95% range (extreme range in brackets)	Mean	Mean		Mean		Mean	95% range (extreme range in brackets)	Mean	Mean	95% range (extreme range in brackets)	Mean	Mean	95% range (extreme range in brackets)	Mean	Mean	95% range (extreme range in brackets)	Mean	95% range		
	$10^6/L$	$10^6/L$	$10^6/L$	$10^6/L$	%	$10^6/L$	%	$10^6/L$	%	$10^6/L$	$10^6/L$	%	$10^6/L$	$10^6/L$	%	$10^6/L$	$10^6/L$	%	$10^6/L$	$10^6/L$	%	$10^6/L$	%	
Birth	18100	(9000–30000)	11000	(6000–26000)	61	1650	9.1	9400	52	400	(20–850)	2.2	100	(0–640)	0.6	5500	(2000–11000)	31	1050	(400–3100)	5.8			33, 34
12 hours	22800	(13000–38000)	15500	(6000–28000)	68	2330	10.2	13200	58	450	(20–950)	2.0	100	(0–500)	0.4	5500	(2000–11000)	24	1200	(400–3600)	5.3	0–1908	0–10	33, 34
24 hours	18900	(9400–34000)	11500	(5000–21000)	61	1750	9.2	9800	52	450	(50–1000)	2.4	100	(0–300)	0.5	5800	(2000–11500)	31	1100	(200–3100)	5.8			33, 34
1 week	12200	(5000–21000)	5500	(1500–10000)	45	830	6.8	4700	39	500	(70–1100)	4.1	50	(0–250)	0.4	5000	(2000–17000)	41	1100	(300–2700)	9.1	0–437	0–3	33, 34
2 weeks	11400	(5000–20000)	4500	(1000–9500)	40	630	5.5	3900	34	350	(70–1000)	3.1	50	(0–230)	0.4	5500	(2000–17000)	48	1000	(200–2400)	8.8	0–102	0–1	33, 34
4 weeks	10800	(5000–19500)	3800	(1000–9000)	35	490	4.5	3300	30	300	(70–900)	2.8	50	(0–200)	0.5	6000	(2500–16500)	56	700	(150–2000)	6.5	–	–	33
2 months	11000	(5500–18000)	3800	(1000–9000)	34	490	4.4	3300	30	300	(70–850)	2.7	50	(0–200)	0.5	6300	(3000–16000)	57	650	(130–1800)	5.9	–	–	33
4 months	11500	(6000–17500)	3800	(1000–9000)	33	450	3.9	3300	29	300	(70–800)	2.6	50	(0–200)	0.4	6800	(3500–14500)	59	600	(100–1500)	5.2	–	–	33
6 months	11900	(6000–17500)	3800	(1000–8500)	32	450	3.8	3300	28	300	(70–750)	2.5	50	(0–200)	0.4	7300	(4000–13500)	61	580	(100–1300)	4.8	–	–	33
8 months	12200	(6000–17500)	3700	(1000–8500)	30	410	3.3	3300	27	300	(70–700)	2.5	50	(0–200)	0.4	7600	(4500–12500)	62	580	(80–1200)	4.7	–	–	33
10 months	12000	(6000–17500)	3600	(1000–8500)	30	400	3.3	3200	27	300	(60–700)	2.5	50	(0–200)	0.4	7500	(4500–11500)	63	550	(50–1200)	4.6	–	–	33
12 months	11400	(6000–17500)	3500	(1500–8500)	31	350	3.1	3200	28	300	(50–700)	2.6	50	(0–200)	0.4	7000	(4000–10500)	61	550	(50–1100)	4.8	–	–	33
2 years	10600	(6000–17000)	3500	(1500–8500)	33	320	3.0	3200	30	280	(40–650)	2.6	50	(0–200)	0.5	6300	(3000–9500)	59	530	(50–1000)	5.0	–	–	33
4 years	9100	(5500–15500)	3800	(1500–8500)	42	270	3.0	3500	39	250	(20–650)	2.8	50	(0–200)	0.6	4500	(2000–8000)	50	450	(0–800)	5.0	–	–	33
6 years	8500	(5000–14500)	4300	(1500–8000)	51	250	3.0	4000	48	230	(0–650)	2.7	50	(0–200)	0.6	3500	(1500–7000)	42	400	(0–800)	4.7	–	–	33
8 years	8300	(4500–13500)	4400	(1500–8000)	53	250	3.0	4100	50	200	(0–600)	2.4	50	(0–200)	0.6	3300	(1500–6800)	39	350	(0–800)	4.2	–	–	33
10 years	8100	(4500–13500)	4400	(1800–8000)	54	240	3.0	4200	51	200	(0–600)	2.4	40	(0–200)	0.5	3100	(1500–6500)	38	350	(0–800)	4.3	–	–	33
12 years	8000	(4500–13500)	4400	(1800–8000)	55	240	3.0	4200	52	200	(0–550)	2.5	40	(0–200)	0.5	3000	(1200–6000)	38	350	(0–800)	4.4	–	–	33
14 years	7900	(4500–13000)	4400	(1800–8000)	56	240	3.0	4200	53	200	(0–500)	2.5	40	(0–200)	0.5	2900	(1200–5800)	37	380	(0–800)	4.7	–	–	33
16 years	7800	(4500–13000)	4400	(1800–8000)	57	230	3.0	4200	54	200	(0–500)	2.6	40	(0–200)	0.5	2800	(1200–5200)	35	400	(0–800)	5.1	–	–	33
18 years	7700	(4500–12500)	4400	(1800–7700)	57	230	3.0	4200	54	200	(0–450)	2.6	40	(0–200)	0.5	2700	(1000–5000)	35	400	(0–800)	5.2	–	–	33
20 years	7500	(4500–11500)	4400	(1800–7700)	59	230	3.0	4200	56	200	(0–450)	2.7	40	(0–200)	0.5	2500	(1000–4800)	33	380	(0–800)	5.0	–	–	33
21 years	7400	(4500–11000)	4400	(1800–7700)	59	220	3.0	4200	56	200	(0–450)	2.7	40	(0–200)	0.5	2500	(1000–4800)	34	300	(0–800)	4.0	–	–	33
Adults	7000	2800–11200	4150	712–7588	59	–	–	–	–	165	0–397	2.4	44	0–112	0.6	2185	1029–3341	31	456	66–846	6.5	0	0	35
	7000	4300–10000	3650	1830–7250	53	520	9.5	3000	43.5	150	0–700	3.2	30	0–150	0.6	2500	1500–4000	36	430	200–950	7.1	–	–	36
	–	3260–9690	–	–	–	–	–	–	–	–	10–480	–	–	0–120	–	–	480–4460	–	–	30–1100	–	–	–	60

'able 13 *Membrane markers of human hematopoietic cells**

Markers	Expression of marker[a] (%)	Lymphoid cells[b]				Occurrence on nonlymphoid cells
		T	B	K	NK	
Antigens						
T-cell antigens[c]	65–85	+	−	(+)	(+)	-
DR antigens	15–25	s	+	s	s	Monocytes, myeloid and erythroid precursors
B-differentiation antigens (BDA)	7–13	−	+	−	−	-
Surface membrane immunoglobulin (sIg)	5–20[d]	−	+	−	−	-
Receptors for						
Sheep erythrocytes	55–80	+	−	(+)[e]	(+)[e]	-
Mouse erythrocytes	5–11	−	+			-
Monkey erythrocytes	60–70	+	−			-
Fc_{μ}	25–43	s[f]	(s)[g]			-
Fc_{γ}[h]	11–30	s	s	+	+	Monocytes, granulocytes, platelets
Fc_{α}[i]	2–13	s				-
Fc_{ε}	2–8		s			Basophils, mast cells
C3b	8–16	s	s	+	−	Monocytes, neutrophils, eosinophils, erythrocytes
C3d	4–14	−	s	−	−	Monocytes, eosinophils
Epstein-Barr virus	5–14	−	+	(s)	−	-
Measles virus	60–70	+	−			-

[a] Number fraction of isolated lymphocytes from adult blood with expression of marker (as percent).
[b] Within a cell group, '+', '−' or 's' indicate that all, none or a subpopulation of cells, respectively, bear the designated marker. Brackets indicate that expression of the marker on cells in a given group is controversial or unconfirmed.
[c] Some T-specific antisera detect functionally distinct subpopulations.
[d] sIg class and subclass frequencies: IgM 10.2%, IgG 4.1% (IgG_1 0.7%, IgG_2 2.3%, IgG_3 0.6%, IgG_4 0.5%), IgA 1.2%, IgD 6.3%, IgE < 1.0%.
[e] *Low*-affinity E_{sheep} rosettes.
[f] *High*-affinity Fc_{μ} receptors, detectable after incubation in serum-free media.
[g] *Low*-affinity Fc_{μ} receptors, detectable on most B cells.
[h] Marked variability is noted with different techniques.
[i] The receptor for IgA on T cells is presumed to be specific for the Fc portion of IgA molecules.

* From VOGLER, L.B., et al., *Progr. Hemat.*, **11**, 7 (1979), with kind permission of the authors, the editor and the publishers.

'ells of granulopoiesis

Normally, mature (band and segmented) neutrophilic, eosino-hilic and basophilic granulocytes as well as monocytes are found the peripheral blood. Metamyelocytes (juvenile cells) occur spo-adically. All these cells are derived from a common precursor cell; orphological differentiation is discernible at the immature mye-cyte stage. The ratio between neutrophilic leukocytes and mono-ytes is constant both in normal individuals and in many patholog-al conditions[31]. In addition, the age-dependence curves of eutrophilic leukocytes and monocytes parallel one another[32].

The absolute concentrations for the different cell forms in whole ood can be determined from their number fraction in the total ukocyte count – determined by counting in a panoptically ained blood smear – and the total leukocyte concentration in hole blood. Counts of cell forms present in relatively low propor-ons (especially basophils and eosinophils) are liable to the error small numbers and thus exhibit a wide range of variation. Ref-ence values are usually based on counts of several hundred cells id therefore have a narrower range of variation than the usual fferential count of 100 cells. The differentiation between band id segmented neutrophils is not well defined, so that here too ere may be differences in the reference values. Reference values otained with automated cell-identification instruments show ood agreement with those obtained with conventional counting chniques[39].

ymphocytes

Although lymphocytes may display a certain morphological riability, a differentiation by the classical staining methods is not ossible, in contrast to the cells of granulopoiesis. This identifica-on requires supplementary immunological and cytochemical chniques, which are able to differentiate T lymphocytes (thy-us-dependent lymphocytes) from B lymphocytes (bursa-ependent or bone-marrow-derived lymphocytes). Lymphocytes at do not carry distinct markers are called null lymphocytes.

There are quite a number of methods available for characteriz-g the membrane properties of the lymphocyte subclasses. The est known characteristic of T lymphocytes is their property of rming rosettes with sheep erythrocytes; the best known feature B lymphocytes is their membrane-bound immunoglobulin. ther methods include the detection of complement receptors and Fc receptors, and the reaction with specific antisera to T- and B-differentiating antigens[40,41] (Table 13). The reference values depend on the type and number of the markers used, and on the method of cell isolation. In addition to those mentioned, further lymphocyte subclasses have been defined, such as killer cells (K cells) and natural killer cells (NK cells). K cells can lyse antibody-coated target cells, and NK cells are capable of spontaneous lysis of tumor cells[42]. Increasingly the distinction between lymphocyte subpopulations and especially the T-lymphocyte subsets is accomplished by using monoclonal antibodies to cell-surface proteins[43] (Table 14).

Table 14 *Reaction of monoclonal antibodies with various types of mononuclear cells from cord blood and adult blood*[44]

Monoclonal antibody used	Cell type	Definition of cells determined	Newborn	Adults
			% of total mononuclear cells	
OKT3	T3+	All peripheral T cells	52.2	65.4
OKT4	T4+	Helper/inducer T-cell subset	43.5	40.3
OKT8	T8+	Suppressor/cytotoxic T-cell subset	16.7	24.2
OKM1	M1+	Monocytes, null cells	29.9	19.5
OK1a	1a+	B cells, monocytes, activated T cells	25.9	18.5

The total lymphocyte count rises a few hours after birth, then declines, and reaches a second peak toward the end of the 1st year of life. In the newborn, the T-cell fraction is low[45,46], but rises to normal adult levels within the first 18 months of life[47] (Table 15). The T-lymphocyte count falls in old age[46,48].

Platelets

Platelets contain no nuclei but are abundantly provided with organelles: they are formed in mature megakaryocytes and enter the blood after fragmentation of the cytoplasm. Their count in the blood stream is dependent not only on their production and sur-

Table 15 *Concentration and distribution of T and B lymphocytes in peripheral blood at different ages*[47]

Subjects	Age	Number	T lymphocytes: Number concentration in whole blood, Mean (10⁶/L)	T lymphocytes: Number concentration in whole blood, 95% range (10⁶/L)	T lymphocytes: Number fraction (relative to total lymphocyte count), Mean (%)	T lymphocytes: Number fraction (relative to total lymphocyte count), 95% range (%)	B lymphocytes: Number concentration in whole blood, Mean (10⁶/L)	B lymphocytes: Number concentration in whole blood, 95% range (10⁶/L)	B lymphocytes: Number fraction (relative to total lymphocyte count), Mean (%)	B lymphocytes: Number fraction (relative to total lymphocyte count), 95% range (%)
Children	1 week to 18 months	18	2970	1620–4320	50.2	33–67	1530	470–2590	26.2	14–39
	18 months to 10 years	23	1840	590–3090	56.9	45–69	720	170–1270	22.7	16–29
Adults	....	42	1910	750–3070	64.0	51–78	540	170–910	17.2	11–23

Table 16 *Kinetic and metabolic data for leukocytes*

Parameter		Unit	Mean	s	(Extreme range)	Re
Half-life	Neutrophilic granulocytes	h	10.5	3.3	–	49
	Neutrophilic granulocytes	h	12.2	2.0	–	50
	Eosinophilic granulocytes	h	44	2	–	50
O_2 uptake in 10^{12} cells	Leukocytes	mmol/h	40	–	–	51
Glucose consumption in 10^{12} cells	Leukocytes	mmol/h	140	–	–	51
Lactate formation in 10^{12} cells	Leukocytes	mmol/h	301	–	–	51
Index of alkaline phosphatase	Neutrophilic granulocytes	–	–	–	(60–100)	52
	Neutrophilic granulocytes, newborn	–	216	27	(164–264)	53
	Neutrophilic granulocytes, adults	–	85	13	–	53

Table 17
Number concentration of platelets in capillary blood at different ages

Subjects	Age	Mean (10⁹/L)	95% range (10⁹/L)	Reference
Children	1 day	–	120–270	59
	3 days	–	120–270	59
	7 days	–	140–300	59
	10 days	–	160–300	59
	15 days	–	180–300	59
Adults	....	–	125–318	60
		250	156–344	61
		250	133–367	62

Table 18
Morphological, kinetic and metabolic data for platelets

Parameter	Unit	Mean	s	95% range	Ref
Diameter:					
Free-floating	µm	3.2	0.5	–	66
Smear	µm	1.83	0.16	–	67
Section (electron microscope)	µm	1.5	–	–	68
Thickness:					
Free-floating	µm	1.1	0.2	–	66
Section (electron microscope)	µm	0.5–1.0	–	–	68
Volume	fL	5.17	0.46	–	69
	fL	5.4	0.7	–	70
	fL	8.0	–	6.3–9.7	71
Life-span	d	8.5	1.3	–	72
	d	9.0	1.2	–	73
	d	9.9	0.6	–	54
Half-life	d	–	–	3.2–5.2	74
O_2 uptake in 10^{12} cells	µmol/h	863	64	–	75
CO_2 formation in 10^{12} cells	µmol/h	957	104	–	75
Pyruvate formation in 10^{12} cells	µmol/h	39	4	–	75
Lactate formation in 10^{12} cells	µmol/h	764	119	–	75

vival, but also, and especially, on their distribution. Normally, about ⅓ of all blood platelets are stored reversibly in the spleen[54]. In splenomegaly, this fraction may be so high that thrombocytopenia occurs despite the fact that platelet production is unimpaired.

The indirect techniques for counting platelets in a stained blood smear are no longer in common use. The values obtained with these techniques were sometimes much higher than those obtained with the direct counting methods now in use. Today, the method most commonly used are optical counting under a phase-contrast microscope (counting chamber) after lysis of erythrocytes with ammonium oxalate[55] or electronic counting in platelet-rich plasma[56] or whole blood[57] (using a multichannel analyzer). Electronic counting in platelet-rich plasma yields values in agreement with those obtained by the counting-chamber method, but is more precise (the coefficient of variation in counts from the same sample is 5% as compared with 11% in the counting chamber)[56,58]. Table 17 presents normal values.

According to most studies there are no essential differences between platelet counts in the newborn and in adults[63]. Sometimes, higher values are found in young women than in men of the same age, a finding which might be due to iron deficiency[64]. The platelet count falls during the premenstrual period[65].

The platelet diameter is dependent on the preparation method. In smears fixed and stained with routine methods it is 1–4 µm, while electron microscope measurements yield a smaller value, and measurements on free-floating platelets show a larger diameter (Table 18). In measurements on smears, large platelets – macroplatelets or megaplatelets – with a diameter of 2.5 µm up to near 5 µm may be distinguished from normal platelets (diameter less than 2.5 µm). These large platelets make up about 10% of the total in normal preparations[76,77].

Data on platelet volume are dependent on the method of determination[64]; furthermore, no single reference range can be given, since an inverse relation between mean platelet volume and platelet count has been reported[78].

References

[1] Miale, J.B., *Laboratory Medicine: Hematology,* 6th ed., Mosby, St. Louis, 1982.
[2] International Committee for Standardization in Haematology (ICSH), *J. clin. Path.,* **31**, 139 (1978).
[3] van Assendelft et al., Methods for the determination of packed cell volume, WHO publication LAB/76.3, Geneva, 1976.
[4] England and Down, *Lancet,* **1**, 701 (1974).
[5] Heimpel et al., *Klin. Wschr.,* **55**, 1149 (1977).
[6] Kelly and Munan, *Brit. J. Haemat.,* **35**, 153 (1977).
[7] Verhoef and Leijnse, *Neth. J. Med.,* **19**, 141 (1976).
[8] Helman and Rubenstein, *Amer. J. clin. Path.,* **63**, 35 (1975); Winkel et al., *Amer. J. clin. Path.,* **75**, 693 (1981).
[9] Dybkaer et al., *Acta med. scand.,* **209**, 1 (1981).
[10] Viteri et al., *Brit. J. Haemat.,* **23**, 189 (1972).
[11] Garn et al., *Amer. J. clin. Nutr.,* **30**, 1935 (1977); Dallman et al., *Amer. J. clin. Nutr.,* **31**, 377 (1978); Garn et al., *Amer. J. clin. Nutr.,* **34**, 1645 (1981).
[12] Wintrobe et al., *Clinical Hematology,* 8th ed., Lea & Febiger, Philadelphia, 1981, page 77.
[13] Wood, W.G., *Brit. med. Bull.,* **32**, 282 (1976).
[14] International Committee for Standardization in Haematology (ICSH), *Brit. J. Haemat.,* **42**, 133 (1979).
[15] Schröter and Nafz, *Helv. paediat. Acta,* **36**, 519 (1981).
[16] Faxén, N., *Acta paediat. (Uppsala),* **19**, suppl. 1, 1 (1937).
[17] Seip, M., *Acta paediat. (Uppsala),* **44**, 355 (1955).
[18] Oski and Naiman, *Pediatrics,* **36**, 104 (1965).
[19] De Chastonay, E., *Helv. paediat. Acta,* **6**, 257 (1951).
[20] Wintrobe et al., *Clinical Hematology,* 8th ed., Lea & Febiger, Philadelphia, 1981, page 1885.
[21] Dacie and Lewis, *Practical Haematology,* 4th ed., Churchill, London, 1968, page 34.
[22] Seip, M., *Acta med. scand.,* **146**, suppl. 282, 1 (1953).
[23] Boroviczény and Balló, *Wien. Z. inn. Med.,* **38**, 196 (1957).
[24] Schröter and Kahsnitz, *J. Pediat.,* **103**, 460 (1983).
[25] Cavill et al., *Brit. J. Haemat.,* **35**, 33 (1977).
[26] Barosi et al., *Brit. J. Haemat.,* **39**, 409 (1978).
[27] Giblett, E., quoted by Mollison, P.L., *Blood Transfusion in Clinical Medicine,* 5th ed., Blackwell, Oxford, 1972, page 22.
[28] Kaplan and Hsu, *Pediatrics,* **27**, 354 (1961).
[29] Berlin et al., *Physiol. Rev.,* **39**, 577 (1959).
[30] Waller, H.D., *Ser. Haematol.,* No. 2, 34 (1965).
[31] Bain and Wickramasinghe, *Acta haemat. (Basel),* **55**, 89 (1976).
[32] Kato, K., *J. Pediat.,* **7**, 7 (1935).
[33] Dittmer, D.S. (Ed.), *Blood and Other Body Fluids,* Federation of American Societies for Experimental Biology, Washington, 1961, page 125.
[34] Forkner, C.E., *Bull. Johns Hopk. Hosp.,* **45**, 75 (1929).
[35] Graham et al., *Blood,* **10**, 467 (1955).
[36] Wintrobe et al., *Clinical Hematology,* 8th ed., Lea & Febiger, Philadelphia, 1981, page 1888.
[37] Karayalcin et al., *N. Y. St. J. Med.,* **72**, 1815 (1972); Caramihai et al., *J. Pediat.,* **86**, 252 (1975).
[38] Sadowitz and Oski, *Pediatrics,* **72**, 405 (1983).
[39] Arkin et al., *Amer. J. clin. Path.,* **67**, 159 (1977).
[40] Winchester and Ross, in Rose and Friedman (Eds.), *Manual of Clinical Immunology,* American Society for Microbiology, Washington, 1976, page 64; Greaves, M.F., *Progr. Hemat.,* **9**, 255 (1975); Kohout and Dutz, *Progr. clin. Path.,* **7**, 197 (1978); Bowman et al., *Advanc. intern. Med.,* **25**, 391 (1980).
[41] Vogler et al., *Progr. Hemat.,* **11**, 1 (1979).
[42] Herberman and Ortaldo, *Science,* **214**, 24 (1981).
[43] Editorial, *Lancet,* **2**, 781 (1980).
[44] Sridama et al., *New Engl. J. Med.,* **307**, 352 (1982).
[45] Christiansen et al., *Acta paediat. scand.,* **65**, 425 (1976).
[46] Diaz-Jouanen et al., *Lancet,* **1**, 688 (1975).
[47] Fleisher et al., *Pediatrics,* **55**, 162 (1975).
[48] Rosenthal and Steinmann, *Dtsch. med. Wschr.,* **103**, 409 (1978).
[49] McMillan and Scott, *Blood,* **32**, 738 (1968).
[50] Dale et al., *J. Lab. clin. Med.,* **87**, 487 (1976).
[51] Valentine, W.N., *Progr. Hemat.,* **1**, 293 (1956).
[52] Vajima and Kraus, *New Engl. J. Med.,* **293**, 918 (1975).
[53] Donato et al., *J. Pediat.,* **94**, 242 (1979).
[54] Harker and Finch, *J. clin. Invest.,* **48**, 963 (1969).
[55] Brecher and Cronkite, *J. appl. Physiol.,* **3**, 365 (1950).
[56] Bull et al., *Amer. J. clin. Path.,* **44**, 678 (1965).
[57] Adam et al., *Blut,* **32**, 347 (1976).
[58] Brecher et al., *Amer. J. clin. Path.,* **23**, 15 (1953).
[59] Göbel et al., *Klin. Wschr.,* **57**, 81 (1979).
[60] Käch et al., *Schweiz. med. Wschr.,* **110**, 1244 (1980).
[61] Karpatkin et al., *Amer. J. Med.,* **51**, 1 (1971).
[62] Tocantins, L.M., *Medicine (Baltimore),* **17**, 155 (1938).
[63] Wintrobe et al., *Clinical Hematology,* 8th ed., Lea & Febiger, Philadelphia, 1981, page 372.
[64] Maupin, B., *Blood Platelets in Man and Animals,* Pergamon, Oxford, 1969.
[65] Pohle, F.J., *Amer. J. med. Sci.,* **197**, 40 (1939).
[66] Frojmovic et al., *J. Lab. clin. Med.,* **91**, 109 (1978).
[67] Weiss et al., *Amer. J. Med.,* **57**, 920 (1974).
[68] Hovig, T., *Ser. Haematol.,* **1**, 3 (1968).
[69] Corash et al., *Blood,* **49**, 71 (1977).
[70] Friedhoff et al., *Blood,* **51**, 317 (1978).
[71] Rowan et al., *Brit. J. Haemat.,* **43**, 490 (1979).
[72] Myers et al., *J. Lab. clin. Med.,* **97**, 854 (1981).
[73] Harker and Slichter, *New Engl. J. Med.,* **287**, 999 (1972).
[74] Murphy et al., *New Engl. J. Med.,* **286**, 499 (1972).
[75] Waller et al., *Thrombos. Diathes. haemorrh. (Stuttg.),* **3**, 520 (1959).
[76] Garg et al., *New Engl. J. Med.,* **284**, 11 (1971).
[77] Sahud, M.A., *New Engl. J. Med.,* **286**, 355 (1972).
[78] Bessman et al., *Amer. J. clin. Path.,* **76**, 289 (1981); Levin and Bessman, *J. Lab. clin. Med.,* **101**, 295 (1983).

Table 1 *Myelogram at different ages*

Type of cell	1st day of life[1]		End of newborn period[1]		Infancy[1]		Preschool age[1]		School age[1]		Adults[2]		12 men[3]	
	Mean	Range	Mean	Range	Mean	Range	Mean	Range	Mean	Range	Mean	Range	Mean	Range
	Number fraction as percent													
Erythroblasts:														
Basophils	5.0	0.5–10.0	1.0	0.0–3.0	2.5	0.5–5.0	2.5	1.0–6.0	3.0	1.0–8.0	3.5	0.5–7.5	2.0	0.3–3.5
Polychromatic	15.0	7.5–30.0	3.0	0.0–10.0	10.0	5.0–20.0	5.0	3.0–10.0	6.0	3.0–10.0	7.0	2.0–15.0	21.6	13.1–30.1
Oxyphils	15.0	7.5–30.0	6.0	2.0–20.0	7.5	5.0–12.5	10.0	5.0–20.0	11.0	5.0–20.0	12.0	5.0–25.0	2.0	0.3–3.7
Total	35.0	–	10.0	–	20.0	–	17.5	–	20.0	–	22.5	–	25.6	15.0–36.2
Granulopoiesis:														
Myeloblasts	2.5	0.2–5.0	2.0	0.2–5.0	1.5	0.2–5.0	1.0	0.2–5.0	1.0	0.2–5.0	1.0	0.5–5.0	0.9	0.1–1.7
Promyelocytes	3.0	0.2–5.0	3.5	0.5–7.5	2.5	0.5–10.0	2.5	0.5–7.5	3.0	0.5–10.0	3.0	0–7.5	3.3	1.9–4.7
Myelocytes	6.0	2.0–20.0	10.0	5.0–20.0	10.0	5.0–15.0	12.5	5.0–20.0	15.0	5.0–25.0	15.0	5.0–25.0	12.7	8.5–16.9
Metamyelocytes	12.5	5.0–25.0	12.5	5.0–25.0	10.0	5.0–15.0	12.5	5.0–20.0	15.0	5.0–25.0	15.0	5.0–20.0	15.9	7.1–24.7
Neutrophils:														
Band	12.5	5.0–25.0	15.0	10.0–25.0	8.0	5.0–15.0	10.0	5.0–15.0	12.5	5.0–20.0	15.0	5.0–25.0	12.4	9.4–15.4
Segmented	15.0	10.0–30.0	15.0	10.0–25.0	7.0	1.0–15.0	8.5	1.0–15.0	8.0	1.0–15.0	7.0	0.5–15.0	7.4	3.8–11.0
Eosinophils	1.0	0.0–5.0	2.5	0.5–7.5	4.0	1.0–7.5	5.0	1.5–7.5	4.0	1.0–7.0	4.0	1.5–7.5	3.1	1.1–5.2
Basophils	0.05	0.0–0.5	0.05	0.0–1.0	<0.05	0–1.0	<0.1	0–0.5	<0.2	0–1.0	<0.5	0–1.0	<0.1	–
Total	52.5	–	60.0	–	43.0	–	52.0	–	58.5	–	60.5	–	56.7	–
Monocytes	7.5	3.0–15.0	5.0	2.0–10.0	2.0	0.5–5.0	3.0	1.0–5.0	1.5	0.5–4.0	2.0	0.5–3.0	0.3	0–0.6
Lymphocytes	...	...	...	...	...	...	...	...	...	...	7.5	2.5–15.0	16.2	8.6–23.8
Reticulum cells	5.0	0.0–10.0	25.0	10.0–40.0	35.0	15.0–50.0	27.5	15.0–40.0	20.0	10.0–35.0	6.5	1.5–20.0	0.3	0–0.8
Plasma cells	0.1	0.0–1.0	0.1	0.0–1.5	<0.5	0–2.0	<0.5	0–2.5	0.5	0.2–2.5	1.0	0.5–3.0	1.3	0–3.4
Megakaryocytes	0.1	–	0.1	–	<0.5	–	<0.5	–	<0.5	–	<0.5	–	<0.1	–

Table 2 *Bone marrow of adults (data relative to body mass)*

Parameter	Unit	Mean or range	Ref.
Mass	g/kg^{-1}	30–50	4
Fat-marrow mass/hematopoietic-marrow mass	–	1	4
Total number of nucleated cells	$10^9/kg^{-1}$	10.4–11.1	5
Granulopoietic cells	$10^9/kg^{-1}$	7.6	6
Erythropoietic cells	$10^9/kg^{-1}$	3.0	5
Megakaryocytes	$10^6/kg^{-1}$	6.1	7
Granulocyte production rate	$10^9 d^{-1} kg^{-1}$	1.63	8
Erythrocyte production rate	$10^9 d^{-1} kg^{-1}$	2.6	9
Platelet production rate	$10^9 d^{-1} kg^{-1}$	2.5	10

Bone-marrow hematopoietic cells have a common pluripotent ancestor cell which, because of its low degree of differentiation, is morphologically indistinguishable from the lymphoid cells. On the other hand, the more mature precursors of the fully differentiated cells of the peripheral blood are distinguishable in terms of their attribution to one cell line and their degree of maturity by means of panoptic staining. The data on the number fractions of the different cell forms (the myelogram) vary over a wide range, depending on the technique used to extract and process the marrow (differences in the relative amount of blood from the marrow sinuses), as well as owing to differences in the nomenclature and the criteria of delimitation for neighboring differentiation stages within a cell series. The latter is, in particular, the reason for the large variations in the ratio between polychromatic erythroblasts and oxyphilic erythroblasts.

The number fraction of cells fixed more firmly in bone-marrow stroma – for example megakaryocytes – is underestimated, especially in smears with abundant blood. The values indicated were obtained with aspirated material by cytological counting and are not directly referable to bone-marrow sections.

The absolute figures for cell content and cell production rates are derived from studies in which isotope methods had been used in addition to the conventional morphological techniques. They are from small references groups, mostly of young males, and in some cases were calculated from data not obtained from the same individual. Exact statistical data are therefore not available.

*This chapter on 'Bone Marrow' has been compiled in collaboration with H. HEIMPEL, Zentrum für innere Medizin, Universität Ulm, Ulm, FRG.

References

[1] OPITZ and WEICKER, in BROCK, J. (Ed.), *Biologische Daten für den Kinderarzt,* 2nd ed., volume 1, Springer, Berlin, 1954, page 160.
[2] ROHR, K., *Das menschliche Knochenmark,* 3rd ed., Thieme, Stuttgart, 1960.
[3] WINTROBE et al., *Clinical Hematology,* 8th ed., Lea & Febiger, Philadelphia, 1981, page 1890.
[4] MECHANIK, N., *Z. Anat. Entwickl.-Gesch.,* **79**, 58 (1926).
[5] HARRISON, W.J., *J. clin. Path.,* **15**, 254 (1962).
[6] WICKRAMASINGHE, S.N., *Human Bone Marrow,* Blackwell, Oxford, 1975.
[7] HARKER, L.A., *J. clin. Invest.,* **47**, 452 (1968).
[8] CARTWRIGHT et al., *Blood,* **24**, 780 (1964).
[9] CAVILL et al., *Brit. J. Haemat.,* **35**, 33 (1977).
[10] HARKER and FINCH, *J. clin. Invest.,* **48**, 963 (1969).

Ferrokinetics[4–6]

The total iron content in the normal male with a body mass of 70 kg is about 3.5–4.0 g (63–72 mmol). In women it is somewhat less. It consists of ⅔ hemoglobin iron, and of ⅓ myoglobin iron, storage iron (ferritin, hemosiderin), and transport iron (transferrin). Iron uptake from food as well as iron loss – identical when iron balance is in equilibrium – are only about 1 mg/d (20 µmol/d). In menstruating and pregnant women, the iron turnover is elevated to 2–3 mg/d (35–55 µmol/d). 5–13% of the iron in an average meal is absorbed depending on how much iron is already in storage[7].

Enteral iron absorption is best measured by whole-body counting after intake of ^{59}Fe-labelled iron compounds, the dose depending on the precise purpose in mind. The older methods of measuring absorption – by determining fecal iron content, or from iron uptake by erythrocytes – are inaccurate and susceptible to error.

A measure for intermediate iron metabolism is the daily plasma-iron turnover. This parameter is calculated from the biological half-life of transferrin-bound plasma iron, the plasma-iron concentration and the plasma volume. The half-life of bound plasma iron, a measure of plasma-iron clearance, can be determined with a ^{59}Fe tracer dose relative to body mass of 0.05 to 0.2 µCi/kg (approximately 0.01–0.04 µg/kg).

Approximately 90% of the iron leaving the plasma compartment is taken up by erythrocyte precursors after breakdown of the transferrin molecule and used for hemoglobin synthesis. The youngest erythroblasts take about 7 days to pass through the bone marrow. Therefore by this time all labelled hemoglobin-containing cells will have left the bone marrow, and more than 70% of the intravenously administered ^{59}Fe will be found in the peripheral erythrocytes. Of the total amount of ^{59}Fe administered, the fraction incorporated in erythrocytes is called 'utilization rate' (for normal values see Table below).

Changes in plasma-iron turnover and iron absorbed in erythrocytes are mainly but not exclusively due to qualitative and quantitative disorders in erythropoiesis. An increase in plasma-iron turnover is always found in elevated total hemoglobin production (e.g. in erythrocytosis, hemolytic anemia, hemorrhage) and in states of ineffective erythropoiesis (e.g. in megaloblastic anemia or dyserythropoietic anemia), and also in hereditary hemochromatosis with increased efflux of iron into the tissue. The iron incorporated in erythrocytes is a semiquantitative parameter of effective erythropoiesis. It is reduced in ineffective erythropoiesis and in erythropoietic hypoplasia.

Exact analysis of iron exchange between the various metabolic compartments and quantitative calculation of total and effective hemoglobin production from ^{59}Fe measurements in plasma and in erythrocytes requires the use of multicompartmental models.

Further information, especially on the distribution of erythropoietic tissue in the body, can be obtained by continuous activity measurements on the body surface after intravenous administration of transferrin-bound ^{59}Fe. The measurements are generally made over the heart, the sacrum, the spleen and the liver. In the case of extramedullary blood formation in the spleen and liver, 'erythropoietic curves' are obtained at these sites as a result of fixation of ^{59}Fe in the first hours after injection and migration into the peripheral blood within a week. Normally, such curves are observed only over parts of the skeleton containing hemopoietic marrow, e.g. over the sacrum.

Ferrokinetic studies usually require measurements over a period of 2 weeks, and in certain cases even longer. For a dose relative to body mass of 0.2 µCi/kg, the whole-body load is about 50 mrd. The critical organ is the bone marrow, with a load of 2–3 mrd. The load on the gonads is approximately equivalent to that for the rest of the whole body.

Blood volume[10, 11]

The most precise determination of blood volume involves simultaneous determination of the cellular and fluid fractions – the erythrocyte and plasma volumes – with two different radionuclides. In clinical practice, however, only one fraction is generally measured; the other fraction and the total blood volume are calculated using the hematocrit (see page 65).

The erythrocyte volume is usually determined with $Na_2{}^{51}CrO_4$ or with the short-lived ^{99}Tc^{m}-sodium pertechnetate[12]. An erythrocyte sample is washed, labelled in vitro, and reinjected. The labelling with ^{51}Cr may alternatively be done in whole blood; then, however, the excess chromate must be reduced with ascorbic acid to prevent relabelling of erythrocytes in the circulation. After a mixing time of, ordinarily, 10 minutes, a blood sample is taken, the erythrocyte activity is determined, and the erythrocyte volume calculated on the isotope dilution principle. The dose relative to body mass is 0.1–0.2 µCi/kg for ^{51}Cr and 0.5–1.5 µCi/kg for ^{99}Tc^{m}; the corresponding whole-body load is 10–20 mrd and 1–3 mrd, respectively. The critical organ is the blood, which gets a load 10 times greater. This determination is used mainly in erythrocytosis for differential diagnosis and control of therapy. Normal values for the erythrocyte volume are given on page 65.

Plasma volume is determined by means of labelled plasma components. The most usual are ^{131}I- or ^{125}I-serum albumin (RISA: radioiodine serum albumin) in a dose relative to body mass of 0.05–0.1 µCi/kg. Because intravascular and extravascular albumin undergo exchange, the emigration of labelled albumin during the mixing time must be adjusted for by correction factors or by measurements of the plasma activity at different time intervals after injection. The plasma volume is calculated from the injected activity and the calculated activity of a plasma sample at time t_0 in accordance with the isotope dilution principle.

To determine the plasma volume, the short-lived indium nuclide ^{113}In^{m} (≈ 5 µCi/kg), which binds to transferrin, is also used[13]. The distribution space of indium transferrin is about 5% greater than that of RISA[13].

The whole-body load is 7–14 mrd for ^{131}I-albumin and about 5 mrd for ^{113}In^{m}.

In the case of severe splenomegaly, the mixing time of labelled erythrocytes or plasma components can be lengthened to 20–40 minutes. Hence, the values obtained from a sample taken 10 minutes after injection will be too low.

Life-span of erythrocytes[14]

Human erythrocytes remain about 100–120 days in the blood, after which they are broken down in macrophages of the mononuclear phagocytic system, especially within the spleen. If a mixed-age erythrocyte population is labelled and its disappearance from the peripheral blood is monitored, elimination curves are obtained which reach the zero line after the afore-mentioned period of time. If ^{32}P-diisopropylfluorophosphate (DF^{32}P) is used as the label, the normal elimination curves are linear, since DF^{32}P binds irreversibly to the cell esterases. For practical reasons, however, erythrocyte life-span is usually determined with $Na_2{}^{51}CrO_4$. Labelling is done as in the determination of erythrocyte volume; however, the dose relative to body mass is 0.5–1.5 µCi/kg. Hexavalent chromium is reduced to trivalent chromium in the cell, the latter leaving the cell at a daily elution rate of 1–2%. The loss is so slight that it is of no importance in the determination of the *erythrocyte volume*. However, in determination of *erythrocyte life-span* the

*This chapter on 'Radioisotope Methods in Hematology' (pages 215 and 216) has been compiled in collaboration with H. Heimpel, Zentrum für innere Medizin, Universität Ulm, Ulm, FRG.

Parameters of ferrokinetics

Parameter	Unit	Cook et al.[8] (6 men)		Ricketts and Cavill[9] (10 subjects)	
		Mean	(Extreme range)	Mean	(Extreme range)
^{59}Fe-plasma-iron clearance (half-life)	min	85	(70–105)	86	(57–128)
Plasma-iron turnover (referred to whole blood)	µmol L^{-1}d^{-1}	134	(124–152)	129	(89–183)
	mg L^{-1}d^{-1}	7.5	(6.9–8.5)	7.2	(4.8–10.2)
^{59}Fe utilization after 14 days	%	82	(80–85)	83	(79–97)

elution – which results in an approximately exponential elimination curve – has to be corrected for. The normal biological half-life of erythrocyte-bound ^{51}Cr is therefore not 50–60 days but closer to only 30 days. In hemolytic anemias and in the case of blood loss it is reduced. In clinical practice, a comparison of the determined biological half-life with the normal value is usually accepted as sufficient measure of accelerated erythrocyte elimination. To determine the real mean life-span of erythrocytes and to assess the elimination kinetics, an analysis of the elimination curves with the aid of tables or kinetic models is necessary.

The site of breakdown of ^{51}Cr-labelled erythrocytes can be ascertained by activity measurements on the body surface[15]. This procedure is necessary for determining the indication for splenectomy in hemolytic anemia with unknown sequestration organ, especially in autoimmunohemolytic forms of anemia.

The whole-body load is 40–120 mrd; the critical organ is the blood and, when erythrocyte absorption is rapid, the spleen as well. Ferrokinetic studies with ^{59}Fe and determinations of erythrocyte life-span with ^{51}Cr may be performed simultaneously to obtain a global evaluation of erythrocyte formation and breakdown, since both isotopes can easily be measured in each other's presence.

Platelet production and platelet decomposition[16,17]

Platelet production can be monitored with ^{75}Se-selenium methionine, which is incorporated into the granules of megakaryocytes. Inferences concerning the kinetics of platelet production may be made from the radioactivity curve of newly formed platelets over a 2-week period; the rate of production, however, cannot be determined. Whereas this method is used exclusively for research purposes, labelling of peripheral platelets is of practical clinical significance for the differential diagnosis of thrombocytopenias. Labelling is done with $DF^{32}P$ in vivo or more frequently with $Na_2{}^{51}CrO_4$ in vitro on the same principle as with erythrocyte-labelling. Since, however, these two radionuclides are absorbed to only a small extent by platelets, the latter must be separated from the other blood components and purified as thoroughly as possible before (^{51}Cr method) or after labelling ($DF^{32}P$ method). Thus, determination of platelet life-span requires considerably more time and effort than that of erythrocytes. Platelets normally remain in the blood for about 10 days. This period is shorter in immunothrombopenias, consumption coagulopathy, and hypersplenism. Radioactivity measurements on the body surface are possible with ^{51}Cr-labelling. In the case of immunothrombopenias, the activity pattern over the spleen permits some prediction to be made concerning the utility of splenectomy.

Granulocytic and lymphoid systems[18]

The isotope methods available for functional studies of these cell systems present so many technical and analytical problems that their use has up to now been limited almost exclusively to research. ^{3}H-Thymidine, which may be detected autoradiographically in the individual cell, is used to study cell formation. Because of radiation exposure, its use in vivo in humans is possible only in selected cases; however, in vitro studies permit some limited statements to be made on the cell cycle and the proliferation status of a cell population. The time granulocytes remain in the peripheral blood can be determined by $DF^{32}P$-labelling; normally it is 9–12 hours. Labelling is also possible with ^{51}Cr or with $^{99}Tc^{m}$-sulfur colloid particles that are phagocytized in vitro by granulocytes and monocytes. ^{3}H-cytidine, $Na_2{}^{51}CrO_4$ or ^{65}Ga-gallium citrate are used for studies of lymphocyte turnover.

Scintigraphy of the spleen

The size of the spleen is an especially important criterion in the differential diagnosis of many hematological diseases. It can be determined more reliably and more precisely by scintigraphy in vivo than by other procedures. Whereas in the older scintigraphic methods, ^{51}Cr-labelled, heat-altered, or ^{197}Hg-mercury-hydroxypropane-treated erythrocytes were used, in the modern procedures these have largely been replaced by short-lived isotopes. Most often the scintigram is obtained with $^{99}Tc^{m}$- or $^{113}In^{m}$-sulfur colloid which is absorbed by spleen macrophages. The liver is visualized at the same time. At a dose related to body mass of 2 μCi/kg or 1 μCi/kg, the radiation load on this organ is 0.9 or 0.6 rd. If it is desired to visualize the spleen selectively, $^{99}Tc^{m}$-labelled erythrocytes that have been altered either by heat or by high doses of tin (which at the same time serves for intracellular fixation of technetium) should be used.

Scintigraphy of bone marrow[3]

The currently available methods permit to visualization of the extent of the erythropoietic marrow fraction as well as the marrow fraction capable of phagocytosis. The erythropoietic cells are labelled with ^{52}Fe, ^{59}Fe or $^{111}InCl_3$, the bone-marrow macrophages with various colloids, preferably gold colloid (^{198}Au) or $^{99}Tc^{m}$-sulfur colloid. The latter method is the simplest and causes the least radiation load on the bone marrow in a dose related to body mass of 60 μCi/kg ($\approx$ 120 mrd). A disadvantage of the colloid method is that the liver and spleen are also labelled, so that the bone marrow in the midportions of the spinal column cannot be delimited with certainty. Erythropoietic and phagocytizing marrow cells are normally found in the same anatomical marrow regions, but in hematological diseases may display different distribution patterns.

References

1 Heimpel and Bitter, in Emrich, D. (Ed.), *Nuclearmedizin, Funktionsdiagnostik und Therapie,* 2nd ed., Thieme, Stuttgart, 1979, page 134.
2 Lewis, M., *Clin. Haemat.,* **6**, No. 3 (1977).
3 McIntyre, P., *Progr. Hemat.,* **10**, 361 (1977).
4 Finch et al., *Medicine (Baltimore),* **49**, 17 (1970).
5 Pollycove and Tono, *Semin. nucl. Med.,* **5**, 11 (1975).
6 Cavill et al., *Clin. Haemat.,* **6**, 583 (1977).
7 Finch and Monsen, *J. Amer. med. Ass.,* **219**, 1462 (1972).
8 Cook et al., *J. clin. Invest.,* **49**, 197 (1970).
9 Ricketts and Cavill, *Ciba Found. Symp.,* NS **51**, 145 (1977).
10 Wright et al., *Semin. nucl. Med.,* **5**, 63 (1975).
11 International Committee for Standardization in Haematology, *Brit. J. Haemat.,* **25**, 801 (1973) and *J. nucl. Med.,* **21**, 793 (1980).
12 Schmidt et al., *Brit. J. Haemat.,* **32**, 411 (1976); Jones and Mollison, *Brit. J. Haemat.,* **38**, 141 (1978).
13 Hosain et al., *Clin. chim. Acta,* **24**, 69 (1969).
14 International Committee for Standardization in Haematology, *Brit. J. Haemat.,* **21**, 241 (1971) and **45**, 659 (1980).
15 International Committee for Standardization in Haematology, *Brit. J. Haemat.,* **30**, 249 (1975).
16 Najean, Y., in Meyniel, G. (Ed.), *Traité de médecine nucléaire,* volume 2, Flammarion, Paris, 1975, page 362.
17 International Committee for Standardization in Haematology, *Blood,* **50**, 1137 (1977).
18 Dresch, C., in Meyniel, G. (Ed.), *Traité de médecine nucléaire,* volume 2, Flammarion, Paris, 1975, page 354.

A wealth of reviews deals with molecular biological as well as clinical aspects of normal and abnormal hemoglobins[1–9,14–16].

The types of hemoglobin found in normal erythrocytes of adults are summarized in Table 1. HbA_{Ia1}, HbA_{Ia2}, HbA_{Ib} and HbA_{Ic} are compounds of HbA with a carbohydrate component – glucose in HbA_{Ic}. HbF, quantitatively the most important hemoglobin of the fetus, is normally contained only in the so-called F cells, which constitute 0.2–5% of the total erythrocytes in adults. HbF_1 is an acetylated form of HbF.

Table 1
Types of hemoglobin present in normal erythrocytes of adults

HbA ~97%		HbA_2 ~2.5%	HbF < 1.0%	
HbA_0 ~90%	$Hb\text{-}A_{Ia}$ 1.6% $Hb\text{-}A_{Ib}$ 0.8% $Hb\text{-}A_{Ic}$ 4%		HbF_0 < 0.9%	HbF_I < 0.1%

Every hemoglobin is composed of 2 pairs of different polypeptide chains and of 4 heme groups. The hemoglobins $\alpha_2^A\beta_2^A$ (HbA), $\alpha_2^A\gamma_2^F$ (HbF) and $\alpha_2^A\delta_2^{A_2}$ (HbA_2) are formed by the combination of 2 α chains with 2 β chains, 2 γ chains or 2 δ chains.

The amino-acid sequence of these 4 polypeptide chains is shown in Table 2. The synthesis of the α chain is coded by 2 genes per haploid chromosome or 4 genes per diploid cell; 1 gene each per haploid chromosome is responsible for the synthesis of the β and δ chains. The synthesis of the γ chain is controlled by 2, or at most 3, genes per haploid chromosome. The γ chain is present in all persons in 2 forms: one with glycine at position 136 ($^G\gamma$ chain), coded for by the gene $^G\gamma$, and the other with alanine at position 136 ($^A\gamma$ chain), coded for by the nonallelic gene $^A\gamma$ which is adjacent to $^G\gamma$ on chromosome 11. The ratio of the glycine-containing chain to the alanine-containing chain in newborn infants is 7:3; after about the 6th month of life it is 2:3. The α and α-like genes are on chromosome 16 in the sequence (from 5′ to 3′) ζ_2, ζ_1, $\Psi\alpha_1$, α_2, α_1– with nontranslated sequences between them. The β cluster of genes is on the short arm of chromosome 11 in the sequence (from 5′ to 3′) $\Psi\beta_2$, ε, $^G\gamma$, $^A\gamma$, $\Psi\beta_1$, δ, β.

If the structure of one or more deoxyribonucleotide triplets (i.e. codons), in the translated portion of the DNA chain forming the gene, is altered (a mutation), a polypeptide chain may be formed which differs from the normal chain in its amino-acid sequence. The combination of a normal pair of polypeptide chains with an abnormal pair, e.g. $\alpha_2^A\beta_2^S$, yields an abnormal hemoglobin, in this case HbS.

The abnormal hemoglobins – about 350 different ones were known up to 1981 – are identified by a letter, the geographic origin or both, for example HbS, Hb Chesapeake, $HbG_{Philadelphia}$. If one knows which polypeptide chain is altered, the chain combination can be given, as has already been shown above for HbS. The complete amino-acid sequence of most of the abnormal hemoglobins is known. Determination of the structure takes place essentially as follows: the chains are split at lysine and arginine residues by hydrolysis of hemoglobin or of the individual polypeptide chains with trypsin. The oligopeptides thus formed can be separated by electrophoretic and chromatographic methods to yield a two-dimensional peptide pattern, the so-called 'fingerprint'. Peptides that are not found in the 'fingerprint' of normal hemoglobin are isolated and their structure determined. If the structure of an abnormal hemoglobin is completely known, the position and type of the change in the chain are cited, for example $\alpha_2^A\beta_2^{6Val}$ for HbS, $\alpha_2^{92Leu}\beta_2^A$ for Hb Chesapeake.

Most of the abnormal hemoglobins so far described show a change in either the α or β chain; for technical reasons few such mutations affecting the γ or δ chain have as yet been found. Base substitution in the DNA chain can result in a chain-termination mutation; for example in Hb McKees Rocks, codon 144 in the *β* gene mRNA, normally UAU coding for tyrosine, has probably changed to UAA, which is a chain-termination or nonsense mutation, resulting in shortened β chains. A similar nonsense mutation near the 5′ end of the gene results in no recognizable β chain being formed, manifested clinically as thalassemia. In Hb Constant Spring (HbCS), the α-chain mRNA termination codon 142, normally UAA, has changed to CAA coding for glutamine, resulting

*This chapter on 'Hemoglobinopathies' (pages 217–221) has been compiled by L.I. Woolf, The University of British Columbia, Vancouver, Canada.

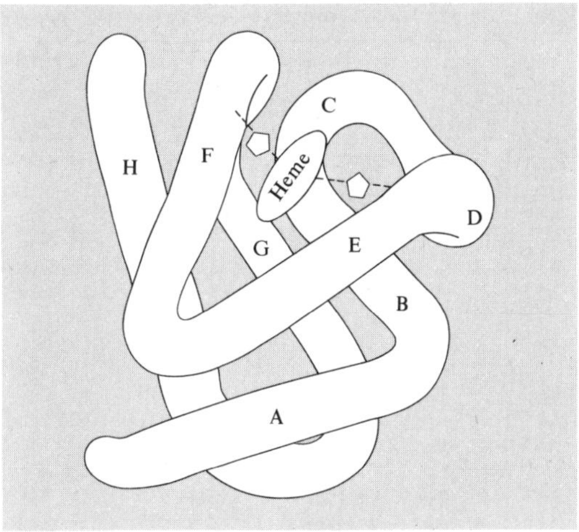

Fig. 1. Tertiary structure of a single globin polypeptide chain[10]. The helix segments labeled A to H are relatively linear. Folding takes place between the helices. The heme group is suspended in a crevice between the E helix and the F helix.

in an α chain 31 amino-acid residues longer than normal. Hb Icaria, Hb Seal Rock and Hb Koya Dora have similarly elongated α chains resulting from different base substitutions in codon 142.

In addition to single amino-acid substitution, resulting from replacement of one purine or pyrimidine base by another in the relevant deoxyribonucleotide triplet, unequal crossing-over at meiosis can result in the insertion into or deletion from the polypeptide chain of one or more (up to 5) amino-acid residues. Such nonhomologous crossing-over can delete variable lengths of the *δ* and *β* genes, as well as the nontranslated DNA between them, resulting in a fused *δβ* gene coding for a hybrid δβ chain (i.e. N-terminal derived from δ and C-terminal from β) which, with normal α chains, forms Hb Lepore (several variants are known depending on the positions of crossing-over). A similar but more extensive deletion leads to Hb Kenya in which the non-α chains are hybrid γβ chains. Unequal crossing-over can also lead to 'anti-Lepore' hemoglobins with the non-α chain having the N-terminal portion derived from a β chain and the C-terminal portion derived from a δ chain, with different crossover points and deleted portions, for example HbMiyada, HbP_{Congo}, and $HbP_{Nilotic}$.

Frame-shift mutations result from unequal crossing-over in which the number of deoxyribonucleotide residues deleted from or inserted into the DNA chain is not an exact multiple of 3. In Hb Wayne, for example, the α-chain amino-acid sequence up to No. 139 is normal, but is followed by an abnormal sequence of 8 amino acids. Deletion of a single nucleotide has disrupted all subsequent triplets, which rearrange themselves to form new triplets coding for amino acids differing from the original. HbCranston and HbTak are frame-shift mutations affecting the β chain; the amino-acid sequences are normal up to No. 145 and No. 147, respectively. Frame-shift mutations can be recognized only if they occur near the 3′ end of the gene.

Whether and in what manner changes in the polypeptide chain cause clinical symptoms depends on how the function of the hemoglobin is interfered with. In accordance with present knowledge of its tertiary structure and folding of the polypeptide chains (Fig. 1), the abnormal hemoglobins can be divided into several groups, depending on the type of impairment of function (Table 3).

The substitution of valine for glutamic acid in the β-6 position at the molecular surface is enough for the HbS in the deoxygenated form to tend to form aggregates in the shape of long rigid fibers which deform the erythrocytes into the characteristic sickle cells. This and similar hemoglobinopathies are summarized in Table 4.

Other substitutions – for example in the interior of the hemoglobin molecule – lead to denaturation, since bonds that hold the three-dimensional structure of the molecule together are weakened. These unstable hemoglobins – more than 70 are known – can be the cause of chronic hemolytic processes which are characterized by intraerythrocytic inclusions (Heinz bodies). Most carriers of unstable hemoglobins show only a slight hemolysis which, how-

(Continued on page 219)

Table 2 *Primary and secondary structure of the hemoglobin polypeptide chains*[10]

Helix	Amino-acid sequence					
	Position	α	β	γ	δ	Position
NA1	1	Val	Val	Gly	Val	1
NA2	2	Leu	His	His	His	2
NA3			Leu	Phe	Leu	3
A1	3	Ser	Thr	Thr	Thr	4
A2	4	Pro	Pro	Glu	Pro	5
A3	5	Ala	Glu	Glu	Glu	6
A4	6	Asp	Glu	Asp	Glu	7
A5	7	Lys	Lys	Lys	Lys	8
A6	8	Thr	Ser	Ala	Thr	9
A7	9	Asn	Ala	Thr	Ala	10
A8	10	Val	Val	Ile	Val	11
A9	11	Lys	Thr	Thr	Asn	12
A10	12	Ala	Ala	Ser	Ala	13
A11	13	Ala	Leu	Leu	Leu	14
A12	14	Trp	Trp	Trp	Trp	15
A13	15	Gly	Gly	Gly	Gly	16
A14	16	Lys	Lys	Lys	Lys	17
A15	17	Val	Val	Val	Val	18
A16	18	Gly				
AB1	19	Ala				
B1	20	His	Asn	Asn	Asn	19
B2	21	Ala	Val	Val	Val	20
B3	22	Gly	Asp	Glu	Asp	21
B4	23	Glu	Glu	Asp	Ala	22
B5	24	Tyr	Val	Ala	Val	23
B6	25	Gly	Gly	Gly	Gly	24
B7	26	Ala	Gly	Gly	Gly	25
B8	27	Glu	Glu	Glu	Glu	26
B9	28	Ala	Ala	Thr	Ala	27
B10	29	Leu	Leu	Leu	Leu	28
B11	30	Glu	Gly	Gly	Gly	29
B12	31	Arg	Arg	Arg	Arg	30
B13	32	Met	Leu	Leu	Leu	31
B14	33	Phe	Leu	Leu	Leu	32
B15	34	Leu	Val	Val	Val	33
B16	35	Ser	Val	Val	Val	34
C1	36	Phe	Tyr	Tyr	Tyr	35
C2	37	Pro	Pro	Pro	Pro	36
C3	38	Thr	Trp	Trp	Trp	37
C4	39	Thr	Thr	Thr	Thr	38
C5	40	Lys	Gln	Gln	Gln	39
C6	41	Thr	Arg	Arg	Arg	40
C7	42	Tyr	Phe	Phe	Phe	41
CD1	43	Phe	Phe	Phe	Phe	42
CD2	44	Pro	Glu	Asp	Glu	43
CD3	45	His	Ser	Ser	Ser	44
CD4	46	Phe	Phe	Phe	Phe	45
CD5	47	Asp	Gly	Gly	Gly	46
CD6	48	Leu	Asp	Asn	Asp	47
CD7	49	Ser	Leu	Leu	Leu	48
CD8			Ser	Ser	Ser	49
D1	50	His	Thr	Ser	Ser	50
D2	51	Gly	Pro	Ala	Pro	51
D3			Asp	Ser	Asp	52
D4			Ala	Ala	Ala	53
D5			Val	Ile	Val	54
D6			Met	Met	Met	55
D7			Gly	Gly	Gly	56
E1	52	Ser	Asn	Asn	Asn	57
E2	53	Ala	Pro	Pro	Pro	58
E3	54	Gln	Lys	Lys	Lys	59
E4	55	Val	Val	Val	Val	60
E5	56	Lys	Lys	Lys	Lys	61
E6	57	Gly	Ala	Ala	Ala	62
E7	58	His	His	His	His	63
E8	59	Gly	Gly	Gly	Gly	64
E9	60	Lys	Lys	Lys	Lys	65
E10	61	Lys	Lys	Lys	Lys	66
E11	62	Val	Val	Val	Val	67
E12	63	Ala	Leu	Leu	Leu	68
E13	64	Asp	Gly	Thr	Gly	69
E14	65	Ala	Ala	Ser	Ala	70
E15	66	Leu	Phe	Leu	Phe	71
E16	67	Thr	Ser	Gly	Ser	72
E17	68	Asn	Asp	Asp	Asp	73
E18	69	Ala	Gly	Ala	Gly	74
E19	70	Val	Leu	Ile	Leu	75
E20	71	Ala	Ala	Lys	Ala	76
EF1	72	His	His	His	His	77
EF2	73	Val	Leu	Leu	Leu	78
EF3	74	Asp	Asp	Asp	Asp	79
EF4	75	Asp	Asn	Asp	Asn	80
EF5	76	Met	Leu	Leu	Leu	81
EF6	77	Pro	Lys	Lys	Lys	82
EF7	78	Asn	Gly	Gly	Gly	83
EF8	79	Ala	Thr	Thr	Thr	84
F1	80	Leu	Phe	Phe	Phe	85
F2	81	Ser	Ala	Ala	Ser	86
F3	82	Ala	Thr	Gln	Gln	87
F4	83	Leu	Leu	Leu	Leu	88
F5	84	Ser	Ser	Ser	Ser	89
F6	85	Asp	Glu	Glu	Glu	90
F7	86	Leu	Leu	Leu	Leu	91
F8	87	His	His	His	His	92
F9	88	Ala	Cys	Cys	Cys	93
FG1	89	His	Asp	Asp	Asp	94
FG2	90	Lys	Lys	Lys	Lys	95
FG3	91	Leu	Leu	Leu	Leu	96
FG4	92	Arg	His	His	His	97
FG5	93	Val	Val	Val	Val	98
G1	94	Asp	Asp	Asp	Asp	99
G2	95	Pro	Pro	Pro	Pro	100
G3	96	Val	Glu	Glu	Glu	101
G4	97	Asn	Asn	Asn	Asn	102
G5	98	Phe	Phe	Phe	Phe	103
G6	99	Lys	Arg	Lys	Arg	104
G7	100	Leu	Leu	Leu	Leu	105
G8	101	Leu	Leu	Leu	Leu	106
G9	102	Ser	Gly	Gly	Gly	107
G10	103	His	Asn	Asn	Asn	108
G11	104	Cys	Val	Val	Val	109
G12	105	Leu	Leu	Leu	Leu	110
G13	106	Leu	Val	Val	Val	111
G14	107	Val	Cys	Thr	Cys	112
G15	108	Thr	Val	Val	Val	113
G16	109	Leu	Leu	Leu	Leu	114
G17	110	Ala	Ala	Ala	Ala	115
G18	111	Ala	His	Ile	Arg	116
G19	112	His	His	His	Asn	117
GH1	113	Leu	Phe	Phe	Phe	118
GH2	114	Pro	Gly	Gly	Gly	119
GH3	115	Ala	Lys	Lys	Lys	120
GH4	116	Glu	Glu	Glu	Glu	121
GH5	117	Phe	Phe	Phe	Phe	122
H1	118	Thr	Thr	Thr	Thr	123
H2	119	Pro	Pro	Pro	Pro	124
H3	120	Ala	Pro	Glu	Gln	125
H4	121	Val	Val	Val	Met	126
H5	122	His	Gln	Gln	Gln	127
H6	123	Ala	Ala	Ala	Ala	128
H7	124	Ser	Ala	Ser	Ala	129
H8	125	Leu	Tyr	Trp	Tyr	130
H9	126	Asp	Gln	Gln	Gln	131
H10	127	Lys	Lys	Lys	Lys	132
H11	128	Phe	Val	Met	Val	133
H12	129	Leu	Val	Val	Val	134
H13	130	Ala	Ala	Thr	Ala	135
H14	131	Ser	Gly	Gly*	Gly	136
H15	132	Val	Val	Val	Val	137
H16	133	Ser	Ala	Ala	Ala	138
H17	134	Thr	Asn	Ser	Asn	139
H18	135	Val	Ala	Ala	Ala	140
H19	136	Leu	Leu	Leu	Leu	141
H20	137	Thr	Ala	Ser	Ala	142
H21	138	Ser	His	Ser	His	143
HC1	139	Lys	Lys	Arg	Lys	144
HC2	140	Tyr	Tyr	Tyr	Tyr	145
HC3	141	Arg	His	His	His	146

*Another form of the normal γ chain contains alanine instead of glycine in position 136.

Table 3 *Functional classification of abnormal hemoglobins*[11]

Functional abnormality	Usual site of substitution	Clinical manifestation	Example
None	Molecular surface	None	Hb$G_{Philadelphia}(\alpha^{68Asn\to Lys})$
Aggregation with reduced solubility	Molecular surface	Hemolytic anemia (homozygotes)	HbS$(\beta^{6Glu\to Val})$
Instability with reduced solubility	Internal nonpolar amino acids, heme pocket region, etc.	Hemolytic anemia (heterozygotes)	HbKöln$(\beta^{98Val\to Met})$
Methemoglobinemia	Proximal (F8) or distal (E7) histidine	Cyanosis	HbM group
Increased oxygen affinity	$\alpha_1\beta_2$ contact or β-C-terminal amino acids	Erythrocytosis	HbChesapeake$(\alpha^{92Arg\to Leu})$
Decreased oxygen affinity	Near heme and $\alpha_1\beta_2$ contact	Cyanosis	HbKansas$(\beta^{102Asn\to Thr})$

Table 4 *Sickle-cell anemias and related anemias*

Disease or abnormal hemoglobin	Hemoglobins present		Clinical manifestation	Original geographical distribution
Sickle-cell anemia	$\alpha_2^A\beta_2^{6Val}$(HbS) $\alpha_2^A\delta_2^A{}_2$(HbA_2) $\alpha_2^A\gamma_2^F$(HbF)	77–87% 2.5% 10–20%	Infarctions and hemolytic anemia	Central and West Africa, India, South Arabia, Mediterranean countries
Sickle-cell trait (heterozygotes for sickle-cell anemia)	$\alpha_2^A\beta_2^A$(HbA_1) $\alpha_2^A\beta_2^{6Val}$(HbS)	56–76% 20–40%	Generally symptomless; sickle-cell crises in anoxia	See above
HbC disease	$\alpha_2^A\beta_2^{6Lys}$ $\alpha_2^A\delta_2^A{}_2$ $\alpha_2^A\gamma_2^F$	88% 9% 2%	Mild hemolytic anemia, splenomegaly	For example northern Ghana
HbSC disease (heterozygotes for HbS and HbC)	$\alpha_2^A\beta_2^{6Val}$ $\alpha_2^A\beta_2^{6Lys}$ $\alpha_2^A\gamma_2^F$	52.5% 43.5% 3.5%	Severe hemolytic anemia	Parts of Ghana and neighboring countries
HbE disease	$\alpha_2^A\beta_2^{26Lys}$		Relatively mild anemia	Thailand and Southeast Asia

ever, is intensified during crises, as, for example, is the case with Hb Zürich after intake of sulfonamides. The presence of some other unstable hemoglobins leads to a very severe hemolysis which cannot be controlled even by splenectomy. Another group of these hemoglobins can be detected only by hemolysis in vitro, while the carriers are symptom-free. An amino-acid substitution can render a variant hemoglobin susceptible to posttranslational changes; for example Hb Providence has, at β chain 82, lysine replaced by asparagine. The asparagine residue is posttranslationally deaminated to aspartic acid, and both forms of abnormal hemoglobin are present in the blood.

Hemoglobinopathies of the M group are caused by the fact that the abnormal methemoglobin cannot be reduced to the corresponding hemoglobin. In 4 of the HbM forms (HbM_{Boston}, HbM_{Iwate}, Hb$M_{Saskatoon}$, Hb$M_{Hyde\ Park}$), one amino acid is replaced by tyrosine, the side chain of which enters into a bond with the Fe^{3+} of the metheme. In Hb$M_{Milwaukee-1}$ such a bond is due to a glutamic acid substitution. Other forms of HbM (for example HbFreiburg) are classed with the unstable hemoglobins. HbM_{Iwate} is the most important hemoglobinopathy in Japan. These hemoglobinopathies have been described only in heterozygotes (the homozygote would probably be nonviable), i.e. this type of methemoglobinemia is inherited as an autosomal dominant character; cyanosis is usually the sole clinical symptom.

In a considerable number of stable hemoglobin variants the oxygen affinity is increased. Of the 35 such variants so far described, in 29 the resultant oxygen deprivation of the tissues is sufficient to cause erythrocytosis. As for the hemoglobins M, all affected individuals are heterozygotes for the relevant gene; the great majority are entirely asymptomatic. Of the 41 unstable hemoglobin variants investigated, 18 have increased oxygen affinity. 6 stable hemoglobin variants have low oxygen affinity; apart from cyanosis in 2 of them (HbKansas and HbBeth Israel), there are no clinical manifestations. A number of unstable hemoglobins show low oxygen affinity, as do HbM_{Boston}, HbM_{Iwate} and Hb$M_{Milwaukee-1}$.

The thalassemias (Table 5) are a heterogeneous group of genetically determined anemias in which the formation of α chains, β chains, or β *and* δ chains is greatly decreased or entirely absent. The α, β or δ chains are normal in structure, if one disregards HbConstant Spring or similar hemoglobins and HbLepore.

Traces of HbPortland can be detected in homozygotes for α-thalassemia (the embryonic hemoglobin HbPortland $\zeta_2\gamma_2$ contains the α-like ζ chain).

Without the synthesis of α chains no HbA, HbA_2 and HbF can be formed. In the α-thalassemias, abnormal hemoglobins with 4 β chains (HbH), 4 γ chains (HbBart's) and probably also one with 4 δ chains are formed, due to the excess of β, γ and δ chains. In the β-thalassemias, excess α chains are formed and combine with the cell membrane, leading to lysis of the erythrocyte precursors; this is a major factor in causing the characteristic anemia of the β-thalassemias.

The classification of the thalassemias in Table 5 is based on the previously mentioned (page 217) number and localization of the genes responsible for the formation of the polypeptide chains. At present, 13 genetic determinants of α-thalassemia are known: 4 in which both α_2 and α_1 genes on chromosome 16 have been deleted (α^0), 2 in which there is deletion of only the α_2 gene (or partial deletion of both α_2 and α_1 genes leaving a single functional fused gene) (α^+), 3 nondeletion types (α^+) and 4 α-chain termination variants. Thus there are 90 theoretically possible α-thalassemia genotypes, including heterozygotes and double heterozygotes, of which 19 have been recognized. In the β-thalassemias there is often a point mutation or small deletion in a nontranslated part of the DNA chain, for example in an intron which thereby inhibits, partially or completely, the splicing necessary to produce mature mRNA, or upstream of the 5′ end, thereby probably changing a transcription promoter. In one type of Afro-Asian β^0-thalassemia, the 3rd coding sequence (exon) of the β gene has been deleted together with neighboring nontranslated nucleotides. It has been reported that, in Ferrara-type β^0-thalassemia, normal β-mRNA is produced, but the reticulocytes contain a protein which inhibits

(Continued on page 221)

Table 5 *Clinical aspects of some thalassemias*[12]

Condition	Parental genotypes	α mRNA or β mRNA	Gene defect	Hemoglobin pattern	Clinical manifestation
Homozygous α-thalassemia (α-chain thalassemia 1; α^0-thalassemia)	– –/αα – –/αα	Absent	All 4 α genes deleted	$\alpha_2^A\beta_2^A$: 0 $\alpha_2^A\gamma_2^F$: 0 $\alpha_2^A\delta_2^{A_2}$: 0 γ_4^F(Hb Bart's): 80–90% β_4^A(Hb H): ~10–20% Hb Portland: trace	Hydrops fetalis; death mostly in utero, between the 34th and 40th weeks of pregnancy, or directly following birth
Hb H disease (α-thalassemia 1-α-thalassemia 2; α^+-thalassemia)	a) – –/αα –α/αα b) – –/αα αCS/αα	Marked deficiency Marked deficiency	3 of the 4 α genes deleted 2 of the 4 α genes deleted; 1 α gene replaced by Hb CS gene	$\alpha_2^A\beta_2^A$: 65–90% β_4^A(Hb H): 5–30% γ_4^F(Hb Bart's): 25% in cord blood Hb CS: 2–3%	Moderate to severe anemia (thalassemia intermedia) Moderate to severe anemia (thalassemia intermedia)
Heterozygous α-thalassemia ('α-thal trait'; heterozygosity for α-chain thalassemia 1)	– – /αα αα/αα or –α/αα –α/αα	Presumed deficiency	2 of the 4 α genes deleted	γ_4^F(Hb Bart's): 5–10% in cord blood	Mild anemia (especially mild in the African variant)
Silent carrier (heterozygosity for α-chain thalassemia 2)	–α/αα αα/αα	Presumed slight deficiency	1 of the 4 α genes deleted	γ_4^F(Hb Bart's): 1–2% in cord blood	Symptomless
Heterozygous Hb Constant Spring carrier	αCS/αα αα/αα	Presumed deficiency	1 α gene replaced by Hb CS gene	Hb CS: ~1%	Symptomless
Homozygous β^+-thalassemia	β^+/β β^+/β	Marked deficiency	β genes present but splicing or promotor defect	$\alpha_2^A\beta_2^A$: reduced $\alpha_2^A\gamma_2^F$: 20–30% $\alpha_2^A\delta_2^{A_2}$: variable	Mild to severe anemia (mostly Cooley's anemia)
Homozygous β^0-thalassemia	β^0/β β^0/β	Absent	β genes present but in some splicing or promotor defect. In others β gene 'amber' mutation or partial deletion	$\alpha_2^A\beta_2^A$: 0 $\alpha_2^A\gamma_2^F$: $\geq$ 95% $\alpha_2^A\delta_2^{A_2}$: variable	Severe anemia (Cooley)
Homozygous $\delta\beta^0$-thalassemia (F-thalassemia)	$\delta\beta^0/\delta\beta$ $\delta\beta^0/\delta\beta$	δ and β mRNA absent	Deletion of β and δ genes; in some types $^A\gamma$ gene also deleted	$\alpha_2^A\beta_2^A$: 0 $\alpha_2^A\gamma_2^F$: 100% $\alpha_2^A\delta_2^{A_2}$: 0	Usually mild to moderate anemia
Homozygous Hb Lepore disease	*Hb Lepore/β* *Hb Lepore/β*	β-Like mRNA present in reduced amount	Normal β and δ genes deleted; βδ-fusion genes present	$\alpha_2^A\beta_2^A$: 0 $\alpha_2^A\gamma_2^F$: 75% $\alpha_2^A\delta_2^{A_2}$: 0 Hb Lepore: 25%	Severe anemia (Cooley)
Heterozygous β^+-thalassemia	β^+/β Normal	Deficient	β genes present but transcription or mRNA processing defective	$\alpha_2^A\beta_2^A$: reduced $\alpha_2^A\gamma_2^F$: slightly increased $\alpha_2^A\delta_2^{A_2}$: increased	Variable manifestation of anemia (thalassemia minor)
Heterozygous β^0-thalassemia	β^0/β Normal	Deficient	One active β gene present	$\alpha_2^A\beta_2^A$: reduced $\alpha_2^A\gamma_2^F$: slightly increased $\alpha_2^A\delta_2^{A_2}$: increased	Variable manifestation of anemia (thalassemia minor)
Heterozygous $\delta\beta^0$-thalassemia	$\delta\beta^0/\delta\beta$ Normal	Presumed deficiency of δ and β mRNA	1 of the 2 β genes and 1 of the 2 δ genes deleted	$\alpha_2^A\beta_2^A$: reduced $\alpha_2^A\gamma_2^F$: 5–20% $\alpha_2^A\delta_2^{A_2}$: reduced	Variable manifestation of anemia (thalassemia minor)
Heterozygous Hb Lepore disease	*Hb Lepore/β* Normal	β-Like mRNA present	1 of the 2 normal β and δ genes replaced by βδ-fusion gene	$\alpha_2^A\beta_2^A$: reduced $\alpha_2^A\gamma_2^F$: increased $\alpha_2^A\delta_2^{A_2}$: reduced Hb Lepore: 5–15%	Variable manifestation of anemia (thalassemia minor)

Table 6 *Hereditary persistence of Hb F*[13]

	Characteristics of γ globin	$\delta\beta$ genes	Hb F (fraction of total hemoglobin)	
			Heterozygotes	Homozygotes
Pancellular forms				
African	$^{G}\gamma/^{A}\gamma$ usually ⅔	Mostly absent	25–30%	100%
African	$^{G}\gamma$	Active	15–20%	Not described
Greek	$^{A}\gamma$	Active	10–20%	Not described
Hb Kenya	$^{G}\gamma$	$^{A}\gamma\beta$ fusion; δ portion absent	6–7%	Not described
Heterocellular forms				
Chinese (may be pancellular)	Mainly $^{A}\gamma$	Active	10–14%	Not described
British	Mainly $^{A}\gamma$	Active	6–12%	20%
Seattle	$^{G}\gamma/^{A}\gamma = ⅔$	Active	3–8%	Not described
Georgia	$^{A}\gamma$	Active	4–7%	Not described
Swiss	?	Active	1–3%	Not described

translation of the β-mRNA; this work requires confirmation. In yet another form of β^0-thalassemia, a base change produces a chain-terminating codon near the 5′ end of the β gene.

Hb Constant Spring to some extent resembles the α-thalassemias insofar as an α chain with an abnormal (lengthened) sequence is indeed formed, but the gene product is formed only in greatly reduced amounts. Because the *Hb Lepore* gene, a product of fusion of the δ and β genes, replaces the normal δ and β genes, it behaves like a δβ-thalassemia mutation with greatly reduced formation of the chain that replaces the normal β and δ chains. Several different fused $\delta\beta$ genes are known; the different gene products, when combined with α chains and heme, are all termed 'Hb Lepore'.

The hereditary persistence of Hb F (HPFH) is closely connected with the δβ-thalassemias, since the formation of δ and β chains is partially or completely suppressed. This defect is compensated for by increased synthesis of $^{G}\gamma$ and/or $^{A}\gamma$ chains. All the erythrocytes are affected in the pancellular forms; in the heterocellular forms, only the F cells, which are either increased in number or richer in Hb F, are affected. At least 7 forms can be distinguished (Table 6). In the African pancellular $^{G}\gamma^{A}\gamma$ form there is deletion of the δ–β region of chromosome 11 (several variants are known, differing in the length of DNA deletion). In contrast, no major deletions have been found in the British, Greek or Chinese variants of $^{A}\gamma$ heterocellular HPFH or in the African pancellular $^{G}\gamma$ (β^+) variant. These hemoglobinopathies usually are clinically harmless; this holds true for most cases of homozygosity, for all cases of heterozygosity and for double heterozygosity in conjunction with Hb C or Hb S.

Despite the relative rarity of most abnormal hemoglobins, the genes for thalassemia, Hb S, Hb C and Hb F are very widely distributed in some areas of the world or in certain populations. Some of these genes, however, are lethal factors; homozygotes for thalassemia or Hb S often die in childhood, hence a continuous reduction of the genes concerned takes place. The *Hb S* gene is found almost exclusively in regions with endemic malignant malaria or in descendants of previous inhabitants of such regions. During childhood, heterozygotes for the Hb S gene are more resistant to malaria than normal homozygotes ('heterozygote advantage'); the thereby increased survival rate of the heterozygotes balances out the losses in homozygotes due to sickle-cell anemia. This can lead to a 'stable polymorphic population' with a sickle-cell gene frequency of up to 20%. The increased proportion of Hb F in thalassemia also seems to bestow a certain protection against malaria. The uneven geographic distribution of the *Hb C* and *Hb E* genes can probably be explained by a similar relationship with a disease.

In some parts of the world some hemoglobinopathies are the most severe inherited disorders. Prenatal diagnosis has been successful for α-thalassemia, β-thalassemia and sickle-cell anemia. The α-thalassemias can be identified by means of fetal DNA, which can be obtained from cultures of amniotic cells, by hybridizing the fetal DNA with radioactively tagged DNA complementary to the α polypeptide chain. A similar technique can be used in some types of β-thalassemia and in many families with sickle-cell anemia. However, in other types of β-thalassemia and in other families with Hb S, fetal erythrocytes must be obtained, incubated with labelled leucine and the ratio of β chains to γ chains, or of β^S to β^A, determined.

References

1 Bunn et al., *Human Hemoglobins,* Saunders, Philadelphia, 1977.
2 Caughey, W.S. (Ed.), *Biochemical and Clinical Aspects of Hemoglobin Abnormalities,* Academic Press, New York, 1978.
3 Bank et al., *Science,* **207**, 486 (1980); Bank, A., *Progr. Hemat.,* **12**, 25 (1981).
4 Schneider et al., Human Hemoglobins and Hemoglobinopathies: a Review to 1981, *Tex. Rep. Biol. Med.,* **40**, (1980/81).
5 Weatherall and Clegg, *The Thalassaemia Syndromes,* 3rd ed., Mosby, St. Louis, 1981.
6 Orkin and Nathan, *Advanc. hum. Genet.,* **11**, 233 (1981).
7 Orkin et al., *Nature,* **296**, 627 (1982).
8 Treisman et al., *Nature,* **302**, 591 (1983).
9 Farquhar et al., *Amer. J. hum. Genet.,* **35**, 611 (1983).
10 Wintrobe et al., *Clinical Hematology,* 8th ed., Lea & Febiger, Philadelphia, 1981, page 75.
11 Wintrobe et al., *Clinical Hematology,* 8th ed., Lea & Febiger, Philadelphia, 1981, page 803.
12 Orkin and Nathan, *New Engl. J. Med.,* **295**, 710 (1976).
13 Nienhuis and Benz, *New Engl. J. Med.,* **297**, 1430 (1977).
14 Spritz and Forget, *Amer. J. hum. Genet.,* **35**, 333 (1983).
15 Kan, Y.W., in Stanbury et al. (Eds.), *The Metabolic Basis of Inherited Disease,* 5th ed., McGraw-Hill, New York, 1983, page 1711.
16 Winslow and Anderson, in Stanbury et al. (Eds.), *The Metabolic Basis of Inherited Disease,* 5th ed., McGraw-Hill, New York, 1983, page 1666.

The physiological function of hemostasis is the prevention of blood loss after injury to a blood vessel. Vessel contraction, platelet adhesion and aggregation, and blood coagulation together promote hemostasis. The role of the coagulation system is the formation of a sufficient amount of fibrin at the site of a vascular lesion in a very short period of time. Fibrin is required for the consolidation of the platelet plug; sometimes it can even form before platelet aggregation has taken place[1]. In addition to its rapid action, which is to prevent or arrest hemorrhage, the coagulation system must remain inert as long as the blood vessel is intact. The quality of the fibrin is also responsible for proper wound-healing and fibroblast growth.

When bleeding occurs, coagulation must start immediately. The initiating impulse is conveyed via two different pathways: on one hand, activation of the contact phase of the 'intrinsic system' when foreign surfaces come into contact with the plasma coagulation factors, and, on the other hand, activation of the 'extrinsic system' due to reaction of the tissue factor thromboplastin with factor VII. In the so-called 'intrinsic system' only plasma factors are involved, whereas for the 'extrinsic system' the tissue factor thromboplastin is required. Despite the presence of these two parallel and simultaneously activated pathways of factor X activation, one system cannot entirely replace the other, as is shown by the bleeding which occurs in hereditary coagulopathies with a deficiency in one coagulation system only. It is extremely difficult to reconstitute the exact chronology of events in coagulation. The onset of the sequence of reactions varies from one case to another.

Contact phase

Interestingly enough the factors participating in this stage of blood coagulation are involved in the activation of other proteolytic systems – fibrinolysis, complement activation, and the kallikrein–kinin system – in addition to coagulation. In spite of this variety of actions the deficiency of one of these factors causes neither an increased bleeding tendency nor any other symptoms. The proteins implicated in the contact phase are described in Table 1.

(Continued on page 224)

Table 1 *Proteins participating in the contact phase*

Protein	Synonyms	Relative molecular mass (M_r)	Concentration in plasma	Reference
Prekallikrein	Fletcher factor	85000	~50 mg/L	2, 3, 19
Factor XII	Hageman factor	80000	30–40 mg/L	See Table 3
High-molecular-weight kininogen (HMWK)	Fitzgerald factor, Flaujeac factor, Williams factor, Reid factor*	110000	70–90 mg/L	5–9, 22, 23
Factor XI	Plasma thromboplastin antecedent (PTA)	160000	3–6 mg/L	See Table 3

*The deficiency in patients with these traits is not absolutely identical; patients with Fitzgerald trait lack HMWK, whereas patients with Flaujeac trait and those with Williams trait have no kininogen at all.

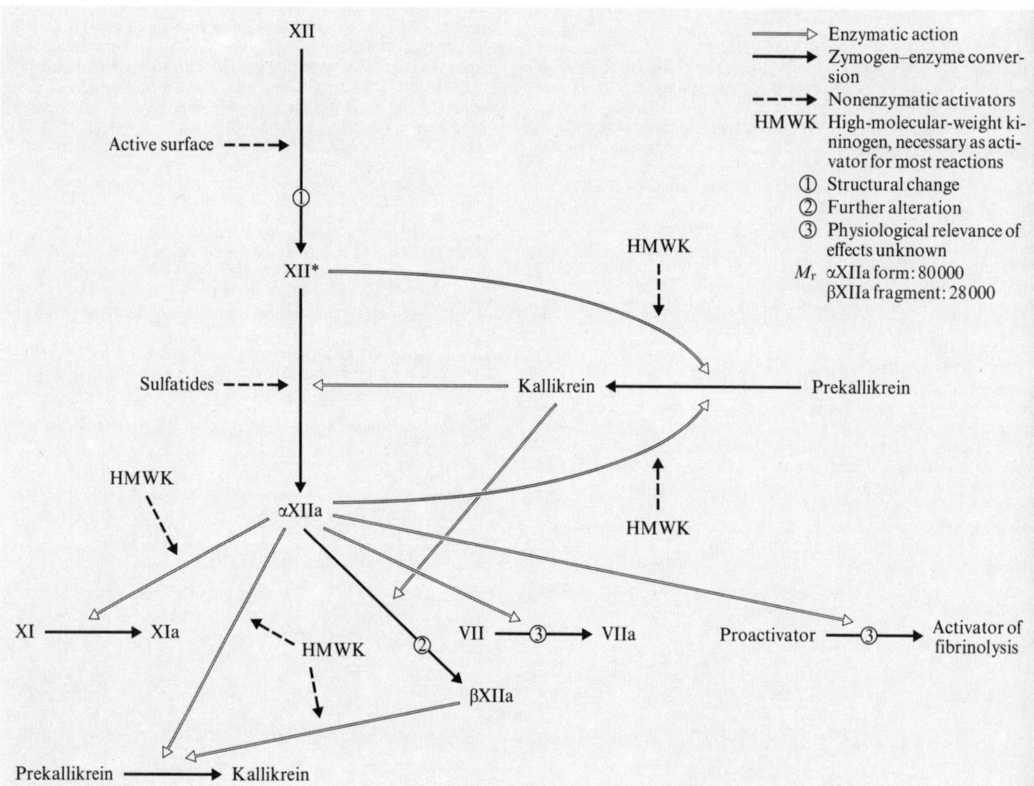

Fig. 1. Contact phase.

*This chapter on 'Blood Coagulation and Fibrinolysis' (pages 222–235) has been written by F. DUCKERT, Gerinnungs- und Fibrinolyselabor, Kantonsspital Basel, Basle, Switzerland.

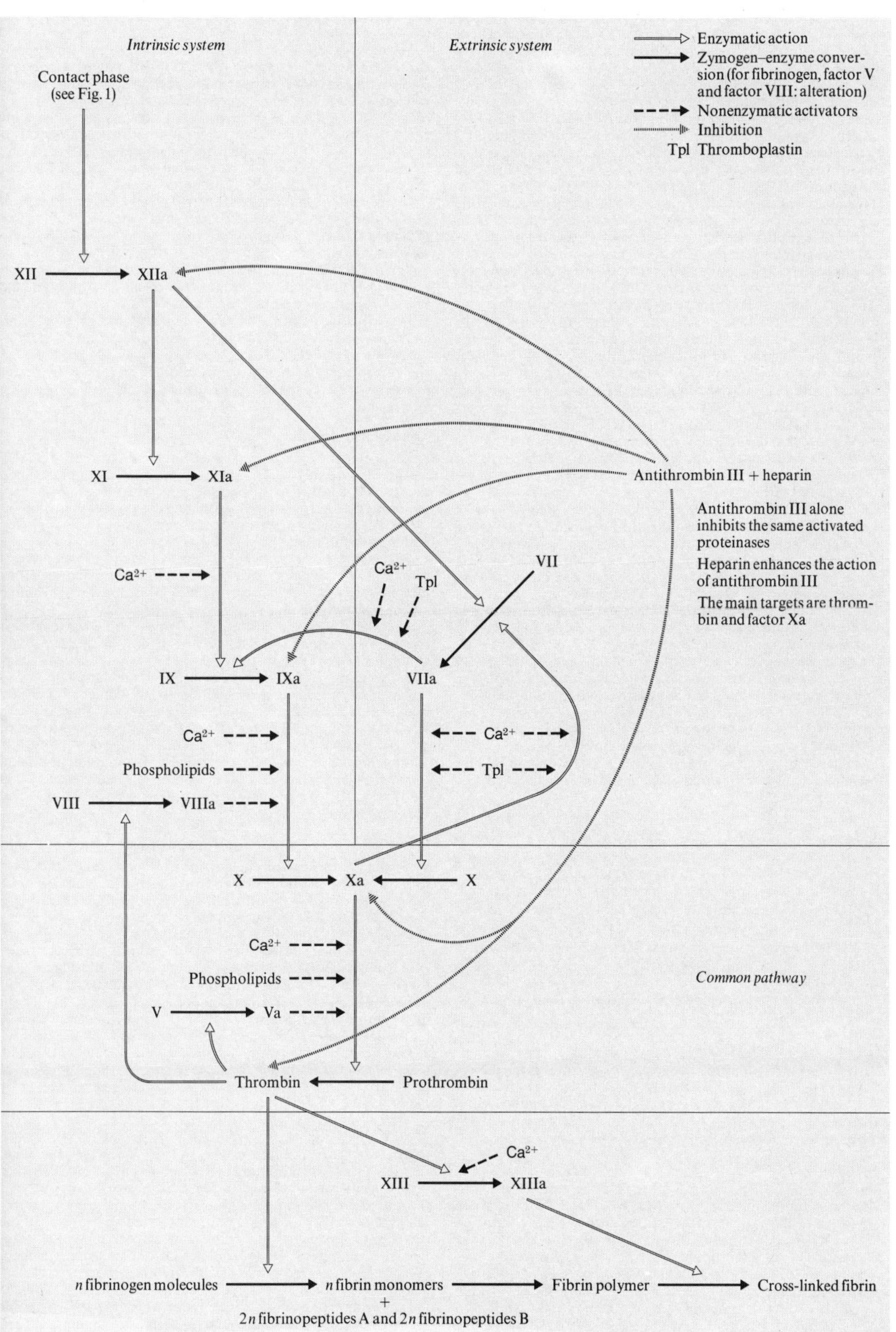

Fig. 2. Interaction of the coagulation factors.

Only factor XI seems to be absolutely necessary. Patients with a factor XI deficiency are prone to bleed after trauma or during operation. In vitro lack of prekallikrein prolongs the contact phase by slowing down the activation which eventually becomes normal. In cases of factor XII or high-molecular-weight-kininogen (HMWK) deficiency, prolongation of contact activation does not normalize the coagulation rate as measured by the aPTT test (*a*ctivated *P*artial *T*hromboplastin *T*ime). In vitro contact activation is produced by negatively charged surfaces such as glass, kaolin, ellagic acid, and in vivo by connective tissue, e.g. collagen, urate crystals and also endotoxins. With the exception of HMWK, the other proteins of the contact phase, as well as most coagulation factors, are serine proteinases present as inactive zymogens in normal plasma. Their activation is due to limited proteolysis. It seems that the first or one of the first possible reactions is a steric modification of factor XII. The surface-bound molecule (XII*) is more susceptible to proteolysis and is readily activated by traces of kallikrein[11]. Once factor XII is activated to factor XIIa ('a' denotes the enzymatically active form of the factor), the reaction rate is greatly increased (Fig. 1). When set into motion, the coagulation cascade functions as an amplifier leading to rapid formation of fibrin (Fig. 2). The term 'cascade' was introduced by MACFARLANE in 1964[12].

Once activated, surface-bound factor XIIa in turn converts prekallikrein to kallikrein; HMWK accelerates both activation reactions[13,14]. In this reaction sequence, HMWK binds to prekallikrein or to factor XI and accelerates the activation of factor XII, kallikrein and subsequently factor XI. HMWK is not an enzyme but functions as an intermediate in the binding of zymogens to negatively charged surfaces.

Factor XII and prekallikrein are single-chain proteins, factor XI is a sort of dimer in which two identical polypeptide chains are linked together by disulfide bonds. The activation of factor XII by kallikrein, of prekallikrein by factor XIIa and of factor XI by XIIa results from the hydrolysis of a single peptide bond in each polypeptide chain; therefore, in factor XI, 2 bonds are split. The 2 chains resulting from this proteolytic cleavage remain attached together by disulfide bridges. Table 2 indicates the substrates of these enzymes. A second cleavage of factor XIIa by kallikrein removes an enzymatically active M_r 28000 fragment called 'βXIIa fragment' as distinct from the first activated form, αXIIa[15]. The βXIIa fragment does not bind to negatively charged surfaces but can still activate prekallikrein[16] (Table 2, Fig. 1). The C-terminal portion of HMWK has a special amino-acid composition; a 50-amino-acid portion is highly positively charged and contains 30% histidine, 30% lysine and 10% glycine[17], which is responsible for the contact activation[18], perhaps in connection with the negatively charged surface.

Table 2 *Substrates of the contact-phase enzymes*

Enzyme	Substrates
αXIIa........	Prekallikrein; factors XI, VII; plasminogen
βXIIa........	Prekallikrein, factor XI (?)
Kallikrein....	Kininogens, factor XII, plasminogen, factor IX
XIa	Factors IX, XII

The substrates are listed in order of their probable decreasing affinity for the corresponding enzyme.

Although much is known about contact activation at the molecular level, the starting point of the first reaction remains a puzzle. It may be that one of the zymogens, as for factor VII, already has weak enzymatic properties which can initiate the process as soon as the substrate has been prepared by contact.

The intrinsic system

After the activation of factor XI to XIa the cascade proceeds with the activation of factor IX to IXa. Whereas the contact phase is possible in the absence of Ca^{2+}, Ca^{2+} is needed for factor IX activation (Fig. 2). Activation of factor IX results from the cleavage of 2 peptide bonds resulting in the loss of a small peptide, the activation peptide, and in the formation of the enzyme IXa consisting of 2 chains linked by disulfide bonds[25,26]. The first cleavage between Ala—Arg leaving 2 chains (M_r 45000 and 18000) is followed by a second cleavage at a Val—Arg bond resulting in the release of a M_r 18000 fragment and leaving the 2-chain factor IXa (M_r 28000 and 18000), where both chains remain linked by disulfide bonds[27]. Factor IX can be activated by enzymes other than XIa (see below).

The next reaction – the activation of factor X – requires the presence of the converting enzyme IXa, factor VIII, phospholipids and Ca^{2+}. With IXa alone the reaction is also possible, but since it is extremely slow it would hardly have any physiological significance. The X→Xa conversion is greatly accelerated by the presence of Ca^{2+} and phospholipids and even more when factor VIII is present. All reactants are bound to the phospholipid membrane (platelet phospholipids). Ca^{2+} is required for the binding of factors IXa and X, whereas factor VIII is directly bound. It seems that the procoagulant unit of factor VIII, VIII:C, is the important part in the reaction itself (see page 227). Factor VIII must be activated by thrombin in order to function as a nonenzymatic catalyst of the reaction, probably binding both factors IXa and X and also being bound to the lipid[28]. The Michaelis constant K_m of the activation reaction becomes smaller in the presence of phospholipids, and the rate constant k_{cat} increases when factor VIII is added.

The activation of factor X to Xa is similar to that of factor IX: an activation peptide is also lost in the middle of the single chain as the result of the cleavage of 2 peptide bonds. Xa consists of 2 chains which are linked together by disulfide bridges. With the activation of factor X the reaction sequence in the intrinsic system is terminated.

The extrinsic system

This system is characterized by the intervention of the tissue factor thromboplastin (Fig. 2), a lipoprotein. Isolated at a purification of × 50000, it is devoid of enzymatic activity. It has no peptidase, amidase or esterase activity and is insensitive to proteinase inhibitors[29]. The protein moiety can be separated from the lipid moiety without denaturation by different solvents, of which ethanol is the most favorable for subsequent reconstitution of the original thromboplastin activity[30]. Reconstitution can be carried out with a mixture of lipids or by specific lipids, phosphatidylethanolamine and phosphatidylcholine being the most active[31].

Also, the sequence of events causing the X→Xa conversion in the extrinsic system is difficult to establish. It has been demonstrated that factor VII, a single-chain zymogen, has weak enzymatic activity. It reacts with diisopropylfluorophosphate (DFP) much faster than all other zymogens and only 4 times more slowly than the 2-chain factor VIIa[32]. This factor VII, together with thromboplastin, can activate factor X. In turn factor Xa, which strongly binds to thromboplastin, can activate factor VII to VIIa[33] without release of an activation peptide. This autocatalytic process (feedback) greatly accelerates the conversion rate of factor X to Xa. Factor VII can be activated by other enzymes such as kallikrein in response to cold[34,35].

Interrelation between the intrinsic and extrinsic systems

As already mentioned, for physiologic blood coagulation both intrinsic and extrinsic systems are required. This implies some links between the two before factor X activation takes place (Fig. 2). In vitro several reactions are possible; factor XIIa can activate factor VII at a similar rate as factor Xa[36] and as kallikrein does. This is one possible link between the two systems[37]. However, there is another link which seems more probable. Factor VIIa together with Ca^{2+} and phospholipids can activate factor IX. In normal plasma the activation rate of factor IX and factor X with dilute thromboplastin is quite similar[38]; twice as many factor X molecules as compared to factor IX are activated because their respective concentrations are 200 nmol/L and 100 nmol/L[39]. The reaction kinetics make it reasonable to suppose that a substantial part of factor X activation is the result of factor IX activation by factor VIIa[39].

The common pathway

After activation of factor X both systems follow the same reaction sequence. The prothrombin–thrombin conversion appears to be very similar to X→Xa activation. Factor Xa is the enzyme, and the reaction helpers are factor V – activated by thrombin –, phospholipids and Ca^{2+}. Thrombin formation is again the result of the cleavage of 2 peptide bonds. The large activation peptide (fragment 1–2) is split off at the amino end of the prothrombin chain (Fig. 3). The released portion of the prothrombin molecule accounts for about half its relative molecular mass, namely 37000. At the amino end, fragment 1 is the domain which allows Ca^{2+}-binding with its 10 γ-carboxyglutamic (4-carboxyglutamic) residues, whereas fragment 2 allows binding and action of factor V which, after activation by thrombin, is required for the conversion of pro-

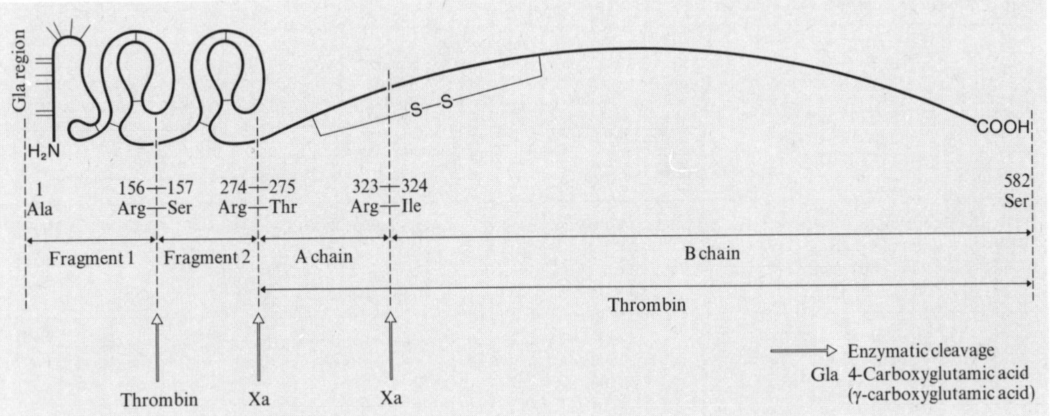

Fig.3. Schematic representation of bovine prothrombin. Fragment 1 with 10 Gla residues is responsible for the Ca^{2+} binding. Fragment 2 reacts with factor Va. The cleavage between fragment 1 and fragment 2 is produced by thrombin itself.

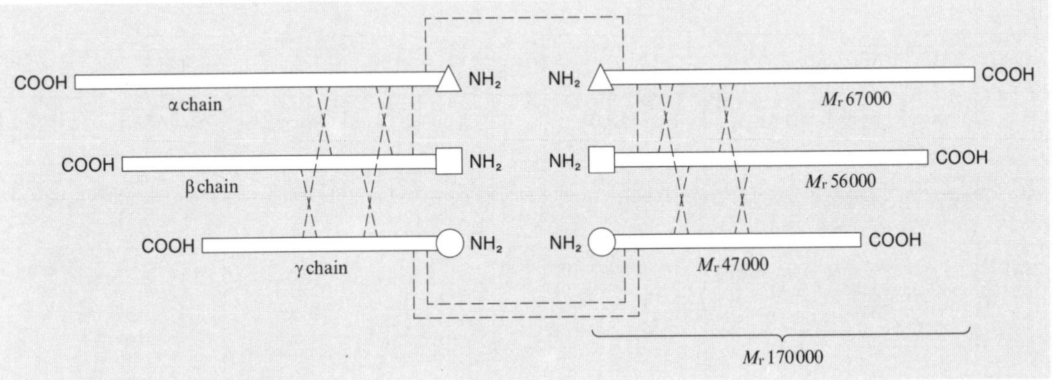

Fig.4. 6-chain structure of fibrinogen[43].

thrombin to thrombin[40–42]. The second cleavage results in the formation of 2-chain thrombin. This serine proteinase, unlike the other vitamin K_1-dependent proteinases (factors VIIa, IXa and Xa), has no remaining γ-carboxyglutamic residues and does not require Ca^{2+} for fibrin formation.

Fibrin formation

Fibrin formation is the only visible reaction of blood coagulation. It is the result of a modification of the fibrinogen molecule by the action of thrombin, followed by the polymerization of the fibrin monomers.

Fibrinogen is made up of 3 pairs of polypeptide chains, the α, β and γ chains (Fig. 4)[43]. The scission of a fibrinopeptide A from each α chain and more slowly of a fibrinopeptide B from each β chain by thrombin gives the fibrin monomer. The relative molecular mass is only slightly diminished, but the removal of the polar peptides reduces the negative charges, and polymerization of the fibrin monomers becomes possible. The polymerization proceeds by end-to-end and lateral attachment of the monomers with a longitudinal displacement of half a monomer[43]. The fibrin threads develop into a 3-dimensional network which can retain the formed elements of the blood and plasma itself. The monomers are held together by electrostatic forces. This fibrin polymer is not yet the physiologic form of fibrin: it must first be stabilized by the action of factor XIII, itself activated by thrombin to factor XIIIa, a transglutaminase. Factor XIIIa introduces covalent bonds between 2 γ-chains of 2 different monomers and between several α chains to form respectively γ dimers and α polymers, the existence of which can be demonstrated by SDS-polyacrylamide-gel electrophoresis of mercaptoethanol-reduced fibrin. The activated factor XIIIa may introduce as many as 6 covalent bonds per fibrin unit[44], but 2 or 3 bonds may be sufficient for fibrin stabilization. This stabilized fibrin is the functional hemostatic form of fibrin with the required mechanical strength[45] and fibrinolysis-refractory properties[46].

The resistance to fibrinolysis is partly due to the covalent binding between the monomers and partly also to the fact that the thrombin-activated factor XIII is able to bind, by the same types of link, α_2-antiplasmin to fibrin[47,48,49], possibly fibrin and fibronectin, and perhaps also fibrin and collagen[50]. However, there is only indirect evidence for the latter reaction. Factor XIII consists of 4 chains: 2 a-chains and 2 b-chains[51]. Platelet factor XIII has only the 2 a-chains[52].

$$\underset{\text{Factor XIII}}{a_2b_2} \xrightarrow{\text{Thrombin}} a_2^{\prime}b_2 \xrightarrow{Ca^{2+}} \underset{\text{Factor XIIIa}}{2\,a^{\prime}} + b_2$$

By the action of thrombin alone the a chain loses a small peptide ($M_r \sim 4000$), but the chains remain attached; dissociation requires the presence of Ca^{2+}, which in a second step unmasks —SH groups essential to the enzymatic action of factor XIIIa. —SH inhibition by iodoacetamide was formerly used for a quantitative assay of factor XIII. The structure as revealed by the electron microscope appears to be similar in both stabilized and nonstabilized fibrin[53,54]. However, treatment of the fibrin membrane with dilute urea destroys the organized structure of nonstabilized fibrin, and the cross-striation of the fibrin threads disappears[53].

Regulation of coagulation

It is not sufficient merely to have fast and efficient fibrin formation at the site of a vessel lesion: the blood must clot only at this site, and coagulation must remain a localized process without further dissemination. Blood clotting should not take place in the absence of bleeding. Several mechanisms assist towards this goal: the coagulation system itself, which may start relatively slowly to be

(Continued on page 227)

Table 3 *Coagulation factors and inhibitors*

Factor	Synonyms	Number of polypeptide chains	Relative molecular mass (M_r)	Number of amino acids: Total	Number of amino acids: 4-Carboxy-glutamic acid	Carbohydrates (M_r of carbohydrate moiety or mass fraction as percentage)	Concentration in plasma	Half-life in plasma	Site of formation	Reference
I	Fibrinogen ($\alpha_2\beta_2\gamma_2$)	2 × 3	340000	2964	...	M_r ~ 5000	1.90–3.65 g/L	89 h	Liver	43, 224
	α chain (Aα chain)	...	67000	610						
	β chain (Bβ chain)	...	56000	461	...	M_r ~ 2500				
	γ chain	...	47000	411	...	M_r ~ 2500				
II	Prothrombin	1	72500	582*	10	~ 11%	140 mg/L	75 h	Liver	226, 227
	Fragment 1-2	...	37000	...	10					
	Thrombin	2	35500	...	0					
	A chain	...	...	49						
	B chain	...	...	259						
III	Thromboplastin (tissue factor)	...	...	...	...	+	...	...	Endothelial cells, monocytes	30, 31, 228
	Protein moiety	...	56000							
IV	Calcium ions (Ca^{2+})									
V	Proaccelerin (labile factor)	1	330000	...	...	~ 20%	11 mg/L	15–26 h	Liver	94–96, 231, 244
VII	Proconvertin (stable factor, serum prothrombin-conversion accelerator)	1	50000	...	~ 9	10%	0.5 mg/L	3–5 h	Liver	229, 230, 245
VIII	Antihemophilic globulin (AHG) (antihemophilic factor A)	...	0.83×10^6 to 20×10^6	...	...	6%	5–10 mg/L	8–18 h	...	93, 225, 232
	VIIIR:VWF (polymer)	...	$< 20 \times 10^6$	...	...	...	...	...	Endothelial cells, megakaryocytes	
	VIII:C	...	100000 to 340000	...	...	...	...	...	Liver (?)	
	VIII:CAg	...	70000							
IX	Plasma thromboplastin component (Christmas factor, antihemophilic factor B)	1	57000	427	8–10	17%	3–5 mg/L	25 h	Liver	26, 233–235
X	Stuart-Prower factor	2	56000	...	12	~ 12%	...	60 h	Liver	236, 237
	Light chain	...	16500	...	12					
	Heavy chain	...	39300							
XI	Plasma thromboplastin antecedent (PTA)	2	160000	...	...	+	3–6 mg/L	48–84 h	...	10, 24, 248
XII	Hageman factor (contact factor)	1	80000	...	...	...	30–40 mg/L	50–60 h	...	4, 20, 21
XIII	Fibrin-stabilizing factor (a_2b_2) (activated form: transglutaminase, fibrinoligase)	4	~ 320000	...	...	...	...	~ 6 d	Liver, megakaryocytes	42, 246, 249
	a chain	...	~ 72000							
	b chain	...	~ 88000	...	...	...	14 mg/L			
Inhibitor										
AtIII	Antithrombin III (heparin cofactor)	1	58000	...	...	15%	290 mg/L	65 h	Endothelial cells	250, 251
$C\bar{1}$Inh	$C\bar{1}$ inhibitor (see page 136)									

*Bovine.

amplified as soon as contact activation develops or thromboplastin becomes available; the inhibitors; the phospholipids.

Inhibitors

The C$\bar{1}$ inhibitor is the main inhibitor for kallikrein, probably for factor XIIa and possibly also for factor XIa; α_2-macroglobulin certainly plays a role, as shown by the presence of an α_2-macroglobulin–kallikrein complex, which has been demonstrated in already minimally activated citrated plasma[55]. However, the major inhibitor of the coagulation cascade is antithrombin III[56] (Fig. 2), a single-chain glycoprotein with 4 carbohydrate residues and 3 disulfide bridges. The primary structure has been described[57]. Antithrombin III inactivates thrombin irreversibly and also factor Xa. Thrombin appears to be more rapidly inhibited than factor Xa[58], which corresponds to the physiologic requirements since more thrombin than factor Xa is formed during coagulation. Normally antithrombin III should rapidly inactivate the thrombin which escapes from a hemostatic clot, or which is formed locally under pathologic conditions. A reduction to 70% of the normal value, or slightly less, considerably increases the risk of thrombosis. The idea that besides antithrombin III a second heparin cofactor exists has been substantiated[58]: a relevant polypeptide has been named 'heparin cofactor II'[60,61], which may be identical to the heparin-dependent thrombin inhibitor, designated 'antithrombin BM'[59]. As for antithrombin III, the inhibiting action of heparin cofactor II is greatly enhanced by heparin. Dermatan sulfate activates heparin cofactor II less markedly than heparin, whereas antithrombin III is not activated at all[60,62]. In contrast to antithrombin III, human heparin cofactor II seems to be unable to inactivate human factor Xa or bovine antithrombin III. The exact physiologic role of heparin cofactor II is not yet known.

Activated protein C (see section on vitamin K_1-dependent coagulation factors) is suppressed by a plasma inhibitor – the protein C inhibitor[67,68]. The mechanism of action has not been established, but the inhibitor does not seem to act as an enzyme.

Localization of coagulation

Certain lipids in the intrinsic and extrinsic system and in the common pathway – phosphatidylethanolamine and phosphatidylcholine, which promote thromboplastin activity, and phosphatidylserine and phosphatidylinositol, which effect other coagulation reactions – are essential catalysts of blood coagulation. These phospholipids are insoluble in aqueous solution; they are fixed to cell structures and are exposed by the rupture of tissue cell membranes and by platelet membranes. In other words, they are available at the site of vessel-wall damage where also platelets adhere and aggregate.

The coagulation process is localized. At this level, coagulation is greatly accelerated, fibrin formation entrapping cells and also activated coagulation factors. When thrombin, factor Xa, kallikrein and other coagulation proteinases reach the circulation, they are rapidly inhibited by antithrombin, C$\bar{1}$ inhibitor or α_2-macroglobulin and cannot normally propagate the clotting reactions.

Properties of the coagulation factors (Table 3, page 226)

The tissue factor thromboplastin is present in endothelial cells[69] and in monocytes, which are the only circulating cells with thromboplastin activity[70]. Brain, lungs and placenta are particularly rich in thromboplastin. These organs are the source of the thromboplastin preparations for the prothrombin-time assay.

Factor VIII is a large molecule with a variable relative molecular mass (0.83×10^6 to 20×10^6), depending on the association grade. Two main hemostatic properties can be distinguished: the procoagulant function VIII:C, and the von Willebrand factor activity VIIIR:VWF, which controls bleeding time. In addition, certain associated properties are recognized: VIIIR:Ag, which is measured immunologically by heterologous antibodies against the VIIIR:VWF moiety, and VIIIR:RCo or ristocetin cofactor, which is required for platelet aggregation induced by the antibiotic ristocetin[71–73] and is missing in von Willebrand's disease[73]. VIIIR:Ag, VIIIR:RCo and VIIIR:VWF are largely identical, at least in regard to their basic unit. VIII:CAg is the procoagulant antigen recognized by homologous and also heterologous antibodies. Both VIIIR:VWF and VIIIR:Ag are synthesized by endothelial cells in culture[74,75] and by megakaryocytes[78]; they have been identified in the endothelial cells of many vessels[78–81] as well as in platelets[76,77]. In the supernatant of endothelial cells in culture, VIIIR:VWF has VIIIR:RCo activity[75] and is composed of M_r 200000 subunits[82]. VIII:C appears to be formed in the liver and spleen[84,85], but certainly not in the same cells as the other clotting factors, since VIII:C activity increases in hepatocellular disease, e.g. in cirrhosis. Factor VIII:C has not been found in endothelial cells in culture or in platelets[83]. Factor VIII can be dissociated into VIIIR:Ag and VIII:C or VIII:CAg at high salt concentrations, more readily with $CaCl_2$ 0.25 mol/L than with NaCl 1.0 mol/L[86]. VIIIR:Ag and VIII:C recombine after concentration and at low ionic strength[86]. The dissociation grade increases in presence of different anticoagulants in the following order: heparin, citrate, EDTA[87]. VIII:CAg can be detected by homologous or heterologous antibodies[88]. It has been postulated that VIII:C (M_r 100000–340000[89]) may consist of several VIII:CAg subunits ($M_r \sim 70000$) linked together by Ca^{2+}[88]. Binding of VIII:C to VIIIR:Ag stabilizes the coagulant activity. VIIIR:VWF is found in plasma as a series of multimers up to a relative molecular mass of 20×10^6[90–92]. Reduction of the multimers gives subunits of M_r 200000[93] or M_r 480000[90]. The basic subunits of the large multimers could be either a dimer (M_r 480000) or a tetramer (M_r 860000) of the monomer obtained by complete reduction[93].

Factor V is a single-chain protein (M_r 330000)[94–96] extremely sensitive to proteolytic enzymes[97]. It is activated by thrombin; as a result the binding sites of factor Xa and prothrombin are unmasked. Thrombin splits at least two different bonds in factor V[95,98]. Factor V binds Ca^{2+}, which stabilizes factor Va[99].

Vitamin K_1-dependent coagulation factors

Prothrombin, factors VII, IX and X, as well as protein C and protein S, have many similar properties. They are quite stable and readily absorbed on barium sulfate and other insoluble salts. These proteins – with the possible exception of protein S[101] – are all zymogens of serine proteinases and have homologous regions in their amino-acid sequence[68] not only with each other but also with other proteinases: fibrinolytic plasmin, chymotrypsin and trypsin. This is particularly true for the polypeptide chain containing active-site serine[42].

The inactive precursors of the coagulation proteinases are synthesized in the liver and transformed in a post-ribosomal vitamin K_1-dependent reaction to the respective zymogens. Inactive precursors are present in the blood in vitamin K deficiency and during treatment with vitamin K antagonists (oral anticoagulants)[103]. These proteins bind Ca^{2+} less strongly than the normal zymogens[104]. The latter contain Ca^{2+}-binding sites made up of γ-carboxyglutamic residues located in the N-terminal region of the molecule[40,105,106]. The carboxylation of glutamic acid (Fig. 5) requires a carboxylase and the reduced form of vitamin K_1[107,108]. The noncarboxylated precursor cannot be activated to the enzyme form physiologically even though it contains the complete enzyme. Acarboxy prothrombin can be converted to normal thrombin by Ca^{2+}-independent pathways with staphylocoagulase or ecarin (a proteinase occurring in *Echis carinatus* venom)[109].

Protein C, a glycoprotein, was first described as autoprothrombin II[63] and then shown to be a vitamin K_1-dependent protein[64,100]. In contrast to the other factors it exerts an inhibiting action on the coagulation process. In the activated form (protein Ca) it inactivates factor Va and factor VIII:C by limited proteolysis[68,101]. Protein C is activated by thrombin[65]. Thrombin as such would physiologically act too slowly[110], but its action is accelerated 20000 times by a membrane-bound cofactor, thrombomodulin[110,111]. The thrombin bound to thrombomodulin has an altered structure which prevents its continuing to convert fibrinogen to fibrin or to activate factor V, although it still reacts with antithrombin III[111].

Protein S exists in plasma in free form and in complex with the complement component C4b-binding protein[102]. It may participate in the inactivation of factor Va by protein C[68].

Factor VII (see page 224), a single-chain protein, is probably the only zymogen in the whole process of coagulation to have sufficient enzymatic activity to initiate blood coagulation, this nor-

Table 3a *Protein C, protein S, and protein C inhibitor*

Protein	M_r	Number of 4-carboxy-glutamic residues	Concentration in plasma	Reference
Protein C	62000	11*	~4 mg/L	66,68
Protein S	69000	~10	~10 mg/L	233,102
Protein C inhibitor...	57000	0	~5 mg/L	67
* Bovine protein.				

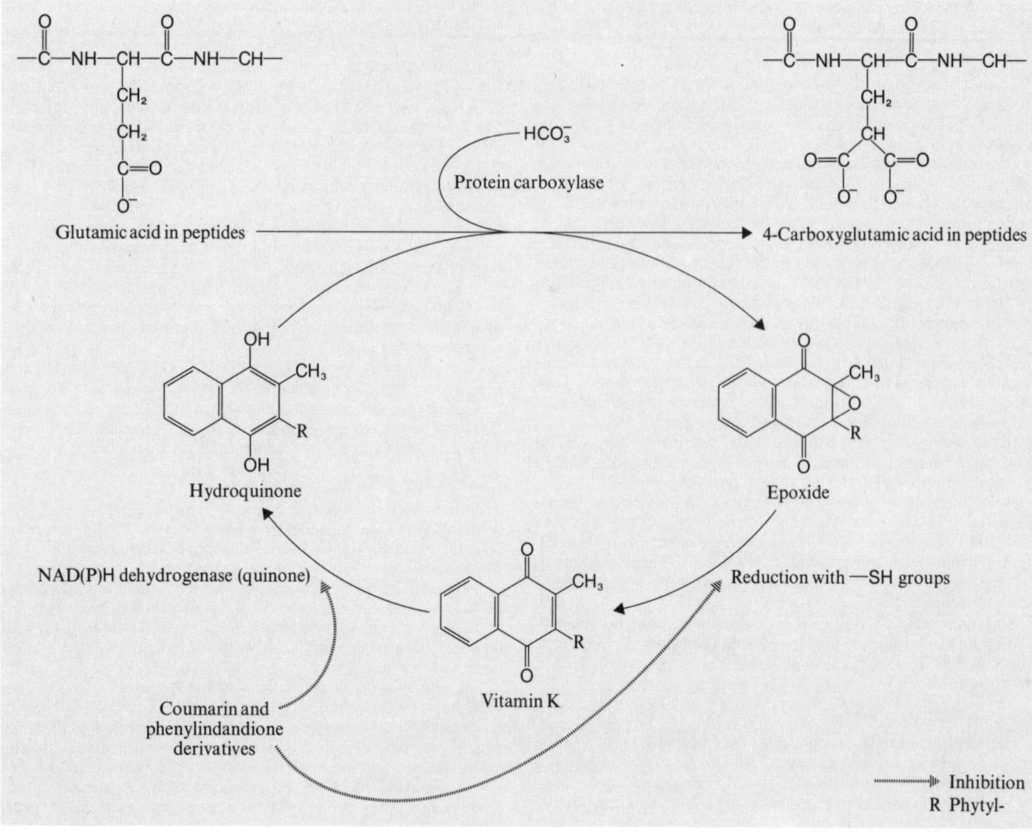

Fig.5. 4-Carboxylation (γ-carboxylation) of glutamic acid in peptides.

mally being prevented by the absence of thromboplastin from the blood: the presence of cell-bound thromboplastin is an absolute requirement for acceleration of the reaction.

The fibrinolytic system

Intravascular fibrin formation and deposition is normally prevented by the absence of contact activation and availability of thromboplastin. When this does occur, however, another proteolytic system, the fibrinolytic system, is brought into action, and this has the ability to remove fibrin (Fig.6). Plasminogen is converted to the fibrinolytic enzyme plasmin by a series of activators. Again, overshooting of the fibrinolytic action is prevented by inhibitors of the activation step and by α_2-antiplasmin.

Three different pathways for the activation of plasminogen are distinguishable: an intrinsic pathway, an extrinsic activation pathway, and a pathway in which exogenous activators are involved, as in thrombolytic therapy. As with coagulation, the intrinsic pathway of plasminogen activation is triggered by the contact phase in which factor XII, prekallikrein and HMWK are involved[112]. The exact physiological role of this activation type is unknown, as is also the case with coagulation. In the extrinsic system, the activators present in blood are released from tissues. The blood, tissue and vascular plasminogen activators are closely related and cross-react with their respective antibodies, but not with antibodies against urokinase[113,114]. These activators are serine proteinases with a relative molecular mass around 70000. It seems quite evident that the blood activator is identical with the vascular activator. The main exogenous activators are urokinase[115] and streptokinase[116]. Urokinase is a proteinase which is synthesized in the kidney - also in cultures of kidney cells - and found in urine. It exists in at least two different forms (M_r 54000 and 33000), possibly also as a larger zymogen. Streptokinase is a catabolic by-product of group C streptococci and a nonenzymatic protein. As was soon recognized[117], streptokinase enters first an equimolecular complex with plasminogen[118], which is rapidly formed[119]. This complex has a very specific proteolytic action on free plasminogen. Streptokinase is successively degraded in the complex from M_r 47000 to M_r 43000 and M_r 37000 fragments[120]. Several of these degraded complexes retain their activator activity. Plasmin is also able to combine with streptokinase[118].

The physiologic equilibrium of the fibrinolytic system, rather like that of coagulation, is maintained by inhibitors, especially α_2-antiplasmin[121-123]. α_2-Antiplasmin inhibits very rapidly and forms stable complexes with plasmin.

Properties of the components of the fibrinolytic system (Table 4)

Plasminogen exists in various forms. Native plasminogen has an N-terminal glutamic-acid residue (Glu plasminogen) and is easily degraded by plasmin to smaller forms with N-terminal lysine, valine or methionine[124]. The main degraded component is Lys plasminogen. The primary structure of Glu plasminogen has been worked out[125,126]. The 790 amino acids are arranged in 2 regions. One region consists of 5 homologous loop structures, the so-called 'kringles'[125] maintained by disulfide bridges. The second region forms after activation of plasminogen the light chain of plasmin with the active serine residue; this chain eventually reacts with α_2-antiplasmin[127]. The activation of Lys plasminogen by urokinase is faster than that of Glu plasminogen[128]. The activation of Glu plasminogen results of the splitting of 2 peptide bonds with release of a peptide[129] at the N-terminal region to give Lys plasminogen, as suggested by WIMAN and WALLÉN[130]; by hydrolysis of the Arg(560)—Val(561) bond it is then activated to plasmin, which is composed of 2 chains. In the presence of α_2-antiplasmin, however, a plasmin is formed which still contains the N-terminal glutamic-acid portion as in native plasminogen and which forms a complex with the inhibitor[131,132].

Hydrolysis of the Arg—Val bond is produced by all plasminogen activators. The activation of plasminogen by urokinase seems to be slightly accelerated in the presence of fibrin[133]. The effect of fibrin on tissue plasminogen activator (t-PA), however, is much

(Continued on page 230)

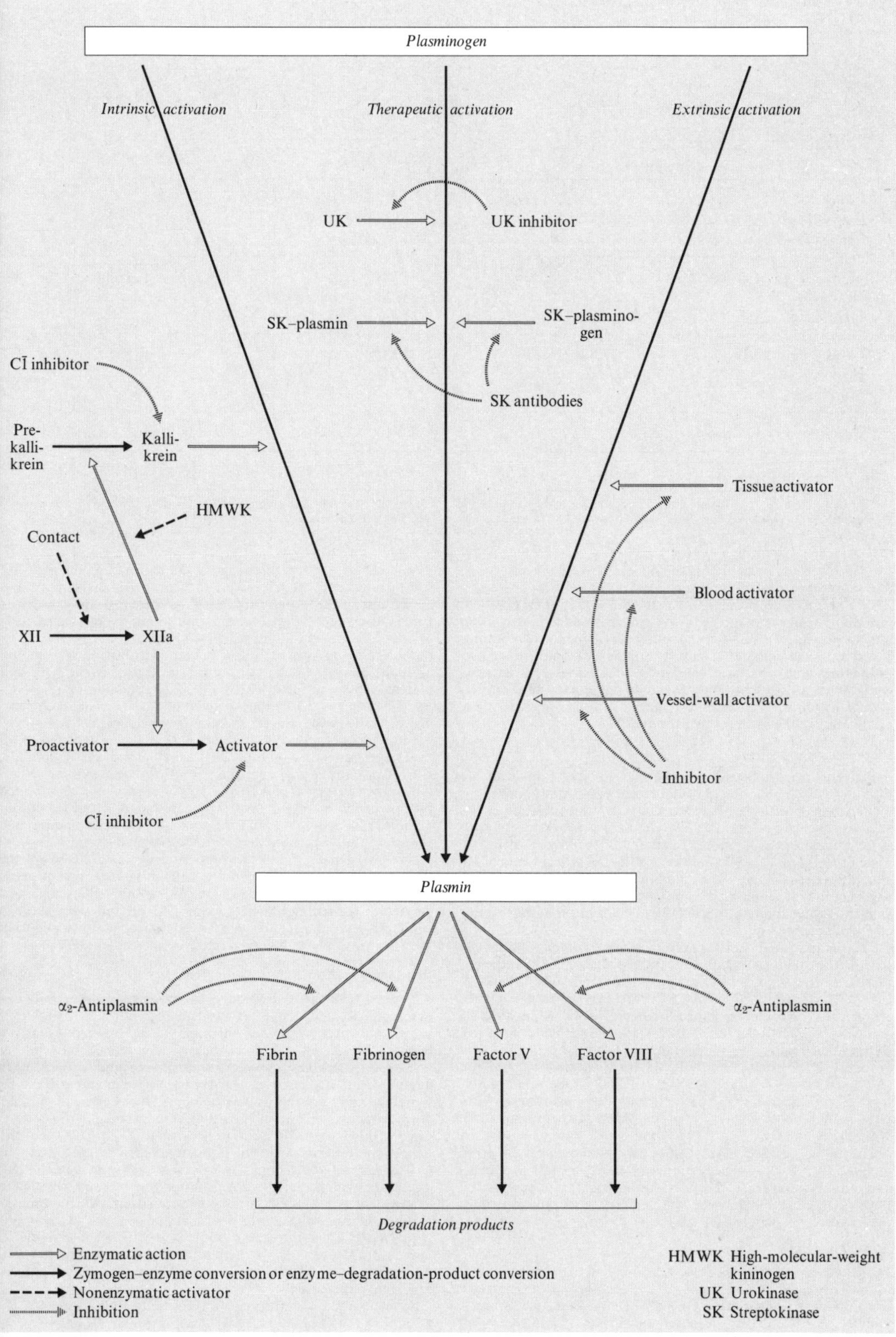

Fig. 6. Fibrinolytic system.

Table 4 *Components of the fibrinolytic system*

Protein	Number of polypeptide chains	Relative molecular mass (M_r)	Number of amino acids	Carbohydrates (mass fraction as percentage)	Concentration in plasma	Half-life in plasma	Site of formation	Reference
Plasminogen	1	90000	790	2%	200 mg/L	53 h	Liver	226, 239
Plasmin	2	...	...	...	...	...	...	238
Heavy chain*	...	...	560					
Light chain	...	...	230					
Urokinase (high-M_r form)	2	54000	...	...	...†	20 min	Kidney	240
Heavy chain	...	33000						
Light chain	...	21000						
Urokinase (low-M_r form)	2	33000	...	...	...†	...	...	241
Heavy chain	...	31000						
Mini chain	...	2426	21					
Tissue plasminogen activator (t-PA)	1	72000◊	...	...	7 µg/L	~5 min	Tissue	140, 219, 242
α_2-Antiplasmin	1	70000	...	13%	70 mg/L	63 h	Liver	123, 239, 243

*The heavy chain of Glu plasmin minus 77 amino acids at the amino end is referred to as 'Lys plasmin', and minus 441 amino acids, as 'Val plasmin'[238].

◊Material secreted by human melanoma cells in culture.

†High-M_r form plus low-M_r form: ~7 µg/L[247].

stronger[133,134], on account of high affinity[134,135]. In the absence of fibrin the conversion of plasminogen to plasmin is rather slow[133,134,136]. This indicates that t-PA has the properties of an excellent thrombolytic agent (page 233), but it is difficult to isolate from human plasma. A tissue-type plasminogen activator can be produced by melanoma cells in culture[137,138] or by cloning of the corresponding gene in bacterial cells[139,140]. t-PA expressed in bacteria contains no carbohydrate, but this should not impair the activation of t-PA by fibrin. t-PA seems to retain its activity after enzymatic elimination of the carbohydrate residues[141].

Platelets

Platelets are cytoplasmic megakaryocyte fragments and are anucleate. Their adhesion to the damaged vessel wall followed by aggregation of further platelets produces the hemostatic plug. The various functions of the platelets are distinct properties of their structural elements: the negative charge of the glycoprotein-rich platelet membrane and that of the endothelial cells prevent adhesion; the external layer of the membrane contains substances such as glycoproteins, implicated as receptors for the triggers of adhesion and aggregation; the phospholipid layer is responsible for the coagulant properties.

The shape of the platelet is maintained by a system of microtubules in the equatorial plane of the discoid platelet. Other filamentous structures align the surface-bound channels. The organelles have well-defined functions: the mitochondria control the metabolism; the α granules contain fibrinogen, factor V, factor VIII in the form of VIIIR:Ag (or VIIIR:VWF), platelet factor 4 (PF-4), β-thromboglobulin, a platelet-derived growth factor, and fibronectin[142,143]; the dense bodies store triggers of aggregation (ADP, serotonin, Ca^{2+}) and vasoconstriction (serotonin) or inhibitors of aggregation (ATP)[142,143,147]; the lysosomes retain hydrolases, and the dense tubular system phospholipases, prostaglandin synthetases, and Ca^{2+}.

The amino-acid sequence of PF-4 (M_r 30800) and β-thromboglobulin (M_r 35400) are very similar[146]. PF-4 neutralizes heparin and inhibits collagenase[144], while β-thromboglobulin may inhibit the prostacyclin synthesis in endothelial cells[145] (for the content of these proteins in platelets see page 164).

Platelet functions

The adhesion of the platelets to a so-called 'foreign surface' – usually damaged endothelium – is the first step in the platelets' contribution to hemostasis. On collagen or basal membranes, platelets spread rapidly and cover the surface[148]. Platelet-membrane glycoproteins act as receptors, and both endothelial and plasma factor VIIIR:VWF are required for normal adhesion. Adhesion to collagen induces a change in shape involving the platelets' contractile system, platelet actomyosin or thrombosthenin[149], and an increase in Ca^{2+} concentration[150]. Activation of the contractile system leads to pseudopode formation and to the release reaction followed by aggregation of platelets to one another. ADP and serotonin released from the dense bodies contribute to aggregation as do the derivatives of arachidonic acid: thromboxane A_2[151] and platelet-activating factor (PAF)[152,153]. The membrane phospholipids become available for the activation of the coagulation cascade. Finally the contractile proteins cause clot retraction.

Inhibitors of aggregation produce a decrease in Ca^{2+} concentration associated with a rise in cAMP, a regulator of the cytoplasmic Ca^{2+} concentration in platelets[154]. cAMP concentration is enhanced by conversion of ATP by adenylate cyclase and diminished by conversion of ATP to AMP by a phosphodiesterase. Prostaglandins play a dual role in the interaction between platelets and the vessel wall. Arachidonic acid is transformed to endoperoxides by cyclooxygenase. Platelet thromboxane synthetase converts the endoperoxides to thromboxane A_2, one of the most potent platelet-aggregating agents. Endothelial-cell endoperoxides are transformed to the strong platelet-aggregation inhibitor, prostacyclin (PGI_2). Acetylsalicylic acid blocks or reduces the production of both derivatives by acetylation of the cyclooxygenase[155].

Physiology

The newborn have a deficient coagulation system especially low in vitamin K_1-dependent factors (Table 5) with a factor IX level occasionally as low as in mild hemophilia B. A discrepancy exists between fibrinogen values as measured by functional clotting assay and those obtained when fibrinogen is estimated with other methods as total fibrinogen. The newborn's plasma thrombin time is prolonged[200], possibly as the result of delayed aggregation of the fibrin monomers[201] and of variations in the α chain of the fibrinogen[202]. Only factor XIII seems to be normal[200]. The content of the main inhibitor, antithrombin III, is markedly reduced to about 60% of normal adult values, as also is the plasminogen content. The absence of bleeding and thrombosis may be explained by the existence of a state of equilibrium between coagulation, anticoagulation and fibrinolysis at a lower level in an intact vascular system. The time taken to reach normal adult levels is variable; it may take a few months. In the mother the activity of factors VII, VIII (VIII:C and VIIIR:VWF), X and XII, as well as that of plasminogen, is increased.

A relatively low antithrombin III activity found immediately after birth is associated to a higher antithrombin III antigen concentration. This may be due to activation of the clotting system followed by consumption of antithrombin III.

Table 5 *Coagulation factors, plasminogen and antithrombin III in the plasma of mother and newborn*[200]

Assay	Unit*	Number of pairs	Mothers		Newborn	
			Mean	s	Mean	s
Fibrinogen:						
Coagulation method	g/L	50	4.00	1.08	1.44	0.35
Heat denaturation	g/L	15	3.77	0.61	2.95	0.67
Factor II	%	50	80	14	26	7
Factor V	%	50	59	46	48	32
Factor VII	%	50	211	58	41	11
Factor VIII	%	50	170	71	53	31
Factor IX	%	50	94	33	14	14
Factor X	%	50	195	90	36	28
Factor XII	%	50	143	38	43	14
Factor XIII	%	50	67	25	86	31
Plasminogen:						
Caseinolytic method	%	50	117	23	30	11
Antithrombin III:						
Activity	%	34	86.6	21.76	60.5	13.56
Immunological assay	%	34	125.5	26.99	87.2	18.9

*Percent data refer to pooled plasma of a great number of normal adults.

The partial thromboplastin time is age-dependent and becomes shorter with increasing age[203]. An increase in factor VIII and a decrease in prekallikrein activity with age have also been observed[204].

Fibrinogen and factor VIII are acute-phase reactants. The activity of factor VIII increases after stress, as does fibrinolytic activity.

Compared with that of other proteins in plasma (pages 136 to 139), the half-life of the coagulation factors is short (Table 3).

Pathology

Coagulation

Hereditary disorders of coagulation are mostly characterized by absence or diminution of the activity of a single factor or inhibitor, while acquired disorders are generally due to complex anomalies. For all coagulation factors, except thromboplastin, hereditary deficiencies have been reported.

Sex-linked hemophilia, the most frequent of the hereditary coagulation diseases, was discovered long ago and was probably first mentioned in the Babylonian Talmud in the 5th century, where it is stated that 'when in the same family 2 male children have died of bleeding after circumcision, the 3rd child should not be circumcised'. The name 'hemophilia' was first used in a thesis by FRIEDRICH HOPFF, one of SCHÖNLEIN's students. The mode of inheritance was clearly described in 1813 by HAY, who noted: 'Children of bleeders are never subject to this disposition, but their grandsons by their daughters.' The term 'conductor' for the female carrier was coined in the first half of the 19th century in Tenna, a Swiss village, by the member of a well-known family of hemophiliacs.

Hemophilia A and B are distinguished by deficient activity of factors VIII and IX, respectively. Their clinical symptoms and mode of inheritance are similar. The seriousness of the condition varies, being severe when the residual clotting activity in plasma is less than 1% (0.01 U/mL), mild when between 0.01 and 0.05 U/mL and light when above 0.05 U/mL. About 80% of cases are hemophilia A patients. Apart from patients with true deficiency of factor VIII:C, variants are known in which a cross-reacting material (CRM) is present in the patient's plasma. CRM is a protein capable of neutralizing the human antibodies found in up to 10% of hemophilia A patients after substitution with factor VIII. These antibodies are directed against the VIII:C portion of factor VIII. CRM is immunologically equivalent to VIII:C. It has been found, for example, in 6 out of 34 patients[156] and in 4 out of 48[157]. The situation is quite different when heterologous antibodies are prepared by rabbit immunization. These antibodies are directed against the carrier protein VIIIR:Ag, which is present in the plasma of all hemophiliacs A.

Table 6 *Abnormal fibrinogens: structural changes*[164]

Fibrinogen	Position of exchange
Lille	Aα7 (Asp→Asn)
Rouen	Aα12 (Gly→Val)
Petoskey	Aα16 (Arg→His)
Manchester	Aα16 (Arg→His)
Bern II	Aα16 (Arg→His)
Metz	Aα16 (Arg→Cys)
Zürich II	Aα16 (Arg→Cys)
Detroit	Aα19 (Arg→Ser)
München	Aα19 (Arg→Asn)

Table 7 *Fibrinopeptides released by thrombin from normal and genetically abnormal fibrinogens (molecules per molecule)*[165]

Fibrinogen	Fibrinopeptide A		B
	Abnormal	Normal	Normal
Normal	–	2	2
Metz	–	–	2
Amsterdam, Frankfurt II, Frankfurt III, London III, Marseille, Schwarzach, Stony Brook, Zürich I	–	1	2
Bicêtre	2	–	2
Louisville, Manchester, New Albany, Rouen, Sydney I, Sydney II	1	1	2
Copenhagen, Frankfurt I, London IV, München I, Münster I, Oslo I, Oslo II, Oslo IV, Philadelphia II, Pontoise, Temple I, Temple II	–	2	2

Hemophilia B also exists with and without factor IX cross-reacting material[159, 160], sometimes showing an abnormal prothrombin time with ox-brain thromboplastin[161].

Patients with von Willebrand's disease have a simultaneous reduction of both VIIIR:Ag and VIII:C. In these patients the reduced platelet adhesiveness results from diminution of VIIIR:Ag complexes which carry the VIIIR:VWF activity. This defect is associated with a prolongation of the bleeding time not seen in true hemophilia. Von Willebrand's disease is autosomal dominant. Heterozygous patients do not generally have hemarthrosis. In homozygous patients, who are usually the offspring of consanguineous parents, the residual activity of both VIII:C and VIIIR:VWF – measured as activity of ristocetin cofactor in an aggregation assay – is very low[158]. Several variants have been described[258].

Afibrinogenemia characterized by the absence of fibrinogen has been demonstrated in more than 100 patients[162, 163]. Hypofibrinogenemia is less well defined; in parents of a person with afibrinogenemia it represents the heterozygous state[163, 164]. Nearly 100 families with dysfibrinogenemia have been identified[165]. In these families the fibrinogen molecules have an abnormal structure due to various anomalies provoking either defective fibrinopeptide A release or delayed polymerization of the fibrin monomers[163]. By 1982, the structural error of 13 fibrinogen variants had been exactly localized[164, 165] (Table 6). A classification of abnormal fibrinogens is possible by analyzing the fibrinopeptides released by thrombin (Table 7).

Defects of prothrombin are rare. In true deficiency the functional activity and the concentration as measured immunologically are reduced in parallel[166], and some activity is always left. Abnormal prothrombin molecules have been detected in at least 10 families. The first detected – in 1969 – is prothrombin Cardeza[167]. The normal thrombin molecule is contained in prothrombin Barcelona[168], but it cannot be activated by the physiological activator, factor Xa. Activation by staphylocoagulase is nevertheless still possible[168]. In this case the abnormality probably lies in one of the cleavage sites for factor Xa[169]. In other cases (prothrombin Brussels, prothrombin Molise), subnormal amounts of prothrombin are measured when it is activated by either ecarin or staphylocoagulase[170].

The clinical manifestations of factor VII deficiency are severe when the residual activity of factor VII is far below 1% (0.01 U/mL). Variants can be distinguished by their variable reaction toward thromboplastins of different sources – ox-brain, or rabbit, monkey or human tissues. Most of these variants have been found in northern Italy[171].

For factor X the number of variants could be very much higher than the total number reported to date. Low residual activity around 1% is coupled with extremely severe hemorrhagic diathesis[172]. No activity was found after activation with either human thromboplastin or Russell's viper venom[177]. In opposition, factor X Friuli is not activated in presence of thromboplastin, but it reacts with Russell's viper venom[173]. Combined deficiencies of several vitamin K_1-dependent factors have been observed, for which a posttranslational defect in γ-carboxylation of glutamic residues may be responsible[174].

About 60 cases with deficiency of factor V are known. Their investigation has been made difficult by the absence of precipitating antibodies. The first family with factor V deficiency was discovered in 1947[175].

The first case of combined deficiency of factors V and VIII was reported in 1954[176]. Inheritance is autosomal. This deficiency may be related to the biochemical similarity of V:C and VIII:C, the clotting moieties of factors V and VIII. In combined deficiency, normal amounts of VIIIR:Ag have been found[177] and the presence of V:CAg and VIII:CAg demonstrated in the plasma of some patients[178]. The combined deficiency may be a secondary defect due to the absence of an inhibitor of activated protein C (page 227)[68]. The uninhibited protein Ca would then be responsible for the abnormally high degradation of factors V and VIII. This hypothesis appears to be questionable or at least not generally valid[179].

Deficiency of factor XI seems to be specific to Jews of Ashkenazi origin. Inheritance is autosomal, and the patients suffer from a true deficiency since both the activity and immunologically measured concentration of factor XI are diminished[180]. It is associated with only mild bleeding even in homozygous patients.

Contact activation of the coagulation system is defective in patients lacking factor XII, prekallikrein or HMWK. Practically all patients are asymptomatic.

The autosomally inherited deficiency of factor XIII[181] is a severe bleeding disorder. Intracranial hemorrhage is observed more frequently than in other hereditary clotting disorders. Here the clotting system is normal, but the quality of the fibrin is hemostatically inadequate[182]. This abnormal fibrin does not permit normal fibroblast growth, at least in some patients characterized by defective wound-healing[183].

The inhibitory capacity of blood coagulation is a major function in protection against thrombosis. Families with reduced antithrombin III activity show an increased tendency to thrombosis[197]. Some families are characterized by a reduction in the concentration of antithrombin III, whereas others have reduced activity with a normal concentration[198]; in some cases the anomaly becomes apparent only in the presence of heparin[199] because the affinity of antithrombin III is diminished. Protein C deficiency, which also predisposes to thromboembolic disorders, has been found in at least 24 families up to 1983[68]. The homozygous state may be incompatible with survival beyond the neonatal period[259].

Fibrinolysis

Hereditary anomalies of the fibrinolytic system have also been recognized. Recurrent thrombosis reflects the abnormal variants of plasminogen, of which 5 had been discovered by 1982 (plasminogens Tochigy, Tokyo, Chicago I, Chicago II and Chicago III); these variants can be classified, by reference to kinetic parameters, into 3 different classes[184]. In contrast, α_2-antiplasmin deficiency is the cause of severe bleeding[185] since secondary activation of the fibrinolytic system is no longer regulated by the presence of this fast-acting inhibitor.

Platelets

Several hereditary platelet defects are known. Various properties may be involved. In the Bernard-Soulier syndrome, platelet adhesiveness to the injured vessel wall is deficient. The disease is autosomal recessive and may be due to the lack of a glycoprotein in the platelet membrane[186]. In thrombasthenia also, abnormal platelet aggregation is caused by deficiency of a membrane glycoprotein[187,188].

In the storage-pool disease, the platelets adhere normally but release insufficient amounts of ADP and Ca^{2+}[189]. The ADP content of the dense bodies is reduced, as is that of ATP, although to a lesser extent. The ratio ATP/ADP is higher than normal[190]. Defects of cyclooxygenase and thromboxane synthetase make the platelets insensitive to stimulation by arachidonic acid[191,192].

Acquired disorders of hemostasis

These are due either to diminished capacity for synthesis of the coagulation factors by the liver or to accelerated consumption, as in disseminated intravascular coagulation (DIC). In liver disease the vitamin K_1-dependent factors are the most sensitive and are the first to be reduced. In cases of liver disease, however, vitamin K is not effective, or only slightly so, because it has no action on the synthesis of polypeptide chains. It is only required for carboxylation of several glutamic residues at the N-terminal portion of these coagulation factors. Carboxylation can also be reduced in liver disease, but especially by vitamin K deficiency, as in obstructive jaundice or during treatment with vitamin K antagonists. In liver cirrhosis, prognosis is bad when, in addition to a decrease in factors II, VII, IX and X, the activity of factors V and XIII and that of plasminogen show a steady fall[193].

Acquired, isolated deficiencies are rarely seen. However, a typical example is the fall in factor X to concentrations as low as 0.10 U/mL seen in patients with amyloidosis[194]. In renal disease platelet anomalies are probably due to the accumulation of guanidinosuccinic acid and hydroxyphenolic acids[195], reversible by dialysis. The concentration of factor VIII is high and those of the other factors frequently reduced in renal insufficiency.

Inhibitors of coagulation have been detected in a variety of disorders, as in systemic lupus erythematosus. The lupus anticoagulant does not inhibit a specific coagulation factor[196].

In disseminated intravascular coagulation (DIC) there is first a phase of fibrin formation with diffuse fibrin deposition and with formation of microthrombi. This is followed by a reactive, secondary activation of fibrinolysis and then bleeding due to consumption and degradation characterized by the disappearance of factors V, VIII and XIII, fibrinogen and platelets, and a reduction in the other factors. These pathological events are associated with the appearance of fibrin(ogen) degradation products (FDP) and soluble complexes of fibrinogen–fibrin monomer in the plasma. During the initial phase, factor VIII levels (VIII:C, VIIIR:Ag) can be very high. Many trigger mechanisms produce DIC: multiple trauma with possible release of thromboplastic material into the circulation, septic shock with endothelial damage and activation of the contact phase, or antigen–antibody activation of the coagulation cascade or platelet aggregation, among others.

Thrombosis

Thrombogenesis is different in the venous and arterial circulations. Venous occlusion is characterized by the formation of red coagulation thrombi, the starting point of which is difficult to determine exactly. Frequently the calf veins are affected first, but thrombi can also form in the valve pockets of the proximal leg veins[205]. Turbulence and minimal alterations of the venous wall may favor thrombus formation. On the arterial side the contribution of the platelets is predominant and leads to the formation of a white thrombus. The normal vascular endothelium is an antithrombotic surface as a result of the negative charge carried by the endothelial cell surface, and the production of antithrombotic substances such as the aggregation inhibitor prostacyclin or t-PA. After injury to the endothelium, platelets and plasma factors come into contact with activating structure-bound substances, i.e. collagen, thromboplastin.

Blood flow plays an important role. Venous stasis produces local ischemia and consequent endothelial damage, the first effect of which is activation of the coagulation system. In arteries the blood flow is more rapid; platelets are brought into contact with the vessel wall by collision with erythrocytes, which are heavier. Platelets adhere to the vessel wall, aggregate and form the starting point for thrombi. Sooner or later the mechanisms for hemostasis are brought into play and contribute to the extension of the thrombus.

Since the hemostatic system participates in thrombogenesis, analysis of hemostatic changes may have a predictive value in the detection of either an existing thrombosis or an increased tendency to thrombosis or atherosclerosis. Reduced antithrombin III activity, diminished fibrinolytic potential and deficiency of protein C predispose to thromboembolic disorders. The preoperative partial thromboplastin time (an expression of the capacity of the intrinsic system) is shorter than normal in patients who suffer postoperative thrombosis[206]. Levels of fibrinogen, factor VII and factor VIII are higher in plasma of patients who die of coronary heart disease than in plasma of survivors[207].

Products of the action of thrombin on fibrinogen – fibrinopeptide A and the complexes of fibrinogen–fibrin monomer – and the fibrin(ogen) degradation products resulting from fibrinolysis are normally not detectable in plasma or present only in very low concentrations[208,209]. An increased concentration is an indication that coagulation and fibrinolysis have been activated. Demonstration of enzyme–inhibitor reaction complexes is another analytical tool. Complexes of thrombin, plasmin and kallikrein with α_2-macroglobulin still have an amidolytic activity[211], but methods based on this property have not until now given the expected results. Another approach is to determine these proteinases complexed by their specific inhibitors: antithrombin III, α_2-antiplasmin and C$\bar{1}$ inhibitor[210].

Prophylaxis and treatment

In hereditary deficiency only the substitution of the deficient factor can restore normality. The hemostatic efficacy, i.e. the concentration of the factor above which bleeding will almost certainly stop, is different for each factor. It varies between about 0.1 U/mL for factor XIII and more than 0.5 U/mL for factor VIII. The rhythm of substitution will therefore depend on the hemostatic level and on the survival time of each factor. Again the situation is more favorable in deficiency of factor XIII (half-life ~6 days) than in deficiency of factor VIII (half-life ~12 hours). In coagulopathies, other drugs – for example antifibrinolytics – have only a complementary effect. In some patients with mild or light hemophilia, deamino-D-arginine vasopressin (DDAVP) stimulates synthesis of factor VIII. In acquired disorders the cause of the failure of hemostasis must be treated.

Thrombosis

Anticoagulation is in fact only a prophylactic treatment to prevent thrombosis or its extension, and pulmonary embolism. Heparin is used for immediate action, and the oral anticoagulants for long-term prophylaxis.

Heparin

Heparin is a direct inhibitor of blood coagulation and works in vivo as well as in vitro. It accelerates the action of antithrombin III on thrombin and other coagulation proteinases. The relatively slow inhibition of thrombin by antithrombin III becomes an immediate reaction in the presence of heparin. In the steady state, commercial heparin (with a large spectrum of molecular size) has a half-life of about 210 minutes. The fractions of low molecular mass (M_r ~6000) have high antifactor Xa activity and low or no antithrombin activity. Heparin-binding of both antithrombin III and thrombin is required. In the case of factor Xa this binding is apparently not necessary.

Heparin is given by infusion after acute thrombosis and pulmonary embolism when immediate and constant anticoagulation is desired. For prophylactic treatment against postoperative thrombosis, the subcutaneous application of 5000 U thrice daily, or the combination of 5000 U or 2500 U heparin with dihydroergotamine mesylate twice daily, is efficacious. Full anticoagulation can be obtained by subcutaneous injections of 10000–20000 U twice daily.

Oral anticoagulants

These are vitamin K antagonists and inhibit the carboxylation of glutamic residues of factors II, VII, IX, X, and of protein C. Their effect in vivo is demonstrable after a time interval necessary for the disappearance of the circulating factors, this depending on the survival time of each factor. Factor VII and protein C disappear first, followed by factors IX, X and finally II (prothrombin). Inactive, acarboxylated proteins are released into the blood instead of the γ-carboxylated zymogens. The aim of oral anticoagulation is to maintain levels of these factors low enough to prevent thrombosis and high enough to avoid the risk of bleeding. The therapeutic range is narrow, and dosage is controlled by determinations of the prothrombin time (PT, Quick, thromboplastin time).

The oral anticoagulants are either coumarin or phenylindandione derivatives, the actions of which are similar. The coumarin derivatives acenocoumarol, warfarin and phenprocoumon are enantiomers. The $S(-)$ forms of phenprocoumon and warfarin are 2 and 5 times more active respectively than the $R(+)$ forms. The reverse is true for acenocoumarol. This difference may be due to variations of receptor affinity or metabolism[212–214]. The interactions with other drugs may also be different.

Drug interactions were first clearly demonstrated with phenylbutazone[215]. This compound and its derivatives are the strongest potentiators of the oral anticoagulants. Barbiturates in contrast reduce the effect of oral anticoagulants[216] because of enzyme induction. Other antirheumatic drugs which do not interfere directly with oral anticoagulation may increase the risk of bleeding through inhibition of platelet functions.

Thrombolysis

Thrombolysis is the only real treatment of thromboembolic disorders which can rapidly restore the patency of blood vessels and preserve the function of venous valves. The patient's fibrinolytic system is activated by infusion of an activator – urokinase or streptokinase – or by plasmin itself. Streptokinase has been by far the most frequently administered activator; it also appears to be the most active[217]. Urokinase of human origin has the advantage of causing practically no side effects except bleeding. However, this advantage does not compensate for its weaker action. Giving the activator by local infusion rather than systemically should reduce the risk of bleeding caused by degradation of fibrinogen, and of factor VIII and factor V, combined with the inhibiting effects of fibrin(ogen) degradation products. Local application is technically more demanding, and its action is limited to one occluded vessel.

The desirable property of an activator – selectivity of action on the thrombus site without inducing a systemic lytic state – is shown by the tissue plasminogen activator (t-PA)[218,219]. By itself t-PA is a poor activator, but its activity is greatly enhanced in the presence of fibrin (page 230).

Another approach consists in the transitory blockade by acylation of the active group of the plasminogen–streptokinase complex. After injection the compound should have enough time to be adsorbed on to the thrombus and possibly to be enriched there before it is deacylated by hydrolysis[220].

Analytical methods

Determination of the activated partial thromboplastin time (aPTT) has generally replaced the less precise and less practical whole-blood coagulation time and recalcification time as a global measure of intrinsic-system activity. In this assay the reagent provides phospholipids and a contact activator. The prothrombin time (PT) is the global assay for the extrinsic system; thromboplastin is the activator. The bleeding time is a measure of platelet count and function. Thrombin time is an assay for inhibitors, for example heparin, and depends on the presence of fibrinogen.

The more specific assays are based on 3 different principles.

The clotting assays use modifications of both aPTT and PT. The assay mixture consists of a reagent containing all necessary factors except the one to be determined, the aPTT or PT activator, the patient's diluted plasma and finally Ca^{2+}. Dilution of the plasma reduces the disturbing effects of other factors and inhibitors present and thus enhances specificity. The clotting time, i.e. the time between addition of Ca^{2+} and visible fibrin formation, reflects the factor activity. The relationship tends to be linear in a double logarithmic graph. For the inhibitor assay, active factor is incubated with inhibitor source; residual factor activity after incubation is an indirect measure of inhibitor activity. For physiological factors and inhibitors, activity is expressed in units or as a percentage of the norm. By definition, the normal value is 1 U/mL or 100%.

The proteinases of coagulation and fibrinolysis are able to hydrolyze esters and amides of amino acids and also the *p*-nitroanilides of tri- or tetrapeptides[221], known collectively as chromogenic or fluorogenic substrates. Specificity, which is not absolute, is controlled by the amino acids and their sequence in the peptides. Sensitivity is less than that of the clotting or fibrinolytic assays, but they have made it possible greatly to simplify the test systems and to develop other test methods. The chromogenic substrates are well suited to the measurement of inhibitors[222,223]. Under some conditions the results of both clotting and substrate assays may differ. α_2-Macroglobulin-linked proteinases are still able to split the *p*-nitroanilides, whereas they are totally inactive in a clotting assay. If this fact is not overlooked, it gives valuable additional information.

A third group of methods uses the antigenic properties of the proteins under investigation. The concentration (not the activity) is measured with specific antibodies and with the help of various techniques: nephelometry, radial immunodiffusion, agglutination of coated particles, electroimmunodiffusion, radioimmunoassays (RIA, IRMA) or the enzyme-linked immunosorbent assay (ELISA). Immunologic assays measure the concentration of precursors, active proteins, inactive forms and degradation products. The specificity can be increased by use of monoclonal antibodies. Quantification of the rapidly formed serine proteinase-inhibitor

Table 8 *Common tests of hemostasis and blood coagulation* [252]

Test	System or function tested	Selected reference values	Common causes of abnormalities
Platelet count	Platelet function	See page 230	Thrombocytopenia; thrombocytosis
Bleeding time	Platelet function		Thrombocytopenia; von Willebrand's disease; platelet dysfunction; vascular disorders (uncommon); severe coagulation disorders (rare)
Template		5.1 (s 1.4) min[253]	
IVY		2.3–7 min[254]	
Activated partial thromboplastin time*	Intrinsic and common pathway	35 (s 4) s[254]	Deficiencies or inhibitors of prekallikrein, HMWK, factors XII, XI, IX, VIII, X, V, prothrombin or fibrinogen; lupus inhibitors
Prothrombin time*	Extrinsic and common pathway	13.1 (s 0.6) s◊[254]	Deficiencies or inhibitors of factors VII, X, V, prothrombin or fibrinogen; dysfibrinogenemia; lupus inhibitors
Thrombin time*	Fibrin formation	15–18 s[254]	Afibrinogenemia, dysfibrinogenemia and hypofibrinogenemia; inhibitors of thrombin or of fibrin polymerization
Fibrinogen assay*	–	1.90–3.65 g/L[255]	Afibrinogenemia, dysfibrinogenemia and hypofibrinogenemia; inhibitors of thrombin or of fibrin polymerization
Assay for fibrin(ogen) degradation products	Fibrinolytic system	< 5 mg/L[256]	DIC; fibrinogenolysis; liver disease; dysfibrinogenemia

*Test affected by heparin. ◊Significant variation depending on thromboplastin used.

complexes, for example plasmin-α_2-antiplasmin[257], is possible with easy techniques when the antibody recognizes only the 'neoantigen'. Immunological methods should be considered as an additional tool and should not replace the activity assay, even though there is good correlation between concentration and activity under normal physiological conditions.

References

1 THILO and BÖHM, *Thrombos. Diathes. haemorrh. (Stuttg.)*, **30**, 363 (1973).
2 WUEPPER and COCHRANE, *J. exp. Med.*, **135**, 1 (1972).
3 HATHAWAY et al., *Blood*, **26**, 521 (1965).
4 RATNOFF and SAITO, *Proc. nat. Acad. Sci. (Wash.)*, **76**, 958 (1979).
5 SAITO et al., *J. clin. Invest.*, **55**, 1082 (1975).
6 DONALDSON et al., *J. Lab. clin. Med.*, **87**, 327 (1976).
7 WUEPPER et al., *J. clin. Invest.*, **56**, 1663 (1975).
8 COLMAN et al., *J. clin. Invest.*, **56**, 1650 (1975).
9 LUTCHER, C.L., *Clin. Res.*, **24**, 440 (1967).
10 ROSENTHAL et al., *Proc. Soc. exp. Biol. (N.Y.)*, **82**, 171 (1953).
11 GRIFFIN, J.H., *Proc. nat. Acad. Sci. (Wash.)*, **75**, 1998 (1978).
12 MACFARLANE, R.G., *Nature*, **202**, 498 (1964).
13 GRIFFIN and COCHRANE, *Proc. nat. Acad. Sci. (Wash.)*, **73**, 2554 (1976).
14 GRIFFIN and COCHRANE, *Semin. Thrombos. Hemostas.*, **5**, 254 (1979).
15 REVAK et al., *J. exp. Med.*, **147**, 719 (1978).
16 COCHRANE and REVAK, *Fed. Proc.*, **38**, 1271 (1979).
17 HAN et al., *J. Biochem. (Tokyo)*, **77**, 55 (1975).
18 SUGO et al., *Biochemistry*, **19**, 3215 (1980).
19 SAITO et al., *J. Lab. clin. Med.*, **92**, 84 (1978).
20 REVAK et al., *J. clin. Invest.*, **54**, 619 (1974).
21 SAITO et al., *J. Lab. clin. Med.*, **88**, 506 (1976).
22 BOUMA et al., *J. Lab. clin. Med.*, **96**, 693 (1980).
23 PROUD et al., *J. Lab. clin. Med.*, **95**, 563 (1980).
24 SAITO and GOLDSMITH, *Blood*, **50**, 377 (1977).
25 FUJIKAWA et al., *Biochemistry*, **13**, 4508 (1974).
26 ØSTERUD et al., *J. biol. Chem.*, **253**, 5946 (1978).
27 DI SCIPIO et al., *J. clin. Invest.*, **61**, 1528 (1978).
28 HEMKER and ZWAAL, *Trends biochem. Sci.*, **7**, 378 (1982).
29 PITLICK and NEMERSON, *Meth. Enzymol.*, **45**, 37 (1976).
30 LIU and MCCOY, *Thrombos. Res.*, **7**, 199 (1975).
31 NEMERSON, Y., *J. clin. Invest.*, **47**, 72 (1968).
32 NEMERSON and ZUR, in BING, D.H. (Ed.), *The Chemistry and Physiology of the Human Plasma Proteins*, Pergamon Press, New York, 1979, page 145.
33 RADCLIFFE and NEMERSON, *J. biol. Chem.*, **251**, 4797 (1976).
34 GJØNNAESS, H., *Thrombos. Diathes. haemorrh. (Stuttg.)*, **28**, 155 (1972).
35 LAAKE and ØSTERUD, *Thrombos. Res.*, **5**, 759 (1974).
36 RADCLIFFE et al., *Blood*, **50**, 611 (1977).
37 SAITO and RATNOFF, *J. Lab. clin. Med.*, **85**, 405 (1975).
38 ØSTERUD and RAPAPORT, *Scand. J. Haemat.*, **24**, 213 (1980).
39 RAPAPORT, S.I., in MÉNACHÉ et al. (Eds.), *Hemophilia and Hemostasis*, Liss, New York, 1981, page 57.
40 MAGNUSSON et al., in REICH et al. (Eds.), *Proteases and Biological Control*, Cold Spring Harbor Laboratory, 1975, page 123.
41 MAGNUSSON et al., in HEMKER and VELTKAMP (Eds.), *Prothrombin and Related Coagulation Factors*, Leiden University Press, Leiden, 1975, page 25.
42 JACKSON and NEMERSON, *Ann. Rev. Biochem.*, **49**, 765 (1980).
43 DOOLITTLE, R.F., *Sci. Amer.*, **245**, No. 6, 92 (1981).
44 PISANO et al., *Proc. nat. Acad. Sci. (Wash.)*, **68**, 770 (1971).
45 GERTH et al., *Biophys. Chem.*, **2**, 208 (1974).
46 MCDONAGH et al., *Brit. J. Haemat.*, **21**, 323 (1971).
47 SAKATA and AOKI, *J. clin. Invest.*, **65**, 290 (1980).
48 SAKATA and AOKI, *J. clin. Invest.*, **69**, 536 (1982).
49 HAYASHI and YAMADA, *Thrombos. Res.*, **16**, 393 (1979).
50 DUCKERT and NYMAN, in GASTPAR, H. (Ed.), *Collagen–Platelet Interaction*, Schattauer, Stuttgart, 1978, page 391.
51 SCHWARTZ et al., *J. biol. Chem.*, **248**, 1395 (1973).
52 BOHN et al., *Blut*, **25**, 235 (1972).
53 DUCKERT et al., in *Proceedings of the 8th Congress of the European Society of Haematology*, Vienna 1961, separate, Karger, Basle, 1962, No. 406.
54 KAY and CUDDIGAN, *Brit. J. Haemat.*, **13**, 341 (1967).
55 LÄMMLE et al., *Thrombos. Res.*, **16**, 245 (1979).
56 ABILDGAARD, U., *Scand. J. clin. Lab. Invest.*, **20**, 207 (1967).
57 PETERSEN et al., in COLLEN et al. (Eds.), *The Physiological Inhibitors of Blood Coagulation and Fibrinolysis*, Elsevier/North-Holland, Amsterdam, 1979, page 43.
58 BRIGINSHAW and SHANBERGE, *Arch. Biochem.*, **161**, 683 (1974); BRIGINSHAW and SHANBERGE, *Thrombos. Res.*, **4**, 463 (1974).
59 WITT et al., *Thrombos. Res.*, **32**, 513 (1983).
60 GRIFFITH, M.J., *J. biol. Chem.*, **257**, 13899 (1982).
61 TOLLEFSEN and BLANK, *J. clin. Invest.*, **68**, 589 (1981).
62 TOLLEFSEN et al., *J. biol. Chem.*, **258**, 6713 (1983).
63 MAMMEN et al., *Thrombos. Diathes. haemorrh. (Stuttg.)*, **5**, 218 (1960).
64 STENFLO, J., *J. biol. Chem.*, **251**, 355 (1976).
65 KISIEL, W., *J. clin. Invest.*, **64**, 761 (1979).
66 OWEN and ESMON, *J. biol. Chem.*, **256**, 5532 (1981).
67 SUZUKI et al., *J. biol. Chem.*, **258**, 163 (1983).
68 GARDINER and GRIFFIN, *Progr. Hemat.*, **13**, 265 (1983).
69 JOHNSEN et al., *Thrombos. Haemostas.*, **49**, 69 (1983).
70 RIVERS et al., *Brit. J. Haemat.*, **30**, 311 (1975).
71 HOWARD and FIRKIN, *Thrombos. Diathes. haemorrh. (Stuttg.)*, **26**, 362 (1971).
72 MEYER et al., *Nature*, **243**, 293 (1973).
73 WEISS et al., *J. clin. Invest.*, **52**, 2697 (1973).
74 JAFFE et al., *J. clin. Invest.*, **52**, 2757 (1973).
75 JAFFE et al., *Proc. nat. Acad. Sci. (Wash.)*, **71**, 1906 (1974).
76 HOWARD et al., *Thrombos. Res.*, **4**, 617 (1974).
77 COLLER et al., *Thrombos. Res.*, **6**, 469 (1975).
78 NACHMAN et al., *J. clin. Invest.*, **60**, 914 (1977).
79 BLOOM et al., *Nature (New Biol.)*, **241**, 217 (1973).
80 HOYER et al., *J. clin. Invest.*, **52**, 2737 (1973).
81 GRUSON and RIZZA, *Blut*, **29**, 241 (1974).
82 JAFFE and NACHMAN, *J. clin. Invest.*, **56**, 698 (1975).
83 BLOOM, A.L., *Clin. Haemat.*, **8**, 53 (1979).
84 NORMAN et al., *Science*, **158**, 1060 (1967).
85 DODDS and HOYER, *Brit. J. Haemat.*, **26**, 497 (1974).
86 TRAN et al., *Schweiz. med. Wschr.*, **109**, 1029 (1979).
87 TRAN et al., *Thrombos. Haemostas.*, **50**, 319 (1983).
88 TRAN et al., *Thrombos. Haemostas.*, **46**, 699 (1981).
89 RICK and HOYER, *Thrombos. Res.*, **7**, 909 (1975).
90 COUNTS et al., *J. clin. Invest.*, **62**, 702 (1978).
91 MEYER et al., *J. Lab. clin. Med.*, **95**, 590 (1980).
92 RUGGERI and ZIMMERMAN, *J. clin. Invest.*, **65**, 1318 (1980).
93 LEGAZ et al., *J. biol. Chem.*, **248**, 3946 (1973).
94 WILSON et al., *J. clin. Invest.*, **73**, 654 (1984).
95 DAHLBÄCK, B., *J. clin. Invest.*, **66**, 583 (1980).
96 KANE et al., *J. biol. Chem.*, **255**, 1170 (1980).
97 COLMAN, R.W., *Biochemistry*, **8**, 1438 and 1445 (1969).
98 ESMON, C.T., *J. biol. Chem.*, **254**, 964 (1979).
99 GREENQUIST and COLMAN, *Blood*, **46**, 769 (1975).
100 SEEGERS et al., *Thrombos. Res.*, **8**, 543 (1976).
101 SUZUKI et al., *J. biol. Chem.*, **258**, 1914 (1983).
102 DAHLBÄCK, B., *Biochem. J.*, **209**, 837 (1983).

[103] HEMKER et al., *Nature,* **200**, 589 (1963); JOSSO et al., *Thrombos. Diathes. haemorrh. (Stuttg.),* **20**, 88 (1968).
[104] STENFLO and GANROT, *Biochem. biophys. Res. Commun.,* **50**, 98 (1973).
[105] STENFLO et al., *Proc. nat. Acad. Sci. (Wash.),* **71**, 2730 (1974).
[106] NELSESTUEN et al., *J. biol. Chem.,* **249**, 6347 (1974).
[107] SADOWSKI et al., *J. biol. Chem.,* **251**, 2770 (1976).
[108] GIRARDOT et al., *Biochem. biophys. Res. Commun.,* **70**, 655 (1976).
[109] MÉNACHÉ et al., in HEMKER and VELTKAMP (Eds.), *Prothrombin and Related Coagulation Factors,* Leiden University Press, Leiden, 1975, p. 159.
[110] ESMON et al., *J. biol. Chem.,* **257**, 859 (1982).
[111] ESMON et al., *Thrombos. Haemostas.,* **50**, 419 (1983).
[112] OGSTON and BENNETT, *Brit. med. Bull.,* **34**, 107 (1978).
[113] RIJKEN et al., *Biochim. biophys. Acta (Amst.),* **580**, 140 (1979).
[114] COLE and BACHMANN, *J. biol. Chem.,* **252**, 3729 (1977).
[115] DUCKERT, F., in MARKWARDT, F. (Ed.), *Fibrinolytics and Antifibrinolytics,* Springer, Berlin, 1978, page 209.
[116] TAYLOR and COMP, in MARKWARDT, F. (Ed.), *Fibrinolytics and Antifibrinolytics,* Springer, Berlin, 1978, page 137.
[117] MÜLLERTZ and LASSEN, *Proc. Soc. exp. Biol. (N.Y.),* **82**, 264 (1953).
[118] CASTELLINO, F.J., *Trends biochem. Sci.,* **4**, 1 (1979).
[119] CEDERHOLM-WILLIAMS et al., *Europ. J. Biochem.,* **100**, 125 (1979).
[120] MCCLINTOCK et al., *Biochemistry,* **13**, 5334 (1974).
[121] COLLEN et al., *Thrombos. Res.,* **7**, 245 (1975).
[122] MÜLLERTZ and CLEMMENSEN, *Biochem. J.,* **159**, 545 (1976).
[123] MOROI and AOKI, *J. biol. Chem.,* **251**, 5956 (1976).
[124] WALLÉN and WIMAN, *Biochim. biophys. Acta (Amst.),* **221**, 20 (1970), and **257**, 122 (1972).
[125] SOTTRUP-JENSEN et al., *Atlas Protein Sequence Struct.,* **5**, suppl. 3, 91 (1978).
[126] WIMAN, B., in GAFFNEY and BALKUV-ULUTIN (Eds.), *Fibrinolysis. Current Fundamental and Clinical Concepts,* Academic Press, London, 1978, p. 47.
[127] WIMAN and COLLEN, *J. biol. Chem.,* **254**, 9291 (1979).
[128] THORSEN et al., *Thrombos. Diathes. haemorrh. (Stuttg.),* **32**, 325 (1974).
[129] RICKLI and OTAWSKY, *Biochim. biophys. Acta (Amst.),* **295**, 381 (1973).
[130] WIMAN and WALLÉN, *Europ. J. Biochem.,* **36**, 25 (1973).
[131] SUMMARIA et al., *J. biol. Chem.,* **250**, 3988 (1975).
[132] VIOLAND and CASTELLINO, *J. biol. Chem.,* **251**, 3906 (1976).
[133] CAMIOLO et al., *Proc. Soc. exp. Biol. (N.Y.),* **138**, 277 (1971).
[134] WALLÉN, P., in PAOLETTI and SHERRY (Eds.), *Thrombosis and Urokinase,* Academic Press, London, 1977, page 91.
[135] MÜLLERTZ, S., *Proc. Soc. exp. Biol. (N.Y.),* **82**, 291 (1953).
[136] NIEUWENHUIZEN et al., *Thrombos. Haemostas.,* **50**, 106 (1983).
[137] WILSON et al., *Cancer Res.,* **40**, 933 (1980).
[138] RIJKEN and COLLEN, *Progr. Fibrinolysis,* **5**, 236 (1981).
[139] PENNICA, D., *Haemostasis,* **11**, suppl. 1, 65 (1982); PENNICA, D., *Thrombos. Haemostas.,* **50**, 94 (1983).
[140] RIJKEN and COLLEN, *J. biol. Chem.,* **256**, 7035 (1981).
[141] LITTLE et al., *Thrombos. Haemostas.,* **50**, 144 (1983).
[142] KAPLAN et al., *Blood,* **53**, 604 (1979); NURDEN et al., *Blood,* **59**, 709 (1982).
[143] HOLMSEN, H., in MIELKE, C.H. (Ed.), *Mechanisms of Hemostasis and Thrombosis,* Symposia Specialists, Miami, 1978, page 73.
[144] HITI-HARPER et al., *Science,* **199**, 991 (1978).
[145] HOPE et al., *Thrombos. Haemostas.,* **42**, 8 (1979).
[146] KAPLAN and OWEN, *Blood,* **57**, 199 (1981).
[147] DA PRADA et al., in DE GAETANO and GATTINI (Eds.), *Platelets: a Multidisciplinary Approach,* Raven Press, New York, 1978, page 331.
[148] BAUMGARTNER and MUGGLI, in GORDON, J.L. (Ed.), *Platelets in Biology and Pathology,* North-Holland, Amsterdam, 1976, page 23.
[149] BETTEX-GALLAND and LÜSCHER, *Advanc. Protein Chem.,* **20**, 1 (1965).
[150] MASSINI et al., *Thrombos. Haemostas.,* **40**, 212 (1978).
[151] SAMUELSSON et al., *Ann. Rev. Biochem.,* **47**, 997 (1978).
[152] BENVENISTE et al., *J. exp. Med.,* **136**, 1356 (1972).
[153] CARGILL et al., *Thrombos. Haemostas.,* **49**, 204 (1983).
[154] HASLAM et al., *Advanc. Cyclic Nucleotide Res.,* **9**, 533 (1978).
[155] ROTH and MAJERUS, *J. clin. Invest.,* **56**, 624 (1975).
[156] HOYER and BRECKENRIDGE, *Blood,* **32**, 962 (1968).
[157] DENSON et al., *Brit. J. Haemat.,* **17**, 163 (1969).
[158] ZIMMERMAN et al., *New Engl. J. Med.,* **301**, 1307 (1979).
[159] KASPER et al., *Blood,* **50**, 351 (1977).
[160] PAREKH et al., *Brit. J. Haemat.,* **40**, 643 (1978).
[161] HOUGIE and TWOMEY, *Lancet,* **1**, 698 (1967).
[162] MAMMEN, E.F., *Semin. Thrombos. Hemostas.,* **1**, 184 (1974).
[163] FLUTE, P.T., *Brit. med. Bull.,* **33**, 253 (1977).
[164] MÉNACHÉ, D., *Ann. N.Y. Acad. Sci.,* **408**, 121 (1983).
[165] HENSCHEN et al., *Ann. N.Y. Acad. Sci.,* **408**, 28 (1983).
[166] OWEN et al., *Mayo Clin. Proc.,* **53**, 29 (1978).
[167] SHAPIRO et al., *J. clin. Invest.,* **48**, 2251 (1969).
[168] JOSSO et al., *Blood,* **38**, 9 (1971).
[169] RABIET et al., *Biochim. biophys. Acta (Amst.),* **584**, 66 (1979).
[170] GIROLAMI et al., *Blood,* **52**, 115 (1978).
[171] GIROLAMI et al., *Blood,* **54**, 46 (1979).
[172] BACHMANN et al., *Thrombos. Diathes. haemorrh. (Stuttg.),* **1**, 87 (1957).
[173] GIROLAMI et al., *Brit. J. Haemat.,* **19**, 179 (1970); GIROLAMI et al., *Acta haemat. (Basel),* **54**, 120 (1975).
[174] GOLDSMITH et al., *J. clin. Invest.,* **69**, 1253 (1982).
[175] OWREN, P.A., *Lancet,* **1**, 446 (1947).
[176] OERI et al., *Bibl. paediat. (Basel),* **58**, 575 (1954).
[177] GIROLAMI et al., *Acta haemat. (Basel),* **55**, 234 (1976).
[178] GIDDINGS et al., *Brit. J. Haemat.,* **37**, 257 (1977).
[179] SUZUKI et al., *Blood,* **62**, 1266 (1983).
[180] FORBES and RATNOFF, *J. Lab. clin. Med.,* **79**, 113 (1972); RIMON et al., *Blood,* **48**, 165 (1976).
[181] BERLINER et al., *Brit. J. Haemat.,* **56**, 495 (1984).
[182] DUCKERT, F., *Ann. N.Y. Acad. Sci.,* **202**, 190 (1972).
[183] BECK et al., *Thrombos. Diathes. haemorrh. (Stuttg.),* **6**, 485 (1961); DUCKERT and BECK, *Semin. Hemat.,* **5**, 83 (1968).
[184] WOHL et al., *Thrombos. Haemostas.,* **48**, 146 (1982).
[185] AOKI et al., *J. clin. Invest.,* **63**, 877 (1979).
[186] NURDEN and CAEN, *Nature,* **255**, 720 (1975).
[187] NURDEN and CAEN, *Brit. J. Haemat.,* **28**, 253 (1974).
[188] PHILLIPS et al., *Nature,* **257**, 599 (1975).
[189] LAGES et al., *Blood,* **46**, 119 (1975); HOLMSEN et al., *Blood,* **46**, 131 (1975).
[190] WEISS et al., *J. clin. Invest.,* **54**, 421 (1974).
[191] LAGARDE et al., *Brit. J. Haemat.,* **38**, 251 (1978).
[192] WEISS and LAGES, *Lancet,* **1**, 760 (1977).
[193] BILAND et al., *Thrombos. Diathes. haemorrh. (Stuttg.),* **39**, 646 (1978).
[194] MÉNACHÉ and BOIVIN, *Nouv. Rev. franç. Hémat.,* **2**, 868 (1962).
[195] RABINER, S.F., *Progr. Hemostas. Thrombos.,* **1**, 233 (1972).
[196] GREEN et al., *Thrombos. Haemostas.,* **49**, 144 (1983).
[197] EGEBERG, O., *Thrombos. Diathes. haemorrh. (Stuttg.),* **13**, 516 (1965).
[198] MACKIE et al., *Brit. med. J.,* **1**, 136 (1978).
[199] TRAN et al., *Thrombos. Haemostas.,* **44**, 87 and 92 (1980).
[200] BILAND and DUCKERT, *Thrombos. Diathes. haemorrh. (Stuttg.),* **29**, 644 (1973).
[201] GUILLIN and MÉNACHÉ, *Thrombos. Res.,* **3**, 117 (1973).
[202] WITT and TESCH, *Thrombos. Haemostas.,* **42**, 79 (1979).
[203] DUCKERT et al., to be published.
[204] CHRISTE et al., to be published.
[205] SEVITT, S., *J. clin. Path.,* **27**, 517 (1974).
[206] GALLUS et al., *Lancet,* **2**, 805 (1973).
[207] MEADE et al., *Lancet,* **1**, 1050 (1980).
[208] COOKE et al., *Lancet,* **2**, 51 (1975); NOSSEL et al., *J. clin. Invest.,* **58**, 1136 (1976).
[209] GODAL and ABILDGAARD, *Scand. J. Haemat.,* **3**, 342 (1966).
[210] FAREED et al., *Clin. Chem.,* **29**, 1641 (1983).
[211] LÄMMLE et al., *Thrombos. Res.,* **16**, 245 (1979).
[212] JÄHNCHEN et al., *Clin. Pharmacol. Ther.,* **20**, 342 (1976).
[213] MEINERTZ et al., *Brit. J. clin. Pharmacol.,* **5**, 187 (1978).
[214] O'REILLY, R.A., *Clin. Pharmacol. Ther.,* **16**, 348 (1974).
[215] SIGG et al., *Schweiz. med. Wschr.,* **86**, 1194 (1956).
[216] KOCH-WESER and SELLERS, *New Engl. J. Med.,* **285**, 487 and 547 (1971).
[217] MARBET et al., *Thrombos. Haemostas.,* **48**, 187, 190 and 196 (1982).
[218] WEIMAR et al., *Lancet,* **2**, 1018 (1981).
[219] VAN DE WERF et al., *New Engl. J. Med.,* **310**, 609 (1984).
[220] SMITH et al., *Nature,* **290**, 505 (1981).
[221] SVENDSEN et al., *Thrombos. Res.,* **1**, 267 (1972).
[222] ABILDGAARD et al., *Scand. J. clin. Lab. Invest.,* **36**, 109 (1976).
[223] TEGER-NILSSON et al., *Scand. J. clin. Lab. Invest.,* **37**, 403 (1977).
[224] LOTTSPEICH and HENSCHEN, *Hoppe-Seylers Z. physiol. Chem.,* **358**, 935 (1977); HENSCHEN and LOTTSPEICH, *Hoppe-Seylers Z. physiol. Chem.,* **358**, 1643 (1977), and *Thrombos. Res.,* **11**, 869 (1977); DOOLITTLE et al., *Nature,* **280**, 464 (1979).
[225] HOYER, L.W., *Blood,* **58**, 1 (1981).
[226] COLLEN et al., *Europ. J. clin. Invest.,* **8**, 185 (1978).
[227] SUTTIE and JACKSON, *Physiol. Rev.,* **57**, 1 (1977).
[228] PITLICK, F.A., *J. clin. Invest.,* **55**, 175 (1975).
[229] BAJAJ et al., *J. biol. Chem.,* **256**, 253 (1981).
[230] BROZE and MAJERUS, *J. biol. Chem.,* **255**, 1242 (1980).
[231] MELLIGER and DUCKERT, *Thrombos. Diathes. haemorrh. (Stuttg.),* **25**, 438 (1971).
[232] OVER et al., *J. clin. Invest.,* **62**, 223 (1978).
[233] DI SCIPIO et al., *Biochemistry,* **16**, 698 (1977).
[234] CHUNG et al., *J. clin. Invest.,* **62**, 1078 (1978).
[235] HJORT et al., *Scand. J. clin. Lab. Invest.,* **13**, 668 (1961).
[236] JACKSON, C.M., *Biochemistry,* **11**, 4873 (1972).
[237] BUCHER et al., *FEBS Lett.,* **68**, 293 (1976).
[238] ROBBINS et al., *Progr. Fibrinolysis,* **5**, 110 (1981).
[239] COLLEN, D., *Thrombos. Haemostas.,* **43**, 77 (1980).
[240] HENSCHEN and LOTTSPEICH, *Haemostasis,* **11**, suppl. 1, 54 (1982).
[241] SCHALLER et al., *Haemostasis,* **11**, suppl. 1, 54 (1982).
[242] WALLÉN et al., *Haemostasis,* **11**, suppl. 1, 53 (1982); RIJKEN et al., *J. Lab. clin. Med.,* **101**, 274 (1983).
[243] HÖGSTORP and SALDEEN, *Haemostasis,* **11**, suppl. 1, 46 (1982).
[244] CHIU et al., *J. clin. Invest.,* **72**, 493 (1983).
[245] FAIR, D.S., *Blood,* **62**, 784 (1983).
[246] IKEMATSU et al., *J. Lab. clin. Med.,* **97**, 662 (1981).
[247] HUBER et al., *J. Lab. clin. Med.,* **103**, 684 (1984).
[248] BOUMA et al., *Blood,* **62**, 1123 (1983).
[249] SARASUA et al., *J. biol. Chem.,* **257**, 14102 (1982).
[250] TRAVIS and SALVESEN, *Ann. Rev. Biochem.,* **52**, 655 (1983).
[251] CHAN et al., *Clin. Sci.,* **60**, 681 (1981).
[252] WINTROBE et al., *Clinical Hematology,* 8th ed., Lea & Febiger, Philadelphia, 1981, page 1045.
[253] MIELKE, C.H., in MIELKE and RODVIEN (Eds.), *Mechanisms of Hemostasis and Thrombosis,* Symposia Specialists Inc., Miami, 1978, page 21.
[254] MIALE, J.B., *Laboratory Medicine: Hematology,* 6th ed., Mosby, St. Louis, 1982.
[255] BOWIE et al., *Mayo Clinic Laboratory Manual of Hemostasis,* Saunders, Philadelphia, 1971.
[256] RICHARDSON et al., *Brit. J. Haemat.,* **42**, 469 (1979).
[257] PLOW et al., *J. Lab. clin. Med.,* **93**, 199 (1979).
[258] ZIMMERMAN et al., *Progr. Hemat.,* **13**, 279 (1983).
[259] SELIGSOHN et al., *New Engl. J. Med.,* **310**, 559 (1984).

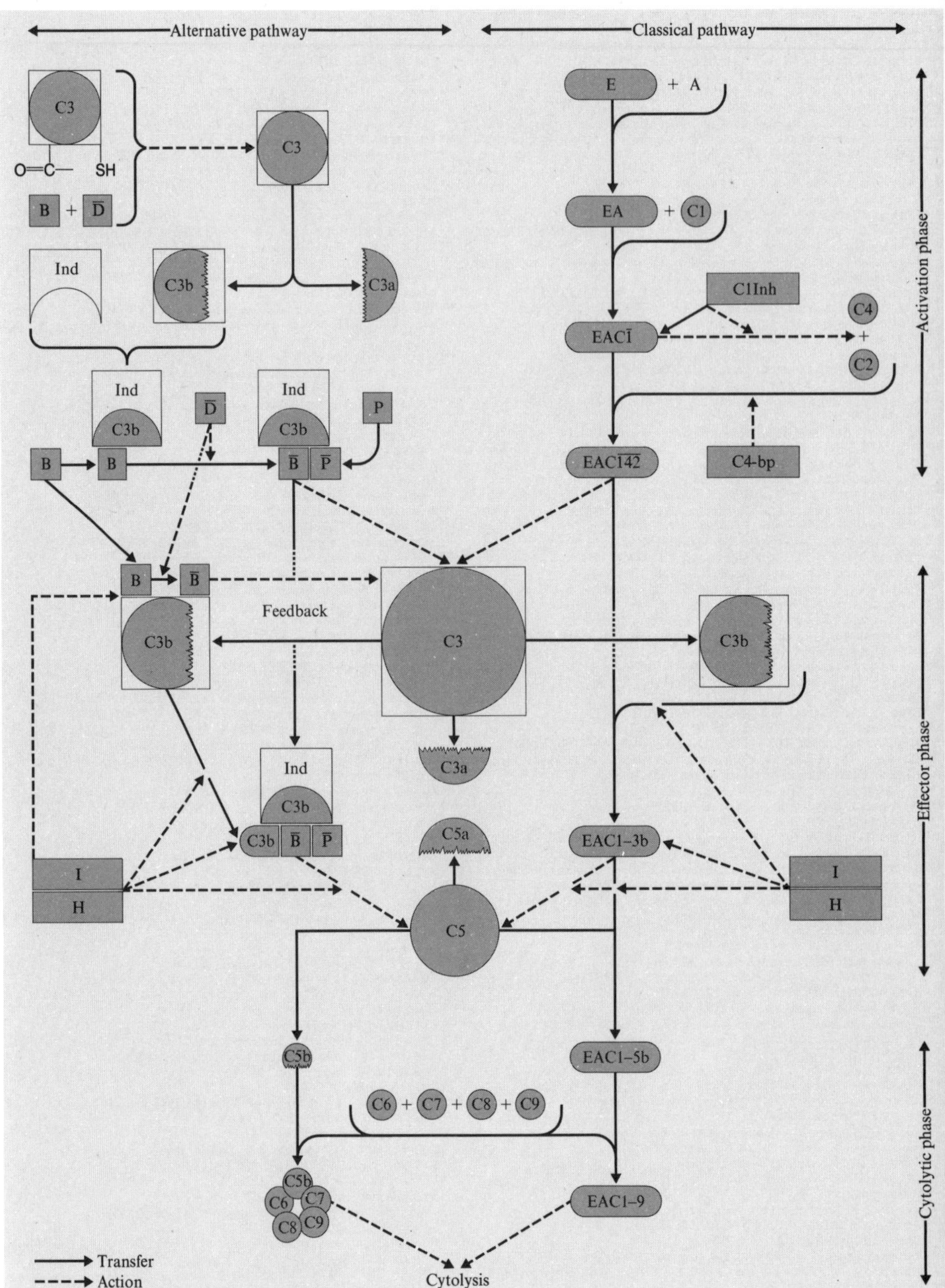

Fig. 1. Scheme of the complement-reaction sequence. It can be divided into activation, effector and cytolytic phases. The activation stage can follow the classical or the alternative pathway. Examples of inducers (Ind) of the alternative pathway include: lipopolysaccharides from the cell walls of gram-negative bacteria (endotoxins), dextran sulfate (polyanions), zymosan (particulate constituents of yeast cell walls), inulin (polyfructose), and antigen-binding segments of antibody molecules. – E: erythrocyte; A: IgG or IgM antibody; B and D: enzymes of the alternative pathway; P: properdin; I and H: inhibitors.

* This chapter (pages 236–244) has been compiled by U. HADDING, Institut für Medizinische Mikrobiologie, Universität Mainz, Mainz, FRG.

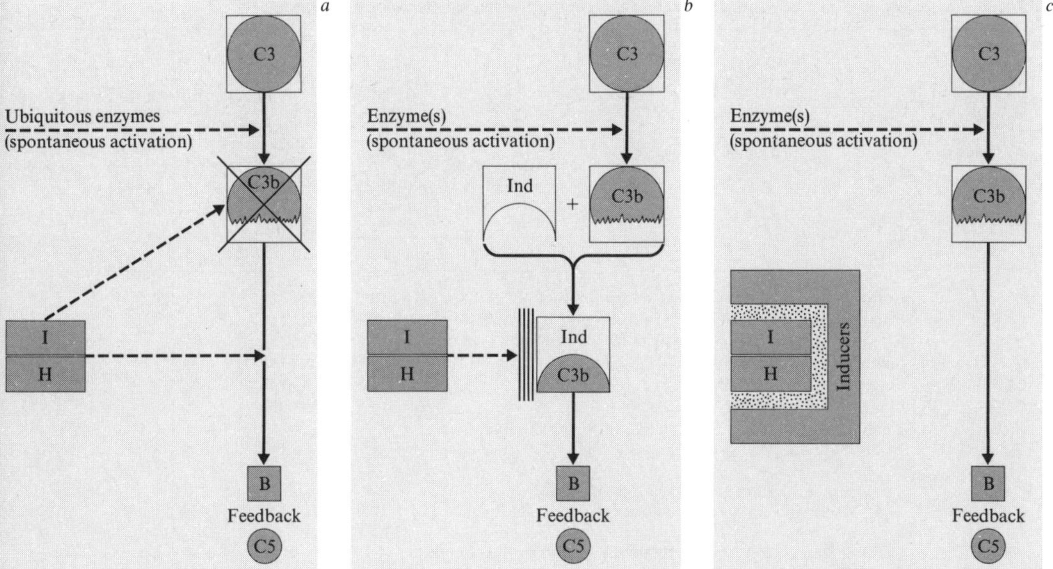

ig. 2. Scheme of the initial reaction of the alternative pathway (complementing Fig. 1). *a* Normal situation: equilibrium between activa-ion and inactivation. The small quantities of C3b continuously produced are captured and controlled by the relevant inhibitors, factor I nd factor H. *b* Inducers of the alternative pathway bind spontaneously produced C3b in such a way that it largely prevents the interven-ion of the inhibitors yet facilitates further reactions. *c* The inducers interact by forming complexes (?) with the inhibitors and block their ctivity, so that – in particular – the positive feedback reaction can proceed unhindered.

)efinition and significance of complement

Complement (C) is a constituent of all normal plasma. It con-ists of an activatable system of proteins reacting with one another n a set sequence. There are 2 activation pathways: the classical, omprising the components C1, C4, and C2, and the alternative, omprising factors B, D, and properdin. Both pathways merge in hat they lead to the formation of C3-activating enzymes, thus en-ering the common final reaction sequence in which C5, C6, C7, 38, and C9 yield membranolytic complexes (Figs. 1 and 2). Since nbalanced complement activation would be deleterious to the rganism, the system is well controlled by inhibitors directed gainst activated C1, C4, C3, and factor B (Table 1). The biological unctions of complement may be summarized in the terms *media-ion of inflammation, defense against infections,* and *participation in he immune response*[1–10] (Fig. 3).

Complement is active, on one hand, in the efferent limb of the mmune response together with antibodies and leukocytes as an nitially humoral, non-antigen-specific effector system, while on he other it plays a part by modulating lymphocyte functions in the fferent limb of the immune response. Activated complement acts nainly on cell membranes, the functions and properties of which re changed by the presence of complement. Acting as a signal, omplement can stimulate the affected cells to physiological esponses – such as release of histamine, serotonin and prosta-landins, enzyme secretion, and directed migration and phagocy-osis – or it can cause new surface characteristics to appear, such as inding capacity and susceptibility to phagocytosis, and finally cell lestruction by cytolysis.

In view of the many-sided interactions of complement with anti-odies, kinins, and enzymes, blood coagulation and fibrinolytic actors, macrophages, B and T lymphocytes, mast cells, granulo-ytes and platelets, it may be stated that complement serves the esponsiveness of the living organism, in conjunction with many ther systems, to preserve its integrity and individuality.

'hysiological functions of the complement system

The most important functions are derived from the 3rd (C3) and ith (C5) components. In the course of their activation, further de-cribed below, enzymatic splitting takes place, with generation of mall polypeptides, C3a or C5a respectively. The remaining larger ragments of the original molecule are designated C3b or C5b Figs. 1 and 5).

Human C3a consists of 77 and C5a of 74 amino-acid residues in known sequence, but only C5a contains an oligosaccharide unit

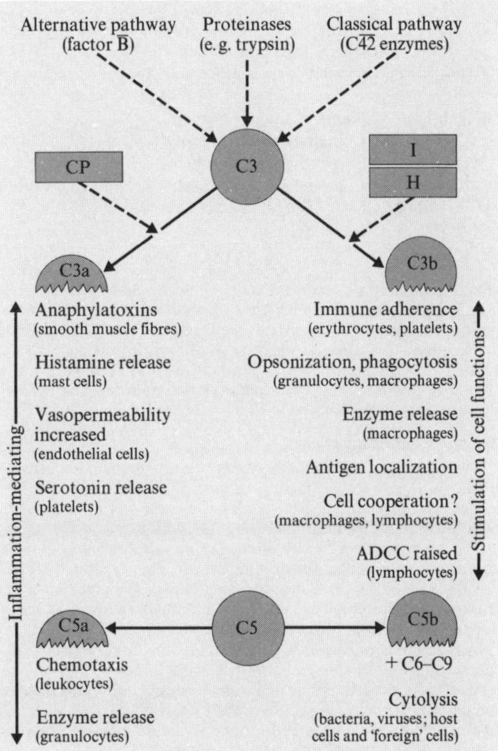

Fig. 3. Simplified reaction sequence showing the biological effects of the complement system. The cells mainly involved are indicated beneath the key word for each biological activity. CP: arginine carboxypeptidase (3.4.17.3) (anaphylatoxin inactivator); ADCC: antibody-dependent, cell-mediated cytotoxicity.

Table 1 *Physicochemical and biological properties of complement components and control proteins*[7,10,63,70,75]

Protein	Structure	Mass of carbohydrates relative to mass of total protein	Sedimentation coefficient (S_{20w})	Relative molecular mass (M_r)	Electrophoretic mobility	Concentration in serum	Turnover rate, related to plasma pool[38] (mean values and s or range)	Rate of synthesis[38] (mean values and s or range)
		%	10^{-13} s			mg/L	$\% h^{-1}$	$mg\,h^{-1}\,kg^{-1}$
C1	Complex of $C1q(C1r)_2(C1s)_2$ held together by Ca^{2+}	+	18	900000	–	–	–	–
C1q	Composed of 18 peptide chains: 6 A-chains (M_r 27550), 6 B-chains (M_r 25200), 6 C-chains (M_r 23800)	8	11.1	459000	γ_2	70	–	–
C1r	Single polypeptide chain	...	7.5	83000	β	34	–	–
C1s	Single polypeptide chain	...	4.5	83000	α_2	31	–	–
C2	Single-chain glycoprotein	+	4.5	108000	β_2	30	–	–
C3	2 polypeptide chains (α: M_r 110000; β: M_r 75000) linked by disulfide bridges[76]	...	9.5	~185000	β_1	1300	1.71 (s0.34)	0.69 (s0.16)
C4	3 polypeptide chains (α: M_r 93000; β: M_r 75000; γ: M_r 33000) linked by disulfide bridges	...	10.0	~200000	β_1	430	1.40 (s0.21)	0.21 (s0.07)
C5	2 polypeptide chains (α: M_r 110000; β: M_r 75000) linked by disulfide bridges[76]	...	8.7	~185000	β_1	75	(1.6–2.2)	(0.06–0.11)
C6	Single-chain glycoprotein[88]	...	5.5	128000	β_2	60	–	–
C7	Single-chain glycoprotein[88]	...	6.0	121000	β_2	55	–	–
C8	3-chain structure consisting of 2 subunits: C8α–γ, C8β[77] (α: M_r 64000; β: M_r 64000; γ: M_r 22000)	...	8.0	151000	γ	80	–	–
C9	Glycoprotein	7.8	4.5	71000	α	60	–	–
B	A serine proteinase composed of fragment Ba (M_r 30000) and fragment Bb (M_r 60000)	...	5–6	92000	β_2	240	(1.4–1.9)	(0.15–0.19)
D	A single-chain serine proteinase (also referred to as $\bar{D}$) consisting of 222 amino acids[90]	...	3	24000	α	2	–	–
P (properdin)	Glycoprotein composed of 4 identical chains (M_r 55000)	9.8	5.4	220000	γ_2	25	–	–
$C\bar{1}$Inh	Single-chain glycoprotein	40	–	~100000	α_2	150	–	–
I (C3bInа)	Composed of 2 polypeptide chains (M_r 50000 and 38000)	...	5.5	88000	β_2	35	–	–
H (β1H)	Single-chain glycoprotein	+	6	150000	β_1	360	–	–
C4-bp (C4-binding protein)	Composed of 7 identical thin, elongated subunits (M_r ~70000) linked to a small central body[89]	...	10.7	540000 to 590000	β_2	?	–	–

linked to asparagine in position 64[11,12]. Both C3a and C5a carry a terminal arginine residue, which is important for their efficacy. A plasma enzyme, arginine carboxypeptidase (3.4.17.3), can split off this arginine – which also exists in kinin – and thus controls the action of these 3 mediators of inflammation. In the early literature, C5a corresponds to the classic 'anaphylatoxin'; later, however, this name has also been applied to C3a[13].

Mediation of inflammation

C3a and C5a can induce *histamine release* from mast cells. In tissue this leads to contraction of smooth muscle fibers, for instance, and probably also of contractile elements in endothelial cells, which thereby lose their lining function.

The polypeptide C5a can stimulate neutrophilic granulocytes and also monocytes to directed migration. This process is termed *chemotaxis*[12,14], and it is among other things responsible for the leukocyte infiltration of inflamed tissues. Furthermore, C5a stimulates *enzyme release* from neutrophils.

In macrophages, *synthesis of prostaglandins* and *thromboxanes* can be triggered by C3a and also by C3b[15].

Mast cells as well as basophilic and neutrophilic granulocytes secrete *platelet-activating factor* (PAF) upon interaction with C3a and especially with C5a. PAF triggers platelet-release reactions but also the oxidative burst in macrophages[16–18].

If inflammation is interpreted as serving to eliminate the damaging agent, then an increase in blood flow and vascular permeability provide for recruitment of macromolecules and cells from the blood. The resulting edema finally makes available all defense and repair mechanisms contained under physiological conditions only inside the blood vessel.

Histamine has vasodilator activity, as does prostaglandin E_2, leading to increased blood flow, which facilitates efflux of macromolecules from the plasma. Various experiments indicated that the bulk of inflammatory edema seems to be dependent on a synergistic action of prostaglandin (e.g. PGE_2) with C5a, explaining its relative resistance to antihistamines[19]. Increased permeability induced by histamine is envisaged as a direct action on the endothelial cells of venules, rapid in onset but short in duration, whereas increased permeability brought about by C5a depends on an interaction between circulating neutrophils and venular endothelial cells and thus is slow in onset but of long duration.

C5a, therefore, is linked to 3 characteristic traits of inflammation: vasodilatation, increased vascular permeability, and accumulation of neutrophils. The chemotactically attracted neutrophils can be aggregated by C5a and triggered to release enzymes and PAF, which in turn increase vascular permeability.

Defense against infection

Complement can take part in defense against infection, both in combination with antibodies and also independently via the alternative activation pathway. The important step here is the coating of foreign structures, for instance the cell membranes or walls of bacteria, with C3b. Since several types of cells possess receptors for C3b, a surface coated with C3b is rendered highly reactive; it behaves as though it were 'adhesive'. In this way, C3b brings about close contact between coated particles and host cells. *Endocytosis by C3b receptors* within coated vesicles has been described for human polymorphonuclear leukocytes and monocytes[20,21]. Since C3b coating commonly takes place in the course of an immune reaction, i.e. the formation of an antigen–antibody complex with subsequent complement activation, the term *immune adherence* has been chosen. An important form of the cell contact mediated by C3b is *opsonization*, by which the phagocytosis of particles difficult to engulf is facilitated by attachment of host proteins. Here too the actions of complement and antibody are complementary, a fact which had inspired PAUL EHRLICH at the beginning of our century to coin the term 'complement' for the 'helping system'. Encapsulated bacteria, such as pneumococci, are much better phagocytized by polymorphonuclear granulocytes after opsonization. Immune adherence can be regarded as the initial stage of opsonization. Opsonization is held to be more important than cytolysis for defense against infection.

Complement can also contribute to *virus neutralization*[22-25]. It prevents adsorption of neutralized virus on to a receptive body cell, thus preventing pinocytosis and cell invasion. Virus neutralization depends on how densely the virus surface is occupied by host proteins. If only a few antibodies are present, neutralization may be carried out, for example, by C2, C4, and C3 fragments. This mechanism may be particularly important in the early phases of a viral infection when antibody is limited. With the help of the C5b–C9 membrane-attack complex, complement may eliminate infectivity of certain viruses by damaging their envelope. In the absence of antibody, C1q is able to interact directly with animal RNA tumor viruses, causing activation of the classical pathway followed by *virolysis*. In man this C1q reactivity may be a natural resistance mechanism to curb the infectivity of the viruses. Many bacterial strains, several viruses and even tumor cells can be lysed by complement. Nevertheless, cytolysis comes second to the above-mentioned mechanisms of defense against infection, since there are bacterial strains which can readily be opsonized but cannot be lysed.

Modulation of the immune response

The influence of C3 and its fragments on the regulation of the immune response has been extensively investigated[26]. Although a definitive picture cannot yet be drawn, there is nevertheless good evidence for functions of C3 in the afferent limb of the immune response. C3 fragments have been implicated as activators of lymphocytes and regulators of blastogenic and antibody responses to antigen by lymphocytes. Elimination of C3 in vivo or antibody-mediated C3 blockade in vitro suppressed the immune response to T-cell-dependent antigens. Both follicular antigen localization and formation of germinal centers in the spleen and lymph nodes are abolished after 'decomplementation', with the result that no B memory cells develop.

It has also been reported that C3a is a potent suppressor of humoral immune responses acting at the level of the T-helper cell[27]. Lymphokine production and therefore macrophage–T-cell interaction seems to be influenced by complement since it was shown that C5a induces macrophages to secrete interleukin 1, resulting in augmentation of the primary humoral immune response[28].

The concept of immune response modulation through complement is supported by genetic analysis. The structural genes for those enzymes ($C\overline{42}$ and factor B) responsible for breaking down C3 and C5 into the biologically active fragments are localized on human chromosome 6, within the region which codes for histocompatibility (HLA antigens) and immune response (see Fig. 1, page 245). This region thus contains the information for specific immunological recognition and the corresponding response capacities[29-31]. The linkage can be interpreted as implying that gene products of this region are essential for the function of the immune system and that the genes, therefore, have been held together closely during evolution. The gene for C3 has been assigned to human chromosome 19, thus rounding off the genetic knowledge regarding the complement system[32,33].

Links with other systems

In addition to the functional relationship already mentioned between the complement system and macrophages, B lymphocytes and granulocytes, there are also links with the intrinsic coagulation–kinin pathway[34,35]. Thus various substances (lipopolysaccharides or 'endotoxins', polyanions, foreign surfaces) or tissue lesions can activate several of these systems simultaneously and in parallel. Moreover, following activation, enzymatic reactions appear in which factors of one pathway activate proteins of neighboring systems. The areas of overlap appear even more prominent, since finally common inactivators block the kinin, coagulation and complement system.

An example is the activated factor XII (Hageman factor), which can bring about transformation of prekallikrein to kallikrein and plasminogen to plasmin. As endopeptidases with low specificity, all the 3 enzymes mentioned are able to split C1, thus initiating complement activation. Kallikrein cleaves C3, while plasmin also splits factor B, in addition to C3. The complement system itself then influences the coagulation pathway via mediators and enzymes released from leukocytes and platelets. A significant role in this is played by C3a-mediated aggregation[36] and cytolysis of platelets with liberation of partial thromboplastins.

Control of the 3 systems is exerted, for instance, by the $C\overline{1}$ inhibitor ($C\overline{1}$Inh) – which is active against $C\overline{1r}$ and $C\overline{1s}$, factor XII, plasmin and kinin-generating kallikrein – and by arginine carboxypeptidase, which inactivates C3a, C5a, and kinin by splitting off the terminal arginine.

Another – primarily nonenzymatic – control mechanism exists for the anaphylatoxins C3a and C5a, termed 'low-zone desensitization of platelets'[37]. Blood platelets can absorb C3a or C5a very rapidly and depending on the concentration will not respond with release reactions and aggregation but only with stimulus-specific reversible refractoriness. Thus, small amounts of anaphylatoxins may constantly be removed from the circulation by this mechanism.

Diagnostics and clinical aspects

Complement components are proteins with known physicochemical properties, their concentration in plasma being under physiological control and determined mainly by the rate of synthesis (Table 1). The daily metabolic turnover amounts to about 50% and is thus appreciably quicker than that for IgM or IgG[38,39].

Complement can be measured in terms of its hemolytic function or as protein. Immunohemolysis permits determination of the total lytic activity, which records all 9 components together. Measurement of the concentration of one individual component in serum requires the use of monospecific antisera, each of which precipitates the component to be studied. In plasma or serum samples, ELISA techniques permit a sensitive determination of whether the classical or alternative pathway has been activated[40,41].

Reference values for complement components in serum are summarized in Table 2. Complement activity in the newborn, as compared with normal adults, has been shown to be generally in the range of 60–100% for the classical pathway components and of about 50% for factor B and properdin[42].

Cell-bound complement can also be determined by Coombs' test, which is used mainly for C3 fragments. Complement determination by means of the Coombs test is of importance in the presence of cold agglutinins (IgM) and in the heterogeneous group of autoimmunohemolytic anemias.

The possible clinical manifestations of disorders of the complement system can readily be deduced from its normal biological functions. Excessive activation or deficient counter-regulation mainly give rise to inflammatory tissue or organ damage. Immune complexes acquire their pathogenic effect only through complement activation. In this way an organ at first completely uninvolved such as the kidney, can be damaged. Secondary complement participation may be regarded as certain in the following diseases: serum sickness, lupus erythematosus, immune vasculitis, immunohemolytic anemias, paroxysmal nocturnal hemoglobinuria, hypocomplementemic chronic glomerulonephritis, and rheumatoid arthritis[43,44].

When there are defects or functional deficiencies in the inhibitor system, the normal level of complement activation may be exceeded. The long-recognized clinical picture of hereditary, nonallergic angioneurotic edema (Quincke's edema) arises from deficiency of $C\overline{1}$Inh. For largely unknown reasons these patients develop spontaneous $C\overline{1}$ activation, localized almost arbitrarily, which is not curbed by $C\overline{1}$Inh as it would be in healthy individuals. In this way the complement sequence (Figs. 1 and 2) can be set in motion, leading to the production of the component fragments that give rise to edema formation. Thus complement is plainly more easily and more commonly activated in vivo than the in-vitro finding leads one to expect.

In addition to $C\overline{1}$Inh deficiency, other genetically determined defects of complement components are known[45-49]: factor I, factor H, properdin, C1q, C1r, C1s, C4, C2, C3, C5, C6, C7, C8, C9 (all in man), C4, C2, and C3 (in guinea pigs[50]), C5 (in mice), and C6 (in rabbits). The C3 defect has the most serious consequences. The great majority of these patients suffer from frequently relapsing, severe bacterial infections. Replacement therapies with complement-sufficient whole blood or with purified complement components have been suggested. Success has been achieved with blood transfusions in a patient with C3 deficiency[51] and with plasma in-

(Continued on page 241)

Table 2 *Complement components in serum or plasma*

Protein	Material	Subjects	Number	Mean	s	95% range	Method	Ref.
				mg/L				
C1q	Serum	Adults	–	65	6.9	–	RID	78
	Serum	Adults	25	69.6	14	–	RID	79
	Serum	Adults	10	65	5	–	Hydroxyproline assay	80
C1r	Serum	Adults	10	39	2	–	RID	80
C1s	Serum	Adults	10	36	3	–	RID	80
C2	Serum	Adults	509	27	5.6	–	RID	81
	Serum	Adults	–	28.4	6.3	–	RID	78
	Serum	Adults	25	32.1	5	–	RID	79
C3	Serum	Newborn, cord blood	24	1089	–	520–1658	RID	82
		Children:						
	Serum	2–7 days	20	1139	–	589–1689	RID	82
	Serum	1–5 months	16	1188	–	652–1724	RID	82
	Serum	6–23 months	25	1238	–	709–1767	RID	82
	Serum	2–5 years	27	1287	–	755–1819	RID	82
	Serum	6–9 years	28	1336	–	790–1882	RID	82
	Serum	10–14 years	23	1386	–	823–1949	RID	82
	Serum	Adults	100	1612	244	–	RID	81
	Serum	Adults	–	1412	149	–	RID	78
	Serum	Adults	25	1390	210	–	RID	79
C3c	Plasma	Adults	25	2	–	–	EID	83
C3d	Plasma		32	5	1	–	Laser nephelometry	84
C4	Serum	Newborn, cord blood	24	536	–	0–1134	RID	82
		Children:						
	Serum	2–7 days	20	568	–	0–1146	RID	82
	Serum	1–5 months	16	599	–	36–1162	RID	82
	Serum	6–23 months	25	631	–	76–1186	RID	82
	Serum	2–5 years	27	663	–	104–1222	RID	82
	Serum	6–9 years	28	694	–	121–1267	RID	82
	Serum	10–14 years	23	726	–	135–1317	RID	82
	Serum	Adults	100	498	151	–	RID	81
	Serum	Adults	–	509	135	–	RID	78
	Serum	Adults	25	514	160	–	RID	79
C5	Serum	Newborn, cord blood	24	67	–	35–98	RID	82
		Children:						
	Serum	2–7 days	20	65	–	35–95	RID	82
	Serum	1–5 months	16	64	–	34–93	RID	82
	Serum	6–23 months	25	62	–	33–91	RID	82
	Serum	2–5 years	27	61	–	31–90	RID	82
	Serum	6–9 years	28	59	–	29–89	RID	82
	Serum	10–14 years	23	58	–	27–89	RID	82
	Serum	Adults	100	153	29	–	RID	81
	Serum	Adults	–	64	13	–	RID	78
	Serum	Adults	25	56.7	7	–	RID	79
C6	Serum	Adults	–	56.2	8.1	–	RID	78
	Serum	Adults	25	50.9	8	–	RID	79
C8	Serum	Adults	25	43.2	6.5	–	RID	79
C9	Serum	Adults	16	58	8	–	RID	85
	Serum	Adults	25	46.8	14	–	RID	79
	Serum	Adults	90	57.5	12.7	–	IRMA	86
	Plasma	Adults	90	60.2	14.9	–	IRMA	86
B	Plasma	Adults	9	306	49	–	EID	87
	Serum	Adults	100	275	55	–	RID	81
	Serum	Adults	–	241	47	–	RID	78
	Serum	Adults	25	227	49	–	RID	79
P	Plasma	Adults	9	17.2	5.1	–	EID	87
	Serum	Adults	–	27.5	3.7	–	RID	78
	Serum	Adults	25	28.4	5	–	RID	79
C$\bar{1}$Inh	Serum	Adults	25	158	14	–	RID	79
I	Serum	Adults	–	39.6	6.7	–	RID	78
	Serum	Adults	25	38.6	5.5	–	RID	79
H	Serum	Adults	–	561	78	–	RID	78
	Serum	Adults	25	525	58	–	RID	79

RID: radial immunodiffusion; EID: electroimmunodiffusion; IRMA: immunoradiometric assay.

Table 3 *Complement deficiencies in man*

Deficiency	Inheritance*	HLA linkage	Symptoms◊
C1q	AR	–	SLE-like syndrome, glomerulonephritis, chronic sepsis
C1r	AR	–	SLE-like syndrome, glomerulonephritis
C4	AR	+	SLE-like syndrome
C2	AR	+	SLE-like syndrome
C3	AR	–	Recurrent pyogenic infection
C5	AR	–	SLE
C6	AR	–	Neisserial infection
C7	AR	–	Neisserial infection
C8	AR	–	Neisserial infection
C9	AR	–	Neisserial infection
C$\bar{1}$ inhibitor	AD	–	Hereditary angioneurotic edema
Factor I	AR	–	Recurrent pyogenic infection

*AR: autosomal recessive; AD: autosomal dominant.
◊SLE: systemic lupus erythematosus (vasculitis; polymyositis, arthritis).

fusions in a patient with factor I deficiency[52]. Table 3 gives a short overview of the mode of inheritance of the deficiencies, their linkage to the major histocompatibility complex and the related symptoms.

Complement activation

Activation of the complement system is present when biological effects take place that can be attributed to one or more of the 9 components. It makes no difference by what route the activation comes about, how many components are concerned, or if the fragments that become active are large or small.

Two main pathways of complement activation are known, each triggered by different chemical structures. The first runs via C1, C4, and C2, whereas the second, alternative pathway bypasses these components to bring about C3 activation with the aid of factors B, D, and P, which formerly were named the 'properdin system'. The first pathway, which has been known longer, is described as the 'classical pathway'. It is dependent on antibodies – hence the name 'complement' to describe a system that 'complements' the action of antibodies.

Activation of C1 takes place in the presence of antigen–antibody complexes (AgAb) formed by IgG or IgM. The partners in this reaction, antibody and C1, are normally present in the plasma in a pre-active form in which they do not react with one another. Only when the antibody becomes bound to its homologous antigen does the intramolecular structure of its Fc region change in such a way that C1q can react with it. The underlying qualitative change in the antibody has, however, not yet been fully elucidated. For C1 activation, 1 IgM molecule suffices, whereas 2 IgG molecules in close proximity are required. There is some evidence that 2 neighboring Fc pairs of the 5 present in the IgM molecule collaborate in the binding and activation of C1. This spatial relationship existing within the IgM macromolecule has first to be created in the case of IgG by the formation of a 'twinned' pair. Independently of their specificity, antibodies of type IgM and IgG have thus proved to bind C1, whereas IgA, IgD and IgE cannot set off the classical pathway.

In summary, C1q can be described as a 4- to 6-valency Fc receptor that reacts with structures of the Fc segment of IgM or IgG which only appear after modification of the antibody. The great multiplicity of antigen specificities is transformed in this way into the structural monotony of C-activating Fc fragments (Fc^x) (Fig. 4).

$$\left.\begin{array}{ll} Ag + IgM & (a) \\ & \longrightarrow AgAb + (Fc^x)_n \\ Ag + 2\,IgG & (b) \end{array}\right\} \quad (1)$$

$$(Fc^x)_2 + (C1q, 2\,C1r, 2\,C1s \xrightarrow{Ca^{2+}} C1) \longrightarrow C\bar{1} \qquad (2)$$

The most important feature of the alternative pathway lies in the fact that a series of substances can activate complement independently of antibodies: polysaccharides (for instance certain dextrans); inulin; agar; zymosan, an insoluble component of yeast cell walls; lipopolysaccharides, known as endotoxins and derived from the cell walls of gram-negative bacteria. Artificial inducers of activation in the alternative pathway can also be synthesized. For example, soluble dextrans transformed into polyanions by sulfatation have produced massive complement activation in all sera so far tested.

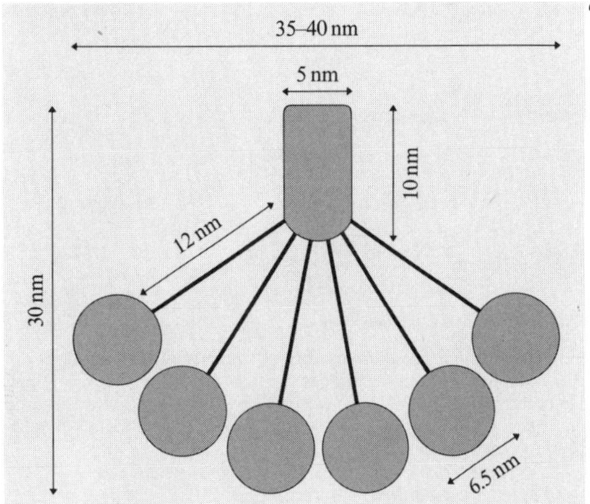

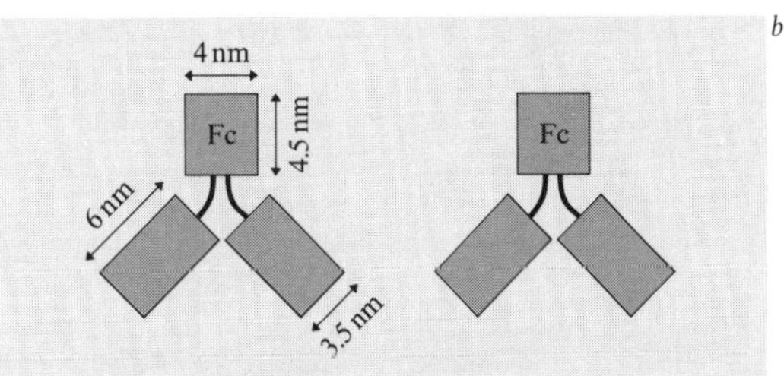

Fig. 4. a Schematic molecular structure of C1q[69–71]. The peripheral spherical subunits interact with the Fc segments of immune complexes. C1r and C1s attach themselves to the central subunit. *b* To portray their comparative size, 2 greatly simplified IgG molecules are illustrated. At least 2 Fc segments are necessary for the binding of C1q with subsequent C1 activation.

The importance of this alternative-pathway activation lies in the fact that the biological functions of the complement system can be employed by this means even in the phases where there is still no reactive antibody present or only small amounts. In the preimmune phase the strict link originally assumed to exist between antigen-antibody reaction and complement activity therefore no longer applies. By means of the alternative pathway, complement can appear as an independent defense system with universal significance in inflammatory processes.

Reaction mechanisms

The reaction mechanisms of the complement system fall naturally into 3 stages. In the 1st stage, or activation phase, enzymes capable of splitting C3 are produced. The 2nd stage, which follows immediately, is the actual biological effector phase in which all the C3 and C5 phenomena described can take place. The 3rd and last stage is the cytotoxic phase directed against cell membranes which culminates in their destruction, with subsequent cell death (Figs. 1–3). The significant differences in the reaction pathways described below lie in the activation phase, which gives rise to different C3-splitting enzymes. By contrast, the effector and cytotoxic phases are the same for all pathways.

The classical pathway

This was elucidated using immunohemolysis as the model. In the form of a complex, 2 components, namely C1 and C2, can be enzymatically active. The reactions determined in vitro are here presented schematically, with C5-splitting shown as the last enzymatic reaction, followed by complex formation with the components C6–C9.

$$\left.\begin{array}{lr} C4 \xrightarrow{C\overline{1s}} C4a + C4b & (a) \\ C2 \xrightarrow{C\overline{1s}} C2a + C2b & (b) \\ C4 + C2 \xrightarrow[Ca^{2+}\ Mg^{2+}]{C\overline{1}} C\overline{4b2a} + C4a + C2b & (c) \end{array}\right\} \textbf{(3)}$$

$$\left.\begin{array}{lr} C3 \xrightarrow{C\overline{4b2a}} C3a + C3b & (a) \\ C5 \xrightarrow{C\overline{4b2a3b}} C5a + C5b & (b) \end{array}\right\} \textbf{(4)}$$

$$\left.\begin{array}{lr} C5b + C6 + C7 \longrightarrow [C5b67] & (a) \\ [C5b67] + C8 + C9 \longrightarrow [C5b\text{–}C9] & (b) \end{array}\right\} \textbf{(5)}$$

In the course of immunohemolysis, the individual reactions take place in the following sequence: antibodies of class IgG or IgM become attached to an erythrocyte (E), giving rise to an immune complex (EA) in which the Fc segments of the antibodies are modified in conformation.

The 'recognition unit' of the C1 macromolecule, i.e. C1q, responds to this structure by binding itself to the immune complex. This leads to autocatalytic activation of C1r, which is transformed into an active enzyme. The subcomponents C1r are thus the point in the reaction sequence at which the conformational changes of the antibody and of C1q result in enzymatic activity. The intramolecular C1 activation is maintained by C1r, which transforms the proesterase C1s proteolytically into the active form $C\overline{1s}$ (formulae **1**, **2**, and **6**).

$$EA + C1 \longrightarrow EAC\overline{1} \qquad \textbf{(6)}$$

As shown in formula **3**, the cell-bound, activated C1 macromolecule ($C\overline{1}$) is now capable of splitting C4 and C2, the subsequent components in the sequence, by means of C1-esterase ($C\overline{1s}$). The large fragment C4b becomes attached to the immune complex and thus forms the site at which native C2 can bind in the presence of Mg^{2+}. Only after this binding does the splitting into C2a and C2b take place, giving rise to the $C\overline{42}$ enzyme, the so-called C3 convertase.

$$\left.\begin{array}{lr} EAC\overline{1} + C4 \longrightarrow EAC\overline{1}4b + C4a & (a) \\ EAC\overline{1}4b + C2 \longrightarrow EAC\overline{1}4b2a + C2b & (b) \\ [\text{Shortened}: EAC\overline{1} + C4 + C2 \longrightarrow EAC\overline{142}] & \end{array}\right\} \textbf{(7)}$$

An important amplification mechanism is present in the C1 reaction, since several $C\overline{42}$ enzymes establish themselves on the cell membrane around one $C\overline{1}$ molecule[53–55]. The C1-esterase is controlled by $C\overline{1}$Inh. The next step in the sequence is represented by formula **4a**, C3 activation marking entry into the biological effector phase. In the α chain of the C3 molecule is a critical thioester bond, probably localized in the C3dg fragment (Figs. 5 and 6). Proteolytic cleavage of the α chain between amino acids 77 and 78 by the C3 convertases of the classical or alternative pathway, for instance, leads to C3a production but also to increased lability of the thioester group. The thioester bond between cysteine and glutamate is broken up, giving rise to a highly reactive but short-lived site which mediates the covalent binding of C3b to cell surfaces, membranes, proteins, etc. (Fig. 6), probably by transesterification. The binding spectrum of C3b is very broad, since for attachment of the molecule only a hydroxy group seems to be required. Virtually the same binding mechanism based on a thioester region has recently been described as being operative in C4 and the α_2-macroglobulin. Each molecule of $C\overline{42}$ enzyme can activate many thousands of C3 molecules – giving further amplification. Thus on one cell at the stage EAC14b2a3b, abbreviated to EAC1-3, there would be an approximate relationship between C1, C4, and C2 or C3 of 1:6:1000. The activation of C5 (formula **4b**) must be preceded by binding of native C5 on cell-bound C3b in the region of the $C\overline{42}$ enzyme, which then carries out the liberation of C5a. The appearance of C5b leads into the cytotoxic phase via formation of the lytic C5b-C9 complex[56–58].

$$\left.\begin{array}{lr} EAC1\text{–}3 + C5b\text{–}C9 \longrightarrow EAC1\text{–}9 & (a) \\ EAC1\text{–}9 \longrightarrow \text{Hb release, cell death} & (b) \end{array}\right\} \textbf{(8)}$$

The molecular processes involved in membrane destruction are only partly understood. By its presence, the lipophilic C5b–C9 complex appears to disturb the membranous structure of the lipophil and lipophobe layers. The resulting turbulence damages the membrane, and its functional collapse leads to osmotic cell lysis

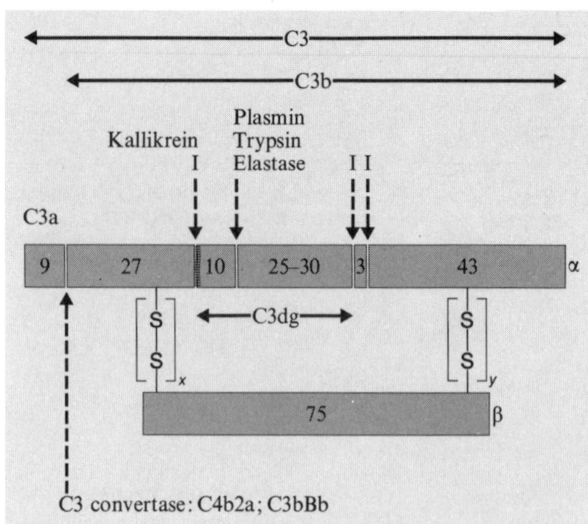

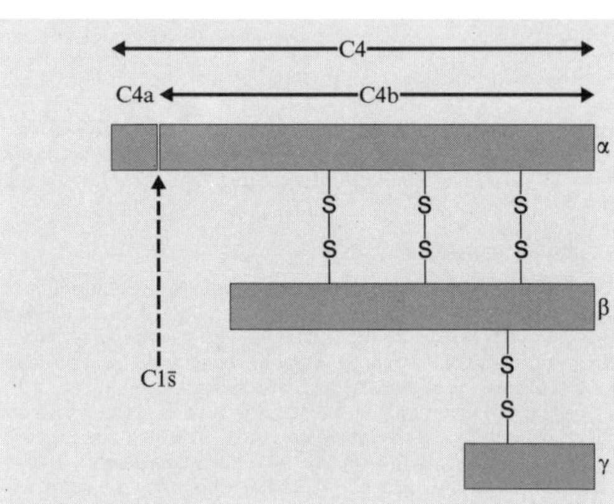

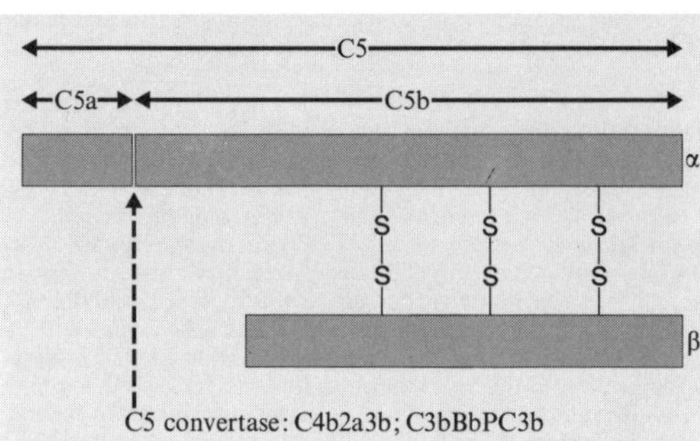

Fig. 5. Diagrams of the polypeptide chain structure of C3, C4 and C5[6,7,72]. Activation of the individual components takes place by enzymatic splitting off a small part of the α chain: C3a, C4a and C5a. (For the positions of the activating enzymes in the sequence see Fig. 1.) – *C3a:* M_r 9000 fragment from the N terminus of the α chain. *C3b:* C3 minus C3a. *C3c:* C3b minus C3dg = β chain plus M_r 27000 and M_r 43000 fragments of the α chain, attached by S—S bridges. *C3dg:* M_r 35000–40000 fragment of the α chain which results from the action of factor I. It can be further cleaved into a M_r 10000 and a M_r 25000–30000 fragment, for instance by trypsin. The C3dg fragment is likely to contain the thioester group (Fig. 6) and, in the hatched area, the active center of C3e, which can induce leukocytosis[72–74]. – Assumed localization of binding sites for receptors in the α chain of C3: for CR_1 (C3b receptor), in the M_r 43000 fragment near to the C terminus; for CR_2 (C3d receptor), in the M_r 25000–30000 fragment; for CR_3 (iC3b receptor), in the M_r 10000 fragment.

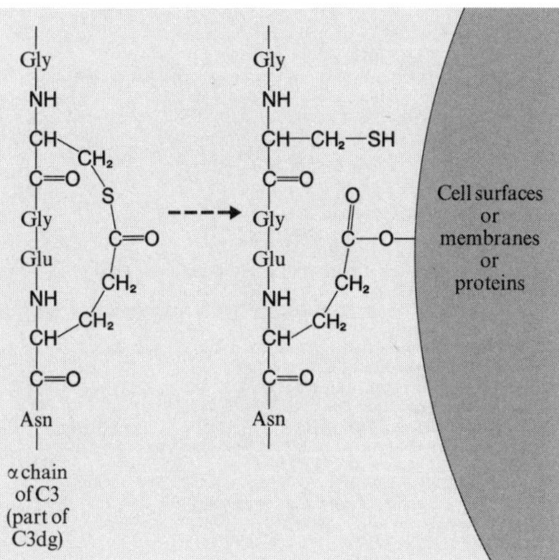

Fig. 6. Chemical composition of the thioester group located in the C3dg fragment of the α chain (Fig. 5). Left: native state. Right: after covalent binding to a cell surface, a membrane or a protein[6,7,72].

with outflow even of compounds of high molecular mass. Nucleated cells, such as leukocytes, can initially compensate for thousands of lytic complement attacks, of which each one would otherwise be fatal for one erythrocyte. These cells apparently possess a potent repair system, but that can eventually become exhausted.

The alternative pathway

Two reaction levels can also be distinguished in the alternative pathway of complement activation. The first yields only traces of C3b after its initial triggering (activation phase). That brings in the second level in which massive C3 activation is possible due to involvement of positive feedback (effector phase).

The early stage of the alternative pathway is now regarded as a 'low-level process' yielding – by spontaneous hydrolysis of the thioester bond described above – a C3 molecule which, though uncleaved, does behave functionally like C3b in that it binds B. Once bound, factor B then acts as a substrate for factor D, which itself acts primarily as an enzyme ($\bar{D}$). Thus bound B will be split by $\bar{D}$, yielding a complex with a new enzymatic site, Bb ('C3b-like C3'Bb), which can activate C3 (formulae **9**a, b, and c).

$$\left.\begin{array}{lll}
\text{C3} \xrightarrow{H_2O} \text{'C3b-like C3'} & & \text{(a)}\\
\text{'C3b-like C3'} + \text{B} + \text{D} \xrightarrow{Mg^{2+}} \text{'C3b-like C3'Bb} + \text{Ba} & & \text{(b)}\\
\text{'C3b-like C3'Bb} + \text{C3} \longrightarrow \text{C3b} + \text{C3a} & & \text{(c)}\\
\text{C3b} + \text{B} \xrightarrow{Mg^{2+}} \text{C3bB} & & \text{(d)}\\
\text{C3bB} + \bar{\text{D}} \longrightarrow [\text{C3bBb}] + \text{Ba} & & \text{(e)}\\
\text{[C3bBb]} + \text{C3} \longrightarrow \text{C3a} + \text{C3b} & & \text{(f)}
\end{array}\right\}\ \textbf{(9)}$$

These small amounts of enzyme are normally controlled without difficulty by the relevant inactivators. According to this hypothesis, the inducers of the alternative pathway of complement activation act by stabilizing the spontaneously produced C3bBb enzyme and thus removing the influence of the control proteins (Fig. 2).

Accordingly the final product is C3b, which either binds on the inducer surface or passes into the fluid phase. In the bound or free form of C3b there is a receptor for factor B. The complex formed by B and C3b can be split by the reaction of $\bar{D}$ into Ba and Bb, giving rise to enzymatic activity against C3, which is localized on the large fragment Bb($\bar{B}$).

Under special conditions, B can also be enzymatically active without being split. Bending of the molecular conformation apparently suffices to make the active center prominent. Factor D appears to be present in the serum as active enzyme ($\bar{D}$). It has not so far been possible to demonstrate an inactive precursor molecule with certainty, although preliminary reports suggest that $\bar{D}$ may be a thrombin fragment[59]. $\bar{D}$ in plasma cannot attack the native factor; only in its bound form does B acquire the properties of a substrate for $\bar{D}$. Such binding of B can take place on C3b (formula **9**d). When B activation takes place, the proteolytically active factor can be replaced by other enzymes – trypsin, plasmin and pronase[60].

When macromolecular inducers (Ind) such as endotoxin or zymosan, on which numerous binding sites are available, have set off the alternative pathway, the reactions so far described lead to the C3-activating intermediate product, IndC3bBb. This enzyme breaks down with a half-life of 4–5 minutes at 30 °C, but it can be stabilized by binding of properdin (P), whereby the half-life is increased 10-fold[61]. Properdin can bind itself in the fluid phase to C3 as well as to fragments C3b and C3c. Interaction with bound C3b is therefore probable. It is not, however, known how free P is transformed into the stabilized enzyme complex, which then contains activated properdin ($\bar{P}$). The following formulae summarize these reactions[62,63].

$$\left.\begin{array}{lll}
\text{IndC3bBb} + \text{P} \longrightarrow \text{Ind}\bar{\text{P}}\text{C3bBb} & & \text{(a)}\\
\text{Ind}\bar{\text{P}}\text{C3bBb} + \text{C3} \longrightarrow \text{Ind}\bar{\text{P}}\text{C3bBbC3b} + \text{C3a} & & \text{(b)}\\
\text{Ind}\bar{\text{P}}\text{C3bBbC3b} + \text{C5} \longrightarrow \text{Ind} \ldots \text{C5b} + \text{C5a} & & \text{(c)}\\
\text{Ind}\bar{\text{P}}\text{C3bBbC3bC5b} + \text{C6–C9} \longrightarrow \text{Ind} \ldots \text{C5b–C9} + [\text{C5b–C9}] & & \text{(d)}
\end{array}\right\}\ \textbf{(10)}$$

Even more marked stabilization of C3bBb enzyme with a half-life of 50 to 60 minutes at 30 °C is brought about by a pathological protein, the C3 nephritis factor (C3NeF). This factor was discovered in the sera of patients with hypocomplementemic membranoproliferative glomerulonephritis but is also present in the serum of patients with partial lipodystrophy, which is closely related to the above-mentioned type of nephritis. In normal serum, C3NeF mediates massive splitting of C3, irrespective of whether the physiologically stabilizing properdin (formula **10**a) is present or not. It is assumed that splitting of C3 comes about through the stabilization of minute quantities of spontaneously arising C3bBb enzyme, and that C3NeF does not, like $\bar{P}$, bind to C3b or perhaps to Bb, but only to the complex formed by both factors. This is consistent with the findings of several laboratories that C3NeF can be defined as an immunoglobulin[64–66]. These antibodies, which may belong to several IgG subgroups, are probably directed against conformation determinants of the C3bBb enzyme. The binding of C3NeF as antibody to C3bBb not only stabilizes the enzyme, but in particular renders it inaccessible to the action of the inactivators. This explains the massive C3 turnover observed.

Two proteins, C3b inactivator (I) and β1H-globulin (H), exercise control over the important but also dangerous biological effector phase and over the amplification and positive feedback mechanism of the alternative pathway. Alongside the enzymatic splitting of C3b and also of free C4b, which requires the simultaneous action of both factors[61–63,67,68], breakdown of the $\bar{P}$C3bBb enzyme takes place in 2 stages: first, H forces Bb out of its binding to C3b, thus freeing inactive Bb (Bbi). Although the enzyme is inactivated by this reaction, it can of course be regenerated. Only enzymatic splitting of C3b by I, such as becomes possible after expulsion of Bb through the action of H, renders the enzyme finally inactive.

$$\left.\begin{array}{lll}
\text{C3b} + (\text{I} + \text{H}) \longrightarrow \text{C3b cleavage} & & \text{(a)}\\
\bar{\text{P}}\text{C3bBb} + \text{H} \longrightarrow \bar{\text{P}}\text{C3b} + \text{Bbi} & & \text{(b)}\\
\bar{\text{P}}\text{C3b} + \text{I} \longrightarrow \bar{\text{P}}\text{C3c} + \text{C3d} & & \text{(c)}
\end{array}\right\}\ \textbf{(11)}$$

Direct enzymatic splitting

Since the activation of C3 is an enzymatic process, it immediately becomes clear that all enzymes are capable of C3 activation, provided they only produce splitting at the correct site. It is thus ensured that the generation of C3a and C3b in this way can be carried out by trypsin, plasmin, thrombin, and also by traumatically-released tissue proteinases and bacterial enzymes.

In summary, Figures 1–3 – portraying all significant aspects of the complement system in schematic form, including the interplay of the various activation pathways – show how the classical pathway can also set off the alternative pathway, via C3b generated from the $\overline{\text{C42}}$ enzyme, employing the positive feedback as amplification stage. On the other hand, the alternative pathway can cross over from C3b via C5 into the classical sequence. Both these possibilities are also open to the C3b produced by direct splitting of C3.

References

[1] ROTHER and TILL (Eds.), *Complement,* Springer, New York, 1984 (in press).
[2] *Transplant. Rev.,* **32** (1976).
[3] HADDING, U., *Monogr. Allergy,* **12**, 36 (1977).
[4] *Meth. Enzymol.,* **80**, section I (1981).
[5] MÜLLER-EBERHARD, H. J., *Springer Semin. Immunopathol.,* **6**, 117 (1983).
[6] TACK, B. F., *Springer Semin. Immunopathol.,* **6**, 259 (1983).
[7] MÜLLER-EBERHARD, H. J., *Ann. Rev. Biochem.,* **44**, 697 (1975), and *Progr. Immunol.,* **4**, 1001 (1980).
[8] OSLER, A. G., *Complement: Mechanisms and Functions,* Prentice-Hall, Englewood Cliffs, 1976.
[9] MINTA and MOVAT, *Curr. Top. Pathol.,* **68**, 135 (1979).
[10] RUDDY, S., in KELLEY et al., *Textbook of Rheumatology,* Saunders, Philadelphia, 1981, page 83.
[11] HUGLI, T. E., *J. biol. Chem.,* **250**, 8293 (1975).
[12] HUGLI, T. E., *CRC Crit. Rev. Immunol.,* **1**, 321 (1981).
[13] VOGT, W., *Pharmacol. Rev.,* **26**, 125 (1974).
[14] WARD and NEWMAN, *J. Immunol.,* **102**, 93 (1969).
[15] HARTUNG et al., *J. Immunol.,* **130**, 1345 and 2861 (1983).
[16] BENVENISTE, J., *Nature,* **249**, 581 (1974); BENVENISTE et al., *Monogr. Allergy,* **12**, 138 (1977).
[17] DEMOPOULOS et al., *J. Biol. Chem.,* **254**, 9355 (1979).
[18] HARTUNG et al., *Int. J. Immunopharmacol.,* **5**, 115 (1983).
[19] WILLIAMS and JOSE, *J. exp. Med.,* **153**, 136 (1981).
[20] ABRAHAMSON and FEARON, *Lab. Invest.,* **48**, 162 (1983).
[21] FEARON and WONG, *Ann. Rev. Immunol.,* **1**, 243 (1983).
[22] DANIELS et al., *Proc. nat. Acad. Sci. (Wash.),* **65**, 528 (1970).
[23] OLDSTONE et al., *J. exp. Med.,* **140**, 549 (1974).
[24] MILLS et al., *J. Immunol.,* **123**, 2518 (1979).
[25] COOPER and NEMEROW, *Springer Semin. Immunopathol.,* **6**, 327 (1983).
[26] WEIGLE et al., *Springer Semin. Immunopathol.,* **6**, 173 (1983).
[27] MORGAN et al., *J. exp. Med.,* **155**, 1412 (1982).
[28] GOODMAN et al., *J. exp. Med.,* **156**, 912 (1982).
[29] PEPYS, M. B., *Transplant. Rev.,* **32**, 93 (1976).
[30] RITTNER, C., *Hum. Genet.,* **35**, 1 (1976).
[31] COLTEN, H. R., *Springer Semin. Immunopathol.,* **6**, 149 (1983).
[32] WHITEHEAD et al., *Proc. nat. Acad. Sci. (Wash.),* **79**, 5021 (1982).
[33] FEY et al., *Springer Semin. Immunopathol.,* **6**, 119 (1983).
[34] KAPLAN et al., *CRC Crit. Rev. Immunol.,* **3**, 75 (1981).
[35] SUNDSMO and FAIR, *Springer Semin. Immunopathol.,* **6**, 231 (1983).
[36] MEUER et al., *J. Immunol.,* **126**, 1506 (1981).
[37] MEUER et al., *J. exp. Med.,* **155**, 698 (1982).
[38] RUDDY et al., *Medicine (Baltimore),* **54**, 165 (1975).
[39] SISSONS et al., *J. clin. Invest.,* **59**, 704 (1977).
[40] COOPER et al., *Springer Semin. Immunopathol.,* **6**, 195 (1983).
[41] MAYES et al., *J. clin. Invest.,* **73**, 160 (1984).
[42] JOHNSTON et al., *Pediatrics,* **64**, 781 (1979).
[43] GOLDSTEIN, I. M., *Amer. J. med. Sci.,* **269**, 172 (1975).
[44] OPFERKUCH et al. (Eds.), *Clinical Aspects of the Complement System,* Thieme, Stuttgart, 1978.
[45] JERSILD et al., *Transplant. Rev.,* **32**, 43 (1976).
[46] AGNELLO, V., *Medicine (Baltimore),* **57**, 1 (1978).
[47] LACHMANN and HOBART, *Ciba Found. Symp.,* NS **66**, 231 (1979).
[48] GLASS et al., in STANBURY et al., *The Metabolic Basis of Inherited Disease,* 5th ed., McGraw-Hill, New York, 1983, page 1934.
[49] SCHIFFERLI and PETERS, *Lancet,* **2**, 957 (1983).
[50] BURGER et al., *Immunobiology,* **164**, 220 (1983); ZANKER et al., *Immunobiology,* **164**, 315 (1983).
[51] OSOFSKY et al., *J. Pediat.,* **90**, 180 (1977).
[52] BARRETT and BOYLE, *J. Pediat.,* **104**, 76 (1984).
[53] OPFERKUCH et al., *J. Immunol.,* **106**, 407 (1971).
[54] LOOS, M., *Progr. Allergy,* **30**, 135 (1982).
[55] ZICCARDI, R. J., *Springer Semin. Immunopathol.,* **6**, 213 (1983).
[56] KOLB and MÜLLER-EBERHARD, *J. exp. Med.,* **141**, 724 (1975).
[57] PODACK et al., *J. Immunol.,* **128**, 2353 (1982), and *J. exp. Med.,* **156**, 268 (1982).
[58] BHAKDI and TRANUM-JENSEN, *Biochim. biophys. Acta (Amst.),* **737**, 343 (1983).
[59] DAVIS et al., *J. Immunol.,* **120**, 1771 (1978).
[60] BRADE et al., *J. Immunol.,* **113**, 1735 (1974).
[61] FEARON et al., *Transplant. Proc.,* **9**, 729 (1977).
[62] GÖTZE et al., *Monogr. Allergy,* **12**, 66 (1977).
[63] MÜLLER-EBERHARD and SCHREIBER, *Advanc. Immunol.,* **29**, 1 (1980).
[64] SCOTT et al., *J. Immunol.,* **120**, 1797 (1978).
[65] DAHA et al., *J. Immunol.,* **119**, 812 (1977), and **120**, 1389 (1978).
[66] HALBWACHS-MECARELLI and GIGLI, *Immunobiology,* **164**, 250 (1983).
[67] WHALEY and RUDDY, *J. exp. Med.,* **144**, 1147 (1976).
[68] PANGBURN et al., *J. exp. Med.,* **146**, 257 (1977).
[69] KNOBEL et al., *Europ. J. Immunol.,* **5**, 78 (1975).
[70] REID and PORTER, *Ann. Rev. Biochem.,* **50**, 433 (1981).
[71] LOOS, M., *Curr. Top. Microbiol. Immunol.,* **102**, 1 (1983).
[72] MEUTH et al., *J. Immunol.,* **130**, 2605 (1983).
[73] ROTHER, K., *Europ. J. Immunol.,* **2**, 550 (1972).
[74] GHEBREHIWET and MÜLLER-EBERHARD, *J. Immunol.,* **123**, 616 (1979).
[75] REID, K. B., *Biochem. Soc. Trans.,* **11**, 1 (1983).
[76] AL SALIHI et al., *FEBS Lett.,* **150**, 238 (1982).
[77] STECKEL et al., *J. biol. Chem.,* **255**, 11997 (1980).
[78] DAVIS and FORRISTAL, *J. Lab. clin. Med.,* **96**, 633 (1980).
[79] WYATT et al., *J. clin. Lab. Immunol.,* **6**, 131 (1981).
[80] ROSANO et al., *J. Lab. clin. Med.,* **103**, 313 (1984).
[81] GLASS et al., *J. clin. Invest.,* **58**, 853 (1976).
[82] NORMAN et al., *J. Pediat.,* **87**, 912 (1975).
[83] ELMGREEN et al., *Acta med. scand.,* **214**, 403 (1983).
[84] VERGANI et al., *Brit. med. J.,* **286**, 926 (1983).
[85] BIESECKER and MÜLLER-EBERHARD, *J. Immunol.,* **124**, 1291 (1980).
[86] MORGAN et al., *Clin. chim. Acta,* **134**, 85 (1983).
[87] ZIEGLER et al., *J. clin. Invest.,* **56**, 761 (1975).
[88] PODACK et al., *J. Immunol.,* **123**, 1071 (1979).
[89] DAHLBÄCK et al., *Proc. nat. Acad. Sci. (Wash.),* **80**, 3461 (1983).
[90] NIEMANN et al., *Biochemistry,* **23**, 2482 (1984).

Leukocyte and thrombocyte groups[1] are inherited characters which can be detected by specific antisera on the surface of leukocytes and platelets. Like the antigenic markers on erythrocytes, they can be classified into several genetically independent systems (Table 1). Furthermore, there are indications that antigens detectable only on monocytes and endothelial cells[2] exist in addition to the leukocyte and thrombocyte groups.

Table 1 *Leukocyte and thrombocyte groups*

Presence of the antigens

1. On leukocytes, thrombocytes and tissues:
   1.1 AB0 blood groups (see page 252)
   1.2 HLA system, class I antigens
   1.3 System Five
2. Mainly on B lymphocytes and monocytes:
   HLA system, class II antigens
3. On leukocytes:
   3.1 Granulocyte-specific systems
   3.2 Lymphocyte-specific systems
4. On thrombocytes:
   Thrombocyte-specific systems

The antisera used to define antigens on leukocytes and thrombocytes other than those of the AB0 blood groups are immune sera. Immunization occurs as a result of pregnancies[3], blood transfusions[4] or transplantations[5] (in the latter case, only antibodies directed against determinants present in the grafted organ can be produced). 'Naturally occurring' antibodies against leukocyte and thrombocyte groups are usually not found.

Leukocyte and thrombocyte groups can be detected by several techniques. The most common methods are listed in Table 2. Apart from these, several other assays have been described, for example cytotoxic tests with granulocytes[12] or platelets[13], immune adherence[14], mixed-cell agglutination[15] or absorption tests. For technical details see *Manual of Tissue Typing Techniques*[16] or DICK and KISSMEYER-NIELSEN[17].

Table 2
Common methods of detecting leukocyte and thrombocyte groups

1. Lymphocytotoxic test[6]:
   On peripheral blood lymphocytes: HLA system, class I antigens
   On B lymphocytes: HLA system, class II antigens
2. Leukoagglutination[7]:
   System Five
   Granulocyte-specific systems
   Some HLA-class I antigens (Bw4, Bw6)
3. Thromboagglutination[8]:
   Thrombocyte-specific systems
4. Complement fixation on thrombocytes[9]:
   HLA system, class I antigens
   Thrombocyte-specific antigens
5. Indirect immunofluorescence on granulocytes[10] (System Five, granulocyte-specific systems)
   Indirect immunofluorescence on thrombocytes[11] (thrombocyte-specific systems)

The HLA system

The HLA system (HLA: *h*uman *l*eukocyte *a*ntigen or *h*uman *l*eukocyte, locus *A*), which represents the major histocompatibility system of man, encompasses approximately one thousandth of the human genome[18] and consists of a series of closely linked loci. It is situated near to band 6p21 on the short arm of chromosome 6 and is linked to other loci: *PGM3*, *GLO*, and possibly *PG5*[19]. The HLA system governs the following gene products:

1. The class I antigens, which consist of 2 noncovalently associated polypeptide chains: a larger chain with a relative molecular mass of 44000 which is glycosylated and which is coded for by the loci *HLA-A*, *-B*, and *-C* of chromosome 6 and a smaller chain, β_2-microglobulin, with a relative molecular mass of 12000 and coded for by chromosome 15. The large chain is fixed in the cell membrane by a sequence of hydrophobic amino acids. The major part of this subunit is extracellular and carries the antigenic determinants which are produced by the amino-acid sequence. It is not clear how the 2 chains are associated, but the presence of β_2-microglobulin is necessary for the expression of the class I alloantigens. The primary structure of some class I antigens is already known. For details of the biochemistry see for example ORR et al.[20]. The class I antigens are present in varying amounts on all the nucleated cells of the organism. It has been possible to show by absorption studies that the greatest amount is present in the spleen, followed by the lung and the liver, while fatty tissue contains practically no absorbing activity[21]. Class I antigens could be detected on reticu-

*This chapter on 'Leukocyte and Thrombocyte Groups' (pages 245–251) has been compiled by W. R. MAYR, Institut für Blutgruppenserologie der Universität Wien, Vienna, Austria.

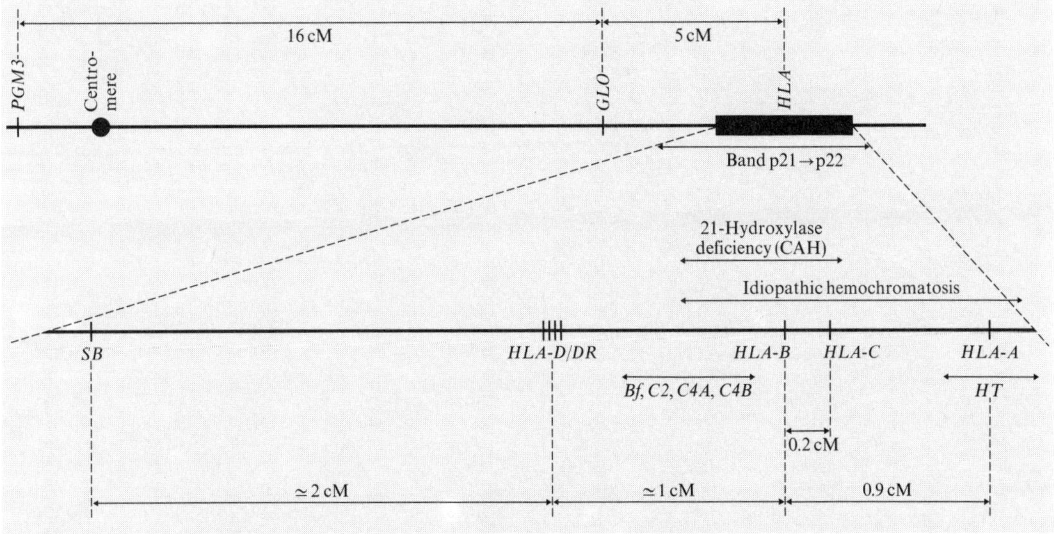

Fig. 1. Scheme of the *HLA* complex on the short arm of chromosome 6.

locytes[22] as well as on mature red blood cells[23]; erythrocyte antigens of the Bg system are closely related to class I antigens on red blood cells (Bg^a = HLA-B7, Bg^b = HLA-B17, Bg^c = HLA-A28)[24], thus showing that some HLA-A, -B, -C determinants are present in small quantities on erythrocytes.

2. The class II antigens, which consist of 2 membrane-associated glycoprotein units, α and β, with relative molecular masses of 34000 and 29000, respectively. The HLA-coded determinants are carried with high probability on the β chain; it is not clear whether the α chain is coded for by the *HLA* complex (see for example ORR et al.[20]). The class II antigens have a restricted tissue distribution and can be detected on B lymphocytes, macrophages, monocytes, activated T lymphocytes, some epithelial and endothelial cells, and spermatozoa. Most probably, the class II antigens are governed by several closely linked loci: *HLA-DR, -MT(DC)* and *-BR*[25]. The exact structure of the *HLA-DR* region of the HLA system, however, is not known. In the *HLA-DR* region, another locus can be found which controls the reactivity of lymphocytes in mixed lymphocyte culture (MLC): *HLA-D*[26]. The HLA-D determinants are possibly carried by the same molecule as HLA-DR, or there may be a very close linkage with an extreme linkage disequilibrium between *HLA-D* and *HLA-DR*.
3. The SB determinants[27] detectable by means of primed lymphocyte typing (PLT). They are preferentially present on B lymphoycytes, and 5 specificities have been described[28]. By cytotoxicity assays it has been possible to identify a monocyte antigen showing a high association with SB4[29]. It therefore seems possible to define SB determinants by serological tests.
4. Antigens detectable on T-lymphocyte subsets or on lectin-activated T lymphocytes (HT antigens)[30].
5. The complement components C2 (locus *C2*)[31], C4 (α chain)[32] and factor B (locus *Bf*)[33]. The genetic control of the C4 α chain is rather complex (page 272): at least 2 loci are involved, *C4A* and *C4B* (also referred to as *C4F* and *C4S*)[34]. The factors Ch^a and Rg^a are antigenic determinants of the C4 α chain and are passively adsorbed from the plasma on to the surface of erythrocytes[35].
6. 21-Hydroxylase, an enzyme which is necessary for normal cortisol synthesis and the lack of which induces the virilizing and salt-wasting form of congenital adrenal hyperplasia (CAH)[36].
7. A gene product influencing iron metabolism. The homozygous state of a mutant of this gene is the cause of idiopathic hemochromatosis[37].

The genetic structure of the short arm of chromosome 6 and details of the HLA system are given in Figure 1.

The loci *HLA-A, -B, -C,* and *-DR* show extreme multiple allelism. HLA specificities are designated by a letter indicating the locus and a figure indicating the individual specificity. The small letter 'w' indicates a provisional specificity not yet optimally defined. 'w' may be dropped when the specificity is confirmed[38].

(Continued on page 248)

Table 3a *HLA-A-allele frequencies in the 3 main racial groups*

HLA-A		Caucasoids	Negroids	Mongoloids
A1		0.147	0.033	0.004
A2		0.285	0.147	0.246
A3		0.146	0.074	0.004
A9	*Aw23*	0.031	0.108	0.005
	Aw24	0.099	0.029	0.356
A10	*A25*	0.027	0.004	0.001
	A26	0.048	0.038	0.098
A11		0.050	0.006	0.090
A28		0.041	0.087	0.005
A29		0.023	0.063	0.002
Aw30		0.027	0.154	0.002
Aw31		0.023	0.022	0.080
Aw32		0.036	0.015	0.001
Aw33		0.015	0.046	0.068
Aw34		0.001	0.065	0.010
Aw36		0.000	0.017	0.003
Aw43		0.000	0.008	0.000
AX		0.001	0.084	0.025
		1.000	1.000	1.000

Table 3b *HLA-B-allele frequencies in the 3 main racial groups*

HLA-B		Caucasoids	Negroids	Mongoloids
B5	*Bw51*	0.071	0.014	0.083
	Bw52	0.015	0.010	0.109
B7		0.124	0.089	0.059
B8		0.096	0.029	0.001
B12	*Bw44*	0.110	0.071	0.065
	Bw45	0.010	0.039	0.002
B13		0.042	0.007	0.020
B14		0.028	0.041	0.001
B15	*Bw62*	0.057	0.010	0.088
	Bw63	0.005	0.003	0.002
B17	*Bw57*	0.033	0.039	0.000
	Bw58	0.013	0.107	0.009
B18		0.057	0.039	0.000
B27		0.041	0.015	0.004
B37		0.012	0.004	0.005
B40	*Bw60*	0.040	0.014	0.066
	Bw61	0.020	0.004	0.088
Bw16	*Bw38*	0.026	0.000	0.002
	Bw39	0.023	0.018	0.029
Bw21	*Bw49*	0.014	0.025	0.003
	Bw50	0.016	0.007	0.000
Bw22	*Bw54*	0.000	0.000	0.073
	Bw55	0.019	0.008	0.029
	Bw56	0.006	0.000	0.011
Bw35		0.104	0.062	0.073
Bw41		0.013	0.012	0.004
Bw42		0.000	0.077	0.006
Bw46		0.000	0.000	0.066
Bw47		0.003	0.001	0.002
Bw48		0.000	0.011	0.023
Bw53		0.001	0.065	0.001
Bw59		0.000	0.008	0.021
BX		0.001	0.171	0.055
		1.000	1.000	1.000

Table 3c *HLA-C-allele frequencies in the 3 main racial groups*

HLA-C	Caucasoids	Negroids	Mongoloids
Cw1	0.039	0.001	0.176
Cw2	0.058	0.120	0.004
Cw3	0.121	0.093	0.269
Cw4	0.134	0.159	0.047
Cw5	0.061	0.030	0.001
Cw6	0.126	0.090	0.007
Cw7	0.163	0.025	0.011
Cw8	0.028	0.005	0.001
CX	0.270	0.477	0.484
	1.000	1.000	1.000

Table 3d *HLA-DR-allele frequencies in the 3 main racial groups*

HLA-DR	Caucasoids	Negroids	Mongoloids
DR1	0.111	0.049	0.063
DR2	0.165	0.154	0.200
DR3	0.118	0.173	0.016
DR4	0.107	0.048	0.235
DR5	0.157	0.133	0.022
DRw6	0.022	0.053	0.046
DR7	0.128	0.098	0.005
DRw8	0.030	0.056	0.065
DRw9	0.008	0.027	0.122
DRw10	0.005	0.019	0.006
DRX	0.149	0.190	0.220
	1.000	1.000	1.000

Table 4 *Significant positive linkage disequilibria in HLA-A, -B, -C, -DR*

Caucasoids

2-loci haplotypes

A/B	A/C	A/DR	B/C	B/DR	C/DR
A1,B8	Aw33,Cw8	A29,DR7	Bw53,Cw4	B8,DR3	Cw6,DR7
Aw33,B14	A2,Cw5	Aw33,DR1	Bw35,Cw4	B13,DR7	Cw8,DR1
A29,Bw44	Aw23,Cw4	A1,DR3	Bw56,Cw1	Bw52,DR2	Cw4,DR1
A25,B18	A1,Cw7	A25,DR2	Bw60,Cw3	Bw57,DR7	Cw7,DR3
A2,Bw52	A1,Cw6	Aw30,DR7	Bw62,Cw3	Bw50,DR7	Cw5,DR4
A1,B37	Aw30,Cw6	Aw23,DR7	B14,Cw8	B7,DR2	
A26,Bw38	A11,Cw4		B37,Cw6	Bw47,DR7	
A1,Bw57			Bw57,Cw6	Bw41,DR3	
A3,Bw47			B13,Cw6	B14,DR1	
A11,Bw55			Bw44,Cw4	Bw39,DR2	
Aw30,B13			Bw55,Cw3	Bw45,DR4	
A2,Bw41			Bw61,Cw2	Bw35,DR1	
A3,B7			Bw47,Cw6	Bw38,DRw6	
A28,Bw53			Bw50,Cw6	Bw44,DR7	
Aw23,Bw44			B27,Cw2	Bw62,DR4	
A2,Bw60			Bw45,Cw6	B18,DR5	
A2,Bw62			B27,Cw1		
Aw32,Bw61			B8,Cw7		
Aw30,B18			Bw58,Cw3		
A11,Bw35			Bw51,Cw1		
A2,Bw51					
Aw23,Bw49					

3-loci haplotypes A/B/C	3-loci haplotypes A/B/DR	4-loci haplotypes A/B/C/DR
Aw23,Bw44,Cw4	A1,B8,DR3	A1,B8,Cw7,DR3
Aw33,B14,Cw8	A2,Bw52,DR2	A3,B7,Cw7,DR2
A3,Bw35,Cw4	A29,Bw44,DR7	A2,Bw44,Cw5,DR4
A1,B8,Cw7	A2,Bw41,DR3	A2,Bw62,Cw3,DR5
A2,B27,Cw2	A25,B18,DR2	Aw24,Bw35,Cw4,DR1
Aw30,B13,Cw6	Aw30,B18,DR3	Aw23,Bw44,Cw4,DR7
A25,B18,CX	A29,Bw45,DR4	A2,Bw56,Cw1,DR1
A3,B7,Cw7	Aw23,Bw44,DR7	
A26,Bw38,CX		
A11,Bw55,Cw3		
A2,Bw44,Cw5		
A1,B17,Cw6		
A2,Bw56,Cw1		
A11,Bw35,Cw4		

Negroids

2-loci haplotypes

A/B	A/C	A/DR	B/C	B/DR	C/DR
Aw30,Bw42	Aw36,Cw4	–	Bw53,Cw4	Bw42,DR3	–
A26,Bw58	A26,Cw6		B27,Cw2		
Aw23,Bw45	A28,Cw3		Bw35,Cw4		
Aw24,B7			Bw58,Cw6		
A29,Bw44			Bw57,Cw6		
			Bw44,Cw4		

Mongoloids

2-loci haplotypes

A/B	A/C	A/DR	B/C	B/DR	C/DR
Aw33,Bw58	A26,Cw3	Aw24,DR1	Bw58,Cw3	Bw52,DR2	Cw4,DR4
Aw33,Bw44		Aw24,DR2	Bw54,Cw1	B7,DR1	Cw3,DR5
Aw24,Bw52			Bw59,Cw1	Bw54,DR4	Cw7,DR1
Aw24,B7			Bw35,Cw3	Bw59,DR4	Cw1,DR4
A2,Bw39			Bw55,Cw1	Bw61,DRw9	
A2,B13			Bw62,Cw4	Bw62,DR4	
Aw24,Bw54			Bw61,Cw3	Bw44,DRw6	
			B13,Cw3	Bw61,DR5	
			Bw60,Cw3	Bw39,DRw8	
			B7,Cw7		
			Bw62,Cw3		

Population and family analyses have shown that at the present time not all gene products can be defined. The genes coding for these 'unknown' determinants are called *AX, BX, CX,* and *DRX,* respectively. The frequencies of the *HLA-A, -B, -C,* and *-DR* alleles in the 3 main human racial groups (Caucasoids, Negroids, and Mongoloids) are given in Tables 3a–d[39,40]. As shown in these tables, some supertypic factors (defined by sera with a broader reactivity) can be split into subtypic ones (defined by sera with a narrower reactivity). This phenomenon is due to the fact that one gene product carries several antigenic determinants: for example the polypeptide chain coded for by *HLA-A9* possesses, besides the determinant A9, either Aw23 or Aw24. From the point of view of formal genetics, it is possible to exchange the gene governing the supertypic factor by the genes coding for the subtypic determinants. This splitting corresponds in principle to the subdivision of blood group A into A_1 and A_2. The supertypic factors Bw4 (4a) and Bw6 (4b) can be regarded in the same way: Bw4 is present on the gene products of *B13, B27, B37, Bw38, Bw44, Bw47, Bw49, Bw51, Bw52, Bw53, Bw57, Bw58, Bw59* and *Bw63,* and Bw6 on the gene products of *B7, B8, B14, B18, Bw35, Bw39, Bw41, Bw42, Bw45, Bw46, Bw48, Bw50, Bw54, Bw55, Bw56, Bw60, Bw61,* and *Bw62*[41].

Early investigations with monoclonal antibodies have shown a further heterogeneity of the class I gene products[42], thus indicating that it will be possible to split more factors into subtypic determinants.

The combination of one allele of each *HLA* locus on chromosome 6, which is usually inherited *en bloc,* is called haplotype. The frequency of recombinations between the loci *HLA-A* and *-B* is approximately 0.9%; this means that the map distance between these 2 loci corresponds to 0.9 centi-Morgan (cM). *HLA-C* is situated between *-A* and *-B* 0.2 cM distant from *-B*; the *HLA-DR* region is located between *-B* and *GLO* 1 cM distant from *HLA-B* (see Fig. 1, McKusick, Francke, and Weitkamp[19]). The *SB* locus is situated between *HLA-DR* and *GLO* (approximately 2 cM from *HLA-DR*)[43], while the *HT* locus (*h*uman *T* genetic region) is close to *HLA-A*[30].

Because of the large number of alleles, the HLA system shows prodigious polymorphism. Taking into account 18 *HLA-A,* 33 *-B,* 9 *-C,* and 11 *-DR* alleles, the number of possible HLA phenotypes amounts to 168797552; furthermore, 58806 haplotypes and 1729102221 genotypes can be expected.

The analysis of haplotype frequencies shows a strong linkage disequilibrium within the HLA system, which means that the observed figures often do not correspond with the frequencies obtained by the multiplication of the corresponding allele frequencies. The *HLA-A, -B* 2-loci haplotypes with the strongest positive linkage disequilibria in the 3 main racial groups are given in Table 4, as well as the 3- and 4-loci haplotypes with the strongest positive association in Caucasoids[44,45]. At present not enough data are available for valid frequencies of 3- and 4-loci haplotypes in Negroids and Mongoloids to be computed. It is also not yet possible to include the *C2, C4,* and *Bf* alleles in these calculations, although linkage disequilibria exist between them and *HLA-A, -B, -C,* and/or *-DR* alleles (for example $Bf^{S0.7}$*–Bw50,* Bf^{F1}*–B18, C2°–A25,B18,DR2*)[40,44].

The biological function of the HLA-class I antigens is restriction of specificity of cytotoxic T lymphocytes, while class II antigens have their main role in restriction of regulatory T cells during the immune response[46].

System Five

This system consists of 2 antigens, 5^a and 5^b, governed by autosomal codominant alleles having frequencies of 0.18 and 0.82, respectively, in Caucasoids (Netherlands)[47]. The antigens are present on all cells of the organism, probably including the erythrocytes[47,48]. Sera against 5^b can be found frequently, while anti-5^a are very rare.

Granulocyte-specific antigens

Several antigenic systems which are probably genetically independent can be detected on granulocytes (Table 5)[49].

Lymphocyte-specific antigens

The antigen Ly^{D1} defined by complement fixation is inherited as an autosomal dominant and has a gene frequency of 0.20 in Caucasoids (USA)[58]. The antigen Ly-Co is probably only present on B lymphocytes and also shows an autosomal dominant inheritance with a gene frequency of 0.21 in Caucasoids (France)[59]. *Ly-Co* segregates independently of *AB0, MNSs, Rh, Le, Fy, Ko, HP, Gm, IGKC (Km), ISf, LP, AG, ACP1, PGM1, PGM2, AK1,* and *HLA*[60].

Table 5 *Granulocyte-specific systems*

System	Antigens	Allele frequencies in Caucasoids	Inheritance
Nine[50]	9^a	0.40 (Netherlands)	Autosomal dominant
NA[51]	NA1 = To1 NA2	0.34 (USA) 0.66 (USA)	Autosomal codominant
NB[52]	NB1	0.83 (USA)	Autosomal dominant
NC[53]	NC1 = Vaz	0.72 (USA)	Autosomal dominant
ND[54]	ND1	0.88 (Netherlands)	Autosomal dominant
NE[55]	NE1	0.12 (Netherlands)	Autosomal dominant
G-A, G-B and G-C[56]	14 antigens		Autosomal dominant by alleles on 3 linked loci
Gr[57]	Gr1 .... Gr2	0.18 (USA) 0.35 (USA)	Autosomal codominant

Table 6 *Thrombocyte-specific systems*

System	Antigens	Allele frequencies in Caucasoids	Inheritance
Duzo[62]	Duzo	0.11 (France)	Autosomal dominant
Zw = Pl^{A}[63]	Zw^a = Pl^{A1} Zw^b = Pl^{A2}	0.85 (Netherlands) 0.15 (Netherlands)	Autosomal codominant
Ko[64]	Ko^a .... Ko^b	0.07 (Netherlands 0.93 (Netherlands)	Autosomal codominant
Pl^{E}[58]	Pl^{E1} .... Pl^{E2}	0.97 (USA) 0.03 (USA)	Autosomal codominant
Bak[65]	Bak^a	0.68 (Netherlands)	Autosomal dominant

Several systems can be demonstrated on T lymphocytes, some coded for by the *HLA* complex[30] and others independent of *HLA*[61].

Thrombocyte-specific antigens

The thrombocyte-specific antigen systems are listed in Table 6. For further details and other specificities see Májský[66].

Erythrocyte antigens on leukocytes and thrombocytes

Reports on the presence of erythrocyte antigens on leukocytes and platelets are rather controversial. It is certain that isoagglutinogens A and B of the AB0 blood groups are detectable on leukocytes and thrombocytes[67]. Furthermore, determinants coded for by the interaction of genes at the *H, ABH, Le,* and *Se* loci are passively adsorbed from the serum on to the lymphocyte surface[68]. Other erythrocyte antigens which are probably present on leukocytes and/or platelets are P, U, K_x, Jk^3, and Ge[69].

Practical implications of the leukocyte and thrombocyte groups

The leukocyte and thrombocyte groups have important practical implications in several fields: organ transplantation, blood transfusion, association with diseases, paternity testing and anthropology. The significance of antibodies against leukocyte and thrombocyte groups is summarized in Table 7[70], while the antigens are important for the following subjects:

Organ transplantation

In order to avoid hyperacute rejection of a grafted organ, the recipient must be completely free of any antibodies against the donor's histocompatibility antigens (AB0 blood groups and HLA-A, -B, -C antigens)[75]. For a good prognosis in kidney transplantation, apart from absence of antibodies against the donor's histocompatibility antigens the most significant prerequisite seems to be that the HLA-DR antigens should be identical[76]. Another fac-

Table 7 *Clinical importance of antibodies against leukocyte and thrombocyte groups*

	Specificity of the antibodies				
	AB0	HLA-A, -B, -C	System Five	Granulocyte-specific systems	Thrombocyte-specific systems
Hyperacute graft rejection	+	+	–	–	–
Reduced survival of transfused granulocytes[71]	+	+	+	+	–
Reduced survival of transfused thrombocytes[72]	(+)	+	?	–	+
Febrile transfusion reactions[73]	–	+	+	+	–
Isoimmune neonatal neutropenia (INN)[49]	–	–	–	+	–
Isoimmune neonatal purpura (INP)[58,74]	–	– (?)	–	–	+
Post-transfusion purpura (PTP)[74]	–	–	–	–	+

tor which influences the survival of grafted kidneys is preoperative blood transfusion to the recipient[77]: patients who have never received blood preparations containing HLA-A, -B, -C antigens have a very poor prognosis for graft survival, while recipients who have been transfused with preparations containing such antigens show good transplant survival. The reason for this phenomenon is not known; it is possible that the application of HLA-A, -B, -C antigens induces a relative tolerance by activating T-suppressor lymphocytes.

In bone-marrow transplantation, the danger of rejection and of graft-versus-host reactions, which frequently cause the patient's death, must be kept in mind. HLA-A, -B, -C, -D, and -DR identity between donor and recipient (in most cases the donor and the recipient are siblings) gives the best results in this form of therapy[78].

Association with diseases

The definite associations between HLA gene products and diseases which have been observed in population studies in Caucasoids are listed in Table 8[79,80].

The causes for such associations, which are not mutually exclusive, may be[81]:

- Linkage disequilibrium between an immune response gene governing a pathologic immune response inducing the disorder, and the corresponding *HLA* gene.

Table 8 *Associations between HLA-A, -B, -C, -DR antigens and diseases in Caucasoids*

Disease	Antigen	RR*
Idiopathic hemochromatosis	A3	8.2
Behçet's disease	B5	6.3
Ankylosing spondylitis	B27	87.4
Postinfection arthritis	B27	40.0
Reiter's disease	B27	37.0
Acute anterior uveitis	B27	10.4
de Quervain's thyroiditis	Bw35	13.7
Chronic active hepatitis, type B	Bw35	5.0
Psoriasis vulgaris	Cw6	13.3
Goodpasture's syndrome	DR2	15.9
Multiple sclerosis	DR2	4.1
Dermatitis herpetiformis	DR3	15.4
Idiopathic membraneous nephropathy	DR3	12.0
Celiac disease	DR3	10.8
	DR7	4.0
Sicca syndrome	DR3	9.7
Idiopathic Addison's disease	DR3	6.3
Systemic lupus erythematosus	DR3	5.8
Chronic active hepatitis, type A	DR3	4.5
Grave's disease	DR3	3.7
Myasthenia gravis	DR3	2.6
Diabetes mellitus, type I	DR4	6.4
	DR3	3.3
Rheumatoid arthritis	DR4	4.2
Pernicious anemia	DR5	5.4
Hashimoto's thyroiditis (hypertrophic)	DR5	3.2

*RR: relative risk (indicates how many times more frequent the disease occurs in antigen-carriers than in antigen-negative individuals).

- The HLA factor (or the product of a closely linked locus with high linkage disequilibrium) may act as a receptor for a pathogen, or it may share antigenic determinants with the pathogen (molecular mimicry, so that the organism cannot produce an immune response), or it may be modified by the pathogen (which causes an immune response against the altered determinant and brings about the disease).
- In cases of autosomal recessive diseases with a clear-cut transmission, the mutant gene may be in linkage disequilibrium with *HLA* genes.

The biological function of the HLA-class I gene products (restriction of lysis by cytotoxic T lymphocytes) indicates that the second mechanism is probable for HLA-A-, -B-, -C-associated diseases, especially for those of viral origin.

The function of the class II antigens points to the possibility that the HLA-DR-associated diseases are influenced by *HLA*-linked immune-response genes with a pathologic way of action. Mutant genes can be observed in congenital adrenal hyperplasia (21-hydroxylase deficiency), idiopathic hemochromatosis, and C2 deficiency.

In cases with no linkage disequilibrium between the gene influencing the disease and the *HLA* genes, possible associations can be detected by family investigations or by sophisticated population analyses. Such studies have already shown that the immune response against antigen E of ragweed[82] and against infections (malaria[83], yellow fever, tuberculoid leprosy[84]) is controlled by the HLA system and that genes governing a form of spinocerebellar ataxia[85] and the development of some organs (e.g. the heart[86] or the vertebral column[87]) are localized in the *HLA* complex.

Paternity testing[88]

In order to use a genetic system in cases of disputed paternity, the following conditions must be fulfilled: the mode of inheritance must be known with certainty, the techniques of determination must be reliable and simple, the phenotype must reflect the genotype only, and the characteristics must be developed at birth or soon thereafter.

Regarding the various leukocyte and platelet alloantigens, these criteria apply to the gene products of *HLA-A, -B,* and *-C* which are

Table 9 *Leukocyte and thrombocyte groups: chances of paternity exclusion (in %)*

HLA-A, -B, -C, -DR	98			99.2 (all systems)
Five	13		59.4 (Five to Bak)	
Nine	5	27.1 (Nine to NE)		
NA	17			
NB	0.4			
NC	0.1			
ND	0.02			
NE	7			
Ly^{D}	8	15.4 (Ly^{D}, Ly-Co)		
Ly-Co	8			
Duzo	6	24.3 (Duzo to Bak)		
Zw	11			
Ko	6			
Pl^{E}	3			
Bak	0.7			

routinely used in affiliation cases with excellent results[89] and with some restrictions to those of *HLA-DR*.

Concerning the other leukocyte and thrombocyte groups, the situation is much more difficult[90], because they are defined by complicated and not always reliable techniques, and because of the lack of adequate quantities of specific antisera. Therefore, the detection of these determinants is limited to a few specialized institutions. Furthermore, the amount of family data on the inheritance of these antigens is not large enough to allow their systematic use in paternity testing.

The chance of exclusion in false accusations of paternity by testing the HLA-A, -B, -C gene products is 96%; this figure rises to 98% by including HLA-DR. The investigation of other leukocyte and thrombocyte groups gives an exclusion chance of 59%; the cumulative exclusion chance by testing all the leukocyte and platelet systems mentioned reaches 99.2% (Table 9).

The use of the systems AB0, MNSs, P, Rh, Lu, K, Se, Fy, Jk, Xg, Gm, IGKC (Km), ACP1, PGM1, AK1, ADA, 6PGD, ESD, GLO, GPT, PGP, HP, Gc, C3, Bf, Tf, and PI yields a chance of exclusion of 98.6%. HLA-A, -B, -C, -DR raises this figure to 99.97%, and the inclusion of the other leukocyte and platelet alloantigens to 99.99%.

Anthropology

Because of its polymorphism and of the large variability of its gene frequencies amongst different populations, the HLA system is of great importance for anthropological investigations. As regards the other leukocyte and thrombocyte groups, not enough data are available for anthropological studies.

In this paragraph, only the major differences in the *HLA*-gene frequencies between the 3 main racial groups are mentioned; for details see Dausset and Colombani[91].

Population analyses have shown that A1, A3, and B8 are relatively frequent in Caucasoids, while Aw36, Aw43, Bw42, Bw46, BW48, Bw54, and Bw59 do not exist in this race. Negroids frequently possess A28, Aw23, Aw30, Aw34, Bw58, and DR3. Mongoloids have a high occurrence of A11, Aw24, Bw52, Bw61, Bw62, Cw1, Cw3, DR4, and DRw9, but seem to lack B8, B14, B18, Bw50, Cw2, Cw5, and Cw8. Furthermore, Aw36, Aw43, and Bw42 are probably specificities typical for Negroids, and Bw46 for Mongoloids. The linkage disequilibria between the loci also vary widely amongst the races (see Table 4). Even in Europe, there are considerable divergences in the distribution of HLA-A, -B, -C antigens: from North to South, the frequencies of A2, B15, and B40 decrease, while those of A10, B5, and Bw35 increase significantly[92].

HLA data can also be used for the construction of evolutionary trees: trees from the HLA-A, -B, -C frequencies fit very well with the classical anthropological concepts of racial evolution[93].

References

[1] Some reviews on leukocyte and thrombocyte groups: Bender et al., in Becker, P.E. (Ed.), *Humangenetik,* volume I/3, Thieme, Stuttgart, 1975, page 275; van Rood and van Leeuwen, in Miescher and Müller-Eberhard (Eds.), *Textbook of Immunopathology,* 2nd ed., volume 2, Grune & Stratton, New York, 1976, page 663; Götze, D. (Ed.), *The Major Histocompatibility System in Man and Animals,* Springer, Berlin, 1977; Mayr, W.R., in Brock and Mayo (Eds.), *The Biochemical Genetics of Man,* 2nd ed., Academic Press, London, 1978, page 373; Svejgaard et al., *The HLA System,* 2nd ed., Karger, Basle, 1979; Dausset, J. (Ed.), *HLA 1982,* Flammarion, Paris, 1981; Thorsby, E., *Transplant. Rev.,* **18**, 51 (1974); Amos and Ward, *Physiol. Rev.,* **55**, 206 (1975); Bach and van Rood, *New Engl. J. Med.,* **295**, 806, 872 and 927 (1976); Bodmer, W.F. (Ed.), The HLA System, *Brit. med. Bull.,* **34**, No.3 (1978); Amos and Kostyu, *Advanc. hum. Genet.,* **10**, 137 (1980); Bodmer, W.F., *Tissue Antigens,* **17**, 9 (1981); Dausset, J., *Science,* **213**, 1469 (1981); Dausset and Contu, *Transplant. Proc.,* **13**, 895 (1981).

[2] Moraes and Stastny, *J. clin. Invest.,* **60**, 449 (1977).

[3] Payne and Rolfs, *J. clin. Invest.,* **37**, 1756 (1958); van Rood et al., *Nature,* **181**, 1735 (1958).

[4] Dausset, J., *Vox Sang. (Amst.),* **4**, 190 (1954).

[5] Morris et al., in Curtoni et al. (Eds.), *Histocompatibility Testing 1967,* Munksgaard, Copenhagen, 1967, page 339; Morris et al., *Transplantation,* **6**, 392 (1968).

[6] Gorer and O'Gorman, *Transplant. Bull.,* **3**, 142 (1956).

[7] Dausset and Nenna, *C. R. Soc. Biol. (Paris),* **146**, 1539 (1952).

[8] Dausset, J., *Vox Sang. (Amst.),* **4**, 204 (1954).

[9] Aster et al., *Clin. Res.,* **9**, 157 (1961).

[10] Verheugt et al., *Brit. J. Haemat.,* **36**, 533 (1977).

[11] von dem Borne et al., *Brit. J. Haemat.,* **39**, 195 (1978).

[12] Hasegawa et al., *Transplantation,* **15**, 492 (1973).

[13] Stux et al., *Vox Sang. (Basel)* **39**, 16 (1980); Lizak and Grumet, *Hum. Immunol.,* **1**, 87 (1980).

[14] Thulstrup, H., in Terasaki, P.I. (Ed.), *Histocompatibility Testing 1970,* Munksgaard, Copenhagen, 1970, page 559; Melief et al., *Vox Sang. (Basel),* **12**, 374 (1967).

[15] Milgrom et al., *J. Amer. med. Ass.,* **192**, 845 (1965).

[16] Ray et al. (Eds.), *Manual of Tissue Typing Techniques,* National Institute of Allergy and Infectious Diseases, National Institutes of Health, Bethesda, Md., 1976.

[17] Dick and Kissmeyer-Nielsen (Eds.), *Histocompatibility Techniques,* Elsevier, Amsterdam, 1979.

[18] Bodmer and Bodmer, *Brit. med. Bull.,* **34**, 309 (1978).

[19] McKusick, V.A., *Mendelian Inheritance in Man,* 5th ed., Johns Hopkins University Press, Baltimore, 1978; Francke and Weitkamp, *Cytogenet. Cell Genet.,* **25**, 32 (1979).

[20] Orr, H.T., in Parham and Strominger (Eds.), *Histocompatibility Antigens. Structure and Function,* Chapman & Hall, London, 1982, page 1.

[21] Berah et al., *Transplantation,* **9**, 185 (1970).

[22] Harris and Zervas, *Nature,* **221**, 1062 (1969); Silvestre et al., *Nature,* **228**, 67 (1970).

[23] Perrault and Högman, *Vox Sang. (Basel),* **20**, 356 (1971); Doughty et al., *Tissue Antigens,* **3**, 189 (1973); Nordhagen and Ørjasaeter, *Vox Sang. (Basel),* **26**, 97 (1974); Nordhagen, R., *Vox Sang. (Basel),* **27**, 124 (1974); **29**, 23 (1975); **32**, 82 (1977); **35**, 49, 58 and 375 (1978).

[24] Morton et al., *Vox Sang. (Basel),* **17**, 536 (1969); **21**, 141 (1971).

[25] Tanigaki and Tosi, *Immunol. Rev.,* **66**, 5 (1982).

[26] Reviews: Bach et al., *Transplant. Rev.,* **12**, 30 (1972); Eijsvoogel, V.P., *Semin. Hematol.,* **11**, 305 (1974); Bach et al., *Nature,* **259**, 273 (1976); Termijtelen et al., *Immunol. Rev.,* **66**, 79 (1982).

[27] Shaw et al., *J. exp. Med.,* **152**, 565 (1980).

[28] Shaw et al., *Immunogenetics,* **14**, 153 (1981).

[29] van Leeuwen et al., *Nature,* **298**, 565 (1982).

[30] Gazit et al., *Nature,* **284**, 275 (1980); Ferrara et al., *Hum. Immunol.,* **2**, 213 (1981).

[31] Fu et al., *J. exp. Med.,* **140**, 1108 (1974).

[32] Rittner et al., in Kissmeyer-Nielsen, F. (Ed.), *Histocompatibility Testing 1975,* Munksgaard, Copenhagen, 1975, page 945; Hauptmann et al., *Ann. Derm. Syph. (Paris),* **101**, 479 (1974).

[33] Allen, F.H., *Vox Sang. (Basel),* **27**, 382 (1974).

[34] O'Neill et al., *Proc. nat. Acad. Sci. (Wash.),* **75**, 5165 (1978).

[35] O'Neill et al., *Nature,* **273**, 668 (1978).

[36] Dupont et al., in Terasaki, P.I. (Ed.), *Histocompatibility Testing 1980,* University of California, Los Angeles, 1980, page 693.

[37] Fauchet et al., in Terasaki, P.I., (Ed.), *Histocompatibility Testing 1980,* University of California, Los Angeles, 1980, page 707.

[38] Nomenclature: Dausset and Colombani (Eds.), *Histocompatibility Testing 1972,* Munksgaard, Copenhagen, 1973, page 7; Kissmeyer-Nielsen, F. (Ed.), *Histocompatibility Testing 1975,* Munksgaard, Copenhagen, 1975, page 5; Bodmer et al. (Eds.), *Histocompatibility Testing 1977,* Munksgaard, Copenhagen, 1978, page 14; Terasaki, P.I. (Ed.), *Histocompatibility Testing 1980,* University of California, Los Angeles, 1980, page 18.

[39] Arnold and Mayr, *Anthropol. Anz.,* **40**, 57 (1982).

[40] Baur and Danilovs, in Terasaki, P.I. (Ed.), *Histocompatibility Testing 1980,* University of California, Los Angeles, 1980, page 955.

[41] Schreuder et al., in Terasaki, P.I. (Ed.), *Histocompatibility Testing 1980,* University of California, Los Angeles, 1980, page 346.

[42] Beckman et al., *Tissue Antigens,* **18**, 341 (1981); Grumet et al., *Hum. Immunol.,* **5**, 61 (1982).

[43] Shaw et al., *Nature,* **293**, 745 (1981).

[44] Baur and Danilovs, in Terasaki, P.I. (Ed.), *Histocompatibility Testing 1980,* University of California, Los Angeles, 1980, page 994.

[45] Arnold and Mayr, *Ärztl. Lab.,* **27**, 239 (1981).

[46] Reviews: Parham and Strominger (Eds.), *Histocompatibility Antigens. Structure and Function,* Chapman & Hall, London, 1982; Zinkernagel and Doherty, *Advanc. Immunol.,* **27**, 51 (1979).

[47] van Leeuwen et al., *Vox Sang. (Basel),* **9**, 431 (1964).

[48] Rosenfield et al., *Vox Sang. (Basel),* **13**, 461 (1967).

[49] Review: Lalezari and Radel, *Semin. Hematol.,* **11**, 281 (1974).

[50] van Rood, J.J., in *Histocompatibility Testing 1965,* Munksgaard, Copenhagen, 1965, page 37.

[51] Lalezari and Bernard, in *Histocompatibility Testing 1965,* Munksgaard, Copenhagen, 1965, page 167; Ceppelini et al., in Curtoni et al. (Eds.), *Histocompatibility Testing 1967,* Munksgaard, Copenhagen, 1967, page 149; van der Weerdt and Lalezari, *Vox Sang. (Basel),* **22**, 438 (1972).

[52] Lalezari and Bernard, *Fed. Proc.,* **25**, 371 (1966).

[53] Lalezari et al., in Terasaki, P.I. (Ed.). *Histocompatibility Testing 1970,* Munksgaard, Copenhagen, 1970, page 319.

[54] Verheugt et al., *Vox Sang. (Basel),* **35**, 13 (1978).

[55] Claas et al., *Tissue Antigens,* **13**, 129 (1979).

[56] Hasegawa et al., in Schlesinger et al., *Transplantation Today,* volume 3, Grune & Stratton, New York, 1975, page 75.

[57] Caplan et al., *Vox Sang. (Basel),* **33**, 206 (1977).

[58] Shulman et al., *Progr. Hemat.,* **4**, 222 (1964).

[59] Legrand and Dausset, in Schlesinger et al., *Transplantation Today,* volume 3, Grune & Stratton, New York, 1975, page 5.

[60] Legrand and Dausset, in Kissmeyer-Nielsen, F. (Ed.), *Histocompatibility Testing 1975,* Munksgaard, Copenhagen, 1975, page 665.

[61] van Leeuwen et al., *Hum. Immunol.,* **4**, 109 (1982).

[62] Moulinier, J., in Videbaek et al. (Eds.), *Transactions of the 6th Congress of the European Society of Haematology,* Copenhagen 1957, part 2, Karger, Basle, 1958, page 817.

[63] van Loghem et al., *Vox Sang. (Basel),* **4**, 161 (1959); van der Weerdt et al., *Vox Sang. (Basel),* **8**, 513 (1963).

[64] van der Weerdt et al., in *Proceedings of the 8th Congress of the European Society of Haematology,* Vienna 1961, Karger, Basle, 1962, article No.379; van der Weerdt, C.M., *Platelet Antigens and iso-Immunization,* thesis, Drukkerij Aemstelstad, Amsterdam, 1965.

[65] von dem Borne et al., *Vox Sang. (Basel)*, **39**, 113 (1980).
[66] Májský, A., in Perlick et al. (Eds.), *Fortschritte der Hämatologie*, volume 1, Barth, Leipzig, 1970, page 445.
[67] Race and Sanger, *Blood Groups in Man*, 6th ed., Blackwell, Oxford, 1975; Dausset and Tangün, *Vox Sang. (Basel)*, **10**, 641 (1965); Thierfelder, S., *Klin. Wschr.*, **46**, 1 (1968).
[68] Oriol et al., in Terasaki, P.I. (Ed.), *Histocompatibility Testing 1980*, University of California, Los Angeles, 1980, page 585.
[69] Review: Benbunan and Lepage, in Dausset, J. (Ed.), *HLA 1982*, Flammarion, Paris, 1981, page 291.
[70] Mayr, W.R., in *Wissenschaftliche Tabellen Geigy*, Teilband Hämatologie und Humangenetik, 8th ed., Basle, 1979, page 234.
[71] Graw et al., *Lancet*, **2**, 77 (1970); Goldstein et al., *Transfusion (Philad.)*, **11**, 19 (1971); Higby et al., *Vox Sang. (Basel)*, **27**, 186 (1974).
[72] Bosch et al., in *Proceedings of the 8th Congress of the European Society of Haematology*, Vienna, 1961, Karger, Basle, 1962, article No. 380; Pfisterer et al., *Blut*, **17**, 1 (1968); Yankee, R.A., *Vox Sang. (Basel)*, **20**, 419 (1971); Lohrmann et al., *Ann. intern. Med.*, **80**, 9 (1974); van Rood, J.J., *Semin. Hematol.*, **11**, 253 (1974).
[73] Brittingham and Chaplin, *J. Amer. med. Ass.*, **165**, 819 (1957).
[74] Svejgaard, A., *Ser. Haematol.*, **2**, No. 3, 5 (1969).
[75] Kissmeyer-Nielsen et al., *Lancet*, **2**, 662 (1966); Manzler, A.D., *Transplantation*, **6**, 787 (1968); Williams et al., *New Engl. J. Med.*, **279**, 611 (1968); Patel and Terasaki, *New Engl. J. Med.*, **280**, 735 (1969).
[76] Review: Morris and Ting, *Immunol. Rev.*, **66**, 103 (1982).
[77] Opelz and Terasaki, in Terasaki, P.I. (Ed.), *Histocompatibility Testing 1980*, University of California, Los Angeles, 1980, page 592; Opelz et al., *Lancet*, **1**, 868 (1972); Opelz and Terasaki, *Transplant. Proc.*, **4**, 433 (1972).
[78] Review: Baum and Ledney (Eds.), *Experimental Hematology Today: 1978*, Springer, New York, 1978.
[79] Mayr, W.R., *Med. Labor. (Stuttg.)*, **33**, 175 (1980).
[80] Reviews: Dausset and Svejgaard (Eds.), *HLA and Disease*, Munksgaard, Copenhagen, 1977; Ryder et al. (Eds.), *HLA and Disease Registry*, 3rd report, Munksgaard, Copenhagen, 1979.
[81] Bodmer, W.F., *J. roy. Coll. Phycns Lond.*, **14**, 43 (1980); Svejgaard et al., *Transplant. Proc.*, **13**, 913 (1981).
[82] Levine et al., *Science*, **178**, 1201 (1972).
[83] Piazza et al., in Dausset and Colombani (Eds.), *Histocompatibility Testing 1972*, Munksgaard, Copenhagen, 1973, page 73.
[84] de Vries and van Rood, *Arch. derm. Res.*, **264**, 89 (1979).
[85] Morton et al., *Amer. J. med. Genet.*, **6**, 251 (1980).
[86] Mohl and Mayr, *Tissue Antigens*, **10**, 121 (1977).
[87] Amos et al., *Transplant. Proc.*, **7**, suppl. 1, 93 (1975).
[88] Mayr, W.R., in *9. Internationale Tagung der Gesellschaft für forensische Blutgruppenkunde*, reports, Berne, 1981, page 1.
[89] Mayr et al., in *8. Internationale Tagung der Gesellschaft für forensische Blutgruppenkunde*, repórts, London, 1979, page 269; Mayr et al., in Hummel and Gerchow (Eds.), *Biomathematical Evidence of Paternity*, Springer, Berlin, page 177.
[90] Engelfriet et al., in *8. Internationale Tagung der Gesellschaft für forensische Blutgruppenkunde*, reports, London, 1979, page 289.
[91] Dausset and Colombani (Eds.), *Histocompatibility Testing 1972*, Munksgaard, Copenhagen, 1973; Bodmer et al. (Eds.), *Histocompatibility Testing 1977*, Munksgaard, Copenhagen, 1978; Terasaki, P.I. (Ed.), *Histocompatibility Testing 1980*, University of California, Los Angeles, 1980.
[92] Mayr, W.R., *Homo*, **27**, 75 (1976); Ryder et al., *Hum. Hered.*, **28**, 171 (1978).
[93] Piazza and Viganotti, in Dausset and Colombani (Eds.), *Histocompatibility Testing 1972*, Munksgaard, Copenhagen, 1973, page 731; Piazza et al., *Tissue Antigens*, **5**, 445 (1975).

The blood groups[1] consist of inherited characters of the erythrocytes, identifiable as antigens by their reaction with specific antibodies. The genes responsible for the presence of these antigens are inherited in accordance with Mendelian principles. Most of the blood group characters are already identifiable in the young embryo and remain unchanged throughout life. In very exceptional cases they can be changed as a result of disease (leukemia etc.)[2].

The blood group characters inherited on a common gene locus form a so-called system. The best-known systems are: AB0, MNSs, P, Rh, Lutheran, Kell, Lewis, Duffy, Kidd, Diego, Ii, Yt, Auberger, Xg, Dombrock, Colton. With the exception of the Xg group, whose genes are inherited via the X chromosome, each of these systems is inherited independently of the others as an autosomal character. Also known are blood group antigens of very rare occurrence ('private' antigens, see page 258) as well as others only rarely absent from human erythrocytes ('public' antigens, see page 258), such as Vel, Ge, Lan.

The blood group characters carried by an individual's erythrocytes are identifiable by means of specific antibodies contained as either complete or incomplete antibodies in test sera. Phytagglutinins extracted from vegetable seeds can also be used for this purpose.

At the right temperature, the complete antibodies react with the erythrocytes suspended in physiological saline. The reaction with incomplete antibodies can be carried out in various ways:

1. In colloidal reaction media such as beef albumin, antibody-free human serum or plasma, gelatin, dextran, polyvinylpyrrolidone, gum arabic, etc.
2. In the enzyme test using proteolytic enzymes such as trypsin, papain, bromelain, ficin.
3. In the indirect antiglobulin test (Coombs' test).

Combinations of tests (for instance a trypsin test combined with an indirect antiglobulin test) are particularly sensitive.

AB0 blood groups (LANDSTEINER, 1900[3])◇

The isoantibodies anti-A and anti-B are normal and regular constituents of human blood sera, the presence or absence of one or the other or both being dependent on the individual's blood group. 2 antigens (agglutinogens), A and B, reacting respectively with anti-A and anti-B, enable a particular blood to be assigned to one of the 4 groups A, B, AB or 0 (Table 1).

The antigens are located on the surface of the erythrocytes, while the serum contains the isoantibody, anti-A and/or anti-B, corresponding to the antigen not carried by the erythrocytes (Table 1).

Table 1

Blood group	Antigen carried by erythrocytes	Antibodies in serum
0	–	Anti-A + anti-B
A	A	Anti-B
B	B	Anti-A
AB	A and B	Neither

From the genetic aspect, one of the allelic genes (*A*, *B* or *0*) is situated at a chromosomal locus, the blood group being determined by the combined effect of the 2 genes situated on the corresponding loci. Phenotypically, the character 0 is found only in the homozygous form.

The 6 possible genotypes (Table 2) give rise to the 4 blood groups (phenotypes). It is impossible to distinguish serologically between *AA* and *A0* or between *BB* and *B0*.

Table 2

Blood group (phenotype)	Genotype
0	*00*
A	*AA* or *A0*
B	*BB* or *B0*
AB	*AB*

*This chapter on 'Blood Groups' (pages 252–263) has been compiled by the late L. P. HOLLÄNDER, Universität Basel, Basle, Switzerland.

◇The internationally recognized blood group systems are described here in the order of their discovery and first description.

The frequencies with which the various blood groups occur within a population differ widely. From these phenotype frequencies the corresponding gene frequencies can be calculated. For a summary of published data in this respect see MOURANT et al.[1]. Such data are of great importance in anthropological studies.

Subgroups of the AB0 system

The blood group A can be subdivided into A_1 and A_2 (VON DUNGERN and HIRSCHFELD[4]), the blood group AB into A_1B and A_2B. Anti-A sera (from B individuals) contain both anti-A and anti-A_1. Anti-A_1 reacts only with erythrocytes of groups A_1 and A_1B, anti-A on the other hand with erythrocytes of groups A_1 and A_2 or A_1B and A_2B. This subdivision of A increases the number of possible AB0 blood groups from 4 to 6, namely 0, A_1, A_2, B, A_1B and A_2B. These phenotypes correspond to 10 genotypes (Table 3).

Table 3

Blood group (phenotype)	Genotype	Frequency† (%)
0	*00*	40.41
A_1	A_1A_1, A_1A_2, A_10	36.72
A_2	A_2A_2, A_20	7.72
B	*BB*, *B0*	10.65
A_1B	A_1B	3.58
A_2B	A_2B	0.92

†In Central European populations (HUMMEL[5]).

Anti-A_1 is present as an irregular antibody in the serum of 1–2% of A_2 individuals and of about 26% of A_2B individuals.

The AB0 subgroups are summarized in Table 4.

Table 4

Blood group	Reaction with test serum: anti-A	anti A_1	anti B	Antibodies regularly present in serum	Antibodies occasionally present in serum
0	–	–	–	Anti-A (+ anti-A_1) Anti-B	–
A_1	+	+	–	Anti-B	–
A_2	+	–	–	Anti-B	Anti-A_1 in about 1–2%
B	–	–	+	Anti-A (+ anti-A_1)	–
A_1B	+	+	+	None	–
A_2B	+	–	+	None	Anti-A_1 in about 26%

Table 5

	A_1	A_2	A_3	A_x	A_m
Reaction of subgroup with					
– test serum anti-A (blood group B)	+	+	+†	– (+)	– (+)
– test serum anti-A + B (blood group 0)	+	+	+†	+	– (+)
– test serum anti-A_1	+	–	–	–	–
Reaction of serum with					
– erythrocytes with A_1 character	–	(+)	–	+	–
– erythrocytes with A_2 character	–	–	–	–	–
– erythrocytes with B character	+	+	+	+	+
Substance A present in saliva of secretors	Yes	Yes	Yes	No	Yes

†Partial agglutination.

The A subgroups can also be determined by means of phythemagglutinins. Thus *Dolichos biflorus* extract reacts specifically with A_1, and an extract of the seeds of *Lotus tetragonolobus* or *Ulex europaeus* can be uséd as 'anti-A_2 reagent'. In very rare cases a blood cannot be assigned to one of the A subgroups since it reacts with both anti-A_1 and 'anti-A_2'. In this event the blood is assumed to belong to an intermediate group (A_{int}). In addition to the A subgroups A_1 and A_2, other – weaker and rarer – A subgroups are known, such as A_3, A_x and A_m (Table 5).

Variants of blood group B are also known. These react weakly or negatively with anti-B test sera. In such individuals the serum contains an anti-B (not reacting with the individual's own B) as well as B substance. B bloods with no anti-B in the serum have also been reported and have been designated B_w (LEVINE et al.[6]) or B_x (YOKOYAMA et al.[7]). Such individuals secrete B substance in the saliva. A weak B property (B_3) of the erythrocytes, with secretion of H substance but not of B substance, has been described (MOULLEC et al.[8]).

In the very rare *Bombay* or *0_h phenotype* the ABH properties of the erythrocytes are suppressed[11], supposedly as a result of the presence of the gene *h* in homozygous form (*hh*). The serum of these individuals contains anti-A, anti-B and anti-H.

The antigens A and B have also been identified on platelets (GUREVITCH and NELKEN[9]) and leukocytes (DAUSSET[10]). The H, A and B substances are glycosphingolipids or glycoproteins. The part of their structure responsible for the antigenic properties has been largely elucidated (page 258).

MNSs blood groups (LANDSTEINER and LEVINE, 1927[12])

The M and N antigens of human erythrocytes can be identified by means of heterospecific immune sera from rabbits. Phenotypes and genotypes of the MN system are shown in Table 6.

Table 6

Phenotype (group)	Reaction with anti-M	Reaction with anti-N	Genotype
M	+	−	*MM*
MN	+	+	*MN*
N	−	+	*NN*

SANGER and RACE were able to show that a serum described by WALSH and MONTGOMERY[13] in 1947 defines an antigen closely related to M and N. This antigen they designated S. In 1951, LEVINE et al.[14] discovered an antibody reacting with the product of the allele *s* already postulated.

The antibodies anti-M and anti-N also occur in human sera as irregular specific cold agglutinins. Anti-S and anti-s cannot be produced experimentally in animals. The use of the 4 antisera anti-M, anti-N, anti-S and anti-s enables 9 phenotypes to be distinguished (Table 7). The phenotype M + N + S + s + comprises 2 genotypes, *MS/Ns* and *Ms/NS*, that cannot be distinguished serologically.

Table 7

	MS/MS	*MS/Ms*	*Ms/Ms*	*MS/NS*	*MS/Ns* or *Ms/NS*	*Ms/Ns*	*NS/NS*	*NS/Ns*	*Ns/Ns*
Anti-M	+	+	+	+	+	+	−	−	−
Anti-N	−	−	−	+	+	+	+	+	+
Anti-S	+	+	−	+	+	−	+	+	−
Anti-s	−	+	+	−	+	+	−	+	+
Frequency (%)	6.35	15.18	9.07	3.76	23.26	22.41	0.56	5.56	13.85

U is an almost universal antigen present in all Caucasians and in most Blacks. The antibody anti-U, discovered in a black woman by WIENER et al.[15], defines the groups U + and U −. U − individuals are found only among Blacks (frequency 1.6%), they are at the same time S − s −.

MN alleles. The gene M^c (DUNSFORD et al.[16]) is responsible for the formation of an antigen that reacts weakly with most anti-M and some anti-N sera. The antigen corresponding to M^g (ALLEN et al.[17]) has intrinsic specificity and reacts neither with anti-M nor with anti-N. The specific antibody anti-M^g is found relatively often in normal sera. N_2 is responsible for the formation of a weak N antigen. This and other *MN* alleles, as well as the so-called MNSs satellites, are all very rare. The last-named are antigens defined by specific antibodies and are inherited *together with* an MS, Ms, NS or Ns complex (in some cases with resultant weakening or strengthening of the M, N or s antigens). The satellites, as reported by RACE and SANGER[18], are: Hu (Hunter)[19] and He (Henshaw)[20] – both found in Blacks – Mi^a, Vw, Mur, Hil, Hut (these 5 satellites form the so-called Miltenberger system), Vr, Ri^a, St^a, Mt^a, Cl^a, Ny^a, Sul, Far. M^k is a silent allele at the *MNSs* double locus (METAXAS and METAXAS-BÜHLER[21]): it forms neither M nor N and neither S nor s, and its presence unrecognized in two generations of a family can simulate exclusion of paternity or maternity (this also applies to M^g).

P blood groups (LANDSTEINER and LEVINE, 1927[22])

Up to 1955 it was assumed that the P system consisted of P-positive and P-negative individuals, as decided by the reaction of the blood with the anti-P originally discovered. Today, persons reacting with anti-P_1 (the original anti-P) are designated P_1, those not so reacting P_2. P_1 individuals react with anti-P_1 with differing inherited degrees of intensity. P_2 individuals almost regularly form cold-active anti-P_1 antibodies; in addition, various animal species, particularly horses, goats, swine and cattle, form satisfactory antibodies suitable for preparing test sera.

In 1951, LEVINE et al.[23] described a hemolysing antibody, anti-Tj^a, that reacted with 99.99% of the erythrocyte samples against which it was tested. In 1955, SANGER[24] showed that the antigen Tj^a belonged to the P system. The original anti-Tj^a is now known as anti-PP_1P^k and is found in the serum of the very rare p individuals.

A further addition to the P system came with the discovery of the antigen P^k (MATSON et al.[25]). The antibody 'Luke' described by TIPPETT et al.[26] is associated with the P system.

The reactions of the phenotypes in the P system are summarized in Table 8.

Table 8

Phenotype	Reaction with anti-P_1	Reaction with anti-P^k*	Reaction with anti-P	Reaction with anti-PP_1P^k	Frequency
P_1	+	−	+	+	80.2%
P_2	−	−	+	+	19.8%
P^k_1	+	+	−	+	Very rare
P^k_2	−	+	−	+	Very rare
p	−	−	−◊	−	Very rare

*Anti-P^k serum is obtained by absorption of anti-PP_1P^k on P_1 erythrocytes.
◊Or weakly +.

Rhesus blood groups (LANDSTEINER and WIENER, 1940[27])

The discovery of the Rh blood groups by LANDSTEINER and WIENER[27] proved to be of great practical importance, since Rh-negative persons form Rh antibodies fairly often after contact with the Rh antigen (transfusion or injection of blood, pregnancy). A second transfusion with Rh-positive blood may result in a hemolytic transfusion reaction. In women it may cause hemolytic disease in their newborn children. For clinical purposes the distinction between Rh(D)-positive and Rh(D)-negative is usually sufficient, but in fact the Rh blood group system is extremely complex. This complexity is one of the reasons why various genetic explanations of the Rh groups have been put forward, and 3 different nomenclatures are in use. WIENER's concept[28] assumes the existence of a single gene locus on the chromosome with multiple alleles. Each allele results in the formation of an agglutinogen possessing several factors. These factors act as antigens and can be detected by means of the corresponding antibodies. According to FISHER and to RACE[29], the Rh group to which a blood belongs is determined by 3 closely linked gene pairs. Any individual inherits 3 Rh genes from each of his parents, namely *C* or *c*, *D* or *d* and *E* or *e*, in the form of an indivisible gene complex. For instance, an individual inherits *CDe* from one parent and *cde* from the other. Table 9 illustrates the 2 concepts using *CDe* as an example. The genetic information for the Rh antigens is inherited via chromosome 1.

Table 9

	Gene	Agglutinogen	Factors	Antibodies
WIENER	R^1	Rh_1	Rh_0	Anti-Rh_0
			rh′	Anti-rh′
			hr″	Anti-hr″
FISHER and RACE	*C*	C		Anti-C
	D	D		Anti-D
	e	e		Anti-e

The correspondence between WIENER's factors and the antigens of FISHER and RACE, together with that between the respective antibodies, is shown in Table 10.

Table 10

Rh_0 = D	Anti-Rh_0 = anti-D
rh′ = C	Anti-rh′ = anti-C
rh″ = E	Anti-rh″ = anti-E
hr′ = c	Anti-hr′ = anti-c
hr″ = e	Anti-hr″ = anti-e

Antigens have since been discovered which correspond partially to further alleles on the same single gene locus.

Alleles and variants of D. STRATTON[30] has described the antigen D^u, which reacts positively with some anti-D sera, negatively with others. D^u occurs in various strengths (high grade and low grade) and appears to be identical with WIENER's intermediate form ($\mathcal{R}h_0$). In D^u individuals the antigen D can cause the formation of anti-D.

The fact that D-positive individuals can also form anti-D (ARGALL et al.[31]) led WIENER and UNGER[32] to assume the existence of partial antigens of D. Individuals not possessing one of these partial factors can form antibodies against it. $\mathcal{R}h^a$ indicates a blood in which the partial factor Rh^A is missing and which reacts with anti-Rh_0 as well as with anti-Rh^B, anti-Rh^C and anti-Rh^D. These variants and their reactions are shown in Table 11.

Table 11

Variant	Reaction with				
	anti-Rh_0	anti-Rh^A	anti-Rh^B	anti-Rh^C	anti-Rh^D
$\mathcal{R}h^a$	+	−	+	+	+
$\mathcal{R}h^b$	+	+	−	+	+
$\mathcal{R}h^c$	+	+	+	−	+
$\mathcal{R}h^d$	+	+	+	+	−
$\mathcal{R}h^{ab}$	+	−	−	+	+
$\mathcal{R}h^{abc}$	+	−	−	−	+
$\mathcal{R}h^{ac}$	+	−	+	−	+

A further, very rare partial antigen of D appears to be that reacting with the antibody anti-Wiel (anti-D^w) described by CHOWN et al.[33].

Alleles and variants of C and c. C^w (CALLENDER and RACE[34]) is a third allele, the corresponding antigen C^w reacts with a specific anti-C^w serum. Most anti-C sera also possess an anti-C^w component.

A rare and weakly reacting antigen is C^u (RACE et al.[35]), a parallel to D^u.

The antibody anti-C^x is quite commonly found and reacts with the very rare antigen C^x (STRATTON and RENTON[36]).

Alleles and variants of E and e. The antigen E^u (CEPPELLINI et al.[37]) is analogous to D^u and C^u. E^w (GREENWALT and SANGER[38]) has been found only in a very few families, e^s (SANGER et al.[39]) only in Blacks. SHAPIRO[40] found the antibody anti-hr^s in the serum of a Bantu woman; the factor hr^s occurs not only among the Bantu but also in Whites. The antigen e^i was found among the Columbian Indians (LAYRISSE et al.[41]).

Rh genotypes. Table 12 shows the distribution of the *Rh* genotypes among the English people as determined by RACE et al.[43]. Data on their distribution among the white population of New York City are to be found in WIENER and WEXLER[42].

Compound Rh antigens. 'Joint products' of the CDE genes have been discovered, for instance ce, which reacts with the antiserum originally designated anti-f (ROSENFIELD et al.[44]). Other compound antigens are rh_i (or Ce) (ROSENFIELD and HABER[45]), CE (TIPPETT et al.[46]) and ce^s, which reacts with the serum originally designated anti-V (DENATALE et al.[47]). The antigen G described by ALLEN and TIPPETT[48] is not a compound antigen in the same sense; it is closely related to C and D, since most C- or D-positive individuals are also G-positive. Anti-G is found in the serum of cde and cdE individuals, most of whom also form the antibody anti-D + C.

'Deficient' Rh gene complex. The first case of a 'deficient' Rh gene was described by RACE et al.[49] and designated by them $-D-$ ($\bar{R}h_0$ in WIENER's nomenclature). Others have since come to light, namely C^wD- (GUNSON and DONOHUE[50]), $cD-$ (TATE et al.[51]).

A special Rh property is the (apparently) complete absence of Rh antigens. The erythrocytes react negatively to all the Rh antibodies. This phenotype is designated Rh_{null}[11]. Rh_{null} persons suffer from hemolytic anemia (Rh_{null} syndrome).

Gene depression. An Rh complex with gene depression has been given the designation r^G (ALLEN and TIPPETT[48]). Similar behavior is shown by the antigens of the complexes r^M (TIPPETT et al.[46]) and r^L (METAXAS-BÜHLER[52]).

'Rh factor'. It has been shown that the D (Rh_0) reacting with the human anti-D sera is not identical with the so-called 'Rh factor' detected by reaction with animal immune sera. The latter factor is known as anti-LW and reacts not only with erythrocytes that are Rh-positive but also, though less strongly, with those that are Rh-negative. It is assumed that Rh and LW are controlled by 2 different gene loci.

Rh nomenclature. In 1962, ROSENFIELD et al.[53] proposed a new terminology for the Rh groups in which the Rh antibodies were given numbers in the chronological order of their identification. The original publication listed 21 antibodies, a number that has risen to over 30 (RACE and SANGER[54]). This nomenclature is without prejudice to any eventual solution of the genetic problems and simply indicates the phenotype. Thus Rh: 1, 2, −3, 4, 5 denotes a blood giving the following reactions: anti-D +, anti-C +, anti-E −, anti-c +, anti-e + (WIENER: Rh_1rh; FISHER and RACE: *CcDee*). The nomenclatures of the most important antigens of the Rh blood group system are given in Table 13.

Lutheran blood groups (CALLENDER and RACE, 1946[34])

This system is determined by the 2 allelic genes Lu^a and Lu^b. The corresponding antigens Lu^a and Lu^b react with the antibodies anti-Lu^a (CALLENDER and RACE[34]) and anti-Lu^b (CUTBUSH and CHANARIN[55]) respectively. The following phenotypes are possible: Lu(a + b −), Lu(a + b +) and Lu(a − b +) corresponding to the genotypes Lu^aLu^a, Lu^aLu^b and Lu^bLu^b. CRAWFORD et al.[56] described the rare phenotype Lu(a − b −) in a family in whom the Kidd group reactions were also unusual. An autosomal linkage between the Lutheran and Lewis genes has been suggested by MOHR[57]. According to SANGER and RACE[58], such a linkage exists between the genes of the Lutheran groups and those determining the secretion of the ABH blood-group substances. Lu(a − b −) persons can form an antibody with the specificity anti-Lu^aLu^b (DARNBOROUGH et al.[59]). CONTRERAS and TIPPETT[125] postulate the existence of an inhibitor gene, *In(Lu)*, genetically independent of the Lutheran locus, which also inhibits the occurrence of the antigens Au^a, i and P_1.

Kell blood groups (COOMBS et al., 1946[60])

The Kell blood-group system owes its discovery to the use of the antiglobulin test (COOMBS et al.[60]) in blood-group serology. The detection of the antibody anti-Kell (COOMBS et al.[60]) was followed

(Continued on page 256)

Table 12 *Rh genotypes of English people* (RACE et al.[43])

Calculated group frequency (%)	Reaction with antisera fairly widely available				Reaction with rarer antisera					Genetic and antigenic constitution	Short symbols		Calculated genotype frequency (%)
	CC^w	c	D	E	Pure C	Pure C^w	e	f	d		Much used	WIENER and WEXLER[42]	
15.1020	−	+	−	−	−	−	+	+	+	*cde/cde*	rr	rr	15.1020
2.0609	−	+	+	−	−	−	+	+	+	*cDe/cde*	R_0r	R^0r	1.9950
					−	−	+	+	−	*cDe/cDe*	R_0R_0	R^0R^0	0.0659
0.9376	−	+	−	+	−	−	+	+	+	*cdE/cde*	$R''r$	$r''r$	0.9235
					−	−	−	−	+	*cdE/cdE*	$R''R''$	$r''r''$	0.0141
14.0769	−	+	+	+	−	−	−	−	−	*cDE/cDE*	R_2R_2	R^2R^2	1.9906
					−	−	−	−	+	*cDE/cdE*	R_2R''	R^2r''	0.3353
					−	−	+	+	−	*cDE/cDe*	R_2R_0	R^2R^0	0.7243
					−	−	+	+	+	*cDE/cde*	R_2r	R^2r	10.9657
										cDe/cdE	R_0R''	R^0r''	0.0610
0.7644	+	+	−	−	+	−	+	+	+	*Cde/cde*	$R'r$	$r'r$	0.7644
					−	+	+	+	+	C^wde/cde	R'^wr	r'^w	0.0000
34.8899	+	+	+	−	+	−	+	+	−	*CDe/cDe*	R_1R_0	R^1R^0	2.0922
					+	−	+	+	+	*CDe/cde*	R_1r	R^1r	31.6759
										cDe/Cde	R_0R'	R^0r'	0.0505
					−	+	+	+	−	C^wDe/cDe	$R_1^wR_0$	$R^{1w}R^0$	0.0664
					−	+	+	+	+	C^wDe/cde	R_1^wr	$R^{1w}r$	1.0049
										C^wde/cDe	R'^wR_0	r'^wR^0	0.0000
0.0234	+	+	−	+	+	−	+	−	+	*cdE/Cdc*	$R''R'$	$r''r'$	0.0234
					+	−	+	+	+	*CdE/cde*	R_yr	r^yr	0.0000
					+	−	−	−	+	*CdE/cdE*	R_yR''	r^yr''	0.0000
					−	+	+	−	+	C^wde/cdE	R'^wR''	r'^wr''	0.0000
13.4178	+	+	+	+	+	−	+	−	−	*CDe/cDE*	R_1R_2	R^1R^2	11.5000
					+	−	+	+	−	*cDe/CDE*	R_0R_z	R^0R^z	0.0125
					+	−	+	−	+	*CDe/cdE*	R_1R''	R^1r''	0.9685
										cDE/Cde	R_2R'	R^2r'	0.2775
					+	−	+	+	+	*CDE/cde*	R_zr	R_zr	0.1893
										CdE/cDe	R_yR_0	r^yR^0	0.0000
					+	−	−	−	−	*cDE/CDE*	R_2R_z	R^2R^z	0.0687
					+	−	−	−	+	*cdE/CDE*	$R''R_z$	$r''R^z$	0.0058
										CdE/cDE	R_yR_2	r_yR^2	0.0000
					−	+	+	−	−	C^wDe/cDE	$R_1^wR_2$	$R^{1w}R^2$	0.3648
					−	+	+	−	+	C^wDe/cdE	R_1^wR''	$R^{1w}r''$	0.0307
										C^wde/cDE	R'^wR_2	r'^wR^2	0.0000
0.0097	+	−	−	−	+	−	+	−	+	*Cde/Cde*	$R'R'$	$r'r'$	0.0097
					+	+	+	−	+	C^wde/Cde	R'^wR'	r'^wr'	0.0000
					−	+	+	−	+	C^wde/C^wde	$R'^wR'^w$	$r'^wr'^w$	0.0000
18.5073	+	−	+	−	+	−	+	−	−	*CDe/CDe*	R_1R_1	R^1R^1	16.6097
					+	−	+	−	+	*CDe/Cde*	R_1R'	R^1R'	0.8016
					+	+	+	−	−	CDe/C^wDe	$R_1R_1^w$	R^1R^{1w}	1.0539
					+	+	+	−	+	C^wDe/Cde	R_1^wR'	$R^{1w}r'$	0.0254
										C^wde/CDe	R'^wR_1	r'^wR^1	0.0000
					−	+	+	−	−	C^wDe/C^wDe	$R_1^wR_1^w$	$R^{1w}R^{1w}$	0.0167
					−	+	+	−	+	C^wde/C^wDe	$R'^wR_1^w$	r'^wR^{1w}	0.0000
0.2101	+	−	+	+	+	−	+	−	−	*CDe/CDE*	R_1R_z	R^1R^z	0.1985
					+	−	+	−	+	*Cde/CDE*	$R'R_z$	$r'R^z$	0.0048
										CdE/CDe	R_yR_1	r^yR^1	0.0000
					+	−	−	−	−	*CDE/CDE*	R_zR_z	R^zR^z	0.0006
					+	+	+	−	−	C^wDe/CDE	$R_1^wR_z$	$R^{1w}R^z$	0.0062
					+	−	−	−	+	*CdE/CDE*	R_yR_z	r^yR^z	0.0000
					+	+	+	−	+	CdE/C^wDe	$R_yR_1^w$	r^yR^{1w}	0.0000
										C^wde/CDE	R'^wR_z	r'^wR^z	0.0000
0.0000	+	−	−	+	+	−	+	−	+	*CdE/Cde*	R_yR'	r^yr'	0.0000
					+	−	−	−	+	*CdE/CdE*	R_yR_y	r^yr^y	0.0000
					+	+	+	−	+	CdE/C^wde	$R_yR'^w$	$r^yr'^w$	0.0000

Table 13 *Numerical and synonymous designations of the Rh antigens* (ROSENFIELD et al.[58])

	CDE	Rh-Hr		CDE	Rh-Hr		CDE	Neutral	Rh-Hr
Rh1	D	Rh_0	Rh13	*	Rh^A	Rh25	–	LW	–
Rh2	C	rh′	Rh14	*	Rh^B	Rh26	–	‘Deal’	–
Rh3	E	rh″	Rh15	*	Rh^C	Rh27	cE	–	–
Rh4	c	hr′	Rh16	*	Rh^D	Rh28	–	–	hr^H
Rh5	e	hr″	Rh17	◊	Hr_0	Rh29	–	‘total Rh’	–
Rh6	f, ce	hr	Rh18	–	Hr	Rh30	–	Go^a	–
Rh7	Ce	rh_i	Rh19	†	hr^s	Rh31	†	–	hr^B
Rh8	C^w	rh^{w1}	Rh20	VS,e^s	–	Rh32	–	$\bar{\bar{R}}^N$	–
Rh9	C^x	rh^x	Rh21	C^G	–	Rh33	–	R^{0Har}	–
Rh10	V, ce^s	hr^v	Rh22	CE	–	Rh34	–	Bas	–
Rh11	E^w	rh^{w2}	Rh23	Wiel, D^w	–	Rh35	–	1114	–
Rh12	G	rh^G	Rh24	E^T	–				

*The anti-D antibodies are formed by D-positive individuals (see Table 11).

◊The antibodies are formed by – D – / – D – individuals.

† e-positive individuals who form an apparent anti-e.

by that of anti-Cellano (k) by LEVINE et al.[61]. The apparently simple system with the phenotypes KK, Kk and kk became more complicated as a result of the discovery (STROUP et al.[62]) that not only Kp^a and Kp^b of the Penney–Rautenberg ‘system’ but also Js^a and Js^b of the Sutter ‘system’ belong to the Kell system. The rare phenotype K_0 reacts with none of the antibodies making up the Kell system. K_0 individuals form the antibody anti-Ku (CORCORAN et al.[63]), which reacts with all the Kell phenotypes except K_0. Other unusual phenotypes have been described by ALLEN et al.[64] (McLeod) and by VAN DER HART et al.[65] (Claas).

Among the Whites, about 9% of individuals are K-positive, including 0.2% KK. Except for the antibodies of the Rh system, anti-K is the commonest immune antibody occurring in man[63].

A numerical nomenclature for the Kell system has been proposed by ALLEN and ROSENFIELD[66] and is shown in Table 14.

Table 14

K1	K	(Kell)
K2	k	(Cellano)
K3	Kp^a	(Penney)
K4	Kp^b	(Rautenberg)
K5	Ku	(Peltz)
K6	Js^a	(Sutter)
K7	Js^b	(Matthews)
K8	K^w	(Williams)
K9	KL	(Claas)

By 1979 the number of antibodies belonging to the Kell blood-group system had risen to 19[67].

The Lewis system (MOURANT[68]) **and the secretor character for ABH substances**

The detection of the antibodies anti-Le^a (MOURANT[68]) and anti-Le^b (ANDRESEN[69]) enabled the three phenotypes of human erythrocytes to be distinguished: Le(a + b –), Le(a – b +), Le(a – b –).

A number of other antibodies of the Lewis system have been discovered in addition to the anti-Le^a and anti-Le^b. One of these, reacting with A_1,Le(b +) erythrocytes, was originally designated ‘Siedler’ (SEAMAN et al.[74]), later anti-A_1Le^b (CROOKSTON et al.[75]). The serum of Le(a – b –) persons may contain antibodies directed against Le^a and Le^b; these antibodies have been designated Le^x (JORDAL[76]). The antibody Le^c (GUNSON and LATHAM[77]) reacts with Le(a – b –) erythrocytes of ABH nonsecretors, the antibody Le^d (POTAPOV[78]) with Le(a – b –) erythrocytes of ABH secretors.

Allowing for anti-Le^a, anti-Le^b, anti-Le^c and anti-Le^d, 4 phenotypes can be distinguished[128] (Table 15).

A further antibody, designated ‘Magard’, has been found in the serum of an A_2 Le(a – b +) person (ANDERSEN[79]).

The Lewis system is related to the AB0 and secretor characters: individuals with Le(a + b –) on their erythrocytes are nonsecretors for ABH substances, whereas those with Le(a – b +) or, generally, Le(a – b –) are secretors of these substances. There are exceptions to this rule among non-Europeans.

Table 15

Phenotype	Reaction with		Frequency	
	anti-Le^a	anti-Le^b	Whites	Blacks
Le(a + b –)	+	–	22%	23%
Le(a – b +)	–	+	72%	55%
Le(a – b – c – d +)	–	–	4.8%*	17.6%*
Le(a – b – c + d –)	–	–	1.2%*	4.4%*

*Estimates calculated on the basis of an 0.8 frequency for secretors and 0.2 frequency for nonsecretors.

The Lewis antigens are primarily components of various body fluids. Thus they occur not only in the serum but also in saliva, gastric juice, lacrimal secretion, semen, amniotic fluid, meconium, and other fluids, while the erythrocytes carry them as a result of adsorption from the serum (SNEATH and SNEATH[70]).

Responsible for the formation of the Lewis substances are the genes *Se, Le* and *H*. The allelic genes *se, le* and *h* have no known function (silent genes). The *Le* gene results in formation of Le^a substance. H substance is found in the secretions only when the *Se* gene is present in addition to the *H* gene, in which case the former must be regarded as the control gene. The genes *Le, H* and *Se* are necessary for formation of Le^b substance. The AB substances arise by action of the gene products (enzymes) of the AB0 system on H substance. These biochemical relationships are summarized in Table 20 and in Figure 1. The connection between the above gene combinations, the erythrocyte phenotypes and substances formed

Table 16 *AB0 (ABH) and Lewis substances on the erythrocytes and in the saliva in the presence of various combinations of the Lele, Sese, Hh and AB0 genes*[80]

Genes present				Erythrocyte phenotype	Substances in saliva
Lewis	Hh	Secretor	AB0		
Le	*H*	*Se*	*0*	0,Le(a – b +)	H,Le^a,Le^b
le	*H*	*Se*		0,Le(a – b –)	H
Le	*H*	*se*		0,Le(a + b –)	Le^a
le	*H*	*se*		0,Le(a – b –)	None
Le	*H*	*Se*	A_1	A_1,Le(a – b +)	A,H◊,Le^a◊,Le^b◊
le	*H*	*Se*		A_1,Le(a – b –)	A,H◊
Le	*H*	*se*		A_1,Le(a + b –)	Le^a◊
le	*H*	*se*		A_1,Le(a – b –)	None
Le	*h*	*Se*	*0* or *A* or *B*	0_h,Le(a + b –)	Le^a
le	*h*	*Se*		0_h,Le(a – b –)	None
Le	*h*	*se*		0_h,Le(a + b –)	Le^a
le	*h*	*se*		0_h,Le(a – b –)	None

◊Less often in individuals with A_1 blood than in those of group 0.

in the saliva is shown in Table 16, based on the work of GRUBB[71], CEPPELLINI[72] and MORGAN and WATKINS[73].

In Great Britain, independently of their AB0 grouping, about 80% of individuals are secretors (*Se/Se* or *Se/se*) and 20% non-secretors (*se/se*), i.e. provided they are homozygous or heterozygous for *H*, they have H substance in the saliva and other body fluids. The formation of Le^a substance is not regarded as conferring secretor status. The rare individuals who are homozygous for *h* (phenotype 0_h or Bombay) form neither H nor Le^b substance and also neither A nor B substance (Table 16).

At birth, the Lewis characters are not present in full. At 3 months about 80% of children react positively to anti-Le^a. The normal frequency distribution is found only from the age of 2 years on.

Duffy blood groups (CUTBUSH et al., 1950[81])

The antibodies anti-Fy^a (CUTBUSH et al.[81]) and anti-Fy^b (IKIN et al.[82]) react respectively with the human erythrocyte antigens Fy^a and Fy^b. The latter are determined by a pair of allelic genes Fy^a and Fy^b (on chromosome 1). SANGER et al.[83] described the phenotype Fy(a – b –), which occurs commonly among Blacks, less often in the Jewish population of the Yemen. The corresponding gene *Fy* is extremely rare in the Whites, while the gene Fy^x occurs quite frequently. The antigen corresponding to the latter also reacts, though weakly, with anti-Fy^b sera. The erythrocytes of homozygotes for *Fy* are resistant to invasion by the malaria pathogen *Plasmodium vivax*[127]. The Duffy blood groups are summarized in Table 17.

Table 17

Phenotype	Reaction with anti-Fy^a	Reaction with anti-Fy^b	Genotype	Frequency
Fy(a + b –)	+	–	Fy^aFy^a	17.16%
Fy(a + b +)	+	+	Fy^aFy^b	48.54%
Fy(a – b +)	–	+	Fy^bFy^b	34.30%
Fy(a – b –)	–	–	$FyFy$	0*

*Over 90% in West African Blacks.

ALBREY et al.[84] described the antibody anti-Fy3, which reacts with all human erythrocytes except the phenotype Fy(a – b –). The finding of anti-Fy4 (BEHZAD et al.[85]) and anti-Fy5 (COLLEDGE et al.[86]) has also been reported.

Kidd blood groups (ALLEN et al., 1951[87])

The antibodies anti-Jk^a (ALLEN et al.[87]) and anti-Jk^b (PLAUT et al.[88]) react respectively with the human erythrocyte antigens Jk^a and Jk^b, determined by the allelic genes Jk^a and Jk^b. In the Kidd groups, individuals have likewise been found whose blood reacts neither with anti-Jk^a nor with anti-Jk^b, i.e. is of phenotype Jk(a – b –). The serum of such persons may contain the antibody anti-Jk^aJk^b (or Jk3) (PINKERTON et al.[89]).

The Kidd blood groups are summarized in Table 18.

Table 18

Phenotype	Reaction with anti-Jk^a	Reaction with anti-Jk^b	Genotype	Frequency
Jk(a + b –)	+	–	Jk^aJk^a	26.4%
Jk(a + b +)	+	+	Jk^aJk^b	50.0%
Jk(a – b +)	–	+	Jk^bJk^b	23.6%
Jk(a – b –)	–	–	$JkJk$	0*

*In Polynesians and Chinese only.

Diego blood groups (LAYRISSE et al., 1955[90])

Only isolated cases of anti-Di^a have been reported. The antigen Di^a is with a few exceptions confined to South American Indians (36%), North American Indians, Japanese and Chinese. The antibody anti-Di^b is likewise of rare occurrence (THOMPSON et al.[91]).

Yt blood groups (EATON et al., 1956[92])

An antibody reacting with 99.6% of English bloods was discovered by EATON et al.[92] and named anti-Yt^a. The antibody anti-Yt^b, which reacts with about 8% of bloods, was described by GILES and METAXAS[93].

Colton blood groups (HEISTÖ et al., 1967[94])

Some 96% of bloods tested reacted with the immune antibody anti-Co^a and are thus Co(a +). The antibody anti-Co^b was discovered by GILES et al.[95]. About 9% of Europeans belong to the Co(b +) group. A case of Co(a – b –) with anti-Co^aCo^b antibodies was described by ROGERS et al.[96].

Dombrock blood groups (SWANSON et al., 1965[97])

Like the Diego system, the Dombrock blood-group system is mainly of anthropological significance. The antibody anti-Do^a has so far been found in 4 or 5 sera only. Anti-Do^b, corresponding to the anticipated antithetic antigen Do^b, was found by MOLTHAN et al.[98].

Auberger blood groups (SALMON et al., 1961[99])

The antibody anti-Au^a has so far been found only twice. The antigen Au^a is equally common among Whites and Blacks. Due to the fact of concomitant suppression of Lu^a, Lu^b, Au^a, P_1 and i antigens by the same inhibitor locus *In(Lu)*, possible links with the Lutheran blood-group system have been suggested (CRAWFORD et al.[100]).

Ii antigenic system (WIENER et al., 1956[101])

The naturally occurring cold-type isoantibody anti-I is formed by the very rare individuals whose erythrocytes carry only small amounts of the antigen I (WIENER et al.[101]). It is also an autoantibody found mainly in persons with acquired hemolytic anemia. Cord-blood erythrocytes react only weakly with anti-I; the normal antigenic reaction develops gradually and attains the adult intensity at the age of 18 months when the antigen i has been broken down and replaced by I. The cold-type autoantibody anti-i was discovered by MARSH and JENKINS in a patient with reticulosis[102]. Anti-i is not uncommon in infectious mononucleosis. There are various definite degrees of prominence among carriers of the antigen I. A distinction is also made between i_1 (rare among Whites) and i_2 (rare among Blacks). A connection between the I and i characters and the AB0 and P systems has been demonstrated (page 258). The determinant groups of I and AB0 and those of I and P_1 are mutually interacting.

The so-called anti-I^T antibody is rare among Whites[103] but common in Melanesians.

Xg blood groups (MANN et al., 1962[104])

The Xg blood group is of particular genetic interest as the only one so far known that is inherited through the X chromosome. The antibody anti-Xg^a is rare. The gene Xg^a, located on the short arm of the X chromosome, has contributed greatly to knowledge of the topography of this chromosome.

The antigen Xg^a and antibody anti-Xg^a distinguish the phenotypes Xg(a +) and Xg(a –). The genes are designated Xg^a and Xg, the latter apparently being a silent allele (Table 19).

Table 19

Phenotype	Reaction with anti-Xg^a	Genotypes Men	Genotypes Women
Xg(a+)	+	Xg^aY	Xg^aXg^a, Xg^aXg
Xg(a–)	–	XgY	$XgXg$

Sid blood group[105,121,129]

The antigen Sd^a varies greatly in its prominence. The strongest reaction is shown by erythrocytes of the Cad family. About 90% of the English population are Sd(a +). Sd^a is not demonstrable on erythrocytes of cord blood; the antigen begins to be detectable at about the age of 10 weeks. 75% of pregnant women react as Sd(a –).

The antigen Sd^a is present in most secretions, with the greatest concentration in urine. Sd^a activity in urine is associated with the Tamm-Horsefall glycoprotein[130].

Scianna blood group[106]

The Scianna blood group possesses 2 allelic antigens, Scl (the former Sm) and Sc2 (the former Bu^a). Gene frequencies: Sc^1 0.992; Sc^2 0.008. The frequency of Sc:2 subjects in Northern Europe is about 1%, whereas the frequency of Sc: −1 is about 0.01%. The phenotype Sc: −1, −2 is extremely rare[126]. An antibody anti-Sc3, reacting with all except Sc: −1, −2 erythrocytes, has been described[131].

Polyagglutinability

Erythrocytes are said to be polyagglutinable when they are agglutinated by almost all human sera. The most common antigens carried by such cells are T and Tn[120,132]. They are exposed by the action of bacterial or viral neuraminidase (for structure see page 261). Polyagglutinability may be due to the inheritance of an antigen for which a corresponding antibody is present in almost all normal sera. Such antigens are Cad[133], NOR[134], and HEMPAS (hereditary erythroblastic multinuclearity with positive acidified serum test)[135].

Widely distributed antigens ('public' antigens)

These are antigens whose absence from human erythrocytes is an extremely rare occurrence. Well described examples are: Vel[107], Ge[108], Lan[109], Gy^a (Gregory)[110], At^a (August)[111], Jr^a[112], Kn^a (Knops)[113], El[114], Dp[114], Gn^a (Gonsowski)[115], Jo^a (Joseph)[116].

The antibodies anti-Cs^a[117] and anti-Yk^a (York)[118] deserve mention on account of their reaction with the erythrocytes of 98% and 95% respectively of persons tested. The relationship between the 2 corresponding antigens remains obscure.

The antigen Chido (Ch^a)[119] occurs in about 98% of individuals tested and is inherited via a gene locus within the *HLA* complex on chromosome 6 (see Fig. 1, page 260). The Bg antigens are also related to the histocompatibility antigens.

Antigens of infrequent occurrence ('private' antigens)

The genetic classification of these antigens, which are often confined to a single family, presents difficulties. Usually it is only possible to demonstrate their serological independence of the established blood groups together with their dominant inheritance. A summary of the many private antigens is to be found in RACE and SANGER[124]. Examples are Levay[34], Wr^a[123], Cad[133] and Bx^a[136].

Chemical structure of blood-group substances

H, A, B, Lewis and Ii substances[137–139]

The antigenic properties of these blood-group substances are determined by terminal sugars on an oligosaccharide chain built up of D-galactose, D-glucose, N-acetyl-D-glucosamine, N-acetyl-D-galactosamine and L-fucose. When L-fucose is added to N-acetyl-D-glucosamine, it acts as the terminal unit on the chain; no other sugar can be added after it (therefore, Le^a cannot be converted to Le^b). The sugars are transferred as UDP or GDP derivatives.

H, A, B, Le and Ii antigens occur as glycosphingolipids or as glycoproteins (Table 20). The glycosphingolipids may contain a relatively simple carbohydrate chain or be highly complex (polyglycosylceramides), while the glycoproteins carry carbohydrate chains O-glycosidically linked to threonine or serine, although some carbohydrate chains may be linked N-glycosidically to asparagine.

The H, A, B, Le and Ii antigens are synthesized by the sequential addition of carbohydrate residues to a precursor substance. Since the antigenic determinants are carbohydrates and not proteins, they cannot be the direct gene products. H, A, B and Le gene products are glycosyltransferases which transfer the immunodominant carbohydrates to an oligosaccharide chain (Table 21). The pathway of biosynthesis of the H, A, B and Lewis glycosphingolipid antigens is shown in Figure 1.

The specificity i is determined by a straight carbohydrate chain containing repeating Galβ1→4GlcNAcβ1→3 sequences attached to ceramide or protein. The development of I is dependent on the presence of a branching enzyme which adds a branch by 1→6 linkage to the galactose in middle position of the unbranched i-active structure:

```
i:
Galβ1→4GlcNAcβ1→3Galβ1→4GlcNAc
                                β1
                                ↓
                                3Galβ1→4Glcβ1→1Cer
I:
Galβ1→4GlcNAcβ1→3Galβ1→4GlcNAc
                  6             β1
                  ↑             ↓
   Galβ1→4GlcNAcβ1              3Galβ1→4Glcβ1→1Cer
```

The carbohydrate sequences associated with both I and i specificity occur as core structures in H, A, B antigen variants on erythrocytes. They can be regarded as incomplete H,A,B-active chains.

P-group substances[137,138,140]

P antigens are formed by 2 different biosynthetic pathways (Fig.2), the precursor in each case being lactosylceramide (the genetic control is shown in Table 22). The gene products are glycosyltransferases which transfer the immunodominant sugars to the precursor.

MN, Ss and U antigens[132,141]

MN blood-group antigen activity has been assigned to glycophorin A. Ss and U antigen activities are located on glycophorin B (Fig.3). The polypeptide chain of glycophorin A consists of 131 amino acids: about 70 amino acids are external to the lipid bilayer of the erythrocyte membrane, while 20 are within the lipid bilayer and 40 are located in the cytoplasm. Amino-acid heterogeneity of glycophorin A at positions 1 and 5 from the amino terminus (Table 23) correlates with the presence of M or N blood-group antigen activity. In M^g, asparagine is substituted for threonine in position 4. Glycophorin B has the same terminal amino-acid sequence as glycophorin A with N activity; S and s antigens differ from one another in a single amino-acid substitution[142], i.e. in position 26 there is a methionine residue in S and a threonine residue in s antigen. In positions 26 to 35 there are differences between glycophorin A and B.

(Continued on page 261)

Table 20 *Occurrence and characteristics of H, A, B, Le and Ii antigens*

Antigen	Occurrence	Substance	Characteristics
H, A, B	Erythrocytes	Glycosphingolipids	Type-2 determinants
		Glycoproteins	Band 3
	Gastrointestinal tissues	Glycosphingolipids	Type-1 and type-2 determinants
	Plasma	Glycosphingolipids	Type-1 determinants
	Secretions	Glycoproteins	–
Le	Plasma*	Glycosphingolipids	Type-1 determinants
	Secretions	Glycoproteins	–
Ii	Erythrocytes, granulocytes, monocytes	Glycosphingolipids	Type-2 determinants
		Glycoproteins	Band 3
i	Plasma	Glycoproteins	M_r 153000
Ii	Secretions	Glycoproteins	–

Type-1 chain: Galβ1 → 3GlcNAcβ1 → 3Galβ1 → 4Glcβ1 → 1Cer
Type-2 chain: Galβ1 → 4GlcNAcβ1 → 3Galβ1 → 4Glcβ1 → 1Cer

* Le antigen is absorbed from plasma if present on erythrocytes (type-1 determinants).

Table 21 *Genetic control of the biosynthesis of carbohydrate chains with properties of the ABH and Lewis blood-group substances*[138]

Gene	Gene product	Sugar added	Pre-cursor	Terminal structure of oligosaccharide chain	Serological specificity
H (Se)	α-L-Fucosyltransferase 1	Fuc	Type 1	Galβ1 → 3GlcNAc—R 2 ↑ α1Fuc	H
			Type 2	Galβ1 → 4GlcNAc—R 2 ↑ α1Fuc	H
Le	α-L-Fucosyltransferase 2	Fuc	Type 1	Galβ1 → 3GlcNAc—R 4 ↑ α1Fuc	Le[a]
			Type 2	No reaction with type-2 chain	
H (Se) and *Le*	α-L-Fucosyltransferase 1 and 2	Fuc	Type 1	Galβ1 → 3GlcNAc—R 2 4 ↑ ↑ α1Fuc α1Fuc	Le[b]
			Type 2	Galβ1 → 4GlcNAc—R 2 ↑ α1Fuc	H
H (Se) and *A*	α-L-Fucosyltransferase 1 and α-N-acetyl-D-galactosaminyltransferase	Fuc GalNAc	Type 1	GalNAcα1 → 3Galβ1 → 3GlcNAc—R 2 ↑ α1Fuc	A
			Type 2	GalNAcα1 → 3Galβ1 → 4GlcNAc—R 2 ↑ α1Fuc	A
H (Se) and *B*	α-L-Fucosyltransferase 1 and α-D-galactosyltransferase	Fuc Gal	Type 1	Galα1 → 3Galβ1 → 3GlcNAc—R 2 ↑ α1Fuc	B
			Type 2	Galα1 → 3Galβ1 → 4GlcNAc—R 2 ↑ α1Fuc	B
H (Se), *A* and *Le*	α-L-Fucosyltransferase 1 and 2 and α-N-acetyl-D-galactosaminyltransferase	Fuc GalNAc	Type 1	GalNAcα1 → 3Galβ1 → 3GlcNAc—R 2 4 ↑ ↑ α1Fuc α1Fuc	ALe[b]
H (Se), *B* and *Le*	α-L-Fucosyltransferase 1 and 2 and α-D-galactosyltransferase	Fuc Gal	Type 1	Galα1 → 3Galβ1 → 3GlcNAc—R 2 4 ↑ ↑ α1Fuc α1Fuc	BLe[b]

Gal: D-galactose
GalNAc: N-acetyl-D-galactosamine
GlcNAc: N-acetyl-D-glucosamine
Fuc: L-fucose

R in glycosphingolipids: Galβ1 → 4Glcβ1 → 1Cer

R in glycoproteins
- *O-glycosidically linked:* Galβ1 → 3GalNAcα1 → Thr (or Ser)
- *N-glycosidically linked:* the polyglycosyl chain contains repeating N-acetyllactosamine units, and N-acetylglucosamine is linked to asparagine.

Table 22 *Genetic control of the biosynthesis of carbohydrate chains with properties of the P-group substances*[138]

Gene	Gene product	Sugar added	Structure of the antigen	Specificity
			Globoside series	
			Galβ1 → 4Glcβ1 → 1Cer	Lactosylceramide
P^k	α-D-Galactosyl-transferase	Gal	Galα1 → 4Galβ1 → 4Glcβ1 → 1Cer	Trihexosylceramide (P^k)
P	β-N-Acetyl-D-galactosaminyl-transferase	GalNAc	GalNAcβ1 → 3Galα1 → 4Galβ1 → 4Glcβ1 → 1Cer	Globoside (P)
	α-N-Acetyl-D-galactosaminyl-transferase	GalNAc	GalNAcα1 → 3GalNAcβ1 → 3Galα1 → 4Galβ1 → 4Glcβ1 → 1Cer	Forssman glycolipid
			Paragloboside series	
			Galβ1 → 4GlcNAcβ1 → 3Galβ1 → 4Glcβ1 → 1Cer	Paragloboside
P^1	α-D-Galactosyl-transferase	Gal	Galα1 → 4Galβ1 → 4GlcNAcβ1 → 3Galβ1 → 4Glcβ1 → 1Cer	P_1
	α-N-Acetylneu-raminic acid transferase	NeuAc	NeuAcα2 → 3Galβ1 → 4GlcNAcβ1 → 3Galβ1 → 4Glcβ1 → 1Cer	Sialosylparagloboside

Gal: D-galactose
Glc: D-glucose
GalNAc: N-acetyl-D-galactosamine
GlcNAc: N-acetyl-D-glucosamine
NeuAc: N-acetylneuraminic acid
Cer: ceramide

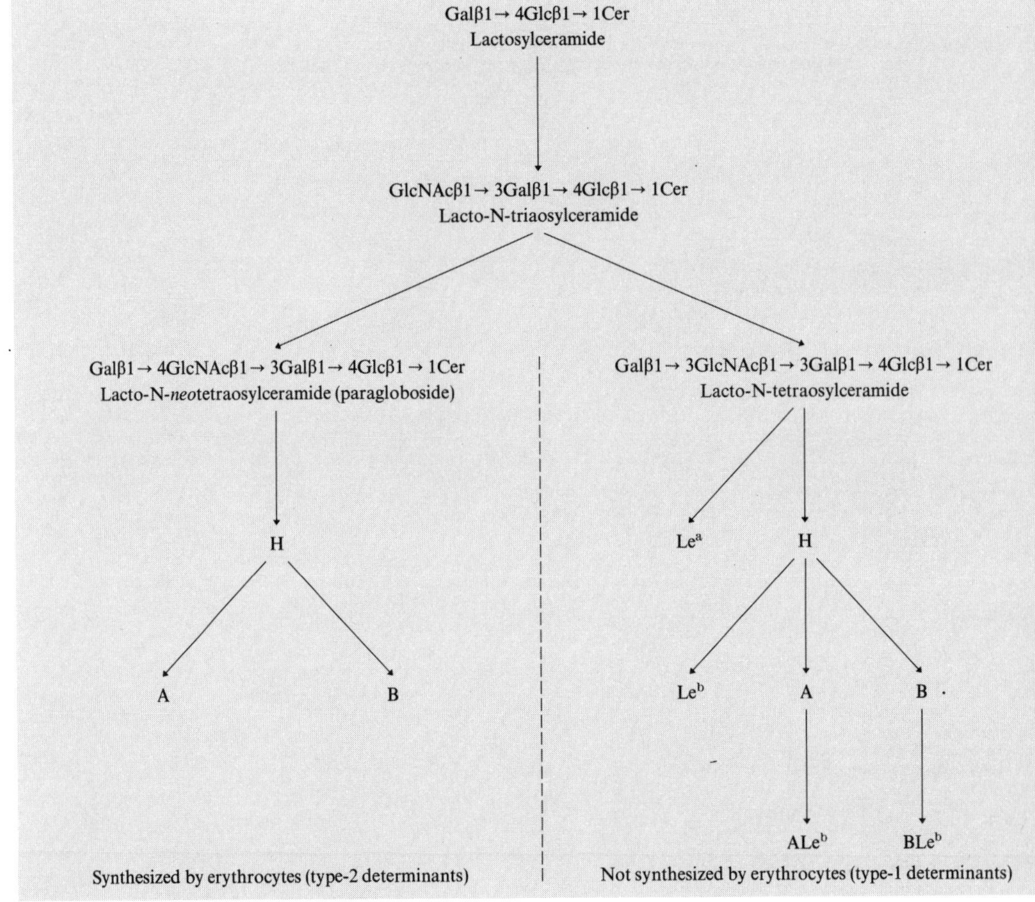

Fig. 1. Biosynthesis of H, A, B and Lewis antigens.

Table 23 *Chemistry of MN and Ss antigens*

Protein of erythrocyte membrane	Antigen	Terminal sequence of amino acids	Positions glycosylated
Glycophorin A (α sialoglycoprotein, MN glycoprotein) ..	M	Ser—Ser—Thr—Thr—Gly—	2, 3, 4, 10, ...
	N	Leu—Ser—Thr—Thr—Glu—	2, 3, 4, 10, ...
	M^c	Ser—Ser—Thr—Thr—Glu—	2, 3, 4, 10, ...
	M^g	Leu—Ser—Thr—Asn—Glu—	Serine and threonine in positions 2 and 3 are not glycosylated
Glycophorin B (δ sialoglycoprotein, Ss glycoprotein)	S,s	Leu—Ser—Thr—Thr—Glu—	2, 3, 4, 10, ...
	U	?	?

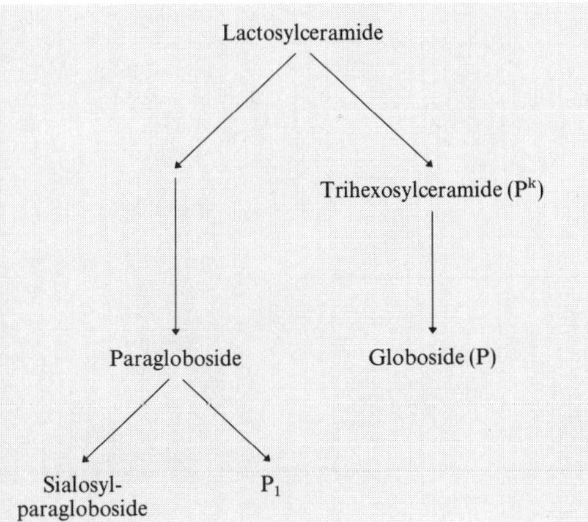

Fig. 2. Biosynthesis of the P antigens.

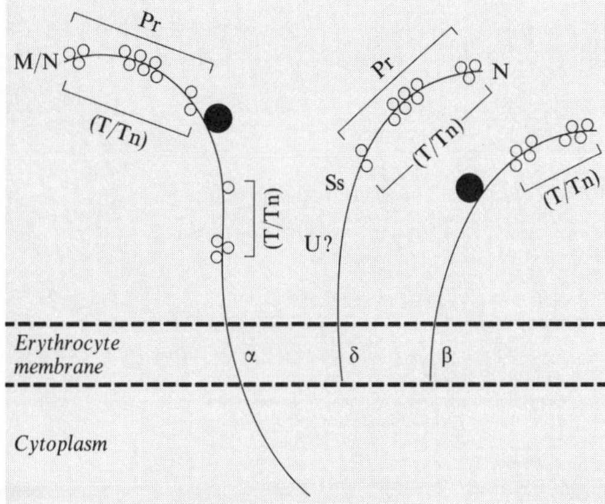

Fig. 3. Schematic representation of antigens on erythrocyte sialoglycoproteins (α: glycophorin A; δ: glycophorin B; β: glycophorin C; ○: O-glycosidically linked oligosaccharide chain; ●: N-glycosidically linked oligosaccharide chain)[132].

Glycophorin A consists of about 60% carbohydrates, all of which are external to the erythrocyte membrane. 15 oligosaccharide chains are O-glycosidically linked, and 1 chain is N-glycosidically linked to the polypeptide chain. The structure of the major O-glycosidically linked oligosaccharide was first reported by THOMAS and WINZLER[143]:

$$\mathrm{NeuAc}\alpha 2 \rightarrow 3\mathrm{Gal}\beta 1 \rightarrow \underset{\substack{\uparrow \\ \alpha 2\mathrm{NeuAc}}}{\overset{}{3\mathrm{GalNAc}}} \rightarrow \mathrm{Ser\ (or\ Thr)}$$

(6 ↑ α2NeuAc attached to GalNAc)

The N-glycosidically linked oligosaccharide chain is rich in N-acetylgalactosamine and mannose, but its exact structure is not known.

The amino-terminal glycopeptide of glycophorin B contains N-acetylneuraminic acid, galactose and N-acetylgalactosamine.

The nature of the U antigen is quite unknown.

Pr antigens[132]

Pr denotes the protease lability of the receptors for certain cold antibodies. Pr determinants are recognized by some anti-Pr sera on glycophorin A and glycophorin B (Fig. 3). The determinants are most probably O-glycosidically linked oligosaccharides within the 26 residues from the amino terminus.

T antigen[132,144]

The T antigen is a cryptantigen that may be transiently exposed on human erythrocytes, platelets and leukocytes by the action of bacterial or viral neuraminidase. T-active structures on the erythrocyte membrane can be connected with sialoglycoproteins as well as with gangliosides.

The proposed structure of the O-glycosidically linked oligosaccharide of the sialoglycoproteins in the T-exposed erythrocyte membrane is as follows:

Galβ1→3GalNAc→Ser (or Thr)

It is misleading to think of the T antigen as a precursor of M- and N-antigen activity: there are 15 O-glycosidically linked oligosaccharide chains on glycophorin A and probably also on glycophorin B and C – all potential T-antigen sites – whereas M-antigen activity is restricted to the amino terminus of glycophorin A, and N-antigen activity to the amino terminus of glycophorin A and B (Fig. 3).

Tn antigen[132,144]

The Tn antigen is a cryptantigen that is exposed on erythrocytes with an acquired and persistent form of polyagglutination. Glycopeptides released from Tn-exposed erythrocytes show a substantial reduction in the content of N-acetylneuraminic acid and galactose when compared with those of normal erythrocytes. The immunodominant group of the Tn antigen is the N-acetylgalactosamine residue O-glycosidically linked to the polypeptide chain of the erythrocyte sialoglycoproteins. It is possible that an N-acetylneuraminic-acid residue is present in some but not all Tn structures:

GalNAc→Ser (or Thr)
[6 ↑ α2NeuAc]

Clinical significance of the blood groups

Blood-group-specific antibodies may interfere with the compatibility test preceding a blood transfusion. If this possibility is not allowed for, the result may be a hemolytic transfusion reaction (Table 24). In addition to AB0 incompatibility, some of these antibodies can cause hemolytic disease of the newborn.

References

[1] WIENER, A. S., *Blood Groups and Transfusion,* 3rd ed., Thomas, Springfield, 1943; STRATTON and RENTON, *Practical Blood Grouping,* Blackwell, Oxford, 1958; WIENER and WEXLER, *Heredity of the Blood Groups,* Grune & Stratton, New York, 1958; DUNSFORD and BOWLEY, *Techniques in Blood Grouping,* 2nd ed., Thomas, Springfield, 1968; GIBLETT, E.R., *Genetic Markers in Human Blood,* Blackwell, Oxford, 1969; BOORMAN and DODD,

Table 24 *The most important blood-group antibodies and their clinical significance*

	Antibody formation*	Physio-logical saline 20 °C	Physio-logical saline 37 °C	Coombs' test	Enzyme test	Optimum temperature (°C)	Transfusion reaction	Probability of hemolytic disease of newborn when mother is antibody-positive and child antigen-positive	Acceptable blood stores (%)
Anti-D	i	–	±	+	+	37	+ +	To be expected	15
Anti-C	i	–	–	+	+	37	+ +	Probable	30
Anti-E	i	–	±	+	+	37	+ +	Probable	70
Anti-c	i	–	–	+	+	37	+ +	Probable	20
Anti-e	i	–	–	+	+	37	+ +	Probable	3
Anti-C^w	i	–	±	+	+	37	+ +	Possible	98
Anti-M	n	+	+	±	–	25	–	Improbable	22
Anti-N	n	+	+	±	–	25	–	Improbable	28
Anti-S	i	–	±	+	–	25–37	+	Possible	45
Anti-s	i	–	–	+	–	37	+	Possible	11
Anti-P_1	n	+	–	–	±	4	–	Improbable	21
Anti-Lu(a)	n/i	+	+	±	–	25	–	Improbable	92
Anti-Lu(b)	i	–	–	+	–	37	+	Possible	<1
Anti-K	i	–	±	+	±	37	+ +	Probable	90
Anti-k	i	–	±	+	±	37	+ +	Probable	0.2
Anti-Le(a)	n	+	+	+	+	4–37	+	Improbable	77
Anti-Le(b)	n	+	+	+	+	4–37	+	Improbable	27
Anti-Fy(a)	i	–	–	+	–	37	+	Probable	33
Anti-Fy(b)	i	–	–	+	–	37	+	Probable	20
Anti-Jk(a)	i	–	–	+	±	37	+	Possible	25
Anti-Jk(b)	i	–	–	+	±	37	+	Possible	25
Anti-Xg(a)	i	–	–	+	?	37	+	Possible	♀13 ♂36

*i: immune; n: natural.

An Introduction to Blood Group Serology, 4th ed., Churchill, London, 1970; Race and Sanger, *Blood Groups in Man,* 6th ed., Blackwell, Oxford, 1975; Mourant et al., *The Distribution of the Human Blood Groups and Other Polymorphisms,* 2nd ed., Oxford University Press, London, 1976; Prokop and Göhler, *Die menschlichen Blutgruppen,* 4th ed., Fischer, Stuttgart, 1976; Mollison, P.L., *Blood Transfusion in Clinical Medicine,* 7th ed., Blackwell, Oxford, 1983.
[2] Gold and Holländer, *Blut,* **9**, 188 (1963).
[3] Landsteiner, K., *Zbl. Bakt., I. Abt. Orig.,* **27**, 357 (1900).
[4] von Dungern and Hirschfeld, *Z. Immun.-Forsch.,* **8**, 526 (1911).
[5] Hummel, K., *Biostatische Abstammungsbegutachtung mit Blutgruppenbefunden,* Fischer, Stuttgart, 1971.
[6] Levine et al., in Holländer, L. (Ed.), *Proceedings of the 6th Congress of the International Society of Blood Transfusion, Boston 1956,* Karger, Basle, 1958, page 132 [*Bibl. haemat. (Basel*), No. 7].
[7] Yokoyama et al., *Vox Sang. (Basel*), NS **2**, 348 (1957).
[8] Moullec et al., *Rev. Hémat.,* **10**, 574 (1955).
[9] Gurevitch and Nelken, *Nature,* **173**, 356 (1954).
[10] Dausset, J., *C.R. Soc. Biol. (Paris*), **148**, 1607 (1954).
[11] Allen, F.H., *Amer. J. clin. Path.,* **66**, 468 (1976).
[12] Landsteiner and Levine, *Proc. Soc. exp. Biol. (N.Y.*), **24**, 600 (1927).
[13] Walsh and Montgomery, *Nature,* **160**, 504 (1947).
[14] Levine et al., *Proc. Soc. exp. Biol. (N.Y.*), **78**, 218 (1951).
[15] Wiener et al., *J. Amer. med. Ass.,* **153**, 1444 (1953).
[16] Dunsford et al., *Nature,* **172**, 688 (1953).
[17] Allen et al., *Vox Sang. (Basel*), NS **3**, 81 (1958).
[18] Race and Sanger, *Blood Groups in Man,* 6th ed., Blackwell, Oxford, 1975, pages 112 and 114/115.
[19] Landsteiner et al., *J. Immunol.,* **27**, 469 (1934).
[20] Ikin and Mourant, *Brit. med. J.,* **1**, 456 (1951).
[21] Metaxas and Metaxas-Bühler, *Nature,* **202**, 1123 (1964).
[22] Landsteiner and Levine, *Proc. Soc. exp. Biol. (N.Y.*), **24**, 941 (1927).
[23] Levine et al., *Proc. Soc. exp. Biol. (N.Y.*), **77**, 403 (1951).
[24] Sanger, R., *Nature,* **176**, 1163 (1955).
[25] Matson et al., *Amer. J. hum. Genet.,* **11**, 26 (1959).
[26] Tippett et al., *Vox Sang. (Basel*), NS **10**, 269 (1965).
[27] Landsteiner and Wiener, *Proc. Soc. exp. Biol. (N.Y.*), **43**, 223 (1940).
[28] Wiener, A.S., *Proc. Soc. exp. Biol. (N.Y.*), **54**, 316 (1943).
[29] Race, R.R., *Nature,* **153**, 771 (1944).
[30] Stratton, F., *Nature,* **158**, 25 (1946).
[31] Argall et al., *J. Lab. clin. Med.,* **41**, 895 (1953).
[32] Wiener and Unger, *J. Amer. med. Ass.,* **169**, 696 (1959).
[33] Chown et al., *Transfusion (Philad.*), **2**, 150 (1962).
[34] Callender and Race, *Ann. Eugen. (Lond.*), **13**, 102 (1946).
[35] Race et al., *Nature,* **161**, 316 (1948).
[36] Stratton and Renton, *Brit. med. J.,* **1**, 962 (1954).
[37] Ceppellini et al., *Boll. Ist. sieroter. milan.,* **29**, 123 (1950).
[38] Greenwalt and Sanger, *Brit. J. Haemat.,* **1**, 52 (1955).
[39] Sanger et al., *Nature,* **186**, 171 (1960).
[40] Shapiro, M., *J. forens. Med.,* **7**, 96 (1960).
[41] Layrisse et al., *Nature,* **191**, 503 (1961).
[42] Wiener and Wexler, in Gedda, L., *Novant'Anni delle Leggi Mendeliane,* Instituto Gregorio Mendel, Rome, 1956, page 147.
[43] Race et al., *Blood,* **3**, 689 (1948).
[44] Rosenfield et al., *Brit. med. J.,* **1**, 975 (1953).
[45] Rosenfield and Haber, *Amer. J. hum. Genet.,* **10**, 474 (1958).
[46] Tippett et al., *Vox Sang. (Basel*), NS **6**, 21 (1961).
[47] DeNatale et al., *J. Amer. med. Ass.,* **159**, 247 (1955).
[48] Allen and Tippett, *Vox Sang. (Basel*), NS **3**, 321 (1958).
[49] Race et al., *Nature,* **166**, 520 (1950).
[50] Gunson and Donohue, *Vox Sang. (Basel*), NS **2**, 320 (1957).
[51] Tate et al., *Vox Sang. (Basel*), NS **5**, 398 (1960).
[52] Metaxas and Metaxas-Bühler, *Vox Sang. (Basel*), NS **6**, 136 (1961).
[53] Rosenfield et al., *Transfusion (Philad.*), **2**, 287 (1962); *Proc. nat. Acad. Sci. (Wash.*), **70**, 1303 (1973).
[54] Race and Sanger, *Blood Groups in Man,* 6th ed., Blackwell, Oxford, 1975, page 183.
[55] Cutbush and Chanarin, *Nature,* **178**, 855 (1956).
[56] Crawford et al., *Transfusion (Philad.*), **1**, 228 (1961).
[57] Mohr, J., *Acta path. microbiol. scand.,* **29**, 339 (1951).

[58] SANGER and RACE, *Heredity,* **12**, 513 (1958).
[59] DARNBOROUGH et al., *Nature,* **198**, 796 (1963).
[60] COOMBS et al., *Lancet,* **1**, 264 (1946).
[61] LEVINE et al., *Science,* **109**, 464 (1949).
[62] STROUP et al., *Transfusion (Philad.),* **5**, 309 (1965).
[63] CORCORAN et al., *Transfusion (Philad.),* **1**, 181 (1961).
[64] ALLEN et al., *Vox Sang. (Basel),* NS **6**, 555 (1961).
[65] VAN DER HART et al., *Vox Sang. (Basel),* NS **15**, 456 (1968).
[66] ALLEN and ROSENFIELD, *Transfusion (Philad.),* **1**, 305 (1961).
[67] SABO et al., *Vox Sang. (Basel),* **36**, 97 (1979).
[68] MOURANT, A.E., *Nature,* **158**, 237 (1946).
[69] ANDRESEN, P.H., *Acta path. microbiol. scand.,* **25**, 728 (1948).
[70] SNEATH and SNEATH, *Nature,* **176**, 172 (1955).
[71] GRUBB, R., *Acta path. microbiol. scand.,* **28**, 61 (1951).
[72] CEPPELLINI, R., in *5ᵉ Congrès international de transfusion sanguine,* Paris, 1955, page 207.
[73] MORGAN and WATKINS, *Brit. med. Bull.,* **25**, 30 (1969).
[74] SEAMAN et al., *Vox Sang. (Basel),* NS **15**, 25 (1968).
[75] CROOKSTON et al., *Lancet,* **2**, 1110 (1970).
[76] JORDAL, K., *Acta path. microbiol. scand.,* **39**, 399 (1956).
[77] GUNSON and LATHAM, *Vox Sang. (Basel),* NS **22**, 344 (1972).
[78] POTAPOV, M.I., *Probl. Hemat. Blood Transfus. (Moscow),* **15**, 45 (1970).
[79] ANDERSEN, J., *Vox Sang. (Basel),* NS **3**, 251 (1958).
[80] ISSITT, P.D., *Applied Blood Group Serology,* 2nd ed., Spectra Biologicals, Oxnard (Cal.), 1975.
[81] CUTBUSH et al., *Nature,* **165**, 188 (1950).
[82] IKIN et al., *Nature,* **168**, 1077 (1951).
[83] SANGER et al., *Brit. J. Haemat.,* **1**, 370 (1955).
[84] ALBREY et al., *Vox Sang. (Basel),* NS **20**, 29 (1971).
[85] BEHZAD et al., *Vox Sang. (Basel),* NS **24**, 337 (1973).
[86] COLLEDGE et al., *Vox Sang. (Basel),* NS **24**, 193 (1973).
[87] ALLEN et al., *Nature,* **167**, 482 (1951).
[88] PLAUT et al., *Nature,* **171**, 431 (1953).
[89] PINKERTON et al., *Vox Sang. (Basel),* NS **4**, 155 (1959).
[90] LAYRISSE et al., *Acta med. venez.,* **3**, 132 (1955).
[91] THOMPSON et al., *Vox Sang. (Basel),* NS **13**, 314 (1967).
[92] EATON et al., *Brit. J. Haemat.,* **2**, 333 (1956).
[93] GILES and METAXAS, *Nature,* **202**, 1122 (1964).
[94] HEISTÖ et al., *Vox Sang. (Basel),* NS **12**, 18 (1967).
[95] GILES et al., *Brit. J. Haemat.,* **19**, 267 (1970).
[96] ROGERS et al., *AABB Abstr. Transfus. (Philad.),* **14**, 508 (1974), quoted by RACE and SANGER, *Blood Groups in Man,* 6th ed., Blackwell, Oxford, 1975, page 393.
[97] SWANSON et al., *Nature,* **206**, 313 (1965).
[98] MOLTHAN et al., *Vox Sang. (Basel),* NS **24**, 382 (1973).
[99] SALMON et al., *Nouv. Rev. franç. Hémat.,* **1**, 649 (1961).
[100] CRAWFORD et al., *Vox Sang. (Basel),* NS **26**, 283 (1974).
[101] WIENER et al., *Ann. intern. Med.,* **44**, 221 (1956).
[102] MARSH and JENKINS, *Nature,* **188**, 753 (1960).
[103] GARRATTY et al., *Transfusion (Philad.),* **12**, 325 (1972).
[104] MANN et al., *Lancet,* **1**, 8 (1962).
[105] MACVIE et al., *Vox Sang. (Basel),* NS **13**, 485 (1967).
[106] SCHMIDT et al., *Transfusion (Philad.),* **2**, 338 (1962); ANDERSON et al., *Transfusion (Philad.),* **3**, 30 (1963).
[107] SUSSMAN and MILLER, *Rev. Hémat.,* **7**, 368 (1952).
[108] ROSENFIELD et al., *Brit. J. Haemat.,* **6**, 344 (1960).
[109] VAN DER HART et al., quoted by RACE and SANGER, *Blood Groups in Man,* 6th ed., Blackwell, Oxford, 1975, page 411.
[110] SWANSON et al., *Transfusion (Philad.),* **7**, 304 (1967).
[111] APPELWHAITE et al., *Vox Sang. (Basel),* NS **13**, 444 (1967).
[112] RACE and SANGER, *Blood Groups in Man,* 6th ed., Blackwell, Oxford, 1975, page 411.
[113] HELGESON et al., *Transfusion (Philad.),* **10**, 137 (1970).
[114] FRANK et al., *Transfusion (Philad.),* **10**, 254 (1970).
[115] FOX and TASWELL, *Transfusion (Philad.),* **9**, 265 (1969).
[116] JENSEN et al., *Transfusion (Philad.),* **12**, 322 (1972).
[117] GILES et al., *Vox Sang. (Basel),* NS **10**, 405 (1965).
[118] MOLTHAN et al., *Transfusion (Philad.),* **9**, 281 (1969).
[119] HARRIS et al., *Vox Sang. (Basel),* NS **12**, 140 (1967).
[120] DAUSSET et al., *Blood,* **14**, 1079 (1959).
[121] RENTON et al., *Vox Sang. (Basel),* NS **13**, 493 (1967).
[122] CAZAL et al., *Rev. franç. Transfus.,* **11**, 209 (1968).
[123] HOLMAN, C.A., *Lancet,* **2**, 119 (1953).
[124] RACE and SANGER, *Blood Groups in Man,* 6th ed., Blackwell, Oxford, 1975, page 432.
[125] CONTRERAS and TIPPETT, *Vox Sang. (Basel),* NS **27**, 369 (1974).
[126] MCCREARY et al., *Transfusion (Philad.),* **13**, 350 (1973).
[127] MILLER et al., *New Engl. J. Med.,* **295**, 302 (1976).
[128] HOSSAINI, A.A., *Progr. clin. Path.,* **7**, 165 (1978).
[129] PICKLES and MORTON, in MOHN et al. (Eds.), *Human Blood Groups,* Karger, Basle, 1977, page 277.
[130] SOH et al., *Biochem. biophys. Res. Commun.,* **93**, 1132 (1980).
[131] NASON et al., *Transfusion (Philad.),* **20**, 531 (1980).
[132] ANSTEE, D.J., *Semin. Hemat.,* **18**, 13 (1981).
[133] CAZAL et al., *Rev. franç. Transfus.,* **11**, 209 (1968).
[134] HARRIS et al., *Vox Sang. (Basel),* **42**, 134 (1982).
[135] CROOKSTON et al., *Brit. J. Haemat.,* **17**, 11 (1969).
[136] CONTRERAS et al., *Vox Sang. (Basel),* **39**, 225 (1980).
[137] WATKINS, W.M., *Proc. roy. Soc. B,* **202**, 31 (1978).
[138] MOLLISON, P.L., *Blood Transfusion in Clinical Medicine,* 7th ed., Blackwell, Oxford, 1983, page 319.
[139] HAKOMORI, S., *Semin. Hemat.,* **18**, 39 (1981).
[140] MARCUS et al., *Semin. Hemat.,* **18**, 63 (1981).
[141] MOLLISON, P.L., *Blood Transfusion in Clinical Medicine,* 7th ed., Blackwell, Oxford, 1983, page 413.
[142] DAHR et al., *Hoppe-Seylers Z. physiol. Chem.,* **361**, 145 (1980).
[143] THOMAS and WINZLER, *J. biol. Chem.,* **244**, 5943 (1969).
[144] MOLLISON, P.L., *Blood Transfusion in Clinical Medicine,* 7th ed., Blackwell, Oxford, 1983, page 468.

Table 1 *Erythrocyte-enzyme groups*

Erythrocyte enzyme		Enzyme groups	Discoverer
EC number	Recommended name		
1.1.1.49	Glucose-6-phosphate dehydrogenase	G6PD groups	BOYER et al., 1962[1]
3.1.3.2	Acid (erythrocyte) phosphatase	ACP_1 groups	HOPKINSON et al., 1963[2]
1.1.1.44	Phosphogluconate dehydrogenase	6PGD groups	FILDES and PARR, 1963[3]
2.7.5.1	Phosphoglucomutase	PGM_1, PGM_2 and PGM_3 groups	SPENCER et al., 1964[4]
2.7.4.3	Adenylate kinase	AK groups	FILDES and HARRIS, 1966[5]
2.7.7.12	UDPglucose-hexose-1-phosphate uridylyltransferase (galactose-1-phosphate uridylyltransferase)	Gt groups	MATHAI and BEUTLER, 1966[6]
3.4.11....	Peptidase A	PepA groups	LEWIS and HARRIS, 1967[7]
3.5.4.4	Adenosine deaminase	ADA groups	SPENCER et al., 1968[8]
3.4.13.9	Proline dipeptidase (peptidase D)	PepD groups	LEWIS and HARRIS, 1969[9]
2.6.1.2	Alanine aminotransferase (glutamic-pyruvic transaminase)	GPT groups	CHEN and GIBLETT, 1971[10]
3.1.1.1	Carboxylesterase (esterase D)	EsD groups	HOPKINSON et al., 1973[11]
2.7.4....	Uridine-5-monophosphate kinase	UMPK groups	GIBLETT et al., 1974[12]
4.4.1.5	Lactoyl-glutathione lyase (glyoxalase I)	GLO groups	KÖMPF et al., 1975[13]
3.1.3.18	Phosphoglycolate phosphatase	PGP groups	BARKER and HOPKINSON, 1978[14]
4.2.1.24	Porphobilinogen synthase (5-aminolevulinate dehydratase)	ALADH groups	BATTISTUZZI et al., 1981[15]

The erythrocyte enzyme groups[16] are systems of genetically controlled molecular (structural) variants of enzymes. Most of these enzymes occur not only in erythrocytes but also in other cells and tissues. Structural variants of a large number of enzymes have been observed. Currently, it is usual to speak of true enzyme polymorphism only when at least 2 alleles have a frequency of 0.01 (1%) or more. A summary of erythrocyte-enzyme polymorphism (erythrocyte-enzyme groups) is to be found in Table 1. It is demonstrable exclusively by electrophoretic separation of the enzymes in the hemolysate.

Unless otherwise stated, the alleles listed under the heading 'Chromosome model' are all of the autosomal codominant type.

In the absence of an indication to the contrary, the data on gene frequencies refer to white populations; figures in brackets are approximate mean values derived from data in the literature for the erythrocyte-enzyme group concerned.

G6PD groups[17-20]
(glucose-6-phosphate dehydrogenase groups)

Detection. Electrophoresis on starch gel or isoelectric focusing followed by multistage enzyme identification with formation of the dye formazan.

Chromosome model. 1 gene locus on the X chromosome with the frequent allele Gd^B, the alleles Gd^A, Gd^{B-} and Gd^{A-} together with over 100 further, very rare alleles.

Phenotypes and genotypes in men are listed in Table 2. In women, heterozygous phenotypes such as AB (2 bands), A− B (2 bands) or AA− (1 band) may occur, corresponding to the genotypes Gd^A/Gd^B, Gd^{A-}/Gd^B and Gd^A/Gd^{A-}.

Table 2 *Phenotypes and genotypes of the G6PD groups in men (for the genes Gd^B, Gd^A, Gd^{B-}, Gd^{A-})*

Starch-gel electrophoresis	Phenotype	Genotype	Occurrence	Relative activity
B bands	B (normal type)	Gd^B	All populations	100%
A bands	A	Gd^A	Blacks	80–100%
Weak B bands	B−	Gd^{B-}	Mediterranean peoples	0–7%
Weak A bands	A−	Gd^{A-}	Blacks	8–20%

Biological significance. The gene products of the *Gd* alleles may result in (a) normal, (b) reduced enzyme activity with hemolysis possibly induced by exogenous factors such as fava beans *(Vicia faba),* primaquine and many other drugs, or (c) reduced enzyme activity combined with chronic hemolytic disease. Girls heterozygous for G6PD deficiency – but not the hemizygous G6PD-deficient boys – enjoy a relative protection against *P. falciparum*[21].

ACP_1 groups[17,18,22-25]
(acid [erythrocyte] phosphatase groups)

Further ACP groups (ACP_2 and ACP_3 groups) occur in other cells and tissues, for instance in leukocytes and the placenta.

Detection. Electrophoresis (starch gel) followed by enzyme identification of the bands by addition of phenolphthalein diphosphate as substrate and of NH_4OH for coloration.

Chromosome model. 1 gene locus on chromosome 2 with the 3 frequent alleles P^A (0.34), P^B (0.61) and P^C (0.05)[26] together with at least 9 further, rare codominant alleles including the silent allele P^0.

Phenotypes and genotypes are summarized in Table 3.

Table 3 *Phenotypes and genotypes of the ACP_1 groups (for the alleles P^A, P^B, P^C)*

Starch-gel electrophoresis	Phenotype	Genotype	Frequency among the Swiss[26]
2 bands	A	P^A/P^A	10.8%
3 bands	AB	P^A/P^B	44.2%
3 bands	AC	P^A/P^C	3.0%
2 bands	B	P^B/P^B	35.6%
2 bands	BC	P^B/P^C	6.0%
2 bands	C	P^C/P^C	0.4%

Biological significance. The enzyme activities of the gene products of the alleles P^A, P^B and P^C differ in the proportions 2:3:4. P^0 heterozygotes exhibit half the enzyme activities of these alleles. The enzyme variants also differ in their resistance to heat. The frequencies of the individual alleles differ widely from one race to another.

6PGD groups[17,18,27,28]
(6-phosphogluconate dehydrogenase groups)

Detection. Electrophoresis (starch gel) followed by multistage enzyme identification with formation of the dye formazan.

Chromosome model. 1 gene locus on chromosome 1 with the 2 frequent alleles PGD^A (0.98) and PGD^C (0.02) (formerly PGD^B) together with a number of very rare alleles: $PGD^{Richmond}$, $PGD^{Freiburg}$, PGD^{Elcho}, PGD^{Kadar}, PGD^0, PGD^W *(Whitechapel)*, $PGD^{Thailand}$, $PGD^{Singapore}$, $PGD^{Wantoat}$, $PGD^{Canberra}$, $PGD^{Caspian}$, PGD^{Natal}, $PGD^{Makiritare}$.

Phenotypes and genotypes are summarized in Table 4.

*This chapter on 'Erythrocyte-Enzyme Groups' (pages 264–267) has been compiled by R. BÜTLER and R. SCHERZ, Zentrallaboratorium des Blutspendedienstes des Schweizerischen Roten Kreuzes, Berne, Switzerland (manuscript completed April 1983).

Table 4 *Phenotypes (for the alleles PGD^A and PGD^C) and genotypes of the 6PGD groups*

Starch-gel electrophoresis	Phenotype	Genotype	Relative activity
	Relatively frequent phenotypes		
1 band	PGD I	PGD^A/PGD^A	100%
3 bands	PGD II	PGD^A/PGD^C	80–100%
3 bands	PGD III	PGD^C/PGD^C	70–90%
	Very rare phenotypes		
	Hackney	PGD^A/PGD^H	100%
	Freiburg (Friendship)	PGD^A/PGD^F	100%
	Newham	PGD^C/PGD^0	40–50%
	Richmond	PGD^A/PGD^R	100%
	Whitechapel	PGD^W/PGD^W	1–5%
	Makiritare	PGD^A/PGD^M	
	Elcho	PGD^A/PGD^E	
	Ilford	PGD^A/PGD^0	50–60%
	Dalston	PGD^A/PGD^W	60–80%

Biological significance. Enzyme activities differ from one PGD type to another (Table 4).

PGM groups[17,18,29–31]
(phosphoglucomutase groups)

Detection. Isoelectric focusing in polyacrylamide or agarose gel followed by multistage enzyme identification with formation of the dye formazan. The bands of the PGM_1 groups appear in 2–4 main zones, those of the PGM_2 and PGM_3 groups likewise in several zones on the anodic side of the PGM_1 range. Erythrocytes contain only very small amounts of PGM_3 enzyme.

Chromosome model. 3 nonlinked gene loci (PGM_1 locus on chromosome 1; PGM_2 locus on chromosome 4; PGM_3 locus on chromosome 6). At the PGM_1 locus, the 4 frequent alleles[32] PGM_1^{a1} (0.63), PGM_1^{a2} (0.19), PGM_1^{a3} (0.13), PGM_1^{a4} (0.05) and at least 8 very rare alleles including the silent allele PGM_1^0. At the PGM_2 locus, the frequent allele PGM_2^1 and at least 12 rare alleles. At the PGM_3 locus, the alleles PGM_3^1, PGM_3^2 and PGM_3^3. The last-named allele has been found only in Oceanians.

The frequently occurring *phenotypes and genotypes* of the PGM_1 groups are summarized in Table 5.

Table 5 *Frequent phenotypes and genotypes of the PGM_1 groups*

Isoelectric focusing	Phenotype	Genotype	Frequency among the Swiss[32]
1 band	PGM_1a_1	PGM_1^{a1}/PGM_1^{a1}	40.4%
2 bands	$PGM_1a_2a_1$	PGM_1^{a2}/PGM_1^{a1}	23.0%
2 bands	$PGM_1a_3a_1$	PGM_1^{a3}/PGM_1^{a1}	16.4%
2 bands	$PGM_1a_4a_1$	PGM_1^{a4}/PGM_1^{a1}	5.5%
1 band	PGM_1a_2	PGM_1^{a2}/PGM_1^{a2}	3.5%
2 bands	$PGM_1a_3a_2$	PGM_1^{a3}/PGM_1^{a2}	6.2%
2 bands	$PGM_1a_4a_2$	PGM_1^{a4}/PGM_1^{a2}	2.4%
1 band	PGM_1a_3	PGM_1^{a3}/PGM_1^{a3}	1.0%
2 bands	$PGM_1a_4a_3$	PGM_1^{a4}/PGM_1^{a3}	1.4%
1 band	PGM_1a_4	PGM_1^{a4}/PGM_1^{a4}	0.2%

Biological significance. In the erythrocytes, phosphoglucomutase activity is shared about equally between the PGM_1 and PGM_2 enzymes. The PGM enzymes differ in their thermostability, with $PGM_2 > PGM_1 > PGM_3$. A genetically determined polymorphism of the PGM_1 enzymes in respect of thermostability has also been observed[33].

AK groups[17,18,31,34]
(adenylate kinase groups)

The AK_1 groups are present in the erythrocytes, while AK_2 and AK_3 occur in other cells and tissues. On account of its differing substrate specificity, AK_3 is also known as nucleoside triphosphate-adenylate kinase (2.7.4.10).

Detection. Electrophoresis (starch gel, agarose gel) followed by multistage enzyme identification with formation of the dye formazan.

Chromosome model. 3 gene loci (AK_1, AK_2, AK_3). At the AK_1 locus on chromosome 9, the 2 alleles[35] AK_1^1 (0.96) and AK_1^2 (0.04) together with at least 4 other, very rare alleles including the silent allele AK_1^0. The AK_1 locus is linked to that of both the AB0 blood groups and the nail-patella syndrome. AK_2 is located on chromosome 1, AK_3 on chromosome 9. Polymorphism of AK_2 or AK_3 has not so far been observed.

The frequently occurring *phenotypes and genotypes* of the AK_1 groups are summarized in Table 6.

Table 6 *Frequent phenotypes and genotypes of the AK_1 groups*

Starch-gel electrophoresis	Phenotype	Genotype	Frequency among the Swiss[35]
3 bands	$AK_1 1$	AK_1^1/AK_1^1	91.6%
4 bands	$AK_1 2\text{-}1$	AK_1^1/AK_1^2	8.2%
3 bands	$AK_1 2$	AK_1^2/AK_1^2	0.2%

Biological significance. Heterozygous carriers of AK_1^0 exhibit only half the normal activity of the AK_1 enzymes.

Gt groups[17,18,36,37]
(galactose-1-phosphate uridylyltransferase groups, GALT groups)

Detection. Electrophoresis (starch gel, agarose gel) or isoelectric focusing followed by multistage enzyme identification with formation of NADH, visualized either by its fluorescence under UV irradiation or by formation of the dye formazan.

Chromosome model. 1 gene locus on chromosome 9 with the alleles[37] Gt^1 (Gt^+) (0.92), Gt^2 (Gt^D, Gt^{Duarte}) (0.08), the very rare allele *gt* (galactosemia gene), and at least 4 further very rare alleles.

Phenotypes and genotypes of the frequent variants are summarized in Table 7.

Table 7 *Phenotypes and genotypes of the Gt groups (for the alleles Gt^1, Gt^2 and gt)*

Agarose-gel or starch-gel electrophoresis	Phenotype	Genotype	Relative activity	Frequency among the Swiss[37]
1 band	Gt1	Gt^1/Gt^1	100%	14.4%
2 bands	Gt2-1	Gt^1/Gt^2	~75%	15.1%
1 band	Gt2	Gt^2/Gt^2	~50%	0.5%
1 weak band	Gt1-0	Gt^1/gt	~50%	Rare
1 weak band	Gt2-0	Gt^2/gt	~25%	Rare
No band	Gt0	gt/gt	<1%	1:51000

Biological significance. Individuals of the genotype *gt/gt* suffer from galactosemia; those carrying the rare genotypes Gt^{Rennes} or Gt^{Negro} sometimes also show clinical manifestations. Heterozygotes of the genotype Gt^2gt react to galactose loading with an excessive elevation of the galactose-1-phosphate level of the cells, probably with clinical effects. Among the Swiss, the frequency of this constellation is circa 0.03%[38].

Pep groups[17,18,39]
(peptidase groups)

There are 7 recognized erythrocyte peptidases (PepA, PepB, PepC, PepD, PepE, PepF, PepS) differing in respect of substrate specificity, molecular size and electrophoretic mobility. Among Whites, there is a genetic polymorphism of the peptidase groups PepA and PepD, whereas, among Pygmies, polymorphism is found in the PepC group; variants of the PepB group, on the other hand, are extremely rare, and the remaining groups show no genetic polymorphism.

Chromosome model. 7 gene loci (*PepA* locus on chromosome 18; *PepB* locus on chromosome 12; *PepC* locus on chromosome 1; *PepD* locus on chromosome 19; *PepE* locus; *PepF* locus; *PepS* locus on chromosome 4). At the *PepA* locus, there are 9 alleles:

Table 8 *Phenotypes and genotypes of the PepA groups*[40]

Starch-gel electrophoresis	Phenotype	Genotype
1 band	PepA 1	$PepA^1/PepA^1$
3 bands	PepA 8-1	$PepA^1/PepA^8$
1 band	PepA 8	$PepA^8/PepA^8$
Among Whites, only the alleles $PepA^1$ and $PepA^8$ are frequent.		

Table 9 *Phenotypes and genotypes of the PepD groups (for the alleles* $PepD^1$ *and* $PepD^2$*)*

Starch-gel electrophoresis	Phenotype	Genotype
1 band	PepD 1	$PepD^1/PepD^1$
3 bands	PepD 2-1	$PepD^1/PepD^2$
1 band	PepD 2	$PepD^2/PepD^2$

$PepA^1$, $PepA^2$, $PepA^3$, $PepA^4$, $PepA^5$, $PepA^6$, $PepA^7$, $PepA^8$, $PepA^9$; at the *PepD* locus, there are 3 alleles: $PepD^1$, $PepD^2$ and $PepD^3$.

Phenotypes and genotypes are summarized in Tables 8 and 9.

Biological significance. The gene product of $PepA^8$ has a markedly lower enzyme activity than that of $PepA^1$.

ADA groups[18,41]
(adenosine deaminase groups)

Detection. Electrophoresis (on starch gel or cellulose-acetate film) followed by multistage enzyme identification with formation of the dye formazan.

Chromosome model. 1 gene locus on chromosome 20 with the 2 alleles[42] ADA^1 (0.94) and ADA^2 (0.06) together with at least 6 further, very rare alleles including the silent allele ADA^0.

Phenotypes and genotypes are summarized in Table 10.

Table 10 *Phenotypes and genotypes of the ADA groups (for the alleles* ADA^1 *and* ADA^2*)*

Starch-gel electrophoresis	Phenotype	Genotype	Frequency among the Swiss[42]
2 bands	ADA 1	ADA^1/ADA^1	88.2%
3 bands	ADA 2-1	ADA^1/ADA^2	11.6%
2 bands	ADA 2	ADA^2/ADA^2	0.2%

Biological significance. In heterozygous ADA^0 individuals, enzyme activity is reduced by a half, while ADA^0/ADA^0 homozygotes show no activity. Complete absence of ADA enzyme activity is associated with combination defects of the immune system.

The phenotypes differ in their resistance to heat, with ADA 1-1 > ADA 2-1 > ADA 2-2.

GPT groups[10,43,44]
(glutamic-pyruvic transaminase groups, alanine aminotransferase groups)

Detection. Starch-gel and polyacrylamide electrophoresis followed by multistage enzyme identification with formation of NAD (fluorescence extinction under UV light).

Chromosome model. 1 gene locus on chromosome 16 with the 2 frequent alleles[42] GPT^1 (0.51) and GPT^2 (0.49) together with at least 11 further, rare alleles[31,45–47] including the silent allele GPT^0 and the allele GPT^{1M} (Marburg variant).

Table 11 *Phenotypes and genotypes of the GPT groups (for the alleles* GPT^1, GPT^2 *and* GPT^3*)*

Starch-gel electrophoresis	Phenotype	Genotype	Frequency among the Swiss[42]
1 band	GPT 1	GPT^1/GPT^1	27.1%
3 bands	GPT 2-1	GPT^1/GPT^2	47.8%
1 band	GPT 2	GPT^2/GPT^2	24.8%
3 bands	GPT 3-1	GPT^1/GPT^3	0.1%
2 bands	GPT 3-2	GPT^2/GPT^3	0.2%

Phenotypes and genotypes are summarized in Table 11.

Biological significance. The enzyme activity of the GPT^1 gene product is noticeably higher than that of the GPT^2 or GPT^{1M} gene product. The latter cannot be distinguished from GPT^1 electrophoretically.

EsD groups[11]
(esterase D groups)

Other erythrocyte esterases (EsA, EsB, EsC) display only very rare variants.

Detection. Electrophoresis (starch gel, agarose gel) or isoelectric focusing with subsequent enzyme identification using 4-methylumbelliferyl acetate as substrate and visualization of the bands by fluorescence of the free 4-methylumbelliferone (UV light).

Chromosome model. 1 gene locus on chromosome 13 with the 2 relatively frequent codominant alleles[42] EsD^1 (0.87) and EsD^2 (0.13) together with at least 6 further, rare alleles including the silent allele EsD^0.

The frequently occurring *phenotypes and genotypes* are summarized in Table 12.

Table 12 *Frequent phenotypes and genotypes of the EsD groups*

Starch-gel electrophoresis	Phenotype	Genotype	Frequency among the Swiss[42]
2 bands	EsD 1	EsD^1/EsD^1	74.9%
4 bands	EsD 2-1	EsD^1/EsD^2	23.5%
2 bands	EsD 2	EsD^2/EsD^2	1.6%

UMPK groups[12,48,49]
(uridine-5-monophosphate kinase groups)

Detection. Starch-gel electrophoresis followed by multistage enzyme identification with formation of the dye formazan.

Chromosome model. 1 gene locus on chromosome 1 with the 2 relatively frequent alleles[49] $UMPK^1$ (0.96) and $UMPK^2$ (0.04) together with at least one further, very rare allele.

Phenotypes and genotypes are summarized in Table 13. The gene product of the allele $UMPK^2$ is considerably more labile than that of the allele $UMPK^1$, with the result that the bands of the allele $UMPK^1$ are much more clearly seen in the electrophoretic pattern than those of the allele $UMPK^2$.

Table 13 *Phenotypes and genotypes of the UMPK groups*

Starch-gel electrophoresis	Phenotype	Genotype
1 band	UMPK 1	$UMPK^1/UMPK^1$
2 bands	UMPK 2-1	$UMPK^1/UMPK^2$
1 band	UMPK 2	$UMPK^2/UMPK^2$

GLO groups[13,50–54]
(glyoxalase groups)

Detection. Electrophoresis (agarose gel, starch gel) followed by multistage enzyme identification with formation of formazan or starch-iodine coloration[50,52].

Chromosome model[51]. 1 gene locus on chromosome 6 with the 2 frequent alleles[50] GLO^1 (0.44) and GLO^2 (0.56) together with the very rare allele GLO^3. In addition, an allele GLO^0 with a gene product lacking enzyme activity has been described[53].

The frequently occurring *phenotypes and genotypes* of the GLO groups are summarized in Table 14.

Biological significance. The *GLO* gene locus is in the neighborhood of the genes of the histocompatibility antigens[48].

Table 14 *Frequent phenotypes and genotypes of the GLO groups*

Agarose-gel electrophoresis	Phenotype	Genotype	Frequency among the Swiss[50]
1 band	GLO 1	GLO^1/GLO^1	19.4%
3 bands	GLO 2-1	GLO^1/GLO^2	49.9%
1 band	GLO 2	GLO^2/GLO^2	30.7%

PGP groups[14, 55]
(phosphoglycolate phosphatase groups)

Detection. Agarose-gel electrophoresis followed by identification making use of specific coloration of the enzyme, whereby phosphate liberated from the phosphoglycolate forms molybdenum blue with ammonium molybdate.

Chromosome model. 1 gene locus on chromosome 16 with the 3 relatively frequent alleles[55] PGP^1 (0.89), PGP^2 (0.09) and PGP^3 (0.02).

Phenotypes and genotypes of the PGP groups are summarized in Table 15.

Table 15 *Phenotypes and genotypes of the PGP groups*

Agarose-gel electrophoresis	Phenotype	Genotype	Frequency among the Swiss[54]
1 band	PGP 1	PGP^1/PGP^1	79.45%
3 bands	PGP 2-1	PGP^1/PGP^2	14.89%
3 bands	PGP 3-1	PGP^1/PGP^3	4.0%
1 band	PGP 2	PGP^2/PGP^2	1.22%
3 bands	PGP 3-2	PGP^2/PGP^3	0.44%
1 band	PGP 3	PGP^3/PGP^3	0

ALADH groups[15, 56]
(5-aminolevulinate dehydratase groups)

Detection. Horizontal starch-gel electrophoresis followed by enzyme identification in the bands with formation of porphobilinogen[56].

Chromosome model. 1 gene locus with the 2 alleles[15] $ALADH^1$ (0.89) and $ALADH^2$ (0.11). Other alleles have not so far been observed.

The frequently occurring *phenotypes and genotypes* of the ALADH groups are summarized in Table 16. The band of the heterozygotic type ALADH 2-1 migrates in the electrophoretic field between the bands of the homozygous types but is somewhat elliptic. Under optimum conditions, 2 bands are recognizable. It should also be noted that the enzyme is extremely labile.

Table 16 *Phenotypes and genotypes of the ALADH groups*

Starch-gel electrophoresis	Phenotype	Genotype
1 band	ALADH 1	$ALADH^1/ALADH^1$
1 band	ALADH 2-1	$ALADH^1/ALADH^2$
1 band	ALADH 2	$ALADH^2/ALADH^2$

References

1 BOYER et al., *Proc. nat. Acad. Sci. (Wash.)*, **48**, 1868 (1962).
2 HOPKINSON et al., *Nature*, **199**, 969 (1963).
3 FILDES and PARR, *Nature*, **200**, 890 (1963).
4 SPENCER et al., *Nature*, **204**, 742 (1964).
5 FILDES and HARRIS, *Nature*, **209**, 261 (1966).
6 MATHAI and BEUTLER, *Science*, **154**, 1179 (1966).
7 LEWIS and HARRIS, *Nature*, **215**, 351 (1967).
8 SPENCER et al., *Ann. hum. Genet.*, **32**, 9 (1968/9).
9 LEWIS and HARRIS, *Ann. hum. Genet.*, **32**, 317 (1968/9).
10 CHEN and GIBLETT, *Science*, **173**, 148 (1971).
11 HOPKINSON et al., *Ann. hum. Genet.*, **37**, 119 (1973).
12 GIBLETT et al., *Amer. J. hum. Genet.*, **26**, 627 (1974).
13 KÖMPF et al., *Hum. Genet.*, **27**, 141 (1975).
14 BARKER and HOPKINSON, *Ann. hum. Genet.*, **42**, 143 (1978).
15 BATTISTUZZI et al., *Ann. hum. Genet.*, **45**, 223 (1981).
16 HOPKINSON, D.A., *Postgrad. med. J.*, **52**, suppl. 2, 59 (1976); GIBLETT, E.R., *Ann. Rev. Genet.*, **11**, 13 (1977).
17 GIBLETT, E.R., *Genetic Markers in Human Blood*, Blackwell, Oxford, 1969.
18 BECKMAN, G., in BROCK and MAYO (Eds.), *The Biochemical Genetics of Man*, 2nd ed., Academic Press, London, 1978, page 186.
19 FLATZ and XIROTIRIS, in BECKER, P.E. (Ed.), *Humangenetik*, volume I/3, Thieme, Stuttgart, 1975, page 494.
20 MODIANO et al., *Proc. nat. Acad. Sci. (Wash.)*, **76**, 852 (1979).
21 LUZZATTO et al., *Ciba Found. Symp.*, **94**, 159 (1983).
22 WALTER and ANANTHAKRISHNAN, in BECKER, P.E. (Ed.), *Humangenetik*, volume I/3, Thieme, Stuttgart, 1975, page 352.
23 YOSHIHARA and MOHRENWEISER, *Amer. J. hum. Genet.*, **32**, 898 (1981).
24 MOHRENWEISER and NOVOTNY, *Amer. J. hum. Genet.*, **34**, 425 (1982).
25 RADAM et al., *Ärztl. Lab.*, **28**, 88 (1982).
26 PFLUGSHAUPT et al., *Hum. Genet.*, **8**, 354 (1970).
27 ANANTHAKRISHNAN, R., in BECKER, P.E. (Ed.), *Humangenetik*, volume I/3, Thieme, Stuttgart, 1975, page 536.
28 BLAKE et al., *Hum. Genet.*, **21**, 347 (1974).
29 WALTER and ANANTHAKRISHNAN, in BECKER, P.E. (Ed.), *Humangenetik*, volume I/3, Thieme, Stuttgart, 1975, page 426.
30 PHILIP et al., *J. Génét. hum.*, **27**, 81 (1979).
31 SPIELMANN and KÜHNL, *Blutgruppenkunde*, Thieme, Stuttgart, 1982.
32 SCHERZ et al., *Hum. Hered.*, **31**, 187 (1981).
33 SCOZZARI et al., *Ann. hum. Genet.*, **45**, 313 (1981).
34 WALTER and ANANTHAKRISHNAN, in BECKER, P.E. (Ed.), *Humangenetik*, volume I/3, Thieme, Stuttgart, 1975, page 445.
35 PFLUGSHAUPT et al., *Hum. Genet.*, **12**, 167 (1971).
36 ANANTHAKRISHNAN and WALTER, in BECKER, P.E. (Ed.), *Humangenetik*, volume I/3, Thieme, Stuttgart, 1975, page 578.
37 STUCKI, M., *Untersuchungen an genetischen Varianten der Galactose-1-phosphaturidyltransferase*, Inauguraldissertation, Berne, 1982.
38 SCHWARZ et al., *J. Pediat.*, **100**, 704 (1982).
39 ANANTHAKRISHNAN, R., in BECKER, P.E. (Ed.), *Humangenetik*, volume I/3, Thieme, Stuttgart, 1975, page 393.
40 LEWIS, W.H., *Ann. hum. Genet.*, **36**, 267 (1973).
41 WALTER and ANANTHAKRISHNAN, in BECKER, P.E. (Ed.), *Humangenetik*, volume I/3, Thieme, Stuttgart, 1975, page 549.
42 PFLUGSHAUPT et al., *Hum. Hered.*, **26**, 161 (1976).
43 ANANTHAKRISHNAN and WALTER, in BECKER, P.E. (Ed.), *Humangenetik*, volume I/3, Thieme, Stuttgart, 1975, page 591.
44 KÖMPF and RITTER, *Hum. Genet.*, **51**, 287 (1979).
45 OLAISEN, B., *Hum. Genet.*, **19**, 289 (1973).
46 SANTACHIARA-BENERECETTI et al., *Hum. Hered.*, **25**, 276 (1975).
47 MCLELLAN, T., *Amer. J. hum. Genet.*, **34**, 623 (1982).
48 TENG et al., *Amer. J. hum. Genet.*, **28**, 138 (1976).
49 KUHN et al., *Hum. Genet.*, **28**, 255 (1975).
50 PFLUGSHAUPT et al., *Hum. Hered.*, **28**, 235 (1978).
51 KAVATHAS and DEMARS, *Amer. J. hum. Genet.*, **33**, 935 (1981).
52 PARR et al., *Biochem. Genet.*, **15**, 109 (1977).
53 RITTNER and WEBER, *Hum. Genet.*, **42**, 315 (1978).
54 WEITKAMP and LAMM, *Cytogenet. Cell Genet.*, **32**, 130 (1982).
55 SCHERZ et al., *Forens. Sci. Int.*, **18**, 267 (1981).
56 GRANICK and MAUZERALL, *J. biol. Chem.*, **232**, 1119 (1958).

Table 1 *Serum groups (summary)*

Serum protein	Serum groups	Detection	Discoverer
Albumin	Alloalbuminemia	Electrophoretic	KNEDEL, 1957[1]
α_1-Acid glycoprotein (orosomucoid)	Or groups	Electrophoretic	SCHMID et al., 1962[2]
α_1-Antitrypsin	Pi groups	Isoelectric focusing	LAURELL, 1965[3]
Haptoglobin	Hp groups	Electrophoretic	SMITHIES, 1955[4]
Gc-Globulin	Gc groups	Isoelectric focusing	HIRSCHFELD, 1959[5]
α_2-Macroglobulin	Xm groups	Immunologic	BERG and BEARN, 1966[6]
Ceruloplasmin	Cp groups	Electrophoretic	SHREFFLER et al., 1967[7]
LDL and VLDL ([very-]low-density lipoprotein)	Ag groups	Immunologic	ALLISON and BLUMBERG, 1961[8]
	Lp groups	Immunologic	BERG, 1963[9]
Apolipoprotein E	Apo-E groups	Electrophoretic	UTERMANN et al., 1977[10]
Transferrin	Tf groups	Electrophoretic	SMITHIES, 1957[11]
Plasminogen	PLG groups	Isoelectric focusing	HOBART, 1979[12]; RAUM et al., 1979[13]
Coagulation factor XIII (subunit A)	F XIII A groups	Electrophoretic	BOARD, 1979[14]
Coagulation factor XIII (subunit B)	F XIII B groups	Electrophoretic	BOARD, 1979[14]
Transcobalamin II	TC II groups	Electrophoretic	DAIGER et al., 1978[15]
Complement factor B	Bf groups	Electrophoretic	ALPER et al., 1972[16]
Complement component 2	C2 groups	Isoelectric focusing	HOBART and LACHMANN, 1976[17]; ALPER, 1976[18]
Complement component 3	C3 groups	Electrophoretic	ALPER and PROPP, 1968[19]
Complement component 4	C4 groups	Electrophoretic	ROSENFELD, 1969[20]
Complement component 6	C6 groups	Electrophoretic	HOBART and LACHMANN, 1974[21]
Complement component 7	C7 groups	Isoelectric focusing	HOBART and LACHMANN, 1976[22]
Complement component 8	C8 groups	Isoelectric focusing	ALPER, 1979[23]; RAUM et al., 1979[24]
IgG	Gm groups	Immunologic	GRUBB and LAURELL, 1956[25]
	Km groups	Immunologic	ROPARTZ, 1960[26]
IgA	A_2m groups	Immunologic	VYAS and FUDENBERG, 1969[27]; KUNKEL et al., 1969[28]
	Km groups	Immunologic	ROPARTZ, 1960[26]
IgM	Km groups	Immunologic	ROPARTZ, 1960[26]
Alkaline phosphatase	Alkaline phosphatase groups	Electrophoretic	ARFORS et al., 1963[29]
Cholinesterase (pseudocholinesterase)	Pseudocholinesterase groups	Enzymatic	KALOW and STARON, 1957[30]

Serum groups are group-specific, genetically determined properties of the serum (or plasma) proteins (genetic protein polymorphism), whereby as a rule the various molecular variants of the serum protein concerned exhibit 'normal' biological activity. In certain serum-group systems (for instance the Pi system, pseudocholinesterase groups), however, some of the protein variants display altered biological activity. In the normal way, a serum-group system is controlled genetically by alleles, i.e. from a single gene locus, though in exceptional cases this function is exercised by genes that are very close neighbors (linked genes) [examples are the Gm groups of IgG, the Ag groups of LDL (low-density lipoproteins)]. Some serum proteins possess more than one serum-group system (for instance the Gm and Km groups of IgG).

Serum groups in which the molecular variants differ in their antigenic structure are also called 'allotypes'. Detection of these allotypic serum groups is based on immunologic reactions. In other serum groups the protein variants show no detectable antigenic differences; detection of these groups makes use of other criteria (such as differences in molecular size and/or electric charge) amenable to physicochemical procedures (for instance starch-gel electrophoresis).

The most important serum-group systems are summarized in Table 1.

In the chromosome models the alleles – when not otherwise specified – are always of the autosomal codominant type.

Unless otherwise stated, data on gene frequencies refer to white populations; figures in brackets are estimates or approximate mean values derived from the literature quoted for the serum group concerned.

Alloalbuminemia[31–34]

Detection by all electrophoretic methods, particularly vertical starch-gel electrophoresis[31]. The albumin appears as a single band in over 99.9% of Europeans. In the remainder it appears as 2 bands (bisalbuminemia); faster and slower migrating variants are known. Some types of alloalbuminemia have been studied by the isoelectric focusing method[35]. The first electrophoretic observations of bisalbuminemia were interpreted as pathological serum-protein patterns ('α_1-paraproteinemia'); alloalbuminemia is not, however, a pathological condition but the expression of a serum-group system. Note that in addition there are rare, acquired, usually drug-induced and transitory types of bisalbuminemia.

Chromosome model. 1 gene locus (probably the structural gene locus of the albumin) with the very frequent allele *A* and over 20 very rare codominant alleles. This gene locus is closely linked to the *Gc* locus.

Phenotypes and genotypes of alloalbuminemia are summarized in Table 2. Three dimeric variants are known in addition to the over 20 monomeric types.

Table 2 *Phenotypes and genotypes of alloalbuminemia*

Electrophoresis	Phenotype	Genotype
1 band	'Normal type'	*A/A*
2 bands (one faster than the normal type)	At least 6, all rare	*A/**
2 bands (one slower than the normal type)	At least 14, all rare	*A/**

* Indicates a rare allele.

Or groups[33, 36–39]
(orosomucoid groups, groups of the α_1-acid glycoprotein)

Detection. Agarose electrophoresis of neuraminidase-treated serum followed by visualization of the orosomucoid bands by immunofixation[37].

*This chapter on 'Serum Groups' (pages 268–275) has been compiled by R. BÜTLER, Zentrallaboratorium des Blutspendedienstes des Schweizerischen Roten Kreuzes, Berne, Switzerland (manuscript completed April 1983).

Table 3 *Phenotypes and genotypes of the Or groups*

Electrophoresis	Phenotype*	Genotype
1 F band and 1 incipient S band	Or FF (Or F)	Or^F/Or^F
1 F band and 1 S band	Or FS	Or^F/Or^S
1 S band and 1 incipient F band	Or SS (Or S)	Or^S/Or^S

*F (for fast) and S (for slow) refer to electrophoretic mobility.

Chromosome model. 1 gene locus on chromosome 9 with 2 alleles, Or^F (0.54) and Or^S (0.46).

Phenotypes and genotypes of the Or groups are summarized in Table 3.

Pi groups[33, 36, 38, 40–46]
(protease-inhibitor groups, α_1-antitrypsin groups)

Detection by high-resolution isoelectric focusing in polyacrylamide gel[33, 42, 43, 45] narrow pH range of 4–5, with or without subsequent immunofixation.

Chromosome model. 1 gene locus on chromosome 14 with the 3 fairly common alleles Pi^{M1} (0.74), Pi^{M2} (0.15), Pi^{M3} (0.08) and 2 rarer alleles, Pi^S (0.02) and Pi^Z (0.01), together with about 40 other very rare alleles including the silent gene Pi^0. The *Pi* locus is closely linked to the *Gm* locus.

Phenotypes and genotypes of the Pi groups are summarized in Table 4. The number of bands identifiable by isoelectric focusing varies with the experimental conditions.

Table 4 *Phenotypes and genotypes of the Pi groups*

Isoelectric focusing	Phenotype	Genotype
3–5 bands	Pi M1 M1 (Pi M1)	Pi^{M1}/Pi^{M1}
6–10 bands	Pi M1 M2	Pi^{M1}/Pi^{M2}
6–10 bands	Pi M1 M3	Pi^{M1}/Pi^{M3}
>6 bands	Pi M1 R	$Pi^{M1}/*$
3–5 bands	Pi M2 M2 (Pi M2)	Pi^{M2}/Pi^{M2}
6–10 bands	Pi M2 M3	Pi^{M2}/Pi^{M3}
>6 bands	Pi M2 R	$Pi^{M2}/*$
3–5 bands	Pi M3 M3 (Pi M3)	Pi^{M3}/Pi^{M3}
>6 bands	Pi M3 R	$Pi^{M3}/*$
Varying numbers of bands	Pi R R	*/*

*Indicates a rare allele; R (= rare variant) indicates the corresponding gene product.

Biological significance. The gene products of the rare alleles Pi^S, Pi^Z and Pi^P show reduced α_1-antitrypsin activity while the Pi^0 gene product has no detectable activity of this kind. Pi^Z/Pi^Z and Pi^Z/Pi^0 individuals have less than 15% of the normal α_1-antitrypsin activity. Clinically, this α_1-antitrypsin deficiency can be manifested in the following disorders[48]: bronchopulmonary symptoms up to panlobular emphysema; hepatic symptoms ranging from portal fibrosis to cirrhosis and possibly hepatoma. The pulmonary and hepatic symptoms can occur either separately or in combination. Heterozygous Pi^Z or Pi^0 carriers can show the same symptoms in weaker form.

Hp groups[36, 38, 49–52]
(haptoglobin groups)

Detection of the classical Hp groups[49]. Starch-gel electrophoresis at pH 8.4 demonstrates 3 haptoglobin band patterns. Detection is made easier by addition of hemoglobin to the serum prior to electrophoretic separation with consequent saturation of the haptoglobin with hemoglobin; as a result of their peroxidase activity, coloration of the Hp-Hb complexes with benzidine is possible.

Detection of the Hp subtypes. 2 types of polypeptide chain (α and β chains) can be demonstrated in all Hp groups by reductive treatment of the isolated haptoglobin with α-mercaptoethanol in urea solution (8 mol/L). In starch-gel electrophoresis at acid pH, 3 subtypes of the Hp 1-1 groups and 2 subtypes of the Hp 2-1 groups can be recognized. Hp polymorphism is a result of structural variations in the α chains.

Phenotypes and genotypes of the classical Hp groups and their subtypes are summarized in Tables 5 and 6.

Table 5 *Phenotypes and genotypes of the classical Hp groups*

Starch-gel electrophoresis	Phenotype	Genotype	Frequency among the Swiss[53]
1 Hp 1 band..................	Hp 1-1	Hp^1/Hp^1	15.5%
1 Hp 1 band and 5 or 6 Hp 2 bands*......................	Hp 2-1	Hp^1/Hp^2	49.5%
5 or 6 Hp 2 bands*...........	Hp 2-2	Hp^2/Hp^2	35.0%

*The multiple bands of types Hp 2-1 and Hp 2-2 are attributable to the formation of polymers of the gene product of Hp^2.

Table 6 *Phenotypes and genotypes of the Hp subtypes*

Electrophoresis	Polypeptide chains	Phenotype*	Genotype
1 β band .... 1 α band	β chains α_1-F chains	Hp 1F-1F	Hp^{1F}/Hp^{1F}
1 β band .... 2 α bands	β chains α_1-F chains α_1-S chains	Hp 1F-1S	Hp^{1F}/Hp^{1S}
1 β band .... 1 α band	β chains α_1-S chains	Hp 1S-1S	Hp^{1S}/Hp^{1S}
1 β band .... 2 α bands	β chains α_1-F chains α_2 chains	Hp 2-1F (Hp 2FS-1F)	Hp^{1F}/Hp^{2FS}
1 β band .... 2 α bands	β chains α_1-S chains α_2 chains	Hp 2-1S (Hp 2FS-1S)	Hp^{1S}/Hp^{2FS}
1 β band .... 1 α band	β chains α_2 chains	Hp 2-2 (Hp 2FS-2FS)	Hp^{2FS}/Hp^{2FS}

*F (for fast) and S (for slow) refer to electrophoretic mobility of the α_1 polypeptide chains.

Rare quantitative variants[36]. These arise from the action of a modified *Hp* gene (or of a modifying gene) resulting in a quantitative reduction in an α-chain type or a change in the polymerizing capacity of α_1 chains with α_2 chains. Hp 2-1 mod. types (Hp 2-1M types) are characterized by a reduction in the intensity of the Hp 2 bands, Hp Ca (Hp Carlberg) by an increase in the number of α_1 chains. Other quantitative variants are Hp 2-1 (trans) and Hp 2-1 (Haw). Hypo- or ahaptoglobinemia (phenotype Hp 0) of genetic origin can occur through the presence of the gene Hp^0, even in the heterozygous condition.

Rare qualitative (structural) variants. These can involve either the α or β chains. α-Chain variants include Hp 1-J and Hp 2-J (Johnson types, originating from the nonhomologous crossing-over of 2 Hp^2 genes), Hp 1-B and Hp 2-B (Ba types), and Hp 2-1D. β-Chain variants are Hp 1Mb and Hp 2-1Mb (Marburg types) together with Hp 1-1Be, Hp 2-1Be and Hp 2-2Be (Bellevue types). Other presumably β-chain variants are Hp 1-P, Hp 2-P, Hp 1-H, Hp 2-H, Hp 2-L and Hp Ab.

Chromosome model[36]. The α-chain gene locus (*Hp* locus, Hp_α locus) has 3 frequently occurring codominant alleles: Hp^{1F}, Hp^{1S} and Hp^2 (Hp^{2FS}); rare alleles are Hp^{2FF}, Hp^{2SS}, Hp^{2M}, Hp^0, Hp^H and Hp^{1D}. The β-chain gene locus (*Bp* locus, Hp_β locus) is not closely linked to the α-chain gene locus; it has a very frequent gene (Bp^A) together with very rare codominant alleles which code for the β-chain variants.

Biological significance[36]. The haptoglobin level is higher in Hp 1-1 individuals than in Hp 2-1 or Hp 2-2 individuals. Hp 1-1 molecules pass the glomerular membrane more easily, however, than Hp 2-1 or Hp 2-2 molecules. Hypo- or ahaptoglobinemia can be due not only to the gene Hp^0 but also to the gene Hp^{2M}.

Gc groups[33, 36, 38, 42, 49, 54–56]
(group-specific component groups, Gc-globulin groups)

Detection of the 'classical' Gc groups by immunoelectrophoresis with monospecific anti-Gc-globulin serum or a polyspecific antiserum allowing recognition not only of Gc-globulin but also of a few other serum proteins whose precipitation lines can serve as guidelines. The Gc type can be confirmed by the immunoelectrophoresis verification test[57]. The 'classical' Gc groups can also be demonstrated by electrophoresis using starch gel or polyacrylamide gel.

Detection of the 'expanded' Gc system by isoelectric focusing in polyacrylamide or agarose gel with subsequent immunofixation. This enables the 'classical' Gc 1-1 type to be divided into 3 and the Gc 2-1 type into 2 subtypes. The band pattern can be altered by neuraminidase treatment of the serum.

Phenotypes and genotypes of the 'classical' Gc groups and the 'expanded' Gc system are summarized in Tables 7 and 8.

Table 7 *Phenotypes and genotypes of the 'classical' Gc groups*

Immunoelectrophoresis	Phenotype	Genotype	Frequency among the Swiss[53]
1 precipitation arc in the anodic range	Gc1-1	Gc^1/Gc^1	56.0%
1 double precipitation arc	Gc2-1	Gc^1/Gc^2	37.4%
1 precipitation arc in the cathodic range	Gc2-2	Gc^2/Gc^2	6.6%

Table 8 *Phenotypes and genotypes of the 'expanded' Gc system*◊

Isoelectric focusing	Phenotype†	Genotype
2 bands	Gc1F-1F	Gc^{1F}/Gc^{1F}
4 bands	Gc1F-1S	Gc^{1F}/Gc^{1S}
2 bands	Gc1S-1S	Gc^{1S}/Gc^{1S}
3 bands	Gc2-1F	Gc^{1F}/Gc^2
3 bands	Gc2-1S	Gc^{1S}/Gc^2
1 band	Gc2-2	Gc^2/Gc^2
1-3 bands	Gc1F-R	$Gc^{1F}/*$
	Gc1S-R	$Gc^{1S}/*$
	Gc2-R	$Gc^2/*$
	GcR-R	*/*

◊Without neuraminidase treatment of the serum.
†F (for fast) and S (for slow) refer to electrophoretic mobility.
*Indicates a rare allele; R (= rare variant) indicates the corresponding gene product.

Chromosome model. 1 gene locus on chromosome 4 with the 3 frequent alleles Gc^{1F} (0.16), Gc^{1S} (0.57) and Gc^2 (0.27) together with over 30 other very rare alleles. The *Gc* locus is linked to the alloalbuminemia locus.

Xm groups[36, 38]
(X-chromosomally controlled antigen of the α_2-macroglobulin)

Detection. Immune double-diffusion test in agar gel (Ouchterlony's test) with absorbed rabbit antihuman serum.

Chromosome model. 1 gene locus of the X chromosome with 1 dominant gene Xm^a and 1 silent allele $Xm^{\cdot}$.

Phenotypes and genotypes of the Xm groups are summarized in Table 9.

Table 9 *Phenotypes and genotypes of the Xm groups*

Phenotype	Genotype
Xm(a +)	Xm^a/Xm^a or $Xm^a/Xm^{\cdot}$
Xm(a −)	$Xm^{\cdot}/Xm^{\cdot}$

Cp groups[33, 36, 38, 58]
(ceruloplasmin groups)

Detection. After separation by starch-gel electrophoresis at pH 9.4, the ceruloplasmin bands are colored specifically on the basis of their oxidase activity (for instance with orthodiaminoanisidine). The Cp groups can also be detected by agarose-gel electrophoresis and subsequent visualization of the Cp bands by immunofixation.

Chromosome model. 1 gene locus with the frequent allele Cp^B (over 0.99) or one of the approximately 4 known, very rare alleles.

Phenotypes and genotypes of the Cp groups are summarized in Table 10.

Table 10 *Phenotypes and genotypes of the Cp groups*[36]

Starch-gel electrophoresis	Phenotype	Genotype
1 band	Cp B ('normal type')	Cp^B/Cp^B
1 band for homozygous types, and 2 bands for heterozygous types	Rare	$Cp^B/*$ or */*

*Indicates a rare gene.

Ag groups[59-62]
('antigen' groups of LDL)

Detection by passive hemagglutination inhibition with human immune sera and erythrocytes coated with purified LDL of a suitable phenotype. For monospecific detection systems, use can also be made of polyspecific immune sera. Another method suitable for monospecific immune sera of precipitating type is immune double diffusion in agar gel (Ouchterlony's test).

The *Ag factors* are listed in Table 11.

Table 11 *Ag factors (Ag antigens)*

Factor	Frequency among the Swiss[61]
Ag(a_1)	72.1%
Ag(c)	51.4%
Ag(d)	75.7%
Ag(g)	90.3%
Ag(h)	16.9%
Ag(i)	98.3%
Ag(t)	95.9%
Ag(x)[Ld(a)]	39.5%
Ag(y)	96.7%
Ag(z)	37.8%

Chromosome model[60, 61]. 5 closely linked *Ag* loci each with 2 codominant alleles: Ag^x–Ag^y, Ag^{a_1}–Ag^d, Ag^c–Ag^g, Ag^t–Ag^z, Ag^h–Ag^i.

Phenotypes. So far 51 phenotypes have been observed. Those occurring with the highest frequency among Whites are listed in Table 12.

Table 12 *Frequent phenotypes of the Ag groups*

Phenotype	Frequency among the Swiss[61]
Ag(x + y + a_1 + d + c + g + t + z − h − i +)	7.4%
Ag(x + y + a_1 + d + c − g + t + z − h − i +)	8.8%
Ag(x + y + a_1 + d − c − g + t + z + h − i +)	9.6%
Ag(x − y + a_1 + d + c + g + t + z + h − i +)	6.9%
Ag(x − y + a_1 + d + c − g + t + z + h − i +)	7.2%
Ag(x − y + a_1 − d + c + g + t + z − h − i +)	10.2%
Ag(x − y + a_1 − d + c + g − t + z − h − i +)	5.0%
Ag(x − y + a_1 − d + c − g + t + z − h − i +)	4.7%

Biological significance. Ag antibodies are formed almost exclusively by post-transfusional alloimmunization in patients who have undergone multiple transfusions, particularly those with Cooley's anemia; as a rule they do not cause transfusion reactions.

Lp groups[9, 36, 38, 62]
(lipoprotein groups of the pre-β_1-lipoprotein closely related to LDL)

Detection by immune double diffusion in agar gel (Ouchterlony's test) with absorbed rabbit antihuman LDL serum[9]. More sensitive methods reveal a higher proportion of Lp(a +) phenotypes. Even Lp(a −) individuals possess very small amounts of Lp(a) protein[63].

Chromosome model. The dominant gene Lp^a probably does not code for a qualitative characteristic; it is more likely that one of the various alleles is responsible for regulation of the concentration of the 'Lp(a) protein', or pre-β_1-lipoprotein, with dominance of regulation of the higher concentrations over that of the lower ones[64].

Phenotypes and genotypes of the Lp groups are summarized in Table 13.

Table 13 *Phenotypes and genotypes of the Lp groups*[9]

Phenotype	Genotype
Lp(a +)	Lp^a/Lp^a or $Lp^a/Lp^{\cdot}$
Lp(a −)	$Lp^{\cdot}/Lp^{\cdot}$

$Lp^{\cdot}$ stands for a silent allele or for an allele coding for low concentrations of Lp(a) protein.

Biological significance. Lp(a +) individuals appear to have rather high cholesterol levels and a significantly greater tendency to develop coronary disease[65–67]. There is moreover a possible genetic correlation with the HLA system[68].

Apo-E groups[10,69–72]
(apolipoprotein-E groups)

Detection either by isoelectric focusing in polyacrylamide gel of the isolated apo-E prepared from purified serum VLDL or by two-dimensional polyacrylamide-gel electrophoresis.

Chromosome model. 1 gene locus (the structural gene locus of apo-E) with the 3 alleles *ε 4* (0.13), *ε 3* (0.75) and *ε 2* (0.12).

Phenotypes and genotypes. The gene products of the 3 apo-E alleles, as revealed by two-dimensional polyacrylamide-gel electrophoresis, consist of 1 (in homozygous individuals) or 2 (in heterozygous individuals) major (asialo) isoproteins, designated apoE-4, apoE-3 and apoE-2, as well as of a number of minor isoproteins containing sialic acid (named apoE-4_{s1}, apoE-4_{s2}, apoE-4_{s3}, etc.). 6 phenotypes can be distinguished, corresponding to the 6 genotypes *E 4/4, E 4/3, E 4/2, E 3/3, E 3/2* and *E 2/2*.

Biological significance. A very strong but not invariate association exists between type-III hyperlipoproteinemia and the apoE phenotype E 2/2 with some type-III HLP individuals having the apoE phenotype E 4/2[73]. Additional correlations between apo-E groups and dyslipoproteinemia have been described[74].

Tf groups[36,38,42,75–80]
(transferrin groups)

Detection by isoelectric focusing in polyacrylamide or agarose gel (PAGIF) with or without addition of Fe^{3+} until the transferrin is saturated; the Tf bands can be specifically visualized by immunofixation. Also recommended is double unidimensional electrophoresis; here immunofixation can be dispensed with on account of the reduced band pattern[77].

Chromosome model. 1 gene locus on chromosome 3 with the 3 frequent alleles Tf^{C1} (0.78), Tf^{C2} (0.15) and Tf^{C3} (0.06) as well as some 25 further, rare or very rare alleles (of the Tf^C, Tf^B and Tf^D series).

Phenotypes and genotypes of the Tf groups are summarized in Table 14. The specific Tf band pattern depends on the degree of Fe^{3+} saturation[78].

Table 14 *Phenotypes and genotypes of the Tf groups*

Isoelectric focusing◊	Phenotype	Genotype
1 band	TfC 1-1	Tf^{C1}/Tf^{C1}
2 bands	TfC 2-1	Tf^{C1}/Tf^{C2}
2 bands	TfC 3-1	Tf^{C1}/Tf^{C3}
1 band	TfC 2-2	Tf^{C2}/Tf^{C2}
2 bands	TfC 3-2	Tf^{C2}/Tf^{C3}
1 band	TfC 3-3	Tf^{C3}/Tf^{C3}
2 bands	TfC 1-R	$Tf^{C1}/*$
2 bands	TfC 3-R	$Tf^{C3}/*$
Various patterns	TfR-R	*/*

◊Patterns of the 'main bands' in the PAGIF according to Kühnl[42].
*Indicates a rare allele; R (= rare variant) indicates the corresponding gene product.

PLG groups[12,13,81,82]
(plasminogen groups)

Detection. Thin-layer isoelectric focusing in polyacrylamide gel in the pH range 3.5–10, followed by immunofixation or application of an enzymatic detection method in which the plasminogen is converted into plasmin by streptokinase or urokinase. The plasmin is visualized by dousing the gel with an agar solution containing casein or fibrin, whereby clear zones appear as a result of lysis of the high-molecular proteins. The polymorphism can also be demonstrated in plasma or serum treated with neuraminidase.

Chromosome model. 1 gene locus on chromosome 4 with the 2 frequent alleles PLG^1 (0.69) and PLG^2 (0.30) as well as a number of rare genes. PLG^1 and PLG^2 are also designated $PLGN^A$ and $PLGN^B$.

Phenotypes and genotypes of the PLG groups are summarized in Table 15. The number of identifiable bands depends on whether native or neuraminidase-treated plasminogen is being studied.

Table 15 *Phenotypes and genotypes of the PLG groups*

Isoelectric focusing		Phenotype	Genotype
Native plasminogen	Neuraminidase-treated plasminogen		
≤ 10 bands ...	3 bands	PLG 1-1	PLG^1/PLG^1
12 bands......	4 bands	PLG 2-1	PLG^1/PLG^2
10 bands......	3 bands	PLG 2-2	PLG^2/PLG^2

F XIII A groups[14,83,84]
(coagulation factor XIII [subunit A] groups)

Detection. Thin-layer agarose-gel electrophoresis followed by immunofixation or detection of glutaminyl-peptide γ-glutamyltransferase activity using monodansylcadaverine-coupled casein in the fluorescence test. The polymorphism can also be demonstrated by isoelectric focusing.

Chromosome model. 1 gene locus with the 2 frequent alleles $FXIIIA^1$ (0.79) and $FXIIIA^2$ (0.21) together with the rare alleles $FXIIIA^3$ and $FXIIIA^4$ and a silent allele $FXIIIA^0$.

Phenotypes and genotypes of the F XIII A groups are summarized in Table 16.

Biological significance. Homozygous carriers of the null gene ($FXIIIA^0$) suffer from impaired fibrin stabilization and wound healing.

Table 16 *Phenotypes and genotypes of the F XIII A groups*

Isoelectric focusing	Phenotype	Genotype
1 band	F XIII A 1-1	$FXIIIA^1/FXIIIA^1$
3 bands	F XIII A 2-1	$FXIIIA^1/FXIIIA^2$
1 band	F XIII A 2-2	$FXIIIA^2/FXIIIA^2$
3 bands	F XIII A 1-4	$FXIIIA^1/FXIIIA^4$
3 bands	F XIII A 2-4	$FXIIIA^2/FXIIIA^4$
2 bands	F XIII A 3-1	$FXIIIA^1/FXIIIA^3$

F XIII B groups[84,85]
(coagulation factor XIII [subunit B] groups)

Detection. Agar-gel electrophoresis followed by immunofixation. The polymorphism can also be demonstrated by isoelectric focusing.

Chromosome model. 1 gene locus with 3 fairly frequent alleles, $FXIIIB^1$ (0.75), $FXIIIB^2$ (0.07) and $FXIIIB^3$ (0.18).

Phenotypes and genotypes of the F XIII B groups are summarized in Table 17.

Table 17 *Phenotypes and genotypes of the F XIII B groups*

Agar-gel electrophoresis	Phenotype	Genotype
2 bands	F XIII B 1-1	$FXIIIB^1/FXIIIB^1$
4 bands	F XIII B 2-1	$FXIIIB^1/FXIIIB^2$
4 bands	F XIII B 3-1	$FXIIIB^1/FXIIIB^3$
2 bands	F XIII B 2-2	$FXIIIB^2/FXIIIB^2$
4 bands	F XIII B 3-2	$FXIIIB^2/FXIIIB^3$
2 bands	F XIII B 3-3	$FXIIIB^3/FXIIIB^3$

TC II groups[15,86–88]
(transcobalamin II groups)

Detection. Thin-layer polyacrylamide-gel electrophoresis after neuraminidase treatment of the serum and incubation with ^{57}Co-labeled vitamin B_{12}. Electrophoresis is followed by autoradiographic visualization. Neuraminidase treatment is necessary in order to remove transcobalamin I and transcobalamin III from the transcobalamin-II identification zone.

Chromosome model. 1 gene locus with 3 fairly frequent alleles, *TC2* X* (0.42), TC2* *S* (0.01) and *TC2* M* (0.56), together with several very rare alleles including *TC2* F* (0.003) and *TC2* DPAV* (0.002).

Phenotypes and genotypes of the TC II groups are summarized in Table 18.

Table 18 *Phenotypes and genotypes of the TC II groups*

Polyacrylamide-gel electrophoresis	Phenotype	Genotype
2 bands	TC2X	*TC2* X/TC2* X*
4 bands	TC2SX	*TC2* S/TC2* X*
4 bands	TC2MX	*TC2* M/TC2* X*
2 bands	TC2S	*TC2* S/TC2* S*
4 bands	TC2MS	*TC2* M/TC2* S*
2 bands	TC2M	*TC2* M/TC2* M*

The heterozygous carriers of the rare alleles so far detected show a pattern of 3 bands.

Biological significance. A relationship between familial TC II deficiency and congenital immune deficiency has been demonstrated[87].

Bf groups (GBG groups, Gb groups)[16,33,89]
(groups of the properdin factor B, or glycine-rich β-glycoprotein)

Detection. Agarose-gel electrophoresis followed by immunofixation.

Chromosome model. 1 gene locus on chromosome 6 with the 2 frequent alleles Bf^{F} (0.18) and Bf^{S} (0.80), the 2 rare alleles Bf^{F1}, (0.01) and $Bf^{S0.7}$ (0.01), together with about 8 very rare alleles including Bf^{0}, the silent allele[90]. The *Bf* locus is closely linked to the *HLA* loci and the *GLO* locus.

Phenotypes and genotypes of the Bf groups are summarized in Table 19.

Table 19 *Phenotypes and genotypes of the Bf groups*

Agarose-gel electrophoresis	Phenotype	Genotype	Frequency among the Swiss[91]
≥4 bands	BfF	Bf^{F}/Bf^{F}	3.2%
≥5 bands	BfF–F1	Bf^{F}/Bf^{F1}	0
≥5 bands	BfF–S	Bf^{F}/Bf^{S}	42.0%
≥5 bands	BfF–S 0.7	$Bf^{F}/Bf^{S0.7}$	1.6%
≥4 bands	BfF1	Bf^{F1}/Bf^{F1}	0
≥5 bands	BfF1–S	Bf^{F1}/Bf^{S}	1.6%
≥5 bands	BfF1–S 0.7	$Bf^{F1}/Bf^{S0.7}$	0
≥4 bands	BfS	Bf^{S}/Bf^{S}	48.4%
≥5 bands	BfS–S 0.7	$Bf^{S}/Bf^{S0.7}$	3.2%
≥4 bands	BfS 0.7	$Bf^{S0.7}/Bf^{S0.7}$	0
Variable number of bands	Rare	...	0

F (for fast) and S (for slow) refer to the rate of migration of the bands concerned, and the numbers following these symbols to the relative length of the reference distance S→F1.

Biological significance. A close association of the rare allele Bf^{F1} with insulin-dependent diabetes has been observed[92,93].

C2 groups[17,18,94–96]
(groups of the complement component 2)

Detection. Isoelectric focusing in polyacrylamide gel followed by functional identification using sensitized sheep erythrocytes and C2-deficient human serum.

Chromosome model. 1 gene locus on chromosome 6, with the 2 fairly frequent alleles $C2^{1}$ (0.96) and $C2^{2}$ (0.03) together with the silent gene $C2^{0}$ (0.01) and a rare allele, $C2^{3}$ (<0.01). The *C2* locus is closely linked to the *Bf* locus.

Phenotypes and genotypes of the C2 groups are summarized in Table 20.

Table 20 *Phenotypes and genotypes of the C2 groups*

Isoelectric focusing	Phenotype	Genotype
1 band	C2 1	$C2^{1}/C2^{1}$
2 bands	C2 2–1	$C2^{1}/C2^{2}$
1 band	C2 2	$C2^{2}/C2^{2}$

Biological significance. The massive reduction in C2 activity suffered by homozygous carriers of the $C2^{0}$ gene is manifested in diseases of the type of lupus erythematodes (LE-like syndrome)[95].

C3 groups[33,97,98]
(groups of the complement component 3)

Detection by high-voltage electrophoresis in agarose gel[97].

Chromosome model. 1 gene locus on chromosome 19 with the 2 frequent alleles $C3^{F}$ (0.20) and $C3^{S}$ (0.79) along with a further 30 rare or very rare alleles.

Phenotypes and genotypes of the C3 groups are summarized in Table 21.

Table 21 *Phenotypes and genotypes of the C3 groups*

Agarose-gel electrophoresis	Phenotype	Genotype	Frequency among the Swiss[99]
1 band	C3 F	$C3^{F}/C3^{F}$	4.4%
2 bands	C3 FS	$C3^{F}/C3^{S}$	31.7%
1 band	C3 S	$C3^{S}/C3^{S}$	63.0%
2 bands	C3 FR	$C3^{F}/*$	0.1%
2 bands	C3 SR	$C3^{S}/*$	0.8%

*Indicates a rare allele; R (= rare variant) indicates the corresponding gene product.

C4 groups[20,100–105]
(groups of the complement component 4)

Detection. Thin-layer agarose-gel electrophoresis or isoelectric focusing followed by immunofixation. Band clarity can be improved by neuraminidase treatment of the samples.

Chromosome model. A model with 2 linked loci (locus *F* and locus *S*) on chromosome 6 has been proposed[102]. Various alleles have been identified on each of these loci, including the fairly common silent alleles f^{0} and s^{0}. There is a close biochemical relationship with the Chido and Rodgers antigens of the erythrocyte surface. All the phenotypes displaying only *F* (C4 F or C4 F–f^{0}) are Chido-negative [Ch(a −)], while all those displaying only *S* (C4 S or C4 S–s^{0}) are Rodgers-negative [Rg(a −)]. The *FS* heterozygotes on the other hand are Ch(a +) Rg(a +). From these observations it has been concluded that the Chido antigen is part of the C4 S molecule and the Rodgers antigen part of the C4 F molecule. There is also a relationship with the HLA system. In addition to the alleles *F, S*, f^{0}, and s^{0}, further rare alleles are known, the most frequent being the allele F^{X}.

The *band patterns and frequencies of the haplotypes* are summarized in Table 22.

Table 22 *Haplotypes of the C4 groups*[103]

Isoelectric focusing	Haplotype	Frequency
4 bands	Fs^{0}	0.147
4 bands	$f^{0}s$	0.172
7 bands	*FS*	0.658
8 bands	$F^{X}S$	0.023
No bands	$f^{0}s^{0}$	Very rare

Biological significance. Homozygous carriers of the haplotype f^0s^0 lack the complement component C4 and therefore suffer from a syndrome of the type of lupus erythematosus (LE-like syndrome).

C6 groups[21,42,90,92,93,106–108]
(groups of the complement component 6)

Detection. Isoelectric focusing in polyacrylamide gel followed by visualization of the C6 bands in a hemolytic overlay.

Chromosome model. 1 gene locus with the 2 frequent alleles $C6^A$ (0.62) and $C6^B$ (0.38) together with about 6 further, very rare alleles.

Phenotypes and genotypes of the C6 groups are summarized in Table 23.

Table 23 *Phenotypes and genotypes of the C6 groups (for the alleles $C6^A$ and $C6^B$)*

Isoelectric focusing	Phenotype	Genotype
7 bands	C6A	$C6^A/C6^A$
9 bands	C6AB	$C6^A/C6^B$
7 bands	C6B	$C6^B/C6^B$

C7 groups[22]
(groups of the complement component 7)

Detection. Isoelectric focusing in polyacrylamide gel followed by visualization of the C7 bands in a hemolytic overlay.

Chromosome model. 1 gene locus with the 3 alleles $C7^1$, $C7^2$ and $C7^3$. The allele $C7^1$ is very frequent among Caucasians, whereas $C7^2$ and $C7^3$ are extremely rare. The *C7* locus is in the neighborhood of the *C6* locus.

Phenotypes. Since only few studies have been made so far on the C7 groups, data on the band patterns of the observed phenotypes will not be reproduced here.

C8 groups[23,24]
(groups of the complement component 8)

Detection. Isoelectric focusing in polyacrylamide gel followed by visualization of the C8 bands in a functionally hemolytic overlay of C8-deficient plasma.

Chromosome model. 1 gene locus with the 2 frequent alleles $C8^a$ (0.65) and $C8^b$ (0.35). A very rare variant $C8^{a1}$ (0.003) has also been observed.

Phenotypes and genotypes of the C8 groups are summarized in Table 24.

Table 24 *Phenotypes and genotypes of the C8 groups*

Isoelectric focusing	Phenotype	Genotype
2 bands	C8a	$C8^a/C8^a$
3 bands	C8ab	$C8^a/C8^b$
2 bands	C8b	$C8^b/C8^b$
2 bands	C8a1	$C8^{a1}/C8^{a1}$
3 bands	C8a1a	$C8^a/C8^{a1}$

Biological significance. An additional silent gene $C8^-$ has been observed so far in 2 individuals in the homozygous form. *C8*-deficient persons suffer from recurrent septic episodes, particularly *Neisseria* infections.

Gm groups[36,38,49,109–112]
(γ-globulin system, IgG groups)

Detection. Hemagglutination inhibition using 0-Rh$^+$ erythrocytes sensitized with anti-D (IgG antibodies to Rhesus factor D) and mono- or polyspecific human anti-Gm sera or monospecific (adsorbed) animal anti-Gm sera. By choosing a suitable Gm phenotype as source of the anti-D antibodies a monospecific detection system can also be built up with polyspecific anti-Gm sera. Immune double diffusion in agar gel (Ouchterlony's test) can also be used with precipitating heteroimmune sera.

Table 25 *Allotypic Gm factors*[111,112]

IgG subclass	Gm factors			Frequency among the Swiss[114]
	WHO*	WHO◇	Earlier designations	
IgG1	G1m(1)	G1m(a)	Gm(a); Gm(1)	48.8%
	G1m(2)	G1m(x)	Gm(x); Gm(2)	16.1%
	G1m(3)	G1m(f)	Gm(b^W), (b2), (f); Gm(3), (4)	90.6%
	G1m(17)	G1m(z)	Gm(z); Gm(17)	–
IgG2	G2m(23)	G2m(n)	Gm(n); Gm(23)	–
IgG3	G3m(11)	G3m(b0)	Gm(b0), (b^β); Gm(11)	–
	G3m(5)	G3m(b1)	Gm(b), (b1), (b^γ); Gm(5), (12)	90.9%
	G3m(13)	G3m(b3)	Gm(b3), (Bet); Gm(13), (25)	–
	G3m(14)	G3m(b4)	Gm(b4); Gm(14)	–
	G3m(10)	G3m(b5)	Gm(b5), (b^α); Gm(10)	–
	G3m(6)	G3m(c3)	Gm-like; Gm(c), (c3); Gm(6)	–
	G3m(24)	G3m(c5)	Gm-like; Gm(c), (c5); Gm(24)	–
	G3m(21)	G3m(g)	Gm(g); Gm(21)	46.8%
	G3m(15)	G3m(s)	Gm(s); Gm(15)	–
	G3m(16)	G3m(t)	Gm(t); Gm(16)	–
	G3m(26)	G3m(u)	Gm(Pa)	–
	G3m(27)	G3m(v)	Gm(Ray)	–
	G3m(28)	G3m(g5)	–	–

Specificities formerly postulated but no longer demonstrable: Gm(7) [Gm(r)]; Gm(8) [Gm(e)]; Gm(9) [Gm(p)]; Gm(18) [Gm(Ro 2)]; Gm(19) [Gm(Ro 3)]; Gm(20); Gm(22) [Gm(y)]

* Numerical nomenclature.
◇ Alphanumerical nomenclature.

The *allotypic Gm factors,* summarized in Table 25, are located on the H chains (heavy chains) of the IgG molecule (γ chains) and are related to the IgG subclasses (γ-chain type).

Isoallotypic IgG markers. These are antigen determinants occurring as allotypic factors in a particular IgG subclass (e.g. in IgG 1: nG1m(1) [non-G1m(1)]) and as isotypic markers in the other subclasses. They are, however, not true genetic markers of IgG.

Chromosome model. 3 closely linked main loci on chromosome 14 for the G1m, G2m and G3m groups. The *G1m* and *G3m* loci are divisible into subloci with codominant alleles. Frequent gene complexes on the 3 main loci are given in Table 26 along with true

Table 26 *Frequent gene complexes on the Gm main loci and true alleles on the subloci*[112]

Gm main locus	Frequent gene complexes	Subloci with true alleles
G1m	$G1m^{1,17}$ $G1m^{1,2,17}$ $G1m^3$	(I) $G1m^3$, $G1m^{17}$ (II) $G1m^1$, $G1m^{1,2}$, $G1m^{-1}$
G2m	–	$G2m^{23}$, $G2m^{-23}$
G3m	$G3m^{21,26,27,28}$ $G3m^{5,10,11,13,14,26,27}$ $G3m^{5,6,11,24,26}$ $G3m^{5,6,10,11,14,26,27}$ $G3m^{10,11,13,15,27}$ $G3m^{10,11,13,15,16,27}$	(I) $G3m^{15}$, $G3m^{15,16}$, $G3m^{26}$ (II) $G3m^5$, $G3m^{-5}$ (III) $G3m^{14}$, $G3m^{-14}$ (IV) $G3m^{21}$, $G3m^{-21}$ (V) $G3m^{11}$, $G3m^{-11}$ (VI) $G3m^6$, $G3m^{13}$ (VII) $G3m^{10}$, $G3m^{28}$ (VIII) $G3m^{24}$, $G3m^{27}$

alleles on the subloci. Frequent *Gm* haplotypes (combined gene complexes for all 3 main loci) include the following:

$Gm^{1, 2, 17; ...; 21, 26, 27, 28}$ and
$Gm^{3; 23; 5, 10, 11, 13, 14, 26, 27}$

The *Gm* loci are linked to the A_2m and *Pi* loci.

Biological significance[113]. Human anti-Gm antibodies occur in patients with rheumatoid arthritis, presumably as a result of autoimmunization against IgG (RAgg sera), as well as in healthy individuals as a result of a (posttransfusional, fetomaternal or maternofetal) alloimmunization or possibly a heteroimmunization (SNAgg sera). In very rare cases, (complement-binding) anti-Gm antibodies cause anaphylactoid transfusion reactions.

Km groups[36, 38, 49, 110–113]
(ϰ light-chain markers of the immunoglobulins; earlier designated Inv groups)

Detection as for the Gm groups.

The *Km factors* (Table 27) occur in all immunoglobulin classes as antigen determinants of the light immunoglobulin chains (ϰ chains).

Table 27 *Km factors*

WHO	Earlier designations	Frequency among the Swiss[66]
Km(1)	Inv(1) [small 1], Inv(1)	18.4%
Km(2)	Inv(a), Inv(2)	17.7%
Km(3)	Inv(b), Inv(3)	–

Chromosome model. 1 gene locus with the 3 alleles Km^1, $Km^{1, 2}$ (together 0.07) and Km^3 (0.93). A very rare silent allele, $Km^{\cdot}$, has also been observed.

Phenotypes and genotypes of the Km groups are summarized in Table 28.

Table 28 *Phenotypes and genotypes of the Km groups*

Phenotype	Genotype
Km(1)	Km^1/Km^1
Km(3)	Km^3/Km^3
Km(1,2)	$Km^1/Km^{1, 2}$ or $Km^{1, 2}/Km^{1, 2}$
Km(1,3)	Km^1/Km^3
Km(1,2,3)	$Km^{1, 2}/Km^3$

Biological significance. The occurrence of human anti-Km antibodies is not linked with the presence of disease (unlike the situation in some cases with anti-Gm); they are formed as a result of allo- or possibly heteroimmunization. Anti-Km antibodies do not cause transfusion reactions.

A_2m groups[111, 112, 115]
(immunoglobulin subclass IgA_2 markers)

Detection by passive hemagglutination inhibition using purified IgA_2 for coating the erythrocytes (preferably by the chrome method) and human anti-A_2m sera.

Chromosome model. 1 gene locus on chromosome 14 with the very frequent allele A_2m^1 (0.99) and the rare allele A_2m^2 (0.01). The A_2m locus is linked to the *Gm* loci.

Phenotypes and genotypes of the A_2m groups are summarized in Table 29. The A_2m antigen determinants are located on the heavy chains of the IgA_2 molecules (α_2 chains).

Table 29 *Phenotypes and genotypes of the A_2m groups*

Phenotype	Genotype
A_2m(1)	A_2m^1/A_2m^1
A_2m(1,2)	A_2m^1/A_2m^2
A_2m(2)	A_2m^2/A_2m^2

Biological significance. Antibodies to A_2m occur as a result of (post-transfusional) alloimmunization or possibly autoimmunization. Most of the patients concerned have a selective IgA deficiency. The antibodies are occasionally the cause of anaphylactoid transfusion reactions.

Alkaline phosphatase groups[36, 116, 117]

Detection. Horizontal or vertical starch-gel electrophoresis in a continuous or discontinuous buffer system, or polyacrylamide-gel electrophoresis. The phosphatase bands are visualized by means of an enzymatic reaction, for example with α-naphthyl phosphate and subsequent coupling with a diazo dye such as fast blue RR.

Genetics. The phenotypes are controlled by the gene locus of the AB0 blood-group system, the secretor-gene locus and an additional gene locus. A role is also played by environmental factors. The phenotype p^{++} is closely related to the 0, B and A_2B blood groups, the phenotype p^0 to the A_1 and A_2 groups.

The *phenotypes* are listed in Table 30. The A bands originate from the alkaline phosphatase of the liver (and/or the bones), the B bands from that of the intestine.

Table 30 *Phenotypes of the alkaline phosphatase groups*[118]

Electrophoresis	Phenotype
1 A band	p^0
1 A band and 1 weak B band	p^+
1 A band and 1 strong B band	p^{++}

Biological significance. The alkaline phosphatase groups (like the AB0 blood groups and the secretor system) are related to the permeability of the cell membranes in the intestinal mucosa and play a part in certain disorders of the gastrointestinal tract.

Cholinesterase (pseudocholinesterase) groups[36, 49, 119–121]

Detection. Determination of the dibucaine number (DN) and the fluoride number (FN). The variants are manifested as quantitative differences in the affinity of the enzyme for the substrate. In starch-gel electrophoresis all the phenotypes produce 4 identically located bands (C_1, C_2, C_3, C_4). There are differences from one phenotype to another in respect of the prominence of the bands, but these do not allow of unambiguous typing.

Chromosome model. 1 gene locus (E_1 locus) on chromosome 3 with the very frequent allele E_1^u (>0.95) and 7 rare alleles (E_1^a, E_1^f, E_1^r, E_1^s, E_1^t, E_1^j, E_1^k). The E_1 locus is linked to the *Tf* locus.

Phenotypes and genotypes are summarized in Table 31, together with the relative enzymatic activity on benzoylcholine substrate. Some rare variants show 5 bands in starch-gel electrophoresis instead of 4, whereby the 5th band is controlled by a 2nd locus (E_2 locus) not linked to the E_1 locus.

Table 31 *Phenotypes and genotypes of the cholinesterase groups*

Phenotype	Genotype	Relative activity	Dibucaine number	Fluoride number
U	$E_1^uE_1^u$	100%	76–87	55–70
A	$E_1^aE_1^a$	50%	8–30	10–28
F	$E_1^fE_1^f$	50%	63–69	30–37
S	$E_1^sE_1^s$	0%	–	–
T	$E_1^tE_1^t$	3%	–	–
ST	$E_1^sE_1^t$	2%	–	–
UR	$E_1^uE_1^r$	52%	–	–
UA	$E_1^uE_1^a$	78%	51–71	42–59
UF	$E_1^uE_1^f$	80%	70–80	45–54
US	$E_1^uE_1^s$	65%	80	64
AF	$E_1^aE_1^f$	60%	39–59	27–38
AS	$E_1^aE_1^s$	20%	21	23
FS	$E_1^fE_1^s$	61%	67	37
UJ	$E_1^uE_1^j$	–	–	–
AJ	$E_1^aE_1^j$	–	–	–
FJ	$E_1^fE_1^j$	–	–	–
UK	$E_1^uE_1^k$	–	–	–
AK	$E_1^aE_1^k$	–	–	–

Biological significance. Individuals with low cholinesterase (pseudocholinesterase) activity (genotypes E_1^a/E_1^a, E_1^a/E_1^f, E_1^f/E_1^f, E_1^a/E_1^s, E_1^f/E_1^s, E_1^s/E_1^s) react to the muscle relaxant suxamethonium (succinyldicholine) used in anesthesia with protracted muscular paralysis.

References

1 Knedel, M., *Blut,* **3**, 129 (1957).
2 Schmid et al., *Biochemistry (Wash.),* **1**, 959 (1962).
3 Laurell, C.B., *Scand. J. clin. Lab. Invest.,* **17**, 271 (1965).
4 Smithies, O., *Biochem. J.,* **61**, 629 (1955).
5 Hirschfeld, J., *Acta path. microbiol. scand.,* **47**, 160 (1959).
6 Berg and Bearn, *J. exp. Med.,* **123**, 379 (1966).
7 Shreffler et al., *Biochem. Genet.,* **1**, 101 (1967).
8 Allison and Blumberg, *Lancet,* **1**, 634 (1961).
9 Berg, K., *Acta path. microbiol. scand.,* **59**, 369 (1963).
10 Utermann et al., *Nature,* **269**, 604 (1977).
11 Smithies, O., *Nature,* **180**, 1482 (1957).
12 Hobart, M.J., *Ann. hum. Genet.,* **42**, 419 (1979).
13 Raum et al., *Clin. Res.,* **27**, 458A (1979).
14 Board, P.G., *Amer. J. hum. Genet.,* **31**, 116 (1979).
15 Daiger et al., *Amer. J. hum. Genet.,* **30**, 202 (1978).
16 Alper et al., *J. exp. Med.,* **135**, 68 (1972).
17 Hobart and Lachmann, *J. Immunol.,* **116**, 1736 (1976).
18 Alper, C.A., *J. exp. Med.,* **144**, 1111 (1976).
19 Alper and Propp, *J. clin. Invest.,* **47**, 2181 (1968).
20 Rosenfeld et al., *J. clin. Invest.,* **48**, 2283 (1969).
21 Hobart and Lachmann, in Peeters, H. (Ed.), *Protides of the Biological Fluids,* Pergamon Press, Oxford, 1975, page 575.
22 Hobart and Lachmann, *Transplant. Rev.,* **32**, 26 (1976).
23 Alper, C.A., *3rd Workshop on the Genetics of the Complement System,* Cologne, 1979.
24 Raum et al., *J. clin. Invest.,* **64**, 858 (1979).
25 Grubb and Laurell, *Acta path. microbiol. scand.,* **39**, 390 (1956).
26 Ropartz, C., *Rev. franç. Etud. clin. biol.,* **5**, 933 (1960).
27 Vyas and Fudenberg, *Proc. nat. Acad. Sci. (Wash.),* **64**, 1211 (1969).
28 Kunkel et al., *Nature,* **223**, 1247 (1969).
29 Arfors et al., *Acta genet. (Basel),* **13**, 89 (1963).
30 Kalow and Staron, *Canad. J. Biochem.,* **35**, 1305 (1957).
31 Weitkamp et al., *Ann. hum. Genet.,* **36**, 381 (1973).
32 Langenbeck, U., in Becker, P.E. (Ed.), *Humangenetik,* volume I/3, Thieme, Stuttgart, 1975, page 1.
33 Séger and Lucotte, *La pratique de l'électrophorèse appliquée à la détection des polymorphismes humains,* Masson, Paris, 1981.
34 Tárnoky, A.L., *Advanc. clin. Chem.,* **21**, 101 (1980).
35 Giuliani et al., *Clin. chim. Acta,* **113**, 43 (1981).
36 Giblett, E.R., *Genetic Markers in Human Blood,* Blackwell, Oxford, 1969.
37 Johnson et al., *J. clin. Invest.,* **48**, 2293 (1969).
38 Cooper, D.W., in Brock and Mayo (Eds.), *The Biochemical Genetics of Man,* 2nd ed., Academic Press, London, 1978, page 271.
39 Beck, W., in Becker, P.E. (Ed.), *Humangenetik,* volume I/3, Thieme, Stuttgart, 1975, page 320.
40 Fagerhol, M.K., *Ser. Haematol.,* **1**, No. 1, 153 (1968).
41 Fagerhol and Laurell, *Progr. med. Genet.,* **7**, 96 (1970).
42 Kühnl, P., *Elektrofokussierung in der forensischen Serologie,* LKB, Gräfelfing, 1979.
43 Weidinger et al., *Z. Rechtsmedizin,* **86**, 1 (1980/81).
44 Cox, D.W., *Amer. J. hum. Genet.,* **33**, 354 (1981).
45 Jeppsson et al., *Clin. Chem.,* **28**, 219 (1982).
46 Cox et al., *Hum. Genet.,* **53**, 429 (1979/80).
47 Buffone et al., *Clin. Chem.,* **29**, 328 (1983).
48 Lieberman, J., *Ann. intern. Med.,* **81**, 850 (1974); Talamo, R.C., *Pediatrics,* **56**, 91 (1975); Fagerhol, M.K., *Postgrad. med. J.,* **52**, suppl. 2, 73 (1976); Tobin and Hutchison, *Arch. intern. Med.,* **142**, 1342 (1982).
49 Prokop and Uhlenbruck, *Human Blood and Serum Groups,* Maclaren, London, 1969.
50 Giblett, E.R., *Ser. Haematol.,* **1**, No. 1, 3 (1968).
51 Ritter et al., in Becker, P.E. (Ed.), *Humangenetik,* volume I/3, Thieme, Stuttgart, 1975, page 50.
52 Sutton, H.E., *Progr. med. Genet.,* **7**, 163 (1970).
53 Beringer, M., *Statistische Auswertung von Blut- und Serumgruppenbestimmungen bei Fällen von strittiger Abstammung,* thesis, Berne, 1967.
54 Reinskou, T., *Ser. Haematol.,* **1**, No. 1, 21 (1968).
55 Jörgensen et al., in Becker, P.E. (Ed.), *Humangenetik,* volume I/3, Thieme, Stuttgart, 1975, page 105.
56 Constans and Cleve, *Hum. Genet.,* **48**, 143 (1979).
57 Hirschfeld, J., *Progr. Allergy,* **6**, 155 (1962).
58 Walter, H., in Becker, P.E. (Ed.), *Humangenetik,* volume I/3, Thieme, Stuttgart, 1975, page 167.
59 Bütler et al., *Vox Sang. (Basel),* **26**, 485 (1974).
60 Bütler and Brunner, *Vox Sang. (Basel),* **27**, 550 (1974).
61 Bütler et al., in Peeters, H. (Ed.), *Protides of the Biological Fluids,* Pergamon Press, Oxford, 1975, page 627.
62 Utermann, G., in Becker, P.E. (Ed.), *Humangenetik,* volume I/3, Thieme, Stuttgart, 1975, page 173.
63 Harvie and Schultz, *Proc. nat. Acad. Sci. (Wash.),* **66**, 99 (1970).
64 Rittner and Wichmann, *Hum. Genet.,* **5**, 42 (1967).
65 Dahlén et al., *Clin. Genet.,* **7**, 334 (1975).
66 López and Bütler, *Vox Sang. (Basel),* **10**, 314 (1965).
67 Berg et al., *Clin. Genet.,* **10**, 97 (1976).
68 Berg, K., *Science,* **172**, 1136 (1971).
69 Utermann et al., *Amer. J. hum. Genet.,* **32**, 339 (1980).
70 Zannis et al., *Amer. J. hum. Genet.,* **33**, 11 (1981).
71 Zannis and Breslow, *Biochemistry (Wash.),* **20**, 1033 (1981).
72 Zannis et al., *J. Lipid Res.,* **23**, 911 (1982).
73 Breslow et al., *J. Lipid Res.,* **23**, 1224 (1982).
74 Ghiselli et al., *Lancet,* **2**, 405 (1982).
75 Bowman, B.H., *Ser. Haematol.,* **1**, No. 1, 97 (1968).
76 Walter, H., in Becker, P.E. (Ed.), *Humangenetik,* volume I/3, Thieme, Stuttgart, 1975, page 137.
77 Altland et al., *Hum. Genet.,* **54**, 221 (1980).
78 Weidinger et al., *Z. Rechtsmedizin,* **85**, 255 (1980).
79 Dykes and Polesky, *Hum. Genet.,* **59**, 365 (1981).
80 Driesel et al., *Z. Rechtsmedizin,* **86**, 133 (1980/81).
81 Mauff et al., in Hummel and Gerchow (Eds.), *Biomathematical Evidence of Paternity,* Springer, Berlin, 1981, page 89.
82 Nishimukai et al., *Hum. Hered.,* **32**, 130 (1982).
83 Board and Coggan, *Hum. Genet.,* **59**, 135 (1981).
84 Kühnl et al., in *9. Internationale Tagung der Gesellschaft für forensische Blutgruppenkunde,* Berne, 1981, abstracts, page 591.
85 Board, P.G., *Amer. J. hum. Genet.,* **32**, 348 (1980).
86 Fräter-Schröder et al., *Blood,* **53**, 193 (1979).
87 Fräter-Schröder et al., *J. inherit. Metab. Dis.,* **4**, 165 (1981).
88 Fräter-Schröder et al., *Hum. Genet.,* **61**, 165 (1982); Fräter-Schröder, M., *Molec. cell. Biochem.,* **56**, 5 (1983).
89 Mauff et al., *Z. Immun-Forsch.,* **154**, 115 (1978).
90 Weidinger et al., *Z. Rechtsmedizin,* **83**, 259 (1979).
91 Scherz et al., *Hum. Hered.,* **27**, 143 (1977).
92 Raum et al., *Lancet,* **1**, 1208 (1979).
93 Bertrams et al., *Lancet,* **2**, 98 (1979).
94 Meo et al., *Proc. nat. Acad. Sci. (Wash.),* **74**, 1672 (1977).
95 Glass et al., *J. clin. Invest.,* **58**, 853 (1976).
96 Olaisen et al., *Hum. Genet.,* **42**, 301 (1978).
97 Teisberg, P., *Vox Sang. (Basel),* **19**, 47 (1970).
98 Bender, K., in Becker, P.E. (Ed.), *Humangenetik,* volume I/3, Thieme, Stuttgart, 1975, page 203.
99 Pflugshaupt et al., in Peeters, H. (Ed.), *Protides of the Biological Fluids,* Pergamon Press, Oxford, 1975, page 559.
100 Teisberg et al., *Nature,* **264**, 253 (1976).
101 Teisberg et al., *J. exp. Med.,* **146**, 1380 (1977).
102 O'Neill et al., *Nature,* **273**, 668 (1978).
103 Petersen et al., *Hum. Genet.,* **53**, 31 (1979/80).
104 Mauff, G., in *9. Internationale Tagung der Gesellschaft für forensische Blutgruppenkunde,* Berne, 1981, abstracts, page 499.
105 Awdeh et al., *Nature,* **282**, 205 (1979).
106 Rittner et al., *Z. Rechtsmedizin,* **83**, 17 (1979).
107 Kunstmann et al., *Immunobiology,* **158**, 55 (1980).
108 Rittner and Mollenhauer, *Ärztl. Lab.,* **27**, 232 (1981).
109 Natvig and Kunkel, *Ser. Haematol.,* **1**, No. 1, 66 (1968).
110 Bender, K., in Becker, P.E. (Ed.), *Humangenetik,* volume I/3, Thieme, Stuttgart, 1975, page 244.
111 WHO Meeting on human immunoglobulin allotypic markers, *J. Immunogenet.,* **3**, 357 (1976).
112 van Loghem, E., in *8. Internationale Tagung der Gesellschaft für forensische Blutgruppenkunde,* London, 1979, abstracts, page 89.
113 Bütler, R., *Bibl. haemat. (Basel),* No. 31 (1969).
114 Scherz et al., unpublished.
115 van Loghem et al., *Vox Sang. (Basel),* **24**, 481 (1973).
116 Beckman, L., *Ser. Haematol.,* **1**, No. 1, 137 (1968).
117 Walter and Ananthakrishnan, in Becker, P.E. (Ed.), *Humangenetik,* volume I/3, Thieme, Stuttgart, 1975, page 352.
118 Bamford et al., *Lancet,* **1**, 530 (1965).
119 Beckman, G., in Brock and Mayo (Eds.), *The Biochemical Genetics of Man,* 2nd ed., Academic Press, London, 1978, page 186.
120 Altland, K., in Becker, P.E. (Ed.), *Humangenetik,* volume I/3, Thieme, Stuttgart, 1975, page 327.
121 Brown et al., *Advanc. clin. Chem.,* **22**, 1 (1981).

In 1956, TJIO and LEVAN[1] demonstrated for the first time in cultured embryonal lung tissue that the number of diploid chromosomes in humans is 46. These consist of 23 homologous pairs, of which 22 play no decisive role in determining sex, and are called autosomal chromosomes. The last pair consists of the sex chromosomes X and Y (XY in the male and XX in the female). Routine chromosome studies have been made possible by the preparation of chromosomes from cultured lymphocytes (blood culture)[2]. The rapid growth of knowledge in the field of cytogenetics has made a standardized international nomenclature necessary. That in common use today is based mainly on the knowledge gained in the early seventies as a result of the visualization of the chromosome banding pattern, and may be traced back to the Paris Conference of 1971[3]. Additional recommendations for standardization were worked out at the Lake Placid Conference in 1974, the Edinburgh Conference in 1975 and more extensively at the Stockholm Conference in 1977[4]. The development and increasing use of high-resolution chromosome preparations in the late seventies prompted another conference in Paris in 1980[5].

Chromosome preparations

Numerous modifications in the technique of making chromosome preparations have been described. Two steps, however, are necessary in most techniques:

1. Addition of colchicine, or substances with a similar effect, which inhibit full mitosis by destroying spindle organization, resulting in accumulation of nuclei undergoing mitosis. Bone marrow cells, in which numerous mitotic nuclei are found, constitute an exception.
2. Treatment of the cells with a hypotonic solution. The chromosomes are scattered by the swelling of the karyoplasm and cytoplasm, making individual chromosomes discernible (Fig. 1).

The contracted and reduplicated chromosomes undergoing mitosis are then rendered visible. For further details, see the literature[6].

A culture of venous blood, which can be harvested after 2–4 days, is usually used for routine cytogenetic studies. The small lymphocytes are transformed by the addition of phytohemagglutinin to blast cells, thereby acquiring the capacity for mitosis. It is not necessary to study the blood immediately; the blood samples, obtained under sterile conditions and heparinized to prevent clotting can be sent to the nearest laboratory.

In the case of mosaicism (presence of more than one cell line), and rare chromosome aberrations, the additional use of fibroblast cultures from skin biopsy specimens is recommended. Often fibroblasts display a different mosaic distribution. Certainly, chromosome analysis from fibroblast cultures takes longer, but the cultures remain stable longer and can be stored in a deep-freezer. Chromosome studies can also be carried out on fibroblast cultures from material obtained post mortem and from abortus material.

Other tissues often used for chromosome determination are bone marrow cells (usually for the study of leukemias), solid tumor cells and amniotic cells (predominantly for prenatal diagnosis of chromosome aberrations).

To obtain high-resolution banding, techniques have now been devised that can partially synchronize peripheral blood cultures and yield sufficient cells in the early phases of mitosis for detailed study. These techniques essentially use some method of blocking the cells in S phase, for instance with methotrexate or bromodeoxyuridine, releasing the block and then timing the subsequent harvest to obtain the maximum number of cells at the appropriate stage[5].

Staining techniques

Until 1970, orcein was mainly used for staining chromosome preparations, since it stains chromatids relatively homogeneously. Reliable identification of the homologues was possible only for chromosomes 1, 2, 3, and 16, sometimes for chromosomes 17, 18, and for the Y chromosome (Fig. 1). The autoradiographic technique, which uses incorporation of radioactively labelled compounds and is based on differences in the time of replication of the different chromosomes, too, cannot identify and classify homologues exactly and reliably.

The classification of the 46 chromosomes according to their size and the position of the centromere (either metacentric, submetacentric, or acrocentric) into 7 groups (A to G, Fig. 2) brought an improvement in that chromosomes with aberrations could henceforth be assigned to their corresponding groups.

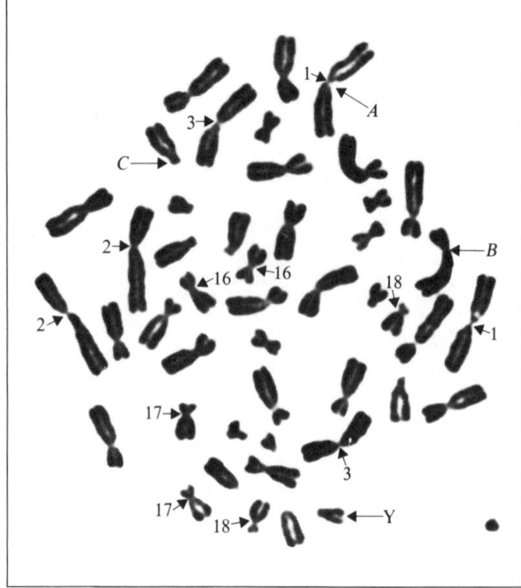

Fig. 1. Metaphase chromosomes stained with orcein. Only the homologues 1, 2, 3, 16, 17, 18, and the Y chromosome are identifiable. *A* Metacentric chromosome. *B* Submetacentric chromosome. *C* Acrocentric chromosome.

Because of the inadequacy of chromosome identification by orcein staining, the additional chromosome of the G group in Down's syndrome, which was discovered in 1959, was ascribed to the larger pair in the G group because of its size, and assigned the number 21 (trisomy 21). However, with the banding technique described below it was found that this chromosome actually belonged to the smaller pair of the G group and was actually a chromosome 22. Nevertheless, by agreement the smaller homologues of the G group continued to be designated chromosome 21, and the larger homologues chromosome 22.

The banding technique was first described by CASPERSSON et al.[7] in 1970. After treatment of the preparation with quinacrine mustard or quinacrine dihydrochloride, the chromatids appear under UV light (fluorescence microscope) with their characteristic band patterns. This Q-banding technique is especially suited for observing chromosome polymorphisms (see page 281) and for investigating the Y chromosome. In the Q-banding technique the Y chromosome exhibits a band with particularly intense fluorescence in the distal portion of the long arm (Figs. 3 and 13); this segment of the Y chromosome is recognizable as a brightly fluorescent point (Y body) even in the interphase nucleus (Fig. 4).

Shortly after Q-banding was introduced, other staining techniques were presented. After pretreatment of the chromosome preparations with various proteolytic agents or detergents at various pH values and temperatures, Giemsa staining or staining with another dye is carried out[6,8]. Apart from the Q-banding technique, the following methods are the most widely used today:

1. G-banding [Giemsa]. The preparation is first treated with trypsin and then stained with Giemsa dye. A simple light microscope is sufficient to evaluate these preparations, which are quite stable (Figs. 2, 5, 8, 9, 10, 11).
2. C-banding [constitutive heterochromatin]. After treatment with alkaline solution, the chromosome preparations are heated in a saline solution at 60 °C. The preparations are then stained with Giemsa, after which the chromosomes assume a darker color, especially in the area of the centromere. For chromosomes 1, 9, and 16 intensive staining of the centromere region extends into the long arm (Fig. 9). In the Y chromosome the distal segment also is stained a dark color. The extent of the intensely stained segment of chromosomes 1, 9, and 16, and of the Y chromosome is variable, and is inherited (chromosome polymorphism, page 281).

(Continued on page 278)

*This chapter on 'Human Chromosomes' (pages 276–290) has been compiled by H.W. GOEDDE and J.J. HOO, Institut für Humangenetik der Universität Hamburg, Hamburg, FRG.

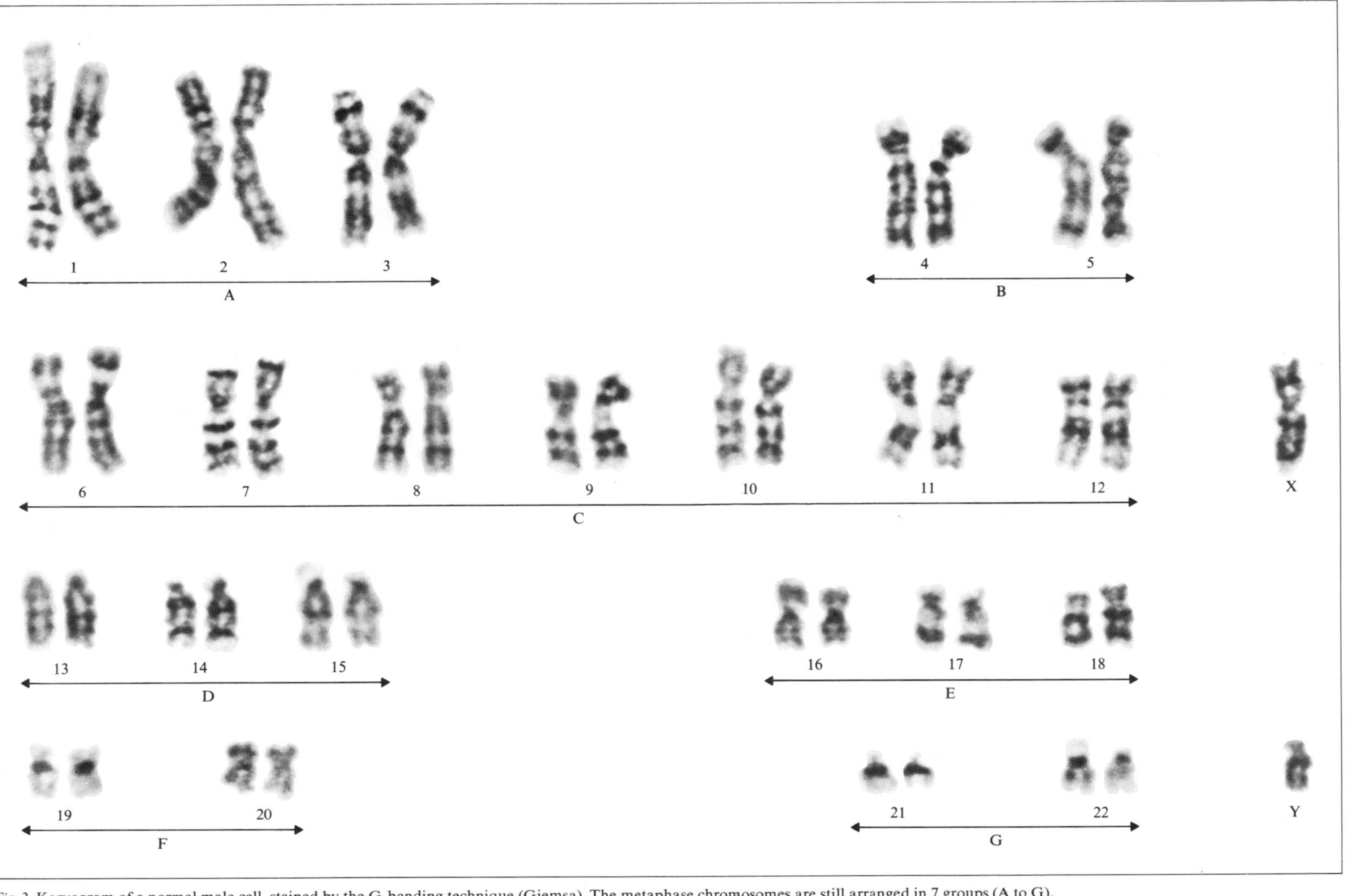

Fig. 2. Karyogram of a normal male cell, stained by the G-banding technique (Giemsa). The metaphase chromosomes are still arranged in 7 groups (A to G).

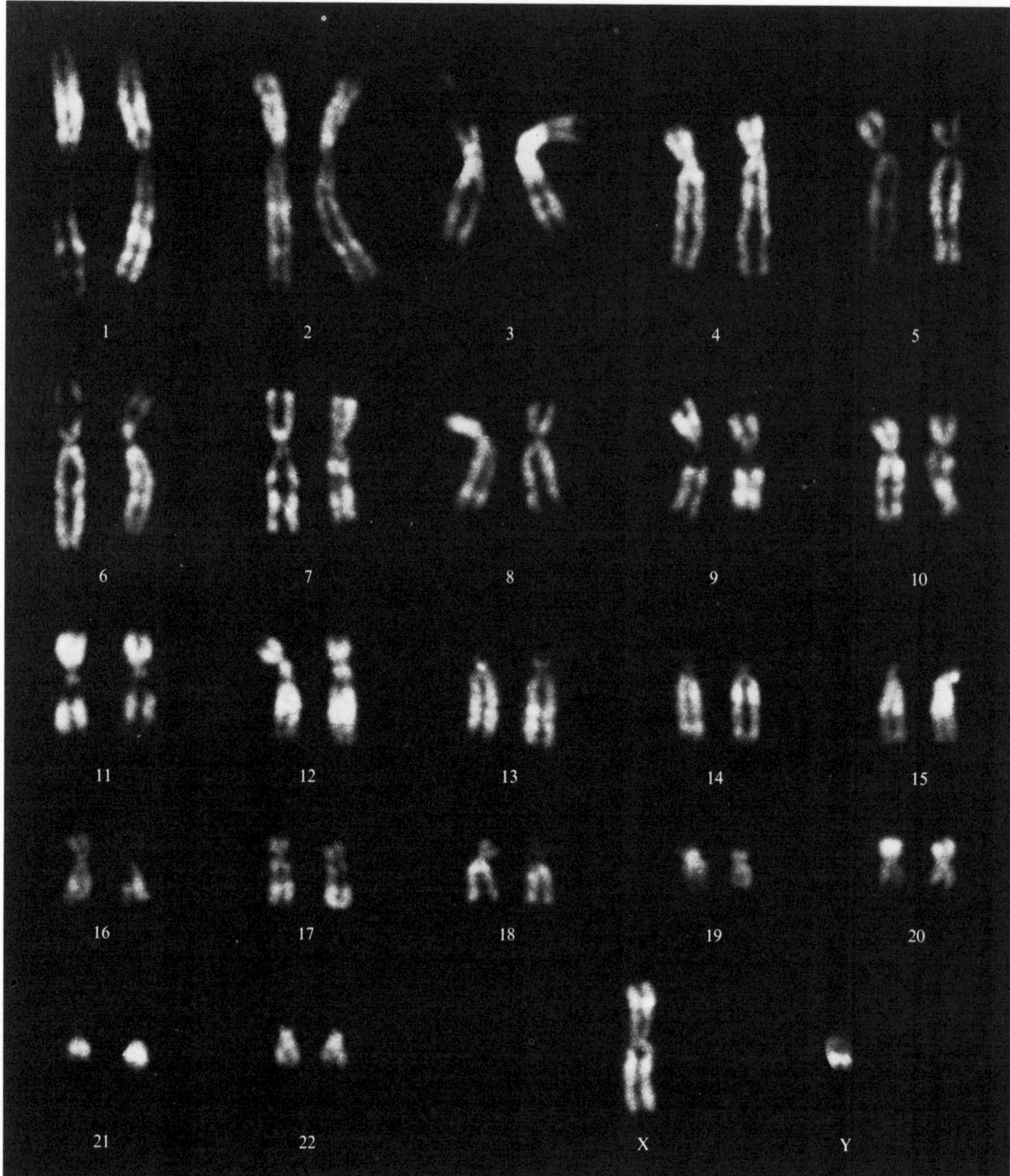

Fig. 3. Karyogram of a normal male cell, stained with the Q-banding technique.

3. R-banding [reverse]. The preparations are first heated in saline at 87 °C and then stained with Giemsa. The banding pattern thereby obtained is the reverse of the G-banding pattern (Fig. 5): The places that appear dark in G-banding are light in R-banding, and vice versa. This method, and its variant T-banding (terminal) are especially suited for detecting smaller deletions at the end of the chromosome (telomeric portion of the chromosome).

Yet to be mentioned is the use of 5-bromodeoxyuridine (BrdU), an analogue of thymidine. If this is added to a lymphocyte culture in late S phase, the late-replicating inactivated X chromosome is recognized by its showing a weaker fluorescence of acridine orange than the non-inactivated X chromosome. On the other hand, if BrdU is present in early S phase and thymidine is added in late S phase, the late-replicating inactivated X chromosome would appear darker after staining with Hoechst 33258 and Giemsa (Fig. 6).

The formation of the banding patterns are only partly understood[9]. Positive Q and G bands correspond to later-replicating chromosome segments in DNA-replication patterns.

The banding patterns visualized by treating and staining the chromosomes in various ways are often designated in the literature by a 3-letter code[4]:

QFQ: Q bands by fluorescence using quinacrine
GTG: G bands by trypsin using Giemsa
RHG: R bands by heating using Giemsa
THA: T bands by heating using acridine orange
CBG: C bands by barium hydroxide using Giemsa

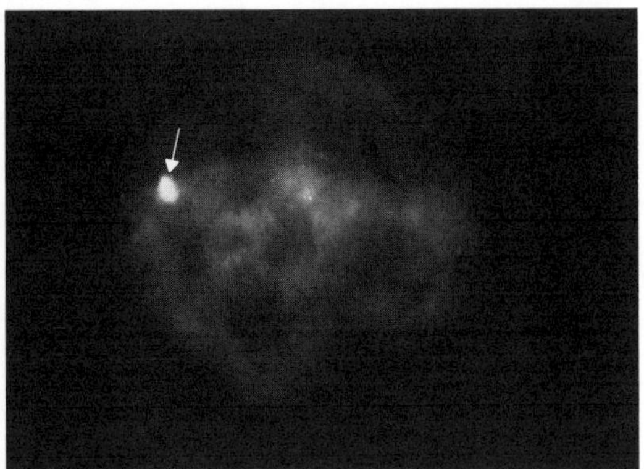

Fig. 4. Interphase nucleus with Y body.

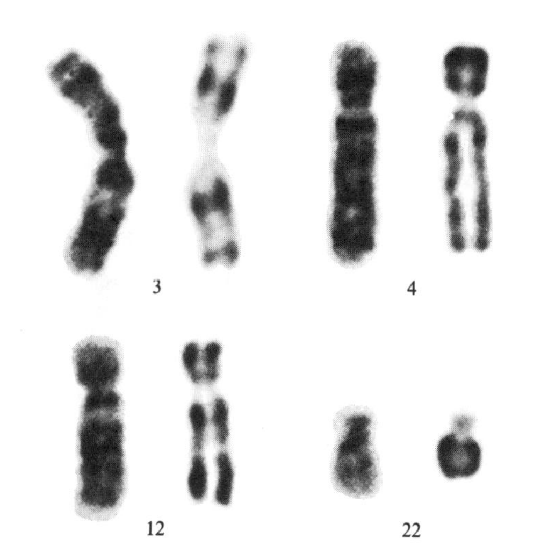

Fig. 5. Examples of reverse pattern in G-banding (left) and R-banding (right).

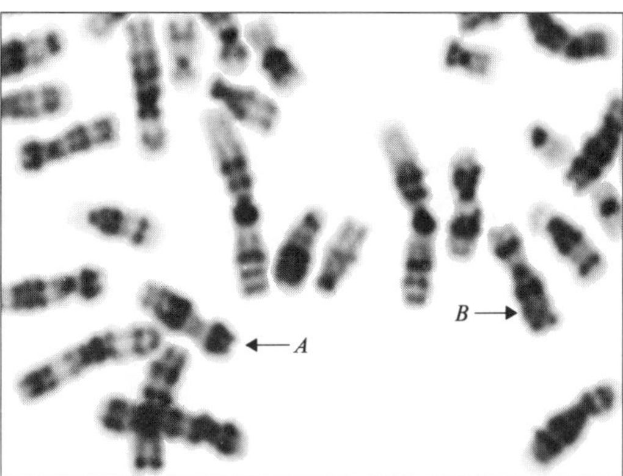

Fig. 6. Metaphase chromosomes, prepared by sequential labelling with BrdU and thymidine, showing DNA-replication banding, which is very similar to the G-band pattern. The late-replicating and inactivated X chromosome (*A*) is stained darker than the non-inactivated X chromosome (*B*).

Nomenclature

Since the Paris Conference of 1971[3] the short and long arms of chromosomes (p: short arm, q: long arm) have been subdivided into several regions on the basis of the banding pattern, and the regions in turn subdivided into several bands (Fig. 7). A karyotype is described by the following set of data: total number of chromosomes, type and number of sex chromosomes, type of autosomal aberration (Table 1). See also ISCN (1978)[4] and ISCN (1981)[5].

Chromosome aberrations

Chromosome anomalies are reported to occur in about 0.6% of all human life births, 5% of stillbirths and 40–50% of all spontaneous abortions[10,11]. The frequency of chromosome aberrations at conception – depending on the method of calculation – is perhaps 20% or more[11]. Aberrations may be numerical (excessive numbers or absence of certain chromosomes), or they may consist in some structural modification (deletion, inversion, ring formation, translocation, etc.). The most frequent aberrations in the newborn are presented together with their clinical symptoms in Table 2 (page 282). The most frequent aberration found in abortus material is monosomy 45,X0, at about 20%. Among trisomies, which make up a total of 50%, trisomy 16 is the most frequent at about 15%. Triploidy (usually 69,XXY, or 69,XXX), comprises about 15%. Differences in frequency compared with those in the newborn are to be attributed to the fact that many chromosome aberrations lead to early miscarriage.

(Continued on page 281)

Table 1 *Examples of karyotypes*

Symbol	Explanation
46,XY	Normal male karyotype (Figs. 2 and 3)
48,XXYY	Numerical aberration of sex chromosomes with an additional X chromosome and an additional Y chromosome
45,X0/46,XX	Turner's syndrome with mosaic; there are 2 cell lines, 45,X0 and 46,XX
46,XX,16qh +	The long arm of one chromosome 16 is lengthened by secondary constriction (Fig. 9) (see 'Chromosome polymorphisms', page 281)
47,XY, + 21	Male karyotype with an additional chromosome 21 (Down's syndrome with free trisomy 21)
46,XX, – 14, + t(14q21q)	Female karyotype with Down's syndrome (translocation trisomy 21). One chromosome 14 is missing; instead there is a chromosome consisting of the long arms of chromosomes 14 and 21 (centric translocation; synonym: Robertson's translocation)
46,XY,inv(10)(p15q22)	Pericentric inversion in chromosome 10. The 2 breaks between which the centromere-containing chromosome fragment has rotated by 180° are in region 1, band 5 of the short arm, and in region 2, band 2 of the long arm of chromosome 10 (Fig. 8)
46,XX,del(5)(p13)	Terminal deletion of the short arm of chromosome 5. There is a break in region 1, band 3, the small fragment being lost (girls with cat-cry syndrome [*cri-du-chat* syndrome])
46,XX,t(11;13)(q23;q14)	Reciprocal translocation between chromosome 11 (break: region 2, band 3) and chromosome 13 (break: region 1, band 4) (Fig. 10)
46,XY,r(13)(p11q34)	One chromosome 13 is in ring form, the ring being formed by the union of the break on the short arm (region 1, band 1) and the break on the long arm (region 3, band 4) (Fig. 11)

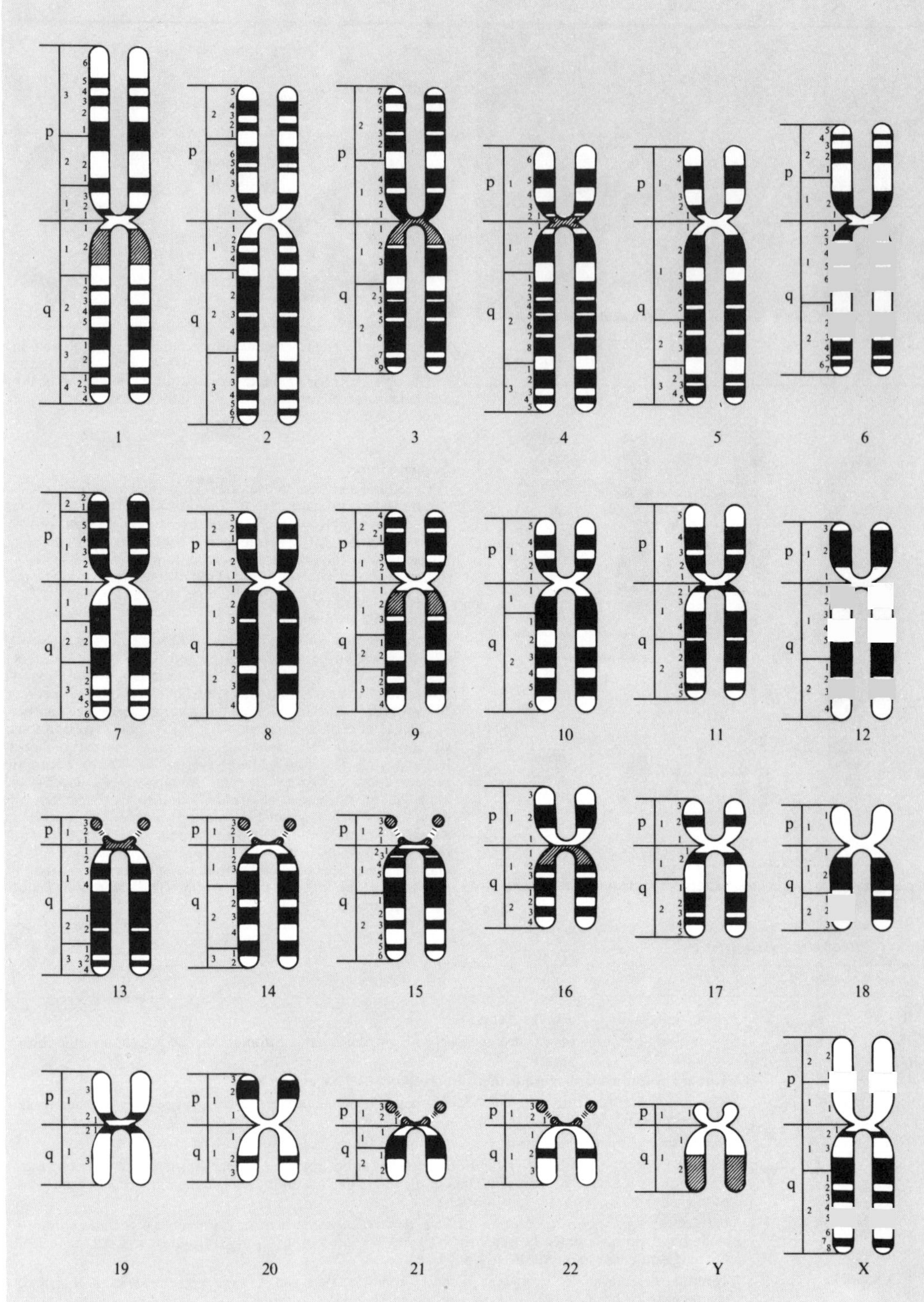

Fig. 7. Schematic representation of chromosome bands using the Q-, G- or R-banding technique according to the Paris Conference 1971[3]. White: negative or slightly stained Q and G bands, positive (dark) R bands. Black: positive Q and G bands, negative R bands. Hatched: variable bands.

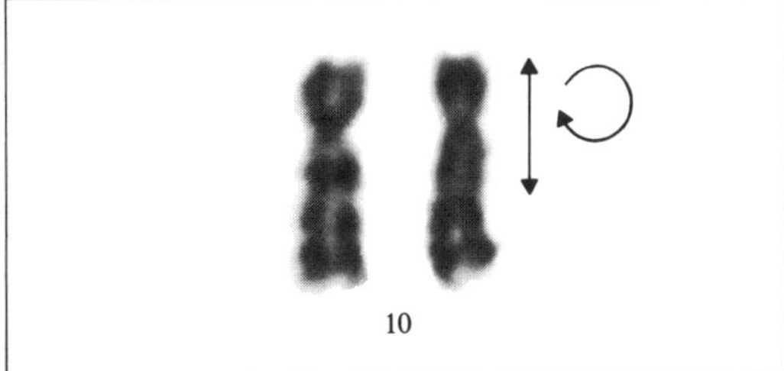

Fig. 8. Picture of a pericentric inversion of chromosome 10: inv(10)(p15q22).

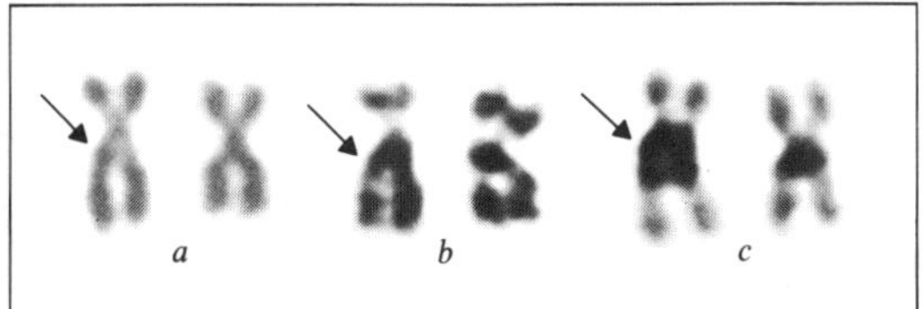

Fig. 9. Lengthening of the long arm of a chromosome 16 due to elongated secondary constriction (*a*) and enlargement of heterochromatin (*b* and *c*). *a* Orcein. *b* G-banding. *c* C-banding.

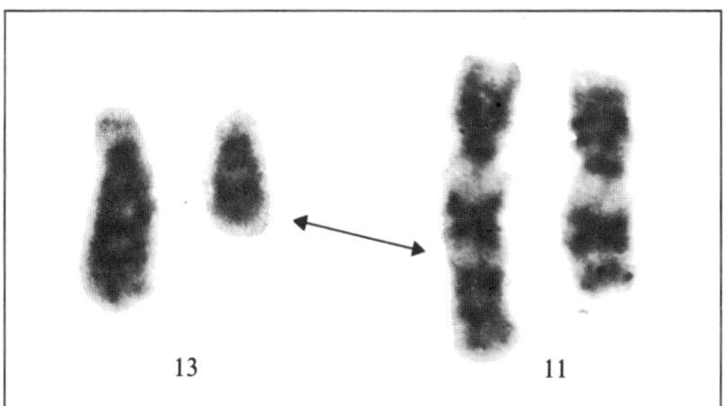

Fig. 10. Reciprocal translocation between chromosomes *11* and *13*: t(11;13)(q23;q14). Phenotypically normal woman with clinical diagnosis of 'habitual miscarriage'.

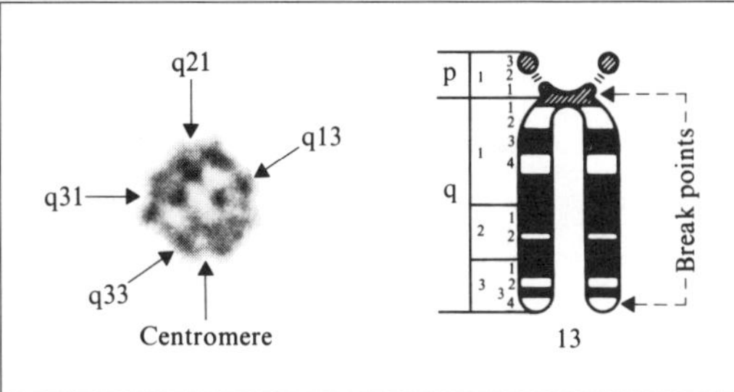

Fig. 11. A chromosome 13 appears in ring form. The break points can be precisely localized: r(13)(p11q34).

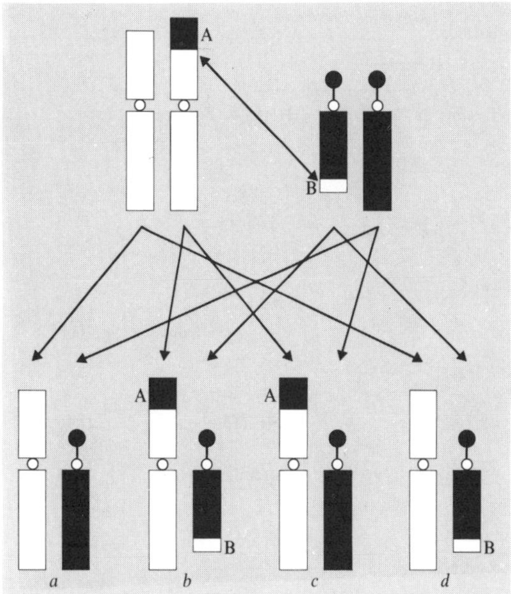

Fig. 12. Possibilities of segregation during meiosis of a carrier with balanced translocation. *a* Leading to a normal karyotype. *b* Leading to a balanced translocation. *c* Leading to trisomy of segment A and monosomy of segment B. *d* Leading to trisomy of segment B and monosomy of segment A.

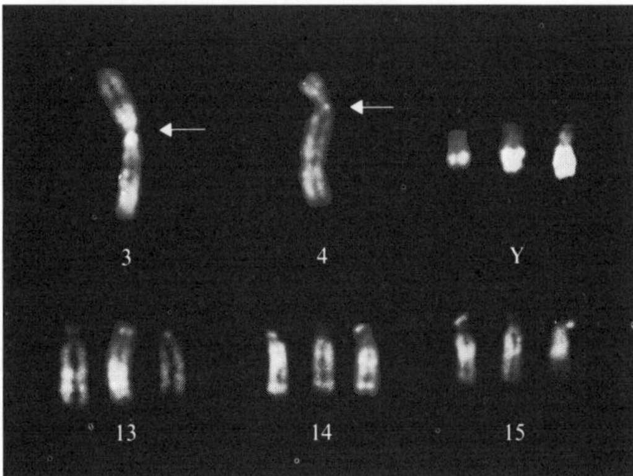

Fig. 13. Chromosome polymorphism, shown on chromosomes with Q-banding.

Chromosome aberrations usually result from a nondisjunction (i.e. in numerical aberrations) or from a break (i.e. in structural aberrations) during meiosis of a parent cell: they are of prezygotic origin. In mosaicism 45,X0/46,XY or 46,XY/46,XY,5p –, for example, the aberration is attributable to defective postzygotic division. In rare cases, defective divisions and breaks, as well as prezygotic and postzygotic defects, occur in combination.

A considerable number of chromosome aberrations which are grouped together under the collective term 'partial trisomies and partial monosomies' are now known. They are usually the result of unbalanced segregations of parental balanced translocations (Fig. 12). The carriers of the balanced translocation are usually themselves phenotypically normal, although early miscarriages often take place. Their carrier status is usually discovered in cytogenetic investigations due to habitual miscarriage, or when a child with multiple anomalies is born. Extended cytogenetic follow-up investigations among relatives as well as a prenatal investigation are indicated in these cases. Thanks to the banding technique a large number of partial trisomies and partial monosomies are now known. Some of them have been delineated as characteristic syndromes[12], the cat-cry syndrome (Table 2), the Hirschhorn-Wolf syndrome (4p –), the de Grouchy syndrome I (18p –), the de Grouchy syndrome II (18q –), the Rethoré syndrome (partial trisomy 9p) for instance and yet others without eponyms.

Chromosome polymorphisms

The term 'chromosome polymorphisms' refers to those structural differences which are inherited and which as far as is currently known cause no phenotypic anomaly. Their distinguishing features are the following:

Table 2 *Chromosome aberrations*

Aberration	Synonym	Frequency in the newborn	Clinical symptoms
Trisomy 21	Down's syndrome	1:600	Mental retardation, heart defects, upward slanting palpebral fissures, epicanthus, short cranium, small ears, Brushfield's spots, flat nasal bridge, large tongue, clinodactyly, simian crease, hypotonic musculature, hyperextensibility of joints, dysplastic pelvis, susceptibility to infections
Trisomy 18	Edward's syndrome	1:5000	Mental and physical retardation, short sternum, heart defects, low-set and malformed ears, microretrognathia, dolichocephaly, flexed and intertwined fingers, arched pattern on many finger tips, pes equinovarus with prominent calcaneus, dorsiflexed halluces, muscular hypertonia
Trisomy 13	Patau's syndrome	1:8000	Mental and physical retardation, microcephaly, scalp defect, coloboma and microphthalmia, cleft lip and palate, low-set and malformed ears, deafness, abnormal nails, heart defects, kidney malformations, uterus bicornis, hexadactyly (little fingers and toes)
47,XXY...............	Klinefelter's syndrome	1:1000 of male births	Hypoplasia of testicles, great height as well as occasional gynecomastia, female distribution of body hair and mental disorder
45,X0.................	Turner's syndrome	1:2000 of female births	Stunted growth, pterygium colli, scutate thorax, stenosis of aortic isthmus, widely spaced nipples, cubitus valgus, no secondary sexual characteristics, rudimentary ovaries, peripheral lymphedema at birth, hairline low at nape
47,XYY...............	....	1:1000 of male births	Great height, in some cases mental and behavioral disorders
5p –	Cat-cry syndrome, Lejeune's syndrome	1:100000	Psychomotor retardation, cat-like cries, microcephaly, microretrognathia, hypertelorism, strabismus, moonface, low-set and malformed ears, muscular hypotonia

Other chromosomal aberrations such as 47,XXX, 48,XXYY, 48,XXXY, for example, as well as the various partial trisomies and monosomies, including the ring chromosomes, are much rarer. For a detailed description of the various chromosomal aberrations see the literature[12].

1. Variable length of the short arm of the acrocentric chromosomes (D and G groups) (Fig. 13).
2. The occurrence of satellites, and their size on the acrocentric chromosomes (Fig. 13).
3. The presence and size of silver-stain-positive nucleolus-organizing regions on the short arms of acrocentric chromosomes.
4. Secondary constrictions in chromosomes 1, 9, and 16 (Fig. 9).
5. Variable length of the Y chromosome (Fig. 13).
6. The occurrence of intensely fluorescent bandings in the proximity of the centromeres of chromosomes 3 and 4, and on the acrocentric chromosomes (Fig. 13).
7. Constriction of the short arm of chromosome 17 (rare).

A knowledge of chromosomal polymorphisms is important as they may be relevant in the following situations:

1. In *prenatal diagnosis,* to detect possible contamination with maternal cells and to prevent the misinterpretation of certain findings.
2. In *family studies,* to determine linkage of some genetic marker (e.g. protein polymorphisms) with a specific marker chromosome (e.g. 1qh +).
3. In *trisomy syndrome* (e.g. trisomy 21) or *triploidy,* to determine the origin of the extra chromosome or the additional haploid.
4. In paternity cases, occasionally, as additional evidence.

Balanced translocations, insertions and inversions are not considered as chromosome polymorphisms since the associated meiotic events often result in habitual miscarriage or the birth of a chromosomally unbalanced child, even when the carriers are themselves phenotypically normal.

Gene mapping

Staining of the banding pattern not only makes possible the exact identification of homologues and precise localization of break points, it also constitutes a basis for a major progress in gene mapping (localization of the different genes to specific chromosomes). This is done by the following methods, among others:

1. *Formal genetic analysis of X-chromosomal inheritance.* Genetic traits and diseases, such as the Xg^a blood group, the enzymes glucose-6-phosphate dehydrogenase and hypoxanthine phosphoribosyltransferase, and the diseases hemophilia, colorblindness, and Duchenne muscular dystrophy, which are X-chromosomally inherited, have their genes on the X chromosome. These genes can be further localized to specific segments on the basis of the various structural anomalies of the X chromosome, for instance the locus for Duchenne muscular dystrophy at Xp21, etc.
2. *Family studies.* Certain genetic traits can be localized on a marker chromosome by concomitant familial studies of the karyotype and the genetic traits. Examples would be the ascription of the Duffy blood group to chromosome 1 and the localization of the α chain of haptoglobin in chromosome 16. Further linkage studies have made it possible to link yet other genetic traits to the same chromosome.
3. *DNA–RNA in situ hybridization.* In hybridization experiments with radioactively tagged bases, it was found that 5*S* and 28*S* ribosomal RNA are synthesized in the short arms of acrocentric chromosomes.
4. *Gene dosage method.* In a monosomy, half of the alleles located in the chromosomal segment are lost. This is manifested in the loss of the codominant genetic traits. Thus, for example, the Rhesus factor has been linked to the short arm of chromosome 1. The attempt in general to link an enzyme to a specific trisomic or monosomic chromosome segment on the basis of its approximately 50% increase or 50% decrease in activity has been proven to be successful: for example the assignment of the gene for esterase D to chromosome 13, i.e. 13q14.
5. *Somatic cell hybridization.* Fusion of human and animal cells (for example cells of hamsters, rats, or mice) results in the gradual loss of human chromosomes. Certain selection methods, or even a systematic study of karyotypes and various genetic traits (for example enzyme polymorphisms) in newly formed cell clones make it possible to localize genes on specific chromosomes. Example: If in newly formed clones the human chromosome 11 and human lactate dehydrogenase A (LDHA) disappear at the same time, it may be inferred that the gene for LDHA is localized on chromosome 11. This method especially has been responsible for considerable advances in gene mapping in past years.

Up to 1984 about 800 genes have been assigned to specific chromosomes[14]. These include more than 200 genes assigned to the X chromosome[15], about 600 assigned to specific autosomes, and at least one assigned to the Y chromosome[13]. A selection is given in Table 3, pages 283–287.

(Continued on page 287)

Table 3 *A selection of known genes assigned to chromosomes*[13]

Chromosome	Region	Marker name	Marker symbol
1	pter→p36.13	Glucose dehydrogenase	GDH
	p	Complement component 8	C8
	p36	U1 small-nuclear RNA	RNU1
	p36	Adenovirus-12 chromosome modification site 1A	A12M2
	pter→p36.13	Enolase 1	ENO1
	pter→p36.13	Phosphogluconate dehydrogenase	PGD
	p31.1→p22.1	Neuroblastoma oncogene	NRAS
	pter→p34	Elliptocytosis 1 (Rh-linked)	EL1
	pter→p32	UDPgalactose 4-epimerase	GALE
	p36→p34	Rhesus blood group	Rh
	p34	α-L-Fucosidase 1 (tissue)	FUCA1
	p34→p32	Scianna blood group	Sc
	p34	Adenylate kinase 2	AK2
	p32	Uridine monophosphate kinase	UMPK
	p22.1	Phosphoglucomutase 1	PGM1
	p21	α-Amylase (salivary)	AMY1
	p21	α-Amylase (pancreatic)	AMY2
	p21→qter	α-Actin (skeletal muscle)	ACTA
	p21→qter	Renin	REN
	q12→q21	Duffy blood group	Fy
	cen→q25	Zonular pulverulent cataract (Fy-linked)	CAE
	q21	Adenovirus-12 chromosome modification site 1B	A12M3
	q21→q22	Glucose-1-phosphate uridylyltransferase (UDPglucose pyrophosphorylase 1)	UGP1
	q23	Antithrombin III	AT3
	cen→q32	Phosphofructokinase (muscle type)	PFKM
	q32→q42	Guanylate kinase 1	GUK1
		Guanylate kinase 2	GUK2
	q25 or q42	Peptidase C	PEPC
	q42.1	Fumarate hydratase	FH
	q42→q43	Adenovirus-12 chromosome modification site 1C	A12M1
	q42→q43	5*S* RNA	RN5S
		Tetrahydropteroylglutamate methyltransferase	MTR
	q21→q31 or q42	Glucosylceramidase (β-glucosidase [acid]) (Gaucher's disease)	GBA
	p22.1→qter	Succinate dehydrogenase	SDH
		Dombrock blood group	Do
2	p25 or p23	Acid phosphatase 1	ACP1
	p23	Malate dehydrogenase (soluble)	MDH1
	p23	Proopiomelanocortin	POMC
		Flavoprotein-linked monooxygenase (arylhydrocarbon hydroxylase)	AHH
		Galactose enzyme activator	GLAT
		Immunoglobulin ϰ polypeptide	IGK
		Kidd blood group	Jk
	p23→qter	Interferon 1 (fibroblast)	IF1
		Regulator of acetylcholinesterase (acetylcholinesterase derepressor)	RACH
		Adenosine-deaminase-complexing protein 2	ADCP2
		Glucose-1-phosphate uridylyltransferase (UDPglucose pyrophosphorylase 2)	UGP2
		Fibronectin (identified with monoclonal antibodies)	FN1
	q32→qter	Isocitrate dehydrogenase ($NADP^+$) (soluble)	IDH1
	q32→qter	Ribulosephosphate 3-epimerase	RPE
3		AF8 temperature-sensitivity complementing	AF8T
	p21→cen	β-D-Galactosidase 1	GLB1
	p21	Aminoacylase 1	ACY1
	p13→q12	Glutathione peroxidase 1	GPX1
	q23→qter	Transferrin receptor	TFRC
	q21→qter	Transferrin	TF
		Cholinesterase 1 (serum)	CHE1
	q28	Somatostatin	SST
		Herpes-simplex-virus-type-1 sensitivity	HV1S
4	pter→q21	Amidophosphoribosyltransferase (phosphoribosylpyrophosphate amidotransferase)	PPAT
	p12→q12	Peptidase S	PEPS
	p14→q12	Phosphoglucomutase 2	PGM2

Table 3 *A selection of known genes assigned to chromosomes*[13] *(continued)*

Chromosome	Region	Marker name	Marker symbol
4		Quinoid dihydropteridine reductase	QDPR
	q11→q13	Group-specific component	GC
		Dentinogenesis imperfecta 1	DGI1
		Plasminogen	PLG
	q11→q22	Albumin	ALB
	q11→q22	α-Fetoprotein	AFP
	q28→q31	MN blood group	MN
	q28→q31	Ss blood group	Ss
		Sclerotylosis	TYS
	q21→q31	Fibrinogen (α, β and γ chains)	FGA, FGB, FGG
		Interleukin 2	IL2
		Alcohol dehydrogenase (class I)	ADH
	p14→qter	Formaldehyde dehydrogenase	FDH
5	pter→q11	Leucyl-tRNA synthetase	LARS
	p	Antiviral-state-repressor regulator	AVRR
	p	Interferon 2 (fibroblast)	IF2
	q13	β-N-Acetyl-D-glucosaminidase (hexosaminidase B) (β subunit)	HEXB
		Arylsulfatase B	ARSB
	q15→qter	Diphtheria-toxin sensitivity	DTS
		β_2-Adrenergic receptor	ADRBR
		Glucocorticoid receptor	GRL
6	p23→q12	Prolactin	PRL
	pter→p23	Coagulation factor XII (Hageman)	F12
		Monkey red-blood-cell receptor	MRBC
	p21.3	Major histocompatibility complex	HLA (MHC)
	p21.3→p21.2	Lactoyl-glutathione lyase (glyoxalase I)	GLO1
	q11→q21	Chorionic gonadotropin (α polypeptide)	CGA
	q12	Malate dehydrogenase (malic enzyme) (soluble)	ME1
		Spinocerebellar ataxia	SCA1
	q21	Superoxide dismutase (mitochondrial)	SOD2
	q12	Phosphoglucomutase 3	PGM3
		P blood group	P
		Plasminogen activator	PLA
		Baboon M7 virus integration site	BEVI
		Surface antigen 5 (M_r 45000)	S5
		Adenosine-deaminase-complexing protein 1	ADCP1
		Coagulation factor XIII (a chain)	F13A
7		Surface antigen 7	S7
	pter→q22	Phosphoserine phosphatase	PSP
	p13→p11	Epidermal-growth-factor receptor (surface antigen 6)	EGFR (S6)
	p14→cen	Biliverdin reductase	BLVR
		Growth-control factor 1	GCF1
	p21→q22	Argininosuccinate lyase	ASL
	p13→q22	Malate dehydrogenase (mitochondrial)	MDH2
	cen→q11.2	Myosin heavy polypeptide (skeletal muscle, adult)	MYH4
	cen→q22	β-D-Glucuronidase	GUSB
		Uridine phosphorylase	UP
		3-Hydroxyacyl-CoA dehydrogenase	HADH
		Diaphorase 2	DIA2
	q22→qter	Neutrophil migration	NM
	q22→qter	Trypsin 1	TRY1
	q22→qter	Carboxypeptidase A	CPA
		Nonhistone chromosome protein 2	NHCP2
	q22 or q32→q36	Histones H1, H2A, H2B, H3, H4	H1 to H4
	q21→q22	Collagen type I, α2	COL1A2
		Collagen type III, α1	COL3A1
8		Fibronectin-cell surface	FN3, FNL
	p21.1	Glutathione reductase (NAD[P]H)	GSR

Table 3 *A selection of known genes assigned to chromosomes*[13] *(continued)*

Chromosome	Region	Marker name	Marker symbol
8		Alanine aminotransferase (glutamic-pyruvic transaminase)	GPT
		Spherocytosis	SPH1
		Thyroglobulin	TG
9	pter→p13	Interferon, α type (leukocyte)	IFL, IFA
	p24→p13	Interferon, β type (fibroblast)	IFF, IFB
	p21→p13	Galactose-1-phosphate uridylyltransferase	GALT
	p24→p13	Adenylate kinase 3 (nucleosidetriphosphate–adenylate kinase)	AK3
	p22→p13	Aconitate hydratase (aconitase 1) (soluble)	ACO1
	cen→q34	Folylpolyglutamate synthetase	FPGS
	q12	DNA associated with cytoplasmic membrane	DNCM
	q34→qter	Argininosuccinate synthetase	ASS
	q34	Waardenburg's syndrome type 1	WS1
	q	α_1-Acid glycoprotein (orosomucoid)	ORM
	q34	AB0 blood group	AB0
	q34	Adenylate kinase 1	AK1
	q3	Nail–patella syndrome 1	NPS1
		Porphobilinogen synthase (aminolevulinate dehydratase)	ALAD
10	p	Hexokinase 1	HK1
	pter→p11.1	6-Phosphofructokinase (platelet type)	PFKP
	q11.1→q24	Inorganic pyrophosphatase	PP
		Glutamate-semialdehyde dehydrogenase (glutamate-γ-semialdehyde synthetase)	GSAS
	q11→q24	Adenosine kinase	ADK
	q25.3→q26.1	Phosphoglyceromutase (phosphoglycerate mutase A)	PGAMA
	q25.3→q26.1	Aspartate aminotransferase (glutamic-oxaloacetic transaminase) (soluble)	GOT1
	q	Lipase A (acid, lysosomal)	LIPA
		Chorionic gonadotropin	CGH
11	pter→p11	Parathyroid hormone	PTH
	p13	Catalase	CAT
	p13	Wilms' tumor/aniridia/genitourinary abnormalities/mental retardation	WAGR
	p15	Insulin	INS
	p15	Hemoglobin β-globin cluster	HBBC
	pter→p13	Lethal antigen 1	S1
	pter→p13	Lethal antigen 3	S3
		Species antigen	S4
		Glutathione transferase (isoenzyme 1 or 3)	GST
	p12.08→p12.03	Lactate dehydrogenase A	LDHA
	p11→q13	Apolipoprotein A-I	APOA1
	p11→q13	Apolipoprotein C-III	APOC3
	p12→cen	Acid phosphatase 2 (lysosomal)	ACP2
		Fibronectin (identified with nonmonoclonal antibodies)	FN2
		Collagenase (recessive dystrophic epidermolysis bullosa)	CLG
		Esterase A4	ESA4
	q13→qter	α-D-Glucosidase (neutral AB)	GANAB
	q13→qter	Lethal antigen 2	S2
	q23→qter	Uroporphyrinogen I synthase	UPS
		Herpes-simplex-virus-type-I sensitivity	HV1S
12		Glycerol-3-phosphate dehydrogenase (NAD^+)	GPD1
	pter→q12	Branched-chain-amino-acid aminotransferase 1	BCT1
	p13	Glyceraldehyde-phosphate dehydrogenase	GAPD
	p12.2→p12.1	Lactate dehydrogenase B	LDHB
	p13	Triosephosphate isomerase 1	TPI1
		Triosephosphate isomerase 2	TPI2
	p	Aromatic 2-oxoacid (α-ketoacid) reductase	KAR
	p11→qter	Enolase 2	ENO2
	p11→qter	Citrate (*si*)-synthase	CS
	q12→q14	Serine hydroxymethyltransferase	SHMT
	q21	Peptidase B	PEPB
	q24.1	Interferon (γ type)	IFG

Table 3 *A selection of known genes assigned to chromosomes[13] (continued)*

Chromosome	Region	Marker name	Marker symbol
13	p12	Ribosomal RNA	RNR
	q14.1	Retinoblastoma 1	RB1
	q14.1	Esterase D	ESD
	q34	Coagulation factor VII	F7
	q34	Coagulation factor X	F10
14	p12	Ribosomal RNA	RNR
	q13.1	Purine-nucleoside phosphorylase (nucleoside phosphorylase)	NP
	q32→qter	Creatine kinase (BB isoenzyme)	CKBB
	q21→qter	Tryptophanyl-tRNA synthetase	WARS
	q24.3→q32.2	α_1-Antitrypsin (protease inhibitor)	PI
		Esterase activator	ESAT
	q32.3	Immunoglobulin heavy-chain gene family	IGH
		Phosphoribosylformylglycinamidine synthetase	PFGS
	q22→qter	Phosphoribosylglycinamide formyltransferase	PGFT
		External-membrane protein (M_r 195000)	M195
15	p12	Ribosomal RNA	RNR
	q11→qter	α-D-Mannosidase A (cytosol)	MANA
		α-D-Glucosidase (neutral C)	GANC
	q11	Prader-Willi syndrome	PWS
	q21→q22	β_2-Microglobulin	B2M
	q22→qter	Mannosephosphate isomerase	MPI
	q22→qter	Pyruvate kinase (M2)	PKM2
	q22→q25.1	β-N-Acetyl-D-glucosaminidase (hexosaminidase A) (α subunit)	HEXA
	q21→qter	Isocitrate dehydrogenase ($NADP^+$) (mitochondrial)	IDH2
	pter→q21	L-Iditol dehydrogenase (sorbitol dehydrogenase)	SORD
	q11→qter	α-Actin (cardiac)	ACTC
16		Hydroxyacylglutathione hydrolase	HAGH
	pter→p11	Alanine aminotransferase (glutamic-pyruvic transaminase)	GPT
	pter→p12	Hemoglobin ζ	HBZ
	pter→p11	Hemoglobin α_1 and α_2	HBA1, HBA2
	p13→p12	Phosphoglycolate phosphatase	PGP
	q12→q22	Aspartate aminotransferase (glutamic-oxaloacetic transaminase 2) (mitochondrial)	GOT2
	q12→q22	Adenine phosphoribosyltransferase	APRT
		Chymotrypsinogen B	CTRB
	q21→q22	Haptoglobin	HP
	q21→q22	Lecithin-cholesterol acyltransferase	LCAT
		Thymidine kinase (mitochondrial)	TK2
	q12→q21	Cytochrome b_5 reductase (diaphorase [NADH/NADPH])	DIA4
		Cystathionine γ-lyase (cystathionase)	CTH
		Lipase B (acid, lysosomal)	LIPB
		Interferon-production regulator	IFR
		Esterase B3	ESB3
		Antiviral-state regulator	AVR
17	pter→p11	Skeletal myosin (heavy chain)	MYH
	q21→q22	Collagen type I, α1	COL1A1
	q21→q22	Galactokinase	GALK
	q21→q22	Thymidine kinase (soluble)	TK1
	q21→q22	Adenovirus-12 chromosome modification site 17	A12M4
	q22→q24	Growth hormones 1 and 2	GH1, GH2
	q22→q24	Chorionic somatomammotropins 1 and 2	CSH1, CSH2
	q22→q25	α-D-Glucosidase (acid)	GAA
18		Chorionic gonadotropin	CGH
	q23	Peptidase A	PEPA
		Asparaginyl-tRNA synthetase	NARS
19	pter→q13	Deoxyribonuclease (DNase) (lysosomal)	DNL
	p13.2→p13	Glucosephosphate isomerase	GPI
	pter→q13	Proline dipeptidase (peptidase D)	PEPD
	pter→q13	α-D-Mannosidase B (lysosomal)	MANB

Table 3 *A selection of known genes assigned to chromosomes*[13] *(continued)*

Chromosome	Region	Marker name	Marker symbol
19		Poliovirus sensitivity	PVS
		Branched-chain-amino-acid aminotransferase 2	BCT2
		Luteinizing hormone (β subunit)	LHB
		Lutheran blood group	Lu
		Chorionic gonadotropin (β subunit)	CGB
	pter→q13.2	Complement component 3	C3
		ABH secretion	Se
		Lewis blood group	Le
		Myotonic dystrophy	DM
		H blood-group antigen	H
20	pter→cen	Nucleosidetriphosphate pyrophosphatase (inosine triphosphatase)	ITPA
	p12.2	Multiple endocrine neoplasia type II	MEN2
		Desmosterol-to-cholesterol enzyme	DCE
	cen→q13.1	Adenosylhomocysteinase	AHCY
	q13.2→qter	Adenosine deaminase	ADA
21	p12	Ribosomal RNA	RNR
	q22	Phosphoribosylglycinamide synthetase	PRGS
		Phosphoribosylaminoimidazole synthetase	PAIS
	q21→qter	Interferon receptor	IFRC
	q22.1	Superoxide dismutase (soluble)	SOD1
	q22	6-Phosphofructokinase (liver type)	PFKL
		Cystathionine β-synthase	CBS
		β-Amino-acid (renal) transport	AABT
22	p12	Ribosomal RNA	RNR
	pter→q11	L-Iduronidase	IDUA
	q11	DiGeorge's syndrome	DGS
	q11	Immunoglobulin λ polypeptide	IGL
		β-D-Galactosidase 2	GLB2
	q13.31→qter	Arylsulfatase A	ARSA
	q13.31→qter	Cytochrome b_5 reductase (diaphorase [NADH])	DIA1
	q11→q13	Aconitate hydratase (aconitase 2) (mitochondrial)	ACO2
	q13→qter	α-N-Acetyl-D-galactosaminidase	NAGA
Y	pter→p11.2	Testes-determining factor(s)	TDF
		Y histocompatibility antigen	HYA
		Actin-like sequence	ACT2
X		Y histocompatibility antigen, locus *B* (regulator)	HYB
		Y histocompatibility antigen, locus *C* (receptor)	HYC
	pter→p22.3	Xg blood group	Xg
	pter→p22.3	Steroid sulfatase (microsomal)	STS
	pter→p21	Chronic granulomatous disease	CGD
	pter→p21	Kell blood-group precursor	Xk
	p22	Ocular albinism	OA
		Muscular dystrophy Becker	BMD
	p	Muscular dystrophy Emery	EMD
	p21	Muscular dystrophy Duchenne	DMD
	p11→q11	Menkes' syndrome	MNK
	q13	Phosphoglycerate kinase	PGK
	q21→q24	α-D-Galactosidase A (Fabry's disease)	GLA
	q22→q26	Ribosephosphate pyrophosphokinase (phosphoribosylpyrophosphate synthetase)	PRPS
	q26→q27	Hypoxanthine phosphoribosyltransferase	HPRT
	q26→q28	Coagulation factor IX	F9
	q28	Glucose-6-phosphate dehydrogenase	G6PD
	q26→qter	Hemophilia A (procoagulant component of factor VIII)	HEMA
	q27→qter	Color blindness (deutan)	CBD
	q27→qter	Color blindness (protan)	CBP
		Adrenoleukodystrophy	ALD
		Anemia, sideroblastic/hypochromic	ASB
		Ornithine carbamoyltransferase	OTC
		Sulfoiduronate sulfatase	SIDS

Sister chromatid exchanges[16]

Sister chromatid exchanges (SCE) represent the interchange of DNA replication products at homologous loci. These exchanges presumably involve DNA breakage and reunion, but little is known about the molecular basis of SCE. SCE can be best demonstrated by allowing the cells to undergo 2 cycles in 5-bromodeoxyuridine-containing medium: 5-bromodeoxyuridine will replace the thymidine in the newly synthesized DNA strands. The bifiliary substituted chromatids will appear paler than the unifiliary substituted chromatids. Thus, a change in the intensity of chromatid staining denotes the occurrence of SCE (Fig. 14).

Analysis of SCE has been used to detect the effects of clastogens and mutagens. It has also been used to differentiate between chromosome-fragility diseases. Cells from patients with Bloom's syndrome show about a 5- to 6-fold increase in SCE compared with control cells, whereas other inherited diseases with chromosome fragility and predisposition to development of neoplasia such as Fanconi's anemia, ataxia-telangiectasia and xeroderma pigmentosum do not show any baseline increase in SCE.

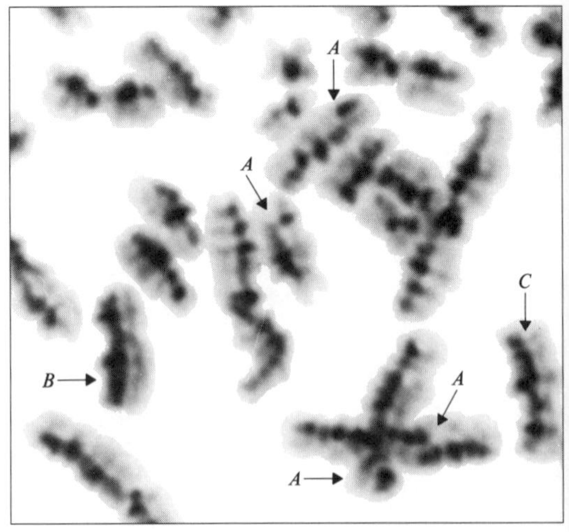

Fig. 14. Sister chromatid exchanges (*A*) in a peripheral lymphocyte which replicated twice in medium containing BrdU and was pulsed with thymidine at the final late S phase. It was stained with Hoechst 33258 and Giemsa. The chromosomes show differential chromatid staining and banding patterns at the same time. The late-replicating X chromosome (*B*) is stained darker than the early-replicating X chromosome (*C*).

High-resolution banding of chromosomes

As much as 1½ to 3 times more bands are seen in prometaphase or prophase chromosomes than in metaphase chromosomes. A single dark band in a metaphase chromosome may be seen as 2 or 3 smaller dark bands in prometaphase or prophase. Frequently, a new dark band will appear in a high-resolution chromosome preparation within the white band originally seen in metaphase (Figs. 15 and 16). Tiny chromosome aberrations, either translocation, duplication, deletion, insertion or inversion, can be better appreciated and indeed may only be detected in high-resolution chromosome preparations.

X-linked mental retardation and the fragile-X syndrome[17]

It has long been known that the ratio of males to females is considerably greater than unity among both institutionalized and non-institutionalized individuals with mental retardation, and that males with mental retardation are more likely to have affected male relatives than mentally retarded females. These familial findings suggested that X-linked disorders might account for much of the male excess in populations with mental retardation.

In 1969, Lubs described a family with nonspecific X-linked mental retardation in which each of the affected males possessed a 'marker X'. The change in the X chromosome was a narrowing in band Xq28 near the distal end of the long arm (Figs. 17 and 18). However, no other family with such a marker X was described in the ensuing years until 1977, when Sutherland revealed that the fragile site on the X chromosome is detectable only when peripheral lymphocytes are cultured in medium deficient in folic acid and thymidine, such as medium TC-199. The marker is not found in all cells, and is usually seen in only 5–50% of the cells examined. A large number of cells must be examined before its presence can be excluded. The fragile X can also be seen in lymphocytes grown in folic acid by adding to the medium methotrexate, a folic acid antagonist, or 5-fluorodeoxyuridine, a potent inhibitor of thymidine monophosphate synthesis. This suggests that the key to the expression of the fragile X is thymidine depletion.

Individuals with the fragile site were estimated to account for one third to one half of all cases of nonspecific X-linked mental retardation. Presence of the marker appears to be associated with specific features that are distinct from those of other forms of X-linked mental retardation. These include the facial appearance with high forehead, large ears and prominent chin. Macroorchidism is usually though not invariably present in postpubertal males, but is frequently absent before puberty, and may be overlooked if testicular volume is not carefully measured using an orchidometer or the formula $V = L \times W^2 \times \pi/6$ (V: volume; L: length; W: width). Behavioral traits in childhood include hyperactivity, anxiety, mood lability and even autistic features.

The clinical expression rate in female heterozygotes, estimated at one third, is higher than for most X-linked disorders, and consists primarily of decreased intelligence without other specific phenotypic features. The fragile X can also be observed in lymphocytes from female heterozygotes, but usually at a much lower rate.

The frequency of the disorder among males has been estimated to be about half that of Down's syndrome. The diagnosis should therefore be considered even in the absence of a family history, because theoretically one third of cases may represent new mutations. Identification of this entity in mildly retarded girls is also important, as one half of their sons may be affected and other relatives may be at risk.

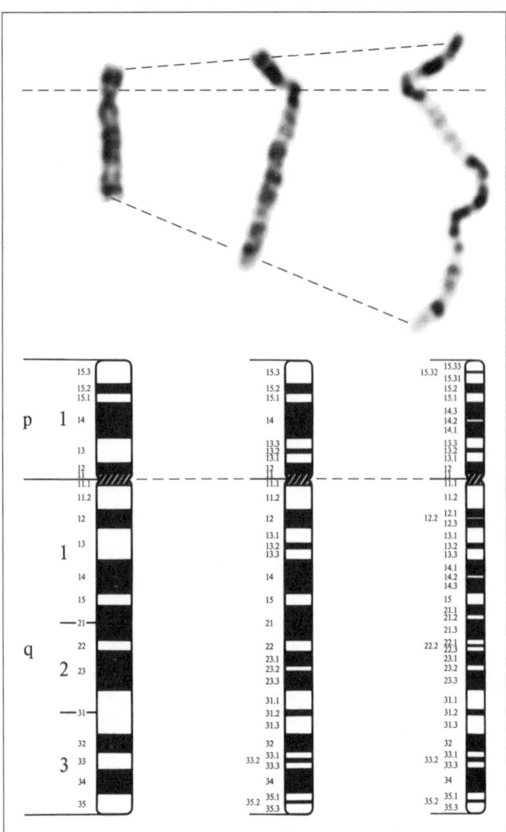

Fig. 15. Chromosome 5 and its diagram, according to the Paris Conference 1980[5], at 3 different stages of chromosome condensation – 400 bands, 550 bands and 850 bands per haploid – which correspond to metaphase, prometaphase and late prophase, respectively.

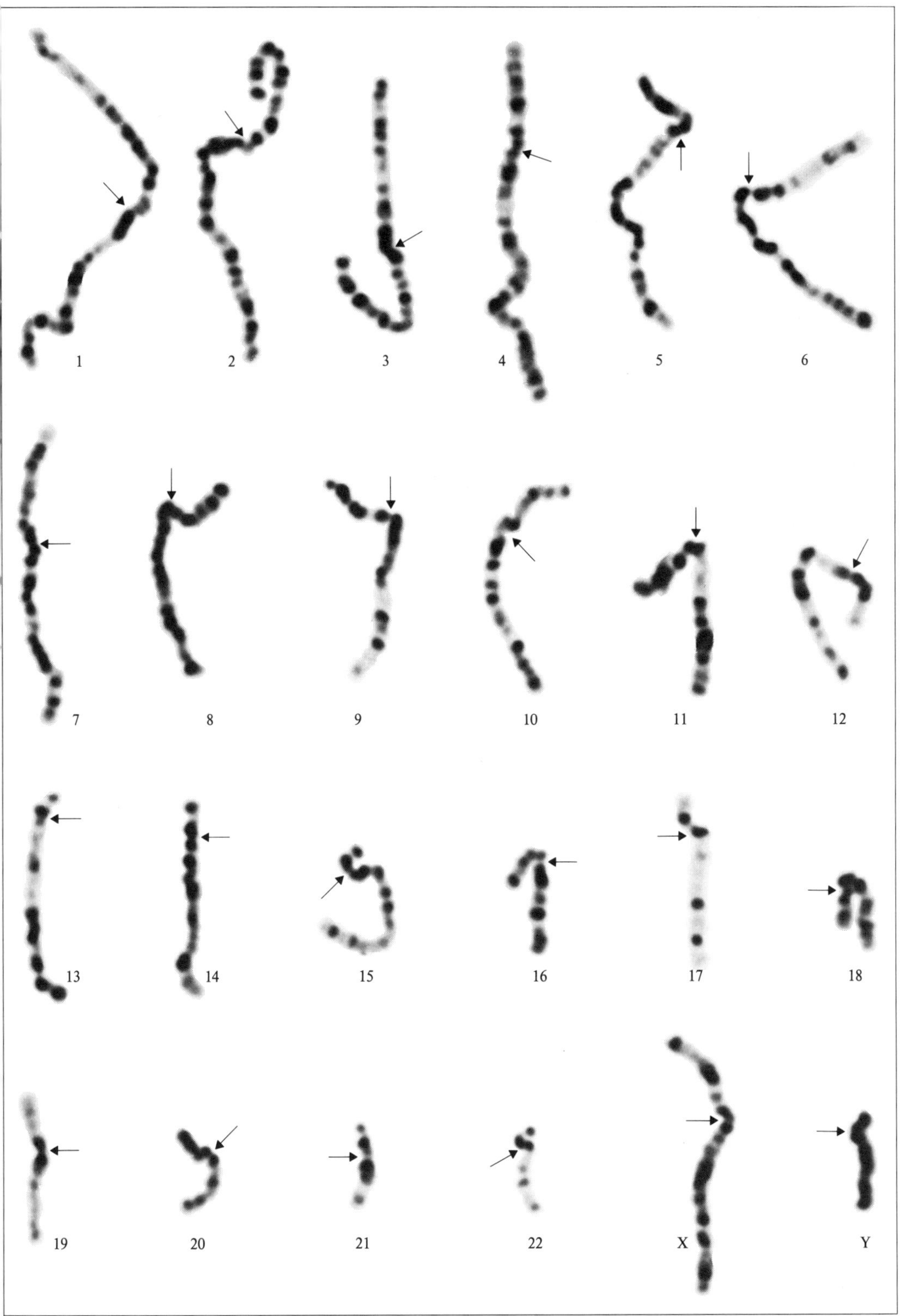

Fig. 16. Haploid set of late-prophase chromosomes, prepared by sequential BrdU (as blocking agent as well) and thymidine labelling, showing DNA-replication pattern with about 850–950 bands per haploid. The arrows point at the centromere.

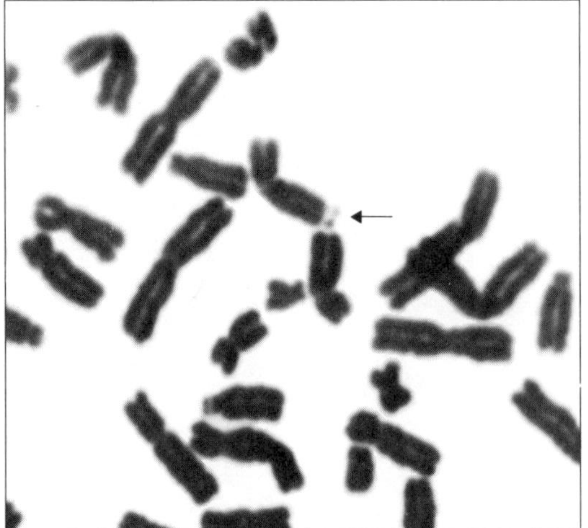

Fig. 17. Unbanded metaphase chromosomes of a male with mental retardation, showing a fragile site at the distal end of the long arm of a C-group chromosome, which is characteristic of a fragile X (arrow). The fragile X can be best and most easily observed in unbanded chromosome preparations. However, destaining and restaining with the banding technique have to be performed to verify that the C-group chromosome is indeed an X chromosome.

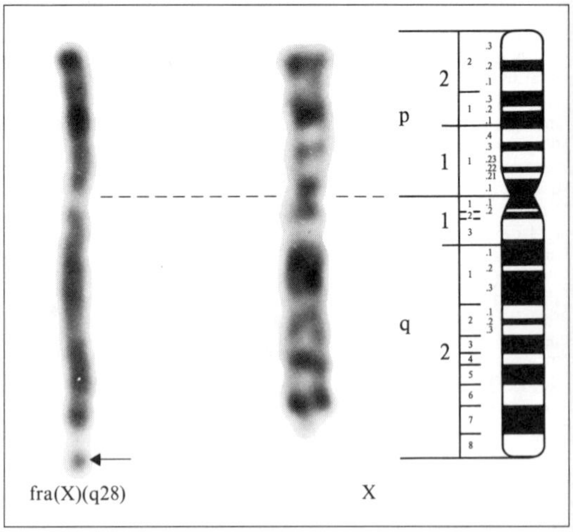

fra(X)(q28)

X

Fig. 18. The prometaphase chromosome on the left with a characteristic fragile site (arrow) was simply stained with Giemsa dye, but the characteristic banding pattern of an X chromosome is only faintly discernible. For comparison purposes, a normal G-banded X chromosome in prometaphase/early metaphase as well as a diagram of the X chromosome in prometaphase are shown on the right.

References

[1] Tjio and Levan, *Hereditas (Lund),* **42**, 1 (1956).
[2] Moorhead et al., *Exp. Cell Res.,* **20**, 613 (1960).
[3] Standardization in human cytogenetics, Paris Conference 1971, *Cytogenet. Cell Genet.,* **11**, 313 (1972).
[4] ISCN (1978), Report of the Standing Committee on Human Cytogenetic Nomenclature (Stockholm Conference 1977), *Cytogenet. Cell Genet.,* **21**, 309 (1978).
[5] ISCN (1981), Report of the Standing Committee on Human Cytogenetic Nomenclature (Paris Conference 1980), *Cytogenet. Cell Genet.,* **31**, 1 (1981).
[6] Schwarzacher et al. (Eds.), *Methods in Human Cytogenetics,* Springer, Berlin, 1974; Yunis, J.J. (Ed.), *Human Chromosome Methodology,* 2nd ed., Academic Press, New York, 1974.
[7] Caspersson et al., *Exp. Cell Res.,* **62**, 490 (1970).
[8] Miller et al., *Progr. med. Genet.,* **9**, 1 (1973).
[9] Evans, H.J., *Advanc. hum. Genet.,* **8**, 347 (1977).
[10] Kleinebrecht and Geisler, *Z. Allgemeinmed.,* **51**, 974 (1975); de Grouchy, J., *Postgrad. med. J.,* **52**, suppl. 2, 5 (1976).
[11] Chandley, A.C., *Ann. Génét.,* **24**, 5 (1981).
[12] de Grouchy and Turleau, *Clinical Atlas of Human Chromosomes,* Wiley, New York, 1977.
[13] Seventh International Workshop on Human Gene Mapping, Los Angeles 1983, *Cyto genet. Cell Genet.,* **37**, 1 (1984).
[14] Miller et al., in [13], page 176.
[15] Miller et al., in [13], page 394.
[16] Latt et al., *Advanc. hum. Genet.,* **10**, 267 (1980).
[17] Gerald, P.S., *Pediatrics,* **68**, 594 (1981); Rhoads, F.A., *Pediatrics,* **69**, 668 (1982); Zollinger et al., *Schweiz. med. Wschr.,* **113**, 238 (1983).

Body Mass in Pregnancy*

Gain of body mass in pregnancy has always been subject to manipulation by dietary restriction, and few if any published data can be said to represent the body mass which would be gained by a healthy population of young pregnant women eating to appetite. Restriction has been particularly practiced in the USA and, although medical opinion there has now raised doubts about the wisdom of restriction, the women themselves, educated for many years to think in terms of their figures and the long-term consequences of adiposity, will certainly continue to practice restraint. From a great many published data compiled by HYTTEN and LEITCH[1], three examples of representative populations are set out in Table 1.

The study made in Aberdeen, Scotland, represents what may be the nearest to a 'natural' situation, where the population practiced little or no dietary restriction and the medical policy was of non-intervention. Details of that body-mass gain are given in Table 2. The median gain of an overall average of about 400–450 g per week was associated with optimum clinical performance, a low rate of preeclampsia (gestosis) and infants of low body mass at birth, and the minimum perinatal mortality rate.

No explanation for most of the large range of body-mass gain can be offered, since most variables examined have only a small influence. Young women and primigravidae tend to gain slightly more than older and more parous women, but it is not possible to assess the effects of age and parity separately. There is no evidence that antecedent body mass has any systematic influence but fat women tend to gain a different composition of body mass, more water and less fat (see below).

Measurements of total body water[2] have shown two major patterns of body-mass gain in healthy pregnant women: those who have no clinical edema, or edema limited to the lower extremities, gain much less water and rather more body fat than those with generalized edema, even though this is usually clinically trivial. Women with clinically observed generalized edema represent about 15% of a normal clinic population. In Table 3, figures referable to the minority who develop generalized edema are shown in parenthesis.

Table 1 *Gain of body mass in pregnancy (per 4-week period)*

4-week period of pregnancy	USA, 1940[3] (2324 women)	Scotland, 1957[4] (2868 women)	India, 1959[5] (130 women)
		kg	
13–16 weeks	1.6	1.4	0.9
17–20 weeks	2.3	1.9	1.1
21–24 weeks	2.3	2.1	1.5
25–28 weeks	2.1	1.9	0.9
29–32 weeks	1.8	1.5	0.9
33–36 weeks	1.8	1.6	0.8
37–40 weeks	1.5	1.5	0.3

Table 2
Gain of body mass in pregnancy (per week) from a study of primigravidae made in the Aberdeen Maternity Hospital (1950–1955)[6]

Weeks of pregnancy	Number	80%				
			50%			
		P_{10}	P_{25}	P_{50}	P_{75}	P_{90}
				kg		
13–19 weeks	2868	0.19	0.29	0.42	0.54	0.66
20–29 weeks	2868	0.27	0.41	0.48	0.60	0.72
30–35 weeks	2868	0.16	0.28	0.42	0.58	0.72
36–40 weeks	2868	0.02	0.19	0.37	0.56	0.65
20 weeks to term (39, 40 or 41 weeks◊................	486	0.14	0.34	0.44	0.56	0.68

P: centiles.
◊Group aged 20–29 years, healthy, no major clinical abnormality.

Table 3 *Analysis of body-mass gain in pregnancy*

	Whole body	Fetus	Placenta	Amniotic fluid	Uterus	Breasts	Plasma	Erythrocytes	Extracellular extravascular water
Gain in total mass (g)									
10 weeks	650 (650)	5	20	30	140	45	100		0 (0)
20 weeks	4000 (4500)	300	170	350	320	180	600		30 (500)
30 weeks	8500 (10000)	1500	430	750	600	360	1300		80 (1530)
40 weeks	12500 (14500)	3400	650	800	970	405	1250		1680 (4900)
Protein storage (g)									
10 weeks	36	0.3	2	0	24	9	0		–
20 weeks	165	27	16	0.5	55	36	30		–
30 weeks	498	160	60	2	102	72	102		–
40 weeks	925	440	100	3	166	81	135		–
Fat storage (g)									
10 weeks	310† (310)†	Min-im	Min-im	–	0.5	1.4	0.4	–	–
20 weeks	2050† (2080)†	2	1	–	1.3	5.4	3.9	–	–
30 weeks	3480† (3530)†	80	3	–	2.4	10.8	17.4	–	–
40 weeks	3345† (2125)†	440	4	–	3.9	12.2	19.6	–	–
Gain in water (g)									
40 weeks	7610 (10830)	2414	540	792	800	304	920	163	1680 (4900)
Gain in extracellular water (g)									
40 weeks	5725 (8945)	1400	260	792	528	148	920	0	1680 (4900)
Gain in intracellular water (g)									
40 weeks	1885	1014	280	0	272	156	0	163	0
Sodium storage (mmol)									
40 weeks	945 (1405)	290	57	100	80	35	140	3	240 (700)
Potassium storage (mmol)									
40 weeks	319 (332)	154	42	3	50	35	4	24	7 (20)
Calcium storage (mmol)									
40 weeks	739 (746)	699	16	1.5	5.5	1.5	3	9	3 (10)

Figures in brackets are for women with generalized edema.
†The values for fat storage in the column 'Whole body' apply to the maternal fatty tissues.

*This chapter on 'Body Mass in Pregnancy' has been compiled in collaboration with F.E. HYTTEN, Clinical Research Centre, Northwick Park Hospital, Harrow (Middlesex), UK.

References

[1] HYTTEN and LEITCH, *The Physiology of Human Pregnancy,* 2nd ed., Blackwell, Oxford, 1971.
[2] HYTTEN et al., *J. Obstet. Gynaec. Brit. Cwlth,* **73**, 553 (1966).
[3] STANDER and PASTORE, *Amer. J. Obstet. Gynec.,* **39**, 928 (1940).
[4] THOMSON and BILLEWICZ, *Brit. med. J.,* **1**, 243 (1957).
[5] VENKATACHALAM et al., *Indian J. med. Res.,* **48**, 511 (1960).
[6] HYTTEN and LEITCH, *The Physiology of Human Pregnancy,* 2nd ed., Blackwell, Oxford 1971, page 265 (and personal communication).

Fitted centiles of body mass at birth (Aberdeen, 1948–1964)

Gestational age (whole weeks)	P_{05}	P_{10}	P_{25}	P_{50}	P_{75}	P_{90}	P_{95}
		90%					
			80%				
			50%				
	kg						
Both sexes, firstborn and later births							
32 weeks	1.11	1.31	1.62	1.91	2.31	2.63	2.77
33 weeks	1.41	1.61	1.91	2.20	2.58	2.89	3.05
34 weeks	1.68	1.88	2.17	2.47	2.83	3.13	3.30
35 weeks	1.92	2.12	2.40	2.70	3.04	3.35	3.52
36 weeks	2.13	2.33	2.61	2.90	3.23	3.53	3.72
37 weeks	2.31	2.50	2.78	3.07	3.40	3.70	3.88
38 weeks	2.47	2.65	2.92	3.22	3.54	3.83	4.02
39 weeks	2.59	2.76	3.03	3.33	3.65	3.95	4.13
40 weeks	2.68	2.84	3.12	3.42	3.73	4.03	4.22
41 weeks	2.74	2.90	3.17	3.47	3.79	4.10	4.27
42 weeks	2.78	2.92	3.20	3.49	3.82	4.13	4.30

Gestational age (whole weeks)	P_{05}	P_{10}	P_{25}	P_{50}	P_{75}	P_{90}	P_{95}
	kg						
Boys, firstborn and later births							
32 weeks	1.17	1.36	1.65	1.93	2.28	2.61	2.76
33 weeks	1.46	1.66	1.94	2.23	2.57	2.89	3.06
34 weeks	1.73	1.93	2.21	2.50	2.83	3.15	3.32
35 weeks	1.97	2.17	2.44	2.74	3.07	3.38	3.56
36 weeks	2.18	2.38	2.65	2.95	3.27	3.58	3.76
37 weeks	2.36	2.56	2.83	3.13	3.45	3.75	3.94
38 weeks	2.51	2.71	2.98	3.28	3.60	3.90	4.08
39 weeks	2.64	2.83	3.10	3.40	3.72	4.02	4.20
40 weeks	2.74	2.92	3.19	3.49	3.81	4.11	4.28
41 weeks	2.80	2.98	3.25	3.56	3.87	4.18	4.33
42 weeks	2.84	3.01	3.28	3.59	3.91	4.22	4.36
Boys, firstborn							
32 weeks	1.00	1.22	1.55	1.76	2.06	2.41	2.72
33 weeks	1.33	1.54	1.85	2.08	2.34	2.68	3.01
34 weeks	1.63	1.83	2.12	2.37	2.67	2.92	3.20
35 weeks	1.89	2.08	2.37	2.62	2.94	3.19	3.42
36 weeks	2.12	2.31	2.58	2.85	3.16	3.43	3.61
37 weeks	2.32	2.50	2.76	3.04	3.33	3.62	3.78
38 weeks	2.48	2.66	2.91	3.20	3.49	3.76	3.91
39 weeks	2.61	2.78	3.03	3.32	3.61	3.88	4.03
40 weeks	2.71	2.87	3.13	3.42	3.71	3.98	4.14
41 weeks	2.77	2.93	3.19	3.48	3.78	4.07	4.22
42 weeks	2.80	2.96	3.23	3.51	3.82	4.13	4.27
Boys, second and later births							
32 weeks	1.30	1.47	1.75	1.99	2.33	2.65	2.79
33 weeks	1.57	1.75	2.03	2.29	2.63	2.94	3.10
34 weeks	1.81	2.00	2.28	2.56	2.89	3.18	3.38
35 weeks	2.03	2.23	2.51	2.80	3.13	3.43	3.62
36 weeks	2.22	2.43	2.70	3.01	3.33	3.64	3.83
37 weeks	2.39	2.60	2.87	3.19	3.51	3.82	4.01
38 weeks	2.54	2.74	3.02	3.34	3.66	3.97	4.15
39 weeks	2.66	2.86	3.13	3.46	3.77	4.09	4.26
40 weeks	2.75	2.95	3.22	3.55	3.86	4.17	4.33
41 weeks	2.83	3.01	3.28	3.60	3.92	4.23	4.37
42 weeks	2.88	3.04	3.31	3.63	3.95	4.25	4.37

Gestational age (whole weeks)	P_{05}	P_{10}	P_{25}	P_{50}	P_{75}	P_{90}	P_{95}
	kg						
Girls, firstborn and later births							
32 weeks	1.05	1.27	1.58	1.90	2.35	2.66	2.78
33 weeks	1.35	1.57	1.87	2.18	2.59	2.90	3.04
34 weeks	1.63	1.83	2.13	2.43	2.81	3.11	3.27
35 weeks	1.87	2.07	2.36	2.65	3.00	3.31	3.47
36 weeks	2.09	2.27	2.56	2.85	3.18	3.48	3.65
37 weeks	2.27	2.44	2.73	3.01	3.33	3.62	3.81
38 weeks	2.42	2.59	2.86	3.15	3.45	3.75	3.94
39 weeks	2.54	2.70	2.97	3.26	3.56	3.85	4.04
40 weeks	2.62	2.78	3.05	3.34	3.64	3.93	4.12
41 weeks	2.68	2.83	3.10	3.39	3.69	3.99	4.17
42 weeks	2.70	2.85	3.11	3.41	3.73	4.02	4.20
Girls, firstborn							
32 weeks	1.05	1.26	1.53	1.83	2.10	2.41	2.71
33 weeks	1.33	1.54	1.81	2.11	2.38	2.64	2.92
34 weeks	1.58	1.79	2.07	2.35	2.63	2.89	3.10
35 weeks	1.81	2.02	2.29	2.58	2.85	3.10	3.30
36 weeks	2.01	2.21	2.49	2.77	3.04	3.31	3.46
37 weeks	2.19	2.38	2.66	2.94	3.21	3.46	3.59
38 weeks	2.34	2.53	2.80	3.08	3.35	3.59	3.71
39 weeks	2.47	2.64	2.91	3.19	3.46	3.70	3.82
40 weeks	2.57	2.73	3.00	3.27	3.54	3.79	3.93
41 weeks	2.65	2.80	3.05	3.33	3.60	3.86	4.02
42 weeks	2.70	2.83	3.08	3.36	3.63	3.91	4.03
Girls, second and later births							
32 weeks	1.22	1.34	1.62	2.00	2.44	2.69	2.78
33 weeks	1.49	1.62	1.91	2.26	2.68	2.94	3.06
34 weeks	1.73	1.88	2.17	2.50	2.89	3.17	3.31
35 weeks	1.95	2.11	2.40	2.71	3.08	3.37	3.53
36 weeks	2.14	2.31	2.59	2.90	3.24	3.54	3.72
37 weeks	2.30	2.48	2.76	3.06	3.39	3.69	3.88
38 weeks	2.44	2.62	2.90	3.19	3.51	3.82	4.01
39 weeks	2.55	2.73	3.00	3.29	3.61	3.92	4.11
40 weeks	2.64	2.81	3.08	3.37	3.69	3.99	4.18
41 weeks	2.70	2.86	3.13	3.42	3.74	4.04	4.22
42 weeks	2.73	2.88	3.14	3.45	3.78	4.07	4.23

(Brackets in each header: 90% spans P_{05}–P_{95} interval between P_{10}… as printed: 90% = P_{05} to P_{95}, 80% = P_{10} to P_{90}, 50% = P_{25} to P_{75}.)

Reference THOMSON et al., *J. Obstet. Gynaec. Brit. Cwlth.*, **75**, 903 (1968) [not including multiple births, macerated stillbirths and mortalities due to deformities].

Centiles of body mass, body length and head circumference at birth (Winterthur, 1969–1974)

Gestational age	Unit	Boys			Girls		
		80%			80%		
		P_{10}	P_{50}	P_{90}	P_{10}	P_{50}	P_{90}
28 weeks							
Mass	kg	0.82	1.13	1.46	0.81	1.11	1.36
Length	cm	35.8	37.8	39.9	34.0	36.8	40.0
Head circumference	cm	24.4	26.2	28.1	23.8	25.6	27.3
30 weeks							
Mass	kg	1.03	1.41	1.74	1.00	1.29	1.62
Length	cm	37.7	39.8	42.2	36.4	39.0	42.2
Head circumference	cm	25.9	27.6	29.4	25.6	27.4	29.3
32 weeks							
Mass	kg	1.35	1.79	2.17	1.27	1.61	2.01
Length	cm	39.6	42.0	44.8	38.9	41.6	44.8
Head circumference	cm	27.5	29.3	31.0	27.5	29.2	31.0
34 weeks							
Mass	kg	1.72	2.22	2.71	1.61	2.09	2.46
Length	cm	41.9	44.6	47.7	41.4	44.2	47.4
Head circumference	cm	29.2	31.1	32.8	29.1	30.8	32.6
36 weeks							
Mass	kg	2.18	2.70	3.29	2.09	2.58	3.03
Length	cm	44.2	47.2	50.4	43.9	46.6	49.7
Head circumference	cm	30.8	32.6	34.4	30.4	32.1	33.9
38 weeks							
Mass	kg	2.61	3.19	3.79	2.53	2.99	3.53
Length	cm	46.2	49.2	52.4	45.8	48.4	51.5
Head circumference	cm	31.9	33.7	35.5	31.4	33.1	35.0
40 weeks							
Mass	kg	2.90	3.50	4.10	2.84	3.31	3.84
Length	cm	47.6	50.5	53.5	47.2	49.8	52.8
Head circumference	cm	32.6	34.4	36.2	32.0	33.8	35.6
42 weeks							
Mass	kg	3.02	3.66	4.30	3.00	3.52	4.02
Length	cm	48.6	51.2	54.2	47.9	50.6	53.5
Head circumference	cm	33.0	34.8	36.6	32.3	34.2	36.0
44 weeks							
Mass	kg	3.09	3.73	4.43	3.05	3.58	4.11
Length	cm	49.0	51.5	54.5	48.3	50.9	53.8
Head circumference	cm	33.2	35.0	36.9	32.5	34.3	36.1

Reference
LARGO et al., *Helv.paediat.Acta,* **35**, 419 (1980).

Centiles of body mass, body length and head circumference after birth (Zurich, 1974–1980)

Gestational age	Unit	Boys			Girls		
		80%			80%		
		P_{10}	P_{50}	P_{90}	P_{10}	P_{50}	P_{90}
34 weeks							
Mass	kg	1.44	1.98	2.41	1.39	1.83	2.32
Length	cm	40.9	43.4	45.9	40.6	43.3	46.0
Head circumference	cm	28.8	30.5	32.2	28.3	30.0	31.8
36 weeks							
Mass	kg	1.85	2.41	2.88	1.84	2.30	2.83
Length	cm	43.2	45.7	48.3	42.6	45.4	48.3
Head circumference	cm	30.6	32.4	34.1	29.8	31.5	33.2
38 weeks							
Mass	kg	2.28	2.88	3.38	2.28	2.78	3.31
Length	cm	45.4	48.0	50.6	44.7	47.5	50.3
Head circumference	cm	32.1	33.9	35.7	31.3	32.9	34.6
40 weeks							
Mass	kg	2.68	3.29	3.83	2.69	3.19	3.75
Length	cm	47.4	49.9	52.4	46.6	49.3	52.0
Head circumference	cm	33.4	35.3	37.0	32.6	34.3	35.9
42 weeks							
Mass	kg	3.08	3.73	4.31	3.06	3.59	4.17
Length	cm	49.3	51.4	54.2	48.3	51.1	53.8
Head circumference	cm	34.7	36.4	38.2	33.8	35.4	37.0
44 weeks							
Mass	kg	3.48	4.16	4.75	3.39	3.97	4.53
Length	cm	51.0	53.3	55.9	50.0	52.7	55.3
Head circumference	cm	35.8	37.5	39.3	34.8	36.4	37.9
46 weeks							
Mass	kg	3.84	4.54	5.19	3.69	4.32	4.89
Length	cm	52.7	54.9	57.6	51.5	54.3	56.8
Head circumference	cm	36.8	38.4	40.2	35.6	37.2	38.8
48 weeks							
Mass	kg	4.18	4.88	5.60	3.99	4.66	5.23
Length	cm	54.0	56.4	60.0	52.8	55.6	58.2
Head circumference	cm	37.5	39.2	40.9	36.3	38.0	39.6
53 weeks							
Mass	kg	4.88	5.72	6.50	4.70	5.42	6.18
Length	cm	56.8	59.6	62.3	55.9	58.7	61.4
Head circumference	cm	39.3	41.0	42.7	37.6	39.3	41.1

Reference
LARGO et al., *Helv.paediat.Acta,* **35**, 419 (1980).

Since suitable abortion material is so scarce, embryological and anatomical studies of the fetus in the early stages of development have yielded only sparse information on growth at this stage of life. By contrast, a number of well-founded studies are available on the body mass of newborn infants from spontaneous deliveries during the 3rd trimester[1].

Centile values for any given gestational age represent centiles of the distribution of 'attained' values, and it is not possible to say whether a child born for example at the end of the 36th week of gestation would have been on the same centile had it remained in the uterus until 40 weeks. That is to say, the centile standards are necessarily based on single cross-sectional values and are in no sense *growth* charts. There are no standard curves for fetal body mass, length or head circumference which are valid for all populations[2]. Thus the standard values given in this chapter for fetal body mass are for instance much too high for Indian populations[3]. Even within one and the same population, standard values may change with the years[4]. THOMSON et al.[5] have published values for the adjustment of birth mass to be added to or subtracted from it – depending on the height and body mass of the mother in mid-pregnancy – *before* comparison with standard values. According to TANNER[6], at least the greater part of the discrepancies between the various standard curves to be found in the literature disappear when the body mass and height of the mother are allowed for. Swiss investigators have likewise come to the conclusion that the birth mass of the fetus at a given gestational age is mainly affected by the body mass of the mother[7].

In practice, intrauterine growth curves are useful for 4 main purposes:

(a) Estimation of the probable gestational age of the newborn infant from its measurements. The centile curves are not designed for this purpose; the median (centile 0.50) gives the expected value of the measurement for a given age and not, conversely, the expected age for a given measurement. From the following tables it will be seen that the error of the estimated age is such that the procedure is for this reason practically useless.

*This chapter on 'Intrauterine Growth' (pages 292–296) has been compiled in collaboration with W.Z. BILLEWICZ, Medical Research Council, Human Reproduction Group, Newcastle upon Tyne, UK.

Body length and body mass of fetuses in the 1st and 2nd trimesters

Gestational age	Crown–rump length	Mass	Gestational age	Crown–rump length	Mass
	cm	g		cm	g
6 weeks	0.5	–	17 weeks	12.1	120
7 weeks	0.8	0.07	18 weeks	13.6	170
8 weeks	1.5	0.22	19 weeks	15.3	253
9 weeks	2.5	0.88	20 weeks	16.4	316
10 weeks	3.5	3.5	21 weeks	17.5	385
11 weeks	4.6	6.0	22 weeks	18.6	460
12 weeks	5.7	11.0	23 weeks	19.7	542
13 weeks	6.8	19.0	24 weeks	20.8	630
14 weeks	8.1	33.0	25 weeks	21.8	723
15 weeks	9.4	55.0	26 weeks	22.8	823
16 weeks	10.7	80.0	27 weeks	23.8	930
			28 weeks	24.7	1045

Reference

IFFY et al., *Pediatrics*, **56**, 173 (1975) [data summarized from various sources].

Biometric data on fetuses in the 2nd and 3rd trimesters

Gestational age	Biparietal diameter	Fronto-occipital diameter	Head circumference	Transverse diameter of chest	Anteroposterior chest diameter	Circumference of chest	Total length	Mass
	cm							g
14 weeks	2.9	–	–	2.5	–	–		
15 weeks	3.2	3.5	11.0	2.7	2.6	9.0		
16 weeks	3.5	3.9	12.4	3.1	2.9	9.8		
17 weeks	3.8	4.3	13.5	3.4	3.1	10.9		
18 weeks	4.2	4.8	14.7	3.7	3.5	11.8		
19 weeks	4.6	5.2	15.9	4.0	3.8	12.6		
20 weeks	4.9	5.7	17.0	4.3	4.0	13.5		
21 weeks	5.2	6.0	18.3	4.5	4.3	14.5		
22 weeks	5.5	6.4	19.4	4.9	4.7	15.5		
23 weeks	5.8	6.7	20.7	5.1	4.9	16.5		
24 weeks	6.1	7.2	22.0	5.3	5.2	17.3		700
25 weeks	6.4	7.5	23.3	5.7	5.5	18.3	31	800
26 weeks	6.8	7.8	24.5	6.0	5.8	19.1		900
27 weeks	7.1	8.3	25.7	6.3	6.1	20.2	34	1000
28 weeks	7.4	8.6	26.7	6.6	6.4	21.1		1100
29 weeks	7.7	9.0	27.8	7.0	6.7	22.2	37	1250
30 weeks	8.0	9.3	28.6	7.3	7.0	23.0		1400
31 weeks	8.3	9.7	29.5	7.5	7.3	24.0	40	1600
32 weeks	8.5	9.9	30.2	7.8	7.6	24.9		1800
33 weeks	8.7	10.1	30.9	8.1	7.9	25.8	43	2000
34 weeks	8.9	10.3	31.5	8.5	8.2	26.8		2250
35 weeks	9.1	10.5	32.2	8.7	8.4	27.7	45	2550
36 weeks	9.2	10.8	32.7	8.9	8.7	28.7		2750
37 weeks	9.4	10.9	33.3	9.3	9.0	29.6	47	2950
38 weeks	9.5	11.0	33.6	9.5	9.3	30.6		3100
39 weeks	9.6	11.2	34.1	9.9	9.5	31.5	50	3250
40 weeks	9.7	11.4	34.5	10.1	9.7	32.1		3400
41 weeks	9.8	11.5	34.7	10.4	9.8	32.7	51	3500
42 weeks	9.9	11.6	35.0	10.5	9.9	33.1		3600

Reference

HANSMANN, M., *Gynäkologe*, **9**, 133 (1976).

Ultrasonically determined normal ranges of crown–rump length

Gestational age	$-2s$	Mean	$+2s$	Gestational age	$-2s$	Mean	$+2s$
	cm				cm		
7 weeks				14 weeks			
1 day	2.3	6.9	11.5	2 days	51.3	68.8	86.3
2 days	2.8	7.6	12.5	4 days	55.6	72.6	90.6
3 days	3.2	8.3	13.4	6 days	57.8	76.3	94.8
4 days	3.6	9.0	14.3	15 weeks			
5 days	3.9	9.6	15.2	2 days	62.5	81.8	101.1
6 days	4.3	10.2	16.1	4 days	65.6	85.4	105.2
8 weeks	4.7	10.8	16.9	6 days	68.6	88.9	109.2
1 day	5.0	11.4	17.8	16 weeks			
2 days	5.4	12.1	18.7	2 days	72.8	93.9	115.0
3 days	5.8	12.7	19.6	4 days	75.5	97.1	118.7
4 days	6.2	13.3	20.5	6 days	78.0	100.1	122.2
5 days	6.6	14.0	21.4	17 weeks			
6 days	7.0	14.7	22.4	2 days	81.5	104.4	127.3
9 weeks	7.5	15.4	23.4	4 days	83.6	107.0	130.4
1 day	8.0	16.2	24.4	6 days	85.6	109.5	133.4
3 days	9.1	17.8	26.5	18 weeks			
5 days	10.3	19.6	28.8	2 days	88.3	113.0	137.7
10 weeks	11.7	21.5	31.2	4 days	89.9	115.1	140.4
2 days	13.3	23.6	33.9	6 days	91.5	117.2	142.9
4 days	15.1	25.9	36.6	19 weeks			
6 days	17.0	28.3	39.6	2 days	93.5	120.0	146.5
11 weeks				4 days	94.8	121.9	148.9
2 days	20.3	32.4	44.4	6 days	96.2	123.7	151.2
4 days	22.7	35.3	47.9	20 weeks			
6 days	25.2	38.3	51.4	1 day	97.5	125.5	153.6
12 weeks				3 days	98.9	127.4	156.0
2 days	29.3	43.2	57.1	5 days	100.3	129.4	158.5
4 days	32.2	46.6	61.3	21 weeks	102.0	131.6	161.2
6 days	35.3	50.2	65.1	1 day	102.9	132.8	162.6
13 weeks				2 days	104.0	134.0	164.1
2 days	40.0	55.6	71.3				
4 days	43.2	59.4	75.5				
6 days	46.4	63.1	79.8				

Reference

HANSMANN et al., *Geburtsh. u. Frauenheilk.*, **39**, 656 (1979).

(b) Assessment of the growth status of an infant in relation to its gestational age. In this case, the question whether a given set of centiles is appropriate for the population to which the infant belongs may be of importance. One could argue, however, that the population centiles are lower than those of a given standard not for genetic reasons but because of adverse conditions operating in the area (for example poor maternal nutrition) and because there is a preference for using the higher standard centiles in the belief that they reflect postnatal risk more sharply. The decision as to which set of centiles should be used depends on the views of the investigator. In publications, for the sake of comparability, it is advisable to use well-known and well-documented standards.

(c) Centile curves may be used to compare two populations or selected groups with due allowance for fetal age. Since in this case the centiles are used simply as a yardstick common to both groups, the problem whether they are or are not appropriate for the population under study does not arise.

(d) Infants with body mass at birth below a selected centile are frequently used for special investigations in which they are compared to infants of 'normal' body mass. It is necessary to use sex- and pregnancy-number-specific centiles for such a purpose, otherwise the special group will contain an excess of females and first-born infants. Newborn infants below a selected centile are called 'small for dates', which gives the false impression of homogeneity. 'Small-for-dates' infants as a group are not homogeneous either with respect to mass at birth or to fetal age, a point worth keeping in mind when analyzing the results of studies involving this group of newborn infants.

In the table presented on page 292, gestational age is given in completed weeks, i.e. 39 weeks means 273–279 days inclusive. Thus, if smooth centile curves are drawn, the value appropriate to

Centiles of ultrasonically determined biparietal diameter

Gestational age	Number	P_{05}	P_{10}	P_{25}	P_{50}	P_{75}	P_{80}	P_{95}
		cm						
16 weeks	12	3.1	3.2	3.4	3.7	4.0	4.1	4.5
17 weeks	15	3.4	3.5	3.7	4.0	4.3	4.4	4.7
18 weeks	22	3.7	3.8	4.0	4.3	4.5	4.6	4.9
19 weeks	33	3.9	4.2	4.3	4.5	4.8	4.9	5.1
20 weeks	39	4.2	4.5	4.6	4.7	5.0	5.1	5.3
21 weeks	40	4.5	4.8	4.9	5.0	5.3	5.4	5.5
22 weeks	48	4.9	5.0	5.2	5.3	5.6	5.7	5.8
23 weeks	57	5.2	5.3	5.5	5.6	5.9	6.0	6.2
24 weeks	50	5.5	5.6	5.8	5.9	6.2	6.3	6.6
25 weeks	47	5.8	5.9	6.0	6.2	6.5	6.6	7.0
26 weeks	43	6.1	6.2	6.3	6.6	6.8	6.9	7.3
27 weeks	51	6.4	6.5	6.7	6.9	7.1	7.2	7.6
28 weeks	51	6.6	6.7	7.0	7.2	7.4	7.5	7.9
29 weeks	53	6.8	6.9	7.3	7.5	7.8	7.9	8.3
30 weeks	50	7.1	7.2	7.6	7.8	8.0	8.2	8.6
31 weeks	48	7.3	7.4	7.8	8.0	8.2	8.4	8.8
32 weeks	47	7.5	7.6	8.0	8.3	8.4	8.6	9.0
33 weeks	50	7.7	7.8	8.3	8.5	8.6	8.8	9.1
34 weeks	50	7.9	8.0	8.5	8.7	8.9	9.1	9.3
35 weeks	49	8.2	8.3	8.7	8.8	9.1	9.3	9.6
36 weeks	48	8.3	8.5	8.9	9.0	9.3	9.4	9.7
37 weeks	43	8.4	8.8	9.0	9.2	9.4	9.5	9.8
38 weeks	42	8.5	8.9	9.1	9.3	9.5	9.6	9.9
39 weeks	29	8.7	9.0	9.2	9.4	9.6	9.7	10.0
40 weeks	15	8.9	9.3	9.4	9.5	9.7	9.8	10.1

Reference
SABBAGHA et al., *Amer. J. Obstet. Gynec.*, **126**, 479 (1976).

Centiles of ultrasonically determined abdominal circumference

Gestational age	Number	P_{05}	P_{10}	P_{25}	P_{50}	P_{75}	P_{80}	P_{95}
		cm						
18 weeks	3	10.3	10.9	11.9	13.1	14.2	14.5	15.9
19 weeks	10	11.6	12.3	13.3	14.4	15.6	15.9	17.2
20 weeks	24	12.6	13.3	14.3	15.4	16.6	16.9	18.2
21 weeks	26	14.2	14.8	15.9	17.0	18.1	18.4	19.8
22 weeks	28	15.2	15.8	16.9	18.0	19.1	19.4	20.8
23 weeks	30	16.5	17.1	18.2	19.3	20.4	20.7	22.1
24 weeks	28	17.7	18.3	19.4	20.5	21.6	21.9	23.3
25 weeks	18	18.5	19.1	20.2	21.3	22.4	22.7	24.1
26 weeks	11	19.3	19.9	21.0	22.1	23.2	23.5	24.9
27 weeks	9	20.9	21.5	22.6	23.7	24.8	25.1	26.5
28 weeks	2	22.5	23.1	24.2	25.3	26.4	26.7	28.1
29 weeks	15	24.1	24.7	25.8	26.9	28.0	28.3	29.7
30 weeks	24	24.6	25.2	26.3	27.4	28.5	28.8	30.2
31 weeks	48	25.2	25.8	26.9	28.0	29.1	29.4	30.8
32 weeks	51	25.9	26.5	27.6	28.7	29.8	30.1	31.5
33 weeks	34	26.2	26.8	27.9	29.0	30.1	30.4	31.8
34 weeks	28	27.3	27.9	29.0	30.1	31.2	31.5	32.9
35 weeks	18	29.4	30.0	31.1	32.2	33.3	33.6	35.0
36 weeks	14	30.5	31.1	32.2	33.3	34.4	34.7	36.1
37 weeks	18	31.6	32.2	33.3	34.4	35.5	35.8	37.2
38 weeks	37	32.9	33.5	34.6	35.7	36.8	37.1	38.5
39 weeks	34	33.1	33.7	34.8	35.9	37.0	37.3	38.7
40 weeks	23	33.3	33.9	35.0	36.1	37.2	37.5	38.9
41 weeks	3	34.3	34.9	36.0	37.1	38.2	38.5	39.9

Reference
TAMURA and SABBAGHA, *Amer. J. Obstet. Gynec.*, **138**, 478 (1980).

39 completed weeks is best located at the midpoint of that week, i.e. at 276 days.

Nomenclature. It is generally agreed that infants with a body mass at birth of 2500 g or less should no longer be designated

Reference intervals for the assessment of gestational age on the basis of ultrasonically measured crown–rump lengths

Crown–rump length	−2s Weeks	−2s Days	Mean Weeks	Mean Days	+2s Weeks	+2s Days	Crown–rump length	−2s Weeks	−2s Days	Mean Weeks	Mean Days	+2s Weeks	+2s Days
6 mm	6	1	7	1	7	7	52 mm	11	7	13	2	14	4
7 mm	6	3	7	2	8	2	54 mm	11	7	13	3	14	5
8 mm	6	4	7	4	8	3	56 mm	12	1	13	4	14	6
9 mm	6	6	7	6	8	6	58 mm	12	2	13	5	14	7
10 mm	7	1	7	7	8	7	60 mm	12	3	13	6	15	1
11 mm	7	2	8	2	9	1	63 mm	12	4	13	7	15	3
12 mm	7	3	8	3	9	3	66 mm	12	5	14	2	15	5
13 mm	7	5	8	4	9	4	70 mm	12	7	14	3	15	7
14 mm	7	6	8	6	9	6	73 mm	13	1	14	5	16	1
15 mm	7	7	8	7	9	7	76 mm	13	2	14	6	16	3
16 mm	8	2	9	2	10	1	80 mm	13	4	15	1	16	5
17 mm	8	3	9	3	10	2	83 mm	13	5	15	2	16	7
18 mm	8	4	9	4	10	4	86 mm	13	6	15	4	17	2
19 mm	8	5	9	5	10	5	90 mm	14	1	15	6	17	4
20 mm	8	6	9	6	10	6	93 mm	14	3	16	1	17	6
21 mm	8	7	9	7	10	7	96 mm	14	4	16	3	18	1
22 mm	9	1	10	1	11	1	100 mm	14	6	16	5	18	3
23 mm	9	2	10	2	11	2	103 mm	15	1	16	7	18	6
24 mm	9	3	10	3	11	3	106 mm	15	3	17	2	19	1
26 mm	9	5	10	5	11	5	110 mm	15	5	17	4	19	4
28 mm	9	6	10	7	12	1	113 mm	15	7	17	7	19	7
30 mm	10	1	11	2	12	2	116 mm	16	2	18	2	20	2
32 mm	10	2	11	3	12	4	120 mm	16	4	18	4	20	4
34 mm	10	4	11	5	12	5	123 mm	16	7	18	7	20	7
36 mm	10	5	11	6	12	7	126 mm	17	2	19	2	21	3
38 mm	10	6	12	1	13	2	130 mm	17	5	19	6	21	6
40 mm	11	1	12	2	13	3	133 mm	17	7	20	1	22	2
42 mm	11	2	12	3	13	4	136 mm	18	3	20	4	22	6
44 mm	11	3	12	4	13	6	140 mm	18	6	20	7	23	2
46 mm	11	5	12	6	13	7	143 mm	19	1	21	3	23	5
48 mm	11	6	12	7	14	2	146 mm	19	4	21	6	24	1
50 mm	11	6	13	1	14	3	150 mm	19	7	22	3	24	5

(Estimates of gestational age: $-2s$, Mean, $+2s$, in Weeks | Days)

Reference
HANSMANN et al., *Geburtsh. u. Frauenheilk.*, **39**, 656 (1979).

'premature'[8,9]. More appropriate terms are 'large for dates' and 'small for dates', or 'large for gestational age' and 'small for gestational age', with reference to an intrauterine growth standard, even though the limiting values for 'large' and 'small' vary from one authority to another (for instance centiles 0.10 and 0.90, centiles 0.03 and 0.97, mean $-2s$ and mean $+2s$ of the body mass for a given gestational age). As far as gestational age is concerned, the expression 'term' means 37–42 weeks[10] or 38–42 weeks[11]; delivery times lying outside these ranges are known as 'pre-term' or 'post-term'.

Extrauterine growth. In studies of perinatal growth, 3 periods must be distinguished[12]: *intrauterine* growth as judged by measurements made at birth, *transitional* growth during the first 6–12 days of life for which there are no valid norms on account of the wide individual variations, and *extrauterine* growth after the first 6–12 days, the rate of which is greater than that of intrauterine growth.

Ultrasound measurements of fetal growth

Examples of growth patterns as measured by ultrasound are given in the tables on pages 294 and 295. Accurate assessment of gestational age is one of the most important uses of diagnostic ultrasonography. Measurement of the crown–rump length during the first 15 weeks of pregnancy, at the time of least biological variability, is a very precise method of determining gestational age[13–16]. With less precision, an assessment of gestational age in the 2nd trimester is possible by measuring the biparietal diameter[17,18] or the femur length[19,20]. For the calculation of fetal body mass, several formulas using various growth parameters have been developed, for example:

Fetal mass (kg)

$$= -1.05775\,\mathrm{BPD} + 0.649145\,\mathrm{TDC} + 0.0930707\,\mathrm{BPD}^2 - 0.0205620\,\mathrm{TDC}^2 + 0.515263$$ [18]

$$= -1.33450\,\mathrm{BPD} + 0.798429\,\mathrm{APDC} + 0.103458\,\mathrm{BPD}^2 - 0.0254788\,\mathrm{APDC}^2 + 1.35470$$ [18]

$$= 0.378\,\mathrm{BPD} + 0.416\,\mathrm{DC} - 4.450$$ [21]

$$= 0.349\,\mathrm{BPD} + 0.384\,\mathrm{DC} + 0.022\,\mathrm{CR}$$ [21]

Log(fetal mass in kg)

$$= -1.7492 + 0.166\,\mathrm{BPD} + 0.046\,\mathrm{AC} - \frac{2.646(\mathrm{AC} \times \mathrm{BPD})}{1000}$$ [22]

BPD Biparietal diameter (cm)
TDC Transverse diameter of chest (cm)
APDC Anteroposterior diameter of chest (cm)
DC Mean diameter of chest (cm)
CR Crown–rump length (cm)
AC Abdominal circumference (cm)

References

[1] BRENNER et al., *Amer. J. Obstet. Gynec.*, **126**, 555 (1976).
[2] FORBES and SMALLS, *Brit. J. Obstet. Gynaec.*, **90**, 297 (1983).
[3] BALAKRISHNAN and NAMBOODIRI, *Ann. hum. Genet.*, **24**, 5 (1960).
[4] CARR-HILL and PRITCHARD, *Brit. J. Obstet. Gynaec.*, **90**, 718 (1983).
[5] THOMSON et al., *J. Obstet. Gynaec. Brit. Cwlth*, **75**, 903 (1968).
[6] TANNER, J. M., *Pediatrics*, **46**, 1 (1970).
[7] WÄLLI et al., *Helv. paediat. Acta*, **35**, 397 (1980).
[8] GRUENWALD, P., *Ciba Found. Symp.*, NS **27**, 3 (1974).
[9] DUBOWITZ, V., *Ciba Found. Symp.*, NS **27**, 47 (1974).
[10] SECOND European Congress of Perinatal Medicine, *Arch. Dis. Childh.*, **45**, 730 (1970).
[11] SILVERMAN et al., *Pediatrics*, **39**, 935 (1967).
[12] LARGO et al., *Helv. paediat. Acta*, **35**, 419 (1980).
[13] ROBINSON, H. P., *Brit. med. J.*, **4**, 28 (1973).
[14] ROBINSON and FLEMING, *Brit. J. Obstet. Gynaec.*, **82**, 702 (1975).
[15] HANSMANN et al., *Geburtsh. u. Frauenheilk.*, **39**, 656 (1979).
[16] PEDERSEN, J. F., *Brit. J. Obstet. Gynaec.*, **89**, 926 (1982).
[17] CAMPBELL, S., *J. Obstet. Gynaec. Brit. Cwlth*, **76**, 603 (1969), and **77**, 1057 (1970).
[18] HANSMANN, M., *Gynäkologe*, **9**, 133 (1976).
[19] O'BRIEN et al., *Amer. J. Obstet. Gynec.*, **139**, 540 (1981).
[20] YEH et al., *Amer. J. Obstet. Gynec.*, **144**, 519 (1982).
[21] MILLER, E. C., *Zbl. Gynäk.*, **102**, 272 (1980).
[22] SHEPARD et al., *Amer. J. Obstet. Gynec.*, **142**, 47 (1982).

Loss of body mass during the first days of life[1]

	Body mass at birth	3rd day		5th day		7th day	
		Mean	s	Mean	s	Mean	s
	g	Loss as % of body mass at birth					
Normal delivery	3465	7.22	2.52	7.29	3.14	5.72	3.29
Abdominal delivery with labor pains	3580	7.19	2.09	7.65	2.83	6.06	3.31
Abdominal delivery without labor pains	3550	7.27	2.33	7.97	2.17	7.66	3.34

Mean weekly gain in body mass during the 1st year of life as a function of body mass at birth[2]

	Body mass at birth			
	0.91 kg to 1.36 kg	1.36 kg to 1.81 kg	1.81 kg to 2.27 kg	2.27 kg to 2.72 kg
	Gain in kg			
Boys				
0–1 month	113	139	159	164
1–3 months	204	221	235	241
3–6 months	230	213	190	173
6–9 months	145	133	125	113
9–12 months	99	91	85	82
Girls				
0–1 month	113	139	159	145
1–3 months	187	196	193	198
3–6 months	201	187	179	173
6–9 months	156	145	142	130
9–12 months	105	91	79	68

Age at which twice the body mass at birth is reached[3]

	Number	Age	
		Days $\pm s_{\bar{x}}$	Months
Boys	192	111 ± 3	3.6
Girls	165	129 ± 3	4.1
Breast-fed infants (55% boys, 45% girls)	139	124 ± 4	4.0
Infants reared on adapted milk (52% boys, 48% girls)	115	113 ± 4	3.6

The tables on pages 298–300 are summaries of data collected between 1929 and 1975 by the Fels Research Institute, Yellow Springs (Ohio), on children up to the age of 36 months, together with the results of a broadly based study made in the period 1963 to 1975 by the National Center for Health Statistics (NCHS) on children aged from 2 to 18 years. The data constitute the new USA standard (NCHS standard) which replaces the earlier, much quoted Boston standard (also known as the Harvard Tables)[4] based on data from an economically privileged white population.

When using the NCHS standard (pages 298–300) it must be borne in mind that in the children up to the age of 36 months body length was measured in the recumbent position (measurements made on standing children are up to 2 cm lower) and that body mass was determined without clothing. The height of the 2- to 18-year-olds was obtained with children standing in stockinged feet. Data for body mass included standardized examination clothing as follows: 2-year-olds 0.05 kg, 3- to 5-year-olds 0.09 kg, 6- to 18-year-olds 0.11–0.3 kg.

*This chapter on 'Normal Measurements During Growth' (pages 297–312) has been compiled in collaboration with W.Z. Billewicz, Medical Research Council, Human Reproduction Group, Newcastle upon Tyne, UK.

◊Symbol: *P*.

The tables on pages 301–308 show the results of a study made on children in Northwest Switzerland (Basel and Wettingen) in the period 1956–1962. A comparison of these data with those from other European studies is to be found on page 300. The results of the NCHS study mentioned lie within the range of the mean values in these tables.

In view of the effect of genetic and socioeconomic factors, the growth of a child is best judged against a standard from the population to which the child belongs[5]. On account of the special importance of growth data at an early age, standards for South Chinese (Hongkong) and West Nigerian (Imesi) children are reproduced on pages 309 and 310.

The tables and graphs on pages 298–312 provide centiles◊ of values of growth parameters attained at a given age. An estimate of the *average* rate of growth (but not of its variability) can be obtained from differences between the values for the centiles 0.50 at two specified ages. Such estimates, though inefficient due to the cross-sectional nature of the data, are valid up to 8 years of age for girls and up to 10 years for boys. Beyond those ages, the variability in the age of initiation of the adolescent growth spurt makes such differences invalid as estimators of the rate of growth. Data on the variability of growth rates during adolescence, based on measurements made by Tanner and Whitehouse[6], are to be found in detail in monographs on the subject[7,8]. The growth rates given here on pages 311 and 312 were determined by the Fels Research Institute, Yellow Springs (Ohio), between 1929 and 1978 in longitudinal studies on white children and are therefore fairly close to those derivable from the NCHS study[14].

When using the centiles of the 'attained' values the same considerations must be borne in mind as those set out on page 293 under the heading 'Intrauterine Growth'.

A special use of standard values for growth remains to be mentioned. In studies on the relationship between nutrition and morbidity, children are often classified on the basis of their position by allotting them an expectancy value, usually that corresponding to the centile 0.50 of a recognized growth standard. The WHO recommends the following classification when the NCHS standard is used[9]:

(a) Greater than centile 0.97
(b) Between centile 0.97 and centile 0.50
(c) Between centile 0.50 and centile 0.03
(d) Between centile 0.03 and $\bar{x} - 3s$
(e) Between $\bar{x} - 3s$ and $\bar{x} - 4s$
(f) Smaller than $\bar{x} - 4s$

The centiles 0.50 of the growth standard also yield reference data on *body height for age* and *body mass for height*[10,11]. From the first of these, conclusions can be drawn concerning the nutritional status of the child in his earlier years, while the second throws light on the current nutritional status. A suitable parameter for assessing the nutritional status of 1- to 5-year-old children which is independent of age is the nutritional index $10^4 \times M/H^{1.6}$ (M = mass in kg; H = height in cm)[12]. Similar information to that afforded by *body mass for height* is obtainable from the parameter *arm circumference for height;* together with skinfold measurements this yields information on muscle mass and fat mass[10,13].

References

1 Furuhjelm, U., *Etud. néo-natal.*, **3**, 93 (1954) [Women's Hospital, Helsinki, 1947–1952].
2 Levin et al., *Weight Gains. Serum Protein Levels and Health of Breast-Fed and Artificially Fed Infants,* Medical Research Council, Special Report Series, No. 296, H.M.S.O., London, 1959, page 104.
3 Neumann and Alpaugh, *Pediatrics,* **57**, 469 (1976).
4 Nelson, W.E. (Eds.), *Textbook of Pediatrics,* 9th ed., Saunders, Philadelphia, 1969, page 42.
5 Tanner, J.M., *Arch. Dis. Childh.,* **51**, 1 (1976); Goldstein and Tanner, *Lancet,* **1**, 582 (1980).
6 Tanner and Whitehouse, *Arch. Dis. Childh.,* **51**, 170 (1976).
7 Marshall, W.A., *Human Growth and Its Disorders,* Academic Press, London, 1977.
8 Buckler, J.M., *A Reference Manual of Growth and Development,* Blackwell, Oxford, 1979.
9 *A Growth Chart for International Use in Maternal and Child Health Care,* WHO, Geneva, 1978, page 15.
10 Waterlow, J.C., *Brit. med. J.,* **3**, 566 (1972).
11 Graham et al., *Amer. J. clin. Nutr.,* **32**, 703 (1979).
12 Dugdale, A.E., *Amer. J. clin. Nutr.,* **24**, 174 (1971).
13 Frisancho, A.R., *Amer. J. clin. Nutr.,* **27**, 1052 (1974); Burgert and Anderson, *Amer. J. clin. Nutr.,* **32**, 2136 (1979); Hall et al., *Amer. J. clin. Nutr.,* **33**, 1846 (1980).
14 Roche and Himes, *Amer. J. clin. Nutr.,* **33**, 2041 (1980).

	Unit	Boys							Girls						
		90%							90%						
			80%							80%					
				50%							50%				
		P_{05}	P_{10}	P_{25}	P_{50}	P_{75}	P_{90}	P_{95}	P_{05}	P_{10}	P_{25}	P_{50}	P_{75}	P_{90}	P_{95}
Data of Fels Research Institute, Yellow Springs (Ohio); statistics of National Center for Health Statistics (NHCS)◊															
Birth															
Mass................	kg	2.54	2.78	3.00	3.27	3.64	3.82	4.15	2.36	2.58	2.93	3.23	3.52	3.64	3.81
Length	cm	46.4	47.5	49.0	50.5	51.8	53.5	54.4	45.4	46.4	48.2	49.9	51.0	52.0	52.9
Head circumference	cm	32.6	33.0	33.9	34.8	35.6	36.6	37.2	32.1	32.9	33.5	34.3	34.8	35.5	35.9
1 month															
Mass................	kg	3.16	3.43	3.82	4.29	4.75	5.14	5.38	2.97	3.22	3.59	3.98	4.36	4.65	4.92
Length	cm	50.4	51.3	53.0	54.6	56.2	57.7	58.6	49.2	50.2	51.9	53.5	54.9	56.1	56.9
Head circumference	cm	34.9	35.4	36.2	37.2	38.1	39.0	39.6	34.2	34.8	35.6	36.4	37.1	37.8	38.3
3 months															
Mass................	kg	4.43	4.78	5.32	5.98	6.56	7.14	7.37	4.18	4.47	4.88	5.40	5.90	6.39	6.74
Length	cm	56.7	57.7	59.4	61.1	63.0	64.5	65.4	55.4	56.2	57.8	59.5	61.2	62.7	63.4
Head circumference	cm	38.4	38.9	39.7	40.6	41.7	42.5	43.1	37.3	37.8	38.7	39.5	40.4	41.2	41.7
6 months															
Mass................	kg	6.20	6.61	7.20	7.85	8.49	9.10	9.46	5.79	6.12	6.60	7.21	7.83	8.38	8.73
Length	cm	63.4	64.4	66.1	67.8	69.7	71.3	72.3	61.8	62.6	64.2	65.9	67.8	69.4	70.2
Head circumference	cm	41.5	42.0	42.8	43.8	44.7	45.6	46.2	40.3	40.9	41.6	42.4	43.3	44.1	44.6
9 months															
Mass................	kg	7.52	7.95	8.56	9.18	9.88	10.49	10.93	7.00	7.34	7.89	8.56	9.24	9.83	10.17
Length	cm	68.0	69.1	70.6	72.3	74.0	75.9	77.1	66.1	67.0	68.7	70.4	72.4	74.0	75.0
Head circumference	cm	43.5	44.0	44.8	45.8	46.6	47.5	48.1	42.3	42.8	43.5	44.3	45.1	46.0	46.4
12 months															
Mass................	kg	8.43	8.84	9.49	10.15	10.91	11.54	11.99	7.84	8.19	8.81	9.53	10.23	10.87	11.24
Length	cm	71.7	72.8	74.3	76.1	77.7	79.8	81.2	69.8	70.8	72.4	74.3	76.3	78.0	79.1
Head circumference	cm	44.8	45.3	46.1	47.0	47.9	48.8	49.3	43.5	44.1	44.8	45.6	46.4	47.2	47.6
18 months															
Mass................	kg	9.59	9.92	10.67	11.47	12.31	13.05	13.44	8.92	9.30	10.04	10.82	11.55	12.30	12.76
Length	cm	77.5	78.7	80.5	82.4	84.3	86.6	88.1	76.0	77.2	78.8	80.9	83.0	85.0	86.1
Head circumference	cm	46.3	46.7	47.4	48.4	49.3	50.1	50.6	45.0	45.6	46.3	47.1	47.9	48.6	49.1
24 months															
Mass................	kg	10.54	10.85	11.65	12.59	13.44	14.29	14.70	9.87	10.26	11.10	11.90	12.74	13.57	14.08
Length	cm	82.3	83.5	85.6	87.6	89.9	92.2	93.8	81.3	82.5	84.2	86.5	88.7	90.8	92.0
Head circumference	cm	47.3	47.7	48.3	49.2	50.2	51.0	51.4	46.1	46.5	47.3	48.1	48.8	49.6	50.1
30 months															
Mass................	kg	11.44	11.80	12.63	13.67	14.51	15.47	15.97	10.78	11.21	12.11	12.93	13.93	14.81	15.35
Length	cm	87.0	88.2	90.1	92.3	94.6	97.0	98.7	86.0	87.0	88.9	91.3	93.7	95.6	96.9
Head circumference	cm	48.0	48.4	49.1	49.9	51.0	51.7	52.2	47.0	47.3	48.0	48.8	49.4	50.3	50.8
36 months															
Mass................	kg	12.26	12.69	13.58	14.69	15.59	16.66	17.28	11.60	12.07	12.99	13.93	15.03	15.97	16.54
Length	cm	91.6	92.4	94.2	96.5	98.9	101.4	103.1	90.0	91.0	93.1	95.6	98.1	100.0	101.5
Head circumference	cm	48.6	49.0	49.7	50.5	51.5	52.3	52.8	47.6	47.9	48.5	49.3	50.0	50.8	51.4
Data and statistics of National Center for Health Statistics (NHCS)*															
2 years															
Mass................	kg	10.49	10.96	11.55	12.34	13.36	14.38	15.50	9.95	10.32	10.96	11.80	12.73	13.58	14.15
Height..............	cm	82.5	83.5	85.3	86.8	89.2	92.0	94.4	81.6	82.1	84.0	86.8	89.3	92.0	93.6
2½ years															
Mass................	kg	11.27	11.77	12.55	13.52	14.61	15.71	16.61	10.80	11.35	12.11	13.03	14.23	15.16	15.76
Height..............	cm	85.4	86.5	88.5	90.4	92.9	95.6	97.8	84.6	85.3	87.3	90.0	92.5	95.0	96.6
3 years															
Mass................	kg	12.05	12.58	13.52	14.62	15.78	16.95	17.77	11.61	12.26	13.11	14.10	15.50	16.54	17.22
Height..............	cm	89.0	90.3	92.6	94.9	97.5	100.1	102.0	88.3	89.3	91.4	94.1	96.6	99.0	100.6
3½ years															
Mass................	kg	12.84	13.41	14.46	15.68	16.90	18.15	18.98	12.37	13.08	14.00	15.07	16.59	17.77	18.59
Height..............	cm	92.5	93.9	96.4	99.1	101.7	104.3	106.1	91.7	93.0	95.2	97.9	100.5	102.8	104.5

Reference HAMILL et al., *Amer. J. clin. Nutr.*, **32**, 607 (1979) [◊867 children (1929–1975); *20000 children (1963–1975)].

	Unit	Boys							Girls						
		90%							90%						
			80%							80%					
				50%							50%				
		P_{05}	P_{10}	P_{25}	P_{50}	P_{75}	P_{90}	P_{95}	P_{05}	P_{10}	P_{25}	P_{50}	P_{75}	P_{90}	P_{95}
4 years															
Mass	kg	13.64	14.24	15.39	16.69	17.99	19.32	20.27	13.11	13.84	14.80	15.96	17.56	18.93	19.91
Height	cm	95.8	97.3	100.0	102.9	105.7	108.2	109.9	95.0	96.4	98.8	101.6	104.3	106.6	108.3
4½ years															
Mass	kg	14.45	15.10	16.30	17.69	19.06	20.50	21.63	13.83	14.56	15.55	16.81	18.48	20.06	21.24
Height	cm	98.9	100.6	103.4	106.6	109.4	111.9	113.5	98.1	99.7	102.2	105.0	107.9	110.2	112.0
5 years															
Mass	kg	15.27	15.96	17.22	18.67	20.14	21.70	23.09	14.55	15.26	16.29	17.66	19.39	21.23	22.62
Height	cm	102.0	103.7	106.5	109.9	112.8	115.4	117.0	101.1	102.7	105.4	108.4	111.4	113.8	115.6
5½ years															
Mass	kg	16.09	16.83	18.14	19.67	21.25	22.96	24.66	15.29	15.97	17.05	18.56	20.36	22.48	24.11
Height	cm	104.9	106.7	109.6	113.1	116.1	118.7	120.3	103.9	105.6	108.4	111.6	114.8	117.4	119.2
6 years															
Mass	kg	16.93	17.72	19.07	20.69	22.40	24.31	26.34	16.05	16.72	17.86	19.52	21.44	23.89	25.75
Height	cm	107.7	109.6	112.5	116.1	119.2	121.9	123.5	106.6	108.4	111.3	114.6	118.1	120.8	122.7
6½ years															
Mass	kg	17.78	18.62	20.02	21.74	23.62	25.76	28.16	16.85	17.51	18.76	20.61	22.68	25.50	27.59
Height	cm	110.4	112.3	115.3	119.0	122.2	124.9	126.6	109.2	111.0	114.1	117.6	121.3	124.2	126.1
7 years															
Mass	kg	18.64	19.53	21.00	22.85	24.94	27.36	30.12	17.71	18.39	19.78	21.84	24.16	27.39	29.68
Height	cm	113.0	115.0	118.0	121.7	125.0	127.9	129.7	111.8	113.6	116.8	120.6	124.4	127.6	129.5
7½ years															
Mass	kg	19.52	20.45	22.02	24.03	26.36	29.11	32.73	18.62	19.37	20.95	23.26	25.90	29.57	32.07
Height	cm	115.6	117.6	120.6	124.4	127.8	130.8	132.7	114.4	116.2	119.5	123.5	127.5	130.9	132.9
8 years															
Mass	kg	20.40	21.39	23.09	25.30	27.91	31.06	34.51	19.62	20.45	22.26	24.84	27.88	32.04	34.71
Height	cm	118.1	120.2	123.2	127.0	130.5	133.6	135.7	116.9	118.7	122.2	126.4	130.6	134.2	136.2
8½ years															
Mass	kg	21.31	22.34	24.21	26.66	29.61	33.22	36.96	20.68	21.64	23.70	26.58	30.08	34.73	37.58
Height	cm	120.5	122.7	125.7	129.6	133.2	136.5	138.8	119.5	121.3	124.9	129.3	133.6	137.4	139.6
9 years															
Mass	kg	22.25	23.33	25.40	28.13	31.46	35.57	39.58	21.82	22.92	25.27	28.46	32.44	37.60	40.64
Height	cm	122.9	125.2	128.2	132.2	136.0	139.4	141.8	122.1	123.9	127.7	132.2	136.7	140.7	142.9
9½ years															
Mass	kg	23.25	24.38	26.68	29.73	33.46	38.11	42.35	23.05	24.29	26.94	30.45	34.94	40.61	43.85
Height	cm	125.3	127.6	130.8	134.8	138.8	142.4	144.9	124.8	126.6	130.6	135.2	139.8	143.9	146.2
10 years															
Mass	kg	24.33	25.52	28.07	31.44	35.61	40.80	45.27	24.36	25.76	28.71	32.55	37.53	43.70	47.17
Height	cm	127.7	130.1	133.4	137.5	141.6	145.5	148.1	127.5	129.5	133.6	138.3	142.9	147.2	149.5
10½ years															
Mass	kg	25.51	26.78	29.59	33.30	37.92	43.63	48.31	25.75	27.32	30.57	34.72	40.17	46.84	50.57
Height	cm	130.1	132.6	136.0	140.3	144.6	148.7	151.5	130.4	132.5	136.7	141.5	146.1	150.4	152.8
11 years															
Mass	kg	26.80	28.17	31.25	35.30	40.38	46.57	51.47	27.24	28.97	32.49	36.95	42.84	49.96	54.00
Height	cm	132.6	135.1	138.7	143.3	147.8	152.1	154.9	133.5	135.6	140.0	144.8	149.3	153.7	156.2
11½ years															
Mass	kg	28.24	29.72	33.08	37.46	43.00	49.61	54.73	28.83	30.71	34.48	39.23	45.48	53.03	57.42
Height	cm	135.0	137.7	141.5	146.4	151.1	155.6	158.5	136.6	139.0	143.5	148.2	152.6	156.9	159.5
12 years															
Mass	kg	29.85	31.46	35.09	39.78	45.77	52.73	58.09	30.52	32.53	36.52	41.53	48.07	55.99	60.81
Height	cm	137.6	140.3	144.4	149.7	154.6	159.4	162.3	139.8	142.3	147.0	151.5	155.8	160.0	162.7
12½ years															
Mass	kg	31.64	33.41	37.31	42.27	48.70	55.91	61.52	32.30	34.42	38.59	43.84	50.56	58.81	64.12
Height	cm	140.2	143.0	147.4	153.0	158.2	163.2	166.1	142.7	145.4	150.1	154.6	158.8	162.9	165.6

Reference HAMILL et al., *Amer. J. clin. Nutr.*, **32**, 607 (1979) [NCHS, 20000 children (1963–1975)].

	Unit	Boys							Girls						
		90%							90%						
			80%							80%					
				50%							50%				
		P_{05}	P_{10}	P_{25}	P_{50}	P_{75}	P_{90}	P_{95}	P_{05}	P_{10}	P_{25}	P_{50}	P_{75}	P_{90}	P_{95}
13 years															
Mass	kg	33.64	35.60	39.74	44.95	51.79	59.12	65.02	34.14	36.35	40.65	46.10	52.91	61.45	67.30
Height	cm	142.9	145.8	150.5	156.5	161.8	167.0	169.8	145.2	148.0	152.8	157.1	161.3	165.3	168.1
13½ years															
Mass	kg	35.85	38.03	42.40	47.81	55.02	62.35	68.51	35.98	38.26	42.65	48.26	55.11	63.87	70.30
Height	cm	145.7	148.7	153.6	159.9	165.3	170.5	173.4	147.2	150.0	154.7	159.0	163.2	167.3	170.0
14 years															
Mass	kg	38.22	40.64	45.21	50.77	58.31	65.57	72.13	37.76	40.11	44.54	50.28	57.09	66.04	73.08
Height	cm	148.8	151.8	156.9	163.1	168.5	173.8	176.7	148.7	151.5	155.9	160.4	164.6	168.7	171.3
14½ years															
Mass	kg	40.66	43.34	48.08	53.76	61.58	68.76	75.66	39.45	41.83	46.28	52.10	58.84	67.95	75.59
Height	cm	152.0	155.0	160.1	166.2	171.5	176.6	179.5	149.7	152.5	156.8	161.2	165.6	169.8	172.2
15 years															
Mass	kg	43.11	46.06	50.92	56.71	64.72	71.91	79.12	40.99	43.38	47.82	53.68	60.32	69.54	77.78
Height	cm	155.2	158.2	163.3	169.0	174.1	178.9	181.9	150.5	153.2	157.2	161.8	166.3	170.5	172.8
15½ years															
Mass	kg	45.50	48.69	53.64	59.51	67.64	74.98	82.45	42.32	44.72	49.10	54.96	61.48	70.79	79.59
Height	cm	158.3	161.2	166.2	171.5	176.3	180.8	183.9	151.1	153.6	157.5	162.1	166.7	170.9	173.1
16 years															
Mass	kg	47.74	51.16	56.16	62.10	70.26	77.97	85.62	43.41	45.78	50.09	55.89	62.29	71.68	80.99
Height	cm	161.1	163.9	168.7	173.5	178.1	182.4	185.4	151.6	154.1	157.8	162.4	166.9	171.1	173.3
16½ years															
Mass	kg	49.76	53.39	58.38	64.39	72.46	80.84	88.59	44.20	46.54	50.75	56.44	62.75	72.18	81.93
Height	cm	163.4	166.1	170.6	175.2	179.5	183.6	186.6	152.2	154.6	158.2	162.7	167.1	171.2	173.4
17 years															
Mass	kg	51.50	55.28	60.22	66.31	74.17	83.58	91.31	44.74	47.04	51.14	56.69	62.91	72.38	82.46
Height	cm	164.9	167.7	171.9	176.2	180.5	184.4	187.3	152.7	155.1	158.7	163.1	167.3	171.2	173.5
17½ years															
Mass	kg	52.89	56.78	61.61	67.78	75.32	86.14	93.73	45.08	47.33	51.33	56.71	62.89	72.37	82.62
Height	cm	165.6	168.5	172.4	176.7	181.0	185.0	187.6	153.2	155.6	159.1	163.4	167.5	171.1	173.5
18 years															
Mass	kg	53.97	57.89	62.61	68.88	76.04	88.41	95.76	45.26	47.47	51.39	56.62	62.78	72.25	82.47
Height	cm	165.7	168.7	172.3	176.8	181.2	185.3	187.6	153.6	156.0	159.6	163.7	167.6	171.0	173.6

Reference HAMILL et al., *Amer. J. clin. Nutr.*, **32**, 607 (1979) [NCHS, 20000 children (1963–1975)].

Comparison of some European growth studies (body length in cm)

Age	Northwest Switzerland[1] (P_{50})		Zurich[2] (mean)		England[3] (P_{50})		Netherlands[4] (mean)		Northwest Germany[5] (P_{50})	
	Boys	Girls	Boys	Girls	Boys	Girls	Boys	Girls	Boys	Girls
3 months	61.0	59.5	60.9	59.5	60.7	59.0	60.7	59.9	–	–
6 months	68.5	66.5	67.9	66.0	68.2	65.5	68.9	67.6	–	–
1 year	76.5	74.7	76.2	74.5	76.3	74.2	78.9	77.4	–	–
2 years	87.0	86.5	88.3	86.6	86.9	85.6	89.7	88.6	88.2	87.7
3 years	96.3	95.2	97.2	95.4	94.2	93.0	98.3	97.9	98.3	97.0
4 years	103.5	102.3	104.9	102.9	101.6	100.4	105.9	105.0	105.2	104.7
5 years	110.2	109.2	111.4	109.5	108.3	107.2	112.6	111.7	112.5	111.3
6 years	116.5	115.9	117.6	115.7	114.6	113.4	118.1	118.6	118.4	118.0
7 years	122.4	122.4	123.7	121.7	120.5	119.3	124.8	124.1	125.3	124.6
8 years	128.0	128.2	129.8	127.7	126.2	125.0	131.0	130.4	131.2	130.7
9 years	133.3	133.2	135.3	133.2	131.6	130.6	136.6	135.8	136.6	136.0
10 years	138.3	137.5	140.4	138.3	136.8	136.4	140.9	140.8	141.1	141.6
11 years	142.7	141.8	145.0	144.1	141.9	142.7	145.9	145.8	145.7	147.1
12 years	147.0	148.5	150.0	150.0	147.3	149.3	151.5	152.9	150.4	154.1

References
[1] HEIMENDINGER, J., *Helv. paediat. Acta*, **19**, 406 and suppl. 13 (1964).
[2] PRADER and BUDLIGER, *Helv. paediat. Acta*, suppl. 37 (1977).
[3] TANNER et al., *Arch. Dis. Childh.*, **41**, 454 and 613 (1966).
[4] VAN WIERINGEN, J.C., *Seculaire groeiverschuiving*, Nederlands Instituut voor Praeventieve Geneeskunde, Leiden, 1972.
[5] REINKEN et al., *Klin. Pädiat.*, **192**, 25 (1980).

	Unit	Boys								Girls							
			90%								90%						
				80%								80%					
					50%								50%				
		Number	P_{05}	P_{10}	P_{25}	P_{50}	P_{75}	P_{90}	P_{95}	Number	P_{05}	P_{10}	P_{25}	P_{50}	P_{75}	P_{90}	P_{95}
Birth																	
Mass	kg	123	2.60	2.80	3.10	3.40	3.70	3.90	4.01	121	2.64	2.70	2.95	3.20	3.53	3.96	4.06
Length	cm	121	47.0	49.0	49.0	50.5	52.0	52.5	53.0	118	47.0	47.0	48.7	49.5	51.0	52.0	53.0
1 month																	
Mass	kg	54	3.42	3.57	3.72	4.04	4.29	4.58	4.73	48	3.36	3.44	3.63	3.86	4.08	4.42	4.50
Length	cm	54	52.0	52.5	53.2	54.5	55.8	56.8	57.0	49	50.7	51.4	52.5	53.2	54.5	55.5	56.7
Sitting height	cm	51	33.7	34.0	35.0	36.0	36.5	37.0	37.7	42	33.0	33.5	34.2	35.0	36.0	36.9	37.9
Head circumference	cm	54	35.3	36.0	36.5	37.5	38.0	39.0	39.0	44	34.2	35.3	36.0	36.5	37.0	38.1	38.4
2 months																	
Mass	kg	65	4.27	4.43	4.73	4.98	5.34	5.64	5.69	57	4.07	4.19	4.48	4.75	5.02	5.31	5.50
Length	cm	64	55.5	56.0	57.0	58.0	59.0	59.5	60.4	56	53.9	54.5	56.0	56.5	57.5	58.5	59.5
Sitting height	cm	60	35.5	36.5	37.0	38.0	39.0	39.5	40.0	50	35.2	35.5	36.5	37.5	38.0	38.5	39.0
Head circumference	cm	63	37.5	38.0	38.5	39.0	40.0	40.5	40.7	53	36.3	37.0	37.5	38.5	39.0	39.5	40.0
3 months																	
Mass	kg	75	5.18	5.40	5.73	6.00	6.32	6.66	6.90	60	4.80	4.89	5.20	5.53	5.95	6.23	6.46
Length	cm	75	58.3	59.0	60.5	61.0	62.5	63.2	63.6	58	57.4	58.0	58.5	59.5	60.5	61.6	63.0
Sitting height	cm	74	38.0	38.5	39.5	40.5	41.0	41.5	42.0	55	37.5	37.5	38.5	39.0	40.0	40.5	41.1
Head circumference	cm	74	39.0	39.5	40.0	40.5	41.5	42.0	42.5	55	38.0	38.2	39.0	40.0	40.5	41.0	41.2
Chest circumference	cm	26	38.0	38.6	39.7	41.0	41.2	42.0	42.0	16	37.4	38.0	38.5	40.0	40.5	41.0	41.2
4 months																	
Mass	kg	63	5.82	5.91	6.35	6.84	7.23	7.49	7.77	58	5.22	5.42	5.77	6.24	6.85	7.13	7.43
Length	cm	63	60.1	61.3	63.5	64.5	65.5	66.3	67.0	58	59.5	60.0	60.5	62.0	63.5	64.5	64.6
Sitting height	cm	60	39.5	40.0	41.0	42.0	43.0	43.5	44.0	56	38.0	39.0	40.0	40.5	41.5	42.0	42.1
Head circumference	cm	60	40.0	40.5	41.0	41.5	42.5	43.0	43.5	55	39.0	39.2	40.0	41.0	41.6	42.5	43.0
5 months																	
Mass	kg	61	6.19	6.52	6.91	7.37	7.90	8.04	8.29	62	6.00	6.05	6.50	7.00	7.40	7.71	7.86
Length	cm	61	62.5	63.5	65.5	66.5	67.5	68.9	69.0	61	62.0	62.5	63.5	64.0	65.5	66.5	67.0
Sitting height	cm	58	40.9	41.5	42.2	43.5	44.0	44.6	45.0	59	40.5	40.5	41.0	42.0	42.5	43.5	44.0
Head circumference	cm	57	41.0	41.0	42.0	43.0	43.5	44.0	44.5	59	40.0	40.5	41.0	42.0	42.5	43.0	44.0
6 months																	
Mass	kg	73	6.74	7.00	7.48	8.12	8.49	8.77	8.98	74	6.34	6.53	6.92	7.48	7.93	8.27	8.62
Length	cm	73	64.1	65.1	67.1	68.5	69.5	71.3	71.6	74	63.5	64.0	65.0	66.5	67.5	69.3	69.6
Sitting height	cm	73	41.8	42.5	43.5	44.5	45.0	46.0	46.5	73	41.0	41.5	42.5	43.0	44.0	44.7	45.0
Head circumference	cm	73	41.8	42.5	43.0	43.5	44.5	45.0	45.5	73	40.8	41.5	42.0	43.0	43.5	44.0	44.5
Chest circumference	cm	28	42.0	42.4	43.0	44.0	45.0	46.0	46.0	23	39.3	41.0	41.8	43.0	44.0	44.7	45.0
7 months																	
Mass	kg	50	7.19	7.41	7.86	8.36	8.85	9.02	9.15	47	6.72	6.87	7.28	7.87	8.31	8.86	9.13
Length	cm	49	65.2	66.5	68.7	70.0	71.0	72.0	73.2	47	65.1	65.5	66.5	68.0	69.5	70.5	71.0
Sitting height	cm	48	43.0	43.5	44.5	45.0	46.0	47.0	47.3	46	42.1	42.8	43.5	44.0	45.0	45.7	46.8
Head circumference	cm	48	42.5	42.9	43.5	44.0	45.0	45.6	46.0	46	41.5	42.0	43.0	43.5	44.5	45.0	45.3
Chest circumference	cm	20	42.0	42.5	43.0	44.0	45.0	46.0	46.0	16	39.8	41.0	42.5	44.0	45.0	45.0	45.2
8 months																	
Mass	kg	59	7.63	8.06	8.35	8.97	9.37	9.66	9.88	56	7.10	7.16	7.56	8.24	8.78	9.30	9.74
Length	cm	59	66.9	68.0	70.5	71.5	72.6	74.0	74.5	55	66.5	67.0	68.0	69.5	71.0	72.2	73.0
Sitting height	cm	57	43.4	44.0	45.0	46.0	47.0	47.5	48.0	55	42.8	43.5	44.5	45.0	46.0	46.7	47.0
Head circumference	cm	56	43.0	43.0	44.5	45.0	46.0	46.5	46.5	55	42.0	42.7	43.5	44.5	45.0	46.0	46.0
Chest circumference	cm	19	42.8	43.0	44.0	45.0	46.0	46.5	46.9	20	42.5	42.5	43.0	45.0	46.0	47.0	47.5
9 months																	
Mass	kg	66	8.00	8.30	8.71	9.37	9.82	10.36	10.40	72	7.30	7.62	7.90	8.58	9.23	9.71	9.88
Length	cm	66	68.8	71.0	72.0	73.0	74.0	75.0	75.8	72	67.9	68.6	69.5	71.0	72.0	73.5	74.0
Sitting height	cm	63	44.5	45.0	46.0	46.5	47.5	48.3	49.0	72	43.3	44.0	45.0	45.5	46.5	47.0	47.7
Head circumference	cm	65	44.0	44.0	45.0	46.0	46.5	47.0	47.5	72	42.8	43.0	44.0	45.0	45.5	46.0	46.5
Chest circumference	cm	24	43.6	44.0	44.0	45.5	47.0	47.0	47.8	26	42.5	43.0	44.0	45.0	46.2	47.2	47.8

Reference HEIMENDINGER, J., *Helv. paediat. Acta*, **19**, 406 (1964) [341 boys and 326 girls, mostly of German-Swiss descent, in Basel and Wettingen (Switzerland), 1957–1962].

	Unit	Boys[1] Number	Boys[1] P_{05}	Boys[1] P_{10}	Boys[1] P_{25}	Boys[1] P_{50}	Boys[1] P_{75}	Boys[1] P_{90}	Boys[1] P_{95}	Girls[1] Number	Girls[1] P_{05}	Girls[1] P_{10}	Girls[1] P_{25}	Girls[1] P_{50}	Girls[1] P_{75}	Girls[1] P_{90}	Girls[1] P_{95}
			90%								90%						
				80%								80%					
					50%								50%				
10 months																	
Mass	kg	36	8.00	8.30	8.85	9.40	9.82	10.41	10.66	36	7.60	7.84	8.30	8.74	9.25	9.90	10.07
Length	cm	36	69.9	71.0	72.5	73.5	74.5	76.4	77.1	36	68.5	69.1	70.5	72.0	73.0	74.0	74.7
Sitting height	cm	34	45.0	45.0	46.0	46.5	47.5	48.5	49.0	36	43.8	44.3	45.0	46.0	47.0	47.2	48.0
Head circumference	cm	36	44.0	44.0	45.0	46.0	47.0	47.0	47.8	34	43.0	43.0	44.0	45.0	45.7	46.0	46.5
11 months																	
Mass	kg	28	8.50	8.86	9.37	10.00	10.46	10.64	10.86	34	7.77	8.00	8.43	9.14	9.99	10.59	10.90
Length	cm	28	71.3	73.3	74.0	75.5	76.0	77.1	77.8	34	70.5	70.8	71.5	73.5	74.7	75.5	76.6
Sitting height	cm	28	45.4	46.0	46.5	47.5	48.0	49.0	49.6	33	44.3	44.6	45.6	46.7	47.5	48.3	48.8
Head circumference	cm	27	44.5	45.0	45.5	47.0	47.5	48.0	48.0	33	43.8	44.0	44.5	45.5	46.0	46.9	47.1
12 months																	
Mass	kg	58	8.50	9.17	9.57	10.09	10.78	11.13	11.36	73	8.22	8.40	8.86	9.51	10.04	11.05	11.33
Length	cm	58	71.4	73.4	75.0	76.5	77.5	79.0	79.5	72	71.0	72.0	73.0	74.7	76.0	77.0	77.5
Sitting height	cm	56	45.8	46.5	47.5	48.0	49.0	50.7	51.1	71	44.5	45.0	46.3	47.5	48.0	48.9	49.5
Head circumference	cm	58	44.5	45.0	46.0	47.0	48.0	48.5	48.5	72	43.8	44.5	45.0	46.0	46.5	47.0	47.5
Chest circumference	cm	26	44.5	44.8	46.0	47.0	48.0	49.0	49.7	31	42.5	44.0	45.3	46.0	47.1	47.5	48.2
15 months																	
Mass	kg	50	9.45	9.80	10.20	10.90	11.48	12.20	12.93	46	8.92	9.06	9.69	10.15	10.92	11.29	11.61
Length	cm	50	75.2	77.2	78.4	80.0	81.0	82.0	82.5	46	75.0	75.5	76.5	78.0	79.5	80.5	81.0
Sitting height	cm	49	47.8	48.9	49.5	50.0	51.0	52.0	52.2	46	46.5	46.5	48.0	48.5	49.5	50.7	51.3
Head circumference	cm	50	45.5	46.4	47.0	48.0	48.5	49.5	49.5	45	44.5	45.0	46.0	47.0	47.5	48.0	48.5
Chest circumference	cm	24	45.5	45.7	47.0	48.5	49.0	50.0	50.4	28	43.4	44.8	46.0	47.0	47.5	48.1	49.4
18 months																	
Mass	kg	39	10.12	10.36	10.91	11.31	12.02	12.91	13.29	40	9.56	10.15	10.47	10.95	11.90	12.42	13.00
Length	cm	39	78.4	79.9	81.5	83.0	84.1	86.0	86.5	40	78.0	78.5	80.0	81.5	83.0	85.0	86.0
Sitting height	cm	39	49.0	49.5	50.5	51.5	52.5	53.5	54.0	40	47.0	49.0	49.5	50.5	52.0	53.0	53.5
Head circumference	cm	39	45.5	46.5	47.5	49.0	49.0	50.0	50.0	40	45.0	46.5	47.0	47.5	48.5	49.0	49.0
Chest circumference	cm	20	46.0	47.0	48.0	49.0	50.0	51.0	52.0	22	44.8	45.1	46.7	48.0	49.2	51.0	51.4
2 years																	
Mass	kg	23	10.91	11.33	11.82	12.53	13.39	13.93	14.43	24	10.03	10.59	11.22	12.10	12.96	13.70	14.05
Height	cm	24	84.0	84.0	86.0	87.5	90.0	92.9	94.3	24	83.0	83.9	85.0	88.0	89.5	90.8	91.4
Sitting height	cm	24	51.1	51.5	52.5	54.0	55.0	56.0	56.4	24	50.1	50.9	52.0	53.5	54.0	55.3	55.9
Head circumference	cm	24	47.1	47.7	48.0	49.5	50.0	51.3	51.5	24	46.1	46.9	47.5	48.5	49.0	49.5	49.9
Chest circumference	cm	20	47.5	48.0	49.0	50.0	50.5	51.0	52.0	10	–	47.0	48.0	49.5	50.5	51.0	–

	Unit	Boys[2] $P_{2.5}$	Boys[2] P_{10}	Boys[2] P_{25}	Boys[2] P_{50}	Boys[2] P_{75}	Boys[2] P_{90}	Boys[2] $P_{97.5}$	Boys[2] s	Girls[2] $P_{2.5}$	Girls[2] P_{10}	Girls[2] P_{25}	Girls[2] P_{50}	Girls[2] P_{75}	Girls[2] P_{90}	Girls[2] $P_{97.5}$	Girls[2] s
		95%								95%							
			80%								80%						
				50%								50%					
2 years																	
Mass	kg	8.3	9.7	11.0	12.4	13.8	15.1	16.5	2.05	9.1	10.1	10.9	11.9	12.9	13.7	14.7	1.4
Height	cm	78.9	81.7	84.2	87.0	89.8	92.3	95.1	4.1	78.8	81.4	83.8	86.5	89.2	91.6	94.2	3.9
Sitting height	cm	48.1	49.8	51.3	52.9	54.5	56.0	57.7	2.4	46.4	48.6	50.5	52.7	54.9	56.8	59.0	3.2
Shoulder width	cm	12.4	14.8	16.9	19.3	21.7	23.8	26.2	3.5	15.0	16.8	18.3	20.0	21.7	23.2	25.0	2.5
Pelvic width	cm	11.7	13.7	15.6	17.6	19.6	21.5	23.5	3.0	12.4	14.0	15.3	16.8	18.3	19.6	21.2	2.2
Head circumference	cm	46.4	47.4	48.2	49.2	50.2	51.0	52.0	1.4	44.6	45.6	46.4	47.4	48.4	49.2	50.2	1.4
Chest circumference	cm	45.2	46.8	48.1	49.6	51.1	52.4	54.0	2.2	43.5	45.2	46.7	48.3	49.9	51.4	53.1	2.4
Upper arm circumf.	cm	13.5	14.2	14.8	15.5	16.2	16.8	17.5	1.0	10.5	12.0	13.3	14.7	16.1	17.4	18.9	2.1
Wrist circumference	cm	4.1	6.1	8.0	10.0	12.0	13.9	15.9	3.0	4.1	6.0	7.7	9.6	11.5	13.2	15.1	2.8
Calf circumference	cm	17.0	17.7	18.3	19.0	19.7	20.3	21.0	1.0	14.1	15.7	17.0	18.5	20.0	21.3	22.9	2.2

References

[1] HEIMENDINGER, J., *Helv. paediat. Acta*, **19**, 406 (1964) [341 boys and 326 girls, mostly of German-Swiss descent, in Basel and Wettingen (Switzerland), 1957–1962].

[2] HEIMENDINGER, J., *Helv. paediat. Acta*, **19**, suppl. 13 (1964) [2150 boys and 2150 girls in crèches, kindergartens and schools in Basel (Switzerland), 1956–1957].

		Boys								Girls							
		95%							s	95%							s
			80%								80%						
				50%								50%					
	Unit	$P_{2.5}$	P_{10}	P_{25}	P_{50}	P_{75}	P_{90}	$P_{97.5}$		$P_{2.5}$	P_{10}	P_{25}	P_{50}	P_{75}	P_{90}	$P_{97.5}$	
2½ years																	
Mass	kg	9.3	10.8	12.1	13.5	14.9	16.2	17.7	2.11	9.7	10.9	11.9	13.1	14.3	15.3	16.5	1.7
Height	cm	84.1	87.0	89.5	92.4	95.3	97.8	100.7	4.2	82.9	85.7	88.2	91.0	93.8	96.3	99.1	4.1
Sitting height	cm	49.8	51.5	53.1	54.9	56.7	58.3	60.0	2.6	47.7	49.8	51.7	53.8	55.9	57.8	59.9	3.1
Shoulder width	cm	13.1	15.5	17.7	20.2	22.7	24.9	27.3	3.6	15.7	17.5	19.0	20.7	22.4	23.9	25.7	2.5
Pelvic width	cm	11.5	13.7	15.6	17.8	20.0	21.9	24.1	3.2	12.7	14.3	15.7	17.3	18.9	20.3	21.9	2.3
Head circumference	cm	46.8	47.8	48.6	49.6	50.6	51.4	52.4	1.4	45.3	46.3	47.1	48.1	49.1	49.9	50.9	1.4
Chest circumference	cm	45.4	47.1	48.6	50.2	51.8	53.3	55.0	2.4	44.5	46.2	47.7	49.3	50.9	52.4	54.1	2.4
Upper arm circumf.	cm	13.2	14.0	14.8	15.6	16.4	17.2	18.0	1.2	11.0	12.4	13.6	15.0	16.4	17.6	19.0	2.0
Wrist circumference	cm	4.3	6.3	8.2	10.2	12.2	14.1	16.1	3.0	3.9	5.8	7.6	9.6	11.6	13.4	15.3	2.9
Calf circumference	cm	15.5	16.9	18.1	19.5	20.9	22.1	23.5	2.0	14.7	16.3	17.6	19.1	20.6	21.9	23.5	2.2
3 years																	
Mass	kg	10.5	11.9	13.2	14.6	16.0	17.3	18.7	2.06	10.3	11.7	12.9	14.3	15.7	16.9	18.3	2.0
Height	cm	88.2	91.0	93.5	96.3	99.1	101.6	104.4	4.1	86.7	89.6	92.3	95.2	98.1	100.8	103.7	4.3
Sitting height	cm	50.0	52.1	54.0	56.1	58.2	60.1	62.2	3.1	49.2	51.1	52.9	54.9	56.9	58.7	60.6	2.9
Shoulder width	cm	13.8	16.3	18.6	21.1	23.6	25.9	28.4	3.7	16.2	17.9	19.5	21.3	23.1	24.7	26.4	2.6
Pelvic width	cm	11.2	13.6	15.7	18.1	20.5	22.6	25.0	3.5	13.1	14.7	16.1	17.7	19.3	20.7	22.3	2.3
Head circumference	cm	47.1	48.1	48.9	49.9	50.9	51.7	52.7	1.4	45.6	46.7	47.6	48.6	49.6	50.5	51.6	1.5
Chest circumference	cm	43.9	46.3	48.4	50.8	53.2	55.3	57.7	3.5	45.4	47.2	48.7	50.4	52.1	53.6	55.4	2.5
Upper arm circumf.	cm	12.9	13.9	14.7	15.7	16.7	17.5	18.5	1.4	11.5	12.8	14.0	15.3	16.6	17.8	19.1	1.9
Wrist circumference	cm	4.3	6.4	8.3	10.4	12.5	14.4	16.5	3.1	3.9	5.9	7.8	9.8	11.8	13.7	15.7	3.0
Calf circumference	cm	15.7	17.2	18.5	19.9	21.3	22.6	24.1	2.1	15.8	17.1	18.3	19.6	20.9	22.1	23.4	1.9
3½ years																	
Mass	kg	11.7	13.1	14.3	15.7	17.1	18.3	19.7	2.03	10.9	12.5	13.8	15.3	16.8	18.1	19.7	2.2
Height	cm	91.7	94.6	97.1	100.0	102.9	105.4	108.3	4.2	90.1	93.1	95.8	98.8	101.8	104.5	107.5	4.4
Sitting height	cm	49.5	52.1	54.5	57.2	59.9	62.3	64.9	3.9	50.5	52.4	54.1	56.0	57.9	59.6	61.5	2.8
Shoulder width	cm	14.8	17.2	19.4	21.9	24.4	26.6	29.0	3.6	16.9	18.6	20.2	22.0	23.8	25.4	27.1	2.6
Pelvic width	cm	10.7	13.3	15.7	18.4	21.1	23.5	26.1	3.9	13.7	15.3	16.6	18.1	19.6	20.9	22.5	2.2
Head circumference	cm	47.5	48.5	49.3	50.3	51.3	52.1	53.1	1.4	46.5	47.4	48.2	49.1	50.0	50.8	51.7	1.3
Chest circumference	cm	38.7	43.1	47.0	51.4	55.8	59.7	64.1	6.4	46.3	48.1	49.6	51.3	53.0	54.5	56.3	2.5
Upper arm circumf.	cm	12.2	13.5	14.6	15.8	17.0	18.1	19.4	1.8	12.2	13.4	14.4	15.6	16.8	17.8	19.0	1.7
Wrist circumference	cm	4.5	6.6	8.5	10.6	12.7	14.6	16.7	3.1	4.1	6.1	8.0	10.0	12.0	13.9	15.9	3.0
Calf circumference	cm	16.0	17.6	18.9	20.4	21.9	23.2	24.8	2.2	17.1	18.2	19.1	20.1	21.1	22.0	23.1	1.5
4 years																	
Mass	kg	12.6	14.0	15.3	16.7	18.1	19.4	20.8	2.05	11.7	13.3	14.7	16.3	17.9	19.3	20.9	2.3
Height	cm	95.0	97.9	100.6	103.5	106.4	109.1	112.0	4.3	93.4	96.5	99.2	102.3	105.4	108.1	111.2	4.5
Sitting height	cm	50.3	53.0	55.5	58.2	60.9	63.4	66.1	4.0	51.8	53.6	55.3	57.1	58.9	60.6	62.4	2.7
Shoulder width	cm	16.4	19.1	20.8	22.7	24.6	26.3	27.4	2.8	17.6	19.3	20.9	22.7	24.5	26.1	27.8	2.6
Pelvic width	cm	12.3	14.5	16.6	18.8	21.0	23.1	25.3	3.3	14.3	15.8	17.1	18.5	19.9	21.2	22.2	2.1
Head circumference	cm	47.8	48.8	49.6	50.6	51.6	52.4	53.4	1.4	47.0	47.9	48.7	49.6	50.5	51.3	52.2	1.3
Chest circumference	cm	38.6	43.3	47.5	52.1	56.7	60.9	65.6	6.8	46.7	48.5	50.0	51.7	53.4	54.9	56.7	2.5
Upper arm circumf.	cm	11.5	13.1	14.4	15.9	17.4	18.7	20.3	2.2	13.1	14.1	14.9	15.9	16.9	17.7	18.7	1.4
Wrist circumference	cm	4.9	6.9	8.8	10.8	12.8	14.7	16.7	3.0	4.6	6.5	8.3	10.3	12.3	14.1	16.0	2.9
Calf circumference	cm	16.3	17.9	19.3	20.9	22.5	23.9	25.5	2.3	17.9	18.9	19.7	20.7	21.7	22.5	23.5	1.4
4½ years																	
Mass	kg	13.6	15.1	16.4	17.8	19.2	20.5	22.0	2.12	12.5	14.2	15.7	17.3	18.9	20.4	22.1	2.4
Height	cm	98.0	101.1	103.8	106.9	110.0	112.7	115.8	4.5	96.9	100.0	102.7	105.8	108.9	111.6	114.7	4.5
Sitting height	cm	52.7	54.9	57.0	59.2	61.4	63.5	65.7	3.3	52.5	54.4	56.2	58.2	60.2	62.0	63.9	2.9
Shoulder width	cm	17.7	20.3	21.8	23.5	25.2	26.7	27.7	2.5	18.5	20.2	21.7	23.3	24.9	26.4	28.1	2.4
Pelvic width	cm	14.1	15.9	17.4	19.1	20.8	22.3	24.1	2.5	15.3	16.6	17.7	18.9	20.1	21.2	22.5	1.8
Head circumference	cm	48.0	49.0	49.8	50.8	51.8	52.6	53.6	1.4	47.2	48.2	49.0	50.0	51.0	51.8	52.8	1.4
Chest circumference	cm	39.2	43.9	48.1	52.7	57.3	61.5	66.2	6.8	47.0	48.7	50.3	52.1	53.9	55.5	57.2	2.6
Upper arm circumf.	cm	11.7	13.3	14.6	16.1	17.6	18.9	20.5	2.2	13.8	14.6	15.4	16.2	17.0	17.8	18.6	1.2
Wrist circumference	cm	5.2	7.2	9.1	11.1	13.1	15.0	17.0	3.0	5.5	7.3	9.0	10.8	12.6	14.3	16.1	2.7
Calf circumference	cm	16.6	18.3	19.8	21.4	23.0	24.5	26.0	2.4	18.4	19.4	20.2	21.2	22.2	23.0	24.0	1.4

Reference HEIMENDINGER, J., *Helv. paediat. Acta,* **19**, suppl. 13 (1964) [2150 boys and 2150 girls in crèches, kindergartens and schools in Basel (Switzerland), 1956–1957].

	Unit	Boys								Girls							
		95%								95%							
			80%								80%						
				50%								50%					
		$P_{2.5}$	P_{10}	P_{25}	P_{50}	P_{75}	P_{90}	$P_{97.5}$	s	$P_{2.5}$	P_{10}	P_{25}	P_{50}	P_{75}	P_{90}	$P_{97.5}$	s
5 years																	
Mass	kg	14.6	16.1	17.4	18.9	20.4	21.7	23.2	2.19	13.5	15.2	16.7	18.3	19.9	21.4	23.1	2.4
Height	cm	101.1	104.2	107.1	110.2	113.3	116.2	119.3	4.6	100.5	103.5	106.2	109.2	112.2	114.9	117.9	4.4
Sitting height	cm	54.5	56.4	58.2	60.2	62.2	64.0	65.9	2.9	53.2	55.3	57.2	59.3	61.4	63.3	65.4	3.1
Shoulder width	cm	18.9	21.2	22.6	24.2	25.8	27.2	28.1	2.3	19.8	21.3	22.6	24.0	25.4	26.7	28.2	2.1
Pelvic width	cm	15.1	16.7	18.0	19.5	21.0	22.3	23.9	2.2	16.2	17.3	18.3	19.4	20.5	21.5	22.6	1.6
Head circumference	cm	48.0	49.1	50.0	51.0	52.0	52.9	54.0	1.5	47.5	48.5	49.3	50.3	51.3	52.1	53.1	1.4
Chest circumference	cm	40.5	45.0	49.0	53.4	57.8	61.8	66.3	6.5	47.4	49.1	50.7	52.5	54.3	55.9	57.6	2.6
Upper arm circumf.	cm	12.7	14.0	15.1	16.3	17.5	18.6	19.9	1.8	14.4	15.2	15.9	16.6	17.3	18.0	18.8	1.1
Wrist circumference	cm	5.6	7.5	9.3	11.3	13.3	15.1	17.0	2.9	6.7	8.3	9.6	11.1	12.6	13.9	15.5	2.2
Calf circumference	cm	17.0	18.7	20.2	21.8	23.4	24.9	26.6	2.4	19.0	20.0	20.8	21.8	22.8	23.6	24.6	1.4
5½ years																	
Mass	kg	15.5	17.1	18.5	20.0	21.5	22.9	24.5	2.25	14.4	16.2	17.7	19.4	21.1	22.6	24.4	2.5
Height	cm	103.9	107.2	110.1	113.4	116.7	119.6	122.9	4.8	103.7	106.8	109.5	112.6	115.7	118.4	121.5	4.5
Sitting height	cm	55.3	57.3	59.2	61.2	63.2	65.1	67.1	3.0	54.1	56.3	58.2	60.4	62.6	64.5	66.7	3.2
Shoulder width	cm	19.8	22.1	23.4	24.9	26.4	27.7	28.6	2.2	20.7	22.1	23.3	24.7	26.1	27.3	28.7	2.0
Pelvic width	cm	15.6	17.1	18.4	19.8	21.2	22.5	24.0	2.1	16.4	17.6	18.6	19.8	21.0	22.0	23.2	1.7
Head circumference	cm	48.0	49.1	50.1	51.2	52.3	53.3	54.4	1.6	47.4	48.5	49.5	50.6	51.7	52.7	53.8	1.6
Chest circumference	cm	45.7	48.6	51.3	54.2	57.1	59.8	62.7	4.3	47.6	49.4	51.1	52.9	54.7	56.4	58.2	2.7
Upper arm circumf.	cm	14.2	15.0	15.8	16.6	17.4	18.2	19.0	1.2	14.7	15.5	16.2	16.9	17.6	18.3	19.1	1.1
Wrist circumference	cm	6.5	8.3	9.8	11.5	13.2	14.7	16.5	2.5	8.1	9.2	10.2	11.3	12.4	13.4	14.5	1.6
Calf circumference	cm	17.5	19.2	20.7	22.3	23.9	25.4	27.1	2.4	19.3	20.4	21.3	22.3	23.3	24.2	25.3	1.5
6 years																	
Mass	kg	16.4	18.0	19.4	21.0	22.6	24.0	25.6	2.32	14.9	16.8	18.6	20.6	22.6	24.4	26.3	2.9
Height	cm	106.8	110.2	113.2	116.5	119.8	122.8	126.2	4.9	106.0	109.4	112.5	115.9	119.3	122.4	125.8	5.0
Sitting height	cm	55.9	58.1	60.0	62.2	64.4	66.3	68.5	3.2	55.4	57.5	59.4	61.5	63.6	65.5	67.6	3.1
Shoulder width	cm	20.9	22.9	24.1	25.5	26.9	28.1	28.9	2.0	21.3	22.7	23.9	25.3	26.7	27.9	29.3	2.0
Pelvic width	cm	16.2	17.6	18.8	20.2	21.6	22.8	24.2	2.0	16.6	17.9	19.0	20.2	21.4	22.5	23.8	1.8
Head circumference	cm	46.8	48.4	49.8	51.4	53.0	54.4	56.0	2.3	47.2	48.5	49.6	50.8	52.0	53.1	54.4	1.8
Chest circumference	cm	49.6	51.4	53.1	54.9	56.7	58.4	60.2	2.7	47.7	49.6	51.4	53.4	55.4	57.2	59.1	2.9
Upper arm circumf.	cm	14.6	15.4	16.1	16.8	17.5	18.2	19.0	1.1	14.8	15.6	16.4	17.2	18.0	18.8	19.6	1.2
Wrist circumference	cm	7.5	9.0	10.3	11.7	13.1	14.4	15.9	2.1	8.8	9.7	10.5	11.4	12.3	13.1	14.0	1.3
Calf circumference	cm	18.2	19.8	21.2	22.8	24.4	25.8	27.4	2.3	19.7	20.8	21.8	22.9	24.0	25.0	26.1	1.6
6½ years																	
Mass	kg	17.1	18.8	20.4	22.1	23.8	25.4	27.1	2.53	14.9	17.3	19.4	21.8	24.2	26.3	28.7	3.5
Height	cm	109.6	113.0	116.1	119.5	122.9	126.0	129.4	5.0	108.3	112.1	115.5	119.2	122.9	126.3	130.1	5.5
Sitting height	cm	56.9	59.1	61.0	63.2	65.4	67.3	69.5	3.2	56.5	58.6	60.5	62.6	64.7	66.6	68.7	3.1
Shoulder width	cm	21.7	23.7	24.9	26.2	27.5	28.7	29.3	1.9	21.6	23.2	24.5	26.0	27.5	28.8	30.4	2.2
Pelvic width	cm	16.5	17.9	19.1	20.5	21.9	23.1	24.5	2.0	17.0	18.3	19.4	20.6	21.8	22.9	24.2	1.8
Head circumference	cm	46.4	48.1	49.7	51.5	53.3	54.9	56.6	2.6	46.8	48.3	49.6	51.0	52.4	53.7	55.2	2.1
Chest circumference	cm	50.6	52.3	53.9	55.7	57.5	59.1	60.8	2.6	47.7	49.9	52.0	54.2	56.4	58.5	60.7	3.3
Upper arm circumf.	cm	14.8	15.6	16.3	17.0	17.7	18.4	19.2	1.1	14.7	15.7	16.5	17.5	18.5	19.3	20.3	1.4
Wrist circumference	cm	8.3	9.6	10.7	11.9	13.1	14.2	15.5	1.8	9.6	10.3	10.9	11.6	12.3	12.9	13.6	1.0
Calf circumference	cm	18.7	20.3	21.7	23.3	24.9	26.3	27.9	2.3	20.2	21.3	22.3	23.4	24.5	25.5	26.6	1.6
7 years																	
Mass	kg	18.0	19.8	21.4	23.2	25.0	26.6	28.4	2.61	15.8	18.4	20.8	23.5	26.2	28.6	31.2	3.9
Height	cm	112.3	115.8	118.9	122.4	125.9	129.0	132.5	5.1	111.5	115.3	118.7	122.4	126.1	129.5	133.3	5.5
Sitting height	cm	58.3	60.3	62.2	64.2	66.2	68.1	70.1	3.0	57.6	59.7	61.6	63.7	65.8	67.7	69.8	3.1
Shoulder width	cm	22.6	24.5	25.6	26.8	28.0	29.1	29.8	1.8	22.3	23.9	25.2	26.7	28.2	29.5	31.1	2.2
Pelvic width	cm	17.1	18.4	19.6	20.9	22.2	23.4	24.7	1.9	17.4	18.7	19.8	21.0	22.2	23.3	24.6	1.8
Head circumference	cm	46.3	48.1	49.8	51.6	53.4	55.1	56.9	2.7	47.0	48.5	49.8	51.2	52.6	53.9	55.4	2.1
Chest circumference	cm	51.2	53.0	54.7	56.5	58.3	60.0	61.8	2.7	48.3	50.7	52.8	55.2	57.6	59.7	62.1	3.5
Upper arm circumf.	cm	14.8	15.6	16.4	17.2	18.0	18.8	19.6	1.2	14.6	15.7	16.7	17.8	18.9	19.9	21.0	1.6
Wrist circumference	cm	8.9	10.0	11.0	12.1	13.2	14.2	15.3	1.6	9.3	10.2	11.0	11.9	12.8	13.6	14.5	1.3
Calf circumference	cm	19.1	20.7	22.1	23.7	25.3	26.7	28.3	2.3	20.5	21.8	22.9	24.1	25.3	26.4	27.7	1.8

Reference HEIMENDINGER, J., *Helv. paediat. Acta,* **19**, suppl. 13 (1964) [2150 boys and 2150 girls in crèches, kindergartens and schools in Basel (Switzerland), 1956–1957].

	Unit	Boys								Girls							
		95%							s	95%							s
			80%								80%						
				50%								50%					
		$P_{2.5}$	P_{10}	P_{25}	P_{50}	P_{75}	P_{90}	$P_{97.5}$		$P_{2.5}$	P_{10}	P_{25}	P_{50}	P_{75}	P_{90}	$P_{97.5}$	
7½ years																	
Mass	kg	18.3	20.4	22.2	24.3	26.4	28.2	30.3	3.05	16.7	19.6	22.3	25.2	28.1	30.8	33.7	4.3
Height	cm	115.1	118.6	121.7	125.2	128.7	131.8	135.3	5.1	114.9	118.5	121.8	125.4	129.0	132.3	135.9	5.3
Sitting height	cm	59.3	61.3	63.2	65.2	67.2	69.1	71.1	3.0	59.1	61.0	62.8	64.8	66.8	68.6	70.5	2.9
Shoulder width	cm	23.2	25.2	26.3	27.5	28.7	29.8	30.4	1.8	23.5	24.8	26.0	27.3	28.6	29.8	31.1	1.9
Pelvic width	cm	17.6	18.9	20.0	21.2	22.4	23.5	24.8	1.8	18.1	19.3	20.3	21.5	22.7	23.7	24.9	1.7
Head circumference	cm	46.4	48.2	49.9	51.7	53.5	55.2	57.0	2.7	47.2	48.7	50.0	51.4	52.8	54.1	55.6	2.1
Chest circumference	cm	51.6	53.5	55.3	57.3	59.3	61.1	63.0	2.9	48.9	51.4	53.7	56.2	58.7	61.0	63.5	3.7
Upper arm circumf.	cm	14.7	15.7	16.5	17.5	18.5	19.3	20.3	1.4	14.6	15.9	17.0	18.2	19.4	20.5	21.8	1.8
Wrist circumference	cm	9.5	10.5	11.3	12.3	13.3	14.1	15.1	1.4	8.3	9.7	10.9	12.3	13.7	14.9	16.3	2.0
Calf circumference	cm	19.6	21.2	22.6	24.2	25.8	27.2	28.8	2.3	21.0	22.4	23.6	25.0	26.4	27.6	29.0	2.0
8 years																	
Mass	kg	18.4	20.8	22.9	25.3	27.7	29.8	32.2	3.49	17.6	20.7	23.6	26.7	29.8	32.7	35.8	4.6
Height	cm	117.7	121.3	124.5	128.0	131.5	134.7	138.3	5.2	118.3	121.7	124.8	128.2	131.6	134.7	138.1	5.0
Sitting height	cm	59.9	62.1	64.0	66.2	68.4	70.3	72.5	3.2	60.4	62.3	64.0	65.9	67.8	69.5	71.4	2.8
Shoulder width	cm	24.1	25.9	26.9	28.1	29.3	30.3	30.9	1.7	24.6	25.8	26.8	28.0	29.2	30.2	31.4	1.7
Pelvic width	cm	18.6	19.7	20.6	21.6	22.6	23.5	24.6	1.5	18.8	19.8	20.8	21.9	23.0	24.0	25.0	1.6
Head circumference	cm	46.5	48.3	50.0	51.8	53.6	55.3	57.1	2.7	46.9	48.5	49.9	51.5	53.1	54.5	56.1	2.3
Chest circumference	cm	52.0	54.1	56.0	58.1	60.2	62.1	64.2	3.1	49.4	52.0	54.4	57.1	59.8	62.2	64.8	3.9
Upper arm circumf.	cm	14.8	15.9	16.8	17.8	18.8	19.7	20.8	1.5	14.5	15.9	17.1	18.5	19.9	21.1	22.5	2.0
Wrist circumference	cm	9.9	10.8	11.6	12.5	13.4	14.2	15.1	1.3	8.6	10.0	11.2	12.6	14.0	15.2	16.6	2.0
Calf circumference	cm	20.1	21.7	23.1	24.7	26.3	27.7	29.3	2.3	21.2	22.8	24.1	25.6	27.1	28.4	30.0	2.2
8½ years																	
Mass	kg	17.7	20.7	23.4	26.4	29.4	32.1	35.1	4.37	18.3	21.6	24.5	27.8	31.1	34.0	37.3	4.8
Height	cm	120.6	124.1	127.2	130.7	134.2	137.3	140.8	5.1	120.7	124.2	127.3	130.8	134.3	137.4	140.9	5.1
Sitting height	cm	60.5	62.8	64.9	67.2	69.5	71.6	73.9	3.4	61.7	63.5	65.2	67.0	68.8	70.5	72.3	2.7
Shoulder width	cm	24.9	26.6	27.6	28.7	29.8	30.8	31.3	1.6	25.2	26.4	27.4	28.6	29.8	30.8	32.0	1.7
Pelvic width	cm	19.4	20.3	21.1	22.0	22.9	23.7	24.6	1.3	19.2	20.2	21.2	22.3	23.4	24.4	25.4	1.6
Head circumference	cm	46.4	48.3	50.0	51.9	53.8	55.5	57.4	2.8	46.1	48.0	49.7	51.6	53.5	55.2	57.1	2.8
Chest circumference	cm	52.7	54.9	56.8	59.0	61.2	63.1	65.3	3.2	49.6	52.5	55.0	57.9	60.8	63.3	66.2	4.2
Upper arm circumf.	cm	15.1	16.2	17.1	18.1	19.1	20.0	21.1	1.5	14.6	16.1	17.4	18.8	20.2	21.5	23.0	2.1
Wrist circumference	cm	10.1	11.0	11.8	12.7	13.6	14.4	15.3	1.3	9.3	10.5	11.5	12.7	13.9	14.9	16.1	1.7
Calf circumference	cm	20.6	22.2	23.6	25.2	26.8	28.2	29.8	2.3	21.3	22.9	24.3	25.9	27.5	28.9	30.5	2.3
9 years																	
Mass	kg	18.7	21.7	24.5	27.5	30.5	33.3	36.3	4.46	19.3	22.6	25.5	28.8	32.1	35.0	38.3	4.8
Height	cm	123.2	126.7	129.8	133.3	136.8	139.9	143.4	5.1	122.9	126.5	129.7	133.2	136.7	139.9	143.5	5.2
Sitting height	cm	60.8	63.3	65.6	68.1	70.6	72.9	75.4	3.7	61.9	64.0	65.9	68.0	70.1	72.0	74.1	3.1
Shoulder width	cm	25.5	27.2	28.2	29.3	30.4	31.4	31.9	1.6	25.5	26.8	27.9	29.1	30.3	31.4	32.7	1.8
Pelvic width	cm	20.0	20.8	21.6	22.4	23.2	24.0	24.8	1.2	19.6	20.6	21.6	22.7	23.8	24.8	25.8	1.6
Head circumference	cm	46.5	48.4	50.1	52.0	53.9	55.6	57.5	2.8	45.1	47.4	49.5	51.8	54.1	56.2	58.5	3.4
Chest circumference	cm	53.9	56.1	58.0	60.2	62.4	64.3	66.5	3.2	48.9	52.3	55.3	58.6	61.9	64.9	68.3	4.9
Upper arm circumf.	cm	15.6	16.6	17.4	18.4	19.4	20.2	21.2	1.4	14.7	16.3	17.6	19.1	20.6	21.9	23.5	2.2
Wrist circumference	cm	10.5	11.3	12.1	12.9	13.7	14.5	15.3	1.2	9.9	10.9	11.7	12.7	13.7	14.5	15.5	1.4
Calf circumference	cm	21.0	22.6	24.0	25.6	27.2	28.6	30.2	2.3	21.4	23.1	24.6	26.2	27.8	29.3	31.0	2.4
9½ years																	
Mass	kg	19.0	22.3	25.3	28.6	31.9	34.9	38.2	4.86	20.5	23.8	26.7	30.0	33.3	36.2	39.5	4.8
Height	cm	125.3	128.9	132.2	135.8	139.4	142.7	146.3	5.3	124.7	128.4	131.7	135.4	139.1	142.4	146.1	5.4
Sitting height	cm	61.0	63.8	66.3	69.1	71.9	74.4	77.2	4.1	61.0	63.8	66.3	69.1	71.9	74.4	77.2	4.1
Shoulder width	cm	26.7	27.8	28.8	29.9	31.0	32.0	33.1	1.6	25.7	27.0	28.2	29.5	30.8	32.0	33.3	1.9
Pelvic width	cm	20.2	21.1	21.9	22.8	23.7	24.5	25.4	1.3	20.0	21.0	22.0	23.1	24.2	25.2	26.2	1.6
Head circumference	cm	46.6	48.5	50.2	52.1	54.0	55.7	57.6	2.8	44.4	47.0	49.3	51.9	54.5	56.8	59.4	3.8
Chest circumference	cm	55.0	57.2	59.1	61.3	63.5	65.4	67.6	3.2	48.5	52.3	55.7	59.4	63.1	66.5	70.3	5.5
Upper arm circumf.	cm	15.9	16.9	17.7	18.7	19.7	20.5	21.5	1.4	14.8	16.4	17.8	19.4	21.0	22.4	24.0	2.3
Wrist circumference	cm	10.7	11.5	12.3	13.1	13.9	14.7	15.5	1.2	9.9	11.0	11.9	12.9	13.9	14.8	15.9	1.5
Calf circumference	cm	21.5	23.1	24.5	26.1	27.7	29.1	30.7	2.3	21.8	23.5	25.0	26.6	28.2	29.7	31.4	2.4

Reference HEIMENDINGER, J., *Helv. paediat. Acta*, **19**, suppl. 13 (1964) [2150 boys and 2150 girls in crèches, kindergartens and schools in Basel (Switzerland), 1956–1957].

	Unit	Boys $P_{2.5}$ (95%)	Boys P_{10} (80%)	Boys P_{25} (50%)	Boys P_{50}	Boys P_{75} (50%)	Boys P_{90} (80%)	Boys $P_{97.5}$ (95%)	Boys s	Girls $P_{2.5}$ (95%)	Girls P_{10} (80%)	Girls P_{25} (50%)	Girls P_{50}	Girls P_{75} (50%)	Girls P_{90} (80%)	Girls $P_{97.5}$ (95%)	Girls s
10 years																	
Mass	kg	19.9	23.5	26.8	30.5	34.2	37.5	41.1	5.37	21.2	24.8	28.0	31.5	35.0	38.2	41.8	5.2
Height	cm	127.4	131.2	134.6	138.3	142.0	145.4	149.2	5.5	126.4	130.2	133.7	137.5	141.3	144.8	148.6	5.6
Sitting height	cm	60.8	64.0	66.9	70.1	73.3	76.2	79.4	4.7	60.7	64.0	66.9	70.2	73.5	76.4	79.7	4.8
Shoulder width	cm	27.3	28.4	29.4	30.5	31.6	32.6	33.7	1.6	26.0	27.4	28.6	30.0	31.4	32.6	34.0	2.0
Pelvic width	cm	20.5	21.5	22.2	23.3	23.4	25.1	26.1	1.4	20.2	21.4	22.4	23.6	24.8	25.8	27.0	1.7
Head circumference	cm	46.8	48.7	50.4	52.3	54.2	55.9	57.8	2.8	43.9	46.7	49.2	52.0	54.8	57.3	60.1	4.1
Chest circumference	cm	55.5	57.8	59.9	62.2	64.5	66.6	68.9	3.4	48.6	52.6	56.1	60.1	64.1	67.6	71.6	5.8
Upper arm circumf.	cm	16.1	17.2	18.1	19.1	20.1	21.0	22.1	1.5	14.8	16.6	18.1	19.8	21.5	23.0	24.8	2.5
Wrist circumference	cm	10.7	11.6	12.4	13.3	14.2	15.0	15.9	1.3	8.3	10.0	11.5	13.1	14.7	16.2	17.9	2.4
Calf circumference	cm	22.0	23.6	25.0	26.6	28.2	29.6	31.2	2.3	22.1	23.9	25.4	27.1	28.8	30.3	32.1	2.5
10½ years																	
Mass	kg	20.6	24.8	28.5	32.7	36.9	40.6	44.8	6.10	21.3	25.4	29.0	33.0	37.0	40.6	44.7	5.9
Height	cm	129.1	133.1	136.6	140.6	144.6	148.1	152.1	5.8	127.4	131.6	135.3	139.5	143.7	147.4	151.6	6.1
Sitting height	cm	61.2	64.6	67.7	71.1	74.5	77.6	81.0	5.0	61.0	64.6	67.8	71.3	74.8	78.0	81.6	5.2
Shoulder width	cm	27.7	28.9	29.9	31.1	32.3	33.3	34.5	1.7	26.2	27.7	29.0	30.5	32.0	33.3	34.8	2.1
Pelvic width	cm	20.5	21.6	22.6	23.7	24.8	25.8	26.9	1.6	20.4	21.7	22.8	24.0	25.2	26.3	27.6	1.8
Head circumference	cm	47.3	49.0	50.6	52.4	54.2	55.8	57.5	2.6	44.1	46.9	49.4	52.2	55.0	57.5	60.3	4.1
Chest circumference	cm	55.3	57.9	60.2	62.8	65.4	67.7	70.3	3.8	49.0	53.1	56.8	60.9	65.0	68.7	72.8	6.0
Upper arm circumf.	cm	16.1	17.3	18.3	19.5	20.7	21.7	22.9	1.7	15.0	16.7	18.3	20.1	21.9	23.5	25.2	2.6
Wrist circumference	cm	10.7	11.7	12.5	13.5	14.5	15.3	16.3	1.4	8.1	9.9	11.6	13.4	15.2	16.9	18.7	2.7
Calf circumference	cm	22.5	24.1	25.5	27.1	28.7	30.1	31.7	2.3	22.3	24.2	25.9	27.8	29.7	31.4	33.3	2.8
11 years																	
Mass	kg	22.9	27.1	30.8	35.0	39.2	42.9	47.1	6.12	21.9	26.4	30.4	34.8	39.2	43.2	47.7	6.5
Height	cm	130.8	134.9	138.6	142.7	146.8	150.5	154.6	6.0	128.9	133.4	137.4	141.8	146.2	150.2	154.7	6.5
Sitting height	cm	61.8	65.4	68.6	72.1	75.6	78.8	82.4	5.2	61.7	65.4	68.7	72.4	76.1	79.4	83.1	5.4
Shoulder width	cm	27.8	29.1	30.3	31.6	32.9	34.1	35.4	1.9	26.4	28.0	29.4	31.0	32.6	34.0	35.6	2.3
Pelvic width	cm	20.3	21.6	22.8	24.1	25.4	26.6	27.9	1.9	20.7	22.2	23.2	24.5	25.8	26.8	28.3	1.9
Head circumference	cm	48.1	49.7	51.0	52.5	54.0	55.3	56.9	2.2	44.8	47.4	49.7	52.3	54.9	57.2	59.8	3.8
Chest circumference	cm	55.3	58.1	60.6	63.4	66.2	68.7	71.5	4.1	49.3	53.6	57.4	61.6	65.8	69.6	73.9	6.2
Upper arm circumf.	cm	16.1	17.4	18.6	19.9	21.2	22.4	23.7	1.9	15.1	16.9	18.5	20.4	22.3	23.9	25.7	2.7
Wrist circumference	cm	10.6	11.7	12.6	13.6	14.6	15.5	16.6	1.5	9.9	11.2	12.3	13.5	14.7	15.8	17.1	1.8
Calf circumference	cm	22.9	24.5	25.9	27.5	29.1	30.5	32.1	2.3	22.6	24.5	26.2	28.1	30.0	31.7	33.6	2.8
11½ years																	
Mass	kg	24.3	28.8	32.8	37.3	41.8	45.8	50.3	6.59	22.9	27.7	32.0	36.8	41.6	45.9	50.7	7.0
Height	cm	132.0	136.4	140.3	144.7	149.1	153.0	157.4	6.4	130.7	135.6	140.0	144.8	149.6	154.0	158.9	7.1
Sitting height	cm	63.0	66.5	69.6	73.1	76.6	79.7	83.2	5.1	63.4	66.9	70.0	73.5	77.0	80.1	83.6	5.1
Shoulder width	cm	27.5	29.1	30.5	32.1	33.7	35.1	36.7	2.3	26.8	28.5	30.0	31.6	33.2	34.7	36.4	2.4
Pelvic width	cm	19.8	21.5	23.0	24.6	26.2	27.7	29.4	2.4	21.1	22.7	23.7	25.1	26.5	27.5	29.1	2.0
Head circumference	cm	49.0	50.3	51.4	52.6	53.8	54.9	56.2	1.8	46.3	48.4	50.3	52.4	54.5	56.4	58.5	3.1
Chest circumference	cm	55.5	58.5	61.2	64.2	67.2	69.9	72.9	4.4	50.1	54.4	58.2	62.4	66.6	70.4	74.7	6.2
Upper arm circumf.	cm	15.7	17.3	18.7	20.3	21.9	23.3	24.9	2.3	15.5	17.3	18.9	20.7	22.5	24.1	25.9	2.6
Wrist circumference	cm	9.9	11.2	12.4	13.7	15.0	16.2	17.5	1.9	11.6	12.3	12.9	13.6	14.3	14.9	15.6	1.0
Calf circumference	cm	23.2	24.9	26.4	28.0	29.6	31.1	32.8	2.4	22.7	24.6	26.4	28.4	30.4	32.2	34.1	2.9
12 years																	
Mass	kg	25.8	30.6	34.8	39.5	44.2	48.4	53.2	6.91	24.3	29.4	34.0	39.0	44.0	48.6	53.7	7.4
Height	cm	133.5	138.2	142.4	147.0	151.6	155.8	160.5	6.8	133.5	138.7	143.3	148.5	153.7	158.3	163.5	7.6
Sitting height	cm	64.6	67.9	70.8	74.1	77.4	80.3	83.6	4.8	65.1	68.4	71.3	74.6	77.9	80.8	84.1	4.8
Shoulder width	cm	26.6	28.6	30.5	32.5	34.5	36.4	38.4	3.0	27.3	29.1	30.6	32.3	34.0	35.5	37.3	2.5
Pelvic width	cm	19.4	21.3	23.1	25.1	27.1	28.9	30.8	2.9	21.7	23.4	24.5	25.9	27.3	28.4	30.1	2.1
Head circumference	cm	49.3	50.5	51.5	52.7	53.9	54.9	56.1	1.7	48.3	49.8	51.1	52.5	53.9	55.2	56.7	2.1
Chest circumference	cm	56.1	59.2	61.9	65.0	68.1	70.8	73.9	4.5	50.6	54.9	58.8	63.1	67.4	71.3	75.6	6.3
Upper arm circumf.	cm	15.2	17.1	18.8	20.7	22.6	24.3	26.2	2.8	15.8	17.6	19.2	21.0	22.8	24.4	26.2	2.6
Wrist circumference	cm	9.1	10.7	12.1	13.7	15.3	16.7	18.3	2.3	11.8	12.5	13.1	13.8	14.5	15.1	15.8	1.0
Calf circumference	cm	23.7	25.4	26.9	28.5	30.1	31.6	33.3	2.4	23.0	24.9	26.7	28.7	30.7	32.5	34.4	2.9

Reference HEIMENDINGER, J., *Helv. paediat. Acta,* **19**, suppl. 13 (1964) [2150 boys and 2150 girls in crèches, kindergartens and schools in Basel (Switzerland), 1956–1957].

	Unit	Boys								Girls							
		95%							s	95%							s
			80%								80%						
				50%								50%					
		$P_{2.5}$	P_{10}	P_{25}	P_{50}	P_{75}	P_{90}	$P_{97.5}$		$P_{2.5}$	P_{10}	P_{25}	P_{50}	P_{75}	P_{90}	$P_{97.5}$	
12½ years																	
Mass	kg	26.9	32.1	36.7	41.8	46.9	51.5	56.7	7.50	25.8	31.2	36.0	41.4	46.8	51.6	57.0	7.9
Height	cm	135.3	140.4	145.0	150.0	155.0	159.6	164.7	7.4	136.3	141.5	146.3	151.5	156.7	161.5	166.7	7.7
Sitting height	cm	66.4	69.4	72.1	75.1	78.1	80.8	83.8	4.4	67.2	70.1	72.8	75.7	78.6	81.3	84.2	4.3
Shoulder width	cm	24.2	27.1	29.8	32.7	35.6	38.3	41.2	4.3	27.9	29.7	31.2	32.9	34.6	36.1	37.9	2.5
Pelvic width	cm	19.2	21.4	23.5	25.7	27.9	30.0	32.2	3.3	22.4	24.2	25.3	26.8	28.3	29.4	31.2	2.2
Head circumference	cm	49.6	50.7	51.7	52.8	53.9	54.9	56.0	1.6	49.3	50.5	51.5	52.7	53.9	54.9	56.1	1.7
Chest circumference	cm	56.7	60.0	62.9	66.2	69.5	72.4	75.7	4.8	51.3	55.7	59.6	64.0	68.4	72.3	76.6	6.4
Upper arm circumf.	cm	14.5	16.7	18.8	21.0	23.2	25.3	27.5	3.3	16.1	17.9	19.5	21.3	23.1	24.7	26.5	2.6
Wrist circumference	cm	8.8	10.6	12.1	13.8	15.5	17.0	18.8	2.5	12.1	12.8	13.4	14.1	14.8	15.4	16.1	1.0
Calf circumference	cm	23.7	25.5	27.2	29.0	30.8	32.5	34.3	2.7	23.5	25.4	27.2	29.2	31.2	33.0	34.9	2.9
13 years																	
Mass	kg	28.9	34.2	38.9	44.1	49.3	54.0	59.3	7.67	27.9	33.6	38.6	44.3	50.0	55.0	60.7	8.3
Height	cm	138.0	143.3	148.1	153.4	158.7	163.5	168.8	7.8	139.8	144.8	149.2	154.1	159.0	163.4	168.4	7.2
Sitting height	cm	67.8	70.7	73.4	76.3	79.2	81.9	84.8	4.3	69.1	71.7	74.1	76.8	79.5	81.9	84.5	3.9
Shoulder width	cm	22.6	26.5	29.6	33.1	36.6	39.7	42.8	5.1	28.5	30.3	31.8	33.6	35.4	36.9	38.7	2.6
Pelvic width	cm	18.8	21.4	23.7	26.3	28.9	31.2	33.3	3.8	23.2	25.0	26.1	27.6	29.1	30.2	32.0	2.2
Head circumference	cm	49.9	51.0	51.9	52.9	53.9	54.8	55.9	1.5	49.6	50.7	51.7	52.8	53.9	54.9	56.0	1.6
Chest circumference	cm	55.3	59.5	63.2	67.4	71.6	75.3	79.5	6.1	52.3	56.8	60.8	65.2	69.6	73.6	78.1	6.5
Upper arm circumf.	cm	14.7	16.9	19.0	21.2	23.4	25.5	27.7	3.3	16.7	18.5	20.0	21.7	23.4	24.9	26.7	2.5
Wrist circumference	cm	9.1	10.9	12.4	14.1	15.8	17.3	19.1	2.5	–	–	–	14.2	–	–	–	0.9
Calf circumference	cm	22.5	24.9	27.0	29.4	31.8	33.9	36.3	3.5	24.1	26.1	28.0	30.0	32.0	33.9	35.9	3.0
13½ years																	
Mass	kg	30.8	36.2	41.0	46.3	51.6	56.4	61.8	7.81	30.3	36.2	41.4	47.3	53.2	58.4	64.3	8.6
Height	cm	141.2	146.6	151.6	157.0	162.4	167.4	172.8	8.0	143.6	148.0	151.9	156.3	160.7	164.4	169.0	6.4
Sitting height	cm	69.3	72.2	74.9	77.8	80.7	83.4	86.3	4.3	70.8	73.2	75.4	77.9	80.4	82.6	85.0	3.6
Shoulder width	cm	24.8	28.7	31.2	34.1	37.0	39.5	41.4	4.2	29.2	31.0	32.5	34.2	35.9	37.4	39.2	2.5
Pelvic width	cm	20.1	22.5	24.6	27.0	29.4	31.5	33.9	3.5	24.3	26.0	27.1	28.5	29.9	31.0	32.7	2.1
Head circumference	cm	50.0	51.1	52.0	53.0	54.0	54.9	56.0	1.5	50.0	51.1	52.0	53.0	54.0	54.9	56.0	1.5
Chest circumference	cm	54.2	59.4	64.0	69.2	74.4	79.0	84.2	7.6	53.3	57.8	61.8	66.2	70.6	74.6	79.1	6.5
Upper arm circumf.	cm	16.0	17.9	19.6	21.5	23.4	25.1	27.0	2.8	17.2	18.9	20.4	22.0	23.6	25.1	26.8	2.4
Wrist circumference	cm	9.9	11.5	12.9	14.5	16.1	17.5	19.1	2.3	–	–	–	14.3	–	–	–	0.9
Calf circumference	cm	22.7	25.2	27.5	30.0	32.5	34.8	37.3	3.7	24.8	26.9	28.8	30.9	33.0	34.9	37.0	3.1
14 years																	
Mass	kg	32.9	38.3	43.2	48.6	54.0	58.9	64.3	7.92	33.7	39.4	44.4	50.1	55.8	60.8	66.5	8.3
Height	cm	144.8	150.2	155.2	160.6	166.0	171.0	176.4	8.0	146.9	150.8	154.3	158.2	162.1	165.6	169.5	5.7
Sitting height	cm	70.6	73.6	76.3	79.3	82.3	85.0	88.0	4.4	72.3	74.6	76.7	79.0	81.3	83.4	85.7	3.4
Shoulder width	cm	28.8	31.9	33.6	35.4	37.2	38.9	39.4	2.7	30.1	31.8	33.3	34.9	36.5	38.0	39.7	2.4
Pelvic width	cm	23.0	24.8	26.3	28.0	29.7	31.2	33.0	2.5	25.3	26.7	27.9	29.3	30.7	31.9	33.3	2.0
Head circumference	cm	50.1	51.2	52.1	53.1	54.1	55.0	56.1	1.5	50.2	51.3	52.2	53.2	54.2	55.1	56.2	1.5
Chest circumference	cm	57.8	62.4	66.4	70.9	75.4	79.4	84.0	6.6	54.3	58.7	62.6	67.0	71.4	75.3	79.7	6.4
Upper arm circumf.	cm	18.2	19.5	20.7	22.0	23.3	24.5	25.8	1.9	17.7	19.3	20.7	22.3	23.9	25.3	26.9	2.3
Wrist circumference	cm	11.0	12.4	13.6	15.0	16.4	17.6	19.0	2.0	–	–	–	14.4	–	–	–	0.9
Calf circumference	cm	25.5	27.3	29.0	30.8	32.6	34.3	36.1	2.7	25.8	27.8	29.7	31.7	33.7	35.6	37.6	3.0
14½ years																	
Mass	kg	34.3	40.1	45.2	50.9	56.6	61.7	67.5	8.37	36.9	42.1	46.7	51.8	56.9	61.5	66.7	7.5
Height	cm	148.2	153.6	158.4	163.8	169.2	174.0	179.4	7.9	149.7	152.5	156.0	159.8	163.6	167.1	169.9	5.6
Sitting height	cm	72.1	75.1	77.8	80.8	83.8	86.5	89.5	4.4	73.6	75.8	77.9	80.1	82.3	84.4	86.6	3.3
Shoulder width	cm	31.7	33.4	34.9	36.5	38.1	39.6	41.3	2.4	31.0	32.6	34.0	35.6	37.2	38.6	40.2	2.3
Pelvic width	cm	24.8	26.3	27.6	29.0	30.4	31.7	33.2	2.1	26.1	27.4	28.6	29.9	31.2	32.4	33.7	1.9
Head circumference	cm	50.3	51.4	52.3	53.3	54.3	55.2	56.3	1.5	50.2	51.3	52.3	53.4	54.5	55.5	56.6	1.5
Chest circumference	cm	61.5	65.3	68.7	72.4	76.1	79.5	83.3	5.5	55.2	59.5	63.4	67.7	72.0	75.9	80.2	6.3
Upper arm circumf.	cm	18.9	20.2	21.4	22.7	24.0	25.2	26.5	1.9	18.4	19.9	21.2	22.6	24.0	25.3	26.8	2.1
Wrist circumference	cm	12.1	13.2	14.2	15.3	16.4	17.4	18.5	1.6	–	–	–	14.5	–	–	–	0.9
Calf circumference	cm	27.0	28.8	30.3	32.0	33.7	35.2	37.0	2.5	26.4	28.3	30.1	32.1	34.1	35.9	37.8	2.9

Reference HEIMENDINGER, J., *Helv. paediat. Acta,* **19**, suppl. 13 (1964) [2150 boys and 2150 girls in crèches, kindergartens and schools in Basel (Switzerland), 1956–1957].

	Unit	Boys								Girls							
		95%								95%							
			80%								80%						
				50%					s			50%					s
	Unit	$P_{2.5}$	P_{10}	P_{25}	P_{50}	P_{75}	P_{90}	$P_{97.5}$		$P_{2.5}$	P_{10}	P_{25}	P_{50}	P_{75}	P_{90}	$P_{97.5}$	
15 years																	
Mass	kg	36.8	42.5	47.5	53.1	58.7	63.7	69.4	8.22	39.5	44.3	48.5	53.2	57.9	62.1	66.9	6.9
Height	cm	151.9	157.1	161.7	166.8	171.9	176.5	181.7	7.5	151.0	153.8	157.3	161.1	164.9	168.4	171.2	5.6
Sitting height	cm	73.3	76.4	79.1	82.2	85.3	88.0	91.1	4.5	74.9	77.1	79.0	81.2	83.4	85.3	87.5	3.2
Shoulder width	cm	33.0	34.6	35.9	37.4	38.9	40.2	41.8	2.2	31.6	33.2	34.5	36.0	37.5	38.8	40.4	2.2
Pelvic width	cm	25.5	27.0	28.3	29.7	31.1	32.4	33.9	2.1	26.6	27.7	28.9	30.2	31.5	32.7	33.8	1.9
Head circumference	cm	50.4	51.5	52.4	53.4	54.4	55.3	56.4	1.5	50.5	51.6	52.5	53.5	54.5	55.4	56.5	1.5
Chest circumference	cm	64.0	67.4	70.5	73.9	77.3	80.4	83.8	5.0	56.2	60.4	64.1	68.3	72.5	76.2	80.4	6.1
Upper arm circumf.	cm	19.3	20.7	21.9	23.3	24.7	25.9	27.3	2.0	18.9	20.3	21.5	22.9	24.3	25.5	26.9	2.0
Wrist circumference	cm	12.9	13.8	14.6	15.5	16.4	17.2	18.1	1.3	–	–	–	14.5	–	–	–	0.9
Calf circumference	cm	27.9	29.6	31.1	32.7	34.3	35.8	37.5	2.4	27.2	28.9	30.5	32.3	34.1	35.7	37.4	2.6
15½ years																	
Mass	kg	39.4	44.9	49.9	55.4	60.9	65.9	71.4	8.09	41.0	45.6	49.7	54.3	58.9	63.0	67.6	6.7
Height	cm	155.8	160.6	164.8	169.5	174.2	178.4	183.2	6.9	150.6	154.6	158.1	162.1	166.1	169.6	173.6	5.8
Sitting height	cm	75.0	78.0	80.7	83.7	86.7	89.4	92.4	4.4	76.0	78.2	80.1	82.3	84.5	86.4	88.6	3.2
Shoulder width	cm	33.2	35.5	36.8	38.2	39.6	40.9	41.6	2.1	32.0	33.5	34.8	36.2	37.6	38.9	40.4	2.1
Pelvic width	cm	26.1	27.6	28.9	30.3	31.7	33.0	34.5	2.1	26.9	28.2	29.3	30.5	31.7	32.8	34.1	1.8
Head circumference	cm	50.7	51.7	52.5	53.5	54.5	55.3	56.3	1.4	50.9	51.9	52.7	53.7	54.7	55.5	56.5	1.4
Chest circumference	cm	65.9	69.1	72.0	75.2	78.4	81.3	84.5	4.7	57.3	61.3	64.8	68.8	72.8	76.3	80.3	5.8
Upper arm circumf.	cm	19.2	20.8	22.1	23.6	25.1	26.4	28.0	2.2	19.7	21.0	22.1	23.3	24.5	25.6	26.9	1.8
Wrist circumference	cm	13.4	14.2	14.9	15.6	16.3	17.0	17.8	1.1	–	–	–	14.5	–	–	–	0.9
Calf circumference	cm	28.5	30.1	31.5	33.1	34.7	36.1	37.7	2.3	27.7	29.4	30.9	32.5	34.1	35.6	37.3	2.4
16 years																	
Mass	kg	41.9	47.4	52.3	57.7	63.1	68.0	73.5	7.98	41.8	46.4	50.5	55.1	59.7	63.8	68.4	6.7
Height	cm	158.8	163.3	167.3	171.7	176.1	180.1	184.6	6.5	151.2	155.3	158.9	162.9	166.9	170.5	174.6	5.9
Sitting height	cm	77.1	79.9	82.4	85.2	88.0	90.5	93.3	4.1	76.7	78.9	80.8	83.0	85.2	87.1	89.3	3.2
Shoulder width	cm	34.2	36.3	37.5	38.9	40.3	41.5	42.2	2.0	32.4	33.8	35.0	36.4	37.8	39.0	40.4	2.0
Pelvic width	cm	27.1	28.4	29.6	30.9	32.2	33.4	34.7	1.9	27.3	28.6	29.7	30.9	32.1	33.2	34.5	1.8
Head circumference	cm	50.8	51.8	52.6	53.6	54.6	55.4	56.4	1.4	51.1	52.0	52.8	53.7	54.6	55.4	56.3	1.4
Chest circumference	cm	67.7	70.7	73.4	76.4	79.4	82.1	85.1	4.4	58.3	62.1	65.5	69.2	72.9	76.3	80.1	5.5
Upper arm circumf.	cm	19.3	20.9	22.3	23.9	25.5	26.9	28.5	2.3	20.0	21.3	22.4	23.6	24.8	25.9	27.2	1.8
Wrist circumference	cm	13.7	14.4	15.0	15.7	16.4	17.0	17.7	1.0	–	–	–	14.5	–	–	–	0.7
Calf circumference	cm	28.9	30.5	31.8	33.3	34.8	36.1	37.7	2.2	28.0	29.6	31.0	32.6	34.2	35.6	37.2	2.3
16½ years																	
Mass	kg	45.3	50.3	54.9	59.9	64.9	69.5	74.5	7.38	42.4	47.1	51.3	55.9	60.5	64.7	69.4	6.8
Height	cm	161.3	165.5	169.2	173.4	177.6	181.3	185.5	6.1	151.6	155.7	159.4	163.5	167.6	171.3	175.4	6.0
Sitting height	cm	79.7	81.8	83.9	86.3	88.7	90.8	93.5	3.5	77.0	79.2	81.1	83.3	85.5	87.4	89.6	3.2
Shoulder width	cm	35.5	36.9	38.1	39.5	40.9	42.1	43.5	2.0	32.6	33.9	35.1	36.4	37.7	38.9	40.2	1.9
Pelvic width	cm	27.9	29.1	30.1	31.3	32.5	33.5	34.7	1.7	27.6	28.9	30.0	31.2	32.4	33.5	34.8	1.8
Head circumference	cm	50.9	51.9	52.7	53.7	54.7	55.5	56.5	1.4	51.1	52.0	52.8	53.7	54.6	55.4	56.3	1.4
Chest circumference	cm	69.1	72.0	74.5	77.4	80.3	82.8	85.7	4.2	59.1	62.7	65.9	69.4	72.9	76.1	79.7	5.2
Upper arm circumf.	cm	19.7	21.3	22.6	24.1	25.6	26.9	28.5	2.2	20.3	21.6	22.7	23.9	25.1	26.2	27.5	1.8
Wrist circumference	cm	13.8	14.5	15.1	15.8	16.5	17.1	17.8	1.0	–	–	–	14.5	–	–	–	0.7
Calf circumference	cm	29.0	30.6	31.9	33.4	34.9	36.2	37.8	2.2	28.1	29.7	31.1	32.7	34.3	35.7	37.3	2.3
17 years																	
Mass	kg	47.6	52.1	56.2	60.8	65.4	69.5	74.0	6.69	43.0	47.7	51.9	56.5	61.1	65.3	70.0	6.8
Height	cm	162.6	166.7	170.3	174.3	178.3	181.9	186.0	5.9	151.7	155.8	159.6	163.8	168.0	171.8	175.9	6.1
Sitting height	cm	79.9	82.2	84.3	86.6	88.9	91.0	93.3	3.4	77.2	79.4	81.3	83.5	85.7	87.6	89.8	3.2
Shoulder width	cm	36.2	37.5	38.7	40.0	41.3	42.5	43.8	1.9	32.7	34.0	35.2	36.5	37.8	39.0	40.3	1.9
Pelvic width	cm	28.6	29.7	30.6	31.6	32.6	33.5	34.6	1.5	27.9	29.2	30.3	31.5	32.7	33.8	35.1	1.8
Head circumference	cm	50.8	51.9	52.8	53.8	54.8	55.7	56.8	1.5	51.1	52.0	52.8	53.7	54.6	55.4	56.3	1.4
Chest circumference	cm	70.1	73.0	75.5	78.4	81.3	83.8	86.7	4.2	59.8	63.2	66.2	69.5	72.8	75.8	79.2	4.9
Upper arm circumf.	cm	20.0	21.5	22.8	24.2	25.6	26.9	28.4	2.1	20.6	21.9	23.0	24.2	25.4	26.5	27.8	1.8
Wrist circumference	cm	14.0	14.6	15.2	15.8	16.4	17.0	17.6	0.9	–	–	–	14.5	–	–	–	0.7
Calf circumference	cm	29.3	30.8	32.1	33.5	34.9	36.2	37.7	2.1	28.2	29.8	31.2	32.8	34.4	35.8	37.4	2.3

Reference HEIMENDINGER, J., *Helv. paediat. Acta,* **19**, suppl. 13 (1964) [2150 boys and 2150 girls in crèches, kindergartens and schools in Basel (Switzerland), 1956–1957].

	Unit	Boys							Girls						
		94%							94%						
			80%							80%					
				50%							50%				
		P_{03}	P_{10}	P_{25}	P_{50}	P_{75}	P_{90}	P_{97}	P_{03}	P_{10}	P_{25}	P_{50}	P_{75}	P_{90}	P_{97}
Birth															
Mass	kg	2.4	2.6	2.8	3.1	3.4	3.6	3.9	2.4	2.6	2.8	3.0	3.2	3.5	3.8
Length	cm	45.4	46.8	47.8	48.9	50.0	51.3	52.8	45.5	46.2	47.2	48.4	49.4	50.3	51.5
3 months															
Mass	kg	4.6	5.0	5.4	5.8	6.2	6.5	7.0	4.2	4.6	5.0	5.3	5.7	6.1	6.4
Length	cm	55.7	57.2	58.4	59.6	60.8	62.1	63.3	54.7	55.8	57.0	58.4	59.4	60.5	61.5
6 months															
Mass	kg	5.8	6.2	6.7	7.2	7.7	8.5	9.0	5.3	5.6	6.1	6.5	7.0	7.5	8.1
Length	cm	62.2	63.3	64.6	66.0	67.5	68.7	70.1	60.6	61.7	63.0	64.3	65.6	66.7	67.8
9 months															
Mass	kg	6.8	7.2	7.7	8.2	8.8	9.5	10.2	6.1	6.5	7.0	7.5	8.0	8.6	9.3
Length	cm	66.1	67.2	68.6	70.0	71.4	72.9	74.5	64.1	65.2	66.8	68.3	69.8	71.0	72.2
1 year															
Mass	kg	7.5	7.9	8.3	8.9	9.5	10.2	11.0	6.7	7.2	7.7	8.2	8.7	9.3	10.1
Length	cm	68.8	70.1	71.4	73.1	74.6	76.4	78.0	66.9	68.1	69.7	71.4	73.0	74.2	76.0
1½ years															
Mass	kg	8.4	8.9	9.3	9.9	10.7	11.3	12.2	7.7	8.2	8.7	9.3	9.9	10.5	11.3
Length	cm	73.6	75.2	76.6	78.6	80.4	82.2	84.1	72.0	73.5	75.1	77.0	78.9	80.4	82.7
2 years															
Mass	kg	9.2	9.7	10.3	10.9	11.7	12.3	13.3	8.5	9.1	9.6	10.3	11.0	11.6	12.5
Length	cm	78.0	79.7	81.5	83.4	85.2	87.3	89.2	76.4	77.6	79.4	81.7	83.8	85.5	87.9
2½ years															
Mass	kg	9.9	10.5	11.2	11.8	12.7	13.3	14.3	9.2	9.8	10.4	11.3	12.0	12.6	13.6
Length	cm	81.9	83.7	85.4	87.5	89.5	91.8	94.0	80.3	81.4	83.5	86.0	88.3	90.2	92.5
3 years															
Mass	kg	10.6	11.3	12.0	12.8	13.7	14.3	15.3	9.9	10.6	11.2	12.1	13.0	13.6	14.6
Length	cm	85.3	87.2	89.1	91.3	93.3	95.9	98.3	83.7	85.4	87.8	90.1	92.4	95.1	97.3
3½ years															
Mass	kg	11.4	12.0	12.6	13.5	14.5	15.5	16.4	10.6	11.4	12.0	12.8	13.8	14.6	15.5
Length	cm	89.0	91.0	93.1	95.4	98.1	100.4	102.6	87.2	89.3	91.8	94.1	96.6	99.6	101.8
4 years															
Mass	kg	11.9	12.6	13.5	14.2	15.4	16.4	17.5	11.1	12.0	12.8	13.6	14.6	15.5	16.5
Length	cm	92.2	94.2	96.4	99.3	101.4	104.0	106.0	90.1	92.6	95.2	97.9	100.2	103.1	106.0
4½ years															
Mass	kg	12.5	13.3	14.1	14.9	16.0	17.1	18.5	11.6	12.5	13.5	14.4	15.6	16.5	17.5
Length	cm	95.2	97.6	99.8	102.1	104.6	107.0	109.1	93.2	95.8	98.2	101.0	103.9	106.5	109.3
5 years															
Mass	kg	13.0	13.9	14.7	15.5	16.5	17.6	19.2	12.0	13.1	14.2	15.1	16.5	17.5	18.5
Length	cm	98.0	100.0	102.2	105.1	107.8	109.9	112.0	96.0	98.2	101.5	104.0	107.0	109.9	112.1

References CHANG et al., *Far East med.J.*, **1**, 101 (1965); BABER et al., *Asian J. mod. Med.*, **10**, 312 (1974) [length measured in recumbent position; when standing height is measured, add 1 cm before reference to the table].

		Boys							Girls						
		94%							94%						
			80%							80%					
				50%							50%				
	Unit	P_{03}	P_{10}	P_{25}	P_{50}	P_{75}	P_{90}	P_{97}	P_{03}	P_{10}	P_{25}	P_{50}	P_{75}	P_{90}	P_{97}
Birth															
Mass	kg	2.2	2.4	2.7	2.9	3.2	3.4	3.6	2.2	2.4	2.6	2.8	3.1	3.4	3.7
Length	cm	43.2	44.4	47.0	48.3	48.3	50.8	52.1	43.2	44.4	45.7	47.0	48.3	50.8	50.8
3 months															
Mass	kg	4.0	4.4	4.9	5.4	5.9	6.2	7.1	3.9	4.3	4.7	5.1	5.5	5.9	6.4
Length	cm	52.1	54.6	57.2	58.4	59.7	62.2	63.5	53.3	54.6	55.9	58.4	59.7	61.0	62.2
6 months															
Mass	kg	4.9	5.5	6.1	6.6	7.2	7.6	8.4	4.4	5.2	5.7	6.3	6.7	7.4	7.9
Length	cm	58.4	61.0	62.2	64.8	66.0	67.3	68.6	59.7	61.0	62.2	63.5	64.8	67.3	68.6
9 months															
Mass	kg	5.8	6.3	6.9	7.5	8.0	8.7	9.4	5.2	5.9	6.5	6.9	7.7	8.4	8.8
Length	cm	63.5	64.8	67.3	68.6	71.1	72.4	74.9	62.2	64.8	66.0	67.3	68.6	71.1	72.4
1 year															
Mass	kg	6.2	6.9	7.5	8.2	8.9	9.6	10.4	5.8	6.5	7.3	7.9	8.5	9.0	9.7
Length	cm	66.0	68.6	69.8	72.4	73.7	76.2	77.5	66.0	67.3	68.6	71.1	72.4	74.9	77.5
1½ years															
Mass	kg	7.5	8.2	8.9	9.5	10.2	11.2	11.9	6.9	8.0	8.5	9.3	10.0	10.5	11.3
Length	cm	71.1	72.4	74.9	77.5	80.0	82.6	83.8	71.1	72.4	74.9	76.2	78.7	80.0	83.8
2 years															
Mass	kg	9.0	9.3	9.8	10.7	11.7	12.5	13.2	8.3	8.8	9.4	10.2	11.2	11.6	12.5
Length	cm	74.9	78.7	80.0	82.6	85.1	86.4	88.9	76.2	78.7	80.0	82.6	85.1	87.6	91.4
2½ years															
Mass	kg	9.7	10.1	10.6	11.6	12.7	14.0	14.4	9.0	10.0	10.5	11.3	12.3	13.3	14.0
Length	cm	78.7	81.3	83.8	86.4	88.9	91.4	94.0	78.7	81.3	82.6	85.1	87.6	91.4	92.7
3 years															
Mass	kg	10.5	11.1	11.8	12.7	14.0	14.9	15.2	10.3	10.8	11.6	12.5	13.3	14.4	15.2
Length	cm	81.3	85.1	87.6	90.2	91.4	95.2	97.8	81.3	83.8	86.4	88.9	91.4	92.7	95.2
3½ years															
Mass	kg	11.0	11.8	12.7	13.7	14.7	15.7	16.2	10.9	11.8	12.5	13.2	14.3	15.2	16.0
Length	cm	83.8	87.6	91.4	94.0	95.2	99.1	100.3	86.4	87.6	90.2	92.7	95.2	96.5	99.1
4 years															
Mass	kg	11.9	12.5	13.1	14.1	15.5	16.7	17.4	11.4	12.2	12.9	13.9	15.0	15.8	16.3
Length	cm	87.6	91.4	94.0	96.5	99.1	102.9	104.1	88.9	91.4	92.7	95.2	97.8	100.3	101.6
4½ years															
Mass	kg	12.1	13.1	13.7	14.8	16.2	17.5	18.1	12.1	13.0	13.8	14.7	15.4	16.6	17.4
Length	cm	88.9	94.0	96.5	99.1	101.6	104.1	106.7	88.9	94.0	96.5	99.1	101.6	104.1	106.7
5 years															
Mass	kg	12.7	13.6	14.3	15.9	17.2	18.1	18.8	12.8	13.4	14.3	15.4	16.7	17.5	18.5
Length	cm	92.7	96.5	99.1	101.6	105.4	108.0	110.5	88.9	96.5	99.1	101.6	104.1	105.4	108.0

Reference Morley et al., *W. Afr. med. J.*, **17**, 8 (1968) [length measured in recumbent position; when standing height is measured, add 1 cm before reference to the table].

Growth rates assessed from data of the Fels Research Institute Study (USA)

Centiles for 6-month increments of body mass in boys and girls from birth to 3 years

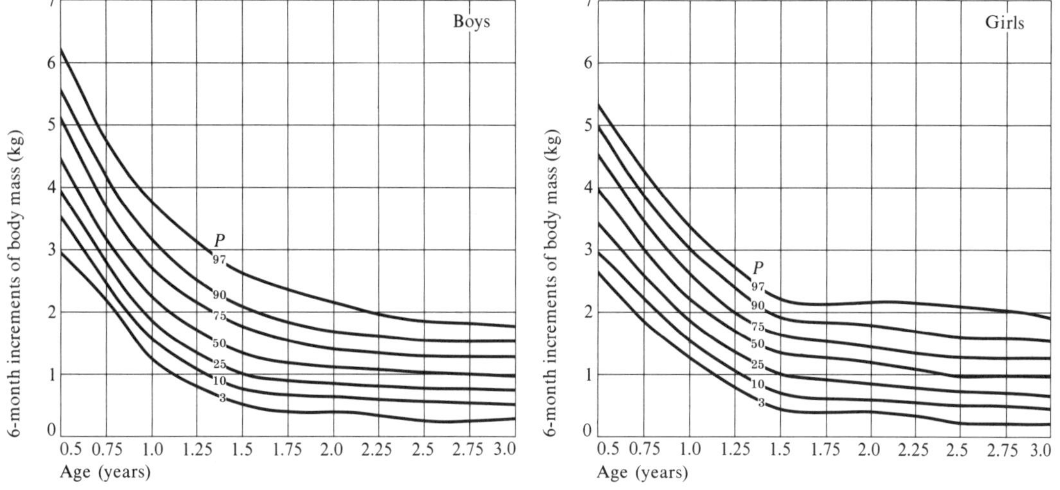

Centiles for 6-month increments of body mass in boys and girls aged from 2 to 18 years

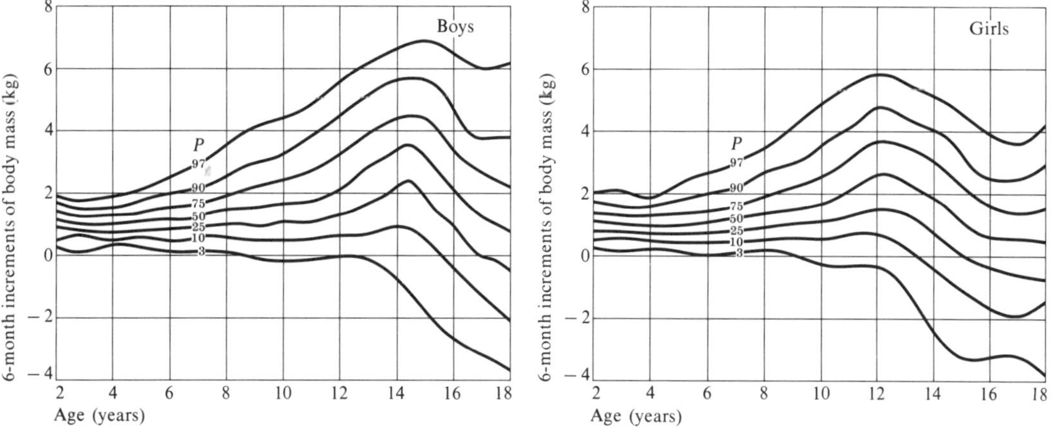

Centiles for 6-month increments of body length in boys and girls from birth to 3 years

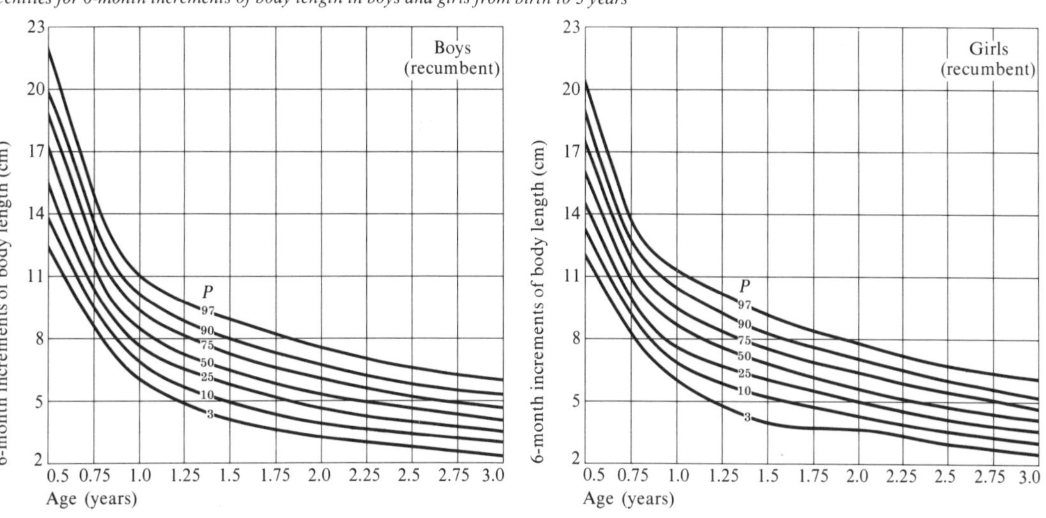

Centiles for 6-month increments of height in boys and girls aged from 2 to 18 years

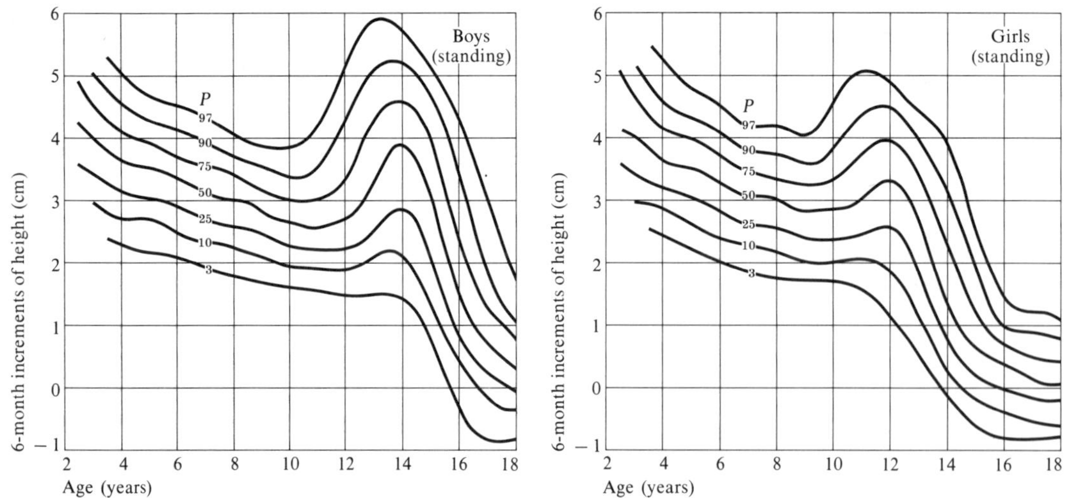

Centiles for 6-month increments of head circumference in boys and girls from birth to 3 years

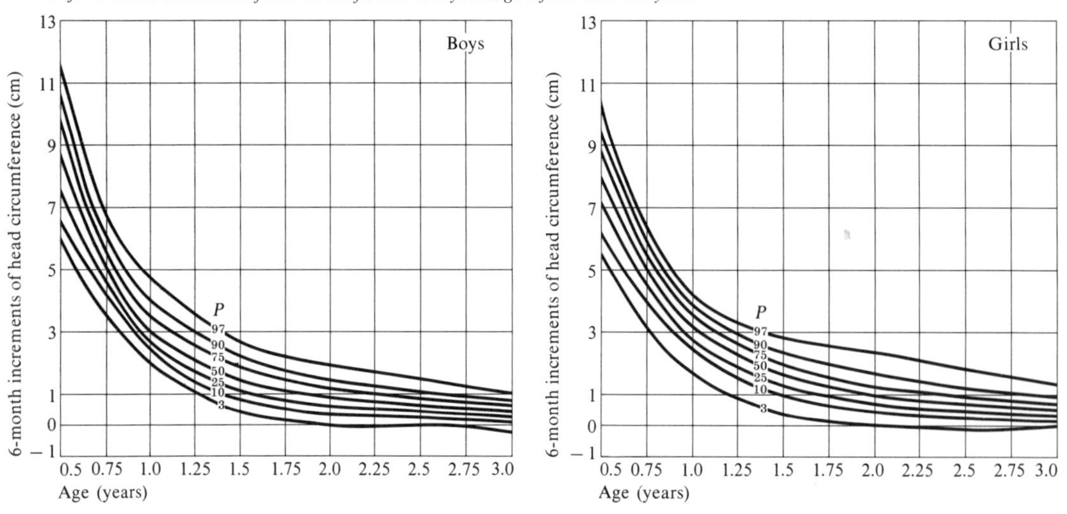

Reference

Roche and Himes, *Amer. J. clin. Nutr.*, **33**, 2041 (1980).

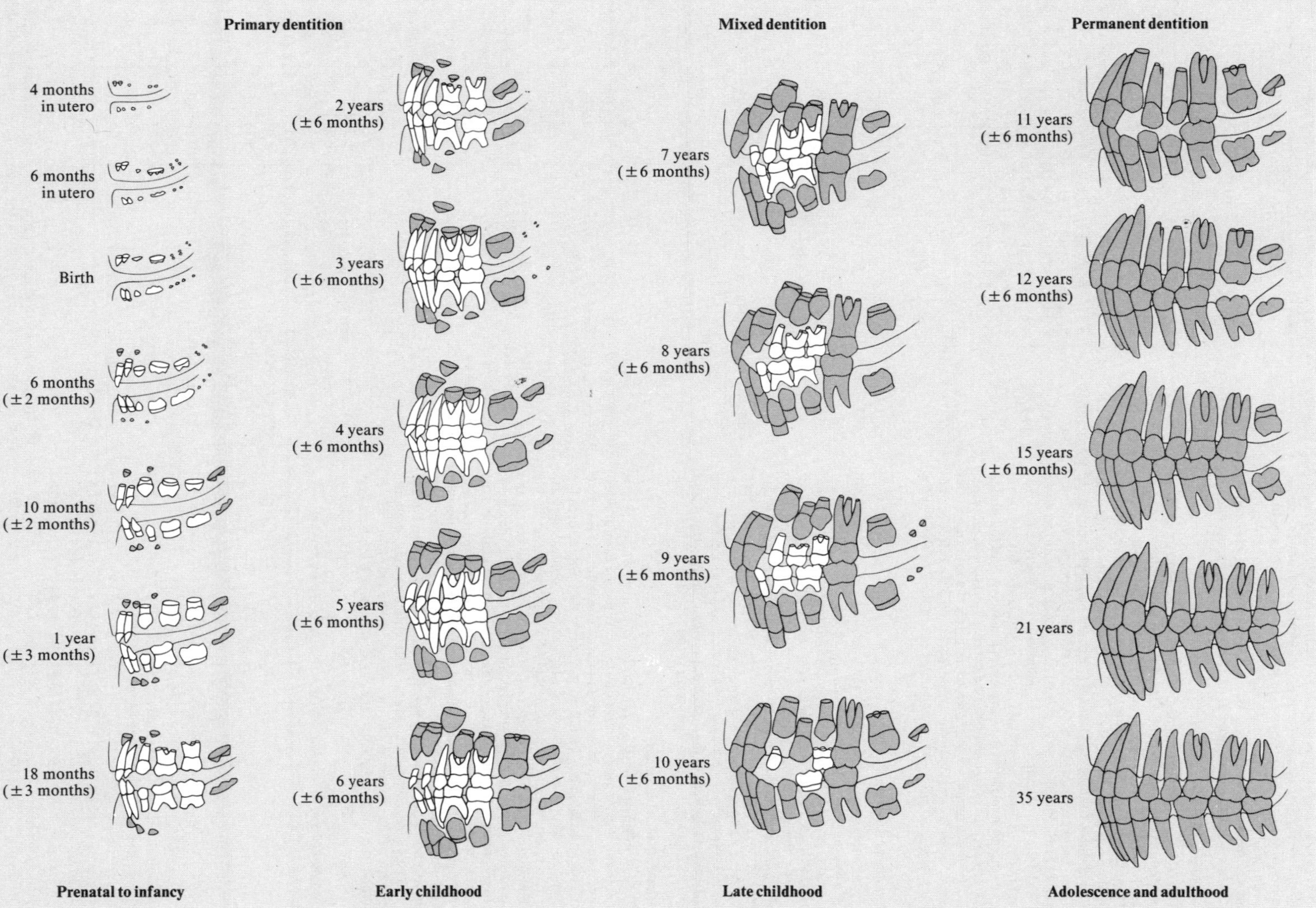
Primary dentition
Mixed dentition
Permanent dentition
4 months in utero
6 months in utero
Birth
6 months (± 2 months)
10 months (± 2 months)
1 year (± 3 months)
18 months (± 3 months)
2 years (± 6 months)
3 years (± 6 months)
4 years (± 6 months)
5 years (± 6 months)
6 years (± 6 months)
7 years (± 6 months)
8 years (± 6 months)
9 years (± 6 months)
10 years (± 6 months)
11 years (± 6 months)
12 years (± 6 months)
15 years (± 6 months)
21 years
35 years
Prenatal to infancy
Early childhood
Late childhood
Adolescence and adulthood

There is a general agreement that the timing of the eruption of deciduous and permanent teeth is predominantly under genetic control. Findings about the association of tooth eruption with the state of health, nutrition, growth and skeletal age vary between the various investigations. In the instances in which such associations have been clearly demonstrated, their effect is rather marginal.

Deciduous dentition

BOAS[1] suggested impaired health as the explanation for delayed dentition. HAMIL et al.[2] found that children with mild scurvy and rickets did not differ from a group of healthy infants. STEARNS and MEREDITH[3] showed that children with superior health records and supplemented with vitamin D erupted their incisors earlier than other children in the study. BILLEWICZ et al.[4] and DELGADO et al.[5] found positive association between dental development and body mass at birth. MCGREGOR et al.[6], BILLEWICZ et al.[4] and DELGADO et al.[5] found that dental development was positively associated with body mass and height attained at a given age. BILLEWICZ et al.[4] found no association between skeletal maturity and the timing of tooth eruption. High-energy food supplementation of maternal diet during pregnancy was shown to influence the eruption of deciduous teeth[5]. Great majority of workers found no difference between boys and girls as regards the age at eruption of the deciduous teeth.

Permanent dentition

Most studies show that teeth in the lower jaw erupt earlier, with the exception of 1st and 2nd premolars, and that girls have earlier eruption ages than boys. BILLEWICZ and MCGREGOR[7] noticed that this difference tended to increase as girls approached the age of puberty. Positive association of dental development with body mass and height attained at a given age was reported by WALLIS[8] and BILLEWICZ and MCGREGOR[7]. The latter observed, however, that there was no association of eruption ages with the position of children on the *body mass for height* standard and inferred that long-term malnutrition may have some effect on the eruption of permanent teeth but that short-term set-backs have no influence.

Estimation of calendar age

The problem of estimating calendar age in areas where there is no reliable birth registration is notoriously difficult; careful questioning and 'clinical assessment' are used. The latter is related to the body mass and height attained and thus rather uncertain in the absence of local growth standards. In addition, 'clinical age' depends on anthropometric measurements frequently used in the same studies to assess the nutritional status. VOORS[9] advocated the use of dental age in such circumstances. Although it has been shown that both deciduous and permanent dentition can be used to estimate calendar age, the limitations should be borne in mind. Firstly, there is a gap between 2½ and about 6 years, where deciduous dentition ceased to be, and permanent dentition has not yet become, useful for estimating age, and data on exfoliation are not reliable in view of extractions, pulp treatment or trauma; secondly, the error of the estimated age increases with the eruption of later teeth. In the table given below, the estimations of age are based on the number of teeth erupted (any tooth being counted which at least partly has broken through the gum). The grouping of the number of teeth is dictated by the fact that in any cross-sectional survey the number of subjects presenting with an even number of teeth at examination greatly outweighs that of those presenting with an odd number of teeth. Reliable local data, if available, should be given preference.

Mean numbers of deciduous teeth at various ages (both sexes)

Age	USA[10]	London[11]	Paris[11]	Zurich[11]	Dakar[11]	Gambia[6]	New Guinea[12]	Hongkong[4]	Guatemala[5] (Ladinos)
6 months	0.4	0.4	0.4	0.4	–	0.3	–	0.3	0.3
9 months	3.1	2.8	2.9	2.5	2.7	2.2	2.4	2.7	2.7
12 months	5.9	6.1	5.8	5.4	4.7	4.5	5.2	5.5	5.6
15 months	–	–	–	–	–	7.5	10.3	8.1	8.6
18 months	12.4	12.9	12.3	12.2	11.4	10.9	13.1	13.1	11.8
21 months	–	–	–	–	–	15.1	15.4	15.4	14.8
24 months	16.7	16.3	16.4	16.3	16.4	17.4	17.7	16.1	16.6
30 months	–	–	–	–	–	19.8	–	19.3	19.3
36 months	19.9	20.0	–	–	–	20.0	–	20.0	20.0

Mean ages (in years) at eruption of the permanent teeth

Permanent teeth	Boys				Girls			
	Britons[13]	Gambians[7]	Bantu[14]	Chinese[15]	Britons[13]	Gambians[7]	Bantu[14]	Chinese[15]
	Years							
Upper jaw								
I_1	7.27	7.38	6.9	7.36	6.94	7.11	6.5	7.23
I_2	8.39	8.59	8.1	8.60	8.04	8.10	7.7	8.19
C	11.33	11.33	10.7	11.03	10.72	10.53	10.2	10.26
PM_1	10.34	10.37	10.0	9.83	10.04	9.79	9.6	9.47
PM_2	11.02	11.25	10.9	10.67	10.91	10.59	10.3	10.48
M_1	6.22	5.99	5.4	6.27	6.12	5.78	5.3	6.29
M_2	11.90	11.93	11.3	12.12	11.68	11.18	10.8	11.80
Lower jaw								
I_1	6.50	6.22	5.8	6.51	6.17	6.08	5.8	6.28
I_2	7.66	7.47	6.9	7.37	7.35	7.07	6.4	7.13
C	10.42	10.58	10.3	10.38	9.60	9.70	9.5	9.51
PM_1	10.80	10.73	10.2	10.04	10.26	9.95	9.6	9.35
PM_2	11.88	11.39	11.0	11.02	11.25	10.66	10.7	10.44
M_1	6.12	5.71	5.4	6.04	5.97	5.48	5.1	5.85
M_2	11.64	11.62	11.2	11.33	11.35	10.93	10.5	10.95

Estimation of calendar age by number of erupted teeth[6,7]

Deciduous teeth	Both sexes	Error of estimate
	Years	
1 or 2 teeth	0.80	~0.16
3 or 4 teeth	1.11	~0.17
5 or 6 teeth	1.17	~0.17
7 or 8 teeth	1.23	~0.20
9 or 10 teeth	1.52	~0.20
11 or 12 teeth	1.59	~0.20
13 or 14 teeth	1.74	~0.25
15 or 16 teeth	1.86	~0.25
17 to 19 teeth	2.09	~0.25

Permanent teeth	Boys	Girls	Error of estimate
	Years		
1 or 2 teeth	5.75	5.67	~0.55
3 or 4 teeth	6.23	5.99	~0.70
5 or 6 teeth	6.80	6.52	~0.75
7 or 8 teeth	7.43	7.05	~0.85
9 or 10 teeth	8.03	7.56	~0.90
11 or 12 teeth	9.16	8.66	~1.00
13 or 14 teeth	9.88	9.59	~1.00
15 or 16 teeth	10.67	9.74	~1.05
17 or 18 teeth	10.69	10.16	~1.05
19 or 20 teeth	11.02	10.24	~1.05
21 or 22 teeth	11.05	10.62	~1.05
23 or 24 teeth	11.65	10.82	~1.05
25 to 27 teeth	12.00	11.44	~1.05

*This chapter on 'Development of the Teeth' (pages 313–315) has been compiled in collaboration with W. Z. BILLEWICZ, Medical Research Council, Human Reproduction Group, Newcastle upon Tyne, UK.

References

[1] BOAS, F., *J. dent. Res.*, **7**, 245 (1927).
[2] HAMIL et al., *Amer. J. Dis. Child.*, **56**, 561 (1938).
[3] MEREDITH, H.V., *J. dent. Res.*, **25**, 43 (1946).
[4] BILLEWICZ et al., *Hum. Biol.*, **45**, 229 (1973).
[5] DELGADO et al., *Amer. J. clin. Nutr.*, **28**, 216 (1975).
[6] MCGREGOR et al., *Brit. J. Nutr.*, **22**, 307 (1968).
[7] BILLEWICZ and MCGREGOR, *Ann. hum. Biol.*, **2**, 117 (1975).
[8] WALLIS, R.S., *Univ. Iowa Stud.*, Studies in Child Welfare, **5**, No. 1 (1931).
[9] VOORS, A.W., *Docum. Med. geogr. trop. (Amst.)*, **9**, 137 (1957).
[10] DOERING and ALLEN, *Child Develop.*, **13**, 113 (1942).
[11] FALKNER, F., *Arch. Dis. Childh.*, **32**, 386 (1957).
[12] BAILEY, K.V., *J. Pediat.*, **64**, 97 (1964).
[13] MILLER et al., *Arch. oral. Biol.*, **10**, 805 (1965).
[14] MACKAY and MARTIN, *J. trop. Med. Hyg.*, **55**, 265 (1952).
[15] LAU, W.H., *J. Formosan med. Ass.*, **70**, 159 (1971).

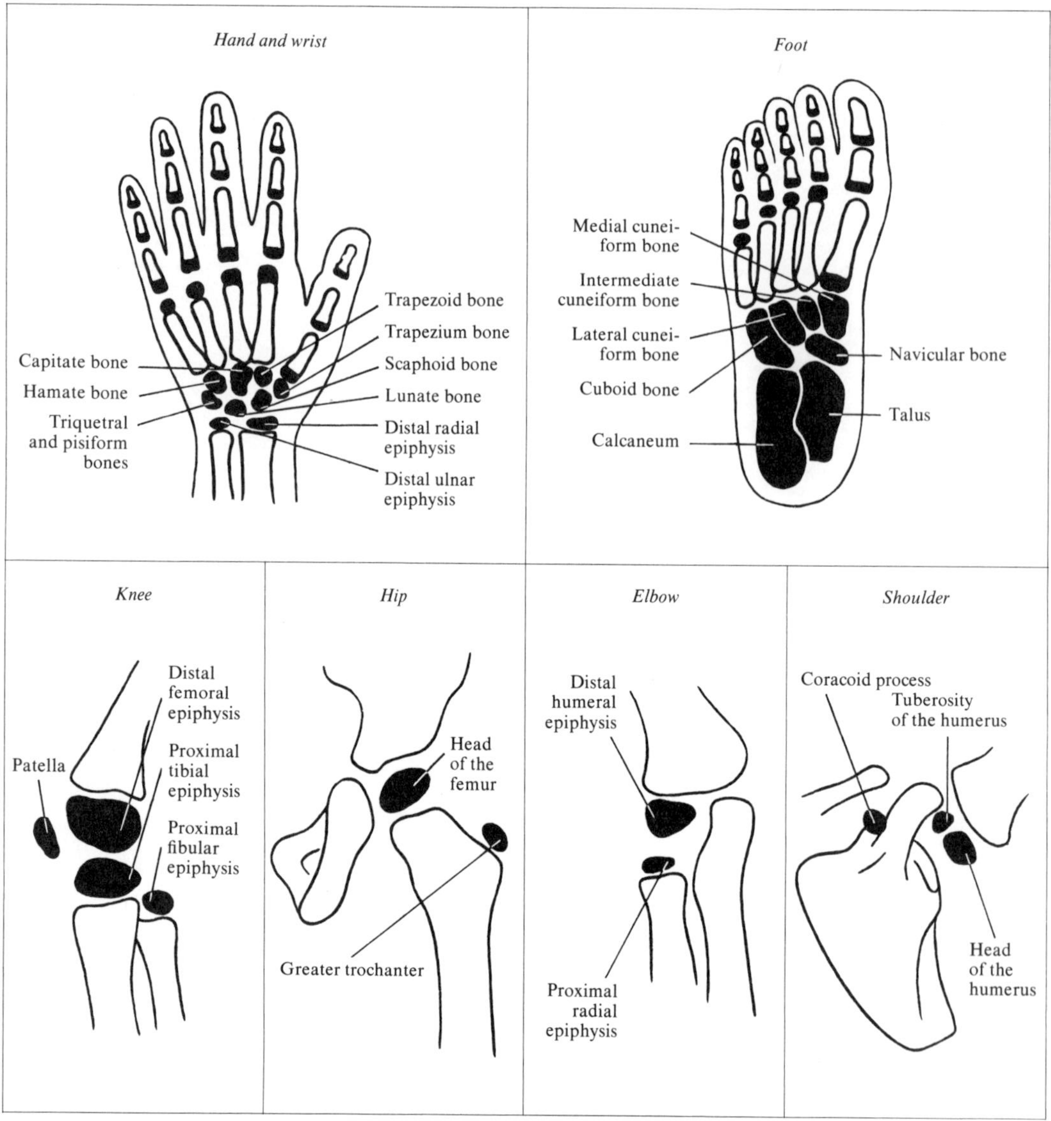

In many clinical situations the assessment of skeletal development is a matter of considerable importance. Various regional ossification processes occurring between birth and maturity can be utilized for this purpose.

For routine clinical purposes the following indications constitute a reliable guide to skeletal development.

Assessment of maturity in the newborn

In the full-term infant, knee X-rays (anteroposterior or lateral) should reveal a distinct and well-formed distal femoral epiphysis.

Assessment of bone age in childhood

The extent to which regional epiphyses are early or late in appearing can be determined by means of the table on page 317. In doing so it must be borne in mind that the range of physiological variation is rather wide, and that a discordance in the time of appearance of various ossification centers is commonly met with. For this reason, diagnostic X-rays should include several regions of the body (wrist, knee and foot, possibly others).

Bone age in the hand can be readily assessed by means of the table on page 318. For other bones and for a more detailed evaluation of bone age see the special atlases[1–4].

In assessing bone development at and during puberty it must be remembered that girls have a bone age about 2 years in advance of that of boys of the same age.

Bone development and the onset of puberty

The onset of puberty can be predicted far more reliably from the state of bone development than from height, while chronological age is an even more unreliable guide. When bone development is rapid and uninterrupted the onset of puberty will be early, and vice versa. In a similar way the time of appearance and state of development of the various ossification centers are directly related to the individual's eventual height. Thus from the age of 6 years onwards the adult height can be calculated with a fair degree of accuracy from the data given in the atlas of Greulich and Pyle[1]. A useful clinical guide is the close relationship between the appearance of the sesamoid bones in the thumb and the onset of puberty. In girls the onset of the menarche can be expected within 6 months of the commencement of ossification of the apophysis of the iliac crest.

*This chapter on 'Appearance of the Secondary Ossification Centers' (pages 316–318) has been compiled in collaboration with H.J. Kaufmann, Kinderklinik der Freien Universität Berlin, West Berlin.

Time of appearance of the ossification centers of the limb bones

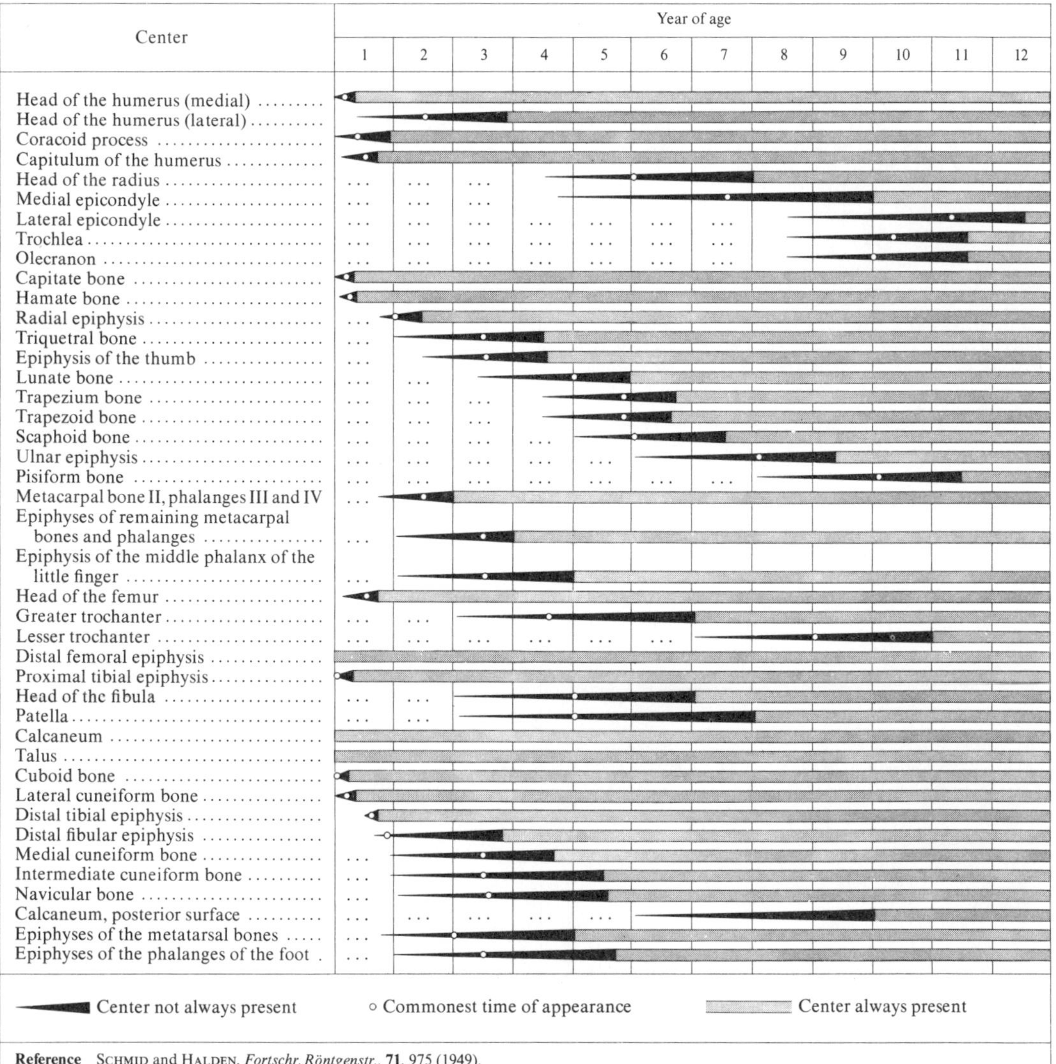

Reference SCHMID and HALDEN, *Fortschr. Röntgenstr.*, **71**, 975 (1949).

Conditions in which it is important to determine bone age

Hypothyroidism. This is marked by a distinct delay in the appearance of the ossification centers. Serial determinations of bone age should accompany treatment. Excessively rapid skeletal development involves the danger of dwarfism.

Pituitary dwarfism. Bone age and longitudinal growth are delayed to the same extent.

Primordial dwarfism. Longitudinal growth is delayed but ossification remains practically normal for the child's age.

Pituitary gigantism. Again due to discordance, longitudinal growth being very advanced while ossification is normal for the child's age.

Adrenogenital syndrome (with precocious puberty). The bone age is far in advance of longitudinal growth; the consequent premature union of the epiphyses results in the height being below normal.

Pseudo-precocious puberty. Here both bone development and longitudinal growth are abnormally rapid, the former more so than the latter.

Help in solving problems concerning the state of development of the secondary ossification centers is obtainable from various publications on the subject, in particular from the atlases and textbooks listed here[1–8].

References

1 PYLE and GREULICH, *A Radiographic Standard of Reference for the Growing Hand and Wrist,* Year Book Medical Publishers, Chicago, 1971.

2 SCHMID and MOLL, *Atlas der normalen und pathologischen Handskeletentwicklung,* Springer, Berlin, 1960.

3 HOERR et al., *Radiographic Atlas of Skeletal Development of the Foot and Ankle,* Thomas, Springfield, 1962.

4 PYLE and HOERR, *A Radiographic Standard of Reference for the Growing Knee,* Thomas, Springfield, 1969.

5 ROCHE et al., *Skeletal Maturity. The Knee Joint as a Biological Indicator,* Plenum, New York, 1975.

6 CAFFEY and SILVERMAN, *Pediatric X-Ray Diagnosis,* 5th ed., Year Book Medical Publishers, Chicago, 1967.

7 SCHMID, F., *Pädiatrische Radiologie,* Springer, Berlin, 1973.

8 MAROTEAUX, P., *Bone Diseases of Children,* Lippincott, Philadelphia, 1979.

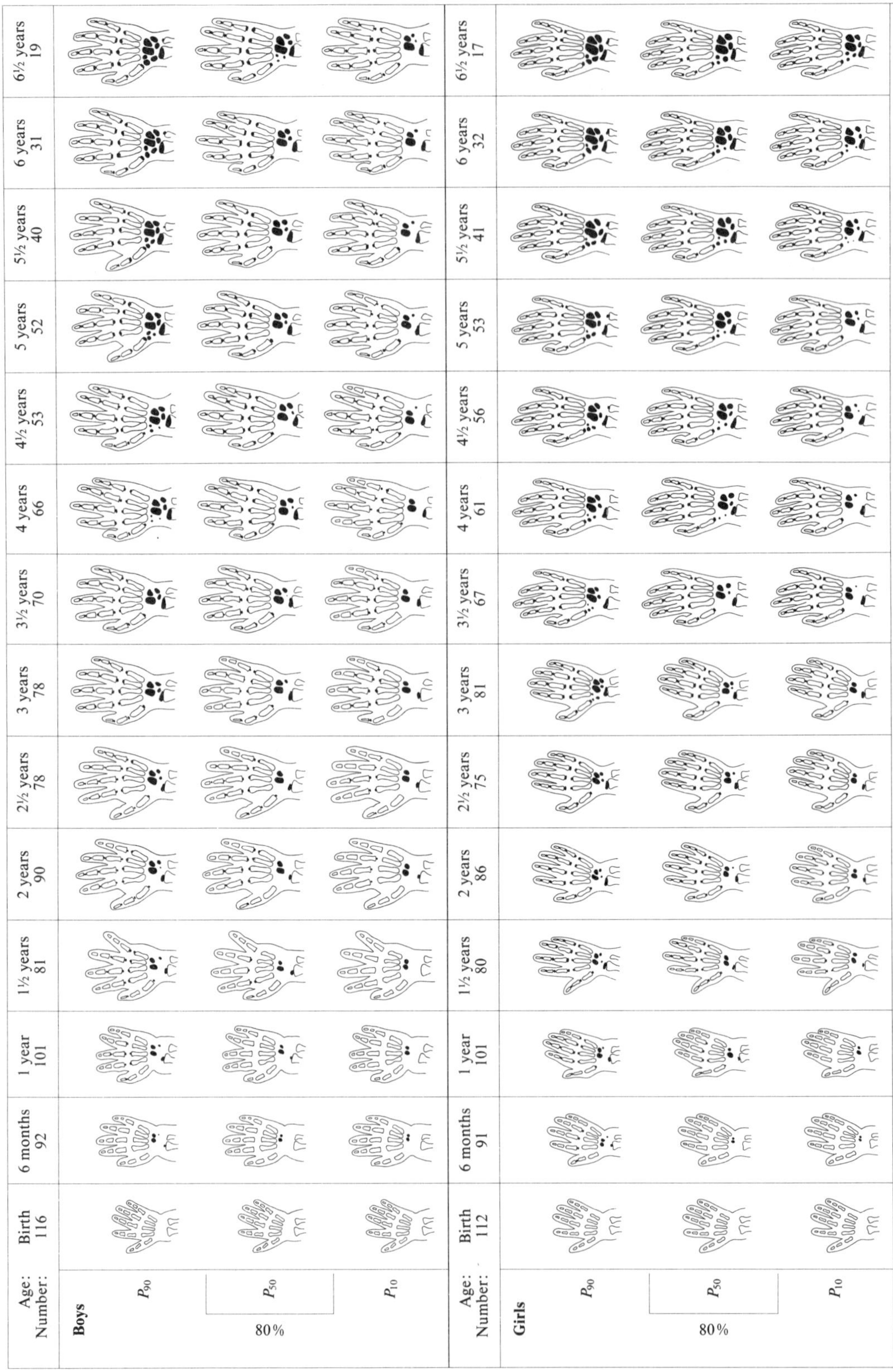

Age: Number:	Birth 116	6 months 92	1 year 101	1½ years 81	2 years 90	2½ years 78	3 years 78	3½ years 70	4 years 66	4½ years 53	5 years 52	5½ years 40	6 years 31	6½ years 19
Boys														
P_{90}														
80% P_{50}														
P_{10}														

Age: Number:	Birth 112	6 months 91	1 year 101	1½ years 80	2 years 86	2½ years 75	3 years 81	3½ years 67	4 years 61	4½ years 56	5 years 53	5½ years 41	6 years 32	6½ years 17
Girls														
P_{90}														
80% P_{50}														
P_{10}														

Reference Vogt and Vickers, *Radiology*, **31**, 441 (1938).

Skinfolds — Triceps and Subscapular Skinfold Thickness in Northwest German Children

Age	Boys						Girls						Reference
	Number	Minimum	80% P_{10}	80% P_{50}	80% P_{90}	Maximum	Number	Minimum	80% P_{10}	80% P_{50}	80% P_{90}	Maximum	
		mm	mm	mm	mm	mm		mm	mm	mm	mm	mm	
Triceps skinfold thickness													
1st month (mid-month)	9	4.8	4.8	5.6	8.9	8.9	8	4.7	4.7	6.4	7.8	7.8	1
2nd month (mid-month)	24	4.3	4.6	6.4	8.6	9.1	27	4.6	6.3	7.3	9.0	9.8	1
3rd month (mid-month)	35	4.4	4.8	7.9	10.6	13.2	24	7.1	7.3	8.9	10.9	11.5	1
4th month (mid-month)	32	4.7	6.6	9.0	10.6	12.6	30	6.2	6.6	9.1	11.0	13.1	1
5th month (mid-month)	26	8.2	8.8	10.6	12.4	13.1	29	7.2	7.8	10.2	12.6	14.1	1
6th month (mid-month)	35	7.6	7.8	10.2	12.7	14.2	48	6.6	7.2	9.6	10.9	13.2	1
7th month (mid-month)	45	6.6	7.6	9.8	11.8	15.8	52	6.4	7.5	9.6	11.6	12.5	1
8th month (mid-month)	16	6.8	7.5	10.2	12.0	15.0	29	5.6	8.2	9.6	11.6	12.2	1
9th month (mid-month)	40	6.8	7.8	10.2	12.2	16.3	48	5.3	6.5	9.3	12.1	15.2	1
10th month (mid-month)	42	5.4	7.6	9.6	13.1	16.0	53	6.4	8.1	9.3	11.3	12.4	1
11th month (mid-month)	14	6.1	7.5	8.7	10.0	10.1	19	6.2	6.8	9.1	12.1	13.5	1
12th month (mid-month)	39	5.1	7.1	9.9	13.3	14.2	36	5.3	7.5	9.6	12.2	14.3	1
13th month (mid-month)	31	5.6	7.8	9.8	11.8	13.0	44	6.4	7.0	9.2	11.8	14.3	1
1½ years	65	5.5	6.8	8.8	11.3	13.0	88	6.1	7.1	9.4	12.8	15.2	2
2 years	90	5.1	6.8	9.8	13.1	15.9	94	5.4	7.1	9.4	11.8	17.6	2
2½ years	94	5.1	6.6	9.1	11.9	15.6	103	5.9	7.1	9.1	12.6	14.4	2
3 years	98	3.2	6.5	9.2	11.9	15.5	110	6.1	7.5	10.1	12.9	14.2	2
4 years	134	5.6	7.4	10.0	12.8	15.8	138	6.0	7.3	10.4	13.5	16.0	2
5 years	167	4.8	7.4	10.0	12.9	21.9	171	4.6	8.3	10.8	14.3	18.6	2
6 years	214	4.4	7.3	9.3	12.9	20.2	213	5.3	7.6	10.7	14.5	22.0	2
7 years	272	3.9	6.3	8.8	12.4	28.1	262	5.2	7.4	10.3	15.0	24.4	2
8 years	301	4.0	6.3	9.0	13.1	21.0	296	4.2	7.6	10.4	15.5	24.4	2
9 years	293	4.1	6.4	9.4	14.3	20.3	302	4.1	7.6	11.0	16.2	25.1	2
10 years	264	4.5	6.6	9.6	14.2	23.2	275	4.8	8.1	11.4	16.8	26.4	2
11 years	179	4.9	6.5	9.8	15.6	22.7	195	5.4	7.9	10.9	15.4	25.7	2
12 years	152	4.8	7.2	10.1	16.4	23.1	150	5.6	7.9	10.2	15.8	25.8	2
13 years	115	5.8	6.8	10.2	17.6	22.5	101	5.6	7.1	10.6	14.6	31.2	2
14 years	71	4.3	5.9	9.0	17.1	29.4	73	5.2	6.9	11.0	16.2	22.6	2
15 years	44	4.2	5.2	8.1	12.0	15.3	43	6.4	7.3	11.8	15.8	20.2	2
16 years	17	5.1	5.4	7.8	10.6	10.9	10	9.0	–	11.3	17.8	22.1	2
Subscapular skinfold thickness													
1st month (mid-month)	9	3.4	3.4	5.4	6.9	6.9	8	4.3	4.3	6.0	7.2	7.2	1
2nd month (mid-month)	24	3.6	4.3	6.1	8.0	10.8	27	4.0	4.9	7.0	8.6	9.6	1
3rd month (mid-month)	35	4.5	5.1	7.1	10.4	11.7	24	5.3	5.4	7.9	9.6	10.0	1
4th month (mid-month)	32	4.2	5.6	7.9	9.3	9.6	29	5.1	5.5	7.6	10.0	10.4	1
5th month (mid-month)	26	5.5	6.2	7.8	9.9	10.2	29	4.0	6.5	8.4	10.2	11.2	1
6th month (mid-month)	35	4.3	5.7	7.2	9.3	12.4	48	4.3	5.8	7.2	9.2	12.1	1
7th month (mid-month)	45	4.4	5.4	6.8	9.3	10.2	52	5.0	5.4	7.0	8.8	11.3	1
8th month (mid-month)	16	4.1	4.4	6.5	8.6	9.2	29	3.1	5.0	6.6	9.6	10.4	1
9th month (mid-month)	40	4.6	5.4	6.6	8.4	9.6	48	3.8	4.6	6.3	8.6	11.1	1
10th month (mid-month)	42	4.2	5.1	6.3	8.6	10.8	53	4.2	4.9	6.3	8.9	11.3	1
11th month (mid-month)	14	4.3	4.6	6.5	7.6	8.4	19	4.6	4.8	5.8	9.1	9.6	1
12th month (mid-month)	39	4.6	4.9	6.2	7.9	9.4	36	4.3	4.5	5.7	8.3	10.4	1
13th month (mid-month)	31	3.6	4.5	5.6	8.1	9.8	44	3.5	4.5	6.2	8.2	10.6	1
1½ years	65	3.5	4.3	5.4	7.0	9.6	88	3.3	4.4	5.5	7.8	9.9	2
2 years	90	3.6	4.3	5.2	7.0	9.8	94	3.3	4.5	5.7	7.4	10.8	2
2½ years	94	3.4	4.2	5.3	6.4	9.8	103	3.5	4.8	5.3	7.3	12.4	2
3 years	98	3.5	4.0	5.3	7.1	11.9	110	3.6	4.2	5.6	7.3	10.4	2
4 years	132	3.4	4.1	5.3	6.8	8.1	138	3.7	4.4	5.7	7.4	11.8	2
5 years	167	3.2	4.1	5.0	6.4	19.4	171	3.4	4.4	5.6	8.3	15.2	2
6 years	213	3.3	4.1	5.0	6.6	18.1	213	3.7	4.3	5.6	8.1	24.6	2
7 years	272	3.1	4.0	5.0	6.6	27.4	262	3.4	4.2	5.7	8.5	22.8	2
8 years	301	3.4	4.0	5.1	7.0	23.4	296	3.5	4.4	5.9	10.1	25.4	2
9 years	293	3.2	4.1	5.2	7.7	28.6	302	3.3	4.5	6.1	11.4	24.2	2
10 years	264	3.1	4.1	5.4	8.6	19.3	275	3.5	4.8	6.5	12.2	33.3	2
11 years	179	3.1	4.1	5.8	9.1	24.3	195	3.4	5.1	6.7	11.4	31.4	2
12 years	152	3.8	4.6	5.9	10.4	19.4	150	3.6	5.0	6.8	12.5	33.8	2
13 years	115	3.8	4.4	6.4	11.5	21.4	101	3.9	5.2	7.2	12.6	25.0	2
14 years	72	4.1	4.8	6.3	11.1	29.8	73	4.1	5.4	7.5	13.4	17.2	2
15 years	44	4.8	5.2	6.5	8.8	16.0	43	4.6	6.2	8.3	13.8	18.6	2
16 years	17	4.9	5.3	6.7	9.2	9.3	10	7.0	–	8.8	12.9	15.1	2

References [1] Reinken et al., *Klin. Pädiat.*, **191**, 556 (1979). [2] Reinken et al., *Klin. Pädiat.*, **192**, 25 (1980).

Skinfolds — Suprailiac and Anterior Axillary Line Skinfold Thickness in Northwest German Children

Age	Boys						Girls						Reference
	Number	Minimum (mm)	80% P_{10} (mm)	80% P_{50} (mm)	80% P_{90} (mm)	Maximum (mm)	Number	Minimum (mm)	80% P_{10} (mm)	80% P_{50} (mm)	80% P_{90} (mm)	Maximum (mm)	
Suprailiac skinfold thickness													
1st month (mid-month)	9	3.1	3.1	4.6	6.8	6.8	7	3.4	3.4	5.1	6.6	6.6	1
2nd month (mid-month)	24	3.5	4.2	5.7	7.8	9.6	27	4.4	5.1	6.4	8.8	9.2	1
3rd month (mid-month)	35	5.5	5.8	7.5	11.1	11.9	24	5.4	5.9	8.3	10.2	11.1	1
4th month (mid-month)	32	5.0	6.2	8.6	11.9	12.8	30	5.3	5.6	9.0	11.6	13.2	1
5th month (mid-month)	26	4.9	5.6	8.8	12.0	14.6	29	5.3	5.8	9.2	13.1	14.6	1
6th month (mid-month)	35	5.4	6.2	8.8	10.6	12.8	48	4.5	5.8	8.5	11.4	11.8	1
7th month (mid-month)	45	4.5	5.4	7.5	10.2	13.8	52	4.9	6.3	8.4	10.6	14.6	1
8th month (mid-month)	16	4.4	5.1	7.5	9.7	11.6	29	4.1	5.4	7.8	11.6	12.6	1
9th month (mid-month)	40	4.9	5.3	7.1	9.5	15.0	48	4.3	5.1	7.1	10.0	12.6	1
10th month (mid-month)	42	4.3	5.5	7.5	10.0	13.2	53	3.8	6.1	7.4	10.2	12.2	1
11th month (mid-month)	14	3.3	4.2	7.2	9.0	11.0	19	4.5	4.6	6.8	9.0	9.1	1
12th month (mid-month)	39	3.8	4.6	6.6	10.0	13.8	36	4.7	5.5	7.1	9.6	10.1	1
13th month (mid-month)	31	4.3	5.3	7.0	8.6	11.2	44	3.8	4.6	6.9	9.3	12.3	1
1½ years	65	2.7	3.2	4.1	5.4	6.9	88	2.5	3.1	4.2	5.8	7.4	2
2 years	90	2.8	3.3	3.9	5.4	8.2	94	2.4	3.3	4.1	5.8	8.4	2
2½ years	94	2.6	3.3	3.9	4.8	6.4	104	2.6	3.3	4.0	5.5	8.4	2
3 years	98	2.4	3.1	4.0	5.3	7.0	110	2.4	3.3	4.2	5.4	8.2	2
4 years	132	2.6	3.3	4.1	5.3	7.0	138	2.8	3.4	4.5	5.8	8.6	2
5 years	167	2.3	3.1	4.0	5.2	12.3	171	2.8	3.4	4.5	6.4	14.1	2
6 years	214	2.6	3.2	4.1	5.3	12.3	213	2.8	3.4	4.5	6.8	18.6	2
7 years	272	2.5	3.1	3.9	5.2	15.9	262	2.7	3.4	4.5	6.9	19.0	2
8 years	301	2.5	3.2	4.1	5.9	17.0	296	2.4	3.5	4.7	7.8	22.3	2
9 years	293	2.5	3.2	4.1	6.8	19.4	302	2.5	3.6	5.0	9.1	23.5	2
10 years	264	2.4	3.4	4.4	7.2	13.2	275	2.9	3.8	5.4	10.1	27.8	2
11 years	179	2.5	3.3	4.6	7.8	18.6	195	2.8	4.0	5.4	9.7	27.6	2
12 years	152	2.5	3.6	4.9	9.5	16.7	150	3.1	3.9	5.4	10.7	29.4	2
13 years	115	2.8	3.7	5.2	10.6	26.3	101	3.3	4.4	5.8	10.4	22.3	2
14 years	72	3.0	3.7	5.2	10.0	21.6	73	3.5	4.5	6.2	12.2	17.2	2
15 years	44	3.3	4.0	4.8	6.6	18.0	43	4.2	4.8	6.8	10.6	18.2	2
16 years	17	3.6	3.7	5.2	–	5.9	10	5.8	–	7.3	12.3	17.4	2
Anterior axillary line skinfold thickness													
1st month (mid-month)	9	2.5	2.5	4.2	6.8	6.8	7	4.0	4.0	4.2	7.1	7.1	1
2nd month (mid-month)	24	2.4	3.0	4.1	5.8	6.5	27	3.1	3.6	4.6	6.5	7.9	1
3rd month (mid-month)	34	3.3	3.6	5.0	7.6	9.4	24	3.6	4.4	6.7	8.2	8.4	1
4th month (mid-month)	32	3.6	3.8	5.5	6.9	9.0	30	2.5	3.8	6.3	8.2	10.8	1
5th month (mid-month)	23	3.6	4.4	5.5	7.8	8.8	29	4.6	5.1	6.3	8.2	9.8	1
6th month (mid-month)	35	3.1	3.6	5.5	6.6	8.2	48	3.0	4.3	5.1	6.4	8.4	1
7th month (mid-month)	45	3.3	3.9	4.8	6.8	8.0	52	3.0	4.2	5.2	6.4	8.4	1
8th month (mid-month)	14	3.0	3.6	4.7	6.4	7.8	29	2.9	3.4	4.3	6.9	7.2	1
9th month (mid-month)	39	3.1	3.4	4.9	7.0	7.5	48	3.1	3.5	4.4	6.2	8.1	1
10th month (mid-month)	42	3.4	3.8	4.8	6.3	7.5	53	3.2	3.6	4.6	6.2	8.1	1
11th month (mid-month)	14	3.4	3.4	4.5	5.4	6.4	19	2.8	3.4	4.3	5.7	6.5	1
12th month (mid-month)	39	3.1	3.5	4.4	5.6	6.3	36	3.3	3.7	4.3	6.3	8.2	1
13th month (mid-month)	31	3.4	3.6	4.4	5.8	6.5	44	2.8	3.5	4.4	5.8	6.4	1
1½ years	65	3.7	4.5	5.8	8.2	10.1	88	3.3	5.1	6.8	9.6	16.4	2
2 years	90	3.2	4.2	5.9	8.3	10.8	94	3.9	4.5	6.3	9.8	14.5	2
2½ years	94	3.3	4.6	5.8	7.8	12.4	103	2.9	4.5	6.1	8.1	12.4	2
3 years	98	3.4	4.3	5.8	8.0	12.7	110	3.0	4.6	6.3	8.6	13.7	2
4 years	132	2.9	4.2	5.5	8.1	10.9	138	3.1	4.4	6.6	9.4	19.2	2
5 years	167	3.2	3.7	5.4	7.6	20.4	171	3.5	4.4	6.5	11.1	16.5	2
6 years	214	2.6	3.9	5.5	8.8	23.1	213	3.1	4.4	6.9	11.2	20.6	2
7 years	272	2.8	3.8	5.3	9.0	30.5	262	2.7	4.3	6.8	12.2	26.6	2
8 years	301	3.0	3.9	5.7	9.6	24.2	296	3.2	4.4	7.0	12.7	27.6	2
9 years	293	2.6	4.1	6.1	11.0	26.4	302	3.5	4.7	7.6	15.0	30.4	2
10 years	264	2.5	4.4	6.7	12.6	27.5	275	3.2	5.1	8.5	17.8	29.4	2
11 years	179	2.7	4.5	7.5	14.6	25.7	195	4.2	5.5	8.6	15.9	29.1	2
12 years	152	3.6	4.8	8.2	16.8	29.8	150	4.4	5.6	9.1	17.3	32.5	2
13 years	115	3.7	5.2	8.7	20.0	35.8	101	3.8	6.5	9.4	17.6	34.4	2
14 years	72	4.3	5.6	8.5	20.4	34.4	73	4.5	6.3	9.6	18.9	24.4	2
15 years	44	4.6	6.6	8.5	12.9	27.6	43	6.2	7.3	11.5	20.3	31.2	2
16 years	17	5.8	–	8.2	9.9	13.3	10	7.2	–	10.9	21.3	26.1	2

References [1] Reinken et al., *Klin. Pädiat.*, **191**, 556 (1979). [2] Reinken et al., *Klin. Pädiat.*, **192**, 25 (1980).

Age	Boys						Girls						Reference
	Number	Minimum	80%			Maximum	Number	Minimum	80%			Maximum	
			P_{10}	P_{50}	P_{90}				P_{10}	P_{50}	P_{90}		
		mm						mm					
Abdominal skinfold thickness													
1st month (mid-month)	7	2.8	2.8	4.5	5.6	5.6	5	3.2	3.2	4.0	5.8	5.8	1
2nd month (mid-month)	23	3.1	3.4	4.8	7.6	9.0	27	3.3	3.9	5.0	8.2	9.2	1
3rd month (mid-month)	35	4.3	5.3	6.5	8.4	11.2	24	5.1	5.3	7.3	9.6	11.0	1
4th month (mid-month)	32	4.1	5.4	7.6	8.6	10.8	27	4.0	5.4	8.1	9.8	11.8	1
5th month (mid-month)	25	4.2	4.4	7.1	9.4	13.0	29	4.8	5.4	7.8	9.6	12.0	1
6th month (mid-month)	35	3.5	4.6	7.0	9.6	11.8	48	4.4	4.9	6.6	9.3	10.8	1
7th month (mid-month)	45	3.6	4.4	6.4	9.1	15.4	52	3.7	4.7	6.8	8.8	10.0	1
8th month (mid-month)	16	3.5	4.1	5.5	7.3	11.4	29	3.4	4.9	6.1	9.2	11.3	1
9th month (mid-month)	40	3.3	3.8	5.6	8.6	11.1	48	2.7	4.1	5.7	8.4	11.4	1
10th month (mid-month)	42	3.6	4.2	6.2	8.0	12.0	53	3.8	4.4	6.0	8.1	11.1	1
11th month (mid-month)	14	3.0	3.2	4.7	7.6	9.0	19	4.1	4.2	5.4	6.4	6.8	1
12th month (mid-month)	39	3.5	3.8	5.4	7.6	9.0	36	3.5	4.5	5.5	7.2	8.8	1
13th month (mid-month)	31	3.5	4.1	5.5	7.0	7.6	44	3.0	3.8	5.3	6.9	9.3	1
1½ years	65	2.6	3.4	4.4	6.3	8.1	88	2.6	3.4	4.7	7.2	10.6	2
2 years	90	2.9	3.4	4.4	6.1	8.6	94	2.3	3.6	4.8	6.5	10.6	2
2½ years	94	2.1	3.4	4.4	6.4	8.5	103	2.4	3.3	4.6	6.3	9.7	2
3 years	98	2.4	3.3	4.4	6.3	9.4	110	2.9	3.9	5.2	6.7	11.3	2
4 years	132	2.3	3.2	4.5	6.5	8.6	138	2.0	3.8	5.3	7.6	13.2	2
5 years	167	2.1	3.1	4.3	6.3	12.4	171	2.4	3.6	5.4	8.6	16.3	2
6 years	214	2.1	3.2	4.2	7.0	16.0	213	2.3	3.6	5.3	8.7	20.4	2
7 years	272	2.4	3.0	4.0	6.9	23.2	262	2.4	3.4	5.2	9.2	29.0	2
8 years	301	2.5	3.1	4.1	7.6	16.1	296	2.5	3.6	5.5	10.8	25.6	2
9 years	293	2.4	3.2	4.5	7.9	19.4	301	2.6	3.9	6.2	11.4	25.9	2
10 years	264	2.1	3.2	4.8	8.8	19.1	275	2.9	4.3	6.6	13.6	25.4	2
11 years	179	2.5	3.4	5.3	9.9	19.5	195	2.8	4.4	6.6	12.1	22.6	2
12 years	152	2.6	3.8	5.8	12.2	24.6	150	3.1	4.5	6.9	13.3	22.5	2
13 years	115	2.6	3.9	6.5	14.4	23.9	101	3.7	4.6	7.2	11.7	27.6	2
14 years	72	3.0	4.0	6.5	15.7	25.2	73	4.3	4.8	8.0	14.3	20.6	2
15 years	44	3.4	4.6	6.5	9.4	18.6	43	4.6	5.6	8.6	14.9	17.4	2
16 years	17	4.8	–	6.8	8.3	8.8	10	5.0	–	8.6	15.1	15.8	2
Sum of triceps, subscapular and suprailiac skinfold thicknesses													
1st month (mid-month)	9	11.5	11.5	15.4	22.6	22.6	7	12.4	12.4	18.2	20.1	20.1	1
2nd month (mid-month)	24	12.0	13.3	18.1	25.5	27.7	27	14.0	16.6	20.6	25.8	26.9	1
3rd month (mid-month)	35	14.9	16.3	22.3	31.5	36.0	24	18.4	19.9	24.5	29.8	32.0	1
4th month (mid-month)	32	15.1	20.1	25.5	30.5	32.8	29	17.6	19.3	25.7	32.6	35.0	1
5th month (mid-month)	26	21.2	21.6	26.7	34.0	36.5	29	18.8	20.6	29.3	34.7	35.9	1
6th month (mid-month)	35	17.4	21.3	25.8	32.1	33.7	48	15.6	20.0	25.2	30.2	34.4	1
7th month (mid-month)	45	16.6	20.4	24.3	29.3	39.8	52	18.2	20.2	24.5	29.2	35.7	1
8th month (mid-month)	16	15.3	17.8	23.9	29.4	35.8	29	12.8	19.8	23.5	31.4	34.2	1
9th month (mid-month)	40	18.0	19.0	23.0	28.8	39.7	48	15.3	16.5	23.0	30.1	36.6	1
10th month (mid-month)	42	14.3	18.6	24.4	31.0	40.0	53	15.0	19.5	23.6	29.5	33.2	1
11th month (mid-month)	14	15.5	17.9	21.7	25.7	25.8	19	16.1	17.4	22.5	28.4	29.7	1
12th month (mid-month)	39	15.5	17.3	23.1	28.9	34.8	36	14.7	18.9	22.6	29.4	33.5	1
13th month (mid-month)	31	16.8	17.8	22.1	27.8	32.6	44	14.4	17.2	22.5	28.3	34.7	1
1½ years	65	13.5	16.1	20.0	24.8	29.8	88	14.7	17.7	21.9	29.4	35.7	2
2 years	90	13.5	16.3	20.2	27.3	32.4	94	13.8	16.9	21.8	27.0	37.5	2
2½ years	94	12.3	16.3	19.7	26.0	30.4	102	13.5	16.4	20.1	27.2	36.2	2
3 years	98	12.1	15.9	20.3	26.5	32.3	110	14.9	17.0	22.1	28.3	36.1	2
4 years	132	14.0	16.4	21.2	25.8	31.0	138	13.7	17.2	23.6	28.3	42.0	2
5 years	167	12.4	16.0	20.2	27.3	61.7	171	13.8	18.1	23.2	33.3	47.2	2
6 years	212	12.5	16.1	19.9	27.0	58.0	213	14.1	17.2	23.5	32.8	63.4	2
7 years	272	11.3	14.7	19.1	27.6	86.0	262	12.2	16.2	22.7	33.6	73.8	2
8 years	301	10.6	14.4	19.7	29.2	68.0	196	11.2	17.2	23.3	39.2	76.4	2
9 years	293	11.5	15.1	20.6	32.1	75.3	302	12.7	17.6	25.1	40.5	69.0	2
10 years	262	10.9	15.8	22.1	35.8	65.0	275	13.4	19.4	26.0	45.8	84.5	2
11 years	179	11.7	15.5	23.6	38.0	67.0	195	14.2	19.6	26.1	42.8	84.1	2
12 years	152	12.6	16.6	24.6	42.9	71.1	150	13.6	19.8	25.8	45.0	88.7	2
13 years	115	15.2	17.3	25.4	49.4	73.4	101	15.0	19.5	27.0	42.8	87.0	2
14 years	70	13.8	16.6	23.8	50.0	93.6	73	15.6	19.6	28.3	48.0	60.4	2
15 years	44	14.0	18.1	23.0	32.1	55.6	43	18.9	20.9	32.3	46.4	68.3	2
16 years	17	16.5	16.8	23.5	27.6	33.5	10	24.6	–	29.8	56.8	58.5	2

References [1] Reinken et al., *Klin. Pädiat.*, **191**, 556 (1979). [2] Reinken et al., *Klin. Pädiat.*, **192**, 25 (1980).

Age	Males							Females						
		90%							90%					
			80%							80%				
				50%							50%			
	P_{05}	P_{10}	P_{25}	P_{50}	P_{75}	P_{90}	P_{95}	P_{05}	P_{10}	P_{25}	P_{50}	P_{75}	P_{90}	P_{95}
	mm							mm						
Whites														
6 years	5.0	6.1	7.2	8.8	10.6	13.1	16.5	5.8	6.1	7.7	9.6	11.6	13.4	15.6
7 years	5.1	6.1	7.3	9.4	11.7	15.0	18.1	6.1	6.5	8.3	10.5	13.0	15.5	18.6
8 years	5.2	6.1	7.5	9.8	12.7	16.8	19.7	6.4	7.0	8.9	11.4	14.5	17.6	21.4
9 years	5.3	6.0	7.5	10.1	13.4	18.3	21.1	6.8	7.5	9.6	12.3	15.9	19.6	24.0
10 years	5.3	5.9	7.5	10.2	13.8	19.4	22.3	7.1	8.0	10.2	13.2	17.2	21.5	26.2
11 years	5.3	5.7	7.4	10.2	13.9	20.1	23.2	7.5	8.6	10.9	14.1	18.4	23.1	28.0
12 years	5.2	5.5	7.3	9.9	13.8	20.4	23.8	7.9	9.1	11.5	14.9	19.4	24.5	29.4
13 years	5.1	5.4	7.1	9.6	13.6	20.3	24.1	8.2	9.6	12.0	15.6	20.2	25.7	30.5
14 years	5.0	5.2	6.9	9.3	13.2	19.9	24.1	8.5	10.1	12.5	16.2	21.0	26.5	31.3
15 years	4.9	5.1	6.7	9.0	12.9	19.4	23.9	8.8	10.5	12.9	16.8	21.6	27.2	31.9
16 years	4.7	5.1	6.6	8.7	12.7	18.9	23.6	9.1	10.9	13.3	17.3	22.1	27.7	32.5
17 years	4.6	5.1	6.5	8.7	12.6	18.6	23.2	9.2	11.1	13.6	17.8	22.5	28.0	32.9
18–20 years	4.4	5.2	6.5	9.2	13.4	18.7	22.2	9.6	11.4	14.1	18.6	23.4	28.9	34.0
21–23 years	4.4	5.3	6.6	9.9	14.3	19.6	22.1	9.6	11.4	14.3	18.9	23.9	29.7	34.6
24–26 years	4.8	5.4	7.2	10.9	15.6	21.1	23.3	9.9	11.4	14.9	19.7	25.5	32.0	35.8
27–29 years	5.0	5.7	7.7	11.3	15.8	21.0	23.9	10.0	11.7	15.3	20.3	26.5	33.2	36.7
30–32 years	5.3	6.4	8.9	12.1	16.0	20.4	23.9	10.7	12.7	16.5	21.8	28.1	34.5	38.3
33–35 years	5.2	6.6	9.3	12.5	16.1	20.3	23.4	11.2	13.2	17.0	22.3	28.5	34.6	38.4
36–38 years	5.0	6.2	9.0	12.3	16.0	20.2	22.6	12.0	13.6	17.9	22.6	28.7	34.7	37.6
39–41 years	5.0	5.9	8.7	11.9	15.8	19.9	22.7	12.0	13.6	18.2	22.9	29.0	34.9	37.7
42–44 years	5.1	6.1	8.4	11.3	15.5	19.6	23.6	11.7	13.9	18.8	24.3	30.2	35.8	39.7
45–47 years	5.3	6.5	8.5	11.4	15.5	19.9	24.1	11.7	14.3	19.2	24.9	30.6	36.1	40.7
48–50 years	5.7	6.8	8.3	11.5	15.3	20.7	24.5	12.7	15.4	19.9	25.0	30.2	36.2	40.6
Blacks														
6 years	4.0	4.0	5.1	6.4	8.4	10.4	13.0	3.7	4.8	6.1	7.4	9.7	11.3	19.4
7 years	4.0	4.2	5.3	6.5	8.8	11.7	15.1	3.9	5.0	6.6	8.1	10.9	14.2	21.1
8 years	4.0	4.3	5.5	6.6	9.1	12.7	16.9	4.1	5.4	7.2	9.0	12.2	17.1	23.0
9 years	4.0	4.4	5.6	6.8	9.2	13.7	18.6	4.5	5.8	7.8	10.1	13.6	19.8	24.9
10 years	4.0	4.4	5.7	6.9	9.3	14.4	20.2	4.9	6.2	8.3	11.1	14.9	22.3	26.9
11 years	4.0	4.4	5.7	7.0	9.3	15.2	21.6	5.4	6.7	8.9	12.0	16.3	24.3	28.7
12 years	3.9	4.4	5.6	7.1	9.4	15.9	22.9	5.8	7.1	9.4	12.9	17.6	25.9	30.3
13 years	3.9	4.3	5.5	7.1	9.5	16.5	24.0	6.3	7.4	9.9	13.7	18.8	27.2	31.7
14 years	3.8	4.2	5.3	7.2	9.7	17.2	24.9	6.6	7.7	10.4	14.4	19.9	28.1	32.8
15 years	3.7	4.1	5.2	7.2	9.9	17.8	25.4	6.9	7.8	10.8	14.9	20.8	28.8	33.6
16 years	3.6	4.0	5.0	7.1	10.1	18.2	25.6	7.0	7.9	11.1	15.4	21.6	29.4	34.1
17 years	3.5	3.9	4.9	7.1	10.3	18.6	25.4	7.1	7.9	11.4	15.8	22.3	29.9	34.5
18–20 years	3.3	3.7	4.8	6.9	10.7	18.7	23.1	7.2	8.4	12.2	16.9	23.8	31.5	34.7
21–23 years	3.3	3.7	4.8	6.9	10.9	18.2	21.7	7.5	9.1	12.7	17.7	24.6	32.5	34.8
24–26 years	3.3	3.7	5.1	7.9	11.8	17.9	23.7	8.4	10.6	13.8	19.8	26.8	33.5	36.5
27–29 years	3.4	3.8	5.5	8.7	12.9	18.4	25.9	8.7	10.6	14.5	21.0	28.5	34.0	38.1
30–32 years	3.6	4.2	6.5	10.3	14.9	19.2	26.3	8.6	9.9	16.3	23.8	31.9	36.5	41.9
33–35 years	3.7	4.5	6.9	10.6	15.0	19.3	24.5	8.7	10.2	17.3	25.0	33.1	38.1	43.4
36–38 years	4.1	4.8	7.0	10.0	13.8	20.1	23.5	9.6	12.3	18.9	26.1	33.3	39.8	44.7
39–41 years	4.2	4.7	6.7	9.4	13.3	20.9	25.4	9.7	13.2	19.2	26.0	32.8	39.9	44.6
42–44 years	3.8	4.2	6.1	8.8	13.5	21.3	27.8	8.6	12.3	18.9	25.8	32.0	40.2	43.6
45–47 years	3.5	4.0	6.0	9.0	13.8	20.3	26.8	8.0	11.3	18.5	26.0	32.5	40.7	43.4
48–50 years	3.1	4.1	6.0	9.8	14.0	18.5	24.8	8.8	11.1	18.4	26.8	34.8	41.4	44.7

Reference CRONK and ROCHE, *Amer. J. clin. Nutr.*, **35**, 347 (1982).

Measurements of skinfold thickness furnish information on the subcutaneous fatty tissues and thence also on the mass of total body fat[1].

Long experience and strict adherence to the measuring instructions are necessary if reproducible results are to be obtained. Not all the instruments (calipers) available on the market yield wholly comparable results. Measurements made with the Harpenden and Holtain calipers are practically congruous[2,3], and the results obtained with these two instruments show satisfactory agreement with those given by the Lange calipers. On the other hand, compared with the other instruments the Best calipers give discordant results[3].

In accordance with recommendations made by the Committee on Nutritional Anthropometry of the Food and Nutrition Board of the National Research Council (USA)[4], measurements should be made on the right side of the body since differences between the two sides cannot be ruled out[5]. Many different sites of the body can be examined in this way.

The commonest measurement sites are the following:

Triceps skinfold. On the posterior aspect of the upper arm, midway between the acromium and olecranon in the vertical direction.

Subscapular skinfold. At the lateral inferior angle of the scapula in the direction of the ribs.

Suprailiac skinfold. In the middle axillary line over the iliac crest in the vertical direction.

Anterior axillary line skinfold. In the anterior axillary line at the level of the 10th rib.

Abdominal skinfold. Midway between navel and anterior superior iliac spine.

From the large number of published studies on skinfold thickness, two have been chosen for reproduction here: the one consists of measurements made on northwest German children in the period 1974–1977 by means of the Harpenden or Holtain calipers (pages 319–321), the other of the results of the First Health and Nutrition Examination Survey, USA (NHANES-I) made in the period 1971–1974, in which the Lange calipers were used (page 322). This latter study is also the source of the body-mass index tables for subjects aged between 6 and 50.9 years on page 328.

Changes in eating habits can naturally give rise to alterations in skinfold thickness in a whole population. Thus according to an English study on children[6], the 0.50 centile of the triceps skinfold thickness of 1-year-olds measured in 1967 corresponds to the 0.95 centile (boys) or 0.75 centile (girls) of measurements made in 1960.

The increase in skinfold thickness occurring up to middle life as recorded in cross-sectional studies has been confirmed in a longitudinal study: in men the increase was most marked in the abdominal skinfold thickness[7].

References

[1] DUGDALE and GRIFFITHS, *Amer. J. clin. Nutr.*, **32**, 2400 (1979).
[2] DAUNCEY and GAIRDNER, *Arch. Dis. Childh.*, **50**, 286 (1975).
[3] REHS et al., *Z. Kinderheilk.*, **120**, 121 (1975).
[4] *Hum. Biol.*, **28**, 111 (1956).
[5] BURGERT and ANDERSON, *Amer. J. clin. Nutr.*, **32**, 2136 (1979).
[6] TANNER and WHITEHOUSE, *Arch. Dis. Childh.*, **50**, 142 (1975).
[7] CHIEN et al., *J. appl. Physiol.*, **39**, 825 (1975).

Interpreting data on body mass is a problem of critical interest to physicians, nutritionists, and epidemiologists – in short, to everyone concerned with health.

As easy as it seems to measure body mass – leaving aside the technical fallacies of balances –, so difficult it is to get representative samples of men and women measured periodically for age, height, and body mass in the nude state. Statistical analysis of the data is tricky, and any attempt at getting clues to mortality, morbidity, and psychological well-being has to overcome many uncertainties[1]. Studies in this field have been done on more than a million subjects in the United States (Build Study, 1979[2]) as well as in Norway[3]. Several other US studies have been summarized by KEYS[4] and SIMOPOULOS and VAN ITALLIE[5].

*This chapter on 'Body Mass and Height of Adults' (pages 324–327) has been compiled in collaboration with W.Z. BILLEWICZ, Medical Research Council, Human Reproduction Group, Newcastle upon Tyne, UK.

Some of the frequently quoted studies relating body mass to height will be discussed in the following sections.

British standard body mass for height (Table 1)

This standard[6] is based on measurements made in 1943 on men and women aged 20–29 years after adjustment of body masses to those without clothing and of heights to those without footwear[7]. The median body mass given for each height constitutes the standard. These median values should be increased as follows to allow for the effect of ageing:

Men		Women	
30–39 years	+ 2.5 kg	30–39 years	+ 2.5 kg
40–49 years	+ 4.5 kg	40–44 years	+ 4.5 kg
50–64 years	+ 2.5 kg	45–64 years	+ 7.0 kg

Table 1 *British standard body mass for height*

Men

Height (without footwear)	Mass (without clothing) as percentage of standard mass: 60% (kg)	70%	80%	90%	100%	110%	120%	130%	140%
145 cm....	26.7	31.1	35.6	40.0	44.4	48.9	53.3	57.8	62.2
146 cm....	27.0	31.5	36.0	40.5	45.0	49.5	54.0	58.5	63.0
147 cm....	27.5	32.0	36.6	41.2	45.7	50.3	54.9	59.5	64.0
148 cm....	27.8	32.5	37.1	41.7	46.3	51.0	55.6	60.2	64.9
149 cm....	28.2	32.9	37.6	42.3	47.0	51.7	56.4	61.1	65.8
150 cm....	28.6	33.4	38.1	42.9	47.6	52.4	57.2	61.9	66.7
151 cm....	29.0	33.9	38.7	43.5	48.3	53.2	58.0	62.8	67.7
152 cm....	29.4	34.3	39.2	44.1	48.9	53.8	58.7	63.6	68.5
153 cm....	29.8	34.8	39.7	44.7	49.6	54.6	59.6	64.5	69.5
154 cm....	30.2	35.2	40.2	45.2	50.2	55.3	60.3	65.3	70.3
155 cm....	30.6	35.7	40.8	45.9	50.9	56.0	61.1	66.2	71.3
156 cm....	30.9	36.1	41.2	46.4	51.5	56.7	61.8	67.0	72.1
157 cm....	31.4	36.6	41.8	47.0	52.2	57.5	62.7	67.9	73.1
158 cm....	31.8	37.1	42.4	47.7	52.9	58.2	63.5	68.8	74.1
159 cm....	32.1	37.5	42.8	48.2	53.5	58.9	64.2	69.6	74.9
160 cm....	32.6	38.0	43.4	48.8	54.2	59.7	65.1	70.5	75.9
161 cm....	32.9	38.4	43.9	49.4	54.8	60.3	65.8	71.3	76.8
162 cm....	33.3	38.9	44.4	50.0	55.5	61.1	66.6	72.2	77.7
163 cm....	33.7	39.3	44.9	50.5	56.1	61.8	67.4	73.0	78.6
164 cm....	34.1	39.8	45.5	51.2	56.8	62.5	68.2	73.9	79.6
165 cm....	34.5	40.2	46.0	51.7	57.4	63.2	68.9	74.7	80.4
166 cm....	34.9	40.7	46.5	52.3	58.1	64.0	69.8	75.6	81.4
167 cm....	35.3	41.1	47.0	52.9	58.7	64.6	70.5	76.4	82.2
168 cm....	35.7	41.6	47.6	53.5	59.4	65.4	71.3	77.3	83.2
169 cm....	36.1	42.1	48.1	54.1	60.1	66.2	72.2	78.2	84.2
170 cm....	36.5	42.5	48.6	54.7	60.7	66.8	72.9	79.0	85.0
171 cm....	36.9	43.0	49.2	55.3	61.4	67.6	73.7	79.9	86.0
172 cm....	37.2	43.4	49.6	55.8	62.0	68.2	74.4	80.6	86.8
173 cm....	37.7	43.9	50.2	56.5	62.7	69.0	75.3	81.6	87.8
174 cm....	38.0	44.4	50.7	57.0	63.3	69.7	76.0	82.3	88.7
175 cm....	38.4	44.8	51.2	57.6	64.0	70.4	76.8	83.2	89.6
176 cm....	38.8	45.3	51.7	58.2	64.6	71.1	77.6	84.0	90.5
177 cm....	39.2	45.8	52.3	58.8	65.3	71.9	78.4	84.9	91.5
178 cm....	39.6	46.2	52.8	59.4	65.9	72.5	79.1	85.6	92.3
179 cm....	40.0	46.7	53.3	60.0	66.6	73.3	80.0	86.6	93.3
180 cm....	40.4	47.2	53.9	60.6	67.3	74.1	80.8	87.5	94.3
181 cm....	40.8	47.6	54.4	61.2	67.9	74.7	81.5	88.3	95.1
182 cm....	41.2	48.1	54.9	61.8	68.6	75.5	82.4	89.2	96.1
183 cm....	41.6	48.5	55.4	62.3	69.2	76.2	83.1	90.0	96.9
184 cm....	42.0	49.0	56.0	63.0	69.9	76.9	83.9	90.9	97.9
185 cm....	42.3	49.4	56.4	63.5	70.5	77.6	84.6	91.7	98.7
186 cm....	42.8	49.9	57.0	64.1	71.2	78.4	85.5	92.6	99.7

Women

Height (without footwear)	Mass (without clothing) as percentage of standard mass: 60% (kg)	70%	80%	90%	100%	110%	120%	130%	140%
140 cm....	25.4	29.6	33.8	38.0	42.2	46.5	50.7	54.9	59.1
141 cm....	25.7	30.0	34.3	38.6	42.8	47.1	51.4	55.7	60.0
142 cm....	26.0	30.4	34.7	39.0	43.3	47.7	52.0	56.3	60.7
143 cm....	26.4	30.8	35.2	39.6	43.9	48.3	52.7	57.1	61.5
144 cm....	26.7	31.1	35.6	40.0	44.4	48.9	53.3	57.8	62.2
145 cm....	27.0	31.5	36.0	40.5	45.0	49.5	54.0	58.5	63.0
146 cm....	27.3	31.9	36.4	41.0	45.5	50.1	54.6	59.2	63.7
147 cm....	27.7	32.3	36.9	41.5	46.1	50.8	55.4	60.0	64.6
148 cm....	28.1	32.7	37.4	42.1	46.7	51.4	56.1	60.8	65.4
149 cm....	28.4	33.1	37.8	42.5	47.2	52.0	56.7	61.4	66.1
150 cm....	28.7	33.5	38.3	43.1	47.8	52.6	57.4	62.2	67.0
151 cm....	29.0	33.9	38.7	43.5	48.3	53.2	58.0	62.8	67.7
152 cm....	29.4	34.3	39.2	44.1	48.9	53.8	58.7	63.6	68.5
153 cm....	29.7	34.6	39.6	44.5	49.4	54.4	59.3	64.3	69.2
154 cm....	30.0	35.0	40.0	45.0	50.0	55.0	60.0	65.0	70.0
155 cm....	30.3	35.4	40.4	45.5	50.5	55.6	60.6	65.7	70.7
156 cm....	30.7	35.8	40.9	46.0	51.1	56.3	61.4	66.5	71.6
157 cm....	31.0	36.2	41.3	46.5	51.6	56.8	62.0	67.1	72.3
158 cm....	31.4	36.6	41.8	47.0	52.2	57.5	62.7	67.9	73.1
159 cm....	31.7	36.9	42.2	47.5	52.7	58.0	63.3	68.6	73.8
160 cm....	32.0	37.4	42.7	48.0	53.3	58.7	64.0	69.3	74.7
161 cm....	32.3	37.7	43.1	48.5	53.8	59.2	64.6	70.0	75.4
162 cm....	32.7	38.1	43.6	49.0	54.4	59.9	65.3	70.8	76.2
163 cm....	33.0	38.5	44.0	49.5	55.0	60.5	66.0	71.5	77.0
164 cm....	33.3	38.9	44.4	50.0	55.5	61.1	66.6	72.2	77.7
165 cm....	33.7	39.3	44.9	50.5	56.1	61.8	67.4	73.0	78.6
166 cm....	34.0	39.7	45.3	51.0	56.6	62.3	68.0	73.6	79.3
167 cm....	34.4	40.1	45.8	51.5	57.2	63.0	68.7	74.4	80.1
168 cm....	34.7	40.4	46.2	52.0	57.7	63.5	69.3	75.1	80.8
169 cm....	35.0	40.9	46.7	52.5	58.3	64.2	70.0	75.8	81.7
170 cm....	35.3	41.2	47.1	53.0	58.8	64.7	70.6	76.5	82.4
171 cm....	35.7	41.6	47.6	53.5	59.4	65.4	71.3	77.2	83.2
172 cm....	36.0	42.0	48.0	54.0	59.9	65.9	71.9	77.9	83.9
173 cm....	36.3	42.4	48.4	54.5	60.5	66.6	72.6	78.7	84.7
174 cm....	36.6	42.7	48.8	54.9	61.0	67.1	73.2	79.3	85.4
175 cm....	37.0	43.2	49.3	55.5	61.6	67.8	73.9	80.1	86.3
176 cm....	37.4	43.6	49.8	56.0	62.2	68.5	74.7	80.9	87.1
177 cm....	37.7	43.9	50.2	56.5	62.7	69.0	75.3	81.6	87.8
178 cm....	38.0	44.4	50.7	57.0	63.3	69.7	76.0	82.3	88.7
179 cm....	38.3	44.7	51.1	57.5	63.8	70.2	76.6	83.0	89.4
180 cm....	38.7	45.1	51.6	58.0	64.4	70.9	77.3	83.8	90.2

Reference KEMSLEY et al., *Brit.J.prev.soc.Med.*, **16**, 189 (1962).

Average body mass for height of North Americans (Table 2)

The well-known tables of the 1959 Build and Blood Pressure Study[8] have been replaced by the 1979 Build Study[2]. This latter study comprises data collected on several million policy holders of 25 United States' and Canadian insurance companies during 1950 and 1972. The population of the study is therefore to some extent self-selected, and this may have produced a bias towards certain income groups.

1983 Metropolitan height and mass tables according to body frame (Table 3)

These tables[9] are based on the pooled data of the aforementioned population of policy holders aged 25–59 years. Body frame was classified according to elbow-breadth measurements taken from the National Health and Nutrition Examination Survey, 1971–1975, as listed in Table 4. These values are so devised that 50% of the population falls within the medium frame, and 25% each falls within the small and large frames respectively.

The 1983 Metropolitan height and mass tables indicate the body mass for height at which mortality has been found to be lowest – or longevity highest. Because the values given in the 1959 tables of this institution had been called 'ideal' or 'desirable', various misinterpretations of their meaning and purpose occurred; so the 1983 tables are referred to more appropriately as a 'health-education tool – a guideline'.

Table 2 *Average body mass of North Americans in 1979 (without clothing and without shoes)*

Men							Women						
Height (without shoes)	20–24 years	25–29 years	30–39 years	40–49 years	50–59 years	60–69 years	Height (without shoes)	20–24 years	25–29 years	30–39 years	40–49 years	50–59 years	60–69 years
	kg							kg					
							142 cm	44.5	46.7	48.5	50.3	52.2	53.1
							143 cm	45.0	47.3	48.9	50.9	52.6	53.5
							144 cm	45.7	48.0	49.5	51.6	53.1	54.0
							145 cm	46.3	48.5	49.9	52.2	53.5	54.4
							146 cm	47.4	49.0	50.3	52.8	54.4	55.3
							147 cm	48.5	49.4	50.8	53.5	55.3	56.2
							148 cm	48.8	49.7	51.2	53.8	55.6	56.6
							149 cm	49.1	50.0	51.7	54.1	55.9	57.1
							150 cm	49.4	50.3	52.2	54.4	56.2	57.6
							151 cm	50.3	51.4	52.8	55.2	57.1	58.2
							152 cm	51.3	52.6	53.5	56.2	58.1	59.0
							153 cm	51.7	52.8	53.8	56.5	58.3	59.3
							154 cm	52.4	53.2	54.4	56.8	58.6	59.8
155 cm	56.7	58.5	60.3	61.2	61.7	61.2	155 cm	53.1	53.5	54.9	57.2	59.0	60.3
156 cm	57.8	59.6	61.3	62.0	62.4	62.0	156 cm	53.8	54.3	55.6	57.9	59.7	61.1
157 cm	59.4	61.2	62.6	63.0	63.5	63.0	157 cm	54.9	55.3	56.7	59.0	60.8	62.1
158 cm	59.7	61.5	63.0	63.5	64.0	63.5	158 cm	55.2	55.6	57.0	59.2	61.2	62.4
159 cm	60.2	62.0	63.7	64.4	64.9	64.4	159 cm	55.7	56.2	57.5	59.8	61.9	63.0
160 cm	60.8	62.6	64.4	65.3	65.8	65.3	160 cm	56.2	56.7	58.1	60.3	62.6	63.5
161 cm	61.5	63.3	65.1	66.2	66.6	66.0	161 cm	56.8	57.4	58.6	60.9	63.1	64.2
162 cm	62.2	64.0	65.8	67.1	67.5	66.7	162 cm	57.3	58.1	59.1	61.4	63.7	64.9
163 cm	62.6	64.4	66.2	67.6	68.0	67.1	163 cm	57.6	58.5	59.4	61.7	64.0	65.3
164 cm	63.9	65.7	67.5	68.6	69.1	68.4	164 cm	58.4	59.0	60.2	62.7	64.7	66.1
165 cm	64.9	66.7	68.5	69.4	69.9	69.4	165 cm	59.0	59.4	60.8	63.5	65.3	66.7
166 cm	65.7	67.3	69.1	70.2	70.7	70.2	166 cm	59.6	60.1	61.4	64.1	66.1	67.5
167 cm	66.6	68.0	69.8	71.1	71.5	71.1	167 cm	60.3	60.8	62.1	64.9	67.0	68.4
168 cm	67.1	68.5	70.3	71.7	72.1	71.7	168 cm	60.8	61.2	62.6	65.3	67.6	68.9
169 cm	68.1	69.7	71.5	72.6	73.1	72.6	169 cm	61.8	62.2	63.6	66.0	68.6	69.7
170 cm	68.9	70.8	72.6	73.5	73.9	73.5	170 cm	62.6	63.0	64.4	66.7	69.4	70.3
171 cm	69.8	71.5	73.3	74.2	74.7	74.2	171 cm	63.3	63.9	65.1	67.4	69.8	70.7
172 cm	70.9	72.4	74.2	75.1	75.6	75.1	172 cm	64.2	65.0	66.0	68.3	70.4	71.3
173 cm	71.7	73.0	74.8	75.7	76.2	75.7	173 cm	64.9	65.8	66.7	68.9	70.8	71.7
174 cm	72.6	74.2	75.8	76.7	77.1	76.7	174 cm	65.5	66.2	67.4	69.6	71.4	72.1
175 cm	73.5	75.3	76.7	77.6	78.0	77.6	175 cm	66.2	66.7	68.0	70.3	72.1	72.6
176 cm	74.0	75.8	77.3	78.2	78.7	78.2	176 cm	67.0	67.5	68.8	70.8	72.6	73.1
177 cm	74.7	76.5	78.2	79.1	79.6	79.1	177 cm	68.1	68.5	69.9	71.5	73.4	73.8
178 cm	75.3	77.1	78.9	79.8	80.3	79.8	178 cm	68.9	69.4	70.8	72.1	73.9	74.4
179 cm	76.4	78.4	80.0	80.9	81.4	80.9							
180 cm	77.6	79.8	81.2	82.1	82.6	82.1							
181 cm	78.3	80.4	81.9	82.8	83.3	82.7							
182 cm	79.3	81.3	83.0	83.9	84.3	83.6							
183 cm	80.3	82.1	83.9	84.8	85.3	84.4							
184 cm	81.3	83.1	84.9	85.8	86.3	85.4							
185 cm	82.6	84.4	86.2	87.1	87.5	86.6							
186 cm	83.2	85.0	86.8	87.7	88.2	87.1							
187 cm	84.2	86.1	87.9	88.8	89.2	87.8							
188 cm	85.3	87.1	88.9	89.8	90.3	88.5							
189 cm	86.2	88.0	89.8	90.7	91.2	89.8							
190 cm	87.1	88.9	90.7	91.6	92.1	91.0							
191 cm	87.5	89.4	91.2	92.1	92.5	91.6							

Reference *Build Study, 1979,* Society of Actuaries and Association of Life Insurance Medical Directors of America, Chicago, 1980. (Data converted to the metric system by the publishers of *Geigy Scientific Tables.*)

Table 3 *1983 Metropolitan Height and Mass Tables* according to body frame (in indoor clothing and in shoes◊)*

Men				Women			
Height (in shoes◊)	Small frame	Medium frame	Large frame	Height (in shoes◊)	Small frame	Medium frame	Large frame
	kg				kg		
				148 cm	46.4–50.6	49.6–55.1	53.7–59.8
				149 cm	46.6–51.0	50.0–55.5	54.1–60.3
				150 cm	46.7–51.3	50.3–55.9	54.4–60.9
				151 cm	46.9–51.7	50.7–56.4	54.8–61.4
				152 cm	47.1–52.1	51.1–57.0	55.2–61.9
				153 cm	47.4–52.5	51.5–57.5	55.6–62.4
				154 cm	47.8–53.0	51.9–58.0	56.2–63.0
				155 cm	48.1–53.6	52.2–58.6	56.8–63.6
				156 cm	48.5–54.1	52.7–59.1	57.3–64.1
				157 cm	48.8–54.6	53.2–59.6	57.8–64.6
158 cm	58.3–61.0	59.6–64.2	62.8–68.3	158 cm	49.3–55.2	53.8–60.2	58.4–65.3
159 cm	58.6–61.3	59.9–64.5	63.1–68.8	159 cm	49.8–55.7	54.3–60.7	58.9–66.0
160 cm	59.0–61.7	60.3–64.9	63.5–69.4	160 cm	50.3–56.2	54.9–61.2	59.4–66.7
161 cm	59.3–62.0	60.6–65.2	63.8–69.9	161 cm	50.8–56.7	55.4–61.7	59.9–67.4
162 cm	59.7–62.4	61.0–65.6	64.2–70.5	162 cm	51.4–57.3	55.9–62.3	60.5–68.1
163 cm	60.0–62.7	61.3–66.0	64.5–71.1	163 cm	51.9–57.8	56.4–62.8	61.0–68.8
164 cm	60.4–63.1	61.7–66.5	64.9–71.8	164 cm	52.5–58.4	57.0–63.4	61.5–69.5
165 cm	60.8–63.5	62.1–67.0	65.3–72.5	165 cm	53.0–58.9	57.5–63.9	62.0–70.2
166 cm	61.1–63.8	62.4–67.6	65.6–73.2	166 cm	53.6–59.5	58.1–64.5	62.6–70.9
167 cm	61.5–64.2	62.8–68.2	66.0–74.0	167 cm	54.1–60.0	58.7–65.0	63.2–71.7
168 cm	61.8–64.6	63.2–68.7	66.4–74.7	168 cm	54.6–60.5	59.2–65.5	63.7–72.4
169 cm	62.2–65.2	63.8–69.3	67.0–75.4	169 cm	55.2–61.1	59.7–66.1	64.3–73.1
170 cm	62.5–65.7	64.3–69.8	67.5–76.1	170 cm	55.7–61.6	60.2–66.6	64.8–73.8
171 cm	62.9–66.2	64.8–70.3	68.0–76.8	171 cm	56.2–62.1	60.7–67.1	65.3–74.5
172 cm	63.2–66.7	65.4–70.8	68.5–77.5	172 cm	56.8–62.6	61.3–67.6	65.8–75.2
173 cm	63.6–67.3	65.9–71.4	69.1–78.2	173 cm	57.3–63.2	61.8–68.2	66.4–75.9
174 cm	63.9–67.8	66.4–71.9	69.6–78.9	174 cm	57.8–63.7	62.3–68.7	66.9–76.4
175 cm	64.3–68.3	66.9–72.4	70.1–79.6	175 cm	58.3–64.2	62.8–69.2	67.4–76.9
176 cm	64.7–68.9	67.5–73.0	70.7–80.3	176 cm	58.9–64.8	63.4–69.8	68.0–77.5
177 cm	65.0–69.5	68.1–73.5	71.3–81.0	177 cm	59.5–65.4	64.0–70.4	68.5–78.1
178 cm	65.4–70.0	68.6–74.0	71.8–81.8	178 cm	60.0–65.9	64.5–70.9	69.0–78.6
179 cm	65.7–70.5	69.2–74.6	72.3–82.5	179 cm	60.5–66.4	65.1–71.4	69.6–79.1
180 cm	66.1–71.0	69.7–75.1	72.8–83.3	180 cm	61.0–66.9	65.6–71.9	70.1–79.6
181 cm	66.6–71.6	70.2–75.8	73.4–84.0	181 cm	61.6–67.5	66.1–72.5	70.7–80.2
182 cm	67.1–72.1	70.7–76.5	73.9–84.7	182 cm	62.1–68.0	66.6–73.0	71.2–80.7
183 cm	67.7–72.7	71.3–77.2	74.5–85.4	183 cm	62.6–68.5	67.1–73.5	71.7–81.2
184 cm	68.2–73.4	71.8–77.9	75.2–86.1				
185 cm	68.7–74.1	72.4–78.6	75.9–86.8				
186 cm	69.2–74.8	73.0–79.3	76.6–87.6				
187 cm	69.8–75.5	73.7–80.0	77.3–88.5				
188 cm	70.3–76.2	74.4–80.7	78.0–89.4				
189 cm	70.9–76.9	74.9–81.5	78.7–90.3				
190 cm	71.4–77.6	75.4–82.2	79.4–91.2				
191 cm	72.1–78.4	76.1–83.0	80.3–92.1				
192 cm	72.8–79.1	76.8–83.9	81.2–93.0				
193 cm	73.5–79.8	77.6–84.8	82.1–93.9				

* Prepared by Metropolitan Life Insurance Company and based on the lowest mortality for men and women at ages 25 to 59. Source of basic data: *Build Study, 1979,* Society of Actuaries and Association of Life Insurance Medical Directors of America, Chicago, 1980.

◊ Indoor clothing weighing 2.3 kg for men and 1.4 kg for women; shoes with 2.5 cm heels.

Reference

Statist. Bull. Metrop. Life Found., **64**, No. 1, 4 (1983).

Table 4 *Mean elbow breadth for height (in shoes with 2.5-cm heels)*

Men		Women	
Height	Elbow breadth	Height	Elbow breadth
158–161 cm	6.4–7.2 cm	148–151 cm	5.6–6.4 cm
162–171 cm	6.7–7.4 cm	152–161 cm	5.8–6.5 cm
172–181 cm	6.9–7.6 cm	162–171 cm	5.9–6.6 cm
182–191 cm	7.1–7.8 cm	172–181 cm	6.1–6.8 cm
192–193 cm	7.4–8.1 cm	182–183 cm	6.2–6.9 cm

Relationships between body mass and height

A *body-mass-for-height* standard is usually applied to decide whether a person is suffering from 'adiposity' ('obesity'). Here, a preferable term to use is 'overweight', since *body-mass-for-height* standards are not a reliable guide to the fat content of the body. The relative adiposity of a group of persons whose body mass for height is 120% of the standard is naturally greater than that of a group whose body mass is 80% of the standard, but the same cannot be said of the individuals making up the group on account of the profound effect exerted on the *mass-to-height* relationship by differences in muscularity.

A commonly accepted classification of *body-mass-for-height* values in relation to an appropriate standard is the following[10]:

Table 5 *Correlation of mass-for-height indices with mass, height and fat content of the body*

Index	477 men			301 women		
	Height	Mass	Fat content	Height	Mass	Fat content
	Correlation coefficient *r*					
M/H	0.131	0.953	0.543	0.012	0.984	0.711
M/H^2 (body-mass index, Quetelet index)	−0.201	0.796	0.551	−0.173	0.931	0.701
M/H^3 (Rohrer index)	−0.472	0.583	0.503	−0.351	0.842	0.662
$M^{1/3}/H$ (ponderal index)	−0.461	0.601	0.517	−0.360	0.836	0.684
$H/M^{1/3}$ (Sheldon index)	0.441	−0.611	−0.521	0.363	−0.821	−0.695
H^3/M (leanness index of NICHOLSON and ZILVA)	0.415	−0.612	−0.516	0.361	−0.796	−0.695

Reference WATSON et al., *Amer. J. clin. Nutr.*, **32**, 736 (1979).

Thin	≤ 80%	Overweight	≥ 110%
Underweight	≤ 90%	Obese	≥ 120%
Normal	91–109%	Superobese	> 159%
		Morbidly obese[11]	> 200%

Various indices are available to replace classification in a particular percentage series of a *body-mass-for-height* standard by a numerical value[12–16] (see Table 5).

The main use of numerical values is to furnish an indication of whether the subject suffers from adiposity. An index can be regarded as suitable for this purpose when it correlates closely with body mass but only poorly with height. This requirement is best met by the ratios mass/height and mass/square of height, even though – especially in males – these indices do not correlate satisfactorily with the fat content of the body as calculated from the water content[16].

Centiles for the body-mass index (or Quetelet index) M/H^2 for white and black North Americans are indicated on page 328. Values for the mean body-mass index in various study populations have been compiled by SIMOPOULOS and VAN ITALLIE[5].

The M/H^2 values (M in kg, H in m) may be classified in the following manner[24]:

Emaciation	< 15	Overweight	25–29.9
Underweight	15–18.9	Obese	30–39.9
Normal	19–24.9	Morbidly obese	≥ 40

The correlation between body-mass index and mortality is described by an U-shaped curve (Fig. 1). Such curves are characterized by a very broad flat bottom, indicating a large range of minimal mortality[3]. In the Norwegian study[3], this minimum has been found to be within the range of 21–25 kg/m².

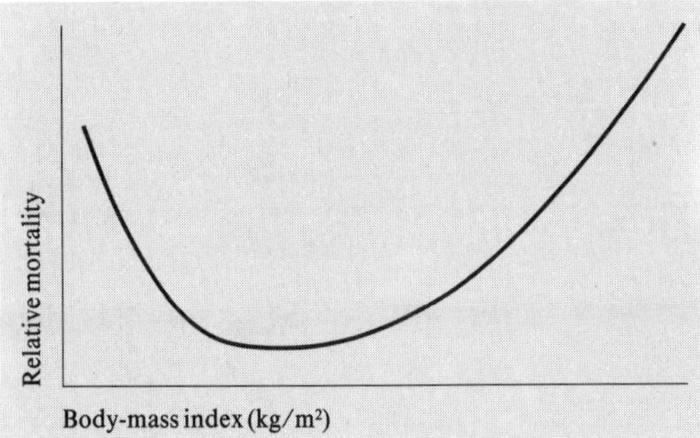

Fig. 1. Mortality-risk curve (schematic)[3].

Changes in body mass and height of adults with age

Practically all cross-sectional studies show an increase in *body mass* with age up to about 60 years, followed by a later decrease[17]. This trend may not be followed however in a population whose nutritional status is subject to changes. The increase in body mass is marked by a loss of body water and an increase in body fat. Data from cross-sectional studies have been confirmed by a number of longitudinal studies[18,19].

Table 6
Decrease in height with age in a northern Norwegian population

Age (in 1966)	Men		Women	
	Number	Height decrease after 5 years (cm)	Number	Height decrease after 5 years (cm)
25–29 years	925	0.0	1138	0.0
30–34 years	1012	0.0	1179	0.0
35–39 years	1304	0.1	1302	0.1
40–44 years	1352	0.3	1386	0.3
45–49 years	1326	0.4	1344	0.4
50–54 years	1221	0.4	1219	0.4
55–59 years	984	0.6	1012	0.6
60–64 years	790	0.6	735	0.7
65–69 years	470	0.5	483	0.8

Reference
FORSDAHL and WAALER, *T. norske Lægeforen.*, **96**, 211 (1976).

It is generally believed that *height* decreases in old age, and in fact the percentage of tall persons among the aged is less than among young adults, while the percentage of short persons among the aged is greater than among young adults[20,21]. The decrease in height with advancing age has also been confirmed in a number of longitudinal studies[17,22,23]. The results of one such study made in northern Norway are shown in Table 6.

References

1 KNAPP, T.R., *J. Amer. med. Ass.*, **250**, 506 (1983).
2 *Build Study, 1979,* Society of Actuaries and Association of Life Insurance Medical Directors of America, Chicago, 1980.
3 WAALER, H.T., *Acta med. scand.*, suppl. 679 (1984).
4 KEYS, A., *Nutr. Rev.*, **38**, 297 (1980).
5 SIMOPOULOS and VAN ITALLIE, *Ann. intern. Med.*, **100**, 285 (1984).
6 KEMSLEY et al., *Brit. J. prev. soc. Med.*, **16**, 189 (1962).
7 KEMSLEY, W.F., *Ann. Eugen. (Lond.)*, **15**, 161 (1950).
8 *Build and Blood Pressure Study,* volume 1, Society of Actuaries, Chicago, 1959, page 16.
9 *Statist. Bull. Metrop. Life Found.*, **64**, No. 1 (1983).
10 KOHRS et al., *Amer. J. clin. Nutr.*, **32**, 2120 (1979).
11 VAN ITALLIE and KRAL, *J. Amer. med. Ass.*, **246**, 999 (1981).
12 BILLEWICZ et al., *Brit. J. prev. soc. Med.*, **16**, 183 (1962).
13 KHOSLA and LOWE, *Brit. J. prev. soc. Med.*, **21**, 122 (1967).
14 FLOREY, C., *J. chron. Dis.*, **23**, 93 (1970).
15 KEYS et al., *J. chron. Dis.*, **25**, 329 (1972).
16 WATSON et al., *Amer. J. clin. Nutr.*, **32**, 736 (1979).
17 SUSANNE, C., in JOHNSTON et al. (Eds.), *Human Physical Growth and Maturation,* Plenum, New York, 1980, page 203.
18 BORKAN and NORRIS, *Hum. Biol.*, **49**, 495 (1977).
19 SUSANNE, C., *J. hum. Evol.*, **6**, 181 (1977).
20 *Weight by Height and Age of Adults,* United States 1960–1962, Public Health Service Publication, series 11, No. 14, Washington, 1966.
21 PAROT et al., *Biom. hum. (Paris)*, **9**, 35 (1974).
22 FORSDAHL and WAALER, *T. norske Laegeforen.*, **96**, 211 (1976).
23 NOPPA et al., *Amer. J. clin. Nutr.*, **33**, 155 (1980).
24 LLEWELLYN-JONES and ABRAHAM, *Brit. med. J.*, **288**, 1800 (1984).

Age	Males							Females						
		90%							90%					
			80%							80%				
				50%							50%			
	P_{05}	P_{10}	P_{25}	P_{50}	P_{75}	P_{90}	P_{95}	P_{05}	P_{10}	P_{25}	P_{50}	P_{75}	P_{90}	P_{95}
	M/H^2 (M in kg, H in m)													
Whites														
6 years	13.0	13.6	14.4	15.3	16.0	17.7	18.7	12.8	13.5	14.0	15.0	16.0	16.9	17.3
7 years	13.3	13.9	14.7	15.7	16.7	18.5	19.9	13.1	13.8	14.5	15.6	16.8	18.4	19.2
8 years	13.6	14.2	15.1	16.1	17.4	19.4	21.1	13.5	14.2	15.1	16.2	17.7	19.9	21.1
9 years	14.0	14.5	15.5	16.6	18.1	20.4	22.3	13.9	14.6	15.6	15.9	18.7	21.3	23.0
10 years	14.5	14.9	15.9	17.1	18.9	21.3	23.4	14.4	15.1	16.2	17.5	19.6	22.7	24.8
11 years	15.0	15.3	16.4	17.6	19.7	22.2	24.5	14.9	15.5	16.7	18.2	20.4	23.8	26.3
12 years	15.5	15.8	16.9	18.2	20.4	23.1	25.5	15.3	16.0	17.3	18.8	21.2	24.8	27.7
13 years	16.0	16.3	17.4	18.8	21.1	24.0	26.5	15.8	16.4	17.8	19.3	21.9	25.6	28.8
14 years	16.5	16.9	18.0	19.4	21.9	24.8	27.3	16.2	16.8	18.2	19.9	22.5	26.1	29.6
15 years	17.0	17.5	18.7	20.1	22.5	25.6	28.0	16.6	17.2	18.6	20.3	23.0	26.5	30.2
16 years	17.4	18.0	19.2	20.8	23.2	26.3	28.6	16.9	17.5	18.9	20.7	23.5	26.7	30.6
17 years	17.8	18.5	19.8	21.4	23.8	26.9	29.2	17.1	17.8	19.2	21.0	23.8	26.9	30.9
18–20 years	18.6	19.7	21.0	23.0	25.3	28.4	30.5	17.6	18.4	19.7	21.6	24.3	27.2	31.2
21–23 years	19.0	20.0	21.4	23.6	26.0	29.0	31.2	17.7	18.5	19.8	21.8	24.4	27.7	31.5
24–26 years	19.4	20.2	21.8	24.2	27.0	30.0	32.4	17.8	18.5	20.0	22.0	24.9	29.6	33.2
27–29 years	19.6	20.5	22.2	24.5	27.3	30.5	32.7	18.0	18.7	20.1	22.1	25.3	30.6	34.1
30–32 years	20.0	21.4	23.1	25.3	27.7	30.7	32.9	18.5	19.2	20.5	22.6	26.2	31.4	35.3
33–35 years	20.1	21.7	23.3	25.7	27.8	30.6	32.7	18.7	19.4	20.7	22.9	26.4	31.3	35.3
36–38 years	20.1	21.6	23.2	25.8	28.1	30.5	32.4	18.8	19.5	21.2	23.4	26.7	31.4	35.2
39–41 years	20.0	21.3	23.2	25.7	28.2	30.6	32.3	18.8	19.5	21.3	23.5	27.0	32.0	35.3
42–44 years	19.8	21.0	23.4	25.8	28.3	30.8	32.7	18.7	19.9	21.5	23.8	28.0	33.2	35.8
45–47 years	19.8	21.0	23.6	25.9	28.3	30.8	32.9	18.8	20.1	21.6	24.0	28.2	33.3	35.9
48–50 years	19.8	21.2	23.6	26.1	28.4	30.9	33.2	19.1	20.2	21.8	24.4	28.0	32.5	35.6
Blacks														
6 years	13.8	14.1	14.8	15.2	16.2	16.9	18.0	13.3	13.4	13.9	14.6	15.4	15.9	17.2
7 years	13.9	14.3	14.9	15.4	16.5	17.9	19.1	13.5	13.7	14.3	15.1	16.4	17.6	19.1
8 years	14.0	14.5	15.1	15.7	16.9	19.0	20.4	13.8	13.9	14.8	15.7	17.4	19.4	21.1
9 years	14.1	14.7	15.4	16.1	17.4	20.0	21.7	14.1	14.3	15.3	16.4	18.5	21.3	23.1
10 years	14.4	15.1	15.7	16.6	17.9	21.1	23.2	14.4	14.7	15.8	17.1	19.6	23.1	25.2
11 years	14.7	15.4	16.2	17.1	18.5	22.1	24.7	14.8	15.2	16.4	17.9	20.7	24.8	27.1
12 years	15.1	15.9	16.7	17.7	19.2	23.1	26.2	15.2	15.7	16.9	18.7	21.7	26.3	28.9
13 years	15.6	16.3	17.2	18.4	19.9	23.9	27.7	15.6	16.2	17.5	19.4	22.6	27.7	30.5
14 years	16.1	16.8	17.9	19.0	20.7	24.7	29.0	16.1	16.7	18.0	20.1	23.4	28.7	31.9
15 years	16.6	17.3	18.5	19.7	21.5	25.3	30.1	16.4	17.2	18.5	20.8	24.0	29.6	33.0
16 years	17.1	17.8	19.1	20.4	22.2	25.9	31.1	16.8	17.7	18.9	21.3	24.6	30.4	33.9
17 years	17.6	18.2	19.6	21.0	23.0	26.4	31.9	17.1	18.0	19.4	21.8	25.0	30.9	34.6
18–20 years	18.6	19.1	20.6	22.6	24.6	27.8	33.2	17.6	18.6	20.2	22.5	26.0	32.0	35.9
21–23 years	18.8	19.4	20.8	23.2	25.4	28.8	33.5	17.7	18.6	20.4	22.8	26.5	32.3	36.4
24–26 years	18.6	19.5	21.0	23.9	26.4	31.1	33.9	17.6	18.6	20.6	23.7	28.0	32.6	37.5
27–29 years	18.6	19.5	21.4	24.2	27.0	32.1	34.6	17.7	18.8	20.9	24.5	28.9	33.1	38.2
30–32 years	19.0	20.0	23.0	25.1	28.3	32.9	36.3	18.2	19.4	22.3	26.1	30.7	35.1	39.6
33–35 years	19.3	20.3	23.9	25.8	28.9	32.7	37.0	18.5	19.6	22.9	26.7	31.4	36.1	40.3
36–38 years	19.5	20.5	24.3	27.0	29.2	31.9	37.1	19.0	20.0	23.3	27.2	32.2	36.8	41.3
39–41 years	19.2	20.4	23.7	26.9	29.0	31.7	36.7	19.0	20.3	23.3	27.3	32.3	36.7	41.7
42–44 years	18.5	20.1	22.1	25.5	28.3	32.4	36.0	19.0	20.9	23.7	27.2	32.0	37.1	42.2
45–47 years	18.4	20.1	21.7	24.8	28.2	33.0	36.0	19.0	20.7	24.0	27.3	32.0	37.4	42.5
48–50 years	18.9	20.6	22.2	24.9	28.9	33.8	36.3	19.0	19.5	24.2	28.3	32.8	37.5	43.9

Reference Cronk and Roche, *Amer. J. clin. Nutr.*, **35**, 347 (1982).

The following formula serves as a model[1] for calculating the body surface area (*SA*) from the height (*H*) and body mass (*M*):

$SA = \alpha_0 H^{\alpha_1} M^{\alpha_2}$ or $\ln SA = \ln\alpha_0 + \alpha_1 \ln H + \alpha_2 \ln M$

[SA in m², H in cm, M in kg]

The parameters α_0, α_1, α_2 (see the table) have been estimated from the data of various investigators or derived from planimetric studies. The values for body surface area calculated by GEHAN and GEORGE[2] from body mass and height are given below.

Many of the physiological functions are related to a parameter of physical size. It is doubtful however whether body surface area is the best reference magnitude for physiological functions[3]. Its most suitable use in this way would seem to be in connection with the cardiac index (the volume of blood expelled by the ventricle in unit time per unit of body surface area).

Parameters α_0, α_1, α_2 for calculation of body surface area

Investigators	Number	α_0	α_1	α_2
GEHAN and GEORGE[2]:				
All ages	401	0.02350	0.42246	0.51456
<5 years	229	0.02667	0.38217	0.53937
5–19 years	42	0.03050	0.35129	0.54375
≥20 years	130	0.01545	0.54468	0.46336
DU BOIS and DU BOIS[1]	9	0.007184	0.725	0.425
BOYD[4]	197	0.01787	0.500	0.4838
HAYCOCK et al.[5]	81	0.024265	0.3964	0.5378

Body surface area as a function of height and body mass[2]

Height ↓ / Mass → (m²)	4 kg	6 kg	8 kg	10 kg	12 kg	14 kg	16 kg	18 kg	20 kg	22 kg	24 kg	26 kg	28 kg	30 kg	32 kg	34 kg	36 kg	38 kg	40 kg	44 kg	48 kg	52 kg	56 kg	60 kg
50 cm	0.25	0.31	0.36	0.40	0.44	0.48	0.51	0.54	0.57	0.60	0.63	0.66	0.68	0.71	0.73	0.75	0.78	0.80	0.82	0.86	0.90	0.94	0.97	1.01
55 cm	0.26	0.32	0.37	0.42	0.46	0.50	0.53	0.57	0.60	0.63	0.66	0.68	0.71	0.74	0.76	0.78	0.81	0.83	0.85	0.90	0.94	0.98	1.01	1.05
60 cm	0.27	0.33	0.39	0.43	0.48	0.52	0.55	0.59	0.62	0.65	0.68	0.71	0.74	0.76	0.79	0.81	0.84	0.86	0.88	0.93	0.97	1.01	1.05	1.09
65 cm	0.28	0.34	0.40	0.45	0.49	0.53	0.57	0.61	0.64	0.67	0.70	0.73	0.76	0.79	0.82	0.84	0.87	0.89	0.91	0.96	1.00	1.05	1.09	1.13
70 cm	0.29	0.36	0.41	0.46	0.51	0.55	0.59	0.63	0.66	0.69	0.73	0.76	0.79	0.81	0.84	0.87	0.89	0.92	0.94	0.99	1.04	1.08	1.12	1.16
75 cm	0.30	0.37	0.42	0.48	0.52	0.57	0.61	0.64	0.68	0.71	0.75	0.78	0.81	0.84	0.87	0.89	0.92	0.95	0.97	1.02	1.07	1.11	1.16	1.20
80 cm	0.31	0.38	0.44	0.49	0.54	0.58	0.62	0.66	0.70	0.73	0.77	0.80	0.83	0.86	0.89	0.92	0.95	0.97	1.00	1.05	1.10	1.14	1.19	1.23
85 cm	0.31	0.39	0.45	0.50	0.55	0.60	0.64	0.68	0.72	0.75	0.79	0.82	0.85	0.88	0.91	0.94	0.97	1.00	1.02	1.08	1.13	1.17	1.22	1.26
90 cm	0.32	0.40	0.46	0.51	0.56	0.61	0.65	0.70	0.73	0.77	0.81	0.84	0.87	0.91	0.94	0.97	0.99	1.02	1.05	1.10	1.15	1.20	1.25	1.29
95 cm	0.33	0.40	0.47	0.53	0.58	0.63	0.67	0.71	0.75	0.79	0.83	0.86	0.89	0.93	0.96	0.99	1.02	1.05	1.07	1.13	1.18	1.23	1.28	1.32

Height ↓ / Mass → (m²)	12 kg	14 kg	16 kg	18 kg	20 kg	22 kg	24 kg	26 kg	28 kg	30 kg	32 kg	34 kg	36 kg	38 kg	40 kg	42 kg	44 kg	48 kg	52 kg	56 kg	60 kg	64 kg	68 kg	72 kg
100 cm	0.59	0.64	0.68	0.73	0.77	0.81	0.84	0.88	0.91	0.95	0.98	1.01	1.04	1.07	1.10	1.13	1.15	1.21	1.26	1.30	1.35	1.40	1.44	1.48
105 cm	0.60	0.65	0.70	0.74	0.78	0.82	0.86	0.90	0.93	0.97	1.00	1.03	1.06	1.09	1.12	1.15	1.18	1.23	1.28	1.33	1.38	1.43	1.47	1.52
110 cm	0.61	0.67	0.71	0.76	0.80	0.84	0.88	0.92	0.95	0.99	1.02	1.05	1.08	1.11	1.14	1.17	1.20	1.25	1.31	1.36	1.41	1.45	1.50	1.55
115 cm	0.63	0.68	0.73	0.77	0.81	0.86	0.89	0.93	0.97	1.00	1.04	1.07	1.10	1.13	1.15	1.19	1.22	1.28	1.33	1.38	1.43	1.48	1.53	1.58
120 cm	0.64	0.69	0.74	0.79	0.83	0.87	0.91	0.95	0.99	1.02	1.06	1.09	1.12	1.15	1.19	1.22	1.24	1.30	1.36	1.41	1.46	1.51	1.56	1.60
125 cm	0.65	0.70	0.75	0.80	0.84	0.89	0.93	0.97	1.00	1.04	1.07	1.11	1.14	1.17	1.21	1.24	1.27	1.32	1.38	1.43	1.49	1.54	1.58	1.63
130 cm	0.66	0.71	0.77	0.81	0.86	0.90	0.94	0.98	1.02	1.06	1.09	1.13	1.16	1.19	1.23	1.26	1.29	1.35	1.40	1.46	1.51	1.56	1.61	1.66
135 cm	0.67	0.73	0.78	0.83	0.87	0.92	0.96	1.00	1.04	1.07	1.11	1.15	1.18	1.21	1.25	1.28	1.31	1.37	1.43	1.48	1.53	1.59	1.64	1.69
140 cm	0.68	0.74	0.79	0.84	0.89	0.93	0.97	1.01	1.05	1.09	1.13	1.16	1.20	1.23	1.26	1.30	1.33	1.39	1.45	1.50	1.56	1.61	1.66	1.71
145 cm	0.69	0.75	0.80	0.85	0.90	0.94	0.99	1.03	1.07	1.11	1.14	1.18	1.22	1.25	1.28	1.32	1.35	1.41	1.47	1.53	1.58	1.64	1.69	1.74

Height ↓ / Mass → (m²)	30 kg	34 kg	38 kg	42 kg	46 kg	50 kg	54 kg	58 kg	62 kg	66 kg	70 kg	74 kg	78 kg	82 kg	86 kg	90 kg	94 kg	98 kg	102 kg	106 kg	110 kg	114 kg	118 kg	122 kg
150 cm	1.12	1.20	1.27	1.34	1.40	1.46	1.52	1.58	1.63	1.69	1.74	1.79	1.84	1.88	1.93	1.98	2.02	2.07	2.11	2.15	2.19	2.23	2.27	2.31
155 cm	1.14	1.21	1.29	1.35	1.42	1.48	1.54	1.60	1.65	1.71	1.76	1.81	1.86	1.91	1.96	2.00	2.05	2.09	2.14	2.18	2.22	2.26	2.30	2.34
160 cm	1.15	1.23	1.30	1.37	1.44	1.50	1.56	1.62	1.68	1.73	1.78	1.84	1.89	1.94	1.98	2.03	2.08	2.12	2.17	2.21	2.25	2.29	2.34	2.38
165 cm	1.17	1.25	1.32	1.39	1.46	1.52	1.58	1.64	1.70	1.75	1.81	1.86	1.91	1.96	2.01	2.06	2.10	2.15	2.19	2.24	2.28	2.32	2.37	2.41
170 cm	1.18	1.26	1.34	1.41	1.48	1.54	1.60	1.66	1.72	1.78	1.83	1.88	1.94	1.99	2.04	2.08	2.13	2.18	2.22	2.27	2.31	2.35	2.40	2.44
175 cm	1.20	1.28	1.35	1.43	1.49	1.56	1.62	1.68	1.74	1.80	1.85	1.91	1.96	2.01	2.06	2.11	2.16	2.20	2.25	2.30	2.34	2.38	2.43	2.47
180 cm	1.21	1.29	1.37	1.44	1.51	1.58	1.64	1.70	1.76	1.82	1.88	1.93	1.98	2.04	2.09	2.13	2.18	2.23	2.28	2.32	2.37	2.41	2.45	2.50

Height ↓ / Mass → (m²)	40 kg	44 kg	48 kg	52 kg	56 kg	60 kg	64 kg	68 kg	72 kg	76 kg	80 kg	84 kg	88 kg	92 kg	96 kg	100 kg	104 kg	108 kg	112 kg	116 kg	120 kg	124 kg	128 kg	132 kg
185 cm	1.42	1.49	1.56	1.63	1.69	1.75	1.81	1.87	1.93	1.98	2.03	2.08	2.13	2.18	2.23	2.28	2.33	2.37	2.42	2.46	2.50	2.55	2.59	2.63
190 cm	1.44	1.51	1.58	1.65	1.71	1.77	1.83	1.89	1.95	2.00	2.06	2.11	2.16	2.21	2.26	2.31	2.35	2.40	2.44	2.49	2.53	2.58	2.62	2.66
195 cm	1.45	1.53	1.60	1.67	1.73	1.79	1.85	1.91	1.97	2.02	2.08	2.13	2.18	2.23	2.28	2.33	2.38	2.43	2.47	2.52	2.56	2.60	2.65	2.69
200 cm	1.47	1.54	1.62	1.68	1.75	1.81	1.87	1.93	1.99	2.05	2.10	2.15	2.21	2.26	2.31	2.36	2.40	2.45	2.50	2.54	2.59	2.63	2.68	2.72
205 cm	1.49	1.56	1.63	1.70	1.77	1.83	1.89	1.95	2.01	2.07	2.12	2.18	2.23	2.28	2.33	2.38	2.43	2.48	2.52	2.57	2.62	2.66	2.70	2.75
210 cm	1.50	1.58	1.65	1.72	1.79	1.85	1.91	1.97	2.03	2.09	2.14	2.20	2.25	2.30	2.36	2.41	2.45	2.50	2.55	2.60	2.64	2.69	2.73	2.77
215 cm	1.52	1.59	1.67	1.73	1.80	1.87	1.93	1.99	2.05	2.11	2.17	2.22	2.27	2.33	2.38	2.43	2.48	2.53	2.58	2.62	2.67	2.71	2.76	2.80
220 cm	1.53	1.61	1.68	1.75	1.82	1.89	1.95	2.01	2.07	2.13	2.19	2.24	2.30	2.35	2.40	2.45	2.50	2.55	2.60	2.65	2.69	2.74	2.79	2.83

References

[1] DU BOIS and DU BOIS, *Arch. intern. Med.*, **17**, 863 (1916).
[2] GEHAN and GEORGE, *Cancer Chemother. Rep.*, **54**, 225 (1970).
[3] KROWETZ, L.J., *J. Pediat.*, **67**, 841 (1965).
[4] BOYD, E., *The Growth of the Surface Area of the Human Body*, University of Minnesota Press, Minneapolis, 1935.
[5] HAYCOCK et al., *J. Pediat.*, **93**, 62 (1978).

A

B

D

E

G

H

J

K

L

M

N

P

T

U

V

W

X

Y

14080/1e USA